JOURNEYSONGS

SECOND EDITION

OCP Publications

Concordat cum originali: † John G. Vlazny, Archbishop of Portland in Oregon

Published with the approval of the Committee on the Liturgy, United States Catholic Conference of Bishops (USCCB).

Publisher: John J. Limb

Editorial Director: Paulette McCoy

Executive Editor: Randall DeBruyn

Managing Editor: Amanda Weller

Assistant Editors: Bari Colombari, Stella García, Steve Grundy, Angie Jáuregui, Argelis Lewis, Melinda Atkins Loomis, Rodolfo López, Theresa Schumacher, Eric Schumock, William Schuster

Editing Assistance: Karl Blume, Barbara Bridge, Mary Rowell, Lori Rux

Director of Engravings: Sharon Norton; Victoria Baker, Monica Germano, Jon Jonsson, Laura C. Kantor, Chris Luttrell, Shannon McNerney, Engravers

Liturgical Advisor: Michael Prendergast

Art Direction and Cover Design: Jean Germano

Graphic Icons: Le Vu

© 2003, OCP Publications
5536 NE Hassalo, Portland, OR 97213
Phone: (503) 281-1191
liturgy@ocp.org
www.ocp.org

Second Printing: November 2003

Assembly	edition 510
Assembly with Readings	edition 515
Choir/Cantor	edition 570
Keyboard Accompaniment	edition 530
Guitar Accompaniment	edition 550
Solo Instrument	edition 590
CD Recording Library	edition 595

ISBN 1-57992-112-4
(RRDSC 1103)

Edition 510
Printed in U.S.A.

PREFACE

Publishing hymnals is an integral part of Oregon Catholic Press's mission of service to the Catholic Church. When *Journeysongs* was first published in 1994, OCP had already been publishing hymnals for many years. Since that time, we have continued to produce hymnals for a variety of worshipping communities, including Spanish-speaking Catholics, young adults and children. OCP now publishes almost half of all the hymnals currently in use in Catholic parishes in the United States. It is, therefore, with a sense of great pride and accomplishment that we present this new, updated edition of *Journeysongs*.

The first edition of *Journeysongs* contained 757 titles: traditional and contemporary hymns and songs of all styles, music for the rites, and service music. Furthermore, with the inclusion of a plastic pocket on the inside back cover, OCP introduced a new era of flexibility in hymnals, allowing new music to be added in yearly supplements. This innovation has contributed over the years to the popularity of *Journeysongs*, adding over 130 new hymns and songs, as well as providing a welcome balance between new music and a stable repertoire.

In *Journeysongs: 2nd Edition* this balance is even more evident. For example, there are almost 100 more hymns and songs than in the original edition, representing a host of different sources and styles: traditional hymns, Latin/English chant, spirituals and gospel-style music, Spanish/English bilingual songs, excellent new hymn texts with both well-known and new tunes, as well as everybody's favorite contemporary songs. In addition, a section of contemporary musical settings of the most-used psalms and canticles for the liturgical year is offered, along with an Order of Mass, additional Mass settings and service music, Rites of Christian Initiation, the Order of Christian Funerals, Eucharistic Exposition and Benediction, additional music for the rites, plus Morning and Evening Prayer. This wealth of music is organized by season or topic, and is fully indexed in the back. Unfortunately, as in the previous edition, some well-known titles by such composers as Marty Haugen and David Haas could not be included here, since we were unable to obtain reprint permission from the publisher. We continue to regret any inconvenience this may cause.

In keeping with the *Journeysongs* tradition of allowing for the future growth of the repertoire, a plastic pocket is again attached to the inside back cover in this second edition. It can be used for custom-made parish music supplements, if desired, or for a variety of music supplements being designed by OCP for several specialized genres: Latin-language chants, Mass settings and hymns, Spanish-language songs and service music, and youth-oriented contemporary songs.

Journeysongs: 2nd Edition is available in two editions: one without scripture readings and one with the complete three-year cycle of *Lectionary* readings, including beautiful musical settings by Fr. John Schiavone of the psalms and gospel acclamations for each Sunday and feast day. A hardbound choir/cantor edition is also available with fully notated scores and arrangements for each title. Other supporting materials include the keyboard and guitar accompaniment editions, a book including a wide variety of instrumental arrangements, and a CD set of demonstration recordings. In addition to the indexes, OCP now offers Liturgy.com™, one of the most advanced online liturgy preparation resources available, to further assist parishes using *Journeysongs: 2nd Edition*.

While there is not enough space to thank each and every person who contributed to this new edition of *Journeysongs*, we do express gratitude to our music advisory committee, whose recommendations added considerably to the contents of this hymnal: Mr. Frank Brownstead, Fr. Ron Krisman, Fr. Edward J. McKenna, Sr. Loretta Manzara, CSI, Dr. Richard Proulx, Dr. Elaine Rendler, Fr. Anthony Ruff, OSB, and Dr. James Savage. Special recognition is also extended to Amanda Weller, whose management of this project was instrumental in seeing it through to completion.

Journeysongs: 2nd Edition Hymnal Committee:

Randall DeBruyn, D.M.A., Chair
Steve Grundy, M.Div., M.A.
Paulette McCoy, M.T.S., B.Mus.
Michael Prendergast, M.T.S., M.A.
Angela Westhoff-Johnson, M.Mus.

CONTENTS

LECTIONARY READINGS

PRAYERS

INDEXES

Note: The following indexes are available in the accompaniment editions: Language Index, Musical Styles Index, and Index of Psalm and Canticle Refrains.

MORNING PRAYER
(LAUDS)

The Liturgy of the Hours is the Church's public worship of Christ, the communal celebration of praise and thanksgiving of the Church at prayer. The Hours, along with the Eucharist, take their meaning solely from the Paschal Mystery of salvation in Christ. Morning Prayer proclaims the themes of Christ as light of the world and sun of justice. It is the praise of God in creation that unites us with the prayer of Christ.

Begin with either the invitatory or the opening dialogue.

VERSE AND RESPONSE *(omit when Prayer begins with the Invitatory)*

1

All make the sign of the cross.

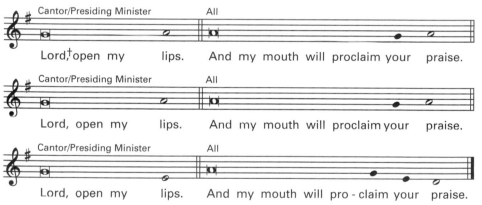

Cantor/Presiding Minister: Lord,†open my lips. All: And my mouth will proclaim your praise.

Cantor/Presiding Minister: Lord, open my lips. All: And my mouth will proclaim your praise.

Cantor/Presiding Minister: Lord, open my lips. All: And my mouth will pro - claim your praise.

MORNING HYMN *(Psalm 95 may be sung in place of the Morning Hymn)*

2

1. This day God gives me Strength of high heav - en, Sun and moon
2. This day God sends me Strength as my guard - ian, Might to up -
3. God's way is my way, God's shield is 'round me, God's host de -
4. Ris - ing I thank you, Might - y and Strong One, King of cre -

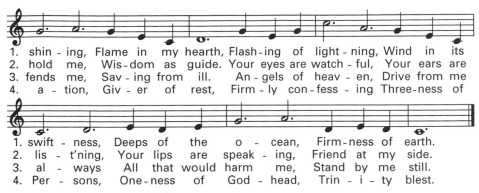

1. shin - ing, Flame in my hearth, Flash-ing of light - ning, Wind in its
2. hold me, Wis - dom as guide. Your eyes are watch - ful, Your ears are
3. fends me, Sav - ing from ill. An - gels of heav - en, Drive from me
4. a - tion, Giv - er of rest, Firm - ly con - fess - ing Three-ness of

1. swift - ness, Deeps of the o - cean, Firm-ness of earth.
2. lis - t'ning, Your lips are speak - ing, Friend at my side.
3. al - ways All that would harm me, Stand by me still.
4. Per - sons, One-ness of God - head, Trin - i - ty blest.

PSALMODY* 3

(Water may be used as a baptismal remembrance during the singing of Psalm 63)

As morn-ing breaks I look to you; I look to you, O Lord, to

be my strength this day, as morn-ing breaks, as morn-ing breaks.

1. O God, you are my God, for you I long;
   for you my soul is thirsting.
   My body pines for you,
   like a dry, weary land without water.
   So I gaze on you in your holy place
   to see your strength and your glory.

2. For your love is better than life,
   my lips will speak your praise.
   So I will bless you all my life,
   in your name I will lift up my hands.
   My soul shall be filled as with a banquet,
   my mouth shall praise you with joy.

3. On my bed I remember you.
   On you I muse through the night,
   for you have been my help;
   in the shadow of your wings I rejoice.
   My soul clings to you;
   your right hand holds me fast.

4. Glory to the Father, and to the Son,
   and to the Holy Spirit:
   as it was in the beginning,
   is now and will be forever. Amen.

*Other psalms, canticles and their antiphons may be taken from the proper of the day. On Wednesday, Friday and other penitential days, Psalm 51 may be used.

PSALM-PRAYER

READING

HOMILY/PREACHING

GOSPEL CANTICLE

All make the sign of the cross.

4

1. Blest be the God of Is - ra - el who comes to set us free
2. With prom-ised mer - cy will God still the cov - e - nant re - call,
3. My child, as proph-et of the Lord you will pre - pare the way,

1. and rais - es up new hope for us: a Branch for Da-vid's tree.
2. the oath once sworn to A - bra - ham from foes to save us all;
3. to tell God's peo - ple they are saved from sin's e - ter-nal sway.

1. So have the proph-ets long de-clared that with a might-y arm
2. that we might wor - ship with - out fear and of - fer lives of praise,
3. Then shall God's mer - cy from on high shine forth and nev - er cease

1. God would turn back our en - e - mies and all who wish us harm.
2. in ho - li - ness and righ-teous-ness to serve God all our days.
3. to drive a - way the gloom of death and lead us in - to peace.

Text: CMD; Luke 1:68–79; adapt. by Carl P. Daw, Jr., b. 1944, © 1989, Hope Publishing Co. All rights reserved. Used with permission.
Music: FOREST GREEN; Trad. English melody.

INTERCESSIONS

5

Cantor   All

(Intercessions) Let us pray to the Lord. Lord, hear our prayer.

Music: Byzantine chant.

LORD'S PRAYER

6

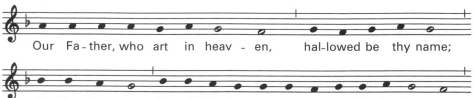

Our Fa - ther, who art in heav - en, hal-lowed be thy name;

thy king-dom come; thy will be done on earth as it is in heav - en.

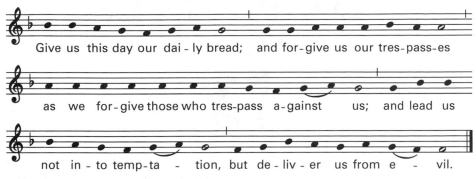

Give us this day our dai - ly bread; and for-give us our tres-pass-es as we for-give those who tres-pass a-gainst us; and lead us not in - to temp-ta - tion, but de - liv - er us from e - vil.

Music: Chant; adapt. by Robert J. Snow, 1926–1998.

CONCLUDING PRAYER

The presiding minister says the concluding prayer.

BLESSING

7

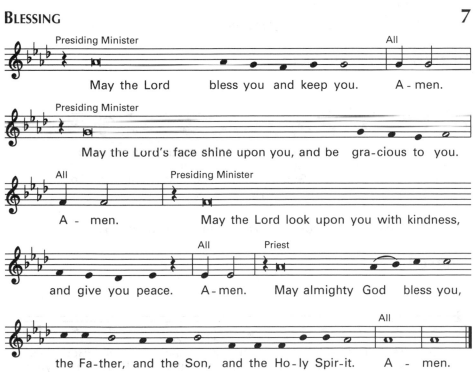

May the Lord bless you and keep you. A - men.

May the Lord's face shine upon you, and be gra-cious to you.

A - men. May the Lord look upon you with kindness,

and give you peace. A-men. May almighty God bless you,

the Fa-ther, and the Son, and the Ho-ly Spir-it. A - men.

SIGN OF PEACE

All share a sign of Christ's peace as a conclusion.

Evening Prayer
(Vespers)

Evening Prayer is an occasion to give thanks for the blessings of the day and for redemption in Christ. Prayer rises "like incense in the Lord's sight," and "upraised hands" become "an evening sacrifice" (Psalm 141:2).

Begin with candle lighting or the opening dialogue.

CANDLE LIGHTING (LUCERNARIUM)

The paschal candle may be lit and brought in to welcome the evening.

THANKSGIVING FOR THE LIGHT

8

Cantor: Light, joy and peace in our Lord Je - sus Christ.
All: Thanks be to God, Al - le - lu - ia.
(Lent: Thanks be to God, thanks be to God.)

Text and music: Paul Inwood, b. 1947, © 1984, 1985, Paul Inwood. Published by OCP Publications. All rights reserved.

All may light their candles from the paschal candle and then sing:

EVENING HYMN

9

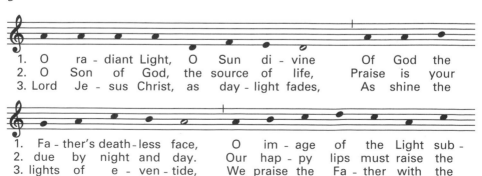

1. O ra - diant Light, O Sun di - vine Of God the
2. O Son of God, the source of life, Praise is your
3. Lord Je - sus Christ, as day - light fades, As shine the

1. Fa - ther's death - less face, O im - age of the Light sub -
2. due by night and day. Our hap - py lips must raise the
3. lights of e - ven - tide, We praise the Fa - ther with the

1. lime   That fills the heav'n - ly dwell - ing place.
2. strain   Of your es - teemed and splen - did name.
3. Son,   The Spir - it blest, and with them one.

Text: LM; *Phos Hilaron*, Greek, ca. 200; tr. by William G. Storey, b. 1923, © William G. Storey.
All rights reserved. Used with permission.
Music: JESU DULCIS MEMORIA; Chant, Mode I.

PSALMODY*   10

(Incense may be used during the singing of Psalm 141)

Refrain: 1st time: Cantor, All repeat; thereafter: All

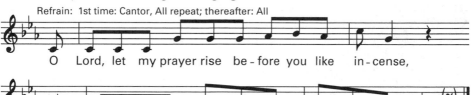

O Lord, let my prayer rise be - fore you like in - cense,

my hands like an ev' - ning of - fer - ing.

Verses: Cantor/Choir

1. Lord, I am calling: hasten to help me.
   Listen to me as I cry to you.
   Let my prayer rise before you like incense,
   my hands like an evening offering.

2. Lord, set a guard at my mouth,
   keep watch at the gate of my lips.
   Let my heart not turn to things that
   are wrong,
   to sharing the evil deeds done by the sinful.
   No, I will never taste their delights.

3. The good may reprove me,
   in kindness chastise me,
   but the wicked shall never anoint my head.
   Every day I counter their malice with prayer.

4. To you, Lord my God, my eyes are turned:
   in you I take refuge; do not forsake me.
   Keep me safe from
   the traps they have set for me,
   from the snares of those who do evil.

Doxology

5. Praise to the Fa - ther, praise to the Son, all praise to the

5. life - giv - ing Spir - it. As it was, is now and shall

to Refrain

5. al - ways be for a - ges un - end - ing. A - men.

Text: Based on Psalm 141:1–5, 8–9, Doxology; Paul Inwood, b. 1947.
Music: Paul Inwood.
Text and music © 1984, 1985, Paul Inwood. Published by OCP Publications. All rights reserved.

*Other psalms, canticles and their antiphons may be taken from the proper of
the day.*

PSALM-PRAYER

READING

HOMILY/PREACHING

GOSPEL CANTICLE

All make the sign of the cross.

11

1. My soul pro - claims the great-ness of the Lord.
2. Through me great deeds will God make man - i - fest,
3. God's might - y arm, pro - tec - tor of the just,
4. Soon will the poor and hun - gry of the earth
5. All glo - ry be to God, Cre - a - tor blest,

1. My spir - it sings to God, my sav - ing God,
2. And all the earth will come to call me blest.
3. Will guard the weak and raise them from the dust.
4. Be rich - ly blest, be giv - en great - er worth.
5. To Je - sus Christ, God's love made man - i - fest,

1. Who on this day a - bove all oth - ers fa - vored me
2. Un-bound-ed love and mer - cy sure will I pro - claim
3. But might - y kings will swift - ly fall from thrones cor - rupt.
4. And Is - ra - el, as once fore-told to A - bra - ham,
5. And to the Ho - ly Spir - it, gen - tle Com - fort - er,

1. And raised me up, a light for all to see.
2. For all who know and praise God's ho - ly name.
3. The strong brought low, the low - ly lift - ed up.
4. Will live in peace through-out the prom-ised land.
5. All glo - ry be, both now and ev - er - more.

INTERCESSIONS

12

Cantor · All

(Intercessions) Let us pray to the Lord. Lord, hear our prayer.

Music: Byzantine chant.

LORD'S PRAYER 13

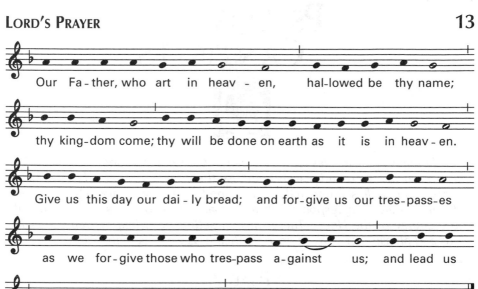

Our Fa-ther, who art in heav-en, hal-lowed be thy name;
thy king-dom come; thy will be done on earth as it is in heav-en.
Give us this day our dai-ly bread; and for-give us our tres-pass-es
as we for-give those who tres-pass a-gainst us; and lead us
not in-to temp-ta - tion, but de-liv-er us from e - vil.

Music: Chant; adapt. by Robert J. Snow, 1926–1998.

CONCLUDING PRAYER

The presiding minister says the concluding prayer.

BLESSING 14

Presiding Minister

May the Lord bless us, protect us from all evil,
and bring us to ever - last - ing life.

All respond:

A
All

A - men, A - men, A - men.

B
Alternate Amen: All

A - men.

Music: Paul Inwood, b. 1947, © 1996, Paul Inwood. Published by OCP Publications. All rights reserved.

SIGN OF PEACE

All share a sign of Christ's peace as a conclusion.

PSALMS & CANTICLES

Biblical psalms and canticles form the heart of the Church's song. Several kinds of religious lyrics, poems and prayers comprise the psalter. The canticles are poems, other than the psalms, found in the Jewish and Christian scriptures. Usually psalms and canticles are sung responsorially at eucharistic celebrations and antiphonally in the Liturgy of the Hours. These musical settings can help us remember key words and phrases and carry them in our hearts as we walk in the world.

---

15   **PSALMS**

---

16   **PSALM 15: THE ONE WHO DOES JUSTICE**

The one who does jus-tice will live in the pres-ence of the Lord.

1. Whoever walks blamelessly
   and does justice;
   who thinks the truth in his heart
   and slanders not with his tongue.

2. Who harms not his fellow man,
   nor takes up a reproach
   against his neighbor;

   by whom the reprobate is despised,
   while he honors those who fear the LORD.

3. Who lends not his money at usury
   and accepts no bribe
   against the innocent.
   Whoever does these things
   shall never be disturbed.

Text: Psalm 15:2–3, 3–4, 4–5. Refrain © 1969, 1981, 1997, ICEL. All rights reserved. Used with permission.
Verses © 1970, 1997, 1998, CCD. All rights reserved. Used with permission.
Music: Owen Alstott, b. 1947, © 1977, 1990, OCP Publications. All rights reserved.

17   **PSALM 16: PROTÉGEME, DIOS MÍO/
YOU ARE MY INHERITANCE**

Estribillo/Refrain

Easter Vigil,	Pro - té - ge - me, Dios mí - o, _____ pro -
33rd Sunday B	You _____ are my in - her - i - tance, my in -
3rd Sunday of Easter A	Se - ñor, me en - se - ña - rás _____ el sen -
	Lord, _____ you will show us, _____
13th Sunday C	Tú e - res, Se - ñor, mi lo - te _____
	You _____ are my in - her - i - tance, my in -

té - ge - me, Dios mí - o, ____ que me re - fu -
her - i - tance, O Lord. ____ ⸒ You ____ are
de - ro de la vi - da. ____ Se - ñor, me en -
show us the path of life. ____ ⸒ Lord, ____
y ____ mi he - re - dad. ____ Tú __ e - res, Se -
her - i - tance, O Lord. ____ ⸒ You ____ are

gio en ti, ____ me re - fu - gio en ti. ____
my in - her - i - tance, my in - her - i - tance, O Lord. __
se - ña - rás __ ⸒ el sen - de - ro de la vi - da.
you will show us, ____ ⸑ show us the path of life. __
ñor, mi lo - te ____ y ____ mi he - re - dad. __
my in - her - i - tance, my in - her - i - tance, O Lord. __

**Estrofas

1. El Señor es el lote de mi heredad y mi copa,
   mi suerte está en tu mano.
   Tengo siempre presente al Señor,
   con él a mi derecha no vacilaré.

2. Por eso se me alegra el corazón,
   se gozan mis entrañas,
   y mi carne descansa serena:
   porque no me entregarás a la muerte
   ni dejarás a tu fiel conocer la corrupción.

3. Me enseñarás el sendero de la vida,
   me saciarás de gozo en tu presencia,
   de alegría perpetua a tu derecha,
   de alegría perpetua a tu derecha.

4. Protégeme, Dios mío, que me refugio en ti;
   yo digo al Señor: "Tu eres mi bien".
   El Señor es el lote de mi heredad y mi copa,
   mi suerte está en tu mano.

5. Bendeciré al Señor que me aconseja;
   hasta de noche me instruye internamente.
   Tengo siempre presente al Señor,
   con él a mi derecha no vacilaré.

**Verses

1. *O Lord, my allotted portion and my cup,*
   you it is who hold fast my lot.
   I set the Lord ever before me;
   with him at my right hand
   I shall not be disturbed.

2. *Therefore my heart is glad*
   and my soul rejoices,
   my body, too, abides in confidence;
   because you will not abandon my soul
   to the netherworld;
   nor will you suffer your faithful one
   to undergo corruption.

3. *You will show me the path to life,*
   fullness of joy in your presence,
   the delights at your right hand forever,
   the delights at your right hand forever.

4. *Keep me, O God, for in you I take refuge;*
   I say to the Lord, "My Lord are you."
   O Lord, my allotted portion and my cup,
   you it is who hold fast my lot.

5. *I bless the Lord who counsels me;*
   even in the night my heart exhorts me.
   I set the Lord ever before me;
   with him at my right hand,
   I shall not be disturbed.

*To perform bilingually, sing the first half of the Refrain in Spanish, and the second half in English.

**Easter Vigil and 33rd Sunday in Ordinary Time, Year B: Verses 1, 2, 3; 3rd Sunday of Easter, Year A and 13th Sunday in Ordinary Time, Year C: Verses 4, 5, 2, 3.

Text: Psalm 16 (Salmo 15):5, 7–8, 9–10, 11; 1–2, 5, 7–8. Spanish © 1970, Comisión Episcopal Española de Liturgia. All rights reserved. Used with permission. English refrains © 1968, 1981, 1997, ICEL. All rights reserved. Used with permission. English verses © 1970, 1997, 1998, CCD. All rights reserved. Used with permission. Music: Bob Hurd, b. 1950, © 1998, 2002, Bob Hurd. Published by OCP Publications. All rights reserved.

18   PSALM 16: YOU ARE MY INHERITANCE, O LORD

You are my in – her – i – tance, O Lord.

1. Keep me, O God,
   for in you I take refuge;
   I say to the LORD, "My LORD are you.
   O LORD, my allotted portion and my cup,
   you it is who hold fast my lot."

2. I bless the LORD who counsels me;
   even in the night my heart exhorts me.
   I set the LORD ever before me;
   with him at my right hand
   I shall not be disturbed.

3. Therefore my heart is glad
   and my soul rejoices,
   my body, too, abides in confidence
   because you will not abandon my soul
   to the netherworld,
   nor will you suffer your faithful one
   to undergo corruption.

4. You will show me the path to life,
   fullness of joys in your presence,
   the delights at your right hand forever.

Text: Psalm 16:1–2, 5, 7–8, 9–10, 11. Refrain © 1968, 1981, 1997, ICEL. All rights reserved. Used with permission.
Verses © 1970, 1997, 1998, CCD. All rights reserved. Used with permission.
Music: Owen Alstott, b. 1947, © 1977, 1990, OCP Publications. All rights reserved.

19   PSALM 18: I LOVE YOU, LORD, MY STRENGTH

I love you, Lord, I love you, Lord, my strength.

1. I love you, O Lord, my strength,
   O Lord, my rock,
   my fortress, and my Savior.

2. My God, my rock of refuge,
   my shield, my help, my stronghold!

The Lord is worthy of all praise.
When I call I am saved from my foes.

3. Long life to the Lord, my rock!
   Praised be the God who saves me.
   You who gave great victories to your king,
   and love shown to your anointed.

Text: Psalm 18:23, 3–4, 47, 51. Refrain © 1969, 1981, 1997, ICEL. All rights reserved. Used with permission.
Verse 1 © 1970, 1997, 1998, CCD. All rights reserved. Used with permission.
Verses 2–3, Jeffrey Honoré, b. 1956, © 2001, Jeffrey Honoré. Published by OCP Publications. All rights reserved.
Music: Jeffrey Honoré, © 2001, Jeffrey Honoré. Published by OCP Publications. All rights reserved.

20   PSALM 19: LORD, YOU HAVE THE WORDS

Lord, you have the words of ev – er – last – ing life.

1. The law of the LORD is perfect,
   refreshing the soul;
   the decree of the LORD is trustworthy,
   giving wisdom to the simple.

2. The precepts of the LORD are right,
   rejoicing the heart;
   the command of the LORD is clear,
   enlightening the eye.

3. The fear of the LORD is pure,
   enduring forever;
   the ordinances of the LORD are true,
   all of them just.

4. They are more precious than gold,
   than a heap of purest gold;
   sweeter also than syrup
   or honey from the comb.

Text: John 6:68, Psalm 19:8–11. Refrain © 1969, 1981, ICEL. All rights reserved. Used with permission.
Verses © 1970, CCD. All rights reserved. Used with permission.
Music: Michael Joncas, b. 1951, © 1981, 1990, Jan Michael Joncas Trust. Published by OCP Publications. All rights reserved.

Psalm 22: Dios Mío, Dios Mío/ My God, My God

Dios mí - o, Dios mí - o, ¿por qué me has a -
My God, ___ my God, ___ ⸮ why ___ have

ban - do - na - do? ___ ¿Por qué me has a -
you a - ban - doned me? ⸮ Why ___ have

ban - do - na - do, ___ Dios mí - o? ___
you a - ban - doned me, my God? ___

1. Al verme se burlan de mí,
   hacen visajes, menean la cabeza:
   "Acudió al Señor,
   que lo ponga a salvo;
   que lo libre si tanto lo quiere".

2. Tú eres quien me sacó del vientre,
   me tenías confiado
   en los pechos de mi madre;
   desde el seno pasé a tus manos,
   desde el vientre materno
   tú eres mi Dios.

3. Me acorrala una jauría de mastines,
   me cerca una banda de malhechores:
   me taladran las manos y los pies,
   puedo contar mis huesos.

4. Se reparten mi ropa,
   echan a suerte mi túnica.
   Pero tú, Señor, no te quedes lejos;
   fuerza mía, ven corriendo a ayudarme.

5. Contaré tu fama a mis hermanos,
   en medio de la asamblea te alabaré.
   Fieles del Señor, alábenlo,
   linaje de Jacob,
   glorifíquenlo, témanle,
   linaje de Israel.

1. I am scorned by all who see me;
   shaking their heads, they deride me:
   "Since he trusted the Lord to save him,
   let the Lord come to his rescue."

2. It was you who brought me forth
   from the womb,
   to my mother's breast you entrusted me.
   Into your care was I cast from my birth,
   from my mother's womb you are my God.

3. Like wild animals
   the wicked surround me,
   like predators they encircle me.
   They tear at my hands and my feet;
   I can number each one of my bones.

4. They divide my garments among them;
   they cast lots for my clothing.
   But you, Lord, be not far from me;
   my strength, hasten to help me.

5. I will proclaim your name to my kindred;
   in the assembly I will praise you.
   Give praise, all you who fear the Lord;
   descendants of Jacob, give glory.

Text: Psalm 22 (Salmo 21):8–9, 10–11, 17–18, 19–20, 23–24. Spanish © 1970, Comisión Episcopal Española de Liturgia.
   All rights reserved. Used with permission. English refrain © 1969, 1981, 1997, ICEL. All rights reserved. Used with permission.
   English verses, Bob Hurd, b. 1950, © 1998, Bob Hurd. Published by OCP Publications. All rights reserved.
Music: Bob Hurd, © 1998, Bob Hurd. Published by OCP Publications. All rights reserved.

22

PSALM 22: MY GOD, MY GOD

My God, my God, why have you a-ban-doned me?

1. All who see me scoff at me;
   they mock me with parted lips,
   they wag their heads:
   "He relied on the LORD; let him deliver him,
   let him rescue him, if he loves him."

2. Indeed, many dogs surround me,
   a pack of evildoers closes in upon me;
   they have pierced my hands and my feet;
   I can count all my bones.

3. They divide my garments among them,
   and for my vesture they cast lots.

But you, O LORD, be not far from me;
O my help, hasten to aid me.

4. I will proclaim your name to my brethren;
   in the midst of the assembly
   I will praise you:
   "You who fear the LORD, praise him;
   all you descendants of Jacob,
   give glory to him;
   revere him, all you descendants of Israel!"

23

PSALM 23: THE LORD IS MY SHEPHERD

I Shall Live in the House of the Lord

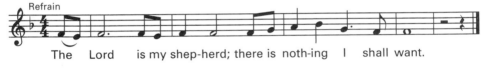

Refrain

The Lord is my shep-herd; there is noth-ing I shall want.

Alternate Refrain

I shall live in the house of the Lord all the days of my life.

1. The LORD is my shepherd; I shall not want.
   In verdant pastures he gives me repose;
   beside restful waters he leads me;
   he refreshes my soul.

2. He guides me in right paths
   for his name's sake.
   Even though I walk in the dark valley
   I fear no evil; for you are at my side
   with your rod and your staff
   that give me courage.

3. You spread the table before me
   in the sight of my foes;
   you anoint my head with oil;
   my cup overflows.

4. Only goodness and kindness
   follow me all the days of my life;
   and I shall dwell in the house of the LORD
   for years to come.

PSALM 23: TÚ VAS CONMIGO/
THE LORD IS MY SHEPHERD

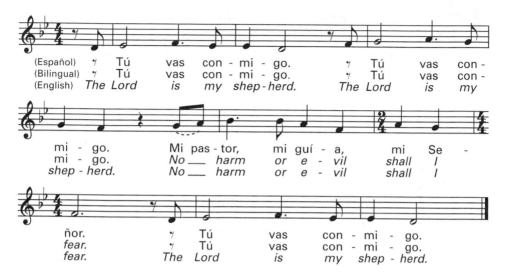

(Español) ⁊ Tú vas con - mi - go. ⁊ Tú vas con -
(Bilingual) ⁊ Tú vas con - mi - go. ⁊ Tú vas con -
(English) The Lord is my shep-herd. The Lord is my

mi - go. Mi pas - tor, mi guí - a, mi Se -
mi - go. No __ harm or e - vil shall I
shep - herd. No __ harm or e - vil shall I

ñor. ⁊ Tú vas con - mi - go.
fear. ⁊ Tú vas con - mi - go.
fear. The Lord is my shep - herd.

1. El Señor es mi pastor,
   nada me falta:
   en verdes praderas me hace recostar;
   me conduce hacia fuentes tranquilas
   y repara mis fuerzas,
   y repara mis fuerzas.

2. Me guía por el sendero justo,
   por el honor de su nombre.
   Aunque camine por cañadas oscuras,
   nada temo porque tú vas conmigo:
   tu vara y tu cayado
   me consuelan, me sosiegan.

3. Preparas una mesa ante mí,
   enfrente de mis enemigos;
   me unges la cabeza con perfume,
   mi copa rebosa, mi copa rebosa.

4. Tu bondad y tu misericordia
   me acompañan
   todos los días de mi vida,
   y habitaré en la casa del Señor
   por años sin término,
   por años sin término.

1. My shepherd is the Lord,
   I shall want nothing.
   In green pastures you give me repose;
   and lead me beside restful waters;
   you revive my spirit,
   you revive my spirit.

2. For the sake of your name
   you guide me in right paths.
   Though I walk in the valley of darkness,
   I shall fear no evil:
   for you walk beside me;
   your rod and your staff give me courage.

3. You spread a table before me
   in the sight of my foes.
   With soothing oil you anoint me;
   my cup runs over, my cup runs over.

4. Surely your goodness and mercy
   shall pursue me all the days of my life
   and I shall dwell in the house of the Lord
   for ever and ever, for ever and ever.

Text: Psalm 23 (Salmo 22):1–3a, 3b–4, 5, 6. Spanish verses © 1970, Comisión Episcopal Española de Liturgia.
    All rights reserved. Used with permission. Spanish refrain and English, Bob Hurd, b. 1950,
    © 1998, Bob Hurd. Published by OCP Publications. All rights reserved.
Music: Bob Hurd, © 1998, Bob Hurd. Published by OCP Publications. All rights reserved.

25

PSALM 24: LET THE LORD ENTER
Lord, This Is the People

Let the Lord en - ter; he is king of glo - ry.

Lord, this is the peo - ple that longs to see your face.

1. The LORD's are the earth and its fullness;
   the world and those who dwell in it.
   For he founded it upon the seas
   and established it upon the rivers.

2. Who can ascend the mountain of the LORD?
   Or who may stand in his holy place?
   One whose hands are sinless,
   whose heart is clean,
   who desires not what is vain.

3. He shall receive a blessing
   from the LORD,
   a reward from God his savior.
   Such is the race that seeks for him,
   that seeks the face of the God of Jacob.

26

PSALM 25: TO YOU, O LORD

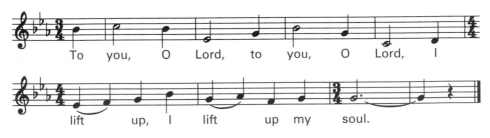

To you, O Lord, to you, O Lord, I

lift up, I lift up my soul.

1. Your ways, O Lord,
   make known to me;
   teach me your paths.
   Guide me in your truth and teach me,
   for you are God my savior.

2. Good and upright is the Lord;
   thus he shows sinners the way.
   The humble he guides to justice;
   he teaches the humble his way.

3. Kindness and constancy
   the paths of the Lord
   for those who keep covenant with him.
   The friendship of the Lord
   with those who revere him,
   his covenant for their instruction.

Psalm 25: A Ti, Señor/To You, O Lord

A ti, Se - ñor, le - van - to mi al - ma, _____
To you, O Lord, I lift up my soul, _____

le - van - to mi al - ma a ti, Se - ñor.
I lift up my soul ___ to you, O Lord.

1. Señor, enséñame tus caminos,
   instrúyeme en tus sendas,
   haz que camine con lealtad;
   enséñame, porque tú eres
   mi Dios y Salvador.

2. El Señor es bueno y recto,
   y enseña el camino a los pecadores;
   hace caminar
   a los humildes con rectitud,
   enseña su camino a los humildes.

3. Las sendas del Señor
   son lealtad y misericordia,
   para los que guardan
   su alianza y sus mandatos.
   El Señor se confía con sus fieles
   y les da a conocer su alianza.

1. *Make me to know your ways, Lord;*
   set my feet upon your pathways.
   Teach me to walk in your truth and lead me,
   for you are my God, my savior.

2. *Good is the Lord and upright,*
   graciously showing the way to sinners,
   leading the humble into paths of justice,
   guiding the poor and the lowly.

3. *All the ways of the Lord are loving*
   toward those who keep the commandments.
   The friendship of God
   embraces all who fear the Lord,
   revealing to them the covenant.

Psalm 25: To You, O Lord

To you, O Lord, I lift up, I lift up my soul, my God.

1. Your ways, O Lord, make known to me;
   teach me your paths.
   Guide me in your truth, for you are my God,
   and for you I will wait.

2. Good and upright is the Lord;
   he shows us the way.
   He guides the meek to justice,
   he teaches the humble to follow his ways.

3. Your way, O Lord,
   is kindness to those who are true.
   Your friendship is
   with those who love you;
   you reveal to them your Word.

29   PSALM 27: THE LORD IS MY LIGHT

The Lord is my light, the Lord is my light, the Lord is my light and my sal - va - tion.

1. The Lord is my light and my salvation;
   if God is my help, whom should I fear?
   The Lord is my refuge,
   my stronghold and my strength;
   why should I be afraid?

2. There is but one thing that I want:
   to live in the dwelling place of God;
   to look all my days on the beauty of the Lord,
   and contemplate God's holy temple.

3. I shall see for myself the grace of God,
   the dawn of that day among the living.
   Wait for the Lord,
   find strength in your hearts;
   have courage and wait for God.

Text: Psalm 27:1, 4, 13–14. Refrain © 1969, 1981, ICEL. All rights reserved. Used with permission.
Verses, Randall DeBruyn, b. 1947, © 1996, OCP Publications. All rights reserved.
Music: Randall DeBruyn, © 1996, OCP Publications. All rights reserved.

30   PSALM 27: THE GOODNESS OF THE LORD

I be - lieve, I be - lieve I shall see the good-ness of the Lord in the land, in the land of the liv - ing.

1. The Lord is my light,
   the Lord is my rock, my salvation.
   The Lord is my refuge, guarding my life;
   of whom should I be afraid?

2. Only one thing I ask:
   may I live in the house of my Lord.
   I shall gaze on God's goodness all of my days;
   I shall live in the shelter of God.

3. I believe I shall see
   the goodness of God
   in the land of the living.
   Be strong, wait for the Lord.

Text: Psalm 27:1, 4, 13–14. Refrain © 1969, 1981, ICEL. All rights reserved. Used with permission.
Verses, Scott Soper, b. 1961, © 1993, Scott Soper. Published by OCP Publications. All rights reserved.
Music: Scott Soper, © 1993, Scott Soper. Published by OCP Publications. All rights reserved.

PSALM 29: THE LORD WILL BLESS US WITH PEACE　　31

The Lord will bless us with peace.

The Lord will bless us with peace.

1. Give today, all you works of the Lord,
   praise and thanks and glory due God's name.
   The name ever blessed, the name so exalted,
   the name of our God!

2. The voice of our God resounds,
   moving upon the water.

The voice of our God
is mighty and strong and clear.

3. Every tongue shall cry out "Glory!"
   to the one enthroned above the flood.
   Everlasting the reign,
   the reign of the God of all!

PSALM 30: I WILL PRAISE YOU, LORD　　32

I will praise you, Lord, you have res-cued me, I will praise you,

Lord, for your mer - cy. I will praise you, Lord,

you have res-cued me: I will praise you, Lord.

1. I will praise you, Lord,
   you have rescued me
   and have not let
   my enemies rejoice over me.
   O Lord, you have raised my soul
   from the dead,
   restored me to life
   from those who sink into the grave.

2. Sing psalms to the Lord,
   you who love him,
   give thanks to his holy name.

His anger lasts but a moment;
his favor through life.
At night there are tears,
but joy comes with dawn.

3. The Lord listened and had pity.
   The Lord came to my help.
   For me you have changed
   my mourning into dancing;
   O Lord my God,
   I will thank you for ever.

33   PSALM 31: FATHER, INTO YOUR HANDS
I COMMEND MY SPIRIT

Fa - ther,   Fa - ther,   in-to your hands I com-mend my spir-it.

1. You, O God, are my refuge;
   in you I shall not be put to shame.
   Rescue me, because you are just.
   Into your hands I commend my soul.
   Save me, save me, my God.

2. By my foes I am hated,
   and all those who see me laugh at me.
   Everyone runs away from my face.
   I am neglected
   like the dead in their grave;
   broken, forgotten my life.

3. All my life I will trust you,
   for you are the God of my heart.
   Rescue me from the hands of my foes.
   Guard me from those who seek
   to harm my life.
   You, Lord, hold me in your hands.

4. Grant that I may behold you;
   redeem your faithful one to life.
   Save me in your compassion and love.
   You are my strength forever, O God.
   Hold fast, all those who love the Lord.

34   PSALM 31: PADRE, EN TUS MANOS/
FATHER, INTO YOUR HANDS

(Español) Pa - dre, _____ en tus ma - nos en - co - mien - do mi es-
(Bilingual) Pa - dre, _____ en tus ma - nos en - co - mien - do mi es-
(English) Fa - ther, ___ in - to your hands ___ I com - mend ___ my

pí - ri - tu.   Pa - dre, _____ en tus
pí - ri - tu.   Fa - ther, ____ in - to your
spir - it.   Fa - ther, ____ in - to your

ma-nos en - co - mien-do mi es - pí - ri - tu.
hands __ I com - mend __ my spir - it.
hands __ I com - mend __ my spir - it.

1. A ti, Señor, me acojo:
   no quede yo nunca defraudado;
   tú que eres justo, ponme a salvo.
   En tus manos encomiendo mi espíritu:
   tú, el Dios leal, me librarás.

2. Soy la burla de todos mis enemigos,
   la irrisión de mis vecinos,
   el espanto de mis conocidos;
   me ven por la calle y escapan de mí.
   Me han olvidado como a un muerto,
   me han desechado
   como a un cacharro inútil.

1. *In you, O LORD, I take refuge;*
   let me not be put to shame.
   In your justice save me.
   Into your hands I commend my spirit;
   you will redeem me, faithful God.

2. *I am scorned by all my enemies,*
   dreaded by friends and neighbors;
   when they see me they turn away.
   I am like one dead and forgotten,
   like a vessel broken and discarded.

3. Pero yo confío en ti, Señor,
te digo: "Tú eres mi Dios".
En tu mano están mis azares;
líbrame de los enemigos,
los enemigos que me persiguen.

4. Haz brillar tu rostro sobre tu siervo,
sálvame por tu misericordia.
Sean fuertes y valientes de corazón,
los que esperan en el Señor.

3. *But Lord, I trust in you;*
I say: "You are my God."
My life is in your hands;
save me from my enemies,
from the hands of those who pursue me.

4. *Let your face shine upon your servant;*
in your steadfast kindness save me.
Take courage, be strong of heart,
all you who wait for the Lord,
all you who hope in the Lord.

PSALM 33: BLESSED THE PEOPLE 35

Bless-ed the peo-ple the Lord has cho-sen to be his own.

1. For upright is the word of the LORD,
and all his works are trustworthy.
He loves justice and right;
of the kindness of the LORD the earth is full.

2. Happy the nation whose God is the LORD,
the people he has chosen
for his own inheritance.

From heaven the LORD looks down;
he sees all mankind.

3. But see, the eyes of the LORD
are upon those who fear him,
upon those who hope for his kindness,
to deliver them from death
and preserve them in spite of famine.

PSALM 33: LORD, LET YOUR MERCY BE ON US 36

Lord, let your mer - cy be on us, as we place our trust in you.

1. Your word, Lord, is faithful
and all your works are to be trusted.
O Lord, you love justice and right
and fill the earth with your love.

2. Lord, you look on those who revere you,
on those who hope in your love,

to rescue their souls from death,
to keep them alive in famine.

3. Our soul is waiting for the Lord.
The Lord is our help and our shield.
May your love be upon us, O Lord,
as we place all our hope in you.

37

PSALM 34: TASTE AND SEE

Taste and see, taste and see that the Lord is good, the Lord is good.

1. I will bless the Lord at all times,
   his praise always on my lips.
   The Lord shall be the glory of my soul;
   the humble shall hear and be glad.

2. Glorify the Lord with me,
   together let us praise his name.
   I sought the Lord: he answered me;
   he set me free from all my fear.

3. Look upon the Lord and be radiant;
   hide not your face from the Lord.
   He heard the cry of the poor;
   he rescued them from all their woes.

4. The angel of the Lord is with his people
   to rescue those who trust in him.
   Taste and see the goodness of the Lord;
   seek refuge in him and be glad.

5. Saints of the Lord, revere him;
   those who fear him lack nothing.
   Lions suffer want and go hungry,
   but those who seek him lack no blessing.

6. Children of the Lord come and hear,
   and learn the fear of the Lord.
   Who is he who longs for life,
   whose only love is for his wealth?

7. Keep evil words from your tongue,
   your lips from speaking deceit.
   Turn aside from evil and do good;
   seek and strive after peace.

Text: Psalm 34:9, 2–15; Stephen Dean, b. 1948.
Music: Stephen Dean.
Text and music © 1981, Stephen Dean. Published by OCP Publications. All rights reserved.

38

PSALM 34: TASTE AND SEE

Taste and see the good-ness of the Lord;

taste and see the good-ness of the Lord.

1. I will bless the Lord at all times,
   with praise always on my lips;
   in the Lord my soul shall make its boast.
   The humble shall hear and be glad.

2. Glorify the Lord with me.
   Together let us praise his name.
   I sought the Lord and was answered;
   from my terrors God set me free.

3. Look towards the Lord and shine in light;
   let your faces be not ashamed.
   This poor man called; the Lord heard him
   and rescued him from all his distress.

4. The angel of the Lord is encamped
   around those who revere him.
   Taste and see that the Lord is good.
   They are happy who seek refuge in him.

Text: Psalm 34:2–3, 4–5, 6–7, 8–9. Refrain © 1969, ICEL. All rights reserved. Used with permission.
   Verses © 1963, The Grail (England). All rights reserved. Used with permission of A.P. Watt, Ltd.
Music: Christopher Willcock, b. 1947, © 1977, 1990, 1997, Christopher Willcock, SJ.
   Published by OCP Publications. All rights reserved.

PSALM 34: GUSTEN Y VEAN/TASTE AND SEE

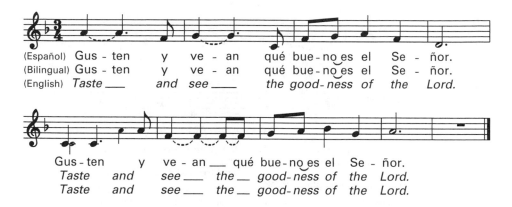

(Español) Gus - ten y ve - an qué bue - no es el Se - ñor.
(Bilingual) Gus - ten y ve - an qué bue - no es el Se - ñor.
(English) Taste ___ and see ___ the good - ness of the Lord.

Gus - ten y ve - an ___ qué bue - no es el Se - ñor.
Taste and see ___ the ___ good - ness of the Lord.
Taste and see ___ the ___ good - ness of the Lord.

1. Bendigo al Señor en todo momento,
su alabanza está siempre en mi boca;
mi alma se gloría en el Señor:
que los humildes lo escuchen
y se alegren.

2. Proclamen conmigo
la grandeza del Señor,
ensalcemos juntos su nombre.
Yo consulté al Señor y me respondió,
me libró de todas mis ansias.

3. Miren al Señor y quedarán radiantes,
no asomará en sus caras la vergüenza.
Si el afligido invoca al Señor,
lo escuchará y lo salva
de sus angustias.

4. El ángel del Señor protege y salva
a los que honran y temen al Señor.
Gusten y vean qué bueno es el Señor,
dichoso aquel que se acoge a Dios.

1. *I will bless the LORD at all times,*
his praise shall be ever in my mouth.
Let my soul glory in the LORD;
the lowly will hear me and be glad.

2. *Glorify the LORD with me,*
let us together extol his name.
I sought the LORD, [who] answered me
and delivered me from my fears.

3. *Look to the Lord; be radiant with joy.*
And let your faces
not blush with shame.
The poor called out,
and the Lord heard and rescued them
from all their distress.

4. *The angel of the Lord*
encamps around those who fear God
and delivers them.
O taste and see that the Lord is good;
happy are those who take refuge in God.

40

PSALM 34: I WILL BLESS THE LORD
Taste and See

I will bless the Lord at all times.

Taste and see the good-ness of the Lord.

1. I will bless the LORD at all times;
   his praise shall be ever in my mouth.
   Let my soul glory in the LORD;
   the lowly will hear me and be glad.

2. Glorify the LORD with me;
   let us extol his name.
   I sought the LORD, and he answered me,
   and delivered me from all my fears.

3. Look to him that you may
   be radiant with joy,
   and your faces may not blush with shame.

When the poor one called out,
the LORD heard
and from all his distress he saved him.

4. The angel of the LORD encamps
   around those who fear him,
   and delivers them.
   Taste and see how good the LORD is;
   blessed the man
   who takes refuge in him.

41

PSALM 40: HERE I AM
God, My God, Come to My Aid

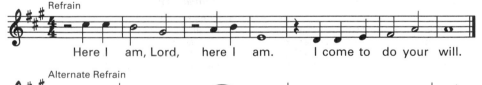

Here I am, Lord, here I am. I come to do your will.

God, my God, come to my aid, come to my aid, come to my aid; come.

1. Long was I waiting for God,
   and then he heard my cry.
   It was he who taught this song to me,
   a song of praise to God.

2. You asked me not for sacrifice,
   for slaughtered goats or lambs.
   No, my heart,
   you gave me ears to hear you,
   then I said, "Here I am."

3. You wrote it in the scrolls of law
   what you would have me do.
   Doing that is what has made me happy,
   your law is in my heart.

4. I spoke before your holy people,
   the good news that you save.
   Now you know that I will not be silent,
   I'll always sing your praise.

PSALM 42/43: AS THE DEER LONGS

As the deer longs for run - ning streams, so I long, so I long, so I long for you.

1. Athirst my soul for you,
the God who is my life!
When shall I see, when shall I see,
see the face of God?

2. Echoes meet
as deep is calling unto deep,
over my head, all your mighty waters,
sweeping over me.

3. Continually the foe delights in taunting me:

"Where is God, where is your God?"
Where, O where, are you?

4. Defend me, God;
send forth your light and your truth.
They will lead me to your holy mountain,
to your dwelling place.

5. Then I shall go unto the altar of my God.
Praising you, O my joy and gladness,
I shall praise your name.

Text: Psalm 42:2, 3, 8, 4; Psalm 43:3, 4; Bob Hurd, b. 1950.
Music: Bob Hurd.
Text and music © 1988, Bob Hurd. Published by OCP Publications. All rights reserved.

PSALM 42/43: MY SOUL IS THIRSTING FOR YOU

My soul is thirst-ing for you, O Lord my God.

1. As the deer longs for running waters,
so my soul longs for you, O God.
Athirst is my soul for God the living God.
When shall I go and behold
the face of God?

2. Send forth your light and your fidelity;
they shall lead me on

and bring me to your holy mountain,
to your dwelling place.

3. Then will I go into the altar of God,
the God of my gladness and joy;
then will I give you thanks upon the harp,
O God, my God.

Text: Psalm 42:2, 3; 43:3, 4. Refrain © 1969, ICEL. All rights reserved. Used with permission.
Verses © 1970, CCD. All rights reserved. Used with permission.
Music: Robert E. Kreutz, 1922–1996, © 1983, OCP Publications. All rights reserved.

PSALM 45: THE QUEEN STANDS

The Queen stands, at your right hand, ar - rayed in gold.

1. The Queen takes her place
at your right hand in gold of Ophir.

2. Hear, O daughter and see; turn your ear,
forget your people and your father's house.

3. So shall the king desire your beauty;
for he is your lord.

4. They are borne in with gladness;
borne in with joy;
they enter the palace of the king.

Text: Psalm 45:10–12, 16. Refrain © 1969, 1981, ICEL. All rights reserved. Used with permission.
Verses © 1970, CCD. All rights reserved. Used with permission.
Music: Kevin Keil, ASCAP, b. 1956, © 1993, Cooperative Ministries, Inc. All rights reserved. Exclusive agent: OCP Publications.

45

PSALM 47: GOD MOUNTS HIS THRONE

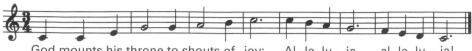

God mounts his throne to shouts of joy: Al - le - lu - ia, al - le - lu - ia!

1. All peoples, clap your hands,
   cry to God with shouts of joy!
   For the Lord Most High we must fear,
   great King over all the earth.

2. God goes up with shouts of joy;
   the Lord goes up with trumpet blast.

   Sing praise for God, sing praise for God,
   sing praise to our King.

3. God is King of all the earth.
   Sing praise with all your skill.
   God is King over the nations;
   he reigns on his holy throne.

46

PSALM 51: BE MERCIFUL, O LORD

Create a Clean Heart

Refrain

Be mer - ci - ful, O Lord, for we have sinned;

be mer - ci - ful, O Lord, for we have sinned.

Alternate Refrain

Cre - ate a clean heart in me, cre - ate a clean heart in me, O God.

1. Have mercy on me, God, in your kindness.
   In your compassion blot out my offense.
   O wash me more and more from my guilt
   and cleanse me from my sin.

2. My offenses truly I know them;
   my sin is always before me.
   Against you, you alone, have I sinned;
   what is evil in your sight I have done.

3. A pure heart create for me, O God,
   put a steadfast spirit within me.
   Do not cast me away from your presence,
   nor deprive me of your holy spirit.

4. Give me again the joy of your help;
   with a spirit of fervor sustain me.
   O Lord, open my lips,
   and my mouth shall declare your praise.

PSALM 51: CREATE IN ME

Cre - ate in me a clean heart, O God, a clean heart, O God, cre - ate in me.

1. O God, in your goodness have mercy
   on me.
   In your compassion wipe out my offense.
   Thoroughly wash me from my guilt,
   and cleanse me from my sins.

2. For I acknowledge my offense
   and my sin is always before me;
   against only you have I sinned,
   and done what is evil in your eyes.

3. A clean heart create for me, O God,
   a steadfast spirit renew in me.
   Cast me not out from your presence,
   O God.
   Take not your Holy Spirit from me.

4. Give us back the joy of our salvation,
   and renew in us a willing spirit.
   O Lord, open my lips, Lord, open my lips.
   And we will sing your praise.

PSALM 51: OH DIOS, CREA EN MÍ/CREATE IN ME

Oh Dios, crea en mí, oh Dios, crea en mí, _____
Cre - ate in _____ me, cre - ate in _____ me a
crea un co - ra - zón, un co-ra-zón pu - ro.
pure _____ heart, O God, a will - ing spir - it.

1. Piedad de mí, Señor,
   por tu bondad,
   por tu inmensa compasión
   borra mi culpa;
   lava del todo mi delito,
   purifícame, tú, de mi pecado.

2. Oh Dios, crea en mí
   un corazón puro,
   pon en mí un espíritu firme;
   no me arrojes lejos de tu rostro,
   no me quites tu santo espíritu.

3. Dame la alegría de tu salvación,
   mantén en mí un alma generosa.
   Enseñaré a los malvados
   tus caminos,
   se volverán a ti los pecadores.

1. *Have mercy on me, O God,*
   in your kindness
   blot out my offenses;
   wash me, wash away my guilt,
   cleanse me completely of my sin.

2. *Create in me, God,*
   a pure heart
   and give me a steadfast spirit;
   do not cast me out
   from your presence,
   nor remove your holy spirit,

3. *Give me back the joy*
   of your salvation,
   sustain in me a willing spirit.
   Open my lips, O Lord,
   and I shall proclaim your praise.

49   PSALM 62: FOR GOD ALONE

For God a-lone my soul waits in si-lence.

1. Only in God is my soul at rest;
from God comes my hope.
Only the Lord is my rock,
my salvation, my fortress;
I shall not be moved.

2. Only in God be at peace, my soul;
from God comes my salvation.

Only the Lord is my strength and my safety
my stronghold;
I shall not be harmed.

3. God is my safety and my glory,
the rock of my strength.
Trust in the Lord at all times, my people,
and pour out your hearts before the Lord.

Text: Psalm 62:6–7, 2–3, 8–9; Scott Soper, b. 1961.
Music: Scott Soper.
Text and music © 1987, Scott Soper. Published by OCP Publications. All rights reserved.

50   PSALM 63: HEAR US, LORD, AND SAVE US

Hear us, Lord, and save us; hear us, Lord, and save us.

1. O God, my God, for you I long;
for you my soul is thirsting.
My body pines for you
like a dry weary land without water.

2. So I gaze on you in your dwelling
to see your strength and glory.

For your love is better than life,
my lips will speak your praise.

3. So I will bless you all my life,
in your name I lift up my hands.
My soul shall be filled as with a banquet,
my mouth shall praise you with joy.

Note: Common (Seasonal) Psalm response for use in Ordinary Time with Common Psalms of petition.

Text: Psalm 63:2, 3–4, 5–6. Refrain © 1969, ICEL. All rights reserved. Used with permission.
  Verses © 1963, The Grail (England). All rights reserved. Used with permission of A.P. Watt, Ltd.
Music: Christopher Willcock, b. 1947, © 1977, 1990, 1997, Christopher Willcock, SJ.
  Published by OCP Publications. All rights reserved.

51   PSALM 63: MY SOUL IS THIRSTING FOR YOU

My soul is thirst-ing for you, O Lord my God.

1. O God, you are my God whom I seek;
for you my flesh pines and my soul thirsts.
Like the earth, parched,
lifeless and without water.

2. Thus have I gazed toward you
in the sanctuary
to see your power and your glory,
for your kindness
is a greater good than life;
my lips shall glorify you.

3. Thus will I bless you while I live;
lifting up my hands,
I will call upon your name.
As with the riches of a banquet
shall my soul be satisfied,
and with exultant lips
my mouth shall praise you.

4. You are my help,
and in the shadow of your wings
I shout for joy.
My soul clings fast to you;
your right hand upholds me.

Text: Psalm 63:2, 3–4, 5–6, 8–9. Refrain © 1968, 1981, 1997, ICEL. All rights reserved. Used with permission.
  Verses © 1970, 1997, 1998, CCD. All rights reserved. Used with permission.
Music: Owen Alstott, b. 1947, © 1977, 1990, OCP Publications. All rights reserved.

PSALM 63: MY SOUL IS THIRSTING 52

My soul is thirst-ing for you, my God. You are my God whom I seek; for you my flesh pines, for you my soul thirsts, thirst-ing for you, my God.

1. Thus have I gazed toward you in the sanctuary
   to see your power and your glory,
   for your kindness is a greater good than life;
   my lips shall glorify you.

2. Thus will I bless you while I live;
   lifting up my hands, I will call upon your name.
   As with the riches of a banquet
   shall my soul be satisfied,
   and with exultant lips my mouth shall praise you.

3. I will remember you as I lie awake,
   and through the night I think of you.
   O Lord, you are my help,
   and I will sing for joy.
   In the shadow of your wings
   I shout for joy.

*Last time, repeat final phrase.

PSALM 66: LET ALL THE EARTH CRY OUT 53

Round

Let all the earth cry out to God with joy, al-le-lu - ia.

1. Shout joyfully to God, all the earth;
   sing praise to the glory of his name;
   proclaim his glorious praise.
   Say to God, "How tremendous
   are your deeds!"

2. "Let all on earth worship
   and sing praise to you,
   sing praise to your name!"
   Come and see the works of God,
   his tremendous deeds
   among the children of Adam.

3. He has changed the sea into dry land;
   through the river they passed on foot;
   therefore let us rejoice in him,
   he rules by his might forever.

4. Hear now, all you who fear God,
   while I declare what he has done
   for me.
   Blessed be God, who refused me not
   my prayer or his kindness!

54

PSALM 67: LA TIERRA YA GERMINÓ/
THE EARTH HAS YIELDED ITS FRUITS

Oh Dios, que Todos los Pueblos Te Alaben/
O God, Let All the Nations Praise You

*Estribillo/Refrain I

La tie - rra ya ger-mi - nó; Dios nos dio sus do - nes.
The earth has yield-ed its fruits; God, our God, has blessed us.

*Estribillo/Refrain II

Oh Dios, que to-dos los pue - blos te a - la - ben.
O God, let all ___ the na - tions ___ praise you.

Oh Dios, que to-dos los pue - blos te a - la - ben.
O God, let all ___ the na - tions ___ praise you.

1. El Señor tenga piedad
   y nos bendiga,
   ilumine su rostro sobre nosotros;
   conozca la tierra sus caminos,
   todos los pueblos tu salvación.

2. Canten de alegría las naciones,
   pues riges al mundo con justicia,
   guías con rectitud los pueblos
   y gobiernas todas las naciones.

3. Oh Dios, que te alaben los pueblos,
   que todos los pueblos te alaben.
   Que Dios nos bendiga;
   que le teman
   hasta los confines del orbe.

1. *May God be gracious and bless us.*
   May God's face shine upon us,
   that all the earth
   may know your ways, Lord,
   and all the nations your salvation.

2. *Let nations exult and rejoice,*
   for you rule the world with justice;
   with fairness you judge the peoples,
   with fairness you govern the nations.

3. *The land has yielded its harvest;*
   God, our God, has blessed us.
   O God, grant us still your blessing,
   that all the ends of the earth
   may revere you.

*Use either refrain for Thanksgiving. Refrain II can also be used for the 6th Sunday of Easter, Year C,
and the 20th Sunday in Ordinary Time, Year A.

Text: Psalm 67 (Salmo 66):2–3, 5, 7–8. Spanish refrain II and verses © 1970, Comisión Episcopal Española de Liturgia.
All rights reserved. Used with permission. Spanish refrain I and English refrains © 1969, 1981, 1997, ICEL.
All rights reserved. Used with permission. English verses, Eleazar Cortés, b. 1947, © 1998, Eleazar Cortés.
Published by OCP Publications. All rights reserved.
Music: Eleazar Cortés, © 1998, Eleazar Cortés. Published by OCP Publications. All rights reserved.

PSALM 67: O GOD, LET ALL THE NATIONS   55

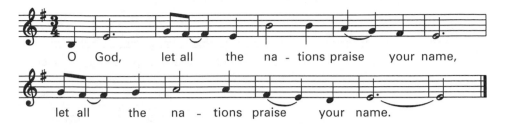

O God, let all the na-tions praise your name,
let all the na-tions praise your name.

1. Lord, look with favor on us;
   show us your face.
   Reveal to the faithful your way, Lord,
   salvation for all the world.

2. May the nations sing and be glad,
   for your word governs all the world.

Your justice will guide all nations,
all people on the earth.

3. Lord, may we sing your praise;
   may we sing to you all of our days.
   O God, we ask you to bless us,
   as we honor your name.

PSALM 69: TURN TO GOD IN YOUR NEED   56

Turn to God in your need. Turn to God in your
need, you shall live! You shall live.

1. This is my prayer to you:
   favor my plea.
   In your great love, O God,
   answer me.
   Come with your help
   and your kindness, I pray:
   be merciful. Turn my way!

2. Here in my poverty, haunted by pain,
   I beg you hear me, raise me again.
   Sweet is your name on my heart
   taking wing.
   Lifted in glory, I sing.

3. The poor ones shall see
   when you rescue my life;
   their hearts, full of hope, will revive.
   O God, hear the needy,
   and do not disdain
   your servants who weep in chains.

4. "Who-Never-Forgets"
   will bring Zion to bloom.
   God who is faithful will build us anew.
   Our daughters and sons
   will receive from God's hand
   this heritage: holy land.

57 PSALM 72: JUSTICE SHALL FLOURISH
Lord, Every Nation

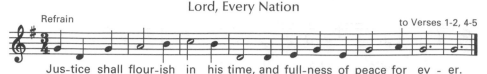

Jus-tice shall flour-ish in his time, and full-ness of peace for ev - er.

Lord, ev-'ry na-tion on earth will a - dore you.

1. O God, with your judgment
   endow the king,
   and with your justice, the king's son;
   he shall govern your people
   with justice
   and your afflicted ones with judgment.

2. Justice shall flower in those days,
   and holy peace,
   'til the moon be no more.
   May he rule from sea to sea,
   and from the River to the ends of the earth.

3. From the islands and Tarshish
   shall kings come with gifts;
   from Arabia and Sheba they come.

All the kings of the earth pay him homage;
all the nations shall serve him.

4. For he shall rescue his poor ones
   when they cry out,
   and the afflicted
   when there is no one to help them.
   He shall have pity for the lowly and poor;
   the lives of the poor he shall save.

5. May his name be blessed forever,
   and while the sun lasts
   his name shall remain.
   In him shall all the tribes
   of the earth be blessed;
   all the nations
   shall proclaim his happiness.

58 PSALM 80: THE VINEYARD OF THE LORD
Lord, Make Us Turn to You

(Ord. Time) The vine-yard of the Lord is the house of Is - ra - el. The
(Advent) Lord, make us turn to you, show your face, we shall be saved. Lord,

vine-yard of the Lord is the house of Is - ra - el.
make us turn to you, show your face, we shall be saved.

Ordinary Time Verses

1. A vine from Egypt you transplanted;
   you drove away the nations and planted it.
   It put forth its foliage to the Sea,
   its shoots as far as the River.

2. Why have you broken down its walls,
   so that every passer-by plucks its fruit,
   the boar from the forest lays it waste,
   and the beasts of the field feed upon it?

3. Once again, O LORD of hosts,
   look down from heaven, and see;
   take care of this vine,

and protect what your right hand
has planted,
the son of man whom you yourself
made strong.

4. Then we will no more withdraw from you;
   give us new life,
   and we will call upon your name.
   O LORD, God of hosts, restore us;
   if your face shine upon us,
   then we shall be saved.

Advent Verses

1. O shepherd of Israel, hearken,
   from your throne upon the cherubim,
   shine forth.
   Rouse your power,
   and come to save us.

2. Once again, O LORD of hosts,
   look down from heaven, and see;
   take care of this vine,
   and protect what your right hand
   has planted,

the son of man whom you yourself
made strong.

3. May your help be with the man
   of your right hand,
   with the son of man whom you yourself
   made strong.
   Then we will no more withdraw from you;
   give us new life,
   and we will call upon your name.

Text: Psalm 80:9, 12, 13–14, 15–16, 19–20; 4, 2–3, 15–16, 8–19. Refrains © 1969, 1981, ICEL. All rights reserved. Used with permission. Verses © 1970, 1997, 1998, CCD. All rights reserved. Used with permission.
Music: Kevin Keil, ASCAP, b. 1956, © 1996, Kevin Keil. Published by OCP Publications. All rights reserved.

PSALM 84: HOW LOVELY IS YOUR DWELLING PLACE   59

How love-ly is your dwell-ing place, O Lord God of Hosts!

1. My soul yearns and pines
   for the courts of the Lord,
   my heart and my flesh cry out;
   Even the sparrow may find a home,
   the swallow a nest for her young;
   Your altars, my king and my God!

2. How happy are they
   who may dwell in your courts,
   how happy when you are their strength;
   Though they might go through
   the valley of death,
   they make it a place of springs.
   Your first rain will bring it to life.

3. O Lord of Hosts, hear my cry,
   and hearken, O God of Jacob;
   One day in your house
   is worth much more to me
   than ten thousand anywhere else;
   The Lord is my sun and my shield!

Text: Psalm 84:2–7, 9, 11–12; Michael Joncas, b. 1951.
Music: Michael Joncas.
Text and music © 1979, New Dawn Music. Published by OCP Publications. All rights reserved.

60 PSALM 85: LORD, SHOW US YOUR MERCY

Lord, show us your mer - cy and love.

1. I will hear what God proclaims;
   the LORD —for he proclaims peace.
   Near indeed is his salvation
   to those who fear him,
   glory dwelling in our land.

2. Kindness and truth shall meet;
   justice and peace shall kiss.
   Truth shall spring out of the earth,
   and justice shall look down from heaven.

3. The LORD himself will give his benefits;
   our land shall yield its increase.
   Justice shall walk before him,
   and prepare the way of his steps.

Note: Common (Seasonal) Psalm for use in Advent.

61 PSALM 85: MUÉSTRANOS, SEÑOR/SHOW US, O LORD

Més - tra - nos, Se - ñor, tu mi - se - ri - cor - dia y
Show __ us, O Lord, your mer - cy and kind-ness and

da - nos tu sal - va - ción, __ y da - nos tu sal - va - ción.
grant us your sal - va - tion, and grant us your sal - va - tion.

1. Quiero escuchar
   lo que dice el Señor;
   paz en favor de su pueblo.
   Dios traerá su salvación
   a todos los que le temen;
   su gloria estará en la tierra.

2. La gracia y la verdad se encuentran,
   la justicia y la paz se abrazan;
   la verdad brotará desde la tierra,
   la justicia bajará del cielo.

3. El Señor mismo nos hará felices;
   nuestra tierra nos dará sus frutos.
   La justicia le abrirá los pasos
   y la paz seguirá sus huellas.

1. *I will hear what the Lord proclaims:*
   peace to the Lord's faithful people.
   Salvation is near
   to those who fear God.
   Glory will dwell in our land.
   Glory will dwell in our land.

2. *Kindness and truth shall meet;*
   justice and peace shall kiss.
   Truth shall spring out of the earth,
   justice shall look down from heaven.

3. *The Lord, our God, will give prosperity*
   and our land shall yield abundant fruit.
   Justice shall march before the Lord,
   salvation and peace will follow.

PSALM 85: SHOW US YOUR KINDNESS

Show us your kind-ness, O God.   Show us your kind-ness, O God.

1. I will hear what God proclaims:
   peace to the people;
   peace to all who change their hearts
   and place their trust in God.

2. Mercy and truth embrace;
   peace and justice.
   Truth shall break forth from the earth,
   and justice from on high.

3. God will give us good things;
   our land will yield its harvest.
   Justice, oh, justice;
   justice, oh, justice will walk before our God
   every step of the way, every step of the way.

Text: Psalm 85:8, 9, 11–12, 13–14; Bob Hurd, b. 1950.
Music: Bob Hurd.

PSALM 89: FOR EVER I WILL SING
THE GOODNESS OF THE LORD

For   ev - er   I   will   sing   the   good-ness   of   the   Lord.

1. I have made a covenant
   with my chosen one,
   I have sworn to David my servant:
   forever will I confirm your posterity
   and establish your throne
   for all generations.

2. Blessed the people who know
   the joyful shout;
   In the light of your countenance,
   O LORD, they walk.
   At your name they rejoice all the day,
   and through your justice they are exalted.

3. He shall say of me,
   "You are my father,
   my God, the rock, my savior."
   Forever I will maintain
   my kindness toward him,
   and my covenant with him stands firm.

4. The promises of the LORD
   I will sing forever,
   through all generations my mouth
   shall proclaim your faithfulness.
   For you have said, "My kindness
   is established forever";
   in heaven you have confirmed
   your faithfulness.

5. You are the splendor of their strength,
   and by your favor our horn is exalted.
   For to the LORD belongs our shield,
   and to the Holy One of Israel, our king.

4th Sunday in Advent, Year B: Verses 4, 1, 3; Christmas: Verses 1, 2, 3;
13th Sunday in Ordinary Time, Year A: Verses 4, 2, 5.

64 PSALM 89: CANTARÉ ETERNAMENTE/FOREVER I WILL SING

Can-ta - ré   e - ter-na-men - te   las mi-se-ri -
cor-dias del Se - ñor.   For - ev - er I will
sing   the good - ness   of   the Lord.

1. Sellé una alianza
   con mi elegido,
   jurando a David mi siervo:
   "Te fundaré un linaje perpetuo,
   edificaré tu trono
   para todas las edades".

2. Dichoso el pueblo
   que sabe aclamarte:
   caminará, oh Señor,
   a la luz de tu rostro;
   tu nombre es su gozo cada día,
   tu justicia es su orgullo.

3. Él me invocará: "Tú eres mi padre,
   mi Dios, mi Roca salvadora".
   Le mantendré eternamente mi favor,
   y mi alianza con él
   será estable.

4. Cantaré eternamente
   las misericordias del Señor,
   anunciaré tu fidelidad
   por todas las edades.
   Porque dije: "Tu misericordia
   es un edificio eterno,
   más que el cielo
   has afianzado tu fidelidad".

5. Porque tú eres su honor y su fuerza,
   y con tu favor realzas nuestro poder.
   Porque el Señor es nuestro escudo,
   y el santo de Israel, nuestro rey.

6. Encontré a David mi siervo
   y lo he ungido con óleo sagrado;
   para que mi mano esté siempre con él
   y mi brazo lo haga valeroso.

7. Mi fidelidad y misericordia
   lo acompañarán,
   por mi nombre crecerá su poder.
   Él me invocará: "Tú eres mi Padre,
   mi Dios, mi Roca salvadora".

1. I have made a covenant
   with my chosen one,
   I have sworn to David my servant:
   forever will I confirm your posterity
   and establish your throne
   for all generations.

2. Happy the people
   who know the joyful shout;
   in the light of your countenance,
   O Lord, they walk.
   At your name they rejoice all the day,
   and through your justice they are exalted.

3. He shall say of me, "You are my father,
   my God, my Rock, my savior."
   Forever I will maintain my
   kindness toward him,
   and my covenant with him stands firm.

4. The promises of the Lord
   I will sing forever;
   through all generations my mouth
   shall proclaim your faithfulness.
   For you have said, "My kindness
   is established forever;"
   in heaven you have confirmed
   your faithfulness.

5. You are the splendor of their strength,
   and by your favor our horn is exalted.
   For to the Lord belongs our shield,
   and to the Holy One of Israel, our king.

6. I have chosen David, my servant;
   with my holy oil I have anointed him.
   My hand will be with him:
   my arm will make him strong.

7. My loyalty and love will be with him;
   through my name
   his horn will be exalted.
   He shall cry to me,
   "You are my Father, my God,
   my Rock that brings me victory."

4th Sunday of Advent, Year B: Verses 4, 1, 3; Christmas: Verses 1, 2, 3;
13th Sunday in Ordinary Time, Year A: Verses 4, 2, 5; Chrism Mass: Verses 6 and 7.

PSALM 90: FILL US WITH YOUR LOVE, O LORD 65

Fill us with your love, O Lord, and we will sing for joy!

1. Make us know the shortness of our life
that we may gain wisdom of heart.
Lord, relent! Is your anger for ever?
Show pity to your servants.

2. In the morning, fill us with your love;
we shall exult and rejoice all our days.
Give us joy to balance our affliction
for the years when we knew misfortune.

3. Show forth your work to your servants;
let your glory shine on their children.
Let the favor of the Lord be upon us:
give success to the work of our hands.

PSALM 90: IN EVERY AGE 66

In ev - 'ry age, O Lord, you have been our ref - uge, you have been our ref - uge.

1. You return us to dust,
saying, "Return, O children, to earth."
For to you a thousand years
are like yesterday passed,
or as a watch of the night.

2. You sweep us away in a dream.
At dawn we are like morning grass
that rises to the morning sun,
then withers and fades.

3. Teach us to treasure our days.
Give wisdom to our hearts.
Return, O Lord, how long must we wait?
Pity your servants.

4. Fill our day-break with your love
that we may rejoice in song.
May your gracious eye watch over us
and the work of our hands.

67 Psalm 91: Be with Me, Lord

Be with me, Lord; be with me, Lord, when I am in trou-ble and need.

1. You who dwell in the shelter
of God, Most High,
who abide in Almighty's shade,
say to the Lord: "My refuge, my
stronghold, my God in whom I trust."

2. Evil shall never befall you,
nor affliction come near to your tent.
Unto his angels he's given command
to guard you in all your ways.

3. On their hands the angels will bear you up,
lest you dash your foot 'gainst a stone.
Lion or viper might strike at your life,
but you will not come to harm.

4. Cling to the Lord and
he'll surely deliver you;
he raises up all who call on his name.
He will bring joy to your hearts and
bless you with peace in all your days.

Text: Based on Psalm 91:15, 1–2, 10–11, 12–13, 14–16; Michael Joncas, b. 1951.
Music: Michael Joncas.

68 Psalm 91: Be with Me, Lord

Be with me Lord, be with me, Lord, when I am in trou-ble.

1. He who dwells in the shadow
of the Most High
and abides in the shade of the Almighty
says to the Lord:
"My refuge, my stronghold,
my God in whom I trust!"

2. Upon you no evil shall fall,
no plague approach where you dwell.
For you has he commanded his angels,
to keep you in all your ways.

3. They shall bear you upon their hands
lest you strike your foot against a stone.
On the lion and the viper you will tread
and trample the young lion and the dragon.

4. "Since he clings to me in love, I will free him;
protect him for he knows my name.
When he calls I shall answer: 'I am with you.'
I will save him in distress and give him glory."

Text: Psalm 91:1–2, 10–11, 12–13, 14–15. Refrain © 1969, ICEL. All rights reserved. Used with permission.
Verses © 1963, The Grail (England). All rights reserved. Used with permission of A.P. Watt, Ltd.
Music: Christopher Willcock, b. 1947, © 1977, 1990, Christopher Willcock, SJ.

Psalm 91: Acompáñame, Señor/ Be with Me, O Lord

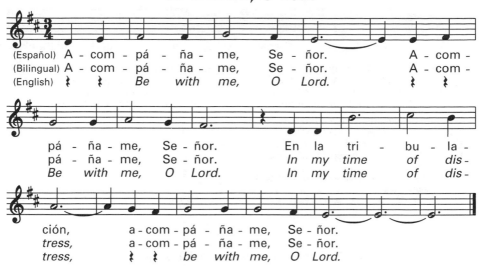

(Español) A - com - pá - ña - me, Se - ñor. A - com -
(Bilingual) A - com - pá - ña - me, Se - ñor. A - com -
(English) Be with me, O Lord.

pá - ña - me, Se - ñor. En la tri - bu - la -
pá - ña - me, Se - ñor. In my time of dis -
Be with me, O Lord. In my time of dis -

ción, a - com - pá - ña - me, Se - ñor.
tress, a - com - pá - ña - me, Se - ñor.
tress, be with me, O Lord.

1. Tú que habitas al amparo
   del Altísimo,
   que vives a la sombra
   del Omnipotente, di al Señor:
   "Refugio mío, alcázar mío,
   Dios mío, confío en ti".

2. No se te acercará la desgracia,
   ni la plaga llegará hasta tu tienda,
   porque a sus ángeles ha dado órdenes
   para que te guarden en tus caminos.

3. Te llevarán en sus palmas,
   para que tu pie
   no tropiece en la piedra;
   caminarás sobre áspides y víboras,
   pisotearás leones y dragones.

4. Se puso junto a mí: lo libraré;
   lo protegeré porque
   conoce mi nombre,
   me invocará y lo escucharé.
   Con él estaré en la tribulación,
   lo defenderé, lo glorificaré.

1. *You who live in the shelter*
   of the Most High,
   in the shadow of the Almighty,
   say to the LORD,
   "My refuge, my fortress,
   my God in whom I trust."

2. *No evil shall overtake you,*
   no harm come near your dwelling.
   For God has commanded the angels
   to guard you in all your ways.

3. *With their hands they shall bear you up,*
   lest you strike your foot against a stone.
   You shall tread upon the viper
   and the cobra,
   you shall trample the lion
   and the serpent.

4. *I will save the one who clings to me,*
   raise on high those who know my name;
   I will answer their call
   and be with them in distress,
   I will save them and give them honor.

Text: Psalm 91 (Salmo 90):1–2, 10–11, 12–13, 14, 16. Spanish © 1970, Comisión Episcopal Española de Liturgia.
All rights reserved. Used with permission. English verse 1 © 1970, 1986, CCD. All rights reserved. Used with permission.
English verses 2–4, Bob Hurd, b. 1950, © 1998, Bob Hurd. Published by OCP Publications. All rights reserved.
Music: Bob Hurd, © 1998, Bob Hurd. Published by OCP Publications. All rights reserved.

70 PSALM 92: IT IS GOOD TO GIVE YOU THANKS

It is good to give you thanks, O Lord, it is good to give you thanks.

1. It is good to give thanks unto the Lord,
   to make music to your name, O Most High,
   to proclaim your love in the morning,
   and your truth throughout the night.

2. The just will flourish like a palm tree,
   and grow like a cedar of Lebanon.
   Planted in the house of the Lord,
   they will flourish in the courts of our God.

3. Still bearing fruit when they are old,
   still full of sap, still green,
   to proclaim the Lord to the just.
   In God, my rock, there is no wrong.

Text: Psalm 92:2–3, 13–14, 15–16; Christopher Willcock, b. 1947.
Music: Christopher Willcock.
Text and music © 1992, 2002, Christopher Willcock, SJ. Published by OCP Publications. All rights reserved.

71 PSALM 95: ESCUCHEN HOY LA VOZ DEL SEÑOR/ LISTEN TODAY TO GOD'S VOICE

Lis-ten to-day to God's voice, hard-en not your heart.

Es - cu - chen hoy la voz del Se-ñor.

1. Vengan, aclamemos al Señor.
   ¡Vivas a la roca que nos salva!
   Entremos hoy a su presencia
   dándole gracias con nuestros cantos.

2. Entren, postrémonos por tierra,
   bendiciendo al Señor, creador nuestro.
   Porque Él es nuestro Dios,
   somos su pueblo y su rebaño.

3. Ojalá escuchen hoy su voz:
   "No endurezcan más el corazón,
   como sus padres me tentaron
   aunque habían visto todas mis obras".

1. *Come with joy before the Lord.*
   Sing out to the Rock of our salvation.
   Come before the Lord with thanks;
   with shouts of joy and songs of praise.

2. *Come, give homage to the Lord.*
   Let us kneel before the one who made us.
   The Lord our God, and we God's people;
   the Lord our Shepherd, and we the flock.

3. *Hear the voice of God today:*
   "Harden not your hearts as at Meribah;
   as on the day in the desert
   when your people put me to the test."

Text: Psalm 95 (Salmo 94):1–2, 6–7, 8–9; Eleazar Cortés, b. 1947.
Music: Eleazar Cortés.
Text and music © 1998, Eleazar Cortés. Published by OCP Publications. All rights reserved.

PSALM 95: IF TODAY YOU HEAR HIS VOICE

72

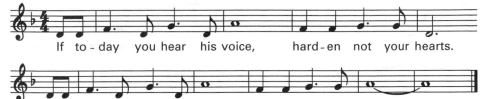

If to-day you hear his voice, hard-en not your hearts.

If to-day you hear his voice, hard-en not your hearts.

1. Come, let us sing joyfully to the LORD;
   Come, let us acclaim
   the Rock of our salvation.
   Let us greet him with thanksgiving;
   let us joyfully sing psalms to him.

2. Come, let us bow down,
   bow down in worship;
   Let us kneel before the LORD,
   the LORD who made us.

For he is our God, and we the people,
the people he shepherds
and the flock he guides.

3. Oh, that today you would hear his voice:
   Oh, "Harden not your hearts as at Meribah,
   as in the day, the day of Massah
   in the desert
   where your fathers tempted me."

PSALM 95: IF TODAY YOU HEAR GOD'S VOICE

73

If to-day you hear God's voice, hard-en not your hearts.

If to-day you hear God's voice, hard-en not your hearts.

1. Come, let us sing joyfully to the LORD;
   let us acclaim the Rock of our salvation.
   Let us come into his presence with
   thanksgiving;
   let us joyfully sing psalms to him.

2. Come, let us bow down and worship;
   let us kneel before the LORD who
   made us.
   For he is our God,
   and we are the people he shepherds,
   the flock he guides.

3. O, that today you would
   hear his voice:
   "Harden not your hearts
   as at Meribah,
   as in the day of Massah in the desert."
   Where your fathers tempted me;
   they tested me though they had seen
   my works.

74

PSALM 96: TODAY A SAVIOR IS BORN

To - day, to - day a Sav-ior has been born; a
Sav-ior has been born to us. He is Christ the Lord,
Christ the Lord, Je - sus Christ the Lord.

1. Sing a new song to the Lord.
   Sing to the Lord, all the earth.
   Sing to the Lord, sing to the Lord.
   Sing to the Lord, bless his name!

2. Proclaim his help day by day.
   Tell among the nations his glory.
   Tell of his works, tell of his works,
   and his wonders among all the peoples.

3. Let the heavens rejoice and earth be glad,
   let the sea and all within it thunder praise.
   All of the land, all that it bears:
   rejoice at the presence of the Lord.

75

PSALM 96: TODAY OUR SAVIOR IS BORN

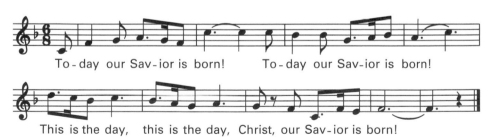

To - day our Sav-ior is born! To - day our Sav-ior is born!
This is the day, this is the day, Christ, our Sav-ior is born!

1. Sing to our God a joyful song!
   Everyone bless God's name.
   Tell of God's wondrous deeds;
   sing to all the world.

2. Heaven be glad and earth rejoice,
   let every ocean roar!

   Every forest, every tree
   joins the song of joy!

3. Cry out with joy for God has come,
   come to rule the earth.
   God will rule the world with love,
   righteousness and truth.

PSALM 98: LOS CONFINES DE LA TIERRA/ ALL THE ENDS OF THE EARTH

1. Canten al Señor un cántico nuevo
   porque ha hecho maravillas.
   Su diestra le ha dado la victoria,
   su diestra, su santo brazo.

2. El Señor da a conocer su victoria,
   revela a las naciones su justicia:
   se acordó de su amor y fidelidad
   en favor de la casa de Israel.

3. Los confines de la tierra
   han contemplado
   la victoria de nuestro Dios.
   Aclama al Señor, tierra entera,
   griten, vitoreen, toquen.

4. Toquen la cítara para el Señor,
   toquen y suenen los instrumentos:
   con clarines y al son de trompetas
   aclamen al rey y Señor.

1. *Sing, sing to the Lord a new song;*
   sing, for our God has worked wonders.
   The right hand of the Lord
   has won the vict'ry,
   the holy arm of the Lord
   has brought salvation.

2. *The Lord makes known salvation,*
   revealing justice to the nations.
   The Lord remembers mercy
   and faithful love for the house of Israel.

3. *All the ends of the earth have seen*
   the vict'ry, the vict'ry of our God.
   Rejoice before the Lord all the earth;
   break forth into songs of praise.

4. *Give praise to the Lord upon the harp,*
   with the harp and tuneful song.
   With trumpets and the sound of the horn
   give praise to the King, the Lord.

77   Psalm 98: All the Ends of the Earth

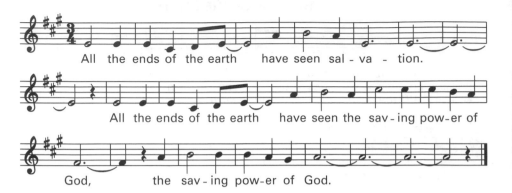

All the ends of the earth have seen sal - va - tion.

All the ends of the earth have seen the sav - ing pow-er of

God, the sav - ing pow-er of God.

1. Let us sing a new song
   for the wondrous deeds of our God,
   whose holy arm has prevailed,
   bringing salvation and victory.

2. All the ends of the earth
   have seen the power of God.
   Ring out your joy, break into song;
   all you lands sing praise.

3. Sing the praises of God;
   with the harp and song give praise.
   O trumpets sound! Joyfully sing;
   sing to the ruler of all.

78   Psalm 98: The Lord Has Revealed

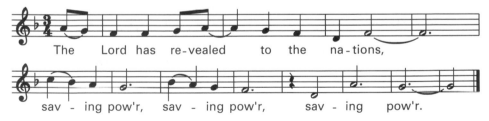

The Lord has re-vealed to the na - tions,

sav - ing pow'r, sav - ing pow'r, sav - ing pow'r.

1. Sing a new song, all you lands,
   of the marvelous deeds of the Lord.
   Salvation is born of God's right hand
   and holy arm.

2. The saving power of God
   has been revealed to all the lands.
   His kindness and truth
   forever faithful to the house of Israel.

3. All of the ends of the earth
   have seen the salvation of God.
   Shout to the Lord, dance for joy,
   sing your praise.

4. Play out your song on the harp,
   create a melodious song.
   With trumpets and horn
   acclaim our King and our God.

PSALM 98: ALL THE ENDS OF THE EARTH

All the ends of the earth have seen the sav-ing pow-er of God.

1. Sing to the Lord a new song,
   for he has done wondrous deeds;
   his right hand has won vict'ry for him,
   his holy arm.

2. The Lord has made his salvation known:
   in the sight of the nations
   he has revealed his justice.
   He has remembered his kindness
   and his faithfulness t'ward the house of Israel.

3. All the ends of the earth
   have seen the salvation of our God.
   Sing joyfully to the Lord, all you lands;
   break into song; sing praise, sing praise,
   O sing praise, sing praise.

PSALM 100: NOSOTROS SOMOS SU PUEBLO/ WE ARE GOD'S PEOPLE

No - so - tros so - mos su pue - blo. *We*

are God's peo - ple. Yo - ve - jas de su re -

ba - ño. *The flock of the Lord.*

1. Aclamen al Señor, oh tierra entera,
   sirvan al Señor con alegría,
   entren en su presencia con vítores.

2. Sepan que el Señor es Dios:
   que Dios nos hizo y somos suyos,
   somos el pueblo de Dios
   y ovejas de su rebaño.

3. El Señor es bueno,
   su misericordia es eterna.
   Su fidelidad abraza
   a todas las edades.

1. *Make a joyful noise to the Lord,
   all the earth.
   Worship the Lord with gladness;
   come into the presence of the Lord
   with singing.*

2. *Know that the Lord is God,
   our maker to whom we belong.
   We are the people of God,
   the flock of the Lord.*

3. *For the Lord is good;
   the kindness of the Lord is everlasting.
   God's faithfulness embraces
   every generation.*

81   PSALM 100: WE ARE GOD'S PEOPLE

We are God's peo-ple, the flock of the Lord.

1. Let all the earth shout for joy.
   Serve the Lord with gladness.
   Sing to the Lord with joyful song.

2. Know that the Lord is God.
   He made us, to him we belong,
   and we are the sheep of his flock.

3. Enter his gates with thanks,
   the courts of the Lord with praise.
   Give thanks and bless his name.

4. Forever God is good.
   His love is everlasting,
   faithful for all generations.

82   PSALM 103: EL SEÑOR ES COMPASIVO/ THE LORD IS KIND AND MERCIFUL

El Se-ñor es com-pa-si-vo y mi-se-ri-cor-dio - so.
The Lord is kind and the Lord is mer-ci-ful.

1. Bendice, alma mía, al Señor,
   y todo mi ser a su santo nombre.
   Bendice, alma mía, al Señor
   y no olvides sus beneficios.

2. Él perdona todas tus culpas
   y cura todas tus enfermedades;
   él rescata tu vida de la fosa
   y te colma de gracia y de ternura.

3. El Señor es compasivo
   y misericordioso,
   lento a la ira y rico en clemencia.
   No nos trata como merecen
   nuestros pecados,
   ni nos paga según nuestras culpas.

4. Como dista el oriente del ocaso,
   así aleja de nosotros nuestros delitos;
   como un padre siente
   ternura por sus hijos,
   siente el Señor ternura por sus fieles.

1. Bless the LORD, O my soul;
   and all my being, bless his holy name.
   Bless the LORD, O my soul,
   and forget not all his benefits.

2. He pardons all your iniquities,
   heals all your ills,
   He redeems your life from destruction,
   crowns you with kindness and compassion.

3. Merciful and gracious is the LORD,
   slow to anger and abounding in kindness.
   Not according to our sins
   does he deal with us,
   nor does he requite us
   according to our crimes.

4. As far as the east is from the west,
   so far has he put our transgressions from us.
   As a father has compassion on his children,
   so the LORD has compassion
   on those who fear him.

PSALM 103: THE LORD IS KIND AND MERCIFUL 83

The Lord is kind and mer - ci - ful.

1. My soul, give thanks to the Lord,
   all my being, bless his holy name.
   My soul, give thanks to the Lord
   and never forget all your blessings.

2. It is he who forgives all your guilt,
   who heals all your ills,
   who redeems your life from the grave,
   who crowns you with love
   and compassion.

3. The Lord is compassion and love,
   slow to anger, rich in mercy,
   treats us not according to sin
   nor repays us according to our faults.

4. As far as the east is from the west
   so far does God remove our sins.
   As a father has regard for his sons,
   the Lord will forgive
   those who are faithful.

Text: Psalm 103:1–2, 3–4, 8, 10, 12–13. Refrain © 1968, 1981, 1997, ICEL. All rights reserved. Used with permission.
Verses © 1963, The Grail (England). All rights reserved. Used with permission of A.P. Watt, Ltd.
Music: Christopher Willcock, b. 1947, © 1977, 1990, Christopher Willcock, SJ.
Published by OCP Publications. All rights reserved.

PSALM 103: THE LORD IS KIND AND MERCIFUL 84

The Lord is kind and mer - ci - ful, and par - dons all our sins.

1. Bless the Lord, O my soul.
   Let all that is in me bless his name.

2. Slow to anger and quick to heal,
   and mighty in justice to those in need.

3. Keep in mind the works of God,
   who redeems you from evil
   and brings you home.

4. As high as the sky is above the earth,
   so far God lifts us above our sins.

Text: Psalm 103:1a, 8, 2a–3, 11a, 12b. Refrain © 1969, 1981, ICEL. All rights reserved. Used with permission.
Verses, Bob Dufford, SJ, b. 1943, © 1992, 1994, Robert J. Dufford, SJ. Published by OCP Publications. All rights reserved.
Music: Bob Dufford, © 1992, 1994, Robert J. Dufford, SJ. Published by OCP Publications. All rights reserved.

85 PSALM 104: LORD, SEND OUT YOUR SPIRIT

Lord, send out your Spir-it, and re - new the face of the earth.

1. Bless the LORD, O my soul!
   O LORD, my God, you are great indeed!
   How manifold are your works, O LORD!
   The earth is full of your creatures.

2. If you take away their breath,
   they perish and return to their dust.
   When you send forth your spirit, they are created,
   and you renew the face of the earth.

3. May the glory of the LORD endure forever;
   may the LORD be glad in his works!
   Pleasing to him be my theme;
   I will be glad, be glad in the LORD.

86 PSALM 104: SEND FORTH YOUR SPIRIT, O LORD

Send forth your Spir- it, O Lord, and re - new the face of the earth.

1. Bless the Lord, O my soul,
   O Lord, how great you are!
   How many are your works, O Lord,
   the earth is full of your riches!

2. You take back your Spirit, they die,
   back to the dust from which they came;
   you send forth your Spirit,
   they are created, the whole earth is renewed!

3. Your glory will last forever,
   may you rejoice in all your works.
   May my thoughts be pleasing to you,
   I find my joy in you Lord.

Alternate Verses for the Easter Vigil

1. Bless the Lord, O my soul,
   O Lord, how great you are!
   With glory and with majesty clothed;
   you are covered with light!

2. Foundation of earth you made sure,
   standing firm from age to age.
   You placed the ocean like a robe,
   the waters covered the hills.

3. The valleys are flowing with springs;
   rivers run between the hills;
   the birds of heaven dwell on their banks,
   they make their nests as they sing.

4. You send down your rain on the hills.
   All your blessings fill the earth.
   You give the cattle grass for their food,
   and plants for crops to be grown.

5. In wisdom you made all these things.
   Lord, they are numberless.
   Your riches fill the whole of the earth.
   Bless the Lord, O my soul!

PSALM 104: RENUEVA LA FAZ DE LA TIERRA/ RENEW THE FACE OF THE EARTH 87

En - ví - a tu Es - pí - ri - tu, Se - ñor,
O Lord, ___ send out your Spir - it,

y re - nue - va la faz de la tie - rra.
and re - new ___ the face of the earth. ___

1. Bendice, alma mía, al Señor,
   ¡Dios mío, qué grande tú eres!
   Cuántas son tus obras, Señor,
   la tierra está llena de tus criaturas.

2. Les retiras el aliento, y expiran,
   y vuelven, vuelven a ser polvo;
   envías tu aliento y los creas,
   y renuevas la faz de la tierra.

3. Gloria a Dios, gloria para siempre,
   goce el Señor con sus obras.
   Que le sea agradable mi poema,
   yo me alegraré con el Señor.

1. O bless the Lord. Bless the Lord, O my soul.
   O Lord God, you are great indeed.
   You are clothed with majesty and power,
   robed in light. Alleluia!

2. In wisdom, you have wrought them all,
   the earth is full, the earth is full of your glory.
   How great are your works, O Lord!
   Bless thou the Lord, O my soul!

3. If you take away their breath then they perish.
   Your creatures return to their ashes.
   When you send out your spirit, they're created,
   and you renew the face of the earth.

PSALM 110: YOU ARE A PRIEST FOREVER 88

You are a priest for ev - er, in the line of Mel - chi - ze - dek.

1. The LORD said to my Lord:
   "Sit at my right hand
   till I make your enemies your footstool."

2. The scepter of your power
   the LORD will stretch forth from Zion:
   "Rule in the midst of your enemies."

3. "Yours is princely power
   in the day of your birth,
   in holy splendor;
   before the daystar,
   like the dew, I have begotten you."

4. The LORD has sworn,
   and he will not repent:
   "You are a priest forever,
   according to the order of Melchizedek."

89

PSALM 116: ALZARÉ LA COPA DE LA SALVACIÓN/ I WILL TAKE THE CUP OF SALVATION

El Cáliz que Bendecimos/Our Blessing Cup

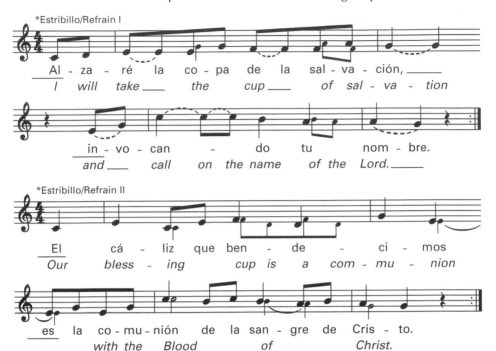

*Estribillo/Refrain I

Al - za - ré la co - pa de la sal - va - ción, ____
I will take ____ the cup ____ of sal - va - tion

in - vo - can - do tu nom - bre.
and ____ call on the name of the Lord. ____

*Estribillo/Refrain II

El cá - liz que ben - de - ci - mos
Our bless - ing cup is a com - mu - nion

es la co - mu - nión de la san - gre de Cris - to.
with the Blood of Christ.

1. ¿Cómo pagaré al Señor
   todo el bien que me ha hecho?
   Alzaré la copa de la salvación,
   invocando tu nombre, Señor.

2. Tenía fe, aún cuando dije:
   "Cómo soy de desgraciado".
   Mucho le cuesta al Señor
   la muerte de sus fieles.

3. Señor, yo soy tu siervo,
   el hijo de tu esclava;
   tú rompiste mis cadenas.
   A ti ofrezco un sacrificio de alabanza,
   invocando tu nombre, Señor.

4. Mis votos al Señor cumpliré
   en presencia de todo su pueblo;
   en el atrio de la casa del Señor,
   en medio de ti, Jerusalén.

1. *What shall I return to the LORD
   for all his bounty to me?
   I will lift the cup of salvation
   and call on the name of the LORD.*

2. *I believed, even when I said,
   "I am greatly afflicted."
   Precious in the eyes of the LORD
   the dying of his faithful ones.*

3. *O LORD, I am your servant,
   your servant, the son of your handmaid;
   you have brought me freedom.
   To you will I offer sacrifice of thanksgiving
   and call upon your name, O LORD.*

4. *My vows to the LORD I will pay
   in the presence of all his people,
   in the courts of the house of the LORD,
   in the midst of you, Jerusalem.*

*The response may be sung in only one language or bilingually. It is repeated in either case.

PSALM 116: I WILL WALK BEFORE THE LORD 90

I will walk be - fore the Lord,
in the land of the liv - ing.

Verses for 24th Sunday of Ordinary Time, Year B

1. I love the LORD
   because he has heard my voice
   in supplication,
   because he has inclined his ear to me
   the day I called.

2. The cords of death encompassed me;
   the snares of the netherworld
   seized upon me;
   I fell into distress and sorrow,
   and I called upon the name of the LORD,
   "O LORD, save my life!"

3. Gracious is the LORD and just;
   yes, our God is merciful.
   The LORD keeps the little ones;
   I was brought low, and he saved me.

4. For he has freed my soul from death,
   my eyes from tears,
   my feet from stumbling.
   I shall walk before the LORD
   in the land of the living.

Verses for 2nd Sunday of Lent, Year B

1. I believed, even when I said,
   "I am greatly afflicted."
   Precious in the eyes of the LORD
   is the death of his faithful ones.

2. O LORD, I am your servant;
   I am your servant,
   the son of your handmaid;
   you have loosed my bonds.
   To you will I offer
   sacrifice of thanksgiving,
   and I will call upon
   the name of the LORD.

3. My vows to the LORD I will pay
   in the presence of all his people,
   In the courts of the house of the LORD,
   in your midst, O Jerusalem.

PSALM 116: OUR BLESSING CUP 91

Our bless-ing cup is a com - mu - nion in the blood of Christ.

1. How shall I make a return to the LORD
   for all the good he has done for me?
   The cup of salvation I will take up,
   and I will call upon the name of the LORD.

2. Taste and see, taste and see
   the sweetness of the Lord,
   the goodness of the Lord.

3. Every time you eat of this bread,
   every time you drink of this cup
   you proclaim the death of the Lord
   until he comes.

PSALM 116: OUR BLESSING CUP

Our bless-ing cup is a com-mun-ion with the blood of Christ; and the bread we break, it is a

Repeat first time only
(or ostinato as desired)
Fine

shar - ing in the bod - y of the Lord.

1. How can we make a return
   for all the goodness God has shown?
   We will take the cup of life,
   and call upon God's name.

2. Precious indeed in your sight,
   the life and death of those you love.
   We are your servants,
   for you have set us free.

3. Gracious and merciful God,
   we give you thanks and bless your name:
   with all your people,
   praise and glory to your name.

4. For you have heard my voice,
   for you have heard my pleading.
   Though death surrounded me,
   you heard and answered me.

Text: 1 Corinthians 10:16; Psalm 116:1, 3, 5, 12–13, 15–16, 17–18; Bob Hurd, b. 1950.
Music: Bob Hurd.
Text and music © 1988, Bob Hurd. Published by OCP Publications. All rights reserved.

93   PSALM 117: GO OUT TO ALL THE WORLD
AND TELL THE GOOD NEWS

Go out to all the world and tell the good news.

1. Praise the LORD, all you nations;
   glorify him, all you peoples!

2. For steadfast is his kindness toward us,
   and the fidelity of the LORD endures forever.

Text: Psalm 117:1, 2. Refrain © 1969, 1981, 1997, ICEL. All rights reserved. Used with permission.
   Verses © 1970, 1997, 1998, CCD. All rights reserved. Used with permission.
Music: Owen Alstott, b. 1947, © 1977, 1990, OCP Publications. All rights reserved.

PSALM 118: ALELUYA/ALLELUIA

Éste Es el Día/This Is the Day

1. Den gracias al Señor
   porque es bueno,
   porque es eterna su misericordia.
   Diga la casa de Israel:
   eterna es su misericordia.

2. La diestra del Señor es poderosa,
   la diestra del Señor es excelsa.
   No he de morir, viviré,
   para contar las hazañas del Señor.

3. La piedra que desecharon
   los arquitectos,
   es ahora la piedra angular.
   Es el Señor quien lo ha hecho,
   ha sido un milagro patente.

1. *Give thanks to the LORD*
   for he is good,
   for his mercy endures forever.
   Let the house of Israel say,
   "His mercy endures forever."

2. *The right hand of the LORD*
   has struck with power;
   the right hand of the LORD is exalted.
   I shall not die but live, and declare
   the works of the LORD.

3. *The stone which*
   the builders rejected,
   has become the cornerstone.
   By the LORD has this been done;
   it is wonderful in our eyes.

*Either refrain may be used throughout the Easter season.

95 Psalm 118: The Stone Which the Builders Rejected

The stone which the build-ers re-ject-ed has be-come the cor-ner-stone.

Al-le-lu - ia, al-le-lu - ia, has be-come the cor-ner-stone.

1. Let the family of Israel say:
"God's love has no end,
God's love has no end."
Let the family of Aaron say:
"God's love has no end,
God's love has no end."
And let all who fear God,
and let all who fear God
say his love is without end.
Alleluia, alleluia,
say his love is without end.

2. I called to the Lord in my distress,
he answered me and set me free.
God is at my side, God is at my side,
God is here to help me now.
Alleluia, alleluia,
God is here to help me now.

3. Open to me the gates of holiness;
I will enter and give thanks.
This is the Lord's own gate,
the gate where the just may enter in.
I will thank you, Lord,
I will thank you, Lord,
for you hear and answer me.
Alleluia, alleluia,
for you hear and answer me.

4. Go forward with branches,
go forward processing,
go to the altar of the Lord
and give thanks to God,
and give thanks to God
for his love is without end.
Alleluia, alleluia,
for his love is without end.

96 Psalm 118: Give Thanks to the Lord for He Is Good

Give thanks to the Lord for he is good, his love is ev-er-last - ing.

1. Let the house of Israel say,
"His mercy endures forever."
Let the house of Aaron say,
"His mercy endures forever."
Let those who fear the LORD say,
"His mercy endures forever."

2. I was hard pressed and was falling,
but the LORD helped me.
My strength and my courage is the LORD,
and he has been my savior.
The joyful shout of victory
in the tents of the just:

3. The stone which the builders rejected
has become the cornerstone.
By the LORD has this been done;
it is wonderful in our eyes.
This is the day the LORD has made;
let us be glad and rejoice in it.

PSALM 118: THIS IS THE DAY

This is the day the Lord has made; let us re-joice and be glad.

This is the day the Lord has made; let us re-joice and be glad.

1. Give thanks to the LORD, for he is good,
   his mercy endures forever.
   Let the house of Israel say,
   "His mercy endures forever."

2. The LORD's right hand has struck with pow'r;
   the LORD's right hand is exalted.
   I shall not die, but live, and
   declare the works of the LORD.

3. The stone which the builders rejected
   has become the cornerstone.
   By the LORD this has been done;
   it is wonderful in our eyes!

Text: Psalm 118:24, 1–2, 16–17, 22–23. Refrain © 1969, 1981, ICEL. All rights reserved. Used with permission.
  Verses © 1970, CCD. All rights reserved. Used with permission.
Music: Michael Joncas, b. 1951, © 1981, 1982, 1988, Jan Michael Joncas Trust.
  Published by OCP Publications. All rights reserved.

PSALM 119: MORE THAN GOLD

Lord, I love your com-mands. More than

gold is your word, so pre-cious to me.

1. I have said, O Lord, that my part
   is in the keeping of your words.
   The law of your mouth
   is more precious to me
   than thousands of pieces of gold—
   than thousands of pieces of gold.

2. Let your kindness comfort me
   according to your word;
   let your compassion give light to my soul,
   for your law is my delight—
   for your law is my delight.

3. For I love your commands
   more than gold, however fine.
   For in your precepts I will go forth.
   Every false way I hate—
   every false way I hate.

Text: Psalm 119:97, 57, 72, 76–77, 127–128. Refrain © 1969, 1981, ICEL. All rights reserved. Used with permission.
  Verses © 1970, CCD. All rights reserved. Used with permission.
Music: Tom Booth, b. 1961, © 1988, Tom Booth. Published by OCP Publications. All rights reserved.

99

PSALM 119: BLESSED ARE THEY

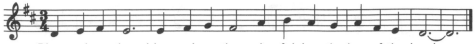

Bless-ed are they, bless-ed are they who fol-low the law of the Lord.

1. They are happy whose life is blameless,
who follow God's law!
They are happy who do his will,
seeking him,
seeking him with all their hearts.

2. You have laid down your precepts
to be obeyed with care, O Lord.
May my footsteps be firm,
my footsteps be firm to obey,
to obey your statutes, O Lord.

3. Bless your servant and I shall live,
obeying your word.
Open my eyes
that I may consider the wonders,
all the wonders of your law.

4. Bend my heart to your will, O Lord,
and not to love of gain.
Keep my eyes from all that is false:
by your word, by your word, O Lord,
give me life.

100

PSALM 121: OUR HELP IS FROM THE LORD

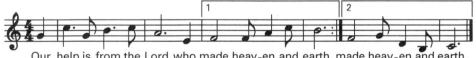

Our help is from the Lord, who made heav-en and earth. made heav-en and earth.

1. I lift up my eyes to the mountains,
when will help come to me?
My help is come from the Lord,
who made heaven and earth.

2. May he not allow me to stumble.
May he who guards me never sleep.
He walks on my path, a force beside me,
the guardian of Israel.

3. The Lord is my help, my protector.
At my right hand he will be.
The sun will not harm me by day,
the moon will not harm me by night.

4. The Lord will protect me from evil;
he will guide me as I go.
The Lord will defend me in my ways,
now and forever.

PSALM 122: LET US GO REJOICING

Let us go re-joic-ing, re-joic-ing to the house of the Lord. Let us go re-joic-ing to the house of the Lord.

1. How I rejoiced to hear them say,
"Let us go to the house of the Lord."
And now within your walls
we are standing, O Jerusalem.

2. Jerusalem, a city firmly built,
knit together in unity and strength.
There the tribes go up,
the tribes of the Lord,
making pilgrimage.

3. There the tribes give thanks
to the name of the Lord,
according to the law of Israel.
There are set the thrones of judgement
for the house of David.

4. Let us pray for the good of Jerusalem,
and for those who love you
prosperity and peace,
peace within your ramparts and your towers,
peace in your dwellings.

5. For the sake of my people and my friends,
I say peace be to you, Jerusalem.
For love of God's house
I pray for you and your prosperity.

PSALM 122: CON QUÉ ALEGRÍA/ LET US GO REJOICING

Con qué a-le-grí-a va - mos a la ca-sa del Se-ñor.

Let us go re - joic - ing to the house of the Lord!

1. Me alegré cuando me dijeron:
   "Vamos a la casa del Señor".
   Ya están pisando nuestros pies
   tus puertas, Jerusalén.

2. Jerusalén está fundada
   como ciudad bien compacta.
   Allá suben las tribus,
   las tribus del Señor.

3. La ley de Israel es dar gracias
   y alabar el nombre del Señor,
   allí donde han de juzgar
   en la casa de David.

4. Deseen la paz a Jerusalén:
   "Vivan seguros los que te aman,
   haya paz dentro de tus muros,
   seguridad en tus palacios".

5. Por el amor de mis compañeros,
   paz para ustedes pediré;
   y el amor de nuestro Dios
   por su bien voy a pedir.

1. *How I rejoiced when I heard them saying:*
   "We go to the house of the Lord."
   And now we stand within your gates,
   your gates, O Jerusalem.

2. *Jerusalem is a city*
   built with unity and strength.
   It is there that the tribes go up,
   the tribes of the Lord.

3. *We go to give thanks to God's holy*
   name according to the law of Israel.
   The thrones of judgment are there,
   the thrones of David's house.

4. *Pray for the peace of Jerusalem:*
   "May those who love you prosper;
   may peace ever reign within your walls,
   and wealth within your house!"

5. *For the sake of my friends*
   and relatives I say,
   "Peace be ever within you."
   For love of the house of the Lord
   I will seek your good.

Text: Psalm 122 (Salmo 121):1–2, 3–4, 4–5, 6–7, 8–9. Spanish verses 1, 2 and 4 © 1970, Comisión Episcopal Española de Liturgia.
All rights reserved. Used with permission. Spanish refrain and verses 3 and 5, and English text, Eleazar Cortés, b. 1947,
© 1994, Eleazar Cortés. Published by OCP Publications. All rights reserved.
Music: Eleazar Cortés, © 1994, 1998, Eleazar Cortés. Published by OCP Publications. All rights reserved.

PSALM 126: THE LORD HAS DONE GREAT THINGS 103

The Lord has done great things for us; we are filled with joy.

1. When the LORD brought back
the captives of Zion,
we were like *people dreaming.
Then our mouth was filled with laughter,
and our tongue with rejoicing.

2. Then they said among the nations,
"The LORD has done great things for them."
The LORD has done great things for us;
we are glad indeed.

3. Restore our fortunes, O LORD,
like the torrents in the southern desert.
Those that sow in tears
shall reap rejoicing.

4. Although they go forth weeping,
carrying the reed to be sown,
They shall come back rejoicing,
carrying their sheaves.

*Original text "men".

PSALM 128: O BLESSED ARE THOSE 104

O blessed are those who fear the Lord and walk in his ways.

1. O blessed are those who fear the Lord
and walk in his ways!
By the labor of your hands you shall eat.
You will be happy and prosper.

2. Your wife like a fruitful vine
in the heart of your house;
your children like shoots of the olive
around your table.

3. Indeed thus shall be blest
all those who fear the Lord.
May the Lord bless you from Zion
all the days of your life!

105 Psalm 130: Del Señor Viene la Misericordia/ With the Lord There Is Fullness of Redemption

Del Se - ñor vie - ne la mi - se - ri - cor - dia, la re - den -
With the Lord, there is full - ness of re - demp - tion, ? with the

ción ? co - pio - sa. Del Se - ñor vie - ne la mi - se - ri -
Lord, there is mer - cy. With the Lord, there is full - ness of re -

cor - dia, ? la re - den - ción co - pio - sa.
demp - tion, ___ ? with the Lord, there is mer - cy.

1. Desde lo hondo a ti grito, Señor;
   Señor, escucha mi voz:
   estén tus oídos atentos
   a la voz de mi súplica.

2. Si llevas cuentas de los delitos, Señor.
   ¿quién podrá resistir?
   Pero de ti procede el perdón
   y así infundes respeto.

3. Mi alma espera en el Señor,
   espera en su palabra.
   Aguarde Israel al Señor,
   como el centinela la aurora.

4. Porque del Señor
   viene la misericordia,
   la redención copiosa;
   y él redimirá a Israel
   de todos sus delitos.

1. From the depths I cry to you O Lord;
   Lord, hear my voice!
   Let your ears attend to my pleading,
   to my voice in supplication.

2. Should you mark our iniquities,
   O Lord, Lord, who could stand?
   But with you there is forgiveness
   so that you may be revered.

3. With trust I wait for the Lord.
   I trust in God's word.
   Let Israel wait for the Lord
   more than sentinels wait for daybreak.

4. For with the Lord
   there is mercy and kindness,
   and fullness of redemption.
   From all sin and iniquity
   the Lord will ransom Israel.

PSALM 130: WITH THE LORD THERE IS MERCY 106

With the Lord there is mer-cy and full-ness of re-

| 1-5 | 1st time: repeat to Verses | Final |

demp-tion.   demp-tion,   re-demp-tion.

1. Out of the depths I cry to you, O Lord.
   Hear my voice.
   Turn not your ears from the sound
   of my voice pleading.

2. Lord, who could stand
   if you recalled our sins?
   But because of your mercy
   we bow to your name.

3. I hold fast to God, I cling to his word.
   Like watching for dawn I wait for the Lord.
   My soul longs for the Lord.

4. With the Lord is mercy and redemption.
   For the Lord's great kindness
   and the Lord's compassion
   will set Israel free.

PSALM 130: OUT OF THE DEPTHS 107

Out of the depths, I cry to you, O Lord.

1. From out of the depths,
   I cry to you, Lord;
   O hear the sound of my voice.
   Lord, open your ears and listen to me;
   I plead for your kindness, O God.

2. If you, O Lord, should number our sins,
   then Lord, who would survive?
   But you are forgiveness for our sins;
   for this we adore you, O God.

3. I trust in you, Lord, my soul looks to you
   as watchmen wait for the dawn.
   And more than the watchmen
   wait for the dawn,
   let Israel wait for the Lord.

4. For with you is found forgiveness of sin;
   you show your mercy to all.
   And you will deliver your chosen ones;
   deliver your people, O God.

108
PSALM 136: GOD'S LOVE IS EVERLASTING

Cantor

1. O give thanks __ to the Lord, for he ____ is good:
   __ O give thanks __ to the Lord, the God ____ of gods:
2. In his wis - dom __ he made the heav - ens. ____
   __ In his love _____ he made the earth: _____
3. He has freed _____ his ser - vant Is - ra - el:
   __ From a land _____ of slav - er - y:
4. He re - mem - bers __ us when we suf - fer: _____
   And he fills _____ us with his joy: _____

All

1-4. God's love is ev - er - last - ing!

Cantor

1. Give thanks to the Lord of lords _____ for his
2. The sun __ to shine by day, _____ the
3. He has led __ us through the wil - der - ness __ and
4. He cares for all liv - ing things, _____ for

1. won - der - ful deeds __ for us;
2. moon and __ the stars __ by night:
3. brought _____ us to ____ our land:
4. great is __ the pow - er of God!

All   **1-3**   **to Verses 2-4**

1-4. God's love is ev - er - last - ing!

Final

4. last - ing!   God's love is ev - er - last - ing!

Text: Psalm 136:1–6, 8–9, 11, 16, 21, 23, 25; Michael Joncas, b. 1951.
Music: Michael Joncas.
Text and music © 1979, New Dawn Music. Published by OCP Publications. All rights reserved.

PSALM 138: ON THE DAY I CALLED 109

Lord, on the day I called for help, you an-swered me, you an-swered me.

1. I shall thank you, God of my heart,
   you have heard my troubled word.
   While angels watch, your name I praise;
   I dance before your holy place.

2. For your love and your faithfulness,
   I thank your name,
   your promise surpasses your fame.
   I called for your help
   all night and day long:
   you heard me, and made me strong.

3. From on high,
   from the heavens the poor you see,
   you drive the proud to their knees.
   Though I live
   in the midst of trouble and woe,
   you save me, and foil my foe.

4. Your strong hand shall come to my aid:
   you shall be all good to me.
   Forever shall your love abide;
   do not cast your child aside.

PSALM 145: I WILL PRAISE YOUR NAME 110
The Hand of the Lord

Refrain
to Verses 1, 3, 4

I will praise your name for ev-er, my king and my God.

Alternate Refrain
to Verses 1, 2, 4

The hand of the Lord feeds us, and an-swers all our needs.

1. God is merciful and gracious,
   slow to anger, full of kindness.
   The Lord is faithful to all his people,
   compassionate to all creation.

2. Lord, we lift our eyes to the heavens,
   and you feed us in due season.
   The treasures, Lord, that you impart
   fulfill every desire.

3. All of your people bless your name
   in a holy song of thanksgiving,
   singing of your eternal reign,
   declaring your holy power.

4. Lord, your justice lasts forever,
   your loving deeds from age to age.
   You are near to all who call,
   never far from faithful hearts.

111
PSALM 145: BENDECIRÉ TU NOMBRE/
I WILL PRAISE YOUR NAME

Ben - de - ci - ré tu nom - bre por
I____ will praise your name____ for

siem - pre ja - más, Dios mí - o, mi Rey.
ev - er, my King and my God.

1. Te ensalzaré, Dios mío, mi Rey,
   bendeciré tu nombre por siempre jamás.
   Día tras día te bendeciré
   y alabaré tu nombre por siempre jamás.

2. El Señor es clemente y misericordioso,
   lento a la cólera y rico en piedad;
   el Señor es bueno con todos,
   es cariñoso con todas sus criaturas.

3. Que todas tus criaturas
   te den gracias, Señor,
   que te bendigan tus fieles;
   que proclamen la gloria de tu reinado,
   que hablen de tus hazañas.

4. El Señor es fiel a sus palabras,
   bondadoso en todas sus acciones.
   El Señor sostiene a los que van a caer,
   endereza a los que ya se doblan.

1. *I will extol you, O my God and King,*
   and I will bless your name forever and ever.
   Every day will I bless you,
   and I will praise your name forever and ever.

2. *The LORD is gracious and merciful,*
   slow to anger and of great kindness.
   The LORD is good to all
   and compassionate toward all his works.

3. *Let all your works give you thanks, O LORD,*
   and let your faithful ones bless you.
   Let them discourse of the glory
   of your kingdom and speak of your might.

4. *The LORD is faithful in all his words,*
   and holy in all his works.
   The LORD lifts up all who are falling
   and raises up all who are bowed down.

Text: Psalm 145 (Salmo 144):1–2, 8–9, 10–11, 13cd–14. Spanish © 1970, Comisión Episcopal Española de Liturgia.
All rights reserved. Used with permission. English refrain © 1968, 1981, 1997, ICEL. All rights reserved. Used with permission.
English verses © 1970, 1997, 1998, CCD. All rights reserved. Used with permission.
Music: John Schiavone, b. 1947, © 1989, 1991, OCP Publications. All rights reserved.

PSALM 145: I WILL PRAISE YOUR NAME

I will praise your name for ev-er, my king and my God.

1. I will give you glory, O God my king,
   I will bless your name for ever.
   I will bless you day after day
   and praise your name for ever.

2. The Lord is kind and full of compassion,
   slow to anger, abounding in love.
   How good is the Lord to all,
   compassionate to all creation.

3. All your creatures
   shall give you thanks, O Lord,
   and your friends shall repeat their blessing.
   They shall speak of the glory of your reign
   and declare your might, O God.

4. The Lord is faithful in all his words
   and loving in all his deeds.
   The Lord supports all who fall
   and raises up all who are bowed down.

PSALM 146: PRAISE THE LORD

Lord, Come and Save Us

Refrain

Praise, praise the Lord, praise the Lord, my soul!

Alternate Refrain

Lord, come and save us; Lord, come and save us.

1. It is he who keeps faith for ever,
   who is just to those who are oppressed.
   It is he who gives bread to the hungry,
   the Lord, who sets prisoners free.

2. It is the Lord who gives sight to the blind,
   who raises up those who are bowed down.

   It is the Lord who protects the stranger
   and upholds the widow and orphan.

3. It is the Lord who loves the just
   but thwarts the path of the wicked.
   The Lord will reign for ever,
   Sion's God, from age to age.

CANTICLES

115   EXODUS 15: TO GOD BE PRAISE AND GLORY

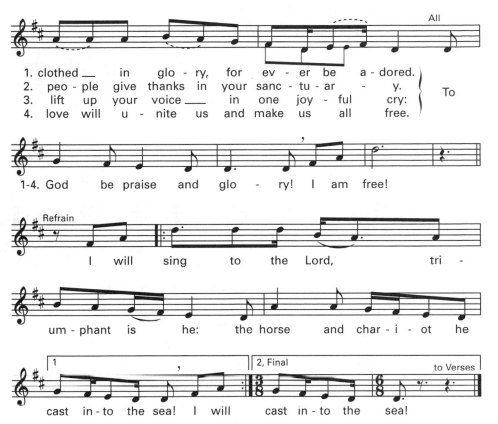

1. clothed __ in glo - ry, for ev - er be a - dored.
2. peo - ple give thanks in your sanc - tu - ar - y.
3. lift up your voice __ in one joy - ful cry:
4. love will u - nite us and make us all free.

To

1-4. God be praise and glo - ry! I am free!

Refrain

I will sing to the Lord, tri -

um - phant is he: the horse and char - i - ot he

cast in - to the sea! I will cast in - to the sea!

Text: Based on Exodus 15:19–21; Janèt Sullivan Whitaker, b. 1958.
Music: Janèt Sullivan Whitaker.

Isaiah 12: Ustedes Sacarán Agua/ You Will Draw Water Joyfully

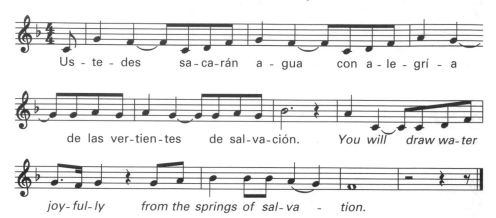

Us - te - des   sa - ca-rán a - gua   con a - le - grí - a

de las ver-tien-tes   de sal-va-ción.   You will   draw wa-ter

joy- ful- ly   from the springs of sal- va - tion.

1. ¡Vean cómo es él,
el Dios que me salva!
Me siento seguro y sin miedo,
pues el Señor
es mi fuerza y mi canción,
él es mi salvación.

2. ¡Denle gracias al Señor;
vitoreen su nombre!
Publiquen entre los pueblos
sus hazañas.
Repitan que su nombre es sublime.

3. ¡Canten al Señor
porque ha hecho maravillas
que toda la tierra debe conocer!
¡Griten de contento y de alegría,
habitantes de Sión, porque grande
se ha portado contigo
el Santo de Israel!

1. *God indeed is my savior;*
I am confident and unafraid.
My strength and my courage is the LORD,
and he has been my savior.
With joy you will draw water
at the fountain of salvation.

2. *Give thanks to the LORD,*
acclaim his name;
among the nations recount
the Lord's deeds,
proclaim how exalted is his name.

3. *Sing praise to the LORD,*
tell the wonders God has done.
Let this be known
throughout all the earth.
Shout with exultation, O city of Zion,
for great in your midst is the Holy One,
the Holy One of Israel!

ISAIAH 12: WE SHALL DRAW WATER 117

We shall draw wa - ter joy - ful-ly, sing-ing joy - ful-ly,

sing-ing joy - ful-ly; we shall draw wa - ter

joy - ful-ly from the well-springs of sal - va - tion.

1. Truly God is our salvation;
   we trust, we shall not fear.
   For the Lord is our strength,
   the Lord is our song;
   he became our Savior.

2. Give thanks, O give thanks to the Lord;
   give praise to his holy name!

Make his mighty deeds known to
all of the nations; proclaim his greatness.

3. Sing a psalm, sing a psalm to the Lord
   for he has done glorious deeds.
   Make known his works to all of the earth;
   people of Zion, sing for joy,
   for great in your midst, great in your midst
   is the Holy One of Israel.

Text: Isaiah 12:3, 2, 4–6; Paul Inwood, b. 1947.
Music: Paul Inwood.
Text and music © 1986, 1988, Paul Inwood. Published by OCP Publications. All rights reserved.

DANIEL 3: GLORY AND PRAISE FOREVER 118

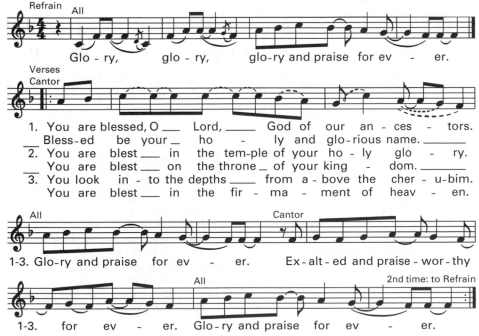

Refrain All

Glo - ry, glo - ry, glo-ry and praise for ev - er.

Verses
Cantor

1. You are blessed, O ___ Lord, ___ God of our an - ces - tors.
   __ Bless-ed be your __ ho - ly and glo-rious name. ___
2. You are blest ___ in the tem-ple of your ho - ly glo - ry.
   __ You are blest ___ on the throne _ of your king - dom. ___
3. You look in - to the depths ___ from a - bove the cher - u-bim.
   __ You are blest ___ in the fir - ma - ment of heav - en.

All   Cantor

1-3. Glo-ry and praise for ev - er. Ex - alt - ed and praise - wor - thy

                  All   2nd time: to Refrain

1-3. for ev - er. Glo-ry and praise for ev - er.

Text: Daniel 3:52–56. Refrain © 1969, 1981, ICEL. All rights reserved. Used with permission. Verses, Laura Ash, b. 1959,
   and David Ash, b. 1958, © 1996, Laura Ash and David Ash. Published by OCP Publications. All rights reserved.
Music: Laura Ash and David Ash, © 1996, Laura Ash and David Ash. Published by OCP Publications. All rights reserved.

119   LUKE 1: MARY'S SONG

Hap-py are they who be-lieve that the prom-ise of the Lord will be ful-filled.

1. I sing with all my soul
   and praise the Lord.
   My heart is glad
   because of God, my Savior;
   for he has looked
   upon his humble servant,
   and who am I to merit his attention?

2. I may henceforth regard myself as
   happy, because my God
   has done great things for me,
   and every generation gives assent:
   the Lord is mighty and his name is holy!

3. He gives his grace anew in every age
   to all who live in reverence with him.

Grace is his strength, but he unmasks all pride
and strips us bare of our self-conceit.

4. Dethroning those who hold authority,
   the poor and humble people
   he makes great.
   He gives in great abundance
   to the hungry,
   sends the rich away with empty hands.

5. His servant Israel he has remembered.
   He has been merciful to all his people,
   for so had been his promise
   to our parents:
   to Abraham and to his seed forever.

120   LUKE 1: MY SOUL PROCLAIMS

Ostinato Refrain

My soul pro-claims your great-ness, O my God. My
spir-it re-joic-es in God my Sav-ior.

Verses: Sung over Refrain

1. You are the God of my heart,
   for you my whole being
   is longing, O God.

2. You look upon your servant
   in her lowliness.
   All ages to come shall call me blessed.

3. You who are mighty
   have done great things for me.
   Holy is your Name.

4. Your mercy is from age to age
   toward those who fear you.

5. You have shown might with your arm
   and confused the proud
   in their inmost thoughts.

6. You depose the mighty
   from their thrones
   and raise the lowly to high places.

7. The hungry you give every good thing;
   the rich you send empty away.

8. You uphold Israel your servant,
   ever mindful of your mercy.

9. As you promised Abraham and Sarah
   and their descendants forever.

LUKE 1: CANTICLE OF ZACHARY

Verses 1, 3, 5

1. Blest be the God of Is - ra - el, The ev - er - liv - ing Lord, Who
3. Of old he gave his sol - emn oath To Fa - ther A - bra - ham; His
5. The ris-ing sun shall shine on us To bring the light of day To

1. comes in pow'r to save his own, His peo - ple Is - ra - el. For
3. seed a might-y race should be And blest for-ev - er-more. He
5. all who dwell in dark - est night And shad-ow of the grave. Our

1. Is - ra - el he rais-es up Sal - va-tion's tow'r on high In
3. vowed to set his peo-ple free From fear of ev - 'ry foe, That
5. foot-steps God shall safe-ly guide To walk the ways of peace; His

1. Da-vid's house who reigned as king And ser - vant of the Lord.
3. we might serve him all our days In good-ness, love, and peace.
5. name for - ev - er-more be blest. Who lives and loves and saves.

Verses 2, 4

2. Through ho - ly proph-ets did he speak His Word in days of old,
4. O ti - ny child, your name shall be The proph-et of the Lord;

2. That he would save us from our foes And all who bear us ill.
4. The way of God you shall pre - pare To make his com-ing known.

2. To our an - ces-tors did he give His cov - e - nant of love,
4. You shall pro-claim to Is - ra - el Sal - va-tion's dawn-ing day,

to Verses 3, 5

2. So with us all he keeps his Word In love that knows no end.
4. When God shall wipe a - way all sins In his re - deem-ing love.

Text: Based on Luke 1:68-79; adapt. by James D. Quinn, SJ, b. 1919, © 1969, 1985, James D. Quinn, SJ. All rights reserved.
Used with permission of Selah Publishing Co., Inc., North American agent.
Music: Michael Joncas, b. 1951, © 1981, 1982, Jan Michael Joncas Trust. Published by OCP Publications. All rights reserved.

122   LUKE 1: BENEDICTUS

1. Blest be the Lord, the God of Is - ra - el,
2. The proph-ets tell a sto - ry just be - gun
3. This is the oath once sworn to A - bra - ham:
4. And you, my child, this day you shall be called
5. The ten - der love God prom-ised from our birth

1. Who brings the dawn and dark - est night dis - pels,
2. Of van-quished foe and glo - rious vic - t'ry won,
3. All shall be free to dwell up - on the land,
4. The prom - ised one, the proph - et of our God,
5. Is soon to dawn up - on this shad-owed earth,

1. Who rais - es up a might - y Sav - ior from the earth,
2. Of prom-ise made to all who keep the law as guide:
3. Free now to praise, un-harmed by the op - pres-sor's rod,
4. For you will go be - fore the Lord to clear the way,
5. To shine on those whose sor - rows seem to nev - er cease,

1. Of Da - vid's line, a son of roy - al birth.
2. God's faith - ful love and mer - cy will a - bide.
3. Ho - ly and righ - teous in the sight of God.
4. And shep-herd all in - to the light of day.
5. To guide our feet in - to the path of peace.

123   LUKE 2: CANTICLE OF SIMEON

Refrain

Christ is the light of all the na - tions and the

glo - ry of his peo - ple Is - ra - el.

Verses

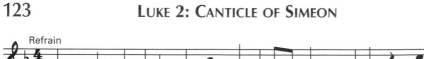

1. Now, __ Lord, you have kept __ your __ word: __ let __
2. With my own eyes I have seen __ the sal - va - tion which __
3. A __ light to re - veal you to the na - tions and the

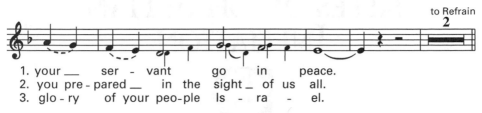

to Refrain
2

1. your __ ser - vant go in peace.
2. you pre - pared __ in the sight __ of us all.
3. glo - ry of your peo - ple Is - ra - el.

Text: *Nunc dimittis;* based on Luke 2:29–32, © 1973, ICEL. All rights reserved. Used with permission.
Music: Randall DeBruyn, b. 1947, © 1988, 1998, OCP Publications. All rights reserved.

LUKE 2: NOW LET YOUR SERVANTS, LORD, DEPART IN PEACE

124

1. Now let your ser - vants, Lord, de - part in peace,
2. What an - cient kings and proph - ets long'd to hear
3. Make us a - pos - tles; we are yours to send
4. Let all the might - y moun - tains leap for joy!
5. We sing your praise, O Ho - ly, Tri - une God:

1. your words with - in our hearts to dwell,
2. calls us to bring the dark - ness light.
3. that all with Sim - eon's eyes may see,
4. Let all the hills re - sound with song
5. you, our Cre - a - tor, Might - y One,

1. for we have seen your sav - ing pow'r,
2. We are your liv - ing bod - y, Lord;
3. and see - ing, live your gos - pel truth
4. bound - less in praise, un - end - ing love
5. for - ev - er in the Spir - it's love

1. the glo - ry of your peo - ple Is - ra - el.
2. let us with liv - ing flame dis - pel the night.
3. like An - na: wise and joy - ful, thank - ful, free.
4. and faith en - dur - ing, deep and true and strong.
5. u - nit - ed with our sav - ing Lord, your Son.

Text: 10 8 8 10; *Nunc dimittis;* based on Luke 2:25–38; M.D. Ridge.
Music: MISSION HILLS; M.D. Ridge.
Text and music © 2001, M.D. Ridge. Published by OCP Publications. All rights reserved.

RITES OF CHRISTIAN INITIATION

---

125   DISMISSAL OF THE CATECHUMENS/ELECT

When the catechumens and the elect are present at liturgy, they are usually dismissed after the homily or preaching. After the dismissal, the catechumens and elect gather with their catechists to pray and break open the scriptures of the day. The following acclamation may be sung during the dismissal to accompany those who are preparing for the sacraments of initiation.

126

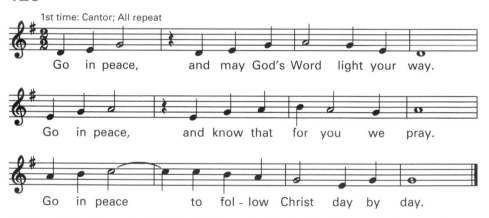

1st time: Cantor; All repeat

Go in peace, and may God's Word light your way.

Go in peace, and know that for you we pray.

Go in peace to fol-low Christ day by day.

Text and music: John Schiavone, b. 1947, © 1997, John Schiavone. Published by OCP Publications. All rights reserved.

---

127   SCRUTINIES

The scrutinies occur on the third, fourth and fifth Sundays of Lent and are accompanied by the readings from Year A. The elect are called before the community to pray for the spirit of repentance. Following the prayer of exorcism the following acclamation may be sung.

128

Those who seek your face, Lord, with a pure heart shall stand in your ho - ly place.

Text: Based on Psalms 27, 26, 32; Christopher Walker, b. 1947.
Music: Christopher Walker.
Text and music © 1987, Christopher Walker. Published by OCP Publications. All rights reserved.

The following song may be sung as the elect are dismissed to continue their reflection on the word of God.

129

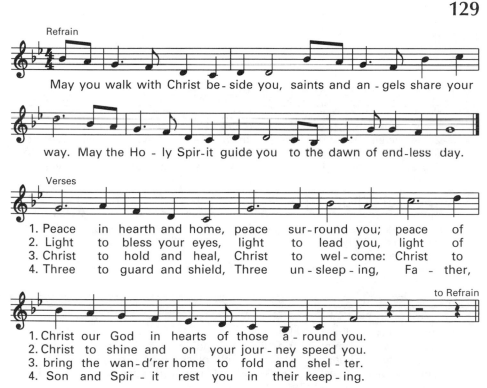

Refrain

May you walk with Christ be - side you, saints and an - gels share your way. May the Ho - ly Spir-it guide you to the dawn of end-less day.

Verses

1. Peace in hearth and home, peace sur-round you; peace of
2. Light to bless your eyes, light to lead you, light of
3. Christ to hold and heal, Christ to wel-come: Christ to
4. Three to guard and shield, Three un - sleep - ing, Fa - ther,

to Refrain

1. Christ our God in hearts of those a - round you.
2. Christ to shine and on your jour - ney speed you.
3. bring the wan - d'rer home to fold and shel - ter.
4. Son and Spir - it rest you in their keep - ing.

Text and music: Stephen Dean, b. 1948, © 1995, Stephen Dean. Published by OCP Publications. All rights reserved.

ORDER OF CHRISTIAN FUNERALS

---

130   VIGIL FOR THE DECEASED

INTRODUCTORY RITES

GREETING

OPENING SONG

131

1. I know that my Re - deem - er lives! What joy the
2. He lives tri - um - phant from the grave; He lives e -
3. He lives to si - lence all my fears; He lives to
4. He lives, all glo - ry to his name! He lives my

1. blest as - sur - ance gives! He lives, he lives, who
2. ter - nal - ly to save; He lives in maj - es -
3. wipe a - way my tears; He lives to calm my
4. Sav - ior, still the same; What joy this blest as -

1. once was dead; He lives, my ev - er - liv - ing head!
2. ty a - bove; He lives to guide his church in love.
3. trou - bled heart; He lives all bless - ings to im - part.
4. sur - ance gives: I know that my Re - deem - er lives!

Text: LM; based on Job 19:25; Samuel Medley, 1738–1799, alt.
Music: DUKE STREET; John Hatton, ca. 1710–1793.

INVITATION TO PRAYER

OPENING PRAYER

LITURGY OF THE WORD

FIRST READING

RESPONSORIAL PSALM   132

The Lord   is   my light   and my sal - va - tion.

Text: Psalm 27:1, 4, 13–14; © 1968, 1981, 1997, ICEL. All rights reserved. Used with permission.
Music: Owen Alstott, b. 1947, © 1977, 1990, OCP Publications. All rights reserved.

GOSPEL

HOMILY/PREACHING

PRAYER OF INTERCESSION

LITANY   133

Response: 1st time: Cantor, All repeat; thereafter: All

Lord,   have   mer - cy.   Lord,   have   mer - cy.

Text: Order of Christian Funerals, © 1985, ICEL. All rights reserved. Used with permission.
Music: Based on Dies Irae; Chant, Mode I; Michael Prendergast, b. 1955;
    © 2002, Michael Prendergast. Published by OCP Publications. All rights reserved.

THE LORD'S PRAYER

CONCLUDING PRAYER

A member or friend of the family may speak in remembrance of the deceased.

CONCLUDING RITE

BLESSING

The vigil may conclude with a song or a few moments of silent prayer or both.

FUNERAL MASS   134

RITE OF RECEPTION AT THE CHURCH

The presiding minister greets the mourners at the entrance of the church. As a baptismal remembrance the coffin is sprinkled with holy water and the pall may be placed on the coffin. The funeral procession then moves into the church accompanied by the following or another appropriate song.

PROCESSIONAL SONG
135

Refrain

Grant them e-ter-nal rest, O Lord, and let per-pet-u-al light shine up-on them.

Text and music: Owen Alstott, b. 1947, © 1983, OCP Publications. All rights reserved.

A symbol of Christian life may be carried in procession, then placed on the coffin.

If the introductory rites have not taken place at the church door, the liturgy begins in the usual manner with a song, the greeting, and the penitential rite.

OPENING PRAYER

LITURGY OF THE WORD

Appropriate readings should be chosen from those provided in the Order of Christian Funerals or the Lectionary.

READINGS

Either one or two readings from scripture may be read before the Gospel reading.

RESPONSORIAL PSALM
136

The Lord is my shep-herd; there is noth-ing I shall want.

Text: Psalm 23:1–3a, 3b–4, 5, 6, © 1968, 1981, 1997, ICEL. All rights reserved. Used with permission.
Music: Owen Alstott, b. 1947, © 1977, 1990, OCP Publications. All rights reserved.

GOSPEL ACCLAMATION

GOSPEL

HOMILY

GENERAL INTERCESSIONS

LITURGY OF THE EUCHARIST

FINAL COMMENDATION

If the Final Commendation takes place in church, the ministers go to a place near the coffin. After a silent prayer, the coffin may be sprinkled with holy water and honored with incense. Meanwhile, the following or another appropriate hymn (see Funeral section, Nos. 580–592) may be sung.

SONG OF FAREWELL

137

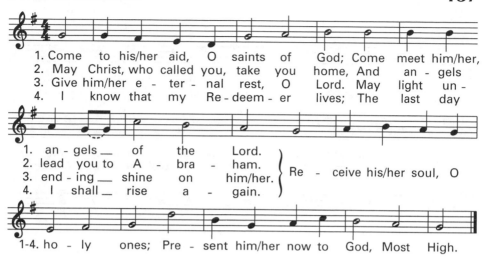

1. Come to his/her aid, O saints of God; Come meet him/her,
2. May Christ, who called you, take you home, And an - gels
3. Give him/her e - ter - nal rest, O Lord. May light un -
4. I know that my Re - deem - er lives; The last day

1. an - gels __ of the Lord.
2. lead you to A - bra - ham.
3. end - ing __ shine on him/her.
4. I shall __ rise a - gain.

Re - ceive his/her soul, O

1-4. ho - ly ones; Pre - sent him/her now to God, Most High.

Text LM; *Subvenite sancti Dei; Requiem aeternam; Credo quod Redemptor;* tr. by Dennis C. Smolarski, SJ, b. 1947,
© 1981, Dennis C. Smolarski, SJ. All rights reserved. Used with permission.
Music: OLD HUNDREDTH; *Genevan Psalter,* 1551; attr. to Louis Bourgeois, ca. 1510–1561, alt.

PRAYER OF COMMENDATION

PROCESSION TO THE PLACE OF COMMITTAL

138

*After the prayer, the following or another appropriate psalm or hymn is sung
while the coffin is being carried to the place of committal.*

Cantor

1. Come, O ev - er liv - ing God,
2. Mak - er of cre - a - tion,
3. You have been our ref - uge,

All

son __ home.
take your daugh-ter home.
*chil-dren home.

Cantor

1. Faith - ful and al - might - y God,
2. Au - thor of re - demp - tion,
3. Through all gen - er - a - tions,

All

son __ home.
take your daugh-ter home.
*chil-dren home.

Cantor

1. Mer - ci - ful and lov - ing God,
2. Source of our sal - va - tion,
3. You are God for - ev - er,

All

son __ home.
take your daugh-ter home.
*chil-dren home.

*Alternate text for All Saints/All Souls Days.

Text and music: John D. Becker, b. 1953, © 1989, OCP Publications. All rights reserved.

OR

139

In pa - ra - dí - sum de - dú - cant te án - ge - li:
May an - gels guide you and bring you in - to par - a - dise:

in tu - o ad - vén - tu su - scí - pi-ant te már - ty - res,
and may all the mar - tyrs come forth to wel-come you home;

et per - dú - cant te in ci - vi - tá - tem san - ctam
and may they lead you in - to the ho - ly cit - y,

Je - rú - sa-lem. Cho - rus an - ge - ló - rum te___
Je - ru - sa-lem. May the an - gel cho - rus sing___

su - scí - pi - at, et cum Lá - za - ro quon-dam
___ to wel-come you, and like Laz - a - rus, for - got -

páu-pe - re ae - tér - nam há - be-as ré - qui-em.
ten and poor, you shall have ev - er - last-ing rest.

Text: *In paradisum* and *Chorus angelorum*; Latin, 11th cent.;
English tr. by Owen Alstott, b. 1947, © 1987, OCP Publications. All rights reserved.
Music: Chant, Mode VII and Mode VIII.

EUCHARISTIC EXPOSITION & BENEDICTION

During the celebration of this rite there should be prayers, songs, readings, silent prayer and a homily or preaching to direct the attention of the faithful to the worship of Christ the Lord.

EXPOSITION

The following or another suitable eucharistic song or seasonal psalm is sung.

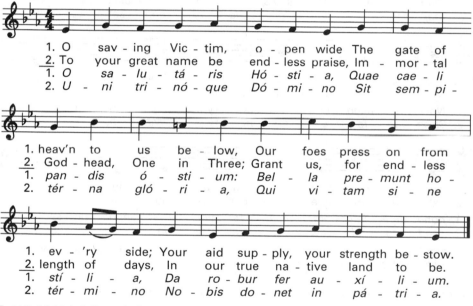

1. O sav - ing Vic - tim, o - pen wide The gate of
2. To your great name be end - less praise, Im - mor - tal
1. O sa - lu - tá - ris Hó - sti - a, Quae cae - li
2. U - ni tri - nó - que Dó - mi - no Sit sem - pi -

1. heav'n to us be - low, Our foes press on from
2. God - head, One in Three; Grant us, for end - less
1. pan - dis ó - sti - um: Bel - la pre - munt ho -
2. tér - na gló - ri - a, Qui vi - tam si - ne

1. ev - 'ry side; Your aid sup - ply, your strength be - stow.
2. length of days, In our true na - tive land to be.
1. stí - li - a, Da ro - bur fer au - xí - li - um.
2. tér - mi - no No - bis do - net in pá - tri - a.

Text: LM; *O Salutaris*; St. Thomas Aquinas, 1227–1274; tr. by Edward Caswall, 1814–1878, alt.
Music: DUGUET; attr. to Abbé Dieudonne Duguet, 1794–1849.

ADORATION

The Liturgy of the Hours may be celebrated during the period of exposition, or there may be prayers, songs, readings from the Word of God and a brief homily or preaching along with time for silent prayer.

Psalms 23, 34, 72, 84, 85, 122 or 128 may be sung during the period of adoration (see Psalms section, No. 15).

BENEDICTION

℣. You have given them Bread from heaven. (Easter: alleluia)
℟. **Having within it all Sweetness. (Easter: alleluia)**

The minister incenses the Blessed Sacrament while the following or another appropriate song is sung.

141

1. Tan-tum er-go Sac-ra-mén-tum Ve-ne-ré-mur
2. Ge-ni-tó-ri, Ge-ni-tó-que Laus et ju-bi-
1. *Ho-ly sac-ra-ment, most ho-ly, Let us bow on*
2. *God Be-get-ter and Be-got-ten, Yours be praise and*

1. cér-nu-i: Et an-tí-quum do-cu-mén-tum
2. lá-ti-o, Sa-lus, ho-nor, vir-tus quo-que
1. *bend-ed knee: Vi-sions of the an-cient prom-ise*
2. *maj-es-ty, Hon-or, glo-ry and sal-va-tion,*

1. No-vo ce-dat rí-tu-i: Prae-stet fi-des
2. Sit et be-ne-dí-cti-o: Pro-ce-dén-ti
1. *Now ful-filled in mys-te-ry. Faith de-clares what*
2. *Bless-ing for e-ter-ni-ty, With the One pro-*

1. sup-ple-mén-tum Sén-su-um de-fé-ctu-i.
2. ab u-tró-que Com-par sit lau-dá-ti-o.
1. *none dare fath-om; Faith re-veals what none may see.*
2. *ceed-ing al-ways, E-qual-ly in u-ni-ty.*

Text: 87 87 87; *Tantum ergo*; St. Thomas Aquinas, 1227–1274; tr. by Harry Hagan, OSB, b. 1947, © 1990, St. Meinrad Archabbey. Published by OCP Publications. All rights reserved.
Music: ST. THOMAS (TANTUM ERGO); John F. Wade, 1711–1786.

After a prayer, the priest or deacon blesses those present with the Blessed Sacrament.

REPOSITION

While a minister places the Blessed Sacrament in the tabernacle the people may sing or recite the following or other appropriate acclamations or hymns.

142

Cantor sings each invocation first; assembly repeats

Bless'd be God. Bless'd be his Ho-ly Name.

Bless'd be Je - sus Christ, true God and true Man.

Bless'd be the Name of Je-sus. Bless'd be his most Sa-cred Heart.

Bless'd be his most Pre-cious Blood. Bless'd be Je-sus in the most Ho-ly

Sac - ra-ment of the Al - tar. Bless'd be the Ho - ly

Spir - it, the Par - a - clete. Bless'd be the great Moth-er of God,

Ma - ry most ho - ly. Bless'd be her ho - ly and Im -

ma - cu-late Con - cep - tion. Bless'd be her glo - ri - ous As - sump - tion.

Bless'd be the name of Ma - ry, Vir - gin and Moth - er.

Bless'd be Saint Jo - seph, her most chaste spouse.

(Fine)

Bless'd be God in his an - gels. Bless'd be God in his saints.

ORDER OF MASS

At the Eucharist, God's people come together to hear the word of the Lord, to pray for the world's needs, to praise God and give thanks for His creative and saving work, to receive Christ Jesus in Communion and then to be sent forth in the Spirit as apostles of the gospel. These central elements of the Order of Mass have changed little throughout history, but variable elements help accommodate this mystery of faith to local church needs and to the feasts and seasons of the liturgical year.

143   INTRODUCTORY RITES

As people gather, their language changes from that of everyday to that which has meaning forever in God's reign. Even "How are you?" has a different meaning as God transforms individuals into members of Christ's body.

ENTRANCE SONG

A processional chant or hymn may be sung. After the entrance song, all make the sign of the cross.

GREETING

In the name of the Father, and of the Son, and of the Holy Spirit.

Amen.

A   The grace of our Lord Jesus Christ and the love of God and the fellowship of the Holy Spirit be with you all.

And also with you.

B   The grace and peace of God our Father and the Lord Jesus Christ be with you.

Blessed be God, the Father of our Lord Jesus Christ.

Or   **And also with you.**

C   The Lord be with you.
(*A bishop says,* "Peace be with you.")

And also with you.

RITE OF BLESSING AND SPRINKLING HOLY WATER   **144**

*On Sundays there may be a blessing and sprinkling of holy water to recall baptism.
This replaces the penitential rite below. During the sprinkling, the following or
another suitable antiphon is sung.*

Refrain

Save us, O God,   wash a - way our sin.   Make us your own,   one

1-5
2   to Verses
Final

peo - ple   in your   name.   name.

Verses: Choir or All   All repeat   to Refrain

1. With wa - ter   of   life,   re - fresh us.
2. Re - new us   in   soul   and bod - y.
3. Your Spir - it   re - news   cre - a - tion.   Give us new life.
4. By   dy - ing to   sin   with Je - sus:
5. By   ris - ing with Christ in   glo - ry:

Text and music: *Celtic Mass;* Christopher Walker, b. 1947, © 1996, Christopher Walker.
Published by OCP Publications. All rights reserved.

Continue with the "Gloria," No. 149.

PENITENTIAL RITE

This celebration of God's mercy takes one of the following forms:

A   **I confess to almighty God,
                 and to you, my brothers and sisters,
                 that I have sinned through my own fault**
(Strike breast) **in my thoughts and in my words,
                 in what I have done,
                 and in what I have failed to do;
                 and I ask blessed Mary, ever virgin,
                 all the angels and saints,
                 and you, my brothers and sisters,
                 to pray for me to the Lord our God.**

                 May almighty God have mercy on us,
                 forgive us our sins, and bring us to everlasting life.
                 Amen.

Continue with the "Kyrie," No. 147 or 148.

B

145

Lord, we have sinned a-gainst you: Lord, have mer - cy.

Lord, show us your mer-cy and love. And grant us your sal - va - tion.

May almighty God have mercy on us,
forgive us our sins,
and bring us to everlasting life.
Amen.

Continue with the "Gloria," No. 149.

C

146

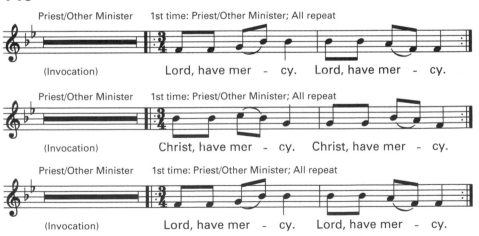

Priest/Other Minister   1st time: Priest/Other Minister; All repeat

(Invocation)   Lord, have mer - cy.   Lord, have mer - cy.

Priest/Other Minister   1st time: Priest/Other Minister; All repeat

(Invocation)   Christ, have mer - cy.   Christ, have mer - cy.

Priest/Other Minister   1st time: Priest/Other Minister; All repeat

(Invocation)   Lord, have mer - cy.   Lord, have mer - cy.

May almighty God have mercy on us,
forgive us our sins,
and bring us to everlasting life.
Amen.

Continue with the "Gloria," No. 149.

KYRIE

The invocations "Lord, have mercy" or "Kyrie eleison" follow as part of form A.

Music: *Celtic Mass;* Christopher Walker, b. 1947, © 1996, Christopher Walker.
Published by OCP Publications. All rights reserved.

OR

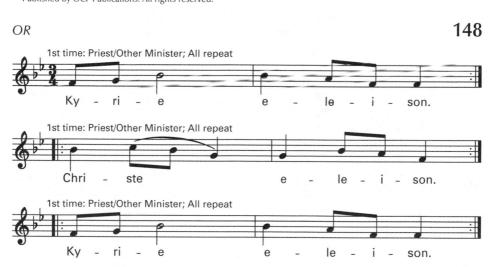

Music: *Celtic Mass;* Christopher Walker, b. 1947, © 1996, Christopher Walker.
Published by OCP Publications. All rights reserved.

GLORIA

On Sundays, solemnities and feasts outside Advent and Lent, all sing or say:

149

Optional Refrain I   to Verses

Glo - ry, glo-ry to God in the high-est, glo-ry to God. ___

Verse 1: Begin here if not using Optional Refrain

1. Glo - ry to God in the high - est, and peace to his peo-ple on

1. earth.   Lord   God,   heav - en - ly King,   al -

1. might - y God and Fa - ther, we wor - ship you, we

to Verse 2 or Optional Refrain I

1. give you thanks, we praise you for your glo - ry.

Verse 2

2. Lord Je - sus Christ,   on - ly Son of the Fa-ther,

Choir/Cantor   All

2. Lord God, Lamb of God, Lord God, Lamb of God, you

2. take a - way the sin of the world: have

2. mer - cy, have mer-cy on us;   you are

2. seat-ed at the right hand of the Fa-ther: re-

to Verse 3 or Optional Refrain I

2. ceive our prayer, re-ceive our prayer.

Verse 3

3. For you a-lone are the Ho-ly One, you a-lone are the

3. Lord, you a-lone are the Most High, Je-sus Christ,

3. with the Ho-ly Spir-it, in the glo-ry of God,

to Amen or Optional Refrain II and Amen

3. the glo-ry of God the Fa-ther.

Optional Refrain II

to Amen

Glo-ry, glo-ry to God in the high-est, glo-ry to God.

Amen

A-men, a-men, a-men.

OPENING PRAYER

After a period of silence, the priest says the opening prayer, and all respond:
Amen.

The Lectionary (book of readings) and the Book of Gospels open the rich treasure of God's word from the Jewish and Christian Scriptures. Sunday readings follow a three-year cycle: Year A emphasizes the Gospel of Matthew; Year B, the Gospel of Mark; Year C, the Gospel of Luke. The Church proclaims the Gospel of John especially during the seasons of Lent and Easter.

FIRST READING

After the reading the lector says, "The word of the Lord," and all respond:

Thanks be to God.

RESPONSORIAL PSALM

Music for the responsorial psalm is found in Nos. 16–113.

SECOND READING

After the reading the lector says, "The word of the Lord," and all respond:

Thanks be to God.

ALLELUIA OR GOSPEL ACCLAMATION

The assembly welcomes the proclamation of the gospel by singing the following acclamation. If it cannot be sung, it is to be omitted.

151

Al - le - lu - ia, al - le - lu - ia.
Al - le - lu - ia, al - le - lu - ia.

Music: *Celtic Mass;* Fintan O'Carroll, d. 1977, and Christopher Walker, b. 1947,
    © 1985, Fintan O'Carroll and Christopher Walker. Published by OCP Publications. All rights reserved.

During Lent:

152

Praise and hon-or, hon-or and glo-ry, glo-ry to you, Lord Je-sus Christ.

Text © 1969, 1981, ICEL. All rights reserved. Used with permission.
Music: *Celtic Mass,* Christopher Walker, b. 1947, © 1996, Christopher Walker.
    Published by OCP Publications. All rights reserved.

GOSPEL

Before the gospel the deacon/priest says, "The Lord be with you," and all respond:
> **And also with you.**

The deacon/priest says, "A reading from the holy Gospel according to N.," and all respond:
> **Glory to you, Lord.**

After the gospel the deacon/priest says, "The Gospel of the Lord," and all respond:
> **Praise to you, Lord Jesus Christ.**

HOMILY

The homilist describes how the good news of Christ's saving mystery applies to this specific community on this particular day.

DISMISSAL OF THE CATECHUMENS AND THE ELECT

In Masses at which catechumens or elect are present for the Liturgy of the Word, the priest may use these or similar words:

> My dear friends, this community now sends you forth to reflect further on God's word, which you have shared with us. Be assured of our loving support and prayers for you. We look forward to the day when you will take part fully in the Lord's Table.

The following or another appropriate song (see No. 126) may be sung while the catechumens/elect are dismissed:

153

Refrain: All
May the word of God strength-en you. May the word of God nour-ish you. May the word of God com-fort you all your life.

Optional Verses: Cantor/Choir/All   to Refrain
1. May it be your light in dark-ness __ as you walk the path of faith.
2. May it lead you to the free-dom __ of the love that calls your name.
3. May it set your hearts on fire _____ to be faith-ful to God's voice.

PROFESSION OF FAITH

On Sundays and solemnities all say the Nicene Creed:

We believe in one God,
>the Father, the Almighty,
>maker of heaven and earth,
>of all that is seen and unseen.

We believe in one Lord, Jesus Christ,
>the only Son of God,
>eternally begotten of the Father,
>God from God, Light from Light,
>true God from true God,
>begotten, not made, one in Being with the Father.
>Through him all things were made.
>For us men and for our salvation
>>he came down from heaven:

(Bow) by the power of the Holy Spirit
>he was born of the Virgin Mary, and became man.
>>*(Genuflect on Christmas and the Annunciation.)*

For our sake he was crucified under Pontius Pilate;
>he suffered, died, and was buried.
>On the third day he rose again
>>in fulfillment of the Scriptures;
>he ascended into heaven
>>and is seated at the right hand of the Father.

He will come again in glory to judge the living and the dead,
>and his kingdom will have no end.

We believe in the Holy Spirit, the Lord, the giver of life,
>who proceeds from the Father and the Son.
>With the Father and the Son he is worshiped and glorified.
>He has spoken through the Prophets.
>We believe in one holy catholic and apostolic Church.
>We acknowledge one baptism for the forgiveness of sins.
>We look for the resurrection of the dead,
>>and the life of the world to come. Amen.

The Apostles' Creed may be used at Masses with children.

**I believe in God, the Father almighty,
creator of heaven and earth.**

**I believe in Jesus Christ, his only Son, our Lord.
He was conceived by the power of the Holy Spirit
and born of the Virgin Mary.**

**He suffered under Pontius Pilate,
was crucified, died, and was buried.
He descended to the dead.
On the third day he rose again.
He ascended into heaven,
and is seated at the right hand of the Father.
He will come again to judge the living and the dead.**

**I believe in the Holy Spirit,
the holy catholic Church,
the communion of saints,
the forgiveness of sins,
the resurrection of the body,
and the life everlasting. Amen.**

GENERAL INTERCESSIONS *(Prayer of the Faithful)*

As priestly people we unite with one another to pray for today's needs in the Church and the world:

154

Deacon/Cantor/Other Minister — All

(Petition) We pray to the Lord: Lord, hear our prayer.

Text and music: *Celtic Mass;* Christopher Walker, b. 1947, © 1996, Christopher Walker.
Published by OCP Publications. All rights reserved.

Christians are baptized into the paschal mystery of Christ's death and resurrection for the forgiveness of sin and fullness of salvation. This mystery is celebrated at every Mass, remembering Christ's loving deed and giving thanks and praise to God. The celebration reaches its high point as the priest concludes the eucharistic prayer, lifting up the vessels containing the Body and Blood of Christ, giving all glory and honor to the almighty Father through Christ in the unity of the Holy Spirit.

PREPARATION OF THE ALTAR AND THE GIFTS

Gifts are collected for the poor and for the Church. Bread and wine are brought to the altar table, and everything is prepared for the celebration. If no song is sung, the priest may pray aloud, and all may respond:

Blessed be God for ever.

The priest invites the assembly to pray ". . . that our sacrifice may be acceptable to God, the almighty Father," and the assembly says:

May the Lord accept the sacrifice at your hands,
for the praise and glory of his name,
for our good and the good of all his Church.

PRAYER OVER THE GIFTS

The priest says the prayer over the gifts, and all respond:

Amen.

EUCHARISTIC PRAYER

PREFACE

156

The Eucharistic Prayer begins with a dialogue between the priest and the assembly.

Priest: The Lord be with you. All: And al-so with you.

Priest: Lift up your hearts. All: We lift them up to the Lord.

Priest: Let us give thanks to the Lord our God.

All: It is right to give him thanks and praise.

Then the priest proclaims the eucharistic prayer; he begins by giving thanks to God through our Lord Jesus Christ, then all sing the following acclamation:

HOLY
157

Ho - ly, ho - ly, ho - ly Lord, God of pow - er, God of might. Heav - en and earth are full of your glo - ry. Ho - san - na in the high - est, ho - san - na in the high - est, ho - san - na in the high - est. Bless - ed is he who comes in the name of the Lord. Ho - san - na in the high - est, ho - san - na in the high - est, ho - san - na in the high - est!

MEMORIAL ACCLAMATION

After the words of institution of the eucharist, the priest sings or says:

Let us proclaim the mystery of faith:

All respond:

A
158

Christ has died, Christ is ris - en, Christ will come a - gain.

B
159

Dy-ing you de-stroyed our death, ris-ing you re-stored our life. Lord Je-sus, come in glo-ry, Lord Je-sus, come in glo-ry.

C
160

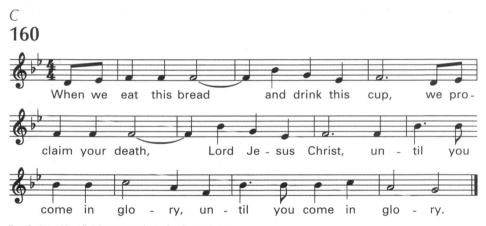

When we eat this bread and drink this cup, we pro-claim your death, Lord Je-sus Christ, un-til you come in glo-ry, un-til you come in glo-ry.

D
161

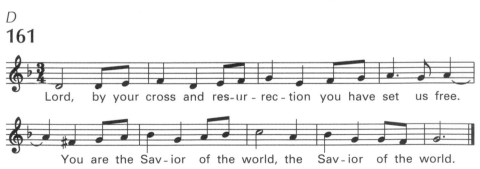

Lord, by your cross and res-ur-rec-tion you have set us free. You are the Sav-ior of the world, the Sav-ior of the world.

GREAT AMEN
162

A-men, a-men, a-men, a-men, a-men, a-men.

COMMUNION RITE

LORD'S PRAYER

The priest invites all to join in the Lord's Prayer:

163

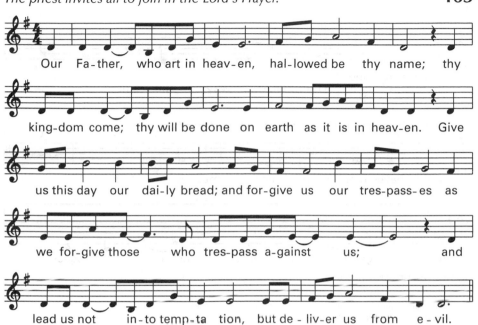

Our Fa-ther, who art in heav-en, hal-lowed be thy name; thy king-dom come; thy will be done on earth as it is in heav-en. Give us this day our dai-ly bread; and for-give us our tres-pass-es as we for-give those who tres-pass a-gainst us; and lead us not in-to temp-ta tion, but de-liv-er us from e-vil.

Deliver us, Lord, from every evil, ...
for the coming of our Savior, Jesus Christ.

For the king-dom, the pow-er, and the glo-ry are yours, now and for ev-er.

SIGN OF PEACE

164

Lord Jesus Christ, ... where you live for ever and ever.

A - men, a - men.

The peace of the Lord be with you always.
And also with you.
Let us offer each other the sign of peace.
The people exchange a sign of peace, according to local custom.

BREAKING OF THE BREAD

The eucharistic bread is broken and the consecrated wine poured in preparation for Communion. The following litany is sung throughout this action:

165

Choir/Cantor   All

Lamb of God,
*Bread of Life, } you take a-way the sins of the
**Lamb of God,

1, 2...   3

world: have mer-cy on us, mer-cy on us.

Final

world: grant us peace, grant us peace.

*Other invocations may be used.
**Last time.

Music: *Celtic Mass;* Christopher Walker, b. 1947, © 1996, Christopher Walker.
Published by OCP Publications. All rights reserved.

COMMUNION

> This is the Lamb of God . . .
>
> **Lord, I am not worthy to receive you,**
> **but only say the word and I shall be healed.**

The minister of Communion says, "The body of Christ" or "The blood of Christ," and the communicant answers:

> **Amen.**

COMMUNION SONG

A Communion song or psalm is sung.

PERIOD OF SILENCE OR SONG OF PRAISE

A period of silence may now be observed, or a psalm or song of praise may be sung.

PRAYER AFTER COMMUNION

The Communion rite concludes with a prayer to which all respond:

> **Amen.**

On Holy Thursday, the Evening Mass of the Lord's Supper concludes at this point with the Transfer of the Holy Eucharist.

GREETING 167

The Lord be with you. And al - so with you.

BLESSING

A 168

May al - might - y God bless you, the Fa - ther,

and the Son, and the Ho - ly Spir- it. A - men.

B   *Or a more solemn blessing or prayer over the people may be chosen by the priest.*

Amen.

C   *A bishop may bless the people using the following form:*

Blessed be the name of the Lord.
Now and for ever.

Our help is in the name of the Lord.
Who made heaven and earth.

DISMISSAL

The deacon/priest invites all to go in the peace of Christ:

A

169

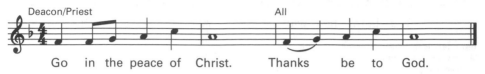

Go in the peace of Christ. Thanks be to God.

B   The Mass is ended, go in peace.
       Thanks be to God.

C   Go in peace to love and serve the Lord.
       Thanks be to God.

During Eastertime, use the following Greeting, Blessing and Dismissal:

170

The Lord be with you. And al - so with you.

May al - might - y God bless you, the Fa - ther,

and the Son, and the Ho - ly Spir - it. A - men.

Go in peace to serve the Lord, Al - le - lu - ia.

Thanks be to God, Al - le - lu - ia.

A final psalm or hymn may be sung.

For Catholics: As Catholics, we fully participate in the celebration of the Eucharist when we receive Holy Communion. We are encouraged to receive Communion devoutly and frequently. In order to be properly disposed to receive Communion, participants should not be conscious of grave sin and normally should have fasted for one hour. A person who is conscious of grave sin is not to receive the Body and Blood of the Lord without prior sacramental confession except for a grave reason where there is no opportunity for confession. In this case, the person is to be mindful of the obligation to make an act of perfect contrition, including the intention of confessing as soon as possible *(Code of Canon Law, canon 916).* A frequent reception of the Sacrament of Penance is encouraged for all.

For our fellow Christians: We welcome our fellow Christians to this celebration of the Eucharist as our brothers and sisters. We pray that our common baptism and the action of the Holy Spirit in this Eucharist will draw us closer to one another and begin to dispel the sad divisions which separate us. We pray that these will lessen and finally disappear, in keeping with Christ's prayer for us "that they may all be one" *(Jn 17:21).*

Because Catholics believe that the celebration of the Eucharist is a sign of the reality of the oneness of faith, life, and worship, members of those churches with whom we are not yet fully united are ordinarily not admitted to Holy Communion. Eucharistic sharing in exceptional circumstances by other Christians requires permission according to the directives of the diocesan bishop and the provisions of canon law *(canon 844 ¶ 4).* Members of the Orthodox Churches, the Assyrian Church of the East, and the Polish National Catholic Church are urged to respect the discipline of their own Churches. According to Roman Catholic discipline, the Code of Canon Law does not object to the reception of communion by Christians of these Churches *(canon 844 ¶ 3).*

For those not receiving Holy Communion: All who are not receiving Holy Communion are encouraged to express in their hearts a prayerful desire for unity with the Lord Jesus and with one another.

For non-Christians: We also welcome to this celebration those who do not share our faith in Jesus Christ. While we cannot admit them to Holy Communion, we ask them to offer their prayers for the peace and the unity of the human family.

MASS SETTINGS

The music with which the Church celebrates the eucharist has developed over the centuries, clothing ancient ritual elements in idioms expressive of the assembly's faith. A broad range of settings — contemporary, gospel, and traditional — invigorates the assembly's celebration and expands its vocabulary of praise. Each of these offers a unified musical approach to the Order of Mass.

---

172   CHANT MASS

---

173   ASPERGES ME

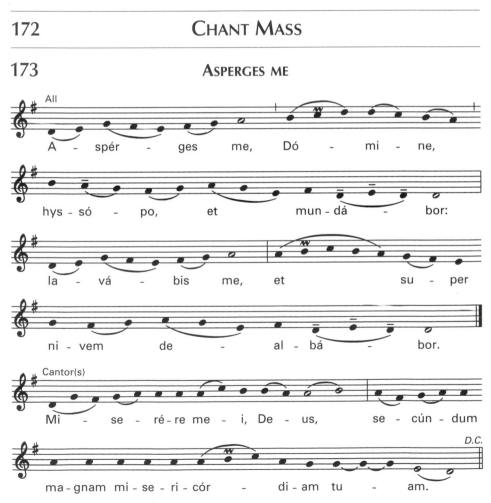

Text and music: *Chant Mass; Graduale Romanum,* 1974.

VIDI AQUAM

Text and music: *Chant Mass; Graduale Romanum*, 1974.

KYRIE

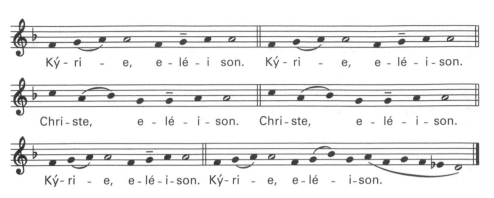

Ký-ri - e, e-lé-i son. Ký-ri - e, e-lé-i-son.

Chri-ste, e-lé-i-son. Chri-ste, e-lé-i-son.

Ký-ri - e, e-lé-i-son. Ký-ri - e, e-lé-i-son.

Text and music: *Chant Mass; Graduale Romanum,* 1974.

176   GLORIA

Gló-ri - a in ex-cél-sis De - o. Et in ter-ra pax ho-mí-ni-bus

bo-nae vo-lun-tá - tis. Lau-dá - mus te.

Be-ne-dí-ci-mus te. A-do-rá - mus te.

Glo-ri-fi-cá-mus te. Grá-ti-as á-gi-mus ti - bi

pro-pter ma-gnam gló-ri-am tu - am. Dó-mi-ne De-us, Rex cae-

lé - stis, De-us Pa-ter o - mní-pot - ens.

Dó-mi-ne Fi - li u-ni-gé-ni-te, Je - su Chri-ste.

Dó-mi-ne De-us, A-gnus De - i, Fí-li-us Pa - tris.

Qui tol-lis pec-cá-ta mun - di, mi-se-ré - re no-bis.

Qui tol-lis pec-cá-ta mun - di, sú-sci-pe de-pre-ca-ti-ó-

nem no - stram. Qui se-des ad déx-te-ram Pa - tris,

mi - se - ré - re no - bis. Quó-ni-am tu so-lus San - ctus.

Tu so-lus Dó - mi - nus. Tu so-lus Al - tís - si-mus,

Je - su Chri - ste. Cum San-cto Spí - ri - tu,

in gló-ri-a De-i Pa - tris. A - men.

Text and music: *Chant Mass; Graduale Romanum*, 1974.

SANCTUS 177

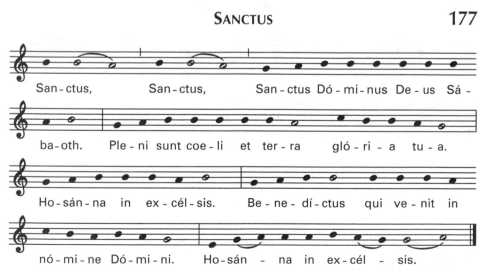

San-ctus, San-ctus, San-ctus Dó-mi-nus De-us Sá-

ba-oth. Ple-ni sunt coe-li et ter-ra gló-ri-a tu-a.

Ho-sán-na in ex-cél-sis. Be-ne-dí-ctus qui ve-nit in

nó-mi-ne Dó-mi-ni. Ho-sán-na in ex-cél-sis.

Text and music: *Chant Mass; Graduale Romanum*, 1974.

178   POST CONSECRATIONEM

Priest   or

My-sté - ri - um fí - de - i. My-sté - ri-um fí - de - i.

All

Mor-tem tu - am an-nun-ti - á-mus, Dó - mi-ne, et tu - am

re-sur-rec - ti - ó-nem con-fi - té - mur, do - nec vé-ni - as.

Text and music: *Chant Mass; Graduale Romanum,* 1974.

179   AMEN

Priest   All

...per ó - mni - a sáe-cu - la sae-cu - ló - rum. A-men.

Text and music: *Chant Mass; Graduale Romanum,* 1974.

180   PATER NOSTER

Pa - ter no-ster, qui es in cae-lis: san-cti - fi - cé-tur no - men

tu - um; ad-vé - ni - at re-gnum tu-um; fi - at vo-lún-tas tu - a,

sic - ut in cae - lo, et in ter - ra.

Pa - nem no-strum co - ti - di - á-num da no - bis hó - di - e;

et di-mít-te no-bis dé-bi-ta no-stra, sic-ut et nos

di-mít-ti-mus de-bi-tó-ri-bus no-stris; et ne nos

in-dú-cas in ten-ta-ti-ó-nem; sed lí-be-ra nos a ma-lo.

Priest: Libera nos, quaesumus, Domine...
et adventum Salvatoris nostri Jesu Christi.

All

Qui-a tu-um est re-gnum, et po-té-

stas, et gló-ri-a in sáe-cu-la.

Priest   All

Pax Dó-mi-ni sit sem-per vo-bís-cum. Et cum spí-ri-tu tu-o.

Text and music: *Chant Mass; Graduale Romanum*, 1974.

AGNUS DEI   181

A-gnus De-i, qui tol-lis pec-cá-ta mun-di: mi-se-

ré-re no-bis. A-gnus De-i, qui tol-lis pec-cá-ta

mun-di: mi-se-ré-re no-bis. A-gnus De-i,

qui tol-lis pec-cá-ta mun-di: do-na no-bis pa-cem.

Text and music: *Chant Mass; Graduale Romanum*, 1974.

183   **LORD, HAVE MERCY**

184   **GLORY TO GOD**

you are seat-ed at the right hand of the Fa-ther: re-ceive our prayer.

For you a-lone are the Ho-ly One, for you a-lone are the

Lord, you a-lone are the Most High, Je-sus

Christ, with the Ho-ly Spir-it, in the glo-ry of

God the Fa-ther. A-men.

Holy 185

Ho-ly, ho-ly, ho-ly Lord, God of pow-er and

might. Heav'n and earth are full of your glo-ry.

Ho-san-na! Ho-san-na in the high-est.

Blessed is he who comes in the name of the Lord.

Ho-san-na! Ho-san-na in the high-est.

186 MEMORIAL ACCLAMATION A

Christ has died, Christ is ris - en, Christ will come a - gain.

187 MEMORIAL ACCLAMATION B

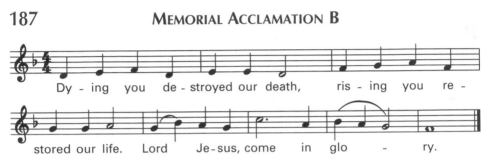

Dy - ing you de - stroyed our death, ris - ing you re -

stored our life. Lord Je - sus, come in glo - ry.

188 MEMORIAL ACCLAMATION C

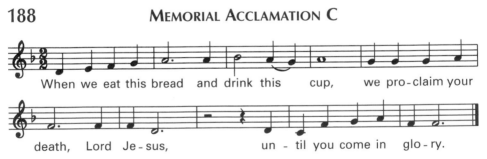

When we eat this bread and drink this cup, we pro - claim your

death, Lord Je - sus, un - til you come in glo - ry.

189 MEMORIAL ACCLAMATION D

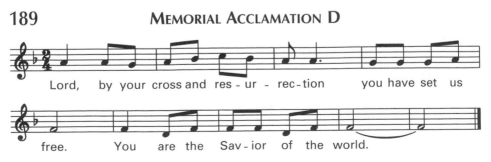

Lord, by your cross and res - ur - rec - tion you have set us

free. You are the Sav - ior of the world.

AMEN

A - men, a - men, a - men.

LAMB OF GOD

191

Lamb of God, you take a - way the sins of the

1, 2 world: have mer - cy on us.
3 world: grant us peace.

MASS OF GOD'S PROMISE

192

KYRIE/LORD, HAVE MERCY

193

Priest 4 All

1. Lord Jesus... Ky - ri - e e - le - i - son.
2. Lord Jesus... Chri - ste e - le - i - son.

1. Lord, have mer - cy on us.
2. Christ, have mer - cy on us.

Priest 4 All

3. Lord Jesus... Ky - ri - e e - le - i - son. Lord, have mer - cy on us.

GLORY TO GOD

Refrain

Glo-ry to God, give glo-ry to God. Glo-ry to God in the high - est. Peace on the earth and glo-ry to God. Peace to all peo-ple, peace to all peo-ple on earth. (3. For)

Verse 1

1. Lord God, heav-en-ly King, al-might-y God and Fa-ther, we

to Refrain

1. wor-ship you, we give you thanks, we praise you for your glo - ry.

Verse 2

2. Lord Je - sus Christ, on - ly Son of the Fa-ther, Lord

2. God, Lamb of God, you take a - way the sin of the world: have mer -

2. cy, have mer - cy, have mer - cy

2. on us; you are seat-ed at the right hand

to Refrain

2. of the Fa - ther: re-ceive our prayer.

Verse 3

(3. For) you a-lone are the Ho-ly One, you a-lone are the Lord,

3. you a-lone are the Most High, Je - sus Christ, with the Ho -

3. ly Spir-it, in the glo-ry of God the Fa - ther.

to Refrain

ALLELUIA 195

Refrain

Al - le - lu - ia, al - le - lu - ia, al - le - lu - ia.

LENTEN GOSPEL ACCLAMATION 196

Praise to you, Lord Je - sus Christ, Word from the heart of God.

HOLY 197

Ho - ly, ho - ly, ho - ly Lord, God of pow-er and might,

heav-en and earth are full of your glo-ry. Ho - san - na in the

high - est. Bless-ed is he who comes in the name of the Lord.

Ho - san - na in the high - est. Ho-san-na in the high - est.

198   MEMORIAL ACCLAMATION A

Christ has died, Christ is ris-en, Christ will come a-gain.

199   MEMORIAL ACCLAMATION B

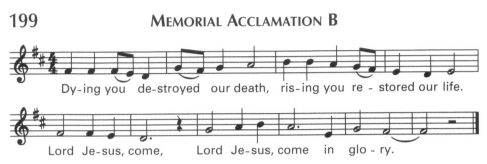

Dy-ing you de-stroyed our death, ris-ing you re-stored our life.

Lord Je-sus, come, Lord Je-sus, come in glo-ry.

200   MEMORIAL ACCLAMATION C

When we eat this bread of life, when we drink of this cup,

we pro-claim your death, O Lord, un-til you come a-gain.

201   MEMORIAL ACCLAMATION D

Lord, by your cross and res-ur-rec-tion you have set us

free. You are the ho-ly Sav-ior of the world.

AMEN

A - men. A - men. A -
men. For ev - er and ev - er, a - men.

LAMB OF GOD LITANY   203

Cantor/Choir   All

(Invocations)   you take a - way   the sins of the
1, 2... world: have   mer-cy   on   us,   have mer-cy, have mer-cy   on
(Final) world: O   grant __ us peace,   O   grant __ us   last - ing

1, 2... | Final
1, 2... us.   (Final) peace,   Lamb of   God.

ST. LOUIS JESUITS MASS   204

LORD, HAVE MERCY   205

Lord, have   mer-cy.   Lord, have mer-cy. Lord, have   mer - cy.
Christ, have mer - cy.   Christ, have mer-cy. Christ, have   mer-cy up-on   us.
Lord, have   mer-cy.   Lord, have mer-cy. Lord, have   mer - cy.

206

GLORY TO GOD

Refrain: 1st time: Cantor/Choir, All repeat; thereafter: All

Give glo - ry to God in the high - est, and

1-5 (Repeat 1st/5th times) to Verses | Final

peace to his peo - ple on earth. earth.

Music: *St. Louis Jesuits Mass;* John Foley, S.J., b. 1939, © 1978, John B. Foley, S.J. and New Dawn Music.
Published by OCP Publications. All rights reserved.

207

ALLELUIA

Refrain

Al - le - lu - ia, al - le - lu - ia, al - le - lu - ia, al - le - lu - ia!

Music: *St. Louis Jesuits Mass;* Dan Schutte, b. 1947, © 1992, Daniel L. Schutte.
Published by OCP Publications. All rights reserved.

208

PRAISE TO YOU, LORD JESUS CHRIST

Refrain

Praise to you, Lord Je-sus Christ, king of end-less glo - ry.

Text: Refrain © 1969, 1981, ICEL. All rights reserved. Used with permission.
Music: *St. Louis Jesuits Mass;* Roc O'Connor, SJ, © 1985, Robert F. O'Connor, SJ, and New Dawn Music.
Published by OCP Publications. All rights reserved.

209

HOLY

Ho - ly, ho - ly, ho - ly Lord, God of pow'r and might.

Heav-en and earth are full of your glo - ry. Ho - san-na, ho -

san - na on high. Bless-ed is he who comes in the

name of the Lord. Ho - san - na in the high - est. Ho -

san - na in the high-est. Ho-san-na, ho-san-na on high.

MEMORIAL ACCLAMATION A 210

Christ has died. Christ is ris-en. Christ will come a-gain.

MEMORIAL ACCLAMATION B 211

Dy - ing you de-stroyed our death. Ris - ing you re-stored our life.

Lord Je - sus, Lord Je - sus, come in glo - ry.

MEMORIAL ACCLAMATION C 212

When we eat this bread of life, when we drink of this ho-ly cup, we pro-

claim your death, O Lord, till you come a-gain. till you come a-gain.

213   MEMORIAL ACCLAMATION D

Lord, by your cross and re-sur-rec-tion you have set us free. You are the Sav-ior of the world.

Text © 1973, ICEL. All rights reserved. Used with permission.
Music: *St. Louis Jesuits Mass;* Bob Dufford, SJ, b. 1943, © 1996, Robert J. Dufford, SJ.
   Published by OCP Publications. All rights reserved.

214   AMEN

A - men, al - lu - ia, for - ev-er and ev - er, for - ev - er, al-le - lu - ia, for - ev-er and ev-er. A-men.

Music: *St. Louis Jesuits Mass;* Bob Dufford, SJ, b. 1943, © 1973, Robert J. Dufford, SJ.
   Published by OCP Publications. All rights reserved.

215   LAMB OF GOD LITANY

Refrain
Lamb of God, you take a-way the sins of the world: have mer-cy on
Lamb of God, you lay __ down your life for the world:

us. have mer-cy on us. O grant us, O grant us your peace.

Verses
1. Praise to you, Je - sus Christ, come to be our bread of life.
2. Praise to you, Son of Light, come to turn a - way the night.
3. Praise to you, Sav - ior King, feed us with the life you bring.
4. Praise to you, Ris - en Christ, clothe us in your sav - ing light.
5. Praise to you, Prince of Peace, come to make our ha - tred cease.
6. Praise to you, Lamb of God, wash us with your ho - ly blood.

Text and music: *St. Louis Jesuits Mass;* Dan Schutte, b. 1947, © 1992, Daniel L. Schutte.
   Published by OCP Publications. All rights reserved.

MISSA UBI CARITAS

KYRIE ELEISON

Ky - ri - e e - le - i - son. Chri - ste e - le - i - son. Ky - ri - e e - le - i - son.

GLORIA

Glo-ri - a in ex - cel - sis De - o, et in ter - ra pax ho-

mi - ni-bus bo - nae vo - lun - ta - tis. ta - tis.

ta - tis. A - men. A - men.

MISERERE NOBIS

Mi-se-re-re no-bis. Mi-se-re-re no-bis. *Oh, _____ hear our prayer.*
(Spanish) *Ó - ye-nos, Se - ñor.*
(Tagalog) *Ding - gin mo ka - mi.*
(Vietnamese) *Xin lắng nghe lời con.*

220   SANCTUS

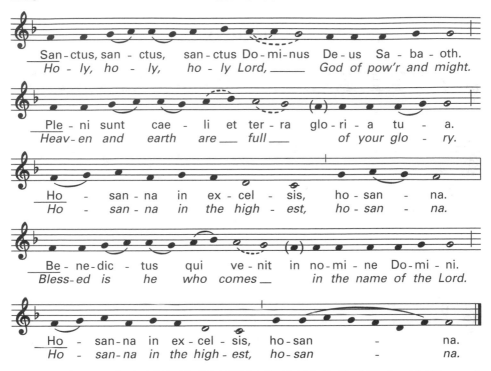

San‐ctus, san‐ctus,   san‐ctus Do‐mi‐nus De‐us Sa‐ba‐oth.
Ho‐ly, ho‐ly,   ho‐ly Lord,___ God of pow'r and might.

Ple‐ni sunt   cae‐li et ter‐ra glo‐ri‐a tu‐a.
Heav‐en and   earth are___ full___ of your glo‐ry.

Ho‐san‐na in ex‐cel‐sis,   ho‐san‐na.
Ho‐san‐na in the high‐est,   ho‐san‐na.

Be‐ne‐dic‐tus   qui ve‐nit in no‐mi‐ne Do‐mi‐ni.
Bless‐ed is   he who comes___ in the name of the Lord.

Ho‐san‐na in ex‐cel‐sis,   ho‐san‐na.
Ho‐san‐na in the high‐est,   ho‐san‐na.

221   MEMORIAL ACCLAMATION A

Christ has died,   Christ is   ris‐en,   Christ will come a‐gain.

Christ has died,   Christ is ris‐en,   Christ   will come   a‐gain.

222   MEMORIAL ACCLAMATION B

Dy‐ing you de‐stroyed our   death,   ris‐ing you re‐stored our life.

Lord   Je - sus, come in glo - ry,   come   in glo   -   ry.

MEMORIAL ACCLAMATION C   223

When we eat   this   bread   and drink this cup,   we pro-claim

your death, Lord Je - sus,   un - til you come in glo   -   ry.

MEMORIAL ACCLAMATION D   224

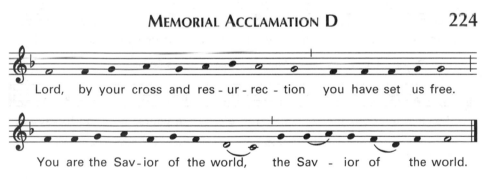

Lord,   by your cross and res - ur - rec - tion   you have set us free.

You are the Sav - ior of the world,   the Sav - ior of   the world.

AMEN   225

A - men,   a - men,   a - men. Al - le - lu - ia.
Lent: *(A   -   men.)*

226   LORD'S PRAYER

Priest: Let us pray for the coming of the kingdom as Jesus taught us:

All

Our Father, who art in heaven, hallowéd be thy name; thy king - dom come; thy will be done on earth as it is in heaven. Give us this day our dai - ly bread; and forgive us our trespasses as we forgive those who trespass a - gainst us; and lead us not in - to temp - tation, but deliver us from evil.

Priest: Deliver us, Lord...for the coming of our Savior, Jesus Christ.

All

For the kingdom, the power and the glo - ry are yours, now and for - ev - er.

227   AGNUS DEI

Invocation: Cantor

Agnus Dei, qui tollis pec - cata mundi:

Response: All

mi - se - re - re no - bis, mi - se - re - re no - bis.
Final: do - na no - bis pa - cem, do - na no - bis pa - cem.

ALLELUIA, WORD OF GOD   229

Refrain

Al-le-lu-ia, al-le-lu-ia, al-le-lu-ia, al-le-lu-ia.

Al-le-lu-ia, al-le-lu-ia, al-le-lu-ia, al-le-lu-ia.

HOLY   230

Ho-ly, ho-ly, ho-ly, Lord God of pow'r, Lord God of might,

Lord God of pow'r and might. Heav'n and earth are

full of your glo-ry. Ho-san-na in the high - est. Ho-san -

na, ho-san - na, ho-san-na in the high - est.

Bless-ed, bless-ed, bless-ed, bless-ed is he who comes in the name, who

comes in the Lord's own name. Ho - san - na, ho -

san - na, ho-san-na in the high - est. Ho-san -

na, ho-san - na, ho-san-na in the high - est.

231   MEMORIAL ACCLAMATION A

Text © 1973, ICEL. All rights reserved. Used with permission.
Music: *Mass of Hope*; Bernadette Farrell, b. 1957, © 1985, Bernadette Farrell.
    Published by OCP Publications. All rights reserved.

232   AMEN

for use with Memorial Acclamation A

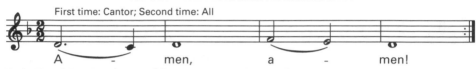

Music: *Mass of Hope*; Bernadette Farrell, b. 1957, © 1986, Bernadette Farrell.
    Published by OCP Publications. All rights reserved.

233   MEMORIAL ACCLAMATION B

Text © 1973, ICEL. All rights reserved. Used with permission.
Music: *Mass of Hope*; Bernadette Farrell, b. 1957, © 1985, Bernadette Farrell.
    Published by OCP Publications. All rights reserved.

234   MEMORIAL ACCLAMATION C

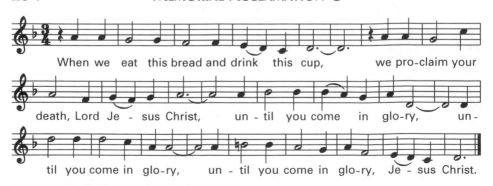

Text © 1973, ICEL. All rights reserved. Used with permission.
Music: *Mass of Hope*; Bernadette Farrell, b. 1957, © 1985, Bernadette Farrell.
    Published by OCP Publications. All rights reserved.

AMEN

when Doxology is spoken

[...for ever and ever.] A - men, A - men, A - men,
A - men, A - men, A - men.

MASS OF GLORY

PENITENTIAL RITE C

Lord, Have Mercy

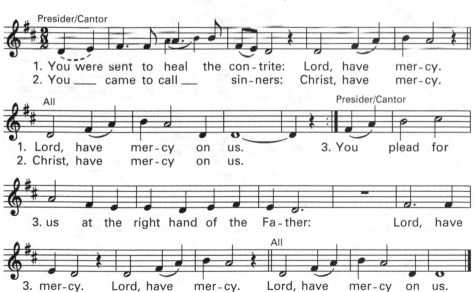

1. You were sent to heal the con-trite: Lord, have mer-cy.
2. You ___ came to call ___ sin-ners: Christ, have mer-cy.

1. Lord, have mer-cy on us. 3. You plead for
2. Christ, have mer-cy on us.

3. us at the right hand of the Fa-ther: Lord, have

3. mer-cy. Lord, have mer-cy. Lord, have mer-cy on us.

238   KYRIE ELEISON

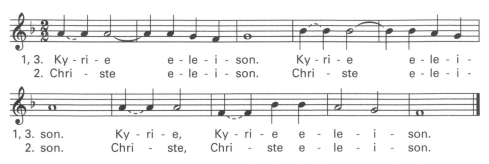

1, 3. Ky - ri - e   e - le - i - son.   Ky - ri - e   e - le - i -
2. Chri - ste   e - le - i - son.   Chri - ste   e - le - i -

1, 3. son.   Ky - ri - e,   Ky - ri - e   e - le - i - son.
2. son.   Chri - ste,   Chri - ste   e - le - i - son.

Music: *Mass of Glory*; Ken Canedo, b. 1953, and Bob Hurd, b. 1950, © 1996, 1998, 2000, Ken Canedo and Bob Hurd. Published by OCP Publications. All rights reserved.

239   GLORY TO GOD

Refrain: 1st time: Cantor, All repeat; thereafter: All

Glo - ry to God,   glo - ry to God,   glo - ry to God   in the high -

- est,   and peace to his peo - ple on earth.   2 to Vss.

Last time

Glo - ry to God,   glo - ry to God,   glo - ry to God in the

high - est,   and peace to his peo - ple on earth.

A - men,   a - men,   a - men.

Music: *Mass of Glory*; Ken Canedo, b. 1953, and Bob Hurd, b. 1950, © 1998, Ken Canedo and Bob Hurd. Published by OCP Publications. All rights reserved.

240   ALLELUIA! GIVE THE GLORY

Refrain

Al - le - lu - ia!   Al - le - lu - ia!

Al-le-lu - ia! Give the glo-ry

1
and the hon-or to the Lord!

2
and the hon-or to the Lord!

Text: Ken Canedo, b. 1953, and Bob Hurd, b. 1950.
Music: *Mass of Glory*; Ken Canedo.
Text and music © 1991, Ken Canedo and Bob Hurd. Published by OCP Publications. All rights reserved.

LENTEN GOSPEL ACCLAMATION · 241

Praise and hon-or to you, O Lord Je - sus Christ.

Text © 1969, 1981, 1997, ICEL. All rights reserved. Used with permission.
Music: *Mass of Glory*; Ken Canedo, b. 1953, and Bob Hurd, b. 1950, © 1998, Ken Canedo and Bob Hurd.
Published by OCP Publications. All rights reserved.

GENERAL INTERCESSIONS · 242

Refrain: 1st time: Cantor, All repeat; thereafter: All

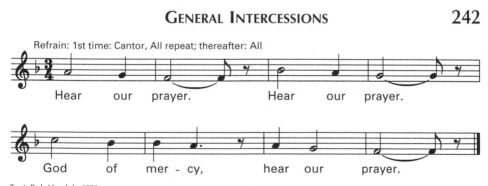

Hear our prayer. Hear our prayer.

God of mer - cy, hear our prayer.

Text: Bob Hurd, b. 1950.
Music: *Mass of Glory*; Bob Hurd.
Text and music © 1991, Bob Hurd. Published by OCP Publications. All rights reserved.

243   EUCHARISTIC PRAYER II: PREFACE DIALOGUE

The Lord be with you. And al-so with you. Lift up your hearts. We lift them up to the Lord. Let us give thanks to the Lord our God. It is right to give him thanks and praise. It is right to give him thanks and praise.

Music: *Mass of Glory*; Ken Canedo, b. 1953, and Bob Hurd, b. 1950, © 1991, Ken Canedo and Bob Hurd.
Published by OCP Publications. All rights reserved.

244   HOLY

Ho-ly, ho-ly, ho-ly Lord, God of pow-er and might. Heav-en and earth are full of your glo-ry. Ho-san-na, ho-san-na, ho-san-na in the high-est. Bless-ed is he who comes in the name of the Lord. Ho-

Music: *Mass of Glory*; Ken Canedo, b. 1953, and Bob Hurd, b. 1950, © 1991, Ken Canedo and Bob Hurd.
Published by OCP Publications. All rights reserved.

MEMORIAL ACCLAMATION A 245

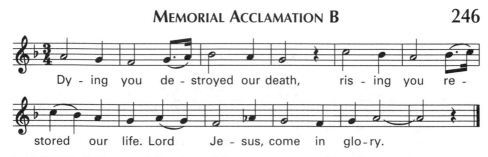

Christ has died, Christ is ris-en, Christ will come, will come a-gain.

MEMORIAL ACCLAMATION B 246

Dy-ing you de-stroyed our death, ris-ing you re-

stored our life. Lord Je-sus, come in glo-ry.

MEMORIAL ACCLAMATION C 247

When we eat this bread and drink this cup,

we pro-claim your death, Lord Je-sus, un - til you

come in glo-ry, un - til you come in glo-ry.

MEMORIAL ACCLAMATION D 248

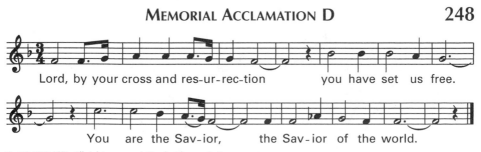

Lord, by your cross and res-ur-rec-tion you have set us free.

You are the Sav-ior, the Sav-ior of the world.

249   AMEN

A - men.   A - men.   Al - le - lu - ia,   a - men.   men.

During Lent: Praise and glo-ry,

250   LAMB OF GOD

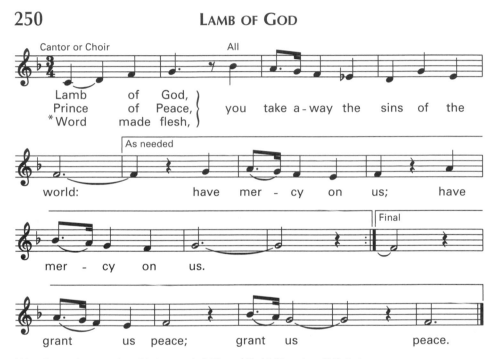

Cantor or Choir   All

Lamb   of   God, ⎫
Prince   of   Peace, ⎬   you   take a - way   the   sins   of   the
*Word   made   flesh, ⎭

As needed

world: have   mer - cy   on   us;   have

Final

mer - cy   on   us.

grant   us   peace;   grant   us   peace.

*More invocations may be added as needed: "Son of God," "Promise of Life," etc.; "Lamb of God," final time.

SERVICE MUSIC

To foster the assembly's sung participation in the ritual moments of the eucharistic celebration, the following selection of acclamations, litanies and other music allows additional choices to suit the community and the occasion. "Music, chosen with care, can serve as a bridge to faith as well as an expression of it" (Music in Catholic Worship, #16).

SPRINKLING RITE   251

AGUA DE VIDA/WATER OF LIFE   252

Estribillo/Refrain:
Todos/All

A-gua de vi - da, _____ san-to re - cuer - do;
Wa-ter of life, _____ ho - ly re - mind - er;

u - ne y re - nue - va _____ al cuer-po de Cris - to.
touch- ing, re - new - ing _____ the bod - y of Christ.

al cuer - po de Cris - to. _____
the bod - y of Christ. _____

Text: Jaime Cortez, b. 1963.
Music: *Misa del Pueblo Inmigrante;* Jaime Cortez.

253

COME TO THE WATER

1. Come to the wa - ter, all who are
2. Come to the wa - ter, all who are
3. Come to the wa - ter, all who are

1. thirst - y; come and re - ceive the gifts
2. lad - en; come to the Lord, for God's
3. bro - ken; come and re - ceive new life

1. wait - ing for you. All _____ who are hun -
2. call - ing to you. Bring _____ all your bur -
3. in the _____ Lord. Here live out the prom -

1. gry, all _____ who have noth - ing, come to the
2. dens, bring all of your sor - rows, come to the
3. ise made _____ to _____ Da - vid; come and be

1. wa - ter, drink of the Lord.
2. wa - ter, drink of the Lord.
3. blessed and drink of the Lord.

Text and music: Grayson Warren Brown, b. 1948, © 1999, Grayson Warren Brown.
Published by OCP Publications. All rights reserved.

254

STREAMS OF LIVING WATER

*Ostinato Refrain

Streams of liv - ing wa - ter shall flow from with - in you.

God will wipe a - way ev - 'ry tear from your eye.

*Verses available in accompaniment books.

Text: Based on Ezekiel 47:1; John 7:38; Revelation 7:17.
Music: Cyprian Consiglio, OSB Cam, b. 1958.
Text and music © 1995, Cyprian Consiglio, OSB Cam. Published by OCP Publications. All rights reserved.

WATER OF LIFE

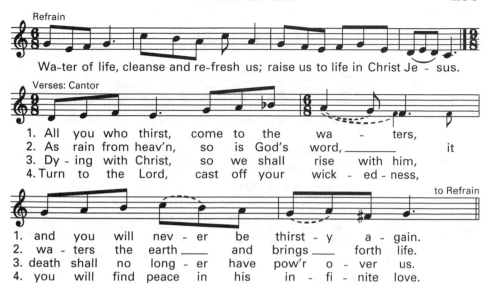

Refrain

Wa-ter of life, cleanse and re-fresh us; raise us to life in Christ Je - sus.

Verses: Cantor

1. All you who thirst, come to the wa - ters,
2. As rain from heav'n, so is God's word, _____ it
3. Dy - ing with Christ, so we shall rise with him,
4. Turn to the Lord, cast off your wick - ed - ness,

to Refrain

1. and you will nev - er be thirst - y a - gain.
2. wa - ters the earth ____ and brings ____ forth life.
3. death shall no long - er have pow'r o - ver us.
4. you will find peace in his in - fi - nite love.

Text and music: Stephen Dean, b. 1948, © 1981, Stephen Dean. Published by OCP Publications. All rights reserved.

LORD, HAVE MERCY

256

KYRIE

257

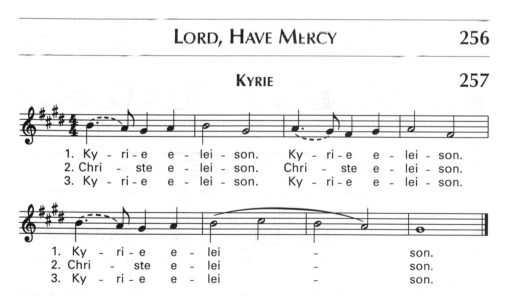

1. Ky - ri - e e - lei - son. Ky - ri - e e - lei - son.
2. Chri - ste e - lei - son. Chri - ste e - lei - son.
3. Ky - ri - e e - lei - son. Ky - ri - e e - lei - son.

1. Ky - ri - e e - lei - son.
2. Chri - ste e - lei - son.
3. Ky - ri - e e - lei - son.

Music: Russian Orthodox.

259   GLORY TO GOD

Cantor: Glo-ry to God in the high - est,   All: and peace to his peo-ple on earth.

Lord God, heav - en - ly King, al - might - y God and

Fa - ther, we wor - ship you, we give you thanks, we

praise you for your glo - ry. Lord Je - sus Christ,

on - ly Son of the Fa - ther, Lord God, Lamb of God,

you take a - way the sin of the world: have mer - cy on

us; you are seat-ed at the right hand of the Fa - ther:

re - ceive our prayer. For you a-lone are the Ho - ly One,

you a - lone are the Lord, you a - lone are the Most High,

Je - sus Christ, with the Ho - ly Spir - it, in the glo - ry of

God, of God the Fa - ther. A - men.

Music: *Mass of the Resurrection;* Randall DeBruyn, b. 1947, © 2002, Randall DeBruyn.
Published by OCP Publications. All rights reserved.

GLORY TO GOD 260

Glo - ry to God in the high - est, and peace to his peo-ple on

earth. Lord God, heav-en-ly King, al-might-y God and Fa - ther,

we wor-ship you, we give you thanks, we praise you for your glo - ry.

Lord Je-sus Christ, on-ly Son of the Fa - ther, Lord God, Lamb of

God, you take a-way the sin of the world: have mer - cy on us;

you are seat-ed at the right hand of the Fa - ther: re - ceive our

prayer. For you a - lone are the Ho - ly One, you a - lone are the

Lord, you a - lone are the Most High, Je - sus Christ, with the

Ho - ly Spir-it, in the glo-ry of God the Fa - ther. A - men.

CHANT GLORY TO GOD

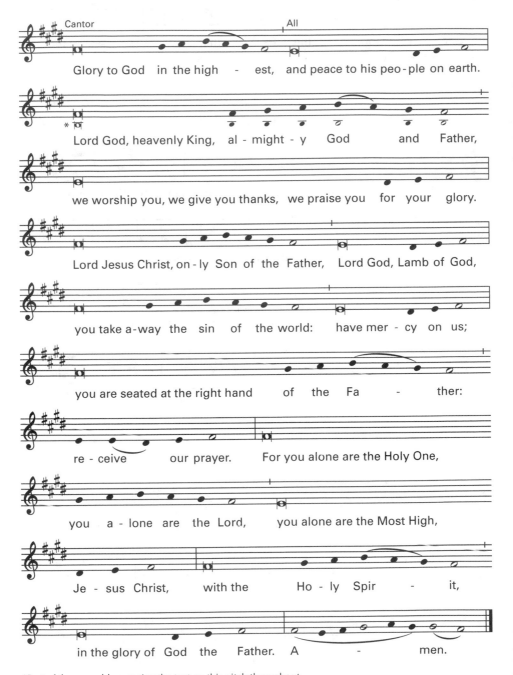

*Part of the assembly may sing the text on this pitch throughout.

GLORY TO GOD

Refrain 1: 1st time: Cantor, All repeat; thereafter: All

Glo - ry to God, glo - ry in the high-est. Peace to his peo-ple, peace on earth.

Cantor/Choir: Lord God, heavenly King,
almighty God
and Father. **(Ref. 1)**
Cantor/Choir: We worship you,

Cantor/Choir: you are seated
at the right hand
of the Father:
receive our prayer,

Refrain 2: All

glo - ry in the high - est.

Cantor/Choir: Give you thanks, **(Ref. 2)**
Cantor/Choir: Praise you for your glory. **(Ref. 1)**
Cantor/Choir: Lord Jesus Christ,
only Son of the Father,
Lord God, Lamb of God,
you take away
the sin of the world:
have mercy on us;

Refrain 4: All

re - ceive our prayer.

Cantor/Choir: Glory to God,
glory in the highest.
Peace to his people,
peace on earth. **(Ref. 1)**
Cantor/Choir: For you alone
are the Holy One,
you alone are the Lord,
you alone are the Most High,
Jesus Christ,
with the Holy Spirit,
in the glory of God,
the glory of God
the Father. **(Ref. 1)**

Refrain 3: All

have mer - cy on us;

Cantor/Choir: Amen, amen.

GLORIA/GLORY TO GOD 263

Estribillo/Refrain

Glo - ria a Dios en el cie - lo,   y en la tie - rra
Glo - ry to God in the high - est,   glo - ry to

paz   a los hom - bres que   a - ma el Se - ñor.
God,   and_ peace to his   peo - ple on earth.

264

GLORY TO GOD

Glo - ri - a in ex - cel - sis De - o; glo - ri - a, et in ter - ra pax.

Glo - ri - a in ex - cel - sis De - o; glo - ri - a, et in ter - ra pax.

Music: Scott Soper, b. 1961, © 1992, Scott Soper. Published by OCP Publications. All rights reserved.

265

GLORY TO GOD

Refrain: 1st time: Choir; All repeat; thereafter: All

Glo - ry to God! Glo - ry to God! Glo - ry to God in the

high - est! Glo - ry to God! Glo - ry to God, and

peace to his peo - ple, his peo - ple on earth.

Music: James Biery, b. 1956, © 1993, James Biery. Published by OCP Publications. All rights reserved.

266

A CHRISTMAS GLORIA

Refrain: All

Glo - ri - a

in ex - cel - sis De - o, De - o.

Music: Trad. French Carol; adapt. by Paul Gibson, b. 1952, © 1988, Paul Gibson.
Published by OCP Publications. All rights reserved.

ADVENT/CHRISTMAS GOSPEL ACCLAMATION 268

Refrain: 1st time: Cantor, All repeat; thereafter: All

Al-le - lu - ia, al-le-lu - ia. Al-le - lu - ia, al-le-lu - ia.

Verse 1
Cantor *3*

1. You are the joy of ev - 'ry hu - man heart,

1. king of all the na - tions. Lord Je-sus, come!

Verses 2, 5, 6, 7
Cantor

2. You are Lord, our jus - tice and our mer - cy,
5. Born to - day our jus - tice and our mer - cy,
6. You are light that shines __ in the dark - ness,
7. You are born of wa - ter and the Spir - it,

2. Show us how to live: Lord Je-sus, come!
5. God in flesh a - mong us: Lord, Je-sus Christ!
6. star to guide the na - tions: Lord, Je-sus Christ!
7. foun - tain of our dreams: Lord, Je-sus Christ!

Verses 3, 4
Cantor *3*

3. E - ter-nal light, and sun __ of jus - tice,
4. Em-man-u - el, the joy of all na - tions,

3. shine in all our dark - ness: Lord Je-sus, come!
4. come to us and save us: Lord Je-sus, come!

269   ADVENT GOSPEL ACCLAMATION

Al - le - lu - ia, al - le - lu - ia, al - le - lu - ia, al - le - lu - ia,

al - le - lu - ia, al - le - lu - ia, al - le - lu - ia, al - le - lu - ia.

270   ALLELUIA! PRAISE TO CHRIST

Al - le - lu - ia! Al - le - lu - ia! Praise to Christ, the Word of Life.

Glo - ry, praise and ju - bi - la - tion, al - le - lu - ia!

271   GALLIARD ALLELUIA

Al - le - lu - ia! Al - le - lu - ia!

Al - le - lu - ia, al - le - lu - ia!

272   PRAISE HIS NAME

Al - le - lu - ia! Al - le - lu - ia! Al - le - lu - ia!

EASTERTIDE GOSPEL ACCLAMATION

Refrain: 1st time: Cantor; thereafter: All

Al - le-lu - ia, al - le - lu - ia, Je-sus, ris - en Lord of life!

Al - le-lu - ia, al - le - lu - ia, al - le - lu - ia!

Verses

Cantor   All   Cantor   All

1. Word of the Fa-ther: Je-sus Christ! Hope of the world: Je-sus Christ!
2. Light of the na-tions: Je-sus Christ! Way, Truth and Life: Je-sus Christ!
3. Liv-ing a-mong us: Je-sus Christ! Word in our flesh: Je-sus Christ!

Cantor   All   Cantor   All   to Refrain

1. Bro-ken and bur-ied: Je-sus Christ! Ris-en to life: Je-sus Christ!
2. Bear-ing our sor-row: Je-sus Christ! With us through time: Je-sus Christ!
3. Ser-vant of oth-ers: Je-sus Christ! Friend of the poor: Je-sus Christ!

ALLELUIA FOR THE EASTER SEASON   274

Al - le-lu - ia! Al - le - lu - ia! Al - le-lu - ia!

Music: O FILII ET FILIAE; Chant, Mode II; *Airs sur les hymnes sacrez, odes et noëls*, 1623.

EASTERTIDE ALLELUIA   275

Al - le-lu - ia, al - le - lu - ia, al - le - lu - ia.

Music: Chant, Mode VI.

SALISBURY ALLELUIA   276

Al - le-lu - ia, al-le - lu - ia, al-le-lu - ia. al-le-lu - ia.

278   LENTEN GOSPEL ACCLAMATION

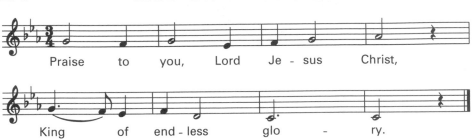

Praise to you, Lord Je - sus Christ,

King of end - less glo - ry.

279   ALABANZA A TI, OH CRISTO/ PRAISE TO YOU, LORD JESUS CHRIST

A - la - ban - za a ti, oh Cris - to, Rey de e - ter - na glo - ria.
Praise to_ you, Lord Je - sus Christ, King of_ end - less glo - ry.

280   LENTEN GOSPEL ACCLAMATION

Praise to you, Lord_ Je - sus Christ, King of end - less glo - ry!
Alt. Ref.: *Praise and glo - ry to you, O Christ, to - day_ and for - ev - er!*

LITANY FOR GENERAL INTERCESSIONS 282

ÓYENOS, SEÑOR/LISTEN TO YOUR PEOPLE 283

O GOD, HEAR US 284

GENERAL INTERCESSIONS 285

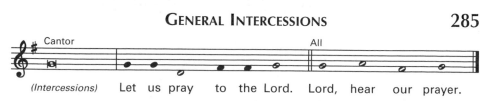

Music: Byzantine Chant.

287   **HOLY**

Ho - ly, ho - ly, ho - ly Lord, God of pow - er,

God of might. Heav - en and earth are full of your glo - ry.

Ho - san - na in the high - est. Bless - ed is he who

comes in the name of the Lord. Ho - san - na

in the high - est. Ho - san - na in the high - est.

288   **MEMORIAL ACCLAMATION A**

Christ has died, Christ is ris - en, Christ will come a - gain.

289   **MEMORIAL ACCLAMATION B**

Dy - ing you de - stroyed our death, ris - ing

you re - stored our life. Lord Je - sus,

come in glo - ry. Lord Je - sus, come in glo - ry.

MEMORIAL ACCLAMATION C

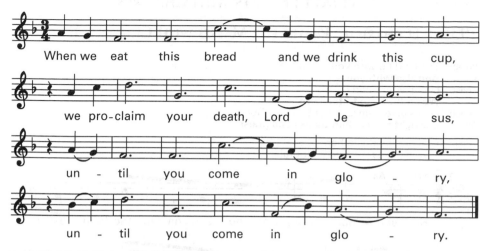

When we eat this bread and we drink this cup,

we pro-claim your death, Lord Je - sus,

un - til you come in glo - ry,

un - til you come in glo - ry.

MEMORIAL ACCLAMATION D 291

Lord, by your cross and res - ur - rec - tion

you have set us free.

You are the Sav - ior of the world.

AMEN 292

A - men, a - men, al-le-lu - ia.   A - men, al-le-lu - ia.
          *a - men.___   a - men.

*Alternate text for Lenten Season.

EUCHARISTIC ACCLAMATIONS
SETTING II: MASSES WITH CHILDREN

293 EUCHARISTIC PRAYER FOR MASSES WITH CHILDREN II

Priest: The Lord be with you.
All: **And also with you.**
Priest: Lift up your hearts.
All: **We lift them up to the Lord.**
Priest: Let us give thanks to the Lord our God.
All: **It is right to give him thanks and praise.**

Priest: God our loving Father...
    ...With Jesus we sing your praise:

Acclamation 1: All

Ho - san - na, ho-san-na, ho - san-na in the high - est! Ho - san - na, ho - san - na, ho - san-na in the high - est!

Priest: Because you love us...
    ...With Jesus we sing your praise: **(to Acclamation 1)**

Priest: Because you love us...
    ...With Jesus we sing your praise: **(to Acclamation 1)**

Priest: For such great love
    we thank you with the angels and saints
    as they praise you and sing:

Acclamation 2: All

Ho - ly, ho - ly, ho - ly Lord, God of pow'r, God of might, ho - ly Lord! Heav'n and earth are full, are full of your glo - ry. Ho - san - na, ho-san - na, ho - san-na in the high-est! Ho - san - na, ho - san - na, ho - san-na in the high - est!

to Acclamation 3

Acclamation 3: All

Blest is he who comes in the name of the Lord. Ho -

san - na, ho-san - na, ho - san-na in the high - est! Ho -

san - na, ho - san - na, ho - san-na in the high - est!

Priest: Blessed be Jesus, whom you sent...
...so that we can live as your children. **(to Acclamation 3)**

Priest: God our Father...
...This is my body which will be given up for you.

Acclamation 4: All

Je - sus died for us, gave his life for us.

He will come a - gain in glo - ry.

Priest: When supper was ended...
...so that sins may be forgiven. **(to Acclamation 4)**

Priest: Then he said to them...
...to be the sacrifice we offer you.

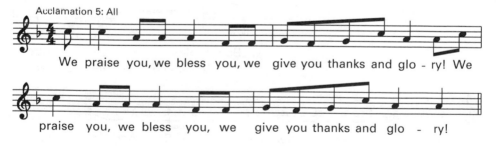

Acclamation 5: All

We praise you, we bless you, we give you thanks and glo - ry! We

praise you, we bless you, we give you thanks and glo - ry!

Priest: Lord our God...
...and all who serve your people. **(to Acclamation 5)**

Priest: Remember, Father, our families and friends...
...to be with you for ever. **(to Acclamation 5)**

Priest: Gather us all together into your kingdom...
...will sing a song of joy. **(to Acclamation 5)**

Priest: Through him...
...for ever and ever.

Acclamation 6: All

A - men, a - men, a - men.

Music: Paul Inwood, b. 1947, © 1995, 1996, Paul Inwood. Published by OCP Publications. All rights reserved.

295　　　　　　　　　　SANTO/HOLY

San - to, San - to, San-to es el Se - ñor,
Ho - ly, ho - ly, ho - ly, ho - ly Lord,

Dios del U - ni - ver - so. San-to es el Se - ñor.
God of pow - er, God of might, ho - ly, ho - ly Lord.

Lle - nos es - tán el cie - lo y la tie - rra de tu glo - ria. Ho -
Heav - en and earth are full of your glo - ry. Ho -

san - na en el cie - lo. Ho - san - na en el cie -
san - na in the high - est. Ho - san - na in the high -

lo. Ben - di - to el que
est. Bless - ed is he who

vie - ne en el nom - bre del Se - ñor. Ho -
comes in the name of the Lord. Ho -

* (Fin/Fine)

D.S. al fine

Note: This can be sung in English or Spanish. If sung bilingually, begin with Spanish and sing the text in between the asterisks in English or vice versa.

Aclamación Conmemorativa I/ Memorial Acclamation B

296

A - nun - cia - mos tu muer - te, pro - cla -
Dy - ing _____ you de- stroyed our

ma - mos tu re - su - rrec - ción.
death, _ ris - ing you re - stored our life.

¡Ven, Se - ñor Je - sús! ¡Ven, Se - ñor Je - sús!
Lord _ Je - sus, come, come in glo - ry.

Aclamación Conmemorativa II/ Memorial Acclamation C

297

Ca - da vez que co - me - mos de es - te pan
When we eat _____ this bread and drink this cup,

y be - be - mos de es - te cá - liz,
we pro - claim your death, Lord Je - sus,

a - nun - cia - mos tu muer - te, Se - ñor,
un - til _ you come _ in glo - ry,

has - ta que vuel - vas, has - ta que vuel - vas.
un - til you come _____ in _ glo - ry.

ACLAMACIÓN CONMEMORATIVA III/
MEMORIAL ACCLAMATION D

Por ____ tu cruz y re - su - rrec - ción ____
Lord, by your cross ____ and re - sur - rec - tion

nos has sal - va - do, Se - ñor.
you ____ have set ____ us free.

Por ____ tu cruz y re - su - rrec - ción
You are the sav - ior of ____ the world, the

nos has sal - va - do, Se - ñor.
sav - ior of ____ the world.

Text: English © 1973, ICEL. All rights reserved. Used with permission.
Music: *Misa de las Américas;* Bob Hurd, b. 1950, © 1999, Bob Hurd. Published by OCP Publications. All rights reserved.

299   AMÉN/AMEN

A - mén, a - mén. A - mén, a - le - lu -
*Te a - la - ba - mos, Se -

ya. A - mén, a - mén.
ñor.

1
A - mén, a - le - lu - ya.
Te a - la - ba - mos, Se - ñor.

2
ya.
ñor.

*For use during Lent.

Music: *Misa de las Américas;* Bob Hurd, b. 1950, and Barbara Bridge, b. 1950, © 1988, Bob Hurd and Barbara Bridge.
    Published by OCP Publications. All rights reserved.

DANISH AMEN

300

A - men, a - men, a - men.

Music: Traditional.

LORD'S PRAYER

LORD'S PRAYER

301

All

Our Fa - ther, who art in heav - en, hal-lowed be thy name;

thy king-dom come; thy will be done on earth as it is in heav-en.

Give us this day our dai - ly bread; and for-give us our tres-pass-es

as we for-give those who tres-pass a-gainst us; and lead us

not in - to temp-ta - tion, but de - liv - er us from e - vil.

Priest
Deliver us, Lord, from every evil,
and grant us peace in our day.
In your mercy keep us free from sin
and protect us from all anxiety
as we wait in joyful hope
for the coming of our Savior, Jesus Christ.

All

For the kingdom, the pow'r and the glo-ry are yours, now and for ev - er.

Music: Chant; adapt. by Robert J. Snow, 1926–1998.

303 LETANÍA PARA LA FRACCIÓN DEL PAN/ LITANY FOR THE BREAKING OF THE BREAD

1. Cor - de - ro de Dios, que qui - tas el pe -
2. Prín - ci - pe de Paz, que qui - tas el pe -
3. Pan de Vi - da, que qui - tas el pe -
1. Lamb of God, you take a - way the
2. Prince of Peace, you take a - way the
3. Bread of Life, you take a - way the
1, 2
1. ca - do del mun - do, ten pie - dad de no -
2. ca - do del mun - do, ten pie - dad de no -
3. ca - do del mun - do,
1. sins of the world: have mer - cy on
2. sins of the world: have mer - cy on
3. sins of the world:
3
1, 2. so - tros.
1, 2. us.
3. da - nos la paz.
3. grant us peace.

Music: Andrea Johnson, CHS, © 1989, 1990, Andrea Johnson, CHS. Published by OCP Publications.

304 LITANY FOR THE BREAKING OF THE BREAD

Cantor
A - gnus De - i, qui tol - lis pec - cá - ta mun - di:
Ostinato Refrain: All
mi - se - ré - re no - bis; do - na no - bis pa - cem.

Music: John Schiavone, b. 1947, © 1988, OCP Publications.

AGNUS DEI

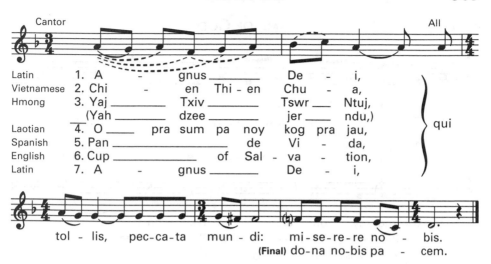

Cantor / All

Latin	1. A - gnus_____ De - i,
Vietnamese	2. Chi - en Thi - en Chu - a,
Hmong	3. Yaj_____ Txiv_____ Tswr___ Ntuj,
	(Yah_____ dzee_____ jer___ ndu,)
Laotian	4. O___ pra sum pa noy kog pra jau,
Spanish	5. Pan_____ de Vi - da,
English	6. Cup_____ of Sal - va - tion,
Latin	7. A - gnus_____ De - i,

qui

tol - lis, pec-ca-ta mun - di: mi-se-re-re no - bis.
(Final) do-na no-bis pa - cem.

Music: Jeffrey Honoré, b. 1956, © 1991, Jeffrey Honoré. Published by OCP Publications. All rights reserved.

ADVENT LAMB OF GOD
306

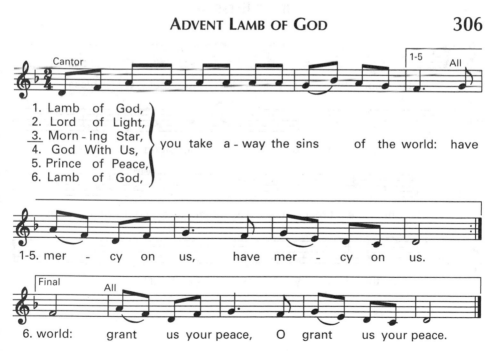

Cantor / 1-5 / All

1. Lamb of God,
2. Lord of Light,
3. Morn - ing Star,
4. God With Us,
5. Prince of Peace,
6. Lamb of God,

you take a - way the sins of the world: have

1-5. mer - cy on us, have mer - cy on us.

Final / All

6. world: grant us your peace, O grant us your peace.

Text and music: Adapt. by Kevin Keil, ASCAP, b. 1956, © 1993, Cooperative Music, Inc.
Exclusive agent: OCP Publications. All rights reserved.

308   LAMB OF GOD

1. Lamb of God,
2. Bread of Life,
3. Word of Truth,
4. Prince of Peace,

you take a-way the sins of the world:

Final: Lamb of God, you take a-way the sins of the world:

1-4. have mer-cy on us, mer-cy on us.
Final: grant __ us peace, grant __ us peace.

Music: Bob Hurd, b. 1950, © 1999, Bob Hurd. Published by OCP Publications. All rights reserved.

309   CUP OF BLESSING

Refrain

Is not the cup of bless-ing that we bless

a shar-ing in the blood of Christ?

Is not the bread that we break a com-mun-ion

in the bod-y of the Lord?

Verses

1. Man - y though we are, _____ we share in this one
2. When we eat this bread, _____ when we drink this
3. Man - y are the gifts: _____ one Spir - it gives them
4. Mem - bers of his bod - y, _____ we are bound to -
5. Let each gift we have _____ be giv - en to up -
6. May this Church stand firm, _____ may our faith a -

1. bread. _____ And so we are made one, _____ one
2. cup, _____ ⅞ we pro - claim Christ's death _____ un -
3. all. _____ ⅞ Man - y ways to serve, _____ in
4. geth - er: ⅞ joined in each one's suf - f'ring and
5. build _____ the bod - y of the Lord, _____ his
6. bound; _____ and let all that we do _____ be

to Refrain

1. bod - y in the Lord.
2. til he comes a - gain.
3. ser - vice to one Lord.
4. shar - ing each one's joy.
5. pres - ence in this world.
6. done in Christ - ly love.

Text: Based on 1 Corinthians 10:16–17; 11:26; 12:4–5, 26–27; 14:26; 16:13–14; Bob Hurd, b. 1950.
Music: Bob Hurd.

DISMISSAL

EASTER SOLEMN DISMISSAL   310

Deacon/Priest

Go in the peace of Christ, al - le - lu - ia, al - le - lu - ia.

All

Thanks be to God, al - le - lu - ia, al - le - lu - ia.

Music: Chant.

HYMNS & SONGS

"Thankfully sing to God psalms, hymns and holy songs" (Colossians 3:16). From the earliest centuries of Christianity, hymns and songs have played a major role in the liturgies and devotions of the faithful. A hymn is a song of praise or thanksgiving to God. All hymns are songs; but in contemporary liturgy the term "song" includes a wide variety of other musical forms: verse-refrain, litany, ostinato, chant, acclamation, spiritual and call-response. Often, but not always, liturgical song is based on scripture. Songs bring to expression and realize externally the inner attitudes of adoration, joy, sadness or petition, and they draw together in unity the diverse dispositions of community members. "A liturgical celebration can have no more solemn or pleasing feature than the whole assembly's expressing its faith and devotion in song" (Musicam Sacram, #16). St. Augustine said simply, "They who love, sing."

SEASONS AND SOLEMNITIES OF THE LORD

311 **O COME, O COME, EMMANUEL**

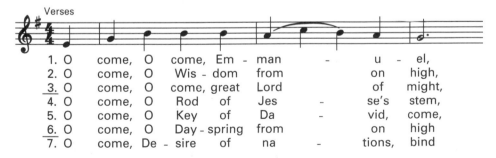

Verses

1. O come, O come, Em - man - u - el,
2. O come, O Wis - dom from on high,
3. O come, O come, great Lord of might,
4. O come, O Rod of Jes - se's stem,
5. O come, O Key of Da - vid, come,
6. O come, O Day - spring from on high
7. O come, De - sire of na - tions, bind

1. And ran - som cap - tive Is - ra - el,
2. Who or - dered all things might - i - ly;
3. Who to your tribes on Si - nai's height
4. From ev - 'ry foe de - liv - er them
5. And o - pen wide our heav'n - ly home;
6. And cheer us by your draw - ing nigh;
7. In one the hearts of hu - man - kind;

1. That mourns in lone - ly ex - ile here
2. To us the path of knowl - edge show,
3. In an - cient times did give the law,
4. That trust your might - y pow'r to save,
5. Make safe the way that leads on high,
6. Dis - perse the gloom - y clouds of night,
7. Make all our sad di - vi - sions cease,

1. Un - til the Son of God ap - pear.
2. And teach us in her ways to go.
3. In cloud, and maj - es - ty, and awe.
4. And give them vic - t'ry o'er the grave.
5. And close the path to mis - er - y.
6. And death's dark shad - ow put to flight.
7. And be for us our King of Peace.

Refrain

Re - joice! Re - joice! Em - man - u - el

Shall come to you, O Is - ra - el!

Text: LM with refrain; Latin, 9th cent.; verses 1, 3–6, para. in *Psalteriolum Cantionum Catholicarum*, Cologne, 1710;
tr. by John M. Neale, 1818–1866; verses 2, 7, tr. from *The Hymnal 1940*, alt.
Music: VENI, VENI, EMMANUEL; Chant, Mode I; *Processionale*, 15th cent. French; adapt. by Thomas Helmore, 1811–1890.

LITANY OF THE WORD 312

Cantor All Cantor All

1. Word of jus - tice, Al - le - lu - ia, Come to dwell here. Ma - ra - na - tha!
2. Word of mer - cy, Al - le - lu - ia, Live a - mong us. Ma - ra - na - tha!
3. Word of pow - er, Al - le - lu - ia, Live with - in us. Ma - ra - na - tha!
*4. Word of free-dom, Al - le - lu - ia, Save your peo - ple. Ma - ra - na - tha!

*Additional verses available in accompaniment books.

Text and music: Bernadette Farrell, b. 1957, © 1987, Bernadette Farrell. Published by OCP Publications. All rights reserved.

A VOICE CRIES OUT

1. Con - sole my peo-ple, the ones dear to me; speak to the
1. heart of Je - ru-sa-lem: the time of your mourn-ing is
1. end-ed now, the Lord of life will come.

Refrain

A voice cries out in the wil - der - ness: "Pre - pare a
way for the Lord!" A voice cries out in the wil - der -
ness: "Make straight a high - way for God!"

Verses 2, 4

2. Ev - 'ry val - ley is made a plain, ev - 'ry moun-tain is
4. Zi - on, shout from the moun-tain top, lift up your voice, O Je -

2. lev - eled; the glo - ry of God __ shall then be re -
4. ru-sa-lem, and say to the peo-ple of God's __ own

to Refrain

2. vealed, and the na - tions will sing in praise.
4. land, "Be - hold, be - hold your God!"

Verse 3

3. A voice shouts: "Cry!" O what shall I cry? All flesh is like
3. grass and its flow-ers: the grass may with - er, the

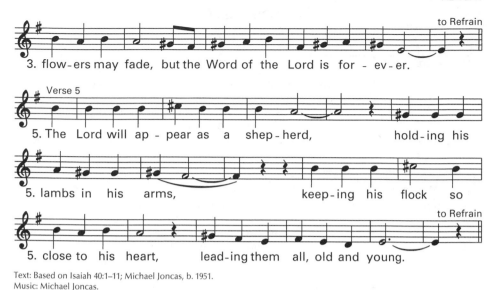

3. flow-ers may fade, but the Word of the Lord is for - ev - er.

Verse 5

5. The Lord will ap - pear as a shep - herd, hold-ing his

5. lambs in his arms, keep-ing his flock so

to Refrain

5. close to his heart, lead-ing them all, old and young.

Text: Based on Isaiah 40:1–11; Michael Joncas, b. 1951.
Music: Michael Joncas.
Text and music © 1981, 1982, Jan Michael Joncas Trust. Published by OCP Publications. All rights reserved.

PATIENCE, PEOPLE 314

Refrain

Pa-tience, peo-ple, till the Lord is come.

Verses

1. See ____ the farm - er a - wait the yield of the soil. He
2. You ____ have seen ____ the pur - pose of the Lord. You
3. Stead - y your hearts, for the Lord is close at hand. And

1. watch - es it in win - ter and in spring rain.
2. know of his com-pas - sion and his mer - cy.
3. do not grum - ble, one a - gainst the oth - er.

1-3. Pa - tience, peo - ple, for the

1-3. Lord is com - ing.

Text: Based on James 5:7–9, 11; John Foley, S.J., b. 1939.
Music: John Foley, S.J.
Text and music © 1977, 1979, John B. Foley, S.J., and New Dawn Music. Published by OCP Publications. All rights reserved.

315

ON JORDAN'S BANK

1. On Jor - dan's bank the Bap - tist's cry An -
2. Then cleansed be ev - 'ry soul from sin; Make
3. We hail you as our Sav - ior, Lord, Our
4. To heal the sick stretch out your hand, And
5. To God the Son all glo - ry be, Whose

1. nounc - es that the Lord is nigh; A - wake and heark - en,
2. straight the way of God with - in, And let each heart pre -
3. ref - uge, and our great re - ward; With - out your grace we
4. bid the fall - en sin - ner stand; Shine forth, and let your
5. ad - vent set your peo - ple free; Whom with the Fa - ther

1. for he brings Glad tid - ings of the King of kings.
2. pare a home, Where such a might - y guest may come.
3. waste a - way Like flow'rs that with - er and de - cay.
4. light re - store Earth's own true love - li - ness once more.
5. we a - dore, And Ho - ly Spir - it, ev - er - more.

Text: LM; Charles Coffin, 1676–1749; tr. by John Chandler, 1806–1876, alt.
Music: WINCHESTER NEW; Georg Wittwe's *Musicalishes Hand-Buch*, Hamburg, 1690;
adapt. by William H. Havergal, 1793–1870.

316

O COME, DIVINE MESSIAH

Verses

1. O come, di - vine Mes - si - ah; The world in
2. O Christ, whom na - tions sigh for, Whom priest and
3. You come in peace and meek - ness And low - ly

1. si - lence waits the day When hope shall sing its
2. proph - et long fore - told, Come, break the cap - tive's
3. will your cra - dle be; All clothed in hu - man

1. tri - umph And sad - ness flee a - way.
2. fet - ters, Re - deem the long - lost fold.
3. weak - ness Shall we your God - head see.

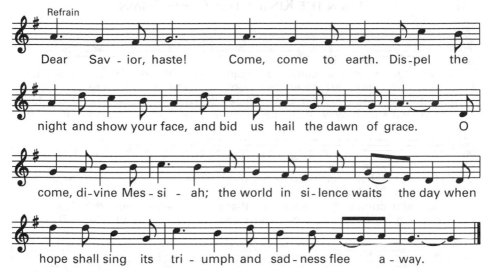

Refrain

Dear Sav - ior, haste! Come, come to earth. Dis-pel the
night and show your face, and bid us hail the dawn of grace. O
come, di-vine Mes - si - ah; the world in si-lence waits the day when
hope shall sing its tri - umph and sad - ness flee a - way.

Text: 78 76 with refrain; Abbé Simon-Joseph Pellegrin, 1663–1745; tr. by Sr. Mary of St. Philip, 1825–1904.
Music: VENEZ, DIVIN MESSIE; Trad. French Carol, 16th cent.

CLEAR THE VOICE 317

1. Clear the voice and clear the warn - ing, Clear
2. "Stir from sleep, and heed the warn - ing! Look
3. "See, the Lamb from Jor - dan's wa - ters Comes
4. "Christ the King comes robed in glo - ry, Scat -
5. Hon - or, glo - ry, praise, and pow - er, King -

1. for all with ears to hear: Voice re - sound - ing
2. a - gain with keen - er eye! In the dark a
3. to par - don and for - give. Turn from sin, and
4. ters night and ev - 'ry fear. Run to meet the
5. ship, might, and maj - es - ty, To the Fa - ther,

1. through the dark - ness, "Trem - ble, Earth! The Christ ap-pears!"
2. new star flash - es, Prom - ise of the morn-ing sky.
3. mark the Gos - pel That for - giv - en you may live.
4. King of glo - ry, Christ whose mer - cy draws us near."
5. Son, and Spir - it Bless - ings for e - ter - ni - ty.

Text: 87 87; based on *Vox clara*, 9th cent.; Harry Hagan, OSB, b. 1947, © 2000, St. Meinrad Archabbey.
Published by OCP Publications. All rights reserved.
Music: RESTORATION; adapt. fr. William Walker's *The Southern Harmony*, 1854.

318 WHEN THE KING SHALL COME AGAIN

1. When the King shall come a - gain All his pow'r re - veal - ing,
2. In the des - ert trees take root Fresh from his cre - a - tion;
3. Strength-en fee - ble hands and knees, Faint - ing hearts, be cheer - ful!
4. There God's high-way shall be seen Where no roar - ing li - on,

1. Splen-dor shall an-nounce his reign, Life and joy and heal - ing;
2. Plants and flow'rs and sweet-est fruit Join the cel - e - bra - tion;
3. God who comes for such as these Seeks and saves the fear - ful;
4. Noth - ing e - vil or un-clean Walks the road to Zi - on:

1. Earth no long - er in de - cay, Hope no more frus - trat - ed;
2. Riv - ers spring up from the earth, Bar - ren lands a - dorn - ing;
3. Deaf ears, hear the si - lent tongues Sing a - way their weep-ing;
4. Ran-somed peo - ple home-ward bound All your prais - es voic - ing,

1. This is God's re-demp-tion day Long - ing - ly a - wait - ed.
2. Val - leys, this is your new birth, Moun-tains, greet the morn-ing!
3. Blind eyes, see the life - less ones Walk - ing, run-ning, leap-ing.
4. See your Lord with glo - ry crowned, Share in his re - joic - ing!

Text: 76 76 D; Isaiah 35; Christopher Idle, b. 1938, © 1982, Jubilate Hymns, Ltd. All rights reserved.
Administered by Hope Publishing Co. Used with permission.
Music: GAUDEAMUS PARITER; Johann Horn, ca. 1495–1547.

319 THE KING SHALL COME WHEN MORNING DAWNS

1. The King shall come when morn - ing dawns And
2. Not, as of old, a lit - tle child, To
3. O bright - er than the ris - ing morn When
4. O bright - er than that glo - rious morn Shall
5. The King shall come when morn - ing dawns And

1. light tri - um-phant breaks, When beau - ty gilds the
2. bear, and fight, and die, But crowned with glo - ry
3. he, vic - to - rious, rose And left the lone-some
4. this fair morn - ing be, When Christ, our King, in
5. light and beau - ty brings. Hail, Christ, the Lord! Thy

1. east - ern   hills And   life   to   joy   a - wakes.
2. like   the   sun That   lights the   morn - ing   sky.
3. place   of   death, De - spite   the   rage   of   foes.
4. beau - ty   comes, And   we   his   face   shall   see!
5. peo - ple   pray: Come   quick - ly   King   of   kings.

Text: CM; Greek; tr. by John Brownlie, 1859–1925, alt.
Music: MORNING SONG; *Sixteen Tune Settings*, Philadelphia, 1812; *Kentucky Harmony*, 1816.

LET THE KING OF GLORY COME 320

Refrain

Lift   up, you   gates, lift   up your arch - es: let the   King of

glo-ry come!   Lift   up your   hearts and   sing, you peo - ple:

(to Verses) | Final

let the   King of   glo-ry come!   Let the King of   glo - ry

| Verses

come!   1. Who   is the King   of   glo - ry?
    2. Come,   O __ come, Em - man-u - el:
    3. Come,   O __ come, bright   Wis - dom:
    4. Come, you __ Key   of   Da-vid, come:

1. Yah - weh,   ho-ly and strong!   Who   is the Lord   of
2. come   and   dwell__ with   us!   Come, O __ come, you
3. come   and   make__ us   wise!   Come, O __ come, you
4. o - pen our heav - en - ly home!   Come, De - sire   of

to Refrain

1. maj - es - ty?   Yah - weh, might-y   and   strong!
2. Lord of   might: ban - ish   death __ and   fear!
3. Day - spring: love, un - close __ our   eyes!
4. na - tions, come: bring   us   in - to your   peace!

Text; Based on Psalm 24 and the "O" Antiphons; Michael Joncas, b. 1951.
Music: Michael Joncas.

Savior of the Nations, Come

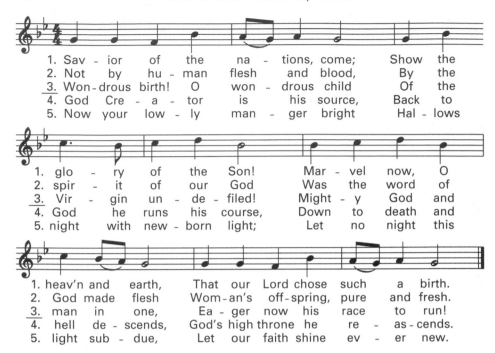

1. Sav - ior of the na - tions, come; Show the
2. Not by hu - man flesh and blood, By the
3. Won - drous birth! O won - drous child Of the
4. God Cre - a - tor is his source, Back to
5. Now your low - ly man - ger bright Hal - lows

1. glo - ry of the Son! Mar - vel now, O
2. spir - it of our God Was the word of
3. Vir - gin un - de - filed! Might - y God and
4. God he runs his course, Down to death and
5. night with new - born light; Let no night this

1. heav'n and earth, That our Lord chose such a birth.
2. God made flesh Wom - an's off - spring, pure and fresh.
3. man in one, Ea - ger now his race to run!
4. hell de - scends, God's high throne he re - as - cends.
5. light sub - due, Let our faith shine ev - er new.

Text: 77 77; *Veni, Redemptor gentium*; Martin Luther, 1483–1546, after St. Ambrose of Milan, 340–397.
Verses 1–3a tr. by William M. Reynolds, 1812–1876. Verses 3b–5 tr. by Martin L. Seltz, 1909–1967, alt.
Music: NUN KOMM, DER HEIDEN HEILAND; *Geystliche Gesangk Buchleyn*, Wittenberg, 1524.

322 The Advent of Our King

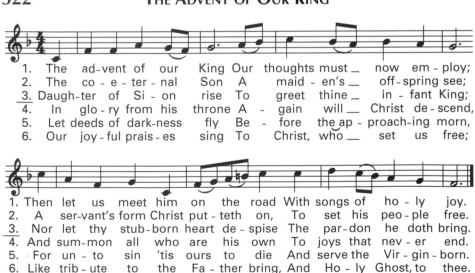

1. The ad-vent of our King Our thoughts must __ now em - ploy;
2. The co - e - ter - nal Son A maid - en's __ off - spring see;
3. Daugh-ter of Si - on rise To greet thine __ in - fant King;
4. In glo - ry from his throne A - gain will __ Christ de - scend,
5. Let deeds of dark-ness fly Be - fore the ap - proach-ing morn,
6. Our joy - ful prais - es sing To Christ, who __ set us free;

1. Then let us meet him on the road With songs of ho - ly joy.
2. A ser-vant's form Christ put - teth on, To set his peo - ple free.
3. Nor let thy stub-born heart de - spise The par - don he doth bring.
4. And sum-mon all who are his own To joys that nev - er end.
5. For un - to sin 'tis ours to die And serve the Vir - gin-born.
6. Like trib - ute to the Fa - ther bring, And Ho - ly Ghost, to thee.

Text: SM; Charles Coffin, fr. *Paris Breviary*, 1736; tr. by Robert Campbell, 1814–1868, alt.
Music: ST. THOMAS (WILLIAMS); *New Universal Psalmodist*, 1770; Aaron Williams, 1731–1776.

READY THE WAY

Verses

1. "Read-y the way of the Lord! Read-y the way of the Lord!" A voice __ cries out in the wil-der-ness: "Read-y the way of the Lord!" (to Verse 2)
2. "Let ev-'ry val-ley be filled. Let ev-'ry val-ley be filled." Let ev-'ry moun-tain be hum-bled; let ev-'ry val-ley be filled." (to Refrain)
3. Des-ert and waste-land will bloom. Des-ert and waste-land will bloom. Glo-ry and splen-dor will fill the land. Des-ert and waste-land will bloom. (to Verse 4)
4. Those who are blind will then see. Those who are deaf will then hear. Those who are lame will then leap for joy. Those who are mute will then sing. (to Refrain)
5. Strength-en the ones who are weak. Strength-en the ones who are weak. Say to the fright-ened: "Have cour-age." Strength-en the ones who are weak. (to Refrain)

Refrain

Here is your God, com-ing with your vin-di-ca - tion.

Look and be-hold the sav - ing pow - er of God.

1, 2 to Verses 3, 5 | Final

2

The sav - ing pow - er of God.

Text: Based on Isaiah 35:1–6; 40:1–5, 9–11; Ezekiel 11:19–20; Bob Hurd, b. 1950.
Music: Bob Hurd.

324   ALLELUIA! HURRY, THE LORD IS NEAR

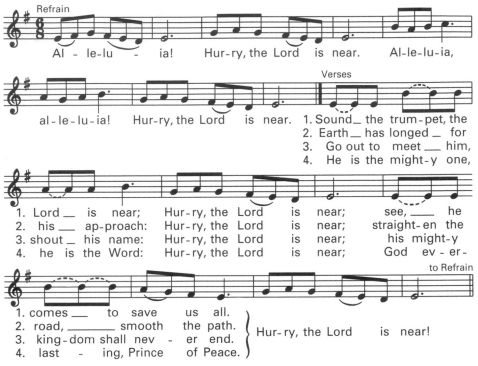

Refrain

Al - le-lu - ia! Hur-ry, the Lord is near. Al-le-lu-ia,

al - le-lu-ia! Hur-ry, the Lord is near.

Verses

1. Sound_ the trum-pet, the
2. Earth_ has longed _ for
3. Go out to meet _ him,
4. He is the might-y one,

1. Lord _ is near; Hur-ry, the Lord is near; see, ____ he
2. his _ ap-proach: Hur-ry, the Lord is near; straight-en the
3. shout _ his name: Hur-ry, the Lord is near; his might-y
4. he is the Word: Hur-ry, the Lord is near; God ev-er-

to Refrain

1. comes ___ to save us all.
2. road, _____ smooth the path.
3. king-dom shall nev - er end.
4. last - ing, Prince of Peace.

Hur-ry, the Lord is near!

Text: Patrick Lee, b. 1930, © 1982, Patrick Lee. Published by OCP Publications. All rights reserved.
Music: Ernest Sands, b. 1949, © 1979, Ernest Sands. Published by OCP Publications. All rights reserved.

325   CREATOR OF THE STARS OF NIGHT

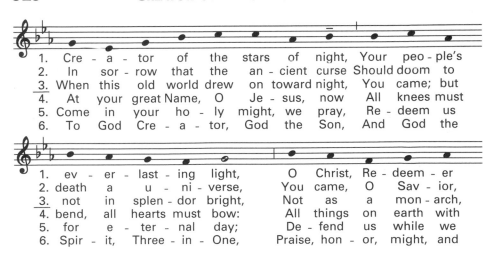

1. Cre - a - tor of the stars of night, Your peo - ple's
2. In sor - row that the an - cient curse Should doom to
3. When this old world drew on toward night, You came; but
4. At your great Name, O Je - sus, now All knees must
5. Come in your ho - ly might, we pray, Re - deem us
6. To God Cre - a - tor, God the Son, And God the

1. ev - er - last - ing light, O Christ, Re - deem - er
2. death a u - ni - verse, You came, O Sav - ior,
3. not in splen - dor bright, Not as a mon - arch,
4. bend, all hearts must bow: All things on earth with
5. for e - ter - nal day; De - fend us while we
6. Spir - it, Three - in - One, Praise, hon - or, might, and

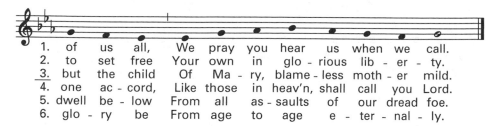

1. of us all, We pray you hear us when we call.
2. to set free Your own in glo - rious lib - er - ty.
3. but the child Of Ma - ry, blame - less moth - er mild.
4. one ac - cord, Like those in heav'n, shall call you Lord.
5. dwell be - low From all as - saults of our dread foe.
6. glo - ry be From age to age e - ter - nal - ly.

Text: LM; Latin, 9th cent.; tr. from *The Hymnal 1982,* © 1985, The Church Pension Fund. All rights reserved. Used with permission.
Music: CONDITOR ALME SIDERUM; Chant, Mode IV.

EVERY VALLEY 326

Refrain

Ev-'ry val-ley shall be ex - alt-ed and ev-'ry hill made low. And

all God's peo-ple shall see to-geth-er the glo-ry of the Lord.

Verses 1, 3

1. A voice cries out in the wil - der - ness, "Pre - pare the way
3. Stand up - on the __ moun-tain-top. O lift your voice

1. of the Lord. Make straight in the des - ert a
3. to the world. Sing joy - ful - ly, Je -

to Refrain

1. high - way, a high - way ___ for our God."
3. ru - sa - lem: "Be - hold, ___ be - hold your God."

Verse 2

2. Com-fort all my peo - ple. The time for war is gone. The

to Refrain

2. blind shall see, the deaf shall hear, the lame shall leap for joy.

Text: Based on Isaiah 40:1, 3, 4, 9; Bob Dufford, SJ, b. 1943.
Music: Bob Dufford, SJ.
Text and music © 1970, Robert J. Dufford, SJ. Published by OCP Productions. All rights reserved.

COMFORT, COMFORT, O MY PEOPLE

1. Com - fort, com - fort, O my peo - ple, Speak of peace, now
2. Hark, the voice of one who's cry - ing In the des - ert
3. O make straight what long was crook - ed, Make the rough - er

1. says our God; Com - fort those who sit in dark - ness,
2. far and near, Bid - ding all to full re - pent - ance
3. plac - es plain; Let your hearts be true and hum - ble,

1. Mourn-ing 'neath their sor-rows' load. Speak un - to Je - ru - sa -
2. Since the king-dom now is here. O that warn - ing cry o -
3. As be - fits his ho - ly reign. For the glo - ry of the

1. lem Of the peace that waits for them; Tell of all the
2. bey! Now pre - pare for God a way; Let the val - leys
3. Lord Now o'er earth is shed a-broad; And all flesh shall

1. sins I cov - er, And that war - fare now is o - ver.
2. rise to meet him And the hills bow down to greet him.
3. see the to - ken That his word is nev - er bro - ken.

Text: 87 87 77 88; based on Isaiah 40:1–8; Johann G. Olearius, 1611–1684; tr. by Catherine Winkworth, 1827–1878, alt.
Music: GENEVA FORTY-TWO; Claude Goudimel, ca. 1514–1572; *Genevan Psalter,* 1551.

328   COME, O LONG-EXPECTED JESUS

1. Come, O long - ex - pect - ed Je - sus, Born to
2. Is - rael's strength and con - so - la - tion, Hope to
3. Born your peo - ple to de - liv - er, Born a
4. By your own e - ter - nal Spir - it Rule in

1. set your peo - ple free! From our fears and
2. all the earth im - part; Dear de - sire of
3. child and yet a king: Born to reign in
4. all our hearts a - lone; By your all - suf -

1. sins re - lease us, You in whom our rest shall be.
2. ev - 'ry na - tion, Joy of ev - 'ry long - ing heart.
3. us for - ev - er, Now your gra - cious king - dom bring.
4. fi - cient mer - it Raise us to your glo - rious throne.

Text: 87 87; Charles Wesley, 1707–1788, alt.
Music: STUTTGART; Christian F. Witt's *Psalmodia Sacra,* Gotha, 1715; adapt. by Henry J. Gauntlett, 1805–1876.

PEOPLE, LOOK EAST 329

1. Peo - ple, look East. The time is near Of the
2. Fur - rows, be glad, though earth is bare. One more
3. Birds, though you long have ceased to build, Guard the
4. Stars, keep the watch when night is dim. One more
5. An - gels, an - nounce on this great feast: Him who

1. crown - ing of the year. Make your house fair as you are
2. seed is plant - ed there; Give up your strength the seed to
3. nest that must be filled. E - ven the hour when wings are
4. light the bowl shall brim. Shin - ing be - yond the frost - y
5. com - eth from the East. Set ev - 'ry peak and val - ley

1. a - ble. Trim the hearth and set the ta - ble. Peo - ple, look
2. nour - ish, That in course the flow'r may flour - ish. Peo - ple, look
3. fro - zen He for fledg - ing time has chos - en. Peo - ple, look
4. weath - er, Bright as sun and moon to - geth - er. Peo - ple, look
5. hum - ming With the word, the Lord is com - ing. Peo - ple, look

1. East, and sing to - day: Love, the Guest, is on the way.
2. East, and sing to - day: Love, the Rose, is on the way.
3. East, and sing to - day: Love, the Bird, is on the way.
4. East, and sing to - day: Love, the Star, is on the way.
5. East, and sing to - day: Love, the Lord, is on the way.

Text: 87 98 87; *The Oxford Book of Carols,* 1928; Eleanor Farjeon, 1881–1965, © 1957, Eleanor Farjeon. All rights reserved.
Reprinted by permission of Harold Ober Assoc., Inc.
Music: BESANÇON; Trad. French Carol.

330   Lift Up Your Heads, Ye Mighty Gates

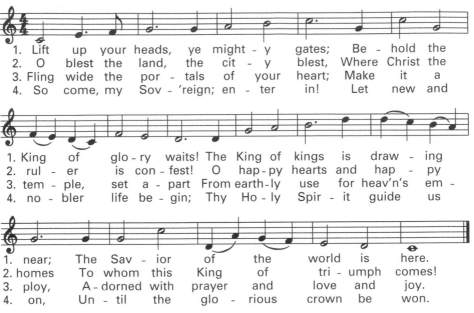

1. Lift up your heads, ye might-y gates; Be-hold the
2. O blest the land, the cit-y blest, Where Christ the
3. Fling wide the por-tals of your heart; Make it a
4. So come, my Sov-'reign; en-ter in! Let new and

1. King of glo-ry waits! The King of kings is draw-ing
2. rul-er is con-fest! O hap-py hearts and hap-py
3. tem-ple, set a-part From earth-ly use for heav'n's em-
4. no-bler life be-gin; Thy Ho-ly Spir-it guide us

1. near; The Sav-ior of the world is here.
2. homes To whom this King of tri-umph comes!
3. ploy, A-dorned with prayer and love and joy.
4. on, Un-til the glo-rious crown be won.

Text: LM; based on Psalm 24; George Weissel, 1590–1635; tr. by Catherine Winkworth, 1827–1878.
Music: TRURO; Williams' *Psalmodia Evangelica, Part II,* 1789.

331   See How the Virgin Waits

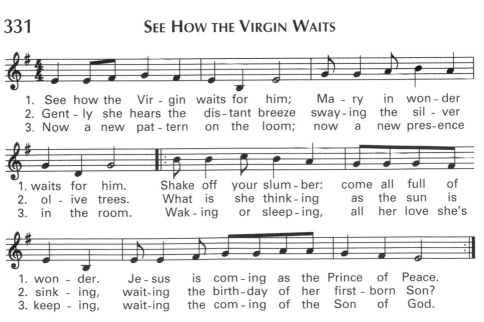

1. See how the Vir-gin waits for him; Ma-ry in won-der
2. Gent-ly she hears the dis-tant breeze sway-ing the sil-ver
3. Now a new pat-tern on the loom; now a new pres-ence

1. waits for him. Shake off your slum-ber: come all full of
2. ol-ive trees. What is she think-ing as the sun is
3. in the room. Wak-ing or sleep-ing, all her love she's

1. won-der. Je-sus is com-ing as the Prince of Peace.
2. sink-ing, wait-ing the birth-day of her first-born Son?
3. keep-ing, wait-ing the com-ing of the Son of God.

Music: Slovakian Folk Melody.

WAKE, O WAKE, AND SLEEP NO LONGER

1. Wake, O wake, and sleep no long - er, For he who calls you
2. Zi - on hears the sound of sing - ing; Our hearts are thrilled with
3. Glo - ry, glo - ry, sing the an - gels, While mu - sic sounds from

1. is no strang - er: A - wake, God's own Je - ru - sa - lem!
2. sud - den long - ing: She stirs, and wakes, and stands pre - pared.
3. strings and cym - bals; All hu - man - kind, with songs a - rise!

1. Hear, the mid-night bells are chim - ing The sig - nal for his
2. Christ, her friend, and lord, and lov - er, Her star and sun and
3. Twelve the gates in - to the cit - y, Each one a pearl of

1. roy - al com - ing: Let voice to voice an - nounce his name!
2. strong re-deem - er— At last his might - y voice is heard.
3. shin-ing beau - ty; The streets of gold ring out with praise.

1. We feel his foot-steps near, The Bride-groom at the
2. The Son of God has come To make with us his
3. All crea - tures round the throne A - dore the ho - ly

1. door— Al - le - lu - ia! The lamps will shine with
2. home: Sing ho - san - na! The fight is won, the
3. One With re - joic - ing: A - men be sung by

1. light di - vine As Christ the Sav - ior comes to reign.
2. feast be - gun; We fix our eyes on Christ a - lone.
3. ev - 'ry tongue To crown their wel - come to the King.

Text: 898 898 664 88; Matthew 25:1–13; tr. and adapt. by Christopher Idle, b. 1938, © 1982, Jubilate Hymns, Ltd.
All rights reserved. Administered by Hope Publishing Co. Used with permission.
Music: WACHET AUF; Philipp Nicolai, 1566–1608; adapt. by Johann Sebastian Bach, 1685–1750.

333 O COME, ALL YE FAITHFUL

Verses

1. O come, all ye faith-ful, joy-ful and tri-um-phant, O
2. God of God, Light of Light,
3. Sing, choirs of an-gels, sing in ex-ul-ta-tion,
4. Yea, Lord, we greet thee, born this hap-py morn-ing,

1. Ad-é-ste fi-dé-les, laé-ti tri-um-phán-tes, Ve-
2. De-um de De-o, Lu-men de Lú-mi-ne
3. Can-tet nunc i-o, cho-rus an-ge-ló-rum,
4. Er-go qui na-tus Di-e ho-di-ér-na,

1. come ye, O come ye to Beth-le-hem;
2. Lo! he comes forth from the Vir-gin's womb.
3. Sing, all ye cit-i-zens of heav'n a-bove!
4. Je-sus, to thee be all glo-ry giv'n;

1. ní-te, ve-ní-te in Béth-le-hem.
2. Ge-stant pu-él-lae ví-sce-ra.
3. Can-tet nunc au-la cae-lés-ti-um.
4. Je-su ti-bi sit gló-ri-a.

1. Come and be-hold him, born the King of an-gels;
2. Our ver-y God, be-got-ten, not cre-a-ted;
3. Glo-ry to God, all glo-ry in the high-est;
4. Word of the Fa-ther, now in flesh ap-pear-ing;

1. Na-tum vi-dé-te Re-gem an-ge-ló-rum.
2. De-um ve-rum, Gé-ni-tum, non fa-ctum.
3. Gló-ri-a, gló-ria, in ex-cél-sis De-o.
4. Pa-tris ae-tér-nae ver-bum ca-ro fa-ctum.

Refrain

O come, let us a-dore him, O come, let us a-dore him, O
Ve-ní-te, a-do-ré-mus, ve-ní-te, a-do-ré-mus, ve-

come, let us a-dore him, Christ, the Lord!
ní-te, a-do-ré-mus Dó-mi-num.

Text: Irregular with refrain; John F. Wade, ca. 1711–1786; tr. by Frederick Oakeley, 1802–1880, alt.
Music: ADESTE FIDELES; John F. Wade.

HE IS BORN

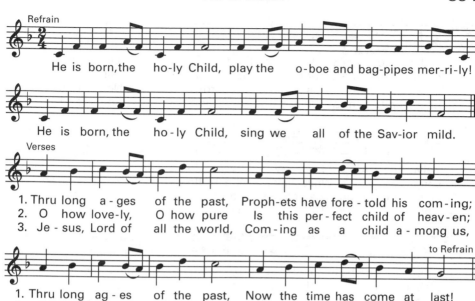

Refrain

He is born, the ho-ly Child, play the o-boe and bag-pipes mer-ri-ly!

He is born, the ho-ly Child, sing we all of the Sav-ior mild.

Verses

1. Thru long a-ges of the past, Proph-ets have fore-told his com-ing;
2. O how love-ly, O how pure Is this per-fect child of heav-en;
3. Je-sus, Lord of all the world, Com-ing as a child a-mong us,

to Refrain

1. Thru long ag-es of the past, Now the time has come at last!
2. O how love-ly, O how pure, Gra-cious gift to hu-man-kind!
3. Je-sus, Lord of all the world, Grant to us thy heaven-ly peace.

Text: 78 77 with refrain; Trad. French Carol, 19th cent.; tr. anon.
Music: IL EST NÉ; Trad. French Carol, 18th cent.

WHAT SHALL WE GIVE

335

1. What shall we give to the child in the man-ger? What shall we
2. What shall we give to the first-born of Ma-ry; things that will
3. This child must grow to in-her-it a king-dom, blos-som and
4. What shall we give to the child in the man-ger? What shall we

1. give him that he will en-joy? Milk and wild hon-ey for
2. nour-ish a new life be-gun? Fruits of the for-est and
3. rip-en like fields of good corn, bear-ing a seed that will
4. give him that he will en-joy? Give of the best to the

1. this lit-tle stran-ger, food to give strength to a new lit-tle boy.
2. figs from the fig tree, nur-tured in so-il and rip-ened by sun.
3. fall and lie bur-ied, spring-ing up new in the bright Eas-ter morn.
4. one who will save us, food to give strength to this man still a boy.

Music: Catalan Carol.

336

JOY TO THE WORLD

1. Joy to the world! the Lord is come; Let earth re-
2. Joy to the world! the Sav - ior reigns; Let us our
3. No more let sins and sor - rows grow, Nor thorns in -
4. He rules the world with truth and grace, And makes the

1. ceive her King; Let ev - 'ry heart pre - pare him
2. songs em - ploy; While fields and floods, rocks, hills and
3. fest the ground; He comes to make his bless - ings
4. na - tions prove The glo - ries of his righ - teous -

1. room, And heav'n and na - ture sing, And heav'n and na - ture
2. plains Re - peat the sound-ing joy, Re - peat the sound-ing
3. flow Far as the curse is found, Far as the curse is
4. ness, And won-ders of his love, And won-ders of his

1. sing, And heav'n, and heav'n and na - ture sing.
2. joy, Re - peat, re - peat the sound - ing joy.
3. found, Far as, far as the curse is found.
4. love, And won - ders, won - ders of his love.

Text: CM with repeats; based on Psalm 98; Isaac Watts, 1764–1748, alt.
Music: ANTIOCH; T. Hawkes' *Collection of Tunes*, 1833; George Frideric Handel, 1685–1759.

337

GOD REST YE MERRY, GENTLEMEN

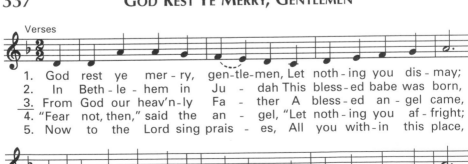

Verses

1. God rest ye mer - ry, gen-tle-men, Let noth-ing you dis - may;
2. In Beth - le - hem in Ju - dah This bless-ed babe was born,
3. From God our heav'n-ly Fa - ther A bless-ed an - gel came,
4. "Fear not, then," said the an - gel, "Let noth-ing you af - fright;
5. Now to the Lord sing prais - es, All you with-in this place,

1. Re - mem-ber Christ our Sav - ior Was born on Christ-mas Day
2. And laid with - in a man - ger Up - on this bless-ed morn:
3. And un - to cer - tain shep - herds Brought tid-ings of the same,
4. This day is born a Sav - ior Of Vir - gin pure and bright,
5. And with true love and char - i - ty Each oth - er now em - brace;

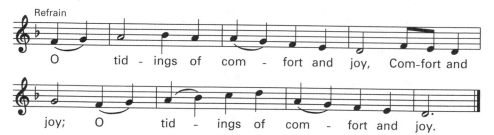

1. To save us all from Sa-tan's pow'r When we were gone a - stray.
2. For which his Moth-er Ma - ry Did noth-ing take in scorn.
3. How that in Beth - le - hem was born The Son of God by name.
4. To free all those who trust in him From Sa-tan's pow'r and might."
5. This ho - ly tide of Christ - mas Is filled with heav'n-ly grace.

Refrain

O tid - ings of com - fort and joy, Com-fort and

joy; O tid - ings of com - fort and joy.

Text: 86 86 86 with refrain; Trad. English Carol, 18th cent.
Music: GOD REST YE MERRY; Trad. English Carol; *Little Book of Christmas Carols*, ca. 1846.

LO, HOW A ROSE E'ER BLOOMING 338

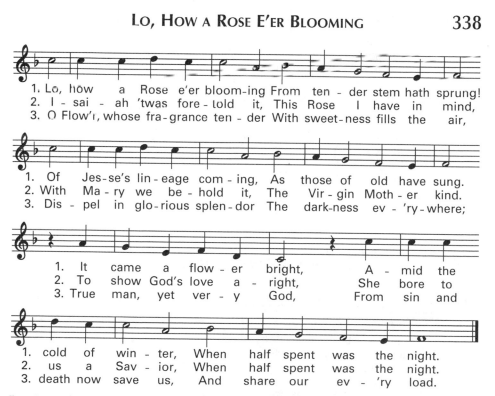

1. Lo, how a Rose e'er bloom-ing From ten - der stem hath sprung!
2. I - sai - ah 'twas fore - told it, This Rose I have in mind,
3. O Flow'r, whose fra-grance ten - der With sweet-ness fills the air,

1. Of Jes-se's lin-eage com - ing, As those of old have sung.
2. With Ma - ry we be - hold it, The Vir - gin Moth - er kind.
3. Dis - pel in glo-rious splen-dor The dark-ness ev - 'ry-where;

1. It came a flow - er bright, A - mid the
2. To show God's love a - right, She bore to
3. True man, yet ver - y God, From sin and

1. cold of win - ter, When half spent was the night.
2. us a Sav - ior, When half spent was the night.
3. death now save us, And share our ev - 'ry load.

Text: 76 76 6 76; based on Isaiah 11:1; Trad. German Carol, 15th cent.; tr. Theodore Baker, 1851-1934.
Music: ES IST EIN' ROS' ENTSPRUNGEN; *Alte Catholische Geistliche Kirchengesänge*, Cologne, 1599.

339   IT CAME UPON THE MIDNIGHT CLEAR

1. It came up-on the mid-night clear, That glo-rious
2. Still through the clo-ven skies they come, With peace-ful
3. And ye, be-neath life's crush-ing load, Whose forms are
4. For, lo, the days are has-tening on, By proph-et

1. song of old, From an-gels bend-ing near the
2. wings un-furled, And still their heav'n-ly mu-sic
3. bend-ing low, Who toil a-long the climb-ing
4. bards fore-told, When with the ev-er-cir-cling

1. earth To touch their harps of gold: "Peace on the earth, good
2. floats O'er all the wea-ry world: A-bove its sad and
3. way With pain-ful steps and slow, Look now! for glad and
4. years Comes 'round the age of gold; When peace shall o-ver

1. will to all From heav'n's all gra-cious King;" The
2. low-ly plains They bend on hov-'ring wing, And
3. gold-en hours Come swift-ly on the wing: O
4. all the earth Its an-cient splen-dors fling, And

1. world in sol-emn still-ness lay, To hear the an-gels sing.
2. ev-er o'er its Ba-bel sounds The bless-ed an-gels sing.
3. rest be-side the wea-ry road And hear the an-gels sing.
4. all the world give back the song Which now the an-gels sing.

Text: CMD; Edmund H. Sears, 1810–1876, alt.
Music: CAROL; Richard S. Willis, 1819–1900, alt.

340   A CHILD IS BORN IN BETHLEHEM

Verses

1. A child is born in Beth-le-hem, al-le-lu-ia!
2. In man-ger bare, in for-eign land, al-le-lu-ia!
3. The vir-gin moth-er bore a son, al-le-lu-ia!
4. The an-gels sing to shep-herds near, al-le-lu-ia!
5. The kings of na-tions from a-far, al-le-lu-ia!
6. With won-drous mis-sion now fore-told, al-le-lu-ia!
7. A world once lost in dark-est night, al-le-lu-ia!
8. Let trum-pet sound and cym-bals ring, al-le-lu-ia!

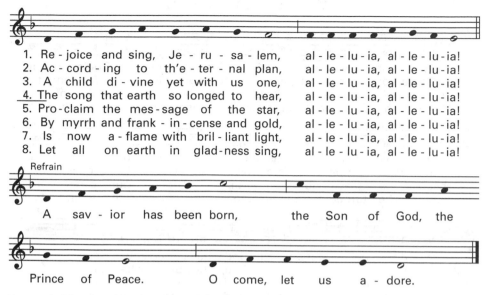

1. Re - joice and sing, Je - ru - sa - lem, al - le - lu - ia, al - le - lu - ia!
2. Ac - cord - ing to th'e - ter - nal plan, al - le - lu - ia, al - le - lu - ia!
3. A child di - vine yet with us one, al - le - lu - ia, al - le - lu - ia!
4. The song that earth so longed to hear, al - le - lu - ia, al - le - lu - ia!
5. Pro - claim the mes - sage of the star, al - le - lu - ia, al - le - lu - ia!
6. By myrrh and frank - in - cense and gold, al - le - lu - ia, al - le - lu - ia!
7. Is now a - flame with bril - liant light, al - le - lu - ia, al - le - lu - ia!
8. Let all on earth in glad - ness sing, al - le - lu - ia, al - le - lu - ia!

Refrain

A sav - ior has been born, the Son of God, the

Prince of Peace. O come, let us a - dore.

Text: 88 with alleluias and refrain; *Puer natus in Bethlehem*; Latin, 14th cent.;
tr. by Owen Alstott, b. 1947, © 2002, OCP Publications. All rights reserved.
Music: PUER NATUS; Chant, Mode I.

ANGELS WE HAVE HEARD ON HIGH 341

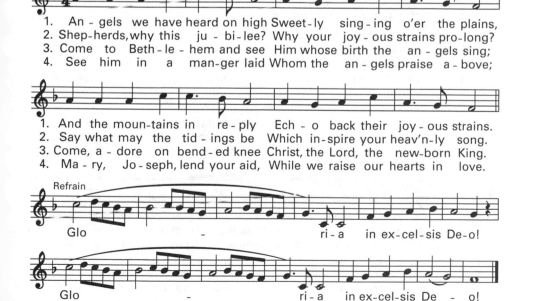

Verses

1. An - gels we have heard on high Sweet - ly sing - ing o'er the plains,
2. Shep - herds, why this ju - bi - lee? Why your joy - ous strains pro - long?
3. Come to Beth - le - hem and see Him whose birth the an - gels sing;
4. See him in a man - ger laid Whom the an - gels praise a - bove;

1. And the moun - tains in re - ply Ech - o back their joy - ous strains.
2. Say what may the tid - ings be Which in - spire your heav'n - ly song.
3. Come, a - dore on bend - ed knee Christ, the Lord, the new - born King.
4. Ma - ry, Jo - seph, lend your aid, While we raise our hearts in love.

Refrain

Glo - ri - a in ex - cel - sis De - o!

Glo - ri - a in ex - cel - sis De - o!

Text: 77 77 with refrain; Trad. French Carol, ca. 18th cent.;
tr. fr. *Crown of Jesus Music, II*, London, 1862; tr. by James Chadwick, 1813–1882, and others, alt.
Music: GLORIA; Trad. French Carol.

342
WAKE FROM YOUR SLEEP

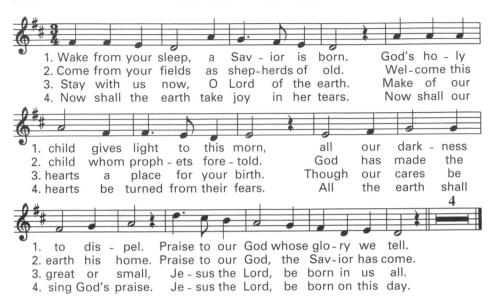

1. Wake from your sleep, a Sav-ior is born. God's ho-ly
2. Come from your fields as shep-herds of old. Wel-come this
3. Stay with us now, O Lord of the earth. Make of our
4. Now shall the earth take joy in her tears. Now shall our

1. child gives light to this morn, all our dark-ness
2. child whom proph-ets fore-told. God has made the
3. hearts a place for your birth. Though our cares be
4. hearts be turned from their fears. All the earth shall

1. to dis-pel. Praise to our God whose glo-ry we tell.
2. earth his home. Praise to our God, the Sav-ior has come.
3. great or small, Je-sus the Lord, be born in us all.
4. sing God's praise. Je-sus the Lord, be born on this day.

Text and music: Dan Schutte, b. 1947, © 1977, 1978, Daniel L. Schutte and New Dawn Music.
Published by OCP Publications. All rights reserved.

343
SILENT NIGHT, HOLY NIGHT/NOCHE DE PAZ,
NOCHE DE AMOR/STILLE NACHT, HEILIGE NACHT

1. Si - lent night! Ho - ly night! All is calm, ___
2. Si - lent night! Ho - ly night! Shep-herds quake ___
3. Si - lent night! Ho - ly night! Son of God, ___

1. No - che de paz, No - che de a-mor; To - do duer-me en
2. No - che de paz, No - che de a-mor; Mi - ra qué gran
3. No - che de paz, No - che de a-mor; Al Di - vi - no

1. Stil - le Nacht! Hei - li - ge Nacht! Al - les schläft, ___
2. Stil - le Nacht! Hei - li - ge Nacht! Hir - ten erst ___
3. Stil - le Nacht! Hei - li - ge Nacht! Got - tes Sohn, ___

1. all is bright Round ___ yon Vir - gin Moth-er and child!
2. at the sight; Glo - ries stream ___ from heav-en a - far;
3. love's pure light Ra - diant beams ___ from thy ho - ly face,

1. de - rre - dor. En - tre los as - tros que es-par-cen su luz
2. res - plan - dor Lu - ce en el ros - tro del Ni - ño Je - sús,
3. Sal - va - dor Que por no - so - tros na - ció en un por - tal.

1. ein - sam wacht Nur ___ das trau - te hoch - hei - li - ge Paar,
2. kund - ge-macht Durch ___ der En - gel Hal - le - lu - ja,
3. o wie lacht Lieb' ___ aus dei - nem gott - li - chen Mund,

1. Ho - ly In - fant so ten - der and mild, Sleep ___ in
2. Heav'n - ly hosts ___ sing "Al - le - lu - ia! Christ ___ the
3. With ___ the dawn of re - deem - ing grace, Je - sus,

1. *Be - lla a - nun - cian - do al ni - ñi - to Je - sús, Bri - lla la es -*
2. *En el pe - se - bre del mun - do la luz, Bri - lla la es -*
3. *Him - nos can - te - mos de a - mor ce - les - tial. ¡Glo - ria por*

1. *Hol - der Kna - be im lo - cki - gem Haar, Schlaf' ___ in*
2. *Tönt ___ es laut ___ von fer - ne und nah: Christ ___ der*
3. *Da ___ uns schlägt ___ die ret - ten - de Stund'. Je - sus in*

1. heav - en - ly peace, Sleep ___ in heav - en - ly peace.
2. Sav - ior is born, Christ ___ the Sav - ior is born."
3. Lord, at thy birth, Je - sus, Lord, at thy birth.

1. *tre - lla de paz, Bri - lla la es - tre - lla de paz.*
2. *tre - lla de paz, Bri - lla la es - tre - lla de paz.*
3. *siem - pre al Se - ñor! ¡Glo - ria por siem - pre al Se - ñor!*

1. *himm - li - scher Ruh'! Schlaf' ___ in himm - li - scher Ruh'!*
2. *Ret - ter ist da! Christ ___ der Ret - ter ist da!*
3. *dei - ner Ge - burt! Je - sus in dei - ner Ge - burt!*

Text: Irregular; Joseph Mohr, 1792–1849; English tr. by John F. Young, 1820–1885;
   Spanish tr. of verse 1 by Federico Fliedner, 1845–1901.
Music: STILLE NACHT; Franz X. Gruber, 1787–1863.

INFANT HOLY, INFANT LOWLY   344

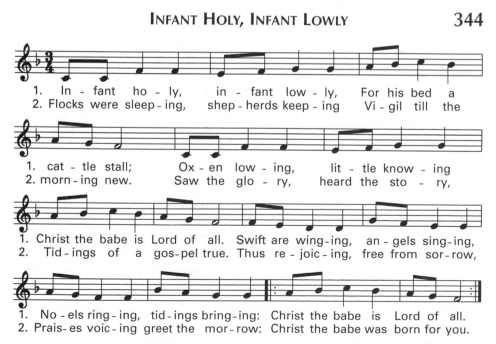

1. In - fant ho - ly, in - fant low - ly, For his bed a
2. Flocks were sleep - ing, shep - herds keep - ing Vi - gil till the

1. cat - tle stall; Ox - en low - ing, lit - tle know - ing
2. morn - ing new. Saw the glo - ry, heard the sto - ry,

1. Christ the babe is Lord of all. Swift are wing - ing, an - gels sing - ing,
2. Tid - ings of a gos - pel true. Thus re - joic - ing, free from sor - row,

1. No - els ring - ing, tid - ings bring - ing: Christ the babe is Lord of all.
2. Prais - es voic - ing greet the mor - row: Christ the babe was born for you.

Text: 87 87 88 77; Polish Carol; tr. by Edith Margaret Gellibrand Reed, 1885–1933.
Music: W ZLOBIE LEZY; Polish Carol.

345   HARK! THE HERALD ANGELS SING

Verses

1. Hark! the her-ald an-gels sing: "Glo-ry to the new-born King; Peace on earth, and mer-cy mild, God and sin-ners rec-on-ciled!" Joy-ful, all ye na-tions, rise, Join the tri-umph of the skies; With an-gel-ic hosts pro-claim: "Christ is born in Beth-le-hem!"

2. Christ, by high-est heav'n a-dored, Christ, the ev-er-last-ing Lord; Late in time, be-hold him come, Off-spring of a vir-gin's womb. Veiled in flesh the God-head see! Hail th'in-car-nate De-i-ty! Pleased as man with us to dwell; Je-sus, our Em-man-u-el!

3. Hail the heav'n-born Prince of Peace! Hail the Sun of Righ-teous-ness! Light and life to all he brings, Ris'n with heal-ing in his wings. Mild he lays his glo-ry by, Born that we no more may die, Born to raise us from the earth, Born to give us sec-ond birth.

Refrain

Hark! the her-ald an-gels sing, "Glo-ry to the new-born King."

Text: 77 77 D with refrain; Charles Wesley, 1707–1788, alt.
Music: MENDELSSOHN; Felix Mendelssohn, 1809–1847; adapt. by William H. Cummings, 1831–1915.

346   GOOD CHRISTIAN FRIENDS, REJOICE

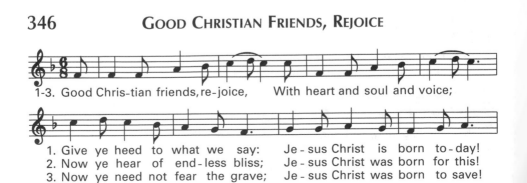

1-3. Good Chris-tian friends, re-joice, With heart and soul and voice;

1. Give ye heed to what we say: Je-sus Christ is born to-day!
2. Now ye hear of end-less bliss: Je-sus Christ was born for this!
3. Now ye need not fear the grave: Je-sus Christ was born to save!

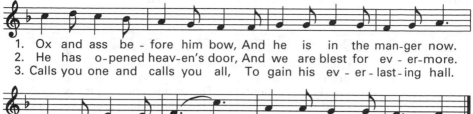

1. Ox and ass be - fore him bow, And he is in the man-ger now.
2. He has o-pened heav-en's door, And we are blest for ev - er-more.
3. Calls you one and calls you all, To gain his ev - er - last-ing hall.

1. Christ is born to - day!   Christ is born to - day!
2. Christ was born for this!   Christ was born for this!
3. Christ was born to save!   Christ was born to save!

Text: 66 77 78 55; Latin and German, 14th cent.; tr. by John M. Neale, 1818–1866, alt.
Music: IN DULCI JUBILO; J. Klug's *Geistliche Lieder*, Wittenberg, 1535.

WHILE SHEPHERDS WATCHED THEIR FLOCKS   347

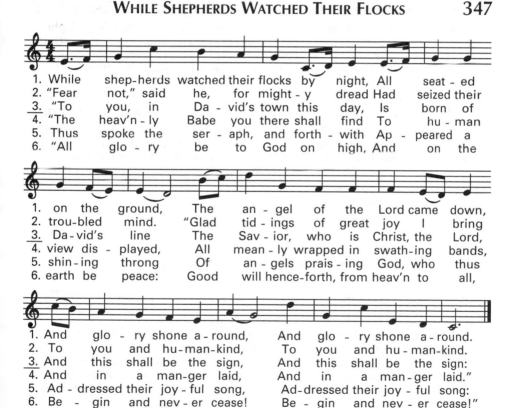

1. While shep-herds watched their flocks by night, All seat - ed
2. "Fear not," said he, for might - y dread Had seized their
3. "To you, in Da - vid's town this day, Is born of
4. "The heav'n - ly Babe you there shall find To hu - man
5. Thus spoke the ser - aph, and forth - with Ap - peared a
6. "All glo - ry be to God on high, And on the

1. on the ground, The an - gel of the Lord came down,
2. trou-bled mind. "Glad tid - ings of great joy I bring
3. Da - vid's line The Sav - ior, who is Christ, the Lord,
4. view dis - played, All mean - ly wrapped in swath-ing bands,
5. shin - ing throng Of an - gels prais - ing God, who thus
6. earth be peace: Good will hence-forth, from heav'n to all,

1. And glo - ry shone a - round, And glo - ry shone a - round.
2. To you and hu-man-kind, To you and hu - man-kind.
3. And this shall be the sign, And this shall be the sign:
4. And in a man-ger laid, And in a man-ger laid."
5. Ad - dressed their joy - ful song, Ad-dressed their joy - ful song:
6. Be - gin and nev - er cease! Be - gin and nev - er cease!"

Text: 86 86 6; Luke 2:8–14; Nahum Tate, 1652–1715.
Music: CHRISTMAS; George Frideric Handel, 1685–1759; adapt. by John Foster, 1762–1822.

348 O LITTLE TOWN OF BETHLEHEM

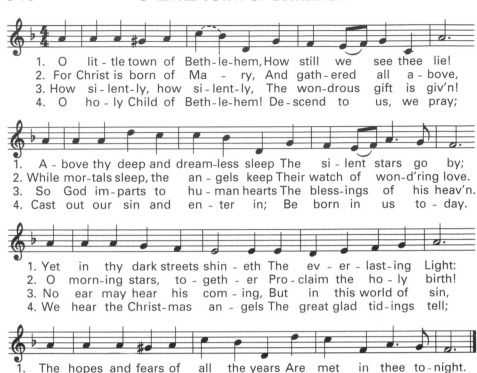

1. O lit - tle town of Beth-le-hem, How still we see thee lie!
2. For Christ is born of Ma - ry, And gath-ered all a - bove,
3. How si - lent-ly, how si - lent-ly, The won-drous gift is giv'n!
4. O ho - ly Child of Beth-le-hem! De - scend to us, we pray;

1. A - bove thy deep and dream-less sleep The si - lent stars go by;
2. While mor-tals sleep, the an - gels keep Their watch of won-d'ring love.
3. So God im-parts to hu - man hearts The bless-ings of his heav'n.
4. Cast out our sin and en - ter in; Be born in us to - day.

1. Yet in thy dark streets shin - eth The ev - er - last-ing Light:
2. O morn-ing stars, to - geth - er Pro - claim the ho - ly birth!
3. No ear may hear his com - ing, But in this world of sin,
4. We hear the Christ-mas an - gels The great glad tid-ings tell;

1. The hopes and fears of all the years Are met in thee to - night.
2. And prais - es sing to God the King, And peace to all on earth.
3. Where meek souls will re - ceive him, still The dear Christ en - ters in.
4. O come to us, a - bide with us, Our Lord Em-man - u - el!

Text: 86 86 76 86; Phillips Brooks, 1835–1893.
Music: ST. LOUIS; Lewis H. Redner, 1831-1908.

349 OF THE FATHER'S LOVE BEGOTTEN

1. Of the Fa-ther's love be - got - ten, Ere the worlds be -
2. Bless - ed was the day for ev - er When the Vir - gin,
3. This is he whom seers in old time Chant-ed of with
4. O ye heights of heav'n, a - dore him; An - gel hosts, his
5. Glo - ry be to God the Fa - ther, Glo - ry be to

1. gan to be, He is Al - pha and O - me - ga,
2. full of grace, By the Ho - ly Ghost con-ceiv - ing,
3. one ac - cord, Whom the voic - es of the proph - ets
4. prais - es sing; All do - min-ions, bow be - fore him,
5. God the Son, Glo - ry to the Ho - ly Spir - it,

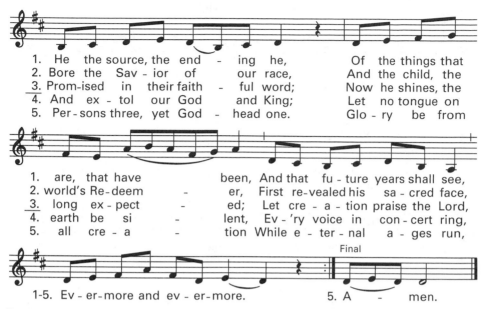

1. He the source, the end - ing he, Of the things that
2. Bore the Sav - ior of our race, And the child, the
3. Prom-ised in their faith - ful word; Now he shines, the
4. And ex - tol our God and King; Let no tongue on
5. Per - sons three, yet God - head one. Glo - ry be from

1. are, that have been, And that fu - ture years shall see,
2. world's Re - deem - er, First re-vealed his sa - cred face,
3. long ex - pect - ed; Let cre - a - tion praise the Lord,
4. earth be si - lent, Ev - 'ry voice in con - cert ring,
5. all cre - a - tion While e - ter - nal a - ges run,

1-5. Ev - er-more and ev - er-more.   5. A - men.

Text: 87 87 87 7; verses 1–4, *Corde natus ex parentis*; Marcus Aurelius Clemens Prudentius, 348–413;
tr. by John M. Neale, 1818–1866, and Henry W. Baker, 1827–1877, alt.; verse 5, Horatius Bonar, 1808–1889.
Music: DIVINUM MYSTERIUM; *Sanctus* trope, 11th cent.; Chant, Mode V; adapt. fr. *Piae Cantiones*, 1582.

CHRIST WAS BORN ON CHRISTMAS DAY 350

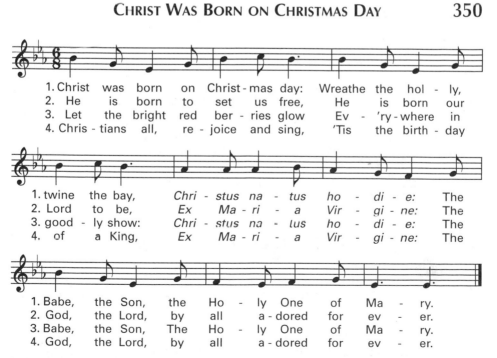

1. Christ was born on Christ-mas day: Wreathe the hol - ly,
2. He is born to set us free, He is born our
3. Let the bright red ber - ries glow Ev - 'ry-where in
4. Chris - tians all, re - joice and sing, 'Tis the birth - day

1. twine the bay, Chri - stus na - tus ho - di - e: The
2. Lord to be, Ex Ma - ri - a Vir - gi - ne: The
3. good - ly show: Chri - stus na - tus ho - di - e: The
4. of a King, Ex Ma - ri - a Vir - gi - ne: The

1. Babe, the Son, the Ho - ly One of Ma - ry.
2. God, the Lord, by all a - dored for ev - er.
3. Babe, the Son, The Ho - ly One of Ma - ry.
4. God, the Lord, by all a - dored for ev - er.

Text: 777 11; Traditional.
Music: RESONET IN LAUDIBUS; German Carol, 14th cent.

351

IN DEEPEST NIGHT

1. In deep-est night we hear the sto - ry: The morn-
2. To us no oth - er sign is giv - en, No oth-
3. The way the sun comes up in glo - ry, A bride-

1. ing star has ris - en plain: For us an in-fant has been
2. er light comes break - ing through: This man a - lone is our com-
3. groom shed - ding light and fire, So comes the king of peace to

1. born, _____ "The Lord-shall - save - us" is his name.
2. pan - ion, A God who is our broth-er, too.
3. join us, And, once for all, has come his hour.

1. O - pen your hearts, be - lieve your sen - ses, And trust in
2. Sing for your God who has un - fold - ed In Je - sus
3. And join-ing ev - 'ry - one to - geth - er, His love doled

1. what you plain - ly see; How God's own Word from high-est
2. his great love for all. The world be-comes a new cre-
3. out as nour - ish - ment, He gives his bod - y to our

1. heav - en Is wrought in us so hu - man - ly.
2. a - tion, All flesh re - ceives his sav - ing call.
3. keep - ing That we may live his cov - e - nant.

Text: 98 98 D; Huub Oosterhuis, b. 1933; tr. by David Smith, © 1967, Gooi en Sticht, bv., Baarn, The Netherlands.
All rights reserved. Exclusive agent for English-language countries: OCP Publications.
Music: RENDEZ À DIEU; attr. to Louis Bourgeois, ca. 1510–1561; *Genevan Psalter*, 1551.

352

GO, TELL IT ON THE MOUNTAIN

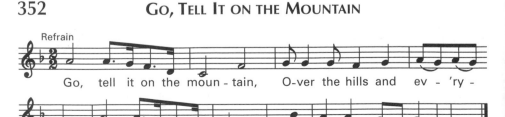

Refrain

Go, tell it on the moun - tain, O-ver the hills and ev - 'ry -

where; Go, tell it on the moun-tain That Je-sus Christ is born.

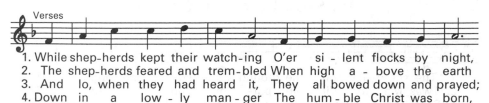

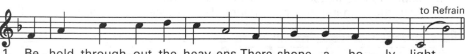

1. While shep-herds kept their watch-ing O'er si - lent flocks by night,
2. The shep-herds feared and trem-bled When high a - bove the earth
3. And lo, when they had heard it, They all bowed down and prayed;
4. Down in a low - ly man-ger The hum - ble Christ was born,

to Refrain

1. Be - hold, through-out the heav-ens There shone a ho - ly light.
2. Rang out the an - gel cho - rus That hailed our Sav - ior's birth.
3. They trav - eled on to - geth - er To where the Babe was laid.
4. And God sent us sal - va - tion That bless - ed Christ-mas morn.

Text: 76 76 with refrain; *American Negro Songs and Spirituals*, 1940; John W. Work, Jr., 1871–1925, alt.
Music: GO TELL IT; Spiritual.

RISE UP, SHEPHERD, AND FOLLOW 353

Verses

1. There's a star in the East on __ Christ-mas morn; Rise up,
2. Leave your sheep, leave your sheep, and __ leave your lambs; Rise up,
3. If you take good __ heed to the an - gel's words; Rise up,

1. shep-herd, and fol-low; It will lead to the place where the
2. shep-herd, and fol-low; Leave your ewes and your rams, leave your
3. shep-herd, and fol-low; You'll for - get your __ flocks, you'll for -

Refrain

1. Christ was born;
2. ewes and rams; } Rise up, shep-herd, and fol-low. Fol - low,
3. get your herds;

fol - low; Rise up, shep-herd, and fol-low. Fol-low the Star of

Beth - le - hem; Rise up, shep-herd, and fol-low.

Text: 10 7 10 7 with refrain; Spiritual.
Music: RISE UP, SHEPHERD; Spiritual.

354 THE SNOW LAY ON THE GROUND

1. The snow lay on the ground, the stars shone bright, When
2. 'Twas Ma - ry, Vir - gin pure of ho - ly Anne, That
3. Saint Jo - seph, too was near to tend the child; To
4. And thus that man - ger poor be - came a throne; For

1. Christ our Lord was born on Christ - mas night. *Ve - ní - te,*
2. brought in - to this world the God made man. She laid him
3. guard him and pro - tect his moth - er mild: The an - gels
4. he whom Ma - ry bore was God the Son. O come, then,

1. *a - do - ré - mus Dó - mi - num,* Ve - ní - te, a - do-
2. in a stall at Beth - le - hem; The ass and ox - en
3. hov - er'd 'round, and sang this song: *Ve - ní - te, a - do-*
4. let us join the heav'n - ly host, To praise the Fa - ther,

Refrain

1. *ré - mus Dó - mi - num.* *Ve - ní - te, a - do - ré - mus*
2. shared the roof with them.
3. *ré - mus Dó - mi - num.*
4. Son, and Ho - ly Ghost.

Dó - mi - num, Ve - ní - te, a - do - ré - mus Dó - mi - num.

Text: 10 10 10 10 with refrain; based on Isaiah 7:14; 19th cent.; anon.
Music: VENITE ADOREMUS; Trad. Melody; adapt. in *Catholic Hymns*, Albany, New York, 1860.

355 SING WE NOW OF CHRISTMAS

Verses

1. ⅞ Sing we now of Christ - mas, No - el, __ sing we here!
2. ⅞ An - gels called to shep - herds, "Leave your __ flocks at rest,
3. In Beth - le - hem they found him; Jo - seph and Ma - ry mild,
4. ⅞ From the east - ern coun - try Came the __ kings a - far,
5. ⅞ Gold and myrrh they took there, Gifts of __ great - est price;

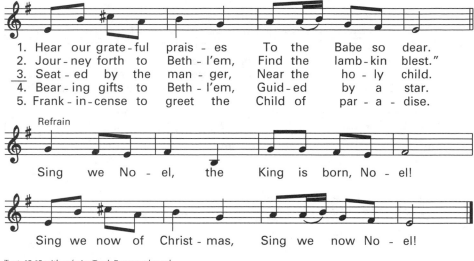

1. Hear our grate-ful prais - es To the Babe so dear.
2. Jour - ney forth to Beth - l'em, Find the lamb-kin blest."
3. Seat - ed by the man - ger, Near the ho - ly child.
4. Bear - ing gifts to Beth - l'em, Guid - ed by a star.
5. Frank - in - cense to greet the Child of par - a - dise.

Refrain

Sing we No - el, the King is born, No - el!

Sing we now of Christ - mas, Sing we now No - el!

Text: 65 65 with refrain; Trad. Provençal carol.
Music: NOËL NOUVELET; Trad. French carol.

SEE AMID THE WINTER'S SNOW 356

1. See a - mid the win - ter's snow, born for us on earth be - low,
2. Say, you ho - ly shep-herds, say, tell your joy-ful news to - day.

1. see, the gen - tle lamb ap - pears, prom-ised from e - ter - nal years.
2. Why have you now left your sheep on the lone-ly moun-tain steep?

1. There with - in a man-ger lies he who built the star - ry skies;
2. "As we watched at dead of night, there ap-peared a won-drous light;

1

to Verse 2

1. he who, throned in heights sub-lime, sits a - mid the cher-u - bim.

Final

2. an-gels sing-ing 'Peace on earth' told us of the Sav - ior's birth."

Text: 77 77 D; Edward Caswall, 1814-1878.
Music: WINTER'S SNOW; Kevin Keil, ASCAP, b. 1956, © 1992, Kevin Keil. Published by OCP Publications. All rights reserved.

O Come, Little Children

1. O come, lit-tle chil-dren; come one and come
2. O see in the man-ger so meek and so
3. His bed, lit-tle chil-dren, a man-ger with

1. all, O come to the man-ger in Beth-le-hem's
2. mild, O see in the soft light the heav-en-ly
3. hay; His Moth-er and Jo-seph in ec-sta-sy

1. stall, And see what our Fa-ther in heav-en a-
2. Child, In swad-dling clothes fold-ed, his beau-ty more
3. pray, The shep-herds in won-der their glad wor-ship

1. bove Has sent to us all on this earth with his love.
2. sweet Than an-gels, whose voic-es his low-ly birth greet.
3. bring, While cho-rus of an-gels sweet Glo-ri-as sing.

Text: 11 11 11 11; Johann C. von Schmid, 1768–1854; tr. by Melanie Schute, 1885–1922, alt.
Music: IHR KINDERLEIN, KOMMET; Johann A. Schulz, 1749–1800.

358   Children, Run Joyfully

Refrain

Chil-dren, run joy-ful-ly, Je-sus is born. Tell all the

moun-tains to sing. Pray to our Fa-ther in

heav-en this day: Thank you, for Je-sus is born.

Verse 1

1. Shep-herds stood watch-ing, keep-ing their sheep, and sud-den-ly

1. an-gels ap-peared. "Don't be a-fraid. We bring you great

1. joy: Your Sav-ior is born this night."

Verse 2
2. "And this will be a sign to you: the ba-by will

2. lie in a man-ger in the cit-y of Da-vid, in

to Refrain
2. Beth - le - hem. Go now, vis - it your Lord."

Text: Verses based on Luke 2:8–12; Bob Dufford, SJ, b. 1943.
Music: Bob Dufford, SJ.
Text and music © 1977, Robert J. Dufford, SJ and New Dawn Music. Published by OCP Publications. All rights reserved.

AWAY IN A MANGER 359

1. A - way in a man-ger, no crib for a bed, The
2. The cat - tle are low-ing, the ba-by a - wakes, But
3. Be near me, Lord Je - sus, I ask thee to stay Close

1. lit - tle Lord Je - sus laid down his sweet head; The
2. lit - tle Lord Je - sus, no cry - ing he makes; I
3. by me for - ev - er, and love me, I pray; Bless

1. stars in the sky ____ looked down where he lay, The
2. love thee, Lord Je - sus! Look down from the sky, And
3. all the dear chil - dren in thy ten - der care, And

1. lit - tle Lord Je - sus, a - sleep on the hay.
2. stay by my cra - dle till morn - ing is nigh.
3. fit us for heav - en to live with thee there.

Text: 11 11 11 11; verses 1–2, *Little Children's Book for Schools and Families,* ca. 1885;
 verse 3, John T. McFarland, 1851–1913; *Gabriel's Vineyard Songs,* 1892, alt.
Music: MUELLER; attr. to James R. Murray, 1841–1905.

360   GOD OF EVE AND GOD OF MARY

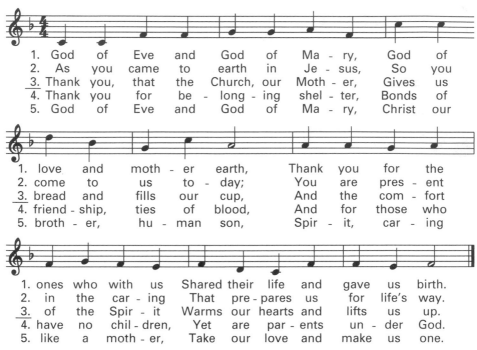

1. God of Eve and God of Ma - ry, God of
2. As you came to earth in Je - sus, So you
3. Thank you, that the Church, our Moth - er, Gives us
4. Thank you for be - long - ing shel - ter, Bonds of
5. God of Eve and God of Ma - ry, Christ our

1. love and moth - er earth, Thank you for the
2. come to us to - day; You are pres - ent
3. bread and fills our cup, And the com - fort
4. friend - ship, ties of blood, And for those who
5. broth - er, hu - man son, Spir - it, car - ing

1. ones who with us Shared their life and gave us birth.
2. in the car - ing That pre - pares us for life's way.
3. of the Spir - it Warms our hearts and lifts us up.
4. have no chil - dren, Yet are par - ents un - der God.
5. like a moth - er, Take our love and make us one.

Text: 87 87; Fred Kaan, b. 1929, © 1989, Hope Publishing Co. All rights reserved. Used with permission.
Music: STUTTGART; Christian F. Witt's *Psalmodia Sacra*, Gotha, 1715; adapt. by Henry J. Gauntlett, 1805–1876.

361   GOD OF ADAM, GOD OF JOSEPH

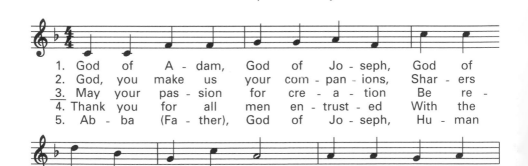

1. God of A - dam, God of Jo - seph, God of
2. God, you make us your com - pan - ions, Shar - ers
3. May your pas - sion for cre - a - tion Be re -
4. Thank you for all men en - trust - ed With the
5. Ab - ba (Fa - ther), God of Jo - seph, Hu - man

1. sow - ing, soil and seed, Thank you for your
2. of your lov - ing cup; Thank you for the
3. flect - ed in our own; For our role in
4. charge of fa - ther - hood, And for those who
5. Christ whose name we bear, Spir - it, womb of

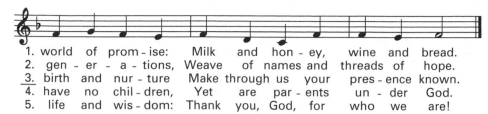

1. world of prom-ise: Milk and hon-ey, wine and bread.
2. gen-er-a-tions, Weave of names and threads of hope.
3. birth and nur-ture Make through us your pres-ence known.
4. have no chil-dren, Yet are par-ents un-der God.
5. life and wis-dom: Thank you, God, for who we are!

Text: 87 87; Fred Kaan, b. 1929, © 1989, Hope Publishing Co. All rights reserved. Used with permission.
Music: STUTTGART; Christian F. Witt's *Psalmodia Sacra*, Gotha, 1715; adapt. by Henry J. Gauntlett, 1805–1876.

ONCE IN ROYAL DAVID'S CITY 362

1. Once in roy-al Da-vid's cit-y
2. He came down to earth from heav-en
3. And through all his won-drous child-hood
4. For he is our child-hood's pat-tern,
5. And our eyes at last shall see him,

1. Stood a low-ly cat-tle shed, Where a
2. Who is God and Lord of all, And his
3. He would hon-or and o-bey, Love and
4. Day by day like us he grew; He was
5. Through his own re-deem-ing love; For that

1. moth-er laid her ba-by In a man-ger
2. shel-ter was a sta-ble, And his cra-dle
3. watch the low-ly maid-en In whose gen-tle
4. lit-tle, weak, and help-less, Tears and smiles like
5. child so dear and gen-tle Is our Lord in

1. for his bed. Mar-y was that moth-er
2. was a stall. With the poor and mean and
3. arms he lay. Chris-tian chil-dren all should
4. us he knew: And he feels for all our
5. heav'n a-bove: And he leads his chil-dren

1. mild, ___ Je-sus Christ her lit-tle Child. ___
2. low-ly Lived on earth our Sav-ior ho-ly.
3. be ___ Kind, o-be-dient, good as he. ___
4. sad-ness, And he shares in all our glad-ness.
5. on ___ To the place where he has gone. ___

Text: 87 87 77; Cecil Frances Alexander, 1818–1895, alt.
Music: IRBY; Henry J. Gauntlett, 1805–1876.

THE FIRST NOWELL

Verses

1. The first No - well, the an - gel did say,
2. They look - ed up and saw ___ a star
3. And by the light of that ___ same star
4. This star drew nigh to the ___ north - west,
5. Then en - tered in those wise ___ men three,
6. Then let us all with one ___ ac - cord

1. Was to cer - tain poor shep-herds in fields as they lay;
2. Shin-ing in ___ the east, ___ be - yond ___ them far;
3. Three ___ wise ___ men came ___ from coun - try far;
4. O'er ___ Beth - le - hem ___ it took ___ its rest,
5. Full ___ rev - 'rent - ly ___ up - on ___ the knee,
6. Sing ___ prais - es to ___ our heav - 'nly Lord;

1. In fields where ___ they lay keep - ing their sheep,
2. And to the ___ earth it gave ___ great light,
3. To seek for a king was their ___ in - tent,
4. And there it ___ did both stop ___ and stay,
5. And of - fered ___ there, in his ___ pres - ence,
6. Who with the ___ Fa - ther we ___ a - dore

1. On a cold win - ter's night ___ that was ___ so deep.
2. And ___ so it con - tin - ued both day ___ and night.
3. And to fol - low the star ___ wher - ev - er it went.
4. Right ___ o - ver the place ___ where Je - sus lay.
5. Their ___ gold ___ and myrrh ___ and frank - in - cense.
6. And ___ Spir - it blest ___ for ev - er - more.

Refrain

No - well, No - well, No - well, No - well,

Born is the King of Is - ra - el.

Note: "Nowell" is the English-language spelling of the French "noël" and is original to this English carol.

Text: Irregular with refrain; Trad. English Carol, 17th cent.; verse 6, alt.
Music: THE FIRST NOWELL; Trad. English Carol, 17th cent.

WE THREE KINGS

Verses

1. We three kings of O - ri - ent are, Bear - ing gifts we
2. Born a King on Beth - le - hem's plain, Gold I bring to
3. Frank - in - cense to of - fer have I: In - cense owns a
4. Myrrh is mine; its bit - ter per - fume Breathes a life of
5. Glo - rious now, be - hold him a - rise, King and God and

1. tra - verse a - far Field and foun - tain, Moor and moun - tain,
2. crown him a - gain; King for - ev - er, Ceas - ing nev - er
3. De - i - ty nigh; Pray'r and prais - ing, Glad - ly rais - ing,
4. gath - er - ing gloom; Sor - r'wing, sigh - ing, Bleed - ing, dy - ing,
5. Sac - ri - fice; "Al - le - lu - ia, Al - le - lu - ia!"

Refrain

1. Fol - low - ing yon - der star. O star of won - der,
2. O - ver us all to reign.
3. Wor - ship him God on high.
4. Sealed in the stone - cold tomb.
5. Sounds through the earth and skies.

star of night, Star with roy - al beau - ty bright, West - ward

lead - ing, still pro - ceed - ing, Guide us to the per - fect light.

Text: 88 44 6 with refrain; Matthew 2:1–11; John H. Hopkins, Jr., 1820–1891.
Music: KINGS OF ORIENT; *Carols, Hymns and Songs*, 1863; John H. Hopkins, Jr.

365

WHAT CHILD IS THIS

Verses

1. What child is this, who, laid to rest, On Mary's lap is
2. Why lies he in such mean es-tate Where ox and ass are
3. So bring him in-cense, gold, and myrrh, Come peas-ant, king, to

1. sleep - ing? Whom an - gels greet with an - thems sweet, While
2. feed - ing? Good Chris - tian, fear: for sin - ners here The
3. own him; The King of kings sal - va - tion brings, Let

Refrain

1. shep - herds watch are keep - ing? This, this is Christ the
2. si - lent Word is plead - ing.
3. lov - ing hearts en-throne him.

King, Whom shep-herds guard and an - gels sing; Haste,

haste to bring him laud, the babe, the son of Ma - ry.

Text: 87 87 with refrain; William C. Dix, 1827-1898.
Music: GREENSLEEVES; Trad. English Melody, 16th cent.

366

CHILD OF THE POOR

Verses

1. Help-less and hun-gry, low - ly, a - fraid, wrapped in the
2. Who is the strang-er here in our midst, look - ing for
3. Bring all the thirst-y, all who seek peace; bring those with

1. chill of mid - win - ter; comes now a-mong us, born in - to
2. shel - ter a - mong us? Who is the out-cast? Who do we
3. noth-ing to of - fer. Strength-en the fee - ble, say to the

1. pov - er - ty's em - brace, new life for the world.
2. see a - mid the poor, the chil - dren of God?
3. fright-ened heart: "Fear not: here is your God!"

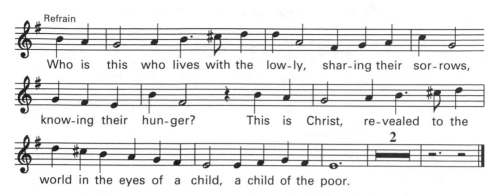

Who is this who lives with the low-ly, shar-ing their sor-rows, know-ing their hun-ger? This is Christ, re-vealed to the world in the eyes of a child, a child of the poor.

Note: *Child of the Poor* may be sung with *What Child Is This* (No. 365) in the following manner: *Child of the Poor*, verse 1, followed by *What Child Is This*, verse 1; *Child of the Poor*, verse 2, followed by *What Child Is This*, verse 2; both songs sung simultaneously on verse 3.

Text and music: Scott Soper, b. 1961, © 1994, Scott Soper. Published by OCP Publications. All rights reserved.

ANGELS FROM THE REALMS OF GLORY 367

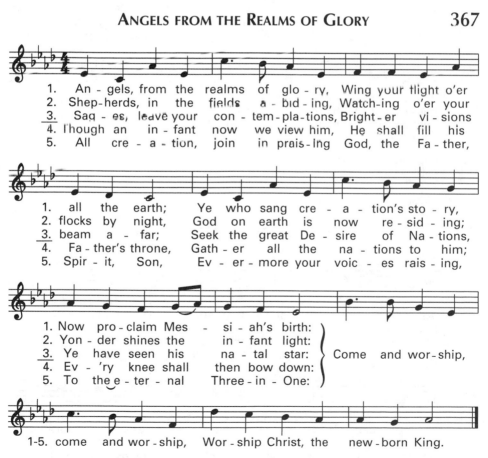

1. An - gels, from the realms of glo - ry, Wing your flight o'er
2. Shep-herds, in the fields a - bid - ing, Watch-ing o'er your
3. Sag - es, leave your con - tem - pla-tions, Bright-er vi - sions
4. Though an in - fant now we view him, He shall fill his
5. All cre - a - tion, join in prais-ing God, the Fa - ther,

1. all the earth; Ye who sang cre - a - tion's sto - ry,
2. flocks by night, God on earth is now re - sid - ing;
3. beam a - far; Seek the great De - sire of Na - tions,
4. Fa - ther's throne, Gath - er all the na - tions to him;
5. Spir - it, Son, Ev - er - more your voic - es rais - ing,

1. Now pro - claim Mes - si - ah's birth:
2. Yon - der shines the in - fant light:
3. Ye have seen his na - tal star: } Come and wor-ship,
4. Ev - 'ry knee shall then bow down:
5. To the e - ter - nal Three - in - One:

1-5. come and wor-ship, Wor-ship Christ, the new-born King.

Text: 87 87 87; verses 1–3, James Montgomery, 1771–1854; verse 4, *Christmas Box*, 1825; verse 5, *Salisbury Hymn Book*, 1857.
Music: REGENT SQUARE; Henry T. Smart, 1813–1879.

368   SONGS OF THANKFULNESS AND PRAISE

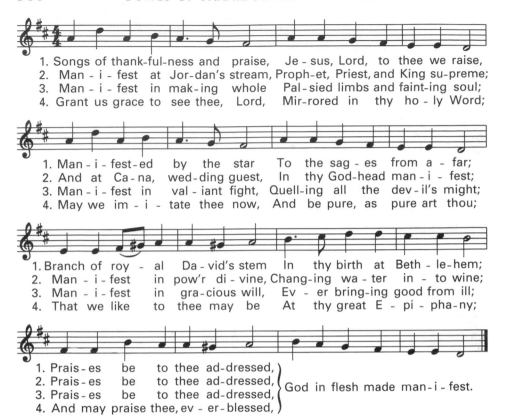

1. Songs of thank-ful-ness and praise, Je - sus, Lord, to thee we raise,
2. Man - i - fest at Jor-dan's stream, Proph-et, Priest, and King su-preme;
3. Man - i - fest in mak-ing whole Pal - sied limbs and faint-ing soul;
4. Grant us grace to see thee, Lord, Mir-rored in thy ho - ly Word;

1. Man - i - fest-ed by the star To the sag - es from a - far;
2. And at Ca - na, wed-ding guest, In thy God-head man - i - fest;
3. Man - i - fest in val - iant fight, Quell-ing all the dev - il's might;
4. May we im - i - tate thee now, And be pure, as pure art thou;

1. Branch of roy - al Da - vid's stem In thy birth at Beth - le-hem;
2. Man - i - fest in pow'r di - vine, Chang-ing wa - ter in - to wine,
3. Man - i - fest in gra-cious will, Ev - er bring-ing good from ill;
4. That we like to thee may be At thy great E - pi - pha-ny;

1. Prais - es be to thee ad-dressed,
2. Prais - es be to thee ad-dressed,
3. Prais - es be to thee ad-dressed,
4. And may praise thee, ev - er-blessed,
} God in flesh made man - i - fest.

Text: 77 77 D; Christopher Wordsworth, 1807–1885.
Music: SALZBURG; Jakob Hintze, 1622–1702.

369   AS WITH GLADNESS MEN OF OLD

1. As with glad - ness men of old Did the guid - ing
2. As with joy - ful steps they sped To that low - ly
3. As they of - fered gifts most rare At that man - ger
4. Ho - ly Je - sus, ev - 'ry day Keep us in the
5. In the heav'n - ly coun - try bright Need they no cre -

1. star be - hold, As with joy they hailed its light,
2. man - ger - bed, There to bend the knee be - fore,
3. rude and bare; So may we with ho - ly joy,
4. nar - row way; And, when earth - ly things are past,
5. at - ed light; Thou, its light, its joy, its crown,

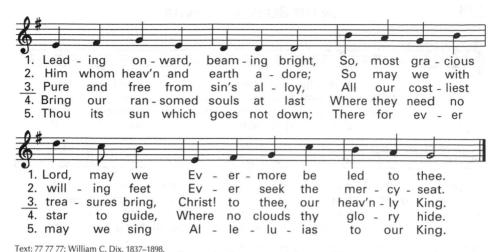

1. Lead - ing on - ward, beam - ing bright, So, most gra - cious
2. Him whom heav'n and earth a - dore; So may we with
3. Pure and free from sin's al - loy, All our cost - liest
4. Bring our ran - somed souls at last Where they need no
5. Thou its sun which goes not down; There for ev - er

1. Lord, may we Ev - er - more be led to thee.
2. will - ing feet Ev - er seek the mer - cy - seat.
3. trea - sures bring, Christ! to thee, our heav'n - ly King.
4. star to guide, Where no clouds thy glo - ry hide.
5. may we sing Al - le - lu - ias to our King.

Text: 77 77 77; William C. Dix, 1837–1898.
Music: DIX; Conrad Kocher, 1786–1872; adapt. by William H. Monk, 1823–1889.

WHAT STAR IS THIS 370

1. What star is this, with beams so bright, More love - ly
2. 'Tis now ful - filled what God de - creed, "From Ja - cob
3. O Je - sus, while the star of grace Im - pels us
4. To God the Fa - ther, heav'n - ly Light, To Christ, re -

1. than the noon - day light? 'Tis sent to an - nounce a
2. shall a star pro - ceed"; And lo! the __ east - ern
3. on to seek thy face, Let not our __ sloth - ful
4. vealed in earth - ly night, To God the __ Ho - ly

1. new - born king, Glad tid - ings of our God to bring.
2. sag - es stand To read in heav'n the Lord's com - mand.
3. hearts re - fuse The guid - ance of thy light to use.
4. Spir - it raise An end - less song of thank - ful praise!

Text: LM; *Quem stella sole pulchrior;* Charles Coffin, 1676–1749; tr. by John Chandler, 1806–1876, alt.
Music: PUER NOBIS; Trier MS, 15th cent.; adapt. by Michael Praetorius, 1571–1621.

371 IN THE BLEAK MIDWINTER

1. In the bleak mid - win - ter, frost - y wind made moan,
2. Our God, heav'n can - not hold him, nor___ earth sus - tain;
3. An - gels and arch - an - gels may have gath - ered there,
4. What___ can I give him, poor___ as I am?

1. Earth stood hard as i - ron, wa - ter like a stone;
2. Heav'n and earth shall flee a - way when he comes to reign.
3. Cher - u - bim and ser - a - phim throng - ed the air;
4. If I were a shep - herd, I would bring a lamb;

1. Snow had fall - en, snow on snow, snow___ on___ snow,
2. In the bleak mid - win - ter a sta - ble place suf - ficed The
3. But his moth - er on - ly, in her maid - en bliss,
4. If I were a Wise___ Man, I would do my part; Yet

1. In the bleak mid - win - ter, long a - go.
2. Lord___ God Al - might - y, Je - sus Christ.
3. Wor - shiped the be - lov - ed with a kiss.
4. what I can I give him: give my heart.

Text: Irregular; Christina G. Rosetti, 1830–1934.
Music: CRANHAM; Gustav T. Holst, 1874–1934.

372 WHEN JESUS COMES TO BE BAPTIZED

1. When Je - sus comes to be bap - tized, He
2. The Spir - it of the Lord comes down, A -
3. He will not quench the dy - ing flame, And
4. O Spir - it help us be like Christ: To
5. We praise you, God, source of all life, We

1. leaves the hid - den years be - hind, The years of safe - ty
2. noints the Christ to suf - fer - ing, To preach the word, to
3. what is bruised he will not break, But heal the wound in -
4. live in love and char - i - ty, To walk in truth and
5. praise you, Christ, e - ter - nal Word, We praise you, Spir - it,

1. and of peace, To bear the sins of hu - man - kind.
2. free the bound, And to the mourn - er, com - fort bring.
3. jus - tice dealt, And out of death his tri - umph make.
4. jus - tice now, And grow in Chris - tian dig - ni - ty.
5. gra - cious gift; Your tri - une pres - ence fills our world.

WHEN JOHN BAPTIZED BY JORDAN'S RIVER   373

1. When John bap - tized by Jor - dan's riv - er   In faith and
2. There as the Lord, bap-tized and pray - ing,   Rose from the
3. O Son of Man, our na - ture shar - ing,   In whose o -

1. hope the peo - ple came,   That John and Jor - dan might de -
2. stream, the sin - less one,   A voice was heard from heav - en
3. be - dience all are blest,   Sav - ior, our sins and sor - rows

1. liv - er   Their trou - bled souls from sin and shame.
2. say - ing,   "This is my own be - lov - ed Son."
3. bear - ing,   Hear us and grant us this re - quest:

1. They came to seek a new be - gin - ning,   The hu - man
2. There as the Fa - ther's word was spo - ken,   Not in the
3. Dai - ly to grow, by grace de - fend - ed,   Filled with the

1. spir - it's age - less quest,   Re - pen - tance, and an
2. pow'r of wind and flame,   But of his love and
3. Spir - it from a - bove;   In Christ bap - tized, be -

1. end of sin - ning,   Re - nounc - ing ev - 'ry wrong con - fessed.
2. peace the to - ken,   Seen as a dove, the Spir - it came.
3. loved, be - friend - ed,   Chil - dren of God in peace and love.

374

ASHES

1. We rise a-gain from ash-es, from the good we've failed to
2. We of-fer you our fail-ures, we ___ of-fer you at-
3. Then rise a-gain from ash-es, let ___ heal-ing come to
4. ⅄ Thanks be to the Fa-ther, who ___ made us like him-

1. do. We rise a-gain from ash-es, to cre-ate our-selves a-
2. tempts, the gifts not ful-ly giv-en, the ___ dreams not ful-ly
3. pain, though spring has turned to win-ter, and ___ sun-shine turned to
4. self. ⅄ Thanks be to his Son, ___ who ___ saved us by his

1. new. If ___ all our world is ash-es, then ___ must our lives be
2. dreamt. Give our stum-bl-ings di-rec-tion, give our vi-sions wid-er
3. rain. The ___ rain we'll use for grow-ing, and cre-ate the world a-
4. death. ⅄ Thanks be to the Spir-it who cre-ates the world a-

1. true, an ___ of-fer-ing of ash-es, an of-fer-ing to you.
2. view, an ___ of-fer-ing of ash-es, an of-fer-ing to you.
3. new from an of-fer-ing of ash-es, an of-fer-ing to you.
4. new from an of-fer-ing of ash-es, an of-fer-ing to you.

375

SIGNED BY ASHES

Ostinato Refrain

Signed by wa-ter; signed by ash-es; se-cure in your love, O God.

Verses

1. Have mercy on us, God, in your compassion.
Wipe out our offenses by your might.
Wash away our guilt;
make us worthy to walk your path in justice.

2. My sinfulness is visible, ever before you.
Against you alone I've transgressed.
But in you is the mighty power of mercy;
when I forgive, I am blest.

3. Cleanse me of my sin and I'll be pure, O Lord.
Wash me so I'm cleaner than the snow.
Let me hear the sounds of joy and gladness
that only those forgiven ever know.

4. Create for me a clean heart,
God of mercy.
Renew a steadfast spirit in me.
Cast me not out
from your loving presence,
that I may worship, sacrifice and sing.

5. O God, my heart and voice
are raised to praise you.
You are not pleased with sacrifice alone.
My sacrifice: a contrite, humble spirit;
I've heard your invitation:
"Child, come home!"

PARCE DOMINE/SPARE YOUR PEOPLE, LORD

Refrain

Par - ce Dó - mi - ne, par - ce pó - pu - lo __ tu - o: __
Spare your peo - ple, Lord, spare your peo - ple in your lov-ing kind-ness!

ne in ae - tér - num i - ra - scá - ris no - bis.
Show us your mer-cy; we have sinned a-gainst you, Lord.

Verses

1. Have mercy on me, God, in your good - ness;
2. For I know my of - fense; _____
3. A clean heart create for me, ____ God;
4. Restore my joy in your sal - va - tion;
5. For you do not de - sire sac - ri - fice;

1. In your abundant compassion blot out my of - fense. _____
2. My sin is always be - fore ____ me.
3. Renew in me a stead - fast spir - it.
4. Sustain in me a will - ing spir - it.
5. A burnt offering you would not ac - cept. _____

1. Wash away all my guilt; _____
2. Against you alone have I sinned; _____
3. Do not drive me away from your pres - ence
4. Lord, open my lips; _____
5. My sacrifice, God, is a bro - ken spir - it;

to Refrain

1. From my sin cleanse me. ____
2. I have done such evil in your sight. ____
3. Nor take from me your Ho - ly Spir - it. ____
4. My mouth will proclaim your praise. ____
5. God, do not spurn a broken, hum - bled heart. _____

Text: Refrain based on Joel 2:17; English refrain by Owen Alstott, b. 1947, © 1973, OCP Publications. All rights reserved.
Verses, Psalm 51:3–6, 12–13, 17–19, © 1970, CCD. All rights reserved. Used with permission.
Music: Refrain, Chant, Mode I. Verses, Randall DeBruyn, b. 1947, © 1992, OCP Publications. All rights reserved.

TURN TO ME

Refrain

Turn to me, O turn, and be saved, says the Lord, for
I am God; there is no oth-er, none be-
side me. I call your name.

Verse 1

1. I am God, who com-forts you; who are
1. you to be a-fraid of flesh that fades, is
1. made like the grass of the field, soon to with-er.

to Refrain

Verses 2, 3

2. Lis-ten __ to me, __ my peo-ple; give ear to __
3. Lift __ up your eyes to the heav-ens, and look at the

2. me, my na-tion: a law will go forth __ from
3. earth down be-low. __ The heav-ens will van-ish like

2. me, __ and my jus-tice for a light to the peo-ple.
3. smoke, and the earth __ will wear out like a gar-ment.

to Refrain

Text: Based on Isaiah 45:22–23, 51:12, 4, 6; John Foley, S.J., b. 1939.
Music: John Foley, S.J.

HAVE MERCY ON US, LORD/ATTENDE DOMINE

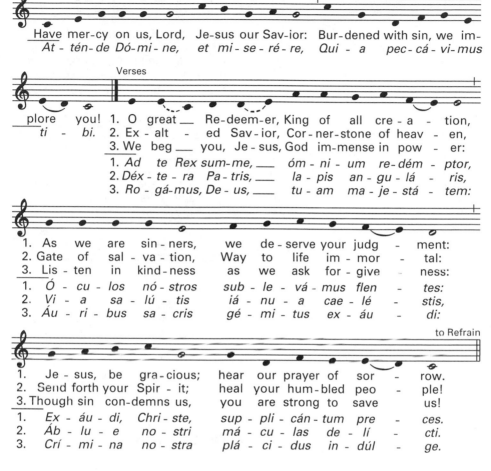

Refrain

Have mer-cy on us, Lord, Je-sus our Sav-ior: Bur-dened with sin, we im-
At - tén- de Dó-mi - ne, et mi - se - ré - re, Qui - a pec - cá - vi-mus

Verses

plore you!
ti - bi.

1. O great __ Re-deem-er, King of all cre - a - tion,
2. Ex - alt - ed Sav-ior, Cor - ner-stone of heav - en,
3. We beg __ you, Je - sus, God im-mense in pow - er:
1. Ad te Rex sum-me, __ óm - ni - um re-dém - ptor,
2. Déx - te - ra Pa - tris, __ la - pis an - gu - lá - ris,
3. Ro - gá-mus, De - us, __ tu - am ma - je - stá - tem:

1. As we are sin - ners, we de - serve your judg - ment:
2. Gate of sal - va - tion, Way to life im - mor - tal:
3. Lis - ten in kind - ness as we ask for - give - ness:
1. Ó - cu - los nó - stros sub - le - vá - mus flen - tes:
2. Vi - a sa - lú - tis iá - nu - a cae - lé - stis,
3. Áu - ri - bus sa - cris gé - mi - tus ex - áu - di:

to Refrain

1. Je - sus, be gra-cious; hear our prayer of sor - row.
2. Send forth your Spir - it; heal your hum-bled peo - ple!
3. Though sin con-demns us, you are strong to save us!
1. Ex - áu - di, Chri - ste, sup - pli - cán - tum pre - ces.
2. Áb - lu - e no - stri má - cu - las de - lí - cti.
3. Crí - mi - na no - stra plá - ci - dus in - dúl - ge.

4. We stand convicted, owning our offenses;
   Guilty before you, yet we seek your pardon:
   O gentle Savior, great is your compassion!

5. Remember, Jesus, you gave all to save us;
   Dying for sinners, you endured the Passion:
   Savior, immortal, grant your gift of freedom!

4. Tibi fatémur, crímina admíssa:
   Contríto corde pándimus occúlta:
   Túa redémptor, píetas ignóscat.

5. Innocens captus, nec repúgnans ductus,
   Téstibus falsis, pro ímpiis damnátus:
   Quos redemísti, tu consérva, Christe.

Text: 11 11 11 with refrain; Latin, 10th cent.
English text by Melvin Farrell, SS, 1930–1986, © 1977, OCP Publications. All rights reserved.
Music: ATTENDE DOMINE; Chant, Mode V; *Paris Processional*, 1824.

379　THE GLORY OF THESE FORTY DAYS

1. The glo-ry of these for-ty days We cel-e-brate with songs of praise; For Christ, by whom all things were made, Him-self has fast-ed and has prayed.
2. A-lone and fast-ing Mo-ses saw The lov-ing God who gave the law; And to E-li-jah, fast-ing, came The steeds and char-i-ots of flame.
3. So Dan-iel trained his mys-tic sight, De-liv-ered from the li-on's might; And John, the Bride-groom's friend, be-came The her-ald of Mes-si-ah's name.
4. Then grant that we like them be true, Con-sumed in fast and pray'r with you; Our spir-its strength-en with your grace, And give us joy to see your face.
5. O Fa-ther, Son, and Spir-it blest, To you be ev-'ry pray'r ad-dressed; Who are in three-fold Name a-dored, From age to age the on-ly Lord.

Text: LM; *Clarum decus jejunii*; St. Gregory the Great, ca. 540–604; tr. fr. the *English Hymnal*, 1906;
　　Maurice F. Bell, 1862–1947, alt.
Music: ERHALT UNS, HERR; J. Klug's *Geistliche Lieder*, Wittenberg, 1543; adapt. by Johann Sebastian Bach, 1685–1750, alt.

380　FORTY DAYS AND FORTY NIGHTS

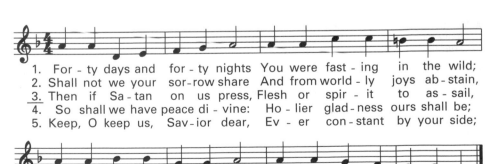

1. For-ty days and for-ty nights You were fast-ing in the wild; For-ty days and for-ty nights Tempt-ed, and yet un-de-filed.
2. Shall not we your sor-row share And from world-ly joys ab-stain, Fast-ing with un-ceas-ing prayer, Strong with you to suf-fer pain?
3. Then if Sa-tan on us press, Flesh or spir-it to as-sail, Vic-tor in the wil-der-ness, Grant we may not faint nor fail!
4. So shall we have peace di-vine: Ho-lier glad-ness ours shall be; Round us, too, shall an-gels shine, Such as served you faith-ful-ly.
5. Keep, O keep us, Sav-ior dear, Ev-er con-stant by your side; That with you we may ap-pear At th'e-ter-nal Eas-ter-tide.

Text: 77 77; George H. Smyttan, 1822–1870, alt.
Music: HEINLEIN; melody attr. to Martin Herbst, 1654–1681, alt.

BEHOLD, BEFORE OUR WOND'RING EYES

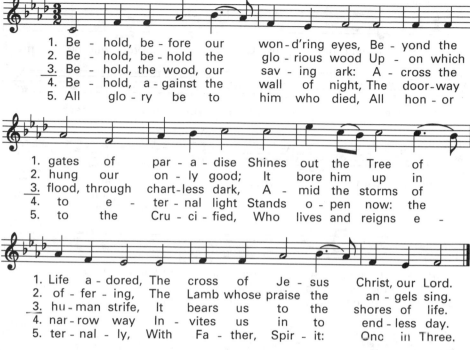

1. Be - hold, be - fore our won - d'ring eyes, Be - yond the
2. Be - hold, be - hold the glo - rious wood Up - on which
3. Be - hold, the wood, our sav - ing ark: A - cross the
4. Be - hold, a - gainst the wall of night, The door - way
5. All glo - ry be to him who died, All hon - or

1. gates of par - a - dise Shines out the Tree of
2. hung our on - ly good; It bore him up in
3. flood, through chart - less dark, A - mid the storms of
4. to e - ter - nal light Stands o - pen now: the
5. to the Cru - ci - fied, Who lives and reigns e -

1. Life a - dored, The cross of Je - sus Christ, our Lord.
2. of - fer - ing, The Lamb whose praise the an - gels sing.
3. hu - man strife, It bears us to the shores of life.
4. nar - row way In - vites us in to end - less day.
5. ter - nal - ly, With Fa - ther, Spir - it: One in Three.

Text: LM; Genevieve Glen, OSB, b 1945, © 1992, 2000, The Benedictine Nuns of the Abbey of St. Walburga.
Published by OCP Publications. All rights reserved.
Music: BOURBON; attr. to Freeman Lewis, 1780–1859.

THIS SEASON CALLS US

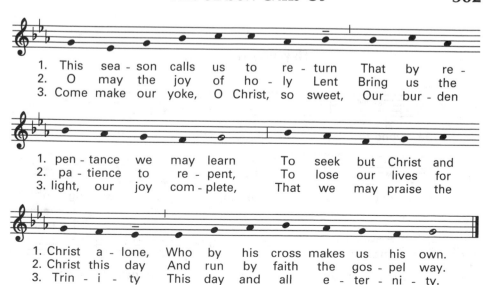

1. This sea - son calls us to re - turn That by re -
2. O may the joy of ho - ly Lent Bring us the
3. Come make our yoke, O Christ, so sweet, Our bur - den

1. pen - tance we may learn To seek but Christ and
2. pa - tience to re - pent, To lose our lives for
3. light, our joy com - plete, That we may praise the

1. Christ a - lone, Who by his cross makes us his own.
2. Christ this day And run by faith the gos - pel way.
3. Trin - i - ty This day and all e - ter - ni - ty.

Text: LM; Harry Hagan, OSB, b. 1947, © 1999, St. Meinrad Archabbey. Published by OCP Publications. All rights reserved.
Music: CONDITOR ALME SIDERUM; Chant, Mode IV.

383
I WILL BE YOUR GOD

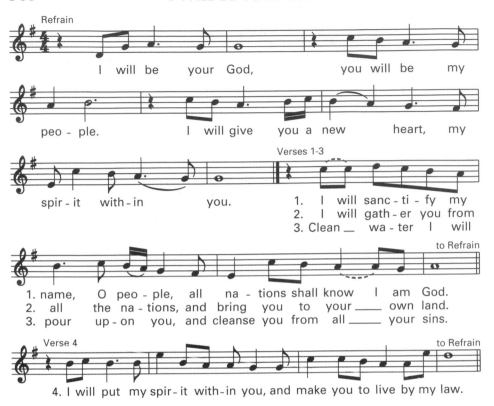

Refrain

I will be your God, you will be my peo - ple. I will give you a new heart, my spir - it with - in you.

Verses 1-3

1. I will sanc - ti - fy my
2. I will gath - er you from
3. Clean __ wa - ter I will

1. name, O peo - ple, all na - tions shall know I am God.
2. all the na - tions, and bring you to your ___ own land.
3. pour up - on you, and cleanse you from all ___ your sins.

to Refrain

Verse 4

4. I will put my spir - it with - in you, and make you to live by my law.

to Refrain

Text: Based on Ezekiel 36:23–27; Gerard Chiusano, b. 1953.
Music: Gerard Chiusano.

384
BEYOND THE DAYS

Refrain

Be - yond the days of hope and mys - t'ry we see a light of faith re - newed, and in our long - ing we thirst for guid - ance to walk with you day by day.

1-4
to Verses

day, to walk with you day by day.

Final | **Verses**

1. For - ty days and
2. Not on bread a -
3. In your hands, O
4. On our Lent - en

1. nights, you guide the steps of our jour - ney. May your
2. lone are we to walk on this jour - ney. Speak the
3. God, we feel the touch of your guid - ance. Keep us
4. path we see the dawn of a new day. Be our

to Refrain

1. pres - ence be felt in the whis - per of your voice.
2. words that give life to the yearn - ings of our hearts.
3. safe in your care: may your gen - tle - ness be there.
4. vi - sion of hope; be the prom - ise of our lives.

Text and music: Ricky Manalo, CSP, b. 1965, © 1997, Ricky Manalo, CSP. Published by OCP Publications. All rights reserved.

BROKEN CISTERNS WALLED IN STONE 385

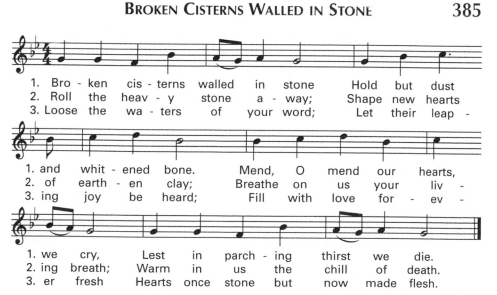

1. Bro - ken cis - terns walled in stone Hold but dust
2. Roll the heav - y stone a - way; Shape new hearts
3. Loose the wa - ters of your word; Let their leap -

1. and whit - ened bone. Mend, O mend our hearts,
2. of earth - en clay; Breathe on us your liv -
3. ing joy be heard; Fill with love for - ev -

1. we cry, Lest in parch - ing thirst we die.
2. ing breath; Warm in us the chill of death.
3. er fresh Hearts once stone but now made flesh.

Text: 77 77; Genevieve Glen, OSB, b. 1945, © 1998, The Benedictine Nuns of the Abbey of St. Walburga.
Published by OCP Publications. All rights reserved.
Music: NUN KOMM, DER HEIDEN HEILAND; *Geystliche Gesangk Buchleyn*, Wittenberg, 1524.

386 FROM THE DEPTHS WE CRY TO THEE

1. From the depths we cry to thee, God of sov-'reign maj-es-ty!
2. Gra-cious God, our hearts re-new; Strength-en us thy will to do.
3. Lord, ac-cept our Len-ten fast And for-give our sin-ful past,

1. Hear our prayers and hymns of praise; Bless our Lent of for-ty days.
2. Wash us, make us pure with-in; Cleanse us from the stain of sin.
3. That we may par-take with thee In the Eas-ter mys-ter-y.

Text: 77 77; Verses 1, 3, Alan G. McDougall, 1895–1964, alt.
Verse 2, Owen Alstott, b. 1947, © 1977, OCP Publications. All rights reserved.
Music: HEINLEIN; attr. to Martin Herbst, 1654–1681.

387 JESUS WALKED THIS LONESOME VALLEY

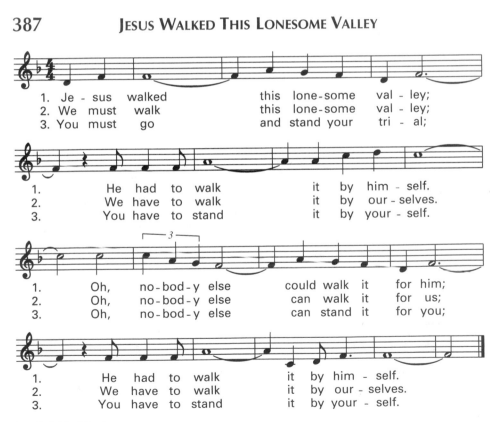

1. Je-sus walked this lone-some val-ley;
2. We must walk this lone-some val-ley;
3. You must go and stand your tri-al;

1. He had to walk it by him-self.
2. We have to walk it by our-selves.
3. You have to stand it by your-self.

1. Oh, no-bod-y else could walk it for him;
2. Oh, no-bod-y else can walk it for us;
3. Oh, no-bod-y else can stand it for you;

1. He had to walk it by him-self.
2. We have to walk it by our-selves.
3. You have to stand it by your-self.

Text: 88 10 8; Traditional.
Music: LONESOME VALLEY; Spiritual.

SOMEBODY'S KNOCKIN' AT YOUR DOOR

1, 6. Some-bod - y's knock-in' at your door; Some-bod - y's

1, 6. knock-in' at your door; O sin - ner, why don't you

1, 6. an - swer? Some-bod - y's knock-in' at your door.

Cantor   All

2. Knocks like Je - sus,
3. Can't you hear him?
4. Je - sus calls you,
5. Can't you trust him?

Some-bod - y's knock-in' at your door.

Cantor   All

2. Knocks like Je - sus,
3. Can't you hear him?
4. Je - sus calls you,
5. Can't you trust him?

Some-bod - y's knock-in' at your

2-5. door. O sin - ner, why don't you

2-5. an - swer? Some-bod - y's knock-in' at your door.

Text and music: Spiritual.

389 O CHRIST, BRIGHT SUN OF JUSTICE

1. O Christ, bright sun of jus - tice, rise
2. As gift, you give this time to heal,
3. May we who keep this Lent - en - tide
4. The day shall come, great day of days,
5. To you, most gen - tle God, we sing,

1. And drive the dark - ness from our eyes.
2. To fire the con - trite heart with zeal.
3. Re - pent of sin and con - quer pride,
4. When earth re - born shall sing your praise;
5. For with this Lent you give us spring

1. May jus - tice with your light in - crease
2. By fast - ing, prayer, and char - i - ty
3. And then with hum - ble hearts draw near
4. Then we shall glo - ry in the cross
5. And make the nar - row way a door

1. And guide us in the way of peace.
2. Re - store to us our dig - ni - ty.
3. To you, the Love that casts out fear.
4. And count all gain but Christ as loss.
5. To life and light for - ev - er - more.

Text: LM; based on *Jam Christe sol justitiae*; Harry Hagan, OSB, b. 1947, © 1998, St. Meinrad Archabbey.
Published by OCP Publications. All rights reserved.
Music: BOURBON; attr. to Freeman Lewis, 1780–1859.

390 ETERNAL LORD OF LOVE

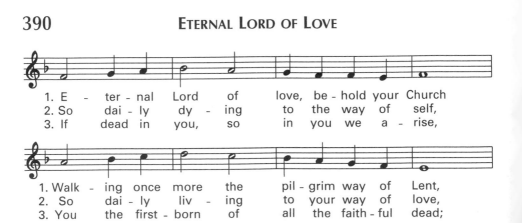

1. E - ter - nal Lord of love, be - hold your Church
2. So dai - ly dy - ing to the way of self,
3. If dead in you, so in you we a - rise,

1. Walk - ing once more the pil - grim way of Lent,
2. So dai - ly liv - ing to your way of love,
3. You the first - born of all the faith - ful dead;

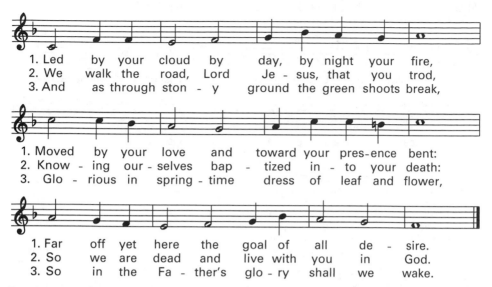

1. Led   by your cloud by   day, by night your fire,
2. We   walk the road, Lord Je - sus, that you trod,
3. And   as through ston - y   ground the green shoots break,

1. Moved by your love and   toward your pres-ence bent:
2. Know - ing our-selves bap - tized in - to your death:
3. Glo - rious in spring - time dress of leaf and flower,

1. Far   off yet here the   goal of all de - sire.
2. So   we are dead and   live with you in God.
3. So   in the Fa - ther's glo - ry shall we wake.

Text: 10 10 10 10 10; Thomas H. Cain, b. 1931, © 1982, Thomas H. Cain. All rights reserved. Used with permission.
Music: OLD 124th; *Genevan Psalter*, 1551.

LORD, WHO THROUGHOUT THESE FORTY DAYS   391

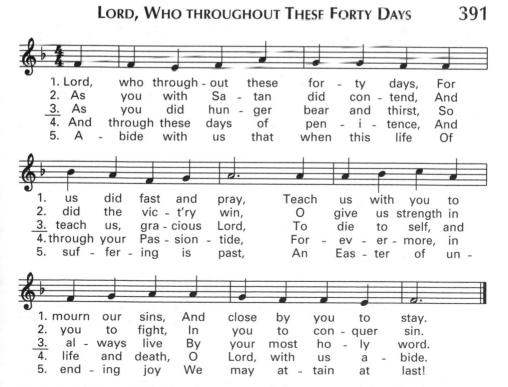

1. Lord,   who through - out these   for - ty days, For
2. As   you with Sa - tan   did con - tend, And
3. As   you did hun - ger   bear and thirst, So
4. And   through these days of   pen - i - tence, And
5. A - bide with us that   when this life Of

1. us   did fast and pray, Teach us with you to
2. did   the vic - t'ry win, O   give us strength in
3. teach us, gra - cious Lord, To   die to self, and
4. through your Pas - sion - tide, For - ev - er - more, in
5. suf - fer - ing is past, An   Eas - ter of un -

1. mourn our sins, And   close by you to stay.
2. you   to fight, In   you to con - quer sin.
3. al - ways live By   your most ho - ly word.
4. life   and death, O   Lord, with us a - bide.
5. end - ing joy We   may at - tain at last!

Text: CM; Claudia F. Hernaman, 1838-1898, alt.
Music: ST. FLAVIAN; *The Whole Psalmes in Foure Partes*, 1563; adapt. by Richard Redhead, 1820–1901.

392   IN THESE DAYS OF LENTEN JOURNEY

Refrain

In these days of Len-ten jour-ney we have seen and we have heard the call to sow jus-tice in the lives of those we serve.

Verses

1. We reach out to those who are home-less, to
2. We o - pen our eyes to the hun - gry and
3. We o - pen our ears to the wea - ry and
4. We call on the Spir - it of Jus - tice and

1. those who live with - out warmth. In the cool-ness of
2. see the fac - es of Christ. As we nour - ish all
3. hear the cry of the poor. To the voic - es that
4. pray for righ-teous-ness' sake. We will sing for the

1. eve - ning we'll shel - ter their dreams; we will
2. peo - ple who hun - ger for food, may their
3. ech - o the song of de - spair, we will
4. free - dom of all the op - pressed; we will

to Refrain

1. clothe them in mer - cy and peace.
2. faith in our God be re - newed.
3. show our com - pas - sion and care.
4. loos - en the bonds of dis - tress.

393   WITH THE LORD

Verse 1

1. Out of the depths I cry to you, I cry to you, O Lord. Lord,

1. o-pen your ears and hear my voice, at-tend to the sound of my plea.

Refrain

With the Lord there is mer-cy and the full-ness of re-
demp-tion, call to him in your tri-als, he will
1, 3 to Vss 2, 4 | 2 to Vs 3 | Final
an-swer when-ev-er you call. call. call.

Verses 2, 4

2. If you ___ O Lord,___ should mark ___ our guilt, then, Lord, who could
4. More than the sen-ti-nels wait for the dawn, let Is-ra-el

2. hope to sur-vive? But with you is found for-give-ness of
4. wait for the Lord. For kind-ness is his, re-demp-tion for

2. sin, and mer-cy that we might re - vere you.
4. all, for-give-ness of sins for his peo - ple.

Verse 3

3. Trust in the Lord, count on his word, wait for the
3. Lord, my soul. I will wait for the Lord all the
3. days of my life as sen-ti-nels wait for the dawn.

394   AGAIN WE KEEP THIS SOLEMN FAST

1. A - gain we keep this sol - emn fast, A gift of
2. The law and proph - ets from of old In fig - ured
3. More spar - ing, there - fore, let us make The words we
4. Let us a - void each harm - ful way That lures the
5. We pray, O bless - ed Three - in - One, Our God while

1. faith from ag - es past, This Lent which binds us
2. ways this Lent fore - told, Which Christ, all ag - es'
3. speak, the food we take, Our sleep, our laugh - ter,
4. care - less mind a - stray; By watch - ful prayer our
5. end - less ag - es run, That this, our Lent of

1. lov - ing - ly To faith and hope and char - i - ty.
2. Lord and Guide, In these last days has sanc - ti - fied.
3. ev - 'ry sense; Learn peace through ho - ly pen - i - tence.
4. spir - its free From schem - ing of the e - ne - my.
5. for - ty days, May bring us growth and give you praise.

Text: LM; *Ex more docti mystico;* ascr. to St. Gregory the Great, ca. 540–604;
   tr. by Peter J. Scagnelli, b. 1949, © Peter J. Scagnelli. All rights reserved. Used with permission.
Music: ERHALT UNS, HERR; J. Klug's *Geistliche Lieder,* 1543; adapt. by Johann Sebastian Bach, 1685–1750, alt.

395   AT THE CROSS HER STATION KEEPING

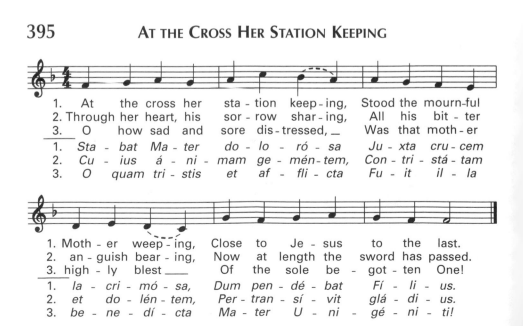

1. At the cross her sta - tion keep - ing, Stood the mourn - ful
2. Through her heart, his sor - row shar - ing, All his bit - ter
3. O how sad and sore dis - tressed, __ Was that moth - er

1. *Sta - bat Ma - ter do - lo - ró - sa Ju - xta cru - cem*
2. *Cu - ius á - ni - mam ge - mén - tem, Con - tri - stá - tam*
3. *O quam tri - stis et af - fli - cta Fu - it il - la*

1. Moth - er weep - ing, Close to Je - sus to the last.
2. an - guish bear - ing, Now at length the sword has passed.
3. high - ly blest ____ Of the sole be - got - ten One!

1. *la - cri - mó - sa, Dum pen - dé - bat Fí - li - us.*
2. *et do - lén - tem, Per - tran - sí - vit glá - di - us.*
3. *be - ne - dí - cta Ma - ter U - ni - gé - ni - ti!*

4. Christ above in torment hangs,
   She beneath beholds the pangs
   Of her dying, glorious Son.

5. Is there one who would not weep,
   Whelmed in miseries so deep,
   Christ's dear Mother to behold?

6. Can the human heart refrain
   From partaking in her pain
   In that Mother's pain untold?

7. Bruised, derided, cursed, defiled,
   She beheld her tender Child,
   All with bloody scourges rent.

8. For the sins of his own nation
   Saw him hang in desolation
   Till his spirit forth he sent.

9. O thou Mother! Font of love,
   Touch my spirit from above,
   Make my heart with thine accord.

10. Make me feel as thou hast felt;
    Make my soul to glow and melt
    With the love of Christ, my Lord.

11. Holy Mother, pierce me through,
    In my heart each wound renew
    Of my Savior crucified.

12. Let me share with thee his pain,
    Who for all my sins was slain,
    Who for me in torment died.

13. Let me mingle tears with thee,
    Mourning him who mourned for me,
    All the days that I may live.

14. By the cross with thee to stay;
    There with thee to weep and pray,
    All I ask of thee to give.

15. Virgin of all Virgins best!
    Listen to my fond request:
    Let me share thy grief divine.

4. *Quae maerébat et dolébat,*
   Pia Mater, dum vidébat
   Nati poenas íncliti.

5. *Quis non posset contristári,*
   Piam Matrem contemplári
   Doléntem cum Fílio?

6. *Quis est homo qui non fleret,*
   Matrem Christi si vidéret
   In tanto supplício?

7. *Pro peccátis suae gentis*
   Vidit Jesum in torméntis,
   Et flagéllis súbditum.

8. *Vidit suum dulcem Natum*
   Moriéntem desolátum,
   Dum emísit spíritum.

9. *Eia Mater, fons amóris,*
   Me sentíre vim dolóris
   Fac, ut tecum lúgeam.

10. *Fac ut árdeat cor meum*
    in amándo Christum Deum,
    ut sibi compláceam.

11. *Sancta Mater, istud agas,*
    Crucifíxi fige plagas
    Cordi meo válide.

12. *Tui Nati vulneráti,*
    Tam dignáti pro me pati,
    Poenas mecum dívide.

13. *Fac me vere tecum flére,*
    Crucifíxo condolére,
    Donec ego víxero.

14. *Juxta crucem tecum stáre,*
    Ac me tibi sociáre
    In planctu desídero.

15. *Virgo vírginum praeclára,*
    Mihi iam non sis amára:
    Fac me tecum plángere.

Text: 88 7; *Stabat Mater dolorosa*; Jacapone da Todi, 1230-1306; tr. by Edward Caswall, 1814-1878, alt.
Music: STABAT MATER; *Maintzisch Gesangbuch*, 1661.

396 HOSANNA TO THE SON OF DAVID

Refrain

Ho - san - na   to the Son of Da - vid!   O blest is he,   O blest is he   who comes   in the name   of the Lord!

Verses

1. Re - joice, daugh - ter of Zi - on,
2. Re - joice, all who are thirst - ing
3. Re - joice, all who are long - ing
4. Re - joice, all who are search - ing
5. Re - joice, all who are hop - ing
6. Re - joice, all who are wait - ing
7. Re - joice, all who are call - ing
8. Re - joice, all who are hun - gry

1. in the One who brings great joy!
2. for the streams of liv - ing joy!
3. to be - hold the face of God!
4. for the truth of ho - ly light!
5. for the reign of peace and love!
6. for the dawn of heav - en's light!
7. on the name of God on high!
8. for the taste of liv - ing bread!

Sing praise, chil -

to Refrain

1-8. - dren of Ju - dah,   for the Lord   is close at hand!

Text: Refrain based on Matthew 21:9; Dan Schutte, b. 1947.
Music: Dan Schutte.
Text and music © 1995, Daniel L. Schutte. Published by OCP Publications. All rights reserved.

397 HOSANNA TO THE SON OF DAVID

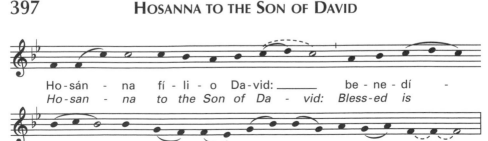

Ho - sán - na fí - li - o Da - vid: _____ be - ne - dí -
Ho - san - na to the Son of Da - vid: Bless-ed is

ctus qui ve - nit in nó - mi - ne Dó - mi - ni.
he who comes in the name of the Lord. _____

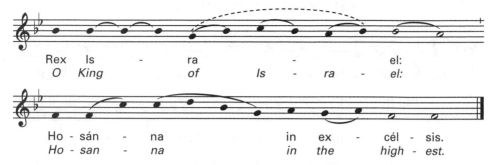

Rex Is - ra - el:
O King of Is - ra - el:

Ho - sán - na in ex - cél - sis.
Ho - san - na in the high - est.

Text: Matthew 21:9.
Music: Chant, Mode VII.

RIDE ON, KING JESUS 398

Refrain

Ride on, King Je - sus, No man can a -
hin - der me, Ride on, King Je - sus,
ride on, No man can a - hin - der me.

Verses

1. King Je - sus __ rides on a milk - white horse,
2. I know that __ my re - deem - er lives,
3. If you want to find your __ way to God,

1-3. No man can a - hin-der me; { The riv - er of Jor - dan
                                   And of __ his bless - ing
                                   The gos - pel high - way

to Refrain

1. he did cross,
2. free - ly gives, } No man can a - hin-der me.
3. must be trod,

Text and music: Spiritual.

399   ALL GLORY, LAUD AND HONOR

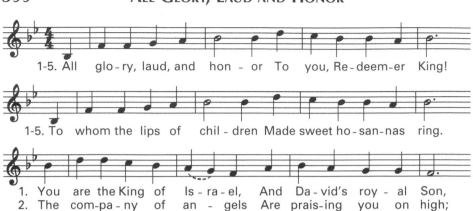

1-5. All glo-ry, laud, and hon - or To you, Re-deem-er King!

1-5. To whom the lips of chil - dren Made sweet ho-san-nas ring.

1. You are the King of Is - ra - el, And Da - vid's roy - al Son,
2. The com-pa - ny of an - gels Are prais-ing you on high;
3. The peo-ple of the He - brews With palms be - fore you went:
4. To you be-fore your pas - sion They sang their hymns of praise:
5. Their prais-es you ac - cept - ed, Ac - cept the prayers we bring,

1. Now in the Lord's Name com - ing, Our King and Bless-ed One.
2. And mor - tals, joined with all _ things Cre - a - ted, make re - ply.
3. Our praise and prayers and an - thems Be - fore you we pre - sent.
4. To you, now high ex - alt - ed, Our mel - o - dy we raise.
5. Great source of love and good - ness, Our Sav-ior and our King.

Text: 76 76 D; Theodulph of Orleans, ca. 760–821; tr. by John M. Neale, 1818–1866, alt.
Music: ST. THEODULPH; Melchior Teschner, 1584–1635.

400   AT THE NAME OF JESUS

Refrain

At the name of Je - sus ev - 'ry knee shall bend,

at the name of Je - sus ev - 'ry knee shall bend.

Verses

1. 'Tis our God's great plea - sure we should speak God's name,
2. Hum - bled for a sea - son, to re - ceive a name
3. Christ is tru - ly Sav - ior, Christ, the God a - dored,
4. In your hearts en - throne him, there let him sub - due
5. Sis - ters, broth - ers, Je - sus dwells with us a - gain

1. who from the be - gin - ning was for - e'er the same.
2. from the lips of peo - ples un - to whom he came.
3. ev - er to be wor - shiped, ev - er - more a - dored.
4. all that is not ho - ly, all that is not true.
5. now to let his vi - sion o'er our hearts to reign.

Text: Phillippians 2:5–7; Caroline M. Noel, 1817–1877, alt.
Music: Suzanne Toolan, RSM, b. 1927, © 1995, Suzanne Toolan, RSM. Published by OCP Publications. All rights reserved.

JESUS TOOK A TOWEL 401

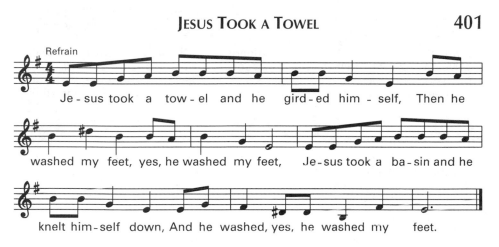

Je - sus took a tow - el and he gird - ed him - self, Then he washed my feet, yes, he washed my feet, Je - sus took a ba - sin and he knelt him - self down, And he washed, yes, he washed my feet.

Verses

1. The heavens are the Lord's,
and the earth is his,
The clouds are his chariot, glory his cloak;
He made the mountains,
set the limits of the sea;
And he stooped and washed my feet.

2. The hour had come, the Pasch was near;
Jesus loved his own,
loved them to the end.
O Lord, let me see, let me understand
Why you stooped and washed my feet.

3. Jesus came to Peter; Peter said to him,
"Do you wash my feet?
Lord, do you wash my feet?"
Jesus knelt down, but Peter cried out,
"Lord, you'll never wash my feet!"

4. Jesus said to Peter,
"Don't you understand?
If you want to be mine,
I must wash your feet."
"Then not just my feet,
but my head and my hands!
O Lord, I want to be yours."

5. He is King of kings and Lord of lords,
Who dwells in light inaccessible;

No one has seen him
where he sits on high,
Yet he stooped to wash my feet.

6. "Do you know, little children,
what I've done for you?
You call me Master, and you call me Lord.
If I am your Master, and if I am your Lord,
Then, what I've done, you must do."

7. Now friends, let's be glad,
let our joy be full.
For God is love, and he abides in us.
He washed our feet, he washes them still
When we do what he once did.

8. Who is like you, Lord,
now enthroned on high,
Where you look upon the heavens
and the earth below?
Before your face
the earth trembles and quakes,
Yet you stoop to wash my feet!

9. Oh, the path is rugged,
and the going is rough,
The journey is long to our heav'nly home,
Our feet are weary and covered with mud,
So the Lord still washes our feet.

Text: Based on John 13; Chrysogonus Waddell, OSCO, b. 1930.
Music: Chrysogonus Waddell, OSCO.
Text and music © Gethsemani Abbey. All rights reserved. Used with permission.

402 JESU, JESU

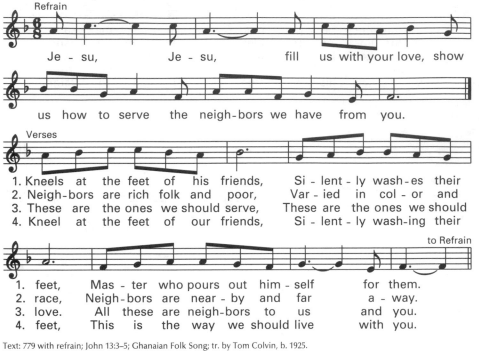

Refrain

Je - su, Je - su, fill us with your love, show us how to serve the neigh-bors we have from you.

Verses

1. Kneels at the feet of his friends, Si - lent - ly wash - es their
2. Neigh-bors are rich folk and poor, Var - ied in col - or and
3. These are the ones we should serve, These are the ones we should
4. Kneel at the feet of our friends, Si - lent - ly wash-ing their

to Refrain

1. feet, Mas - ter who pours out him - self for them.
2. race, Neigh-bors are near - by and far a - way.
3. love. All these are neigh-bors to us and you.
4. feet, This is the way we should live with you.

Text: 779 with refrain; John 13:3–5; Ghanaian Folk Song; tr. by Tom Colvin, b. 1925.
Music: CHEREPONI; Ghanaian Folk Song; adapt. by Tom Colvin.
Text and music © 1969, Hope Publishing Co. All rights reserved. Used with permission.

403 AS I HAVE DONE FOR YOU

Refrain

I, your Lord and Mas-ter, now be-come your ser-vant.

I who made the moon and stars will kneel to wash your feet.

This is my com-mand-ment: to love as I have loved you.

Kneel to wash each oth-er's feet as I have done for you.

Verses

1. All the world will know you are my dis - ci - ples
2. I must leave you now on - ly for a mo - ment.
3. I am like a vine, you are like the branch-es.
4. I have called you friends, now no long - er ser - vants.
5. You will weep for now while the world re - joic - es.
6. I will give you peace; this will be my bless - ing.

1. by the love that you of - fer, the kind - ness you
2. I must go to my Fa - ther to make you a
3. If you cling to my teach - ing you sure - ly will
4. What I told you in se - cret, the world longs to
5. But the tears of your sor - row will soon turn to
6. Though the world churns a - round you, I leave you my

1. show. You have heard the voice of God in the
2. home. On the day of my re - turn, I will
3. live. If you make your home in me, I will
4. know. There can be no great - er love than to
5. joy. As a moth - er cries in child - birth and her
6. peace. I have told you all these things that my

1. words that I have spo - ken. You be - held heav - en's
2. come to take you with me to the place I have
3. come to dwell with - in you. You can count on my
4. give your life for oth - ers. As the Fa - ther has
5. pain is turned to glad - ness, you will know great re -
6. peace may dwell with - in you. Let your faith be un -

to Refrain

1. glo - ry and have seen the face of God.
2. prom - ised where your joy will have no end.
3. mer - cy when you ask for what you need.
4. loved me, so I love you as my own.
5. joic - ing on the day of my re - turn.
6. shak - en and your hope be ev - er strong.

Text: Based on John 13–16; Dan Schutte, b. 1947.
Music: Dan Schutte.

PANGE LINGUA GLORIOSI/SING OF GLORY

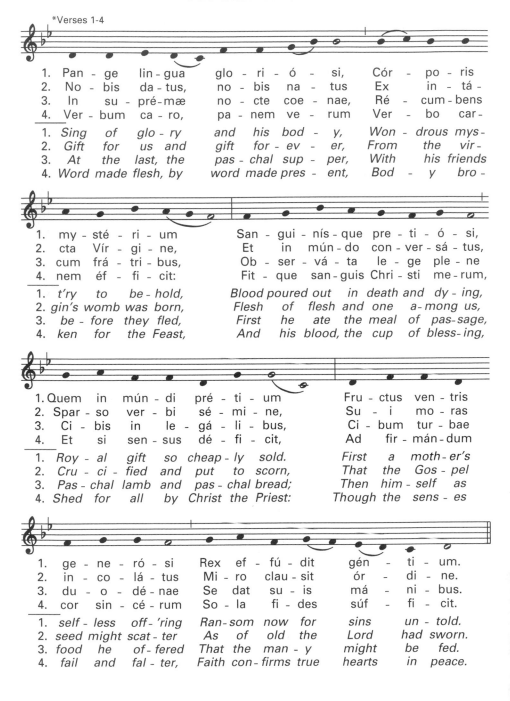

*Verses 1-4

1. Pan - ge lin - gua glo - ri - ó - si, Cór - po - ris
2. No - bis da - tus, no - bis na - tus Ex in - tá -
3. In su - pré - mæ no - cte coe - nae, Ré - cum - bens
4. Ver - bum ca - ro, pa - nem ve - rum Ver - bo car -

1. Sing of glo - ry and his bod - y, Won - drous mys -
2. Gift for us and gift for - ev - er, From the vir -
3. At the last, the pas - chal sup - per, With his friends
4. Word made flesh, by word made pres - ent, Bod - y bro -

1. my - sté - ri - um San - gui - nís - que pre - ti - ó - si,
2. cta Vír - gi - ne, Et in mún - do con - ver - sá - tus,
3. cum frá - tri - bus, Ob - ser - vá - ta le - ge ple - ne
4. nem éf - fi - cit: Fit - que san - guis Chri - sti me - rum,

1. t'ry to be - hold, Blood poured out in death and dy - ing,
2. gin's womb was born, Flesh of flesh and one a - mong us,
3. be - fore they fled, First he ate the meal of pas - sage,
4. ken for the Feast, And his blood, the cup of bless - ing,

1. Quem in mún - di pré - ti - um Fru - ctus ven - tris
2. Spar - so ver - bi sé - mi - ne, Su - i mo - ras
3. Ci - bis in le - gá - li - bus, Ci - bum tur - bae
4. Et si sen - sus dé - fi - cit, Ad fir - mán - dum

1. Roy - al gift so cheap - ly sold. First a moth - er's
2. Cru - ci - fied and put to scorn, That the Gos - pel
3. Pas - chal lamb and pas - chal bread; Then him - self as
4. Shed for all by Christ the Priest: Though the sens - es

1. ge - ne - ró - si Rex ef - fú - dit gén - ti - um.
2. in - co - lá - tus Mi - ro clau - sit ór - di - ne.
3. du - o - dé - nae Se dat su - is má - ni - bus.
4. cor sin - cé - rum So - la fi - des súf - fi - cit.

1. self - less off - 'ring Ran - som now for sins un - told.
2. seed might scat - ter As of old the Lord had sworn.
3. food he of - fered That the man - y might be fed.
4. fail and fal - ter, Faith con - firms true hearts in peace.

**Verses 5-6

5. Tan-tum er - go   Sa - cra-mén - tum   Ve - ne - ré -
6. Ge - ni - tó - ri,   Ge - ni - tó - que   Laus   et ju -

5. Ho - ly sac - ra - ment, most ho - ly,   Let   us bow
6. God Be - get - ter   and   Be - got - ten,   Yours   be praise

5. mur cér - nu - i: Et an - tí - quum do - cu - mén-tum
6. bi - lá - ti - o,   Sa - lus, ho - nor, vir - tus quo-que

5. on bend - ed knee: Vi - sions of the an - cient prom - ise
6. and maj - es - ty,   Hon - or, glo - ry and sal - va - tion,

5. No - vo ce - dat rí - tu - i: Prae-stet fi - des sup - ple -
6. Sit et be - ne - dí - cti - o: Pro - ce - dén - ti ab u -

5. Now ful - filled in mys - te - ry.   Faith de - clares what none dare
6. Bless - ing for e - ter - ni - ty,   With the One pro - ceed - ing

5. mén - tum Sén - su - um de - fé - ctu - i.
6. tró - que Com - par sit lau - dá - ti - o.   A - men.

5. fath - om; Faith re - veals what none may see.
6. al - ways, E - qual - ly in u - ni - ty.   A - men.

*Verses 1–4 are repeated as necessary until the procession reaches the place of reposition.
**Verses 5–6 are sung while the priest, kneeling, incenses the Blessed Sacrament. Then the Blessed Sacrament is placed in the tabernacle of reposition.

Text: 87 87 87; *Pange lingua gloriosi*; St. Thomas Aquinas, 1227–1274;
   tr. by Harry Hagan, OSB, b. 1947, © 1990, St. Meinrad Archabbey. Published by OCP Publications. All rights reserved.
Music: PANGE LINGUA GLORIOSI; Chant, Mode III.

PANGE LINGUA

405

Ostinato Refrain*

**Pan - ge lin - gua glo - ri - ó - si Cór - po -

ris my - sté - ri - um.   Pan - ge lin - gua glo - ri -

ó - si Cór - po - ris my - sté - ri - um.

*Verses are sung by Cantor/Choir in Latin over Refrain.
**Translation: Tell, O tongue, the mystery of the glorious Body.

Text: *Pange lingua gloriosi*; St. Thomas Aquinas, 1227–1274; tr. by Edward Caswall, 1814–1878, alt.
Music: Ricky Manalo, CSP, b. 1965, © 1998, Ricky Manalo, CSP. Published by OCP Publications. All rights reserved.

406 PANGE LINGUA GLORIOSI/SING OF GLORY

1. Pan - ge lin - gua glo - ri - ó - si, Cór - po - ris my - sté - ri - um
2. No - bis da - tus, no - bis na - tus Ex in - tá - cta Vír - gi - ne,
3. In su - pré-mae no - cte coe-nae, Ré - cum-bens cum frá - tri - bus,
4. Ver-bum ca - ro, pa - nem ve - rum Ver - bo car - nem éf - fi - cit:
5. Tan-tum er - go Sa - cra-mén-tum Ve - ne - ré - mur cér - nu - i:
6. Ge - ni - tó - ri, Ge - ni - tó - que Laus et ju - bi - lá - ti - o,

1. San - gui - nís - que pre - ti - ó - si, Quem in mun - di pré - ti - um
2. Et in mun - do con - ver - sá - tus, Spar - so ver - bi sé - mi - ne,
3. Ob - ser - vá - ta le - ge ple - ne Ci - bis in le - gá - li - bus,
4. Fit - que san - guis Chri - sti me - rum, Et si sen - sus dé - fi - cit,
5. Et an - tí - quum do - cu - mén - tum No - vo ce - dat rí - tu - i:
6. Sa - lus, ho - nor, vir - tus quo - que Sit et be - ne - dí - cti - o:

1. Fru - ctus ven - tris ge - ne - ró - si Rex ef - fú - dit gén - ti - um.
2. Su - i mo - ras in - co - lá - tus Mi - ro clau - sit ór - di - ne.
3. Ci - bum tur - bae du - o - dé - nae Se dat su - is má - ni - bus.
4. Ad fir - mán - dum cor sin - cé - rum So - la fi - des súf - fi - cit.
5. Prae - stet fi - des sup - ple - mén - tum Sén - su - um de - fé - ctu - i.
6. Pro - ce - dén - ti ab u - tró - que Com - par sit lau - dá - ti - o.

* 1. Sing of glory and his body,
Wondrous myst'ry to behold,
Blood poured out in death and dying,
Royal gift so cheaply sold.
First a mother's selfless off'ring
Ransom now for sins untold.

2. Gift for us and gift forever,
From the virgin's womb was born,
Flesh of flesh and one among us,
Crucified and put to scorn,
That the Gospel seed might scatter
As of old the Lord had sworn.

3. At the last, the paschal supper,
With his friends before they fled,
First he ate the meal of passage:
Paschal lamb and paschal bread;
Then himself as food he offered
That the many might be fed.

4. Word made flesh, by word made present,
Body broken for the Feast,
And his blood, the cup of blessing,
Shed for all by Christ the Priest:
Though the senses fail and falter,
Faith confirms true hearts in peace.

** 5. Holy sacrament, most holy,
Let us bow on bended knee:
Visions of the ancient promise
Now fulfilled in mystery.
Faith declares what none dare fathom;
Faith reveals what none may see.

6. God Begetter and Begotten,
Yours be praise and majesty,
Honor, glory and salvation,
Blessing for eternity,
With the One proceeding always,
Equally in unity.

*Verses 1–4 are repeated as necessary until the procession reaches the place of reposition.
**Verses 5–6 are sung while the priest, kneeling, incenses the Blessed Sacrament. Then the Blessed Sacrament is placed in the tabernacle of reposition.

Text: 87 87 87; *Pange lingua gloriosi*; St. Thomas Aquinas, 1227–1274;
tr. by Harry Hagan, OSB, b. 1947, © 1990, St. Meinrad Archabbey. Published by OCP Publications. All rights reserved.
Music: ST. THOMAS (TANTUM ERGO); John F. Wade, 1711–1786.

WOOD OF THE CROSS

Refrain

Be - hold the wood of the cross, on which hung the
Sav - ior of the world. O come, O
come, let us wor-ship, let us a - dore.

Verses

1. O God, my God, _____ why have you a - ban-doned me? _
2. I am de-spised, _ re - ject - ed by my peo - ple. _____
3. My bones are bro-ken. They pierce my hands and feet. _____
4. The jaws of death _ are clos - ing in up - on me. ___ The
5. You are en-throned _____ in the ho - ly place. _____ In

to Refrain

1. Why have you for - sak - en me? An - swer me, O God!
2. How could they for - get me? ___ An - swer me, O God!
3. Why have you a - ban-doned me? An - swer me, O God!
4. wick - ed laugh and taunt me. ___ An - swer me, O God!
5. you our fa - thers trust - ed. ___ An - swer me, O God!

Text: Based on *Good Friday Liturgy*; Psalm 22; Owen Alstott, b. 1947.
Music: Owen Alstott.

BY YOUR CROSS 408

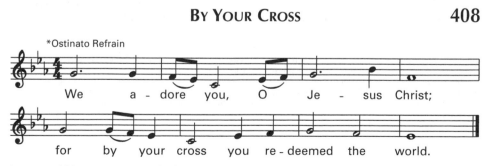

*Ostinato Refrain

We a - dore you, O Je - sus Christ;
for by your cross you re - deemed the world.

*Verses available in accompaniment books.

Text: Based on the trad. prayer for *Stations of the Cross*; Suzanne Toolan, RSM, b. 1927.
Music: Suzanne Toolan, RSM.

O SACRED HEAD, SURROUNDED

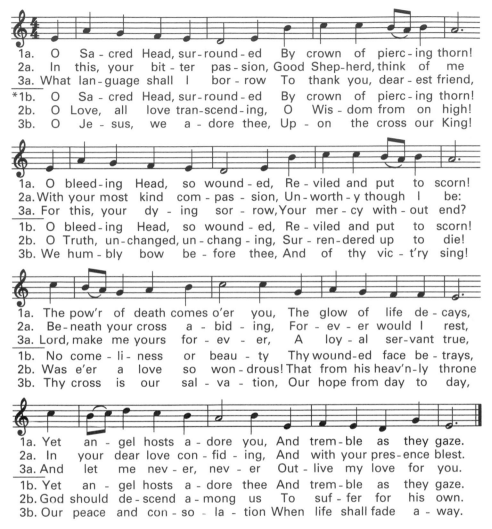

1a. O Sa - cred Head, sur-round-ed By crown of pierc-ing thorn!
2a. In this, your bit - ter pas - sion, Good Shep-herd, think of me
3a. What lan-guage shall I bor - row To thank you, dear - est friend,
*1b. O Sa - cred Head, sur-round-ed By crown of pierc-ing thorn!
2b. O Love, all love tran-scend-ing, O Wis - dom from on high!
3b. O Je - sus, we a - dore thee, Up - on the cross our King!

1a. O bleed-ing Head, so wound - ed, Re - viled and put to scorn!
2a. With your most kind com - pas - sion, Un - worth-y though I be:
3a. For this, your dy - ing sor - row, Your mer - cy with - out end?
1b. O bleed-ing Head, so wound - ed, Re - viled and put to scorn!
2b. O Truth, un-changed, un - chang - ing, Sur - ren-dered up to die!
3b. We hum - bly bow be - fore thee, And of thy vic - t'ry sing!

1a. The pow'r of death comes o'er you, The glow of life de - cays,
2a. Be-neath your cross a - bid - ing, For - ev - er would I rest,
3a. Lord, make me yours for - ev - er, A loy - al ser-vant true,
1b. No come - li - ness or beau - ty Thy wound-ed face be - trays,
2b. Was e'er a love so won - drous! That from his heav'n-ly throne
3b. Thy cross is our sal - va - tion, Our hope from day to day,

1a. Yet an - gel hosts a - dore you, And trem - ble as they gaze.
2a. In your dear love con - fid - ing, And with your pres-ence blest.
3a. And let me nev - er, nev - er Out - live my love for you.
1b. Yet an - gel hosts a - dore thee And trem - ble as they gaze.
2b. God should de - scend a - mong us To suf - fer for his own.
3b. Our peace and con - so - la - tion When life shall fade a - way.

*Alternate verses.

Text: 76 76 D; *Salve caput cruentatum*; ascr. to Bernard of Clairvaux, 1091–1153; tr. by Paul Gerhardt, 1607–1676.
  Verse 1, 2 tr. by Henry W. Baker, 1821–1877, alt.; verse 3 tr. by James W. Alexander, 1804–1859, alt.
  Alternate verses: verse 1 tr. by Henry W. Baker, alt.; verse 2, Owen Alstott, b. 1947; verse 3, Owen Alstott, composite.
  Alternate verses 2, 3 © 1977, OCP Publications. All rights reserved.
Music: PASSION CHORALE; Hans Leo Hassler, 1564–1612; adapt. by Johann Sebastian Bach, 1685–1750.

O Love of God Incarnate 410

1. O Love of God incarnate,
   Our flesh, our blood, our bone,
   Where sin has torn and marred us,
   You make our wounds your own.
   You take our guilt upon you,
   Our burdened spirits bear;
   In death you go before us,
   And you await us there.

2. We meet you in our sorrows;
   We taste you in our tears;
   We know you in our suffering;
   We find you in our fears.

You take the dregs we reach for
And drink our bitter cup;
You die the death we've chosen
And from it raise us up.

3. You rise, our wounds upon you,
   The nail prints clearly seen,
   Your ravaged side still open—
   But love has washed them clean.
   The power that conquers evil
   In you now stands revealed.
   We touch you, unbelieving,
   And find that we are healed.

Note: Music for this hymn is found on previous page, No. 409.

Text: 76 76 D; Genevieve Glen, OSB, b. 1945, © 2001, The Benedictine Nuns of the Abbey of St. Walburga.
Published by OCP Publications. All rights reserved.
Music: PASSION CHORALE; Hans Leo Hassler, 1564–1612; adapt. by Johann Sebastian Bach, 1685–1750.

Behold the Wood 411

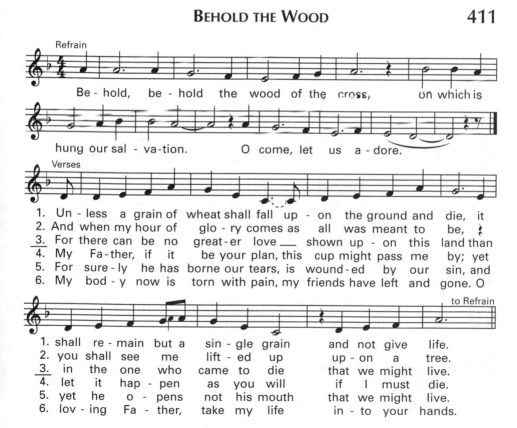

Refrain

Be-hold, be-hold the wood of the cross, on which is hung our sal-va-tion. O come, let us a-dore.

Verses

1. Un-less a grain of wheat shall fall up-on the ground and die, it shall re-main but a sin-gle grain and not give life.
2. And when my hour of glo-ry comes as all was meant to be, you shall see me lift-ed up up-on a tree.
3. For there can be no great-er love __ shown up-on this land than in the one who came to die that we might live.
4. My Fa-ther, if it be your plan, this cup might pass me by; yet let it hap-pen as you will if I must die.
5. For sure-ly he has borne our tears, is wound-ed by our sin, and yet he o-pens not his mouth that we might live.
6. My bod-y now is torn with pain, my friends have left and gone. O lov-ing Fa-ther, take my life in-to your hands.

to Refrain

Text: Based on John 12:24, 32; 15:13; Good Friday Liturgy; Dan Schutte, b. 1947.
Music: Dan Schutte.
Text and music © 1976, Daniel L. Schutte and New Dawn Music. Published by OCP Publications. All rights reserved.

WERE YOU THERE

1. Were you there when they cru - ci - fied my Lord?
2. Were you there when they nailed him to the tree?
3. Were you there when they pierced him in the side?
4. Were you there when the sun re - fused to shine?
5. Were you there when they laid him in the tomb?
6. Were you there when he rose up from the grave?

1. Were you there when they cru - ci - fied my Lord?
2. Were you there when they nailed him to the tree?
3. Were you there when they pierced him in the side?
4. Were you there when the sun re - fused to shine?
5. Were you there when they laid him in the tomb?
6. Were you there when he rose up from the grave?

1-6. Oh! Some - times it caus - es

1-6. me to trem - ble, trem - ble, trem - ble,

1. Were you there when they cru - ci - fied my Lord?
2. Were you there when they nailed him to the tree?
3. Were you there when they pierced him in the side?
4. Were you there when the sun re - fused to shine?
5. Were you there when they laid him in the tomb?
6. Were you there when he rose up from the grave?

Text: 10 10 14 10; Spiritual; *Old Plantation Hymns*, Boston, 1899.
Music: WERE YOU THERE; Spiritual; *Old Plantation Hymns*, Boston, 1899.

413   LORD, WE ADORE YOU

Ostinato Refrain

Lord, we a - dore you, kneel - ing be - fore you; bring - ing our sor - rows,

leav - ing our bur - dens for you, our Re - deem - er, here at your cross.

SING, MY TONGUE, THE SAVIOR'S GLORY

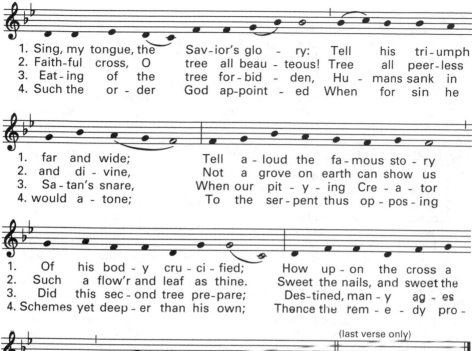

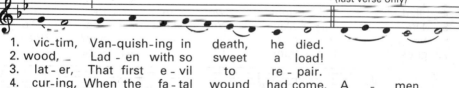

1. Sing, my tongue, the Sav-ior's glo - ry: Tell his tri-umph far and wide; Tell a - loud the fa-mous sto - ry Of his bod - y cru - ci - fied; How up - on the cross a vic-tim, Van-quish-ing in death, he died.

2. Faith-ful cross, O tree all beau - teous! Tree all peer-less and di - vine, Not a grove on earth can show us Such a flow'r and leaf as thine. Sweet the nails, and sweet the wood, Lad - en with so sweet a load!

3. Eat-ing of the tree for-bid - den, Hu - mans sank in Sa-tan's snare, When our pit - y - ing Cre - a - tor Did this sec - ond tree pre-pare; Des-tined, man - y ag - es lat - er, That first e - vil to re - pair.

4. Such the or - der God ap-point - ed When for sin he would a - tone; To the ser-pent thus op - pos - ing Schemes yet deep - er than his own; Thence the rem - e - dy pro - cur-ing, When the fa - tal wound had come. A - men.

(last verse only)

5. So when now at length the fullness
Of the sacred time drew nigh,
Then the Son, the world's Creator,
Left his Father's throne on high;
From a virgin's womb appearing,
Clothed in our mortality.

6. Thus did Christ to perfect manhood
In our mortal flesh attain:
Then of his free choice he goes on
To a death of bitter pain;
And as lamb upon the altar
Of the cross, for us is slain.

7. Lofty tree, bend down your branches,
To embrace your sacred load;
Oh, relax the native tension
Of that all too rigid wood;
Gently, gently bear the members
Of your dying King and God.

8. Blessing, honor everlasting,
To the immortal Deity;
To the Father, Son, and Spirit,
Equal praises ever be;
Glory through the earth and heaven,
Trinity in Unity. Amen.

Text: 87 87 87; Venantius Honorius Fortunatus, 530–609; tr. by John M. Neale, 1818–1866.
Music: PANGE LINGUA GLORIOSI; Chant, Mode III.

MY SONG IS LOVE UNKNOWN

1. My song is love un - known, My Sav - ior's love to
2. He came from his blest throne Sal - va - tion to be -
3. Some - times they strew his way, And his sweet prais - es
4. Why, what hath my Lord done? What makes this rage and
5. They rise and needs will have My dear Lord made a -
6. In life no house, no home My Lord on earth might
7. Here might I stay and sing, No sto - ry so di -

1. me, Love to the love - less shown That they might
2. stow, But all made strange, and none The longed - for
3. sing, Re - sound - ing all the day Ho - san - nas
4. spite? He made the lame to run, He gave the
5. way; A mur - der - er they save, The Prince of
6. have; In death no friend - ly tomb But what a
7. vine! Nev - er was love, dear King, Nev - er was

1. love - ly be. O who am I That
2. Christ would know. But O my friend, My
3. to their King. Then "Cru - ci - fy!" Is
4. blind their sight. Sweet in - ju - ries! Yet
5. Life they slay. Yet stead - fast he To
6. strang - er gave. What may I say? Heav'n
7. grief like thine. This is my friend, In

1. for my sake The Lord should take Frail flesh, and die?
2. friend in - deed, Who at my need His life did spend!
3. all their breath, And for his death They thirst and cry.
4. they at these Them-selves dis-please, And 'gainst him rise.
5. suf - f'ring goes, That he his foes From thence might free.
6. was his home; But mine the tomb Where - in he lay.
7. whose sweet praise I all my days Could glad - ly spend!

Text: 66 66 44; Samuel Crossman, ca. 1624–1683.
Music: LOVE UNKNOWN; John Ireland, 1879–1962, © 1924, 1995, John Ireland. All rights reserved.
Administered by the John Ireland Trust, London. Used with permission.

416   GOOD FRIDAY GENERAL INTERCESSIONS

1st time: Cantor; All repeat

*Christ cru - ci - fied, Je - sus, hear our prayer!

*Verses available in accompaniment books.

Text: *Good Friday General Intercessions,* © 1972, ICEL. All rights reserved. Used with permission.
  Response text, Kevin Keil, ASCAP, b. 1956, © 1992, Kevin Keil. Published by OCP Publications. All rights reserved.
Music: Kevin Keil, ASCAP, © 1992, Kevin Keil. Published by OCP Publications. All rights reserved.

WHEN I SURVEY THE WONDROUS CROSS

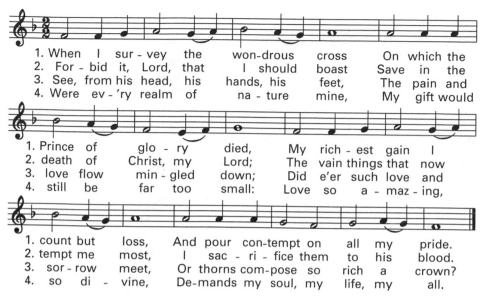

1. When I sur-vey the won-drous cross On which the
2. For-bid it, Lord, that I should boast Save in the
3. See, from his head, his hands, his feet, The pain and
4. Were ev-'ry realm of na-ture mine, My gift would

1. Prince of glo-ry died, My rich-est gain I
2. death of Christ, my Lord; The vain things that now
3. love flow min-gled down; Did e'er such love and
4. still be far too small: Love so a-maz-ing,

1. count but loss, And pour con-tempt on all my pride.
2. tempt me most, I sac-ri-fice them to his blood.
3. sor-row meet, Or thorns com-pose so rich a crown?
4. so di-vine, De-mands my soul, my life, my all.

Text: LM; Isaac Watts, 1674–1748, alt.
Music: HAMBURG; Lowell Mason, 1792–1872.

WHEN JESUS WEPT 418

When Je-sus wept the fall-ing tear In mer-cy

flow'd be-yond all bound, When Je-sus groan'd, a trem-bling

fear Seiz'd all the guil-ty world a-round.

Text: LM; *The New England Psalm Singer*, 1770.
Music: WHEN JESUS WEPT; William Billings, 1746–1800.

LITANY OF THE SAINTS

Cantor Lord, have mer - cy. **All** Lord, have mer - cy.
Christ, have mer - cy. Christ, have mer - cy.
Lord, have mer - cy. Lord, have mer - cy.

Cantor Ho - ly Ma - ry, Moth - er of Gód. **All** Pray for us.
Saint Mí - chael.

Holy angels of Gód	Saint Augústine
Saint John the Báptist	Saint Athanásius
Saint Jóseph	Saint Básil
Saint Peter and Saint Pául	Saint Mártin
Saint Ándrew	Saint Bénedict
Saint Jóhn	Saint Francis and Saint Dóminic
Saint Mary Mágdalene	Saint Francis Xávier
Saint Stéphen	Saint John Viánney
Saint Ignátius	Saint Cátherine
Saint Láwrence	Saint Terésa
Saint Perpetua and Saint Felícity	Saint…
Saint Ágnes	All holy men and wómen
Saint Grégory	

Cantor Lord, be mér - ci - ful. **All** Lord, save your peo - ple.

From all évil | By your coming as mán
From every sín | By your death and rising to new lífe
From everlasting déath | By your gift of the Holy Spírit

Cantor Be mer - ci - ful to us sín - ners. **All** Lord, hear our prayer.

If there are candidates to be baptized
Give new life to these chosen ones
   by the grace of báptism.
Jesus, Son of the living Gód.

If there is no one to be baptized
By your grace bless this font where
   your children will be rebórn.
Jesus, Son of the living Gód.

Cantor; All repeat Christ, hear us. **Cantor; All repeat** Lord Je - sus, hear our prayer.

O Sons and Daughters

Refrain

Al - le - lu - ia! Al - le - lu - ia! Al - le - lu - ia!

Verses

1. O sons and daugh - ters, let us sing! The King of
2. That Eas - ter morn, at break of day, The faith - ful
3. An an - gel clad in white they see, Who sat, and
4. That night the a - pos - tles met in fear; A - mid them
5. When Thom - as first the tid - ings heard, How they had
6. "My wound - ed side, O Thom - as, see; Be - hold my
7. No long - er Thom - as then de - nied; He saw the
8. How blest are they who have not seen, And yet whose
9. On this most ho - ly day of days, To God your

1. heav'n, the glo - rious King, O'er death to - day rose
2. wom - en went their way To seek the tomb where
3. spoke un - to the three: "Your Lord has gone to
4. came their Lord most dear, And said, "My peace be
5. seen the ris - en Lord, He doubt - ed the dis -
6. hands, my feet," said he. "Not faith - less, but be -
7. feet, the hands, the side; "You are my Lord and
8. faith has con - stant been, For they e - ter - nal
9. hearts and voic - es raise, In laud, and ju - bi -

to Refrain

1. tri - um - phing. Al - le - lu - ia!
2. Je - sus lay. Al - le - lu - ia!
3. Gal - i - lee." Al - le - lu - ia!
4. on all here." Al - le - lu - ia!
5. ci - ples' word. Al - le - lu - ia!
6. liev - ing be." Al - le - lu - ia!
7. God," he cried. Al - le - lu - ia!
8. life shall win. Al - le - lu - ia!
9. lee and praise. Al - le - lu - ia!

Text: 888 with alleluias; attr. to Jean Tisserand, d. 1494; tr. by John M. Neale, 1818–1866, alt.
Music: O FILII ET FILIAE; Chant, Mode II; *Airs sur les hymnes sacrez, odes et noëls*, 1623.

CHRISTIANS, TO THE PASCHAL VICTIM

1. Chris-tians, to the Pas-chal Vic-tim   Of - fer your thank-ful prais-es!
1. Ví - cti-mae pa-schá - li lau-des   ím-mo-lent Chri-sti - á - ni.

2.   A Lamb the sheep re-deems; _ Christ, who on - ly is sin - less,
3. Death and life have con - tend - ed   in that com-bat stu-pen-dous:
2.   A - gnus re - dé - mit   o - ves: Chri-stus ín - no-cens Pa - tri
3. Mors et vi - ta du - él - lo   con - fli - xé - re mi-rán - do:

2. Rec - on - ciles____   sin - ners   to   the   Fa - ther.
3. The Prince of   life, who died,   reigns im - mor - tal.
2. re - con - ci - li - á - vit   pec - ca - tó - res.
3. dux   vi - tae mór - tu - us,   re - gnat vi - vus.

4. Speak, Ma - ry, de - clar - ing   What you saw, __ way - far - ing.
6. Bright an-gels, at - test-ing,   The shroud and nap-kin rest-ing.
4. Dic no - bis Ma - rí - a,   quid vi - dí - sti in vi - a?
6. An - gé - li - cos te - stes,   su - dá - ri - um, et ve-stes.

5. "The   tomb   of   Christ,   who   is   liv   -   ing,
7. Yes, Christ my   hope   is   a - ris   -   en;
5. Se - púl - crum Chri - sti   vi - vén   -   tis,
7. Sur - ré - xit Chri - stus spes me   -   a:

5. The   glo - ry   of   Je - sus' res - ur - rec   -   tion;
7. To   Gal - i - lee   he____   goes be - fore   you."
5. et   gló - ri - am   vi - di   re - sur - gén   -   tis:
7. prae - cé - det   su - os   in   Ga - li - laé   -   am.

8. ___ Christ in-deed from death is ris - en,   our new life ob - tain-ing.
8. Sci-mus Chrí-stum sur - re - xís - se   a mór-tu - is ve - re:

8. Have mer - cy, vic - tor King,   ev - er reign   -   ing!
8. tu   no - bis vi - ctor Rex,   mi - se - ré   -   re.

Optional Ending

A - men. Al - le - lú - ia.

CHRIST, THE LORD, IS RISEN TODAY 422

1. Christ, the Lord, is ris'n to-day; Chris-tians, haste your
2. Christ, the Vic-tim un-de-filed, God and sin-ners
3. Say, O won-d'ring Ma-ry, say What you saw a-
4. Christ, who once for sin-ners bled, Now the first-born

1. vows to pay; Make your joy and prais-es known At the
2. re-con-ciled; When in strange and awe-some strife Met to-
3. long the way. "I be-held two an-gels bright, Emp-ty
4. from the dead, Throned in end-less might and pow'r, Lives and

1. Pas-chal Vic-tim's throne; For the sheep the Lamb has bled,
2. geth-er death and life; Chris-tians, on this hap-py day
3. tomb and wrap-pings white; I be-held the glo-ry bright
4. reigns for-ev-er-more. Hail, e-ter-nal Hope on high!

1. Sin-less in the sin-ner's stead; Christ, the Lord, is
2. Haste with joy your vows to pay; Christ, the Lord, is
3. Of the ris-en Lord of light; Christ, my hope, is
4. Hail, our King of Vic-to-ry! Hail, our Prince of

1. ris'n on high; Now he lives, no more to die!
2. ris'n on high; Now he lives, no more to die!
3. ris'n a-gain; Now he lives, and lives to reign!"
4. Life a-dored! Help and save us, gra-cious Lord!

THREE DAYS

1. Three days our world was bro - ken; the
2. Three days— and on the third day, the
3. Three days our world was bro - ken and

1. Lord of life lay dead. "Take up your cross," he
2. wom - en came at dawn. His tomb, they said, was
3. in an in - stant healed, God's cov - e - nant of

1. told us who fol - lowed where he led. Would
2. emp - ty, his bro - ken bod - y gone. Who
3. mer - cy in mys - ter - y re - vealed. Two

1. we now hang in tor - ment with thieves on ev - 'ry side,
2. could be - lieve their sto - ry? The dead do not a - rise,
3. thou - sand years are one day in God's e - ter - nal sight,

1. our Pass - o - ver shat - tered, our hope cru - ci - fied?
2. yet he walks a - mong us, and with our own eyes
3. and yes - ter - day's sor - rows are this day's de - light.

1. Three days we hid in si - lence, in
2. we've seen him at this ta - ble; we've
3. Though still Christ's bod - y suf - fers, pierced

1. bit - ter fear and grief. Three days we clung to -
2. shared his bread and wine. Hearts burn - ing bright with -
3. dai - ly by the sword, yet death has no do -

1. geth - er where he had washed our feet.
2. in us, we've seen his glo - ry shine.
3. min - ion: the ris - en Christ is Lord!

Text: 13 13 13 11 13 13; M.D. Ridge, © 1999, M.D. Ridge. Published by OCP Publications. All rights reserved.
Music: THAXTED; Gustav T. Holst, 1874–1932.

AT THE LAMB'S HIGH FEAST

1. At the Lamb's high feast we sing Praise to our vic -
2. Where the Pas - chal blood is poured, Death's dark an - gel
3. Might - y vic - tim from the sky, Hell's fierce pow'rs be -
4. Eas - ter tri - umph, Eas - ter joy, This a - lone can

1. to - rious King, Who has washed us in the tide
2. sheathes his sword; Is - rael's hosts tri - um - phant go
3. neath you lie; You have con - quered in the fight,
4. sin de - stroy; From sin's pow'r, Lord, set us free,

1. Flow - ing from his wound - ed side; Praise we him, whose
2. Through the wave that drowns the foe. Praise we Christ whose
3. You have brought us life and light: Now no more can
4. New - born souls in you to be. Hymns of glo - ry,

1. love di - vine Gives his sa - cred blood for wine, Gives his
2. blood was shed, Pas - chal vic - tim, Pas - chal bread! With sin -
3. death ap - pall, Now no more the grave en - thrall; You have
4. songs of praise, Fa - ther, un - to you we raise: And to

1. bod - y for the feast, Christ the vic - tim, Christ the priest.
2. cer - i - ty and love Eat we man - na from a - bove.
3. o - pened Par - a - dise, And in you the saints shall rise.
4. you, our ris - en King, With the Spir - it, praise we sing.

Text: 77 77 D; *Ad regias Agni dapes*; Latin, 4th cent.; tr. by Robert Campbell, 1814–1868, alt.
Music: SALZBURG; Jakob Hintze, 1622–1702; adapt. by Johann Sebastian Bach, 1685–1750.

JESUS CHRIST IS RISEN TODAY

1. Je - sus Christ is ris'n to - day,
2. Hymns of praise then let us sing,
3. But the pains which he en-dured,
4. Sing we to our God a - bove,

Al - le - lu - ia!

1. Our tri - um-phant ho - ly day,
2. Un - to Christ, our heav'n-ly King,
3. Our sal - va - tion have pro-cured;
4. Praise e - ter - nal as his love,

Al - le - lu - ia!

1. Who did once up - on the cross,
2. Who en-dured the cross and grave,
3. Now a - bove the sky he's King,
4. One true God by all con-fessed,

Al - le - lu - ia!

1. Suf - fer to re - deem our loss.
2. Sin - ners to re - deem and save.
3. Where the an - gels ev - er sing.
4. Fa - ther, Son, and Spir - it blest.

Al - le - lu - ia!

Text: 77 77 with alleluias; verse 1, Latin, 14th cent.; para. in *Lyra Davidica*, 1708, alt.;
verses 2–3, *The Compleat Psalmodist*, ca. 1750, alt.; verse 4, Charles Wesley, 1707–1788, alt.
Music: EASTER HYMN; later form of melody fr. *Lyra Davidica*, 1708.

426 COME, YE FAITHFUL, RAISE THE STRAIN

1. Come, ye faith-ful, raise the strain Of tri - um-phant glad-ness;
2. 'Tis the spring of souls to - day; Christ has burst his pris - on,
3. Now the queen of sea-sons bright With the day of splen-dor,
4. Nei-ther could the gates of death, Nor the tomb's dark por - tal,
5. "Al - le - lu - ia!" now we cry To our King im - mor - tal,

1. God has brought his Is - ra - el In - to joy from sad-ness;
2. And from three days' sleep in death As a sun has ris - en;
3. With the roy - al feast of feasts Comes its joy to ren - der;
4. Nor the watch - ers, nor the seal Hold him as a mor - tal;
5. Who, tri - um-phant, burst the bars Of the tomb's dark por - tal;

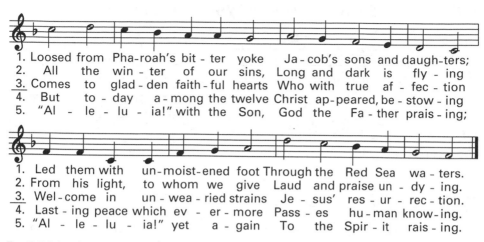

1. Loosed from Pha-roah's bit-ter yoke Ja-cob's sons and daugh-ters;
2. All the win-ter of our sins, Long and dark is fly-ing
3. Comes to glad-den faith-ful hearts Who with true af-fec-tion
4. But to-day a-mong the twelve Christ ap-peared, be-stow-ing
5. "Al - le - lu - ia!" with the Son, God the Fa-ther prais-ing;

1. Led them with un-moist-ened foot Through the Red Sea wa-ters.
2. From his light, to whom we give Laud and praise un-dy-ing.
3. Wel-come in un-wea-ried strains Je-sus' res-ur-rec-tion.
4. Last-ing peace which ev-er-more Pass-es hu-man know-ing.
5. "Al - le - lu - ia!" yet a-gain To the Spir-it rais-ing.

Text: 76 76 D; based on Exodus 15; St. John of Damascus, 8th cent.; tr. by John M. Neale, 1818–1866, alt.
Music: GAUDEAMUS PARITER; Johann Horn, ca. 1495–1547.

CHRIST, THE LORD, IS RISEN TODAY 427

1. Christ, the Lord, is ris'n to - day:
2. Lives a - gain our glo-rious King;
3. Love's re-deem-ing work is done;
4. Soar we now where Christ has led,
Al - le - lu - ia!

1. All on earth with an-gels say:
2. Where, O death, is now your sting?
3. Fought the fight, the bat-tle won;
4. Fol-l'wing our ex-alt-ed Head;
Al - le - lu - ia!

1. Raise your joys and tri-umphs high:
2. Once he died our souls to save;
3. Death in vain for-bids him rise;
4. Made like him, like him we rise:
Al - le - lu - ia!

1. Sing, O heav'ns, and earth re - ply:
2. Where your vic - to - ry, O grave?
3. Christ has o - pened par - a - dise.
4. Ours the cross, the grave, the skies.
Al - le - lu - ia!

Text: 77 77 with alleluias; Charles Wesley, 1707–1788, alt.
Music: LLANFAIR; Robert Williams, 1781–1821.

FESTIVAL CANTICLE: WORTHY IS CHRIST

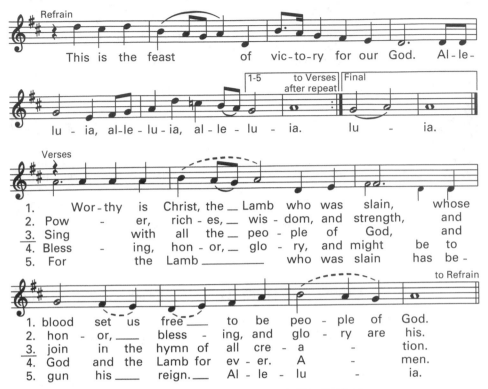

Refrain

This is the feast of vic-to-ry for our God. Al-le-
lu - ia, al-le - lu-ia, al - le - lu - ia. *(1-5 to Verses after repeat)* lu - ia. *(Final)*

Verses

1. Wor-thy is Christ, the __ Lamb who was slain, whose
2. Pow - er, rich - es, __ wis - dom, and strength, and
3. Sing with all the __ peo - ple of God, and
4. Bless - ing, hon - or, __ glo - ry, and might be to
5. For the Lamb _____ who was slain has be -

1. blood set us free ___ to be peo - ple of God.
2. hon - or, ___ bless - ing, and glo - ry are his.
3. join in the hymn of all cre - a - tion.
4. God and the Lamb for ev - er. A - men.
5. gun his ___ reign. ___ Al - le - lu - ia.

Text: Based on Revelation 5; Richard Hillert, b. 1923, © 1978, *Lutheran Book of Worship*. All rights reserved.
Reprinted by permission of Augsburg Fortress.
Music: Richard Hillert, © 1975, 1988, Richard Hillert. All rights reserved. Used with permission.

429   ROLL AWAY THE STONE

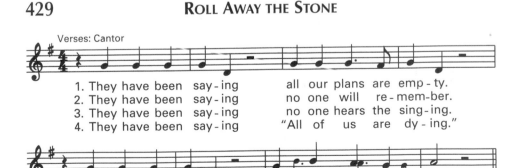

Verses: Cantor

1. They have been say-ing all our plans are emp - ty.
2. They have been say-ing no one will re - mem-ber.
3. They have been say-ing no one hears the sing-ing.
4. They have been say-ing "All of us are dy - ing."

1. They have been say-ing "Where is their God now?"
2. They have been say-ing pow-er rules the world.
3. They have been say-ing all our strength is gone.
4. They have been say-ing "All of us are dead."

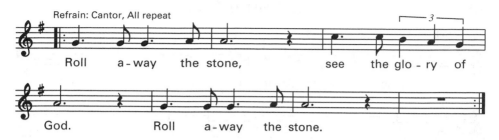

Refrain: Cantor, All repeat

Roll a - way the stone, see the glo - ry of God. Roll a - way the stone.

TWO WERE BOUND FOR EMMAUS 430

1, 5. Two were bound for Em - ma - us, dis - heart - ened
2. On the Sea of Ti - ber - ius, when the night was
3. Then they knew it was Je - sus and they has - tened
4. When the road makes us wea - ry, when our la - bor

1, 5. and __ lost; all their hope for the fu - ture had been
2. near - ly gone and their toil seemed so use - less, not one
3. in to shore; bread and fish for their break - fast from the
4. seems but loss, when the fire of faith weak - ens and too

1, 5. nailed to a cross. Love un-known then walked be-side __ them,
2. fish had they caught, from the shore the strang-er called to them:
3. hands of their Lord. "O __ Pe - ter, if you love __ me
4. high seems the cost, let the Church turn to its ris - en Lord,

1, 5. come __ back from the dead, and they knew he was
2. "Cast your net, friends, once more." And they filled it to
3. you must care for my sheep; if you fol - low your
4. who for us bore the cross, and we'll find our hearts

1, 5. ris - en in the break - ing of bread.
2. burst - ing, but the net was not torn.
3. Shep - herd, then a shep - herd you'll be."
4. burn - ing at the sound of his voice.

431

THE STRIFE IS O'ER

1. The strife is o'er, the bat - tle done;
2. The pow'rs of death have done their worst,
3. On the third morn he rose a - gain,
4. He closed the yawn - ing gates of hell;
5. O Ris - en Lord, all praise to thee,

1. Now is the Vic - tor's tri - umph won; O let the
2. But Christ their le - gions has dis - persed; Let shouts of
3. Glo - rious in maj - es - ty to reign; O let us
4. The bars from heav'n's high por - tals fell; Let hymns of
5. Who from our sin has set us free, That we may

1. song of praise be sung: Al - le - lu - ia!
2. praise and joy out - burst: Al - le - lu - ia!
3. swell the joy - ful strain: Al - le - lu - ia!
4. praise his tri - umph tell: Al - le - lu - ia!
5. live e - ter - nal - ly! Al - le - lu - ia!

Text: 888 with alleluias; *Finita iam sunt praelia*; Latin, 12th cent.; tr. by Francis Pott, 1832–1909, alt.
Music: VICTORY; Giovanni da Palestrina, 1525–1594; adapt. by Willam H. Monk, 1823–1889.

432

BE JOYFUL, MARY, HEAVENLY QUEEN

1. Be joy - ful, Ma - ry, heav'n-ly Queen, Be joy - ful, Ma -
2. The Son you bore by heav-en's grace, Be joy - ful, Ma -
3. The Lord has ris - en from the dead, Be joy - ful, Ma -
4. Now pray to God, O Vir - gin fair, Be joy - ful, Ma -

1. ry! Your Son who died was liv - ing seen,
2. ry! Did all our guilt and sin ef - face,
3. ry! He rose with might as he had said,
4. ry! That he our souls to heav - en bear,

Al -

1-4. le - lu - ia, Re - joice, re - joice, O Ma - ry!

Text: 85 84 7; *Regina Caeli, jubila;* Latin, 17th cent.; tr. anon. in *Psallite,* 1901, alt.
Music: REGINA CAELI; Johann Leisentritt's *Catholicum Hymnologium,* 1584.

THE SUN AROSE IN CLOUDS OF FIRE 433

1. The Sun a - rose in clouds of fire.
2. The wom - en saw no ris - ing light.
3. They had no gold or in - cense kept
4. The cave gaped wide, the swad - dling bands
5. The an - gels at the emp - ty tomb
6. The wom - en ran on feet of fire,
7. From night to day, from day to night

1. From east to west the sky was rent
2. They went in blind, con - sum - ing grief
3. To burn in clouds of prayer - sweet breath.
4. Lay scat - tered where their Love had lain,
5. Sang glo - ry in the ris - ing sun
6. From east to west their gos - pel burned.
7. The Word goes out through all the earth,

1. By si - lent song from un - seen choir
2. To wrap a - gainst the chill stone night
3. They bore but myrrh in hearts that wept
4. Marked by the side, the feet, the hands
5. And hailed the child of Ma - ry's womb
6. Their flam - ing joy rose ev - er high'r
7. Borne by the wise whose cry is light:

1. An - nounc - ing dawn from night far spent.
2. The cold flesh of their dead be - lief.
3. In bit - ter mem - o - ry of death.
4. That bled when all their hope was slain.
5. Who, ris - ing, left death's knots un - done.
6. In clouds of myrrh to in - cense turned.
7. Death, death has died— now all is birth!

Text: LM; Genevieve Glen, OSB, b. 1945, © 1998, The Benedictine Nuns of the Abbey of St. Walburga.
Published by OCP Publications. All rights reserved.
Music: ROCKINGHAM; *Second Supplement to Psalmody in Miniature,* ca. 1780.

434 ALLELUIA! ALLELUIA! LET THE HOLY ANTHEM RISE

1. Al - le - lu - ia! Al - le - lu - ia! Let the ho - ly an - them
2. Al - le - lu - ia! Al - le - lu - ia! Like the sun from out the
3. Al - le - lu - ia! Al - le - lu - ia! He has burst our pris - on
4. Al - le - lu - ia! Al - le - lu - ia! Bless - ed Je - sus, make us

1. rise, And the choirs of heav - en chant it In the
2. wave, He has ris - en up in tri - umph From the
3. bars; He has lift - ed up the por - tals Of our
4. rise From the life of this cor - rup - tion To the

1. tem - ple of the skies; Let the moun - tains skip with
2. dark - ness of the grave. He's the splen - dor of the
3. home be - yond the stars: He has won for us our
4. life that nev - er dies. May your glo - ry be our

1. glad - ness, And the joy - ful val - leys ring With ho -
2. na - tions, He's the lamp of end - less day; He's the
3. free - dom, 'Neath his feet our foes are trod; He has
4. por - tion, When the days of time are past, And the

1. san - nas in the high - est To our Sav - ior and our King!
2. ver - y Lord of glo - ry Who is ris - en up to - day!
3. pur - chased back our birth - right To the king - dom of our God!
4. dead shall be a - wak - ened By the trum - pet's might - y blast!

Text: 87 87 D; Edward Caswall, 1814–1878.
Music: HOLY ANTHEM; *St. Basil's Hymnal*, 1889.

435 LET HEAVEN REJOICE

Refrain

Let heav-en re-joice and earth be glad; let all cre-a-tion sing. Let

chil-dren pro-claim through ev - 'ry land: "Ho-san-na to our King."

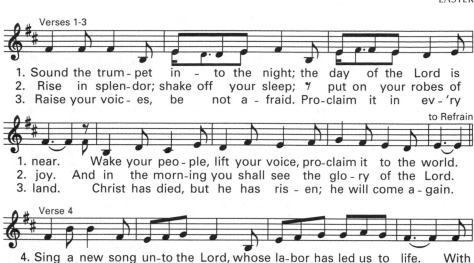

Verses 1-3

1. Sound the trum-pet in-to the night; the day of the Lord is
2. Rise in splen-dor; shake off your sleep; put on your robes of
3. Raise your voic-es, be not a-fraid. Pro-claim it in ev-'ry

to Refrain

1. near. Wake your peo-ple, lift your voice, pro-claim it to the world.
2. joy. And in the morn-ing you shall see the glo-ry of the Lord.
3. land. Christ has died, but he has ris-en; he will come a-gain.

Verse 4

4. Sing a new song un-to the Lord, whose la-bor has led us to life. With

to Refrain

4. grate-ful hearts and joy-ful danc-ing, play be-fore the Lord.

Text and music: Bob Dufford, SJ, b. 1943, © 1972, 1997, Robert J. Dufford, SJ.
Published by OCP Publications. All rights reserved.

REGINA CAELI/O QUEEN OF HEAVEN   436

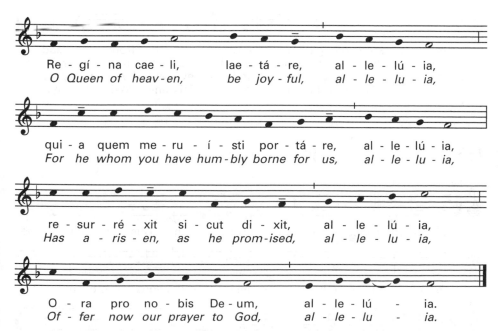

Re - gí - na cae - li, lae - tá - re, al - le - lú - ia,
O Queen of heav-en, be joy-ful, al - le - lu - ia,

qui - a quem me - ru - í - sti por - tá - re, al - le - lú - ia,
For he whom you have hum-bly borne for us, al - le - lu - ia,

re - sur - ré - xit si - cut di - xit, al - le - lú - ia,
Has a - ris - en, as he prom-ised, al - le - lu - ia,

O - ra pro no - bis De - um, al - le - lú - ia.
Of - fer now our prayer to God, al - le - lu - ia.

Text: Irregular; Latin, 12th cent.; tr. by C. Winfred Douglas, 1867–1944, alt.
Music: REGINA CAELI LAETARE; Chant, Mode VI; *Liber Cantualis*, 1983.

ALLELUIA! ALLELUIA!

1. Al - le - lu - ia! Al - le - lu - ia! Hearts and voic - es
2. Now the i - ron bars are bro - ken, Christ from death to
3. Christ is ris - en, we are ris - en! Shed up - on us
4. Al - le - lu - ia! Al - le - lu - ia! Glo - ry be to

1. heav'n - ward raise: Sing to God a hymn of glad - ness,
2. life is born, Glo - rious life and life im - mor - tal,
3. heav'n - ly grace, Rain and dew and gleams of glo - ry
4. God on high; Al - le - lu - ia to the Sav - ior

1. Sing to God a hymn of praise. Christ, who on the
2. On that ho - ly Eas - ter morn. Christ has tri - umphed,
3. From your ho - ly ra - diant face; That, with hearts in
4. Who has won the vic - to - ry; Al - le - lu - ia

1. cross a vic - tim, For the world's sal - va - tion bled, Je - sus
2. and we con - quer By this might - y en - ter - prise, We with
3. heav - en dwell - ing, We on earth, your ser - vants true, Will by
4. to the Spir - it, Fount of love and sanc - ti - ty; Al - le -

1. Christ, the King of glo - ry, Now is ris - en from the dead.
2. Christ to life e - ter - nal By his res - ur - rec - tion rise.
3. an - gel hands be gath - ered, And be ev - er, Lord, with you.
4. lu - ia! Al - le - lu - ia! To the Tri - une Maj - es - ty.

Text: 87 87 D; Christopher Wordsworth, 1807–1885.
Music: HYMN TO JOY; Ludwig van Beethoven, 1770–1827; adapt. by Edward Hodges, 1796–1867.

438   JOIN IN THE DANCE

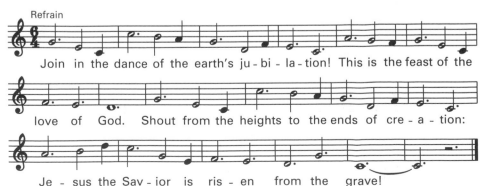

Refrain

Join in the dance of the earth's ju - bi - la - tion! This is the feast of the

love of God. Shout from the heights to the ends of cre - a - tion:

Je - sus the Sav - ior is ris - en from the grave!

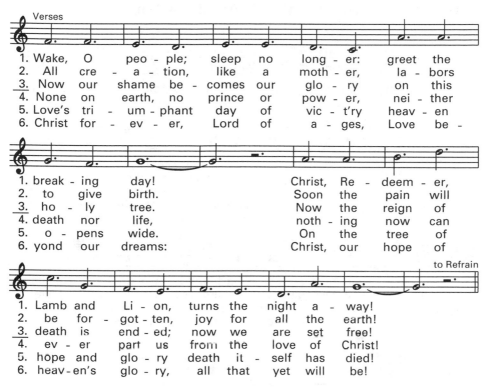

Verses

1. Wake, O peo - ple; sleep no long - er: greet the
2. All cre - a - tion, like a moth - er, la - bors
3. Now our shame be - comes our glo - ry on this
4. None on earth, no prince or pow - er, nei - ther
5. Love's tri - um - phant day of vic - t'ry heav - en
6. Christ for - ev - er, Lord of a - ges, Love be -

1. break - ing day! Christ, Re - deem - er,
2. to give birth. Soon the pain will
3. ho - ly tree. Now the reign of
4. death nor life, noth - ing now can
5. o - pens wide. On the tree of
6. yond our dreams: Christ, our hope of

to Refrain

1. Lamb and Li - on, turns the night a - way!
2. be for - got - ten, joy for all the earth!
3. death is end - ed; now we are set free!
4. ev - er part us from the love of Christ!
5. hope and glo - ry death it - self has died!
6. heav - en's glo - ry, all that yet will be!

Text and music: Dan Schutte, b. 1947, © 1991, Daniel L. Schutte. Published by OCP Publications. All rights reserved.

ALLELUIA NO. 1   439

Refrain

Al - le - lu - ia, al - le - lu - ia! Give thanks to the ris - en Lord. Al - le -

Verses

lu - ia, al - le - lu - ia! Give praise to his name.
1. Je - sus is Lord of
2. Spread the good news o'er
3. We have been cru - ci -
4. Come, let us praise the

to Refrain

1. all the earth; He is the king of cre - a - tion.
2. all the earth: Je - sus has died and has ris - en.
3. fied with Christ; Now we shall live __ for - ev - er.
4. liv - ing God; Joy - ful - ly sing to our Sav - ior.

Text: 8 8 with refrain; Donald Fishel, b. 1950.
Music: ALLELUIA NO. 1; Donald Fishel.
Text and music © 1973, Word of God Music (Administered by The Copyright Company, Nashville, TN.) All rights reserved.
International copyright secured. Used with permission.

440 THIS DAY WAS MADE BY THE LORD

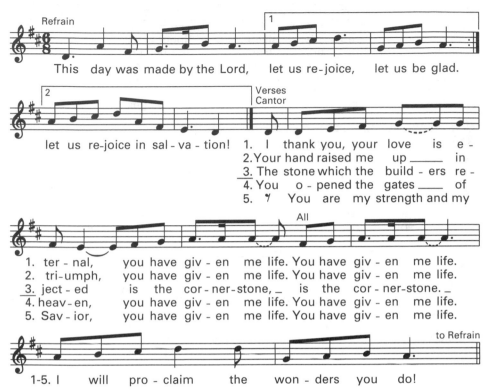

This day was made by the Lord, let us re-joice, let us be glad.

let us re-joice in sal-va-tion! 1. I thank you, your love is e-
2. Your hand raised me up ____ in
3. The stone which the build-ers re-
4. You o-pened the gates ____ of
5. You are my strength and my

1. ter-nal, you have giv-en me life. You have giv-en me life.
2. tri-umph, you have giv-en me life. You have giv-en me life.
3. ject-ed is the cor-ner-stone, _ is the cor-ner-stone. _
4. heav-en, you have giv-en me life. You have giv-en me life.
5. Sav-ior, you have giv-en me life. You have giv-en me life.

1-5. I will pro-claim the won-ders you do!

Text: Based on Psalm 118; Christopher Walker, b. 1947.
Music: Christopher Walker.
Text and music © 1988, 1989, Christopher Walker. Published by OCP Publications. All rights reserved.

441 CHRIST IS ALIVE

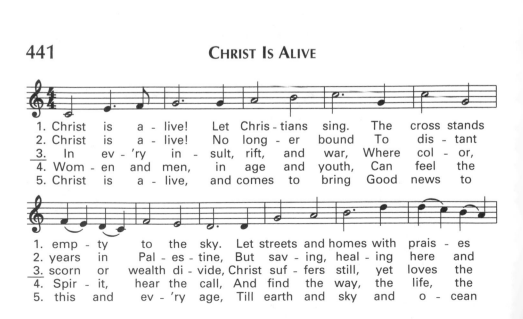

1. Christ is a-live! Let Chris-tians sing. The cross stands
2. Christ is a-live! No long-er bound To dis-tant
3. In ev-'ry in-sult, rift, and war, Where col-or,
4. Wom-en and men, in age and youth, Can feel the
5. Christ is a-live, and comes to bring Good news to

1. emp-ty to the sky. Let streets and homes with prais-es
2. years in Pal-es-tine, But sav-ing, heal-ing here and
3. scorn or wealth di-vide, Christ suf-fers still, yet loves the
4. Spir-it, hear the call, And find the way, the life, the
5. this and ev-'ry age, Till earth and sky and o-cean

1. ring. Love, drowned in death, shall nev - er die.
2. now, And touch - ing ev - 'ry place and time.
3. more, And lives, where e - ven hope has died.
4. truth, Re - vealed in Je - sus, freed for all.
5. ring With joy, with jus - tice, love and praise.

Text: LM; Romans 6:5–11; Brian Wren, b. 1936, © 1975, revised 1995, Hope Publishing Co.
  All rights reserved. Used with permission.
Music: TRURO; Williams' *Psalmodia Evangelica, Part II*, 1789.

CHRIST, THE LORD, IS RISEN AGAIN 442

1. Christ, the Lord, is ris'n a - gain, Christ has
2. Christ who gave for us his life, Who for
3. Christ who bore all pain and loss Com - fort -
4. He who slum - bered in the grave Is ex -
5. Now he bids us tell a - broad How the
6. You, our Pas chal Lamb in - deed, Christ, to -

1. bro - ken ev - 'ry chain! Hark, the an - gels
2. us en - dured the strife, Is our Pas - chal
3. less up - on the cross, Lives in glo - ry
4. alt - ed now to save; Now through Chris - ten -
5. lost may be re - stored, How the pen - i -
6. day your peo - ple feed; Take our sins and

1. shout for joy, Sing - ing ev - er - more on high:
2. Lamb to - day. We, too, sing for joy and say:
3. now on high, Pleads for us and hears our cry:
4. dom it rings That the Lamb is King of kings.
5. tent for - giv'n, How we, too, may en - ter heav'n.
6. guilt a - way, That we all may sing for joy:

1-6. Al - le - lu - ia! Al - le - lu - ia!

1-6. Al - le - lu - ia! Al - le - lu - ia!

Text: 77 77 with alleluias; Michael Weisse, ca. 1480–1534; tr. by Catherine Winkworth, 1827–1878, alt.
Music: CHRIST IST ERSTANDEN; German Melody, 12th cent.

443

NOW THE GREEN BLADE RISES

1. Now the green blade ris - es from the bur-ied grain,
2. In the grave they laid him, love by ha-tred slain,
3. Forth he came at Eas - ter, like the ris - en grain,
4. When our hearts are win - try, griev-ing, or in pain,

1. Wheat that in dark earth man - y days has lain;
2. Think - ing that he would nev - er wake a - gain,
3. He that for three days in the grave had lain;
4. Your touch can call us back to life a - gain,

1. Love lives a - gain, that with the dead has been:
2. Laid in the earth like grain that sleeps un - seen:
3. Raised from the dead, my liv - ing Lord is seen:
4. Fields of our hearts that dead and bare have been:

1-4. Love is come a - gain like wheat a - ris - ing green.

Text: 11 10 11 10; John Macleod Campbell Crum, 1872–1958, alt.; *The Oxford Book of Carols*, 1928,
© 1964, Oxford University Press. All rights reserved. Used with permission.
Music: NOËL NOUVELET; Trad. French Melody.

444

THIS IS THE DAY

Refrain: 1st time: Cantor, All repeat; thereafter: All

This is the day! This is the day! This
is the day that the Lord has made! Let us re-joice!

(to Verses)

Let us re-joice! Let us re-joice and be glad!

Final time only

Let us re-joice and be glad!

Verses: Cantor

1. This is the day that the Lord has made.
Let us rejoice and be glad.

2. Give thanks to the Lord!
Our God is good.
Whose love endures forever.
Let all the children of Israel say:
God's love endures forever.

3. The right hand of God has struck with power.
The right hand of God is exalted.
I shall not die, but I shall live
and proclaim the works of the Lord!

4. The stone which the builders rejected
has become the foundation of our house!
By the Lord has this been done.
How wonderful to behold.

THIS JOYFUL EASTERTIDE 445

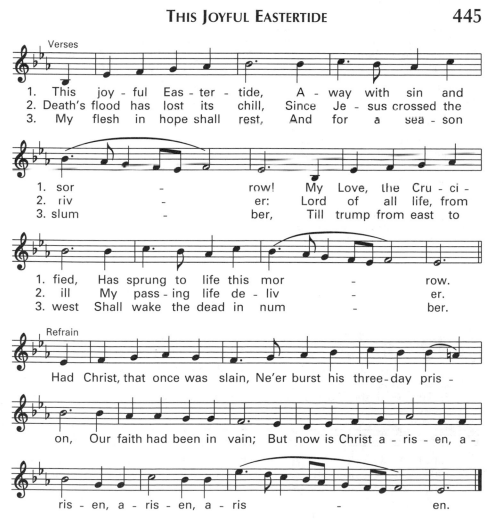

Verses

1. This joy-ful Eas-ter-tide, A-way with sin and sor - row! My Love, the Cru-ci-fied, Has sprung to life this mor - row.

2. Death's flood has lost its chill, Since Jesus crossed the riv - er: Lord of all life, from ill My pass-ing life de-liv - er.

3. My flesh in hope shall rest, And for a sea-son slum - ber, Till trump from east to west Shall wake the dead in num - ber.

Refrain

Had Christ, that once was slain, Ne'er burst his three-day pris-on, Our faith had been in vain; But now is Christ a-ris-en, a-ris-en, a-ris-en, a-ris - en.

Text: 67 67 with refrain; George R. Woodward, 1848–1934.
Music: VREUCHTEN; *Oudaen's David's Psalmen,* 1685, alt.

O GOD, YOU FLAMED ON SINAI'S HEIGHT

1. O God, you flamed on Si - nai's height, In glo - ry
2. O God, in cloud you shad - owed o'er The Mo - ther
3. O God, you burned in flam - ing star To guide the
4. O God, in cloud of fire you claimed As your own
5. On Cal - va - ry the cloud grew cold, And glo - ry
6. O God, up - on that fi - nal height You came in

1. robed, in cloud and light; In thun - der that com -
2. who con - ceived and bore A Child, born un - der
3. ma - gi from a - far; They came and wor - shipped
4. Son the one you named To light with glo - ry
5. fled the Tem - ple's hold With gar - ments rent; the
6. cloud to hide from sight In glo - ry's fire the

1. mand - ed awe You carved in stone the liv - ing Law.
2. fi - ery skies Whose glo - ry daz - zled shep - herd's eyes.
3. glo - ry hid In fra - gile flesh, as they were bid.
4. Ta - bor's hill, Both Law and proph - et to ful - fill.
5. storm burned black A - bove the cross where Life hung slack.
6. liv - ing Son: O God, we praise you, Three in One.

Text: LM; Genevieve Glen, OSB, b. 1945, © 1998, 2000, The Benedictine Nuns of the Abbey of St. Walburga.
  Published by OCP Publications. All rights reserved.
Music: CANONBURY; Robert Schumann, 1810–1856.

447

JESUS IS RISEN

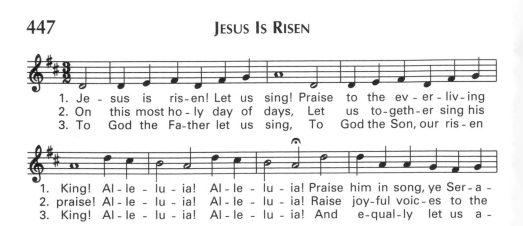

1. Je - sus is ris - en! Let us sing! Praise to the ev - er - liv - ing
2. On this most ho - ly day of days, Let us to - geth - er sing his
3. To God the Fa - ther let us sing, To God the Son, our ris - en

1. King! Al - le - lu - ia! Al - le - lu - ia! Praise him in song, ye Ser - a -
2. praise! Al - le - lu - ia! Al - le - lu - ia! Raise joy - ful voic - es to the
3. King! Al - le - lu - ia! Al - le - lu - ia! And e - qual - ly let us a -

1. phim! Praise him with joy, ye Cher-u - bim!)
2. sky! Sing out, ye heav-ens, in re - ply: } Al - le - lu - ia! Al - le -
3. dore The Ho - ly Spir - it ev - er - more!)

1-3. lu - ia! Al - le - lu - ia! Al - le - lu - ia! Al - le - lu - ia!

Text: LM with alleluias; Compilers, 1978.
Music: LASST UNS ERFREUEN; *Auserlesene Catholische Geistliche Kirchengesänge*, Cologne, 1623.

SING WE TRIUMPHANT HYMNS OF PRAISE 448

1. Sing we triumphant hymns of praise
To greet our Lord these festive days,
Alleluia, alleluia!
Who by a road before untrod
Ascended to the throne of God,
Alleluia, alleluia, alleluia,
alleluia, alleluia!

2. In wond'ring awe his faithful band
Upon the Mount of Olives stand.
Alleluia, alleluia!
And with the Virgin Mother see
Their Lord ascend in majesty.
Alleluia, alleluia, alleluia,
alleluia, alleluia!

3. O risen Christ, ascended Lord,
All praise to you let earth accord,
Alleluia, alleluia!
Who are, while endless ages run,
With Father and with Spirit, One.
Alleluia, alleluia, alleluia,
alleluia, alleluia!

4. To God the Father let us sing,
To God the Son, our risen King,
Alleluia, alleluia!
And equally let us adore
The Holy Spirit evermore,
Alleluia, alleluia, alleluia,
alleluia, alleluia!

Text: LM with alleluias; St. Bede the Venerable, 673–735; verses 1, 2, 4, tr. by John D. Chambers, 1805–1893;
verse 3, tr. by Benjamin Webb, 1819–1885.
Music: LASST UNS ERFREUEN; *Auserlesene Catholische Geistliche Kirchengesänge*, Cologne, 1623.

CREATOR SPIRIT, BY WHOSE AID 449

1. Creator Spirit, by whose aid
The world's foundations first were laid!
Alleluia! Alleluia!
Give us thyself that we may see
The Father and the Son by thee.
Alleluia! Alleluia! Alleluia!
Alleluia! Alleluia!

2. O Source of uncreated light,
The Father's promised Paraclete;
Alleluia! Alleluia!

Thrice holy Font, Thrice holy Fire,
Our hearts with heav'nly love inspire.
Alleluia! Alleluia! Alleluia!
Alleluia! Alleluia!

3. All adoration ever be,
Eternal Paraclete to thee.
Alleluia! Alleluia!
From sin and sorrow set us free
That we may live eternally.
Alleluia! Alleluia! Alleluia!
Alleluia! Alleluia!

Text: LM with alleluias; *Veni, Creator Spiritus*; attr. to Rabanus Maurus, 776–856;
para. by John Dryden, 1631–1700; alt. Compilers, 1977.
Music: LASST UNS ERFREUEN; *Auserlesene Catholische Geistliche Kirchengesänge*, Cologne, 1623.

450   HAIL THEE, FESTIVAL DAY

Refrain

Hail thee, fes-ti-val day! Blest day to be hal-lowed for ev-er;

Day when our Lord was raised, Break-ing the king-dom of death.

Verses 1, 3, 5

Easter   1. All the fair beau-ty of earth   From
Ascension   3. He who was nailed to the cross   Is
Pentecost   5. Bright in the like-ness of fire,   On

1. death of the win-ter a-ris-ing! Ev-'ry good
3. Rul-er and Lord of all peo-ple. All things cre-
5. those who a-wait his ap-pear-ing, He whom the

to Refrain

1. gift of the year Now with its Mas-ter re-turns:
3. a-ted on earth Sing to the glo-ry of God:
5. Lord had fore-told, Sud-den-ly, swift-ly de-scends:

Verses 2, 4, 6

Easter   2. Rise from the grave now, O Lord, The Au-thor of
Ascension   4. Dai-ly the love-li-ness grows, A-dorned with the
Pentecost   6. Forth from the Fa-ther he comes With sev-en-fold

2. life and cre-a-tion. Tread-ing the path-way of
4. glo-ry of blos-som; Heav-en her gates un-
6. mys-ti-cal of-f'ring, Pour-ing on all hu-man

to Refrain

2. death, New life you give to us all:
4. bars, Fling-ing her in-crease of light:
6. souls In-fi-nite rich-es of God:

Text: 79 77 with refrain; Venantius Honorius Fortunatus, ca. 530–609; tr. composite.
Music: SALVE FESTA DIES; Ralph Vaughan Williams, 1872–1958.

HAIL THE DAY THAT SEES HIM RISE

1. Hail the day that sees him rise
2. There for him high tri-umph waits:
3. See! the heav'n its Lord re-ceives,
4. See! he lifts his hands a-bove.
5. Lord, though part-ed from our sight
6. There with you we shall re-main,

Al - le - lu - ia!

1. To his throne be-yond the skies,
2. Lift your heads, e-ter-nal gates,
3. Yet he loves the earth he leaves;
4. See! he shows the wounds of love.
5. Far be-yond the star-ry height,
6. Share the glo-ry of your reign,

Al - le - lu - ia!

1. Christ, the Lamb for sin-ners giv'n,
2. He has con-quered death and sin,
3. Though re-turn-ing to his throne,
4. Hark! his gra-cious lips be-stow,
5. Lift our hearts that we may rise
6. There your face un-cloud-ed view,

Al - le - lu - ia!

1. En-ters now the high-est heav'n!
2. Take the King of glo-ry in.
3. Still he calls the world his own.
4. Bless-ings on his church be-low.
5. One with you be-yond the skies:
6. Find our heav'n of heav'ns in you.

Al - le - lu - ia!

Text: 77 77 with alleluias; Charles Wesley, 1707–1788, and Thomas Cotterill, 1779–1823, alt.
Music: LLANFAIR; Robert Williams, 1781–1821.

452 LORD, YOU GIVE THE GREAT COMMISSION

1. Lord, you give the great com-mis-sion: "Heal the sick and
2. Lord, you call us to your ser-vice: "In my name bap-
3. Lord, you make the com-mon ho-ly: "This my bod-y,
4. Lord, you show us love's true mea-sure: "Fa-ther, what they
5. Lord, you bless with words as-sur-ing: "I am with you

1. preach the word." Lest the church ne-glect its mis-sion
2. tize and teach." That the world may trust your prom-ise,
3. this my blood." Let us all, for earth's true glo-ry,
4. do, for-give." Yet we hoard as pri-vate trea-sure
5. to the end." Faith and hope and love re-stor-ing,

1. And the gos-pel go un-heard, Help us wit-ness to your
2. Life a-bun-dant meant for each, Give us all new fer-vor,
3. Dai-ly lift life heav-en-ward, Ask-ing that the world a-
4. All that you so free-ly give. May your care and mer-cy
5. May we serve as you in-tend And, a-mid the cares that

1. pur-pose With re-newed in-teg-ri-ty:
2. draw us Clos-er in com-mu-ni-ty:
3. round us Share your chil-dren's lib-er-ty: With the Spir-it's
4. lead us To a just so-ci-e-ty:
5. claim us, Hold in mind e-ter-ni-ty:

1-5. gifts em-pow'r us For the work of min-is-try.

Text: 87 87 D; Jeffery Rowthorn, b. 1934, © 1978, Hope Publishing Co. All rights reserved. Used with permission.
Music: ABBOT'S LEIGH; Cyril Vincent Taylor, 1907–1991, © 1942, renewed 1970, Hope Publishing Co.
All rights reserved. Used with permission.

453 VENI, SANCTE SPIRITUS

Ostinato Refrain: All

Ve-ni Sanc-te Spi-ri-tus; Ve-ni Sanc-te Spi-ri-tus;

Ve-ni, ve-ni Sanc-te Spi-ri-tus; Ve-ni Sanc-te Spi-ri-tus.

Verses: Cantor

1. Holy Spirit, Lord of Light,
   radiance give from celestial height.
   Come, O Spirit of the poor,
   come now with treasures that endure:
   Light of all who live.

2. You of all consolers the best.
   You the soul's delightful guest;
   refreshing peace bestow.
   You in toil my comfort sweet.
   You coolness in the heat.
   You my solace in time of woe.

3. Light immortal, light divine;
   fire of love our hearts refine,
   our inmost being fill.

Take your grace away
and nothing pure in us will stay,
all our good is turned to ill.

4. Heal our wounds, our strength renew,
   on our dryness pour your dew;
   wash guilt away,
   bend the stubborn heart,
   melt the frozen,
   warm the chill
   and guide the steps that go astray.

5. Seven-fold gifts on us be pleased to pour,
   who you confess and you adore;
   bring us your comfort when we die;
   give us life with you on high;
   give us joys, give us joys that never end.

Text: Latin, 12th cent.; verses based on the Pentecost Sequence, *Veni, Sancte Spiritus*; adapt. by Christopher Walker, b. 1947.
Music: Christopher Walker.
Text and music © 1981, 1982, Christopher Walker. Published by OCP Publications. All rights reserved.

By the Waking of Our Hearts   454

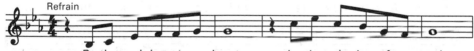

Refrain

By the wak-ing of our hearts,   by the stir-ring of our souls,

may the Spir-it of God a-bide and bring us to-geth-er in Christ.

Verses

1. Come, O Spir - it, from a - bove, come from your ce - les - tial heights.
2. Come, O Sav - ior of the poor, come, O source of gifts en - sured.
3. In our la - bor, rest most sweet; grate - ful cool-ness in the heat.
4. Bend the stub-born heart and will, melt the fro - zen, warm the chill.
5. Grant us vir - tue's sure re - ward, may your gra-cious love be sent.

to Refrain

1. Come with your bless - ed light so ____ ra - diant bright.
2. Come with your gen - tle hope, so ____ won-drous and pure.
3. Con - sole our rest - less lives, by your com - fort, we seek.
4. Come guide our search-ing minds toward your prom - ise ful - filled.
5. Come with your peace and joy that shall nev - er end.

Text: Verses based on the Pentecost Sequence, *Veni, Sancte Spiritus*; Ricky Manalo, CSP, b. 1965.
Music: Ricky Manalo, CSP.
Text and music © 1997, Ricky Manalo, CSP. Published by OCP Publications. All rights reserved.

455

COME, O HOLY SPIRIT, COME/
VENI SANCTE SPIRITUS

1. Come, O Ho - ly Spir - it, come! And from your ce -
2. Come, O Fa - ther of the poor! Come, __ source of
1. Ve - ni San - cte Spí - ri - tus, Et e - mít - te
2. Ve - ni pa - ter páu - pe - rum, Ve - ni da - tor

1. les - tial home Shed a ray of light di - vine!
2. all our store! Come, with - in our bos - oms shine!
1. caé - li - tus Lu - cis tu - ae rá - di - um.
2. mú - ne - rum, Ve - ni lu - men cór - di - um.

3. You, of com - fort - ers the best; You, the soul's most
4. In our la - bor, rest most sweet; Grate - ful cool - ness
3. Con - so - lá - tor ó - pti - me, Dul - cis ho - spes
4. In la - bó - re ré - qui - es, In ae - stu tem -

3. wel - come guest; Sweet re - fresh - ment here be - low;
4. in the heat; Sol - ace in the midst of woe.
3. á - ni - mae, Dul - ce re - fri - gé - ri - um.
4. pé - ri - es, In fle - tu so - lá - ti - um.

5. O most bless - ed Light di - vine, Shine with - in
6. Where you are not, we have naught, Noth - ing good
5. O lux be - a - tís - si - ma, Re - ple cor -
6. Si - ne tu - o nú - mi - ne, Ni - hil est

5. these hearts of yours, And our in - most be - ing fill!
6. in deed or thought, Noth - ing free from taint of ill.
5. dis ín - ti - ma Tu - ó - rum fi - dé - li - um.
6. in hó - mi - ne, Ni - hil est in - nó - xi - um.

7. Heal our wounds, our strength re - new; On our dry - ness
8. Bend the stub - born heart and will; Melt the fro - zen,
7. La - va quod est sór - di - dum, Ri - ga quod est
8. Fle - cte quod est rí - gi - dum, Fo - ve quod est

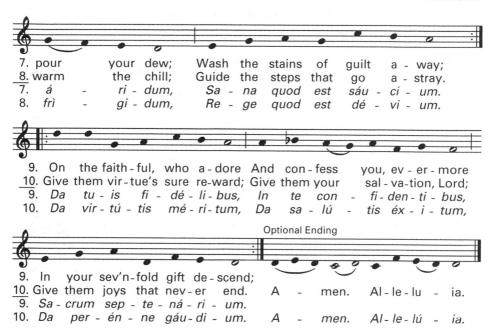

7. pour your dew; Wash the stains of guilt a - way;
8. warm the chill; Guide the steps that go a - stray.
7. á - ri - dum, Sa - na quod est sáu - ci - um.
8. frì - gi - dum, Re - ge quod est dé - vi - um.

9. On the faith - ful, who a - dore And con - fess you, ev - er - more
10. Give them vir - tue's sure re - ward; Give them your sal - va - tion, Lord;
9. Da tu - is fi - dé - li - bus, In te con - fi - den - ti - bus,
10. Da vir - tú - tis mé - ri - tum, Da sa - lú - tis éx - i - tum,

Optional Ending

9. In your sev'n-fold gift de - scend;
10. Give them joys that nev - er end. A - men. Al - le - lu - ia.
9. Sa - crum sep - te - ná - ri - um.
10. Da per - én - ne gáu - di - um. A - men. Al - le - lú - ia.

Text: Poetic Sequence for Pentecost, *Veni, Sancte Spiritus*; fr. *The Roman Missal*, © 1964, National Catholic
Welfare Conference. All rights reserved. Administered by CCD. Used with permission.
Music: Chant, Mode I.

O SPIRIT OF THE LIVING LORD 456

1. O Spir - it of the liv - ing Lord, You
2. O Spir - it, from Christ's heart thrust through, You
3. O Spir - it, burn - ing in us still, You
4. O three - fold God, this fes - tive day Send

1. blow a - cross the wait - ing world; You cleanse and heal earth's
2. wash parched earth with wel - come dew; You wake us in the
3. melt the fro - zen, warm the chill; You cool us in the
4. forth your Spir - it as we pray. Be - fore you the re -

1. wound - ed face With balm poured from the cross of grace.
2. bur - ied seed, You give new bread, the starved to feed.
3. day's long heat, You send, at night - fall, rest most sweet.
4. deemed world bends; You are the joy that nev - er ends.

Text: LM; Genevieve Glen, OSB, b. 1945, © 1998, 2001, The Benedictine Nuns of the Abbey of St. Walburga.
Published by OCP Publications. All rights reserved.
Music: WINCHESTER NEW; *Musicalisches Hand-Buch*, Hamburg, 1690; adapt. by William H. Havergal, 1793–1870.

457

VENI, CREATOR SPIRITUS/
CREATOR SPIRIT, LORD OF GRACE

1. Ve - ni Cre - á - tor Spí - ri - tus, Men - tes tu - ó -
2. Qui dí - ce - ris Pa - rá - cli - tus, ¹Do - num De - i
3. Tu se - pti - fór - mis mú - ne - re, ²De - xtrae De - i
4. Ac - cén - de lu - men sén - si - bus, In - fun - de a - mó -

1. *Cre - a - tor Spir - it, Lord of grace, Come make in us*
2. *O Spir - it, hear your peo - ple's cry! Come down, O Gift*
3. *As once on Christ the Ser - vant's head The oil of sev'n-*
4. *Of ev - 'ry gift the liv - ing source, Of might - y deeds*

1. rum ví - si - ta, Im - ple - su - pér - na grá - ti -
2. al - tís - si - mi, Fons vi - vus, i - gnis, cá - ri -
3. tu dí - gi - tus, Tu ri - te pro - mís - sum Pa -
4. rem cór - di - bus, In - fír - ma nó - stri cór - po -

1. *your dwell - ing place! O pur - est Light in dark - ness*
2. *of God most high! De - scend in peace, O heav'n - ly*
3. *fold grace you shed, So now a - noint from love's deep*
4. *the un - seen force, The Fa - ther sends his Prom - ised*

1. a Quae tu cre - á - sti pé - cto - ra.
2. tas, Et spi - ri - tá - lis ún - cti - o.
3. tris, Ser - mó - ne di - tans gút - tu - ra.
4. ris Vir - tú - te fir - mans pér - pe - ti. (A - men.)

1. *shine; Fill love - less hearts, O Love di - vine!*
2. *Dove; Come, fount of life; come flame of love!*
3. *springs Your cho - sen proph - ets, priests, and kings!*
4. *One To speak for all who serve his Son! (A - men.)*

5. Hostem repéllas lóngius
   Pacémque dones prótinus;
   Ductóre sic te práevio
   Vitémus omne nóxium.

6. Per te sciámus da Patrem,
   Noscámus atque Fílium,
   ³Te utriúsque Spíritum
   Credámus omni témpore.

⁴7. Deo Patri sit glória,
   Et Fílio, quia mórtuis
   Surréxit, ac Paráclito,
   In saeculórum sáecula. Amen.

5. *Keep far all those who wish us ill!*
   O Dove of peace, be with us still!
   In every danger at our side,
   O Friend, befriend us; be our guide!

6. *Reveal to us the Father's love,*
   Reveal his Son, who reigns above!
   To truth, O Truth, make all souls true;
   In love, O Love, make all things new!

7. *To God the Father glory be,*
   And to the Son from death set free;
   And to the Holy Spirit raise
   Our praise to God for endless days. Amen.

Note: The Latin text above is reproduced from the *Graduale Romanum*, 1974. Textual variants are noted below:
1) formerly *Altíssimi donum Dei,*
2) formerly *Dígitus patérnae déxterae,*
3) formerly *Teque utriúsque Spíritum.*
4) Verse 7 does not appear in the *Graduale Romanum*, 1974.

Text: LM; *Veni, Creator Spiritus*; attr. to Rabanus Maurus, 776–856. *Graduale Romanum*, 1974. Verses 1–6, tr. by
James D. Quinn, SJ, b. 1919, © James D. Quinn, SJ. All rights reserved. Used with permission of Selah Publishing Co., Inc.,
North American agent. Verse 7, tr. by Glenn CJ Byer, b. 1961, © 2002, OCP Publications. All rights reserved.
Music: VENI CREATOR SPIRITUS; Chant, Mode VIII.

COME, HOLY GHOST

1. Come, Ho - ly Ghost, Cre - a - tor blest,
2. O Com - fort - er, to thee we cry,
3. To ev - 'ry sense thy light im - part
4. O grant that we through thee may come
5. Praise be to thee, Fa - ther and Son

1. And in our hearts take up thy rest;
2. Thou heav'n - ly gift of God most high;
3. And shed thy love in ev - 'ry heart.
4. To know the Fa - ther and the Son,
5. And Ho - ly Spir - it, with them one;

1. Come with thy grace and heav'n - ly aid
2. Thou font of life, and fire of love,
3. To our weak flesh, thy strength sup - ply;
4. And hold with firm, un - chang - ing faith,
5. And may the Son on us be - stow

1. To fill the hearts which thou hast made,
2. And sweet a - noint - ing from a - bove,
3. Un - fail - ing cour - age from on high,
4. That thou art Spir - it of them both,
5. The gifts that from the Spir - it flow,

1. To fill the hearts which thou hast made.
2. And sweet a - noint - ing from a - bove.
3. Un - fail - ing cour - age from on high.
4. That thou art Spir - it of them both.
5. The gifts that from the Spir - it flow.

Text: LM with repeat; *Veni, Creator Spiritus;* attr. to Rabanus Maurus, 776–856; tr. by Edward Caswall, 1814–1878, alt.
Music: LAMBILLOTTE; Louis Lambillotte, SJ, 1796–1855.

459   COME, O HOLY SPIRIT

1. Come, O Ho-ly Spir-it, come! And from your ce-
2. You, of com-fort-ers the best; You, the soul's most
3. O most bless-ed Light di-vine, May that Light with-
4. Heal our wounds, our strength re-new; On our dry-ness
5. On the faith-ful who a-dore And con-fess you

1. les-tial home Shed a ray of light di-vine!
2. wel-come guest; Sweet re-fresh-ment here be-low;
3. in us shine, And our in-most be-ing fill!
4. pour your dew; Wash the stains of guilt a-way:
5. ev-er more, In your sev'n-fold gift de-scend;

1. Come, O Ho-ly Spir-it, come! Come, O Fa-ther of the
2. Come, O Ho-ly Spir-it, come! In our la-bor, rest most
3. Come, O Ho-ly Spir-it, come! In your ab-sence, we have
4. Come, O Ho-ly Spir-it, come! Bend the stub-born heart and
5. Come, O Ho-ly Spir-it, come! Give them vir-tue's sure re-

1. poor! Come, O Source of all our store! Come, with-
2. sweet; Grate-ful cool-ness in the heat; Sol-ace
3. naught, Noth-ing good in deed or thought, Noth-ing
4. will; Melt the fro-zen, warm the chill; Guide the
5. ward; Give them your sal-va-tion, Lord; Give them

1. in our bos-oms shine! Come, O Ho-ly Spir-it, come!
2. in the midst of woe. Come, O Ho-ly Spir-it, come!
3. free from taint of ill. Come, O Ho-ly Spir-it, come!
4. steps that go a-stray. Come, O Ho-ly Spir-it, come!
5. joys that nev-er end. Come, O Ho-ly Spir-it, come!

Text: 77 77 D; fr. the Pentecost Sequence, *Veni, Sancte Spiritus*, alt.; Owen Alstott, b. 1947,
   © 1980, OCP Publications. All rights reserved.
Music: HYMN TO JOY; Ludwig van Beethoven, 1770–1827; adapt. by Edward Hodges, 1796–1867.

460   SONG OF THE HOLY SPIRIT

1. The Spir-it of the Lord has brought new life to earth,
2. Bap-tized in God's own breath, made pure by fire and oil,
3. The Spir-it finds a home in ev-'ry hu-man breast.

1. Whose breath, as seed out-poured, now calls all things to birth.
2. Our hope of life in death our strength in thirst and toil.
3. That God's own cho - sen Son may guide us to our rest,

1. God's Spir - it now re - vives, our hearts of stone it thaws.
2. Who knows from where it flows, this gen - tle light so warm,
3. May save us from the storm, and raise us from the dust.

1. Re - build-ing bro-ken lives, our shat-tered world re - stores.
2. Which deep with - in us glows, to heal and make us one.
3. Cre - a - tor Spir-it come, com - plete your work in us.

Text: 12 12 12 12; Huub Oosterhuis, b. 1933; tr. by Tony Barr, b. 1945, © 1967, Gooi en Sticht, bv., Baarn, The Netherlands.
All rights reserved. Exclusive agent for English-language countries: OCP Publications.
Music: GELUKKIG IS HET LAND; Trad. Dutch Melody.

COME DOWN, O LOVE DIVINE 461

1. Come down, O Love di - vine, Seek thou this soul of
2. O let it free - ly burn, Till earth - ly pas - sions
3. And so the yearn - ing strong, With which the soul will

1. mine, And vis - it it with thine own ar - dor glow - ing;
2. turn To dust and ash - es in its heat con - sum - ing;
3. long, Shall far out-pass the pow'r of hu - man tell - ing;

1. O Com -fort - er, draw near, With - in my heart ap -
2. And let thy glo - rious light Shine ev - er on my
3. For none can guess its grace, Till we be - come the

1. pear, And kin - dle it, thy ho - ly flame be - stow - ing;
2. sight, And clothe me round, the while my path il - lum - ing.
3. place Where - in the Ho - ly Spir - it makes a dwell - ing.

Text: 66 11 D; Bianco da Siena, d. 1434; tr. by Richard F. Littledale, 1833–1890.
Music: DOWN AMPNEY; Ralph Vaughan Williams, 1872–1958.

462
SEND US YOUR SPIRIT

1. Send us your spir - it, O Lord. Eve - ning en - folds us and
2. Hold us with mer - cy, O Lord. Sor - row has spo - ken, has
3. Teach us your wis - dom, O Lord. Shad - ows have cloud - ed, have
4. Send us good sum - mer, O Lord. Win - ters have chilled us, and

1. holds us too near. Wake the morn - ing light. Make our liv - ing
2. bro - ken our hearts. Clothe us in your care. Be the life we
3. crowd - ed our sight. Give us hearts that see. Set our lov - ing
4. stilled us too long. Give us love's own fire. Be our true de-

1. bright. Shine on our dark - ness, O Lord.
2. bear. Feed us and fill us, O Lord.
3. free. Hear us and help us, O Lord.
4. sire. Send us your spir - it, O Lord.

Text: Inspired by *Veni, Sancte Spiritus*; Dan Schutte, b. 1947.
Music: Dan Schutte.
Text and music © 1985, Daniel L. Schutte and New Dawn Music. Published by OCP Publications. All rights reserved.

463
ENVÍA TU ESPÍRITU

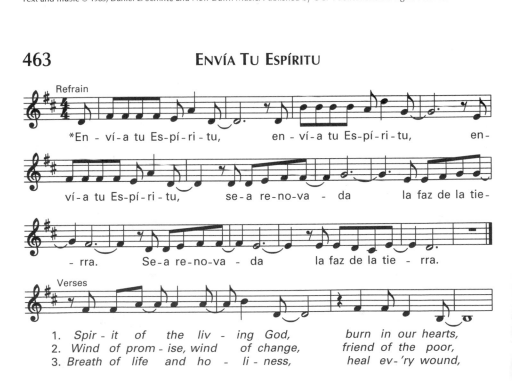

*En - ví - a tu Es - pí - ri - tu, en - ví - a tu Es - pí - ri - tu, en -
ví - a tu Es - pí - ri - tu, se - a re - no - va - da la faz de la tie -
- rra. Se - a re - no - va - da la faz de la tie - rra.

Verses

1. *Spir - it of the liv - ing God,* burn in our hearts,
2. *Wind of prom - ise, wind of change,* friend of the poor,
3. *Breath of life and ho - li - ness,* heal ev - 'ry wound,

to Refrain

1. *and make us a peo - ple of hope and com-pas - sion.*
2. *em - pow- er your peo - ple to make peace and jus - tice.*
3. *and lead us be-yond ev-'ry sin that di-vides us.*

*Send out your spirit, and renew the face of the earth.

Text: Psalm 104:30 and *Veni, Sancte Spiritus*; Latin, 12th cent.; adapt. by Bob Hurd, b. 1950.
Music: Bob Hurd.
Text and music © 1988, Bob Hurd. Published by OCP Publications. All rights reserved.

COME, HOLY SPIRIT 464

Refrain

Come, Ho-ly Spir-it, come fill us with your fire, Al-le-lu - ia!

Verses

1. Ho - ly Spir - it, Lord of light, from the clear cel -
2. Of con - sol - ers you are best, you the soul's de -
3. Light im - mor - tal, light most pure, vis - it now these
4. Heal our wounds, our strength re - new; on our dry - ness
5. Now on those who ev - er - more wor - ship and with

1. es - tial height, your pure beam - ing ra - diance give.
2. light - ful guest, give re - fresh - ing peace to grow.
3. hearts of yours, and our in - most be - ing fill.
4. pour your dew; wash the stains of guilt a - way.
5. faith a - dore, in your sev'n - fold gifts de - scend.

1. Come, O Spir - it of the poor, come with trea - sures
2. You, in toil, are com - fort sweet; pleas - ant cool - ness
3. If you take your grace a - way, noth - ing pure in
4. Bend the stub - born heart and will; melt the fro - zen,
5. Give them com - fort when they die; give them life with

to Refrain

1. that en - dure; come, O light of all who live.
2. in the heat, so - lace in the midst of woe.
3. us will stay; all our good is turned to ill.
4. warm the chill; guide the steps that go a - stray.
5. you on high; give them joys that nev - er end.

Text: Based on the Pentecost Sequence, *Veni, Sancte Spiritus*; Christopher Walker, b. 1947.
Music: Christopher Walker.
Text and music © 1999, Christopher Walker. Published by OCP Publications. All rights reserved.

SEND OUT YOUR SPIRIT

Refrain

Lord, send out your Spir - it; re-new the face of the earth.

Lord, send out your Spir - it; re-new the face of the earth.

Verses

1. You set the earth on its foun-da-tion
2. You sprang up springs run-ning down to the
3. From sea to shore how your won-ders are
4. You reign down rains on the earth all be-
5. He comes with bright wings a - wash-ing the

1. firm, not to be moved ___ in all its days;
2. streams, wind-ing their ways through moun-tains and hills.
3. seen, care-ful-ly planned in wis-dom and love.
4. low; or-chards bear fruit, ___ fields yield your grain.
5. world; all is made new in wa-ter and fire.

1. clothed it with o - ceans and robed it in light:
2. Birds dwell in tree - tops where wa - ters run,
3. All of your world is a - bun - dant with life:
4. Earth, brown and fur - rowed, bears fruit in your gaze,
5. Morn - ing a - ris - es a - new in the sky:

to Refrain
2

1. O bless the Lord, all you his works.
2. send - ing their song in - to the world.
3. O my ___ soul, bless you the Lord.
4. giv - ing us bread; giv - ing us life.
5. God re - cre - ates in a new day.

All Praise and Glad Thanksgiving

1. All praise and glad thanks-giv-ing To God the Fa-ther
2. Christ Je-sus, we a-dore you, The Son of God most
3. O Ho-ly Spir-it, bless-ing To You who reign a-

1. be: The Font of all things liv-ing, Who reigns e-
2. high; With thanks we sing be-fore you, Who came for
3. bove! Your won-drous gifts con-fess-ing, The Church sings

1. ter-nal-ly.
2. us to die.   Praise to God for-ev-er be,
3. forth your love!

1-3. One in life, in Per-sons three: Might-y God,

1-3. sav-ing God, God e-ter-nal Trin-i-ty!

Text. 76 /6 77 67; based on *Trisagion*, Greek, 5th cent.; Melvin Farrell, SS, 1930–1986;
© 1976, OCP Publications. All rights reserved.
Music: GOTT VATER SEI GEPRIESEN; *Limburg Gesangbuch*, 1838.

All Hail, Adored Trinity

1. All hail, a-dor-ed Trin-i-ty! All hail, e-
2. Three per-sons praise we ev-er-more, One on-ly
3. O Trin-i-ty! O U-ni-ty! Be pres-ent

1. ter-nal U-ni-ty! O God the Fa-ther,
2. God our hearts a-dore: In thy sure mer-cy,
3. as we wor-ship thee; And with the songs that

1. God the Son, And God the Spir-it, ev-er One.
2. ev-er kind, May we your strong pro-tec-tion find.
3. an-gels sing U-nite the hymns of praise we bring.

Text: LM; *Ave colenda Trinitas*, ca. 11th cent.; tr. by John D. Chambers, 1805–1893, alt.
Music: OLD HUNDREDTH; *Genevan Psalter*, 1551; attr. to Louis Bourgeois, ca. 1510–1561, alt.

468

ON THIS DAY, THE FIRST OF DAYS

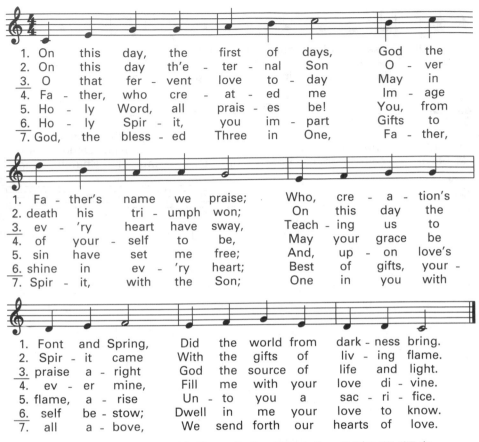

1. On this day, the first of days, God the
2. On this day th'e - ter - nal Son O - ver
3. O that fer - vent love to - day May in
4. Fa - ther, who cre - at - ed me Im - age
5. Ho - ly Word, all prais - es be! You, from
6. Ho - ly Spir - it, you im - part Gifts to
7. God, the bless - ed Three in One, Fa - ther,

1. Fa - ther's name we praise; Who, cre - a - tion's
2. death his tri - umph won; On this day the
3. ev - 'ry heart have sway, Teach - ing us to
4. of your - self to be, May your grace be
5. sin have set me free; And, up - on love's
6. shine in ev - 'ry heart; Best of gifts, your -
7. Spir - it, with the Son; One in you with

1. Font and Spring, Did the world from dark - ness bring.
2. Spir - it came With the gifts of liv - ing flame.
3. praise a - right God the source of life and light.
4. ev - er mine, Fill me with your love di - vine.
5. flame, a - rise Un - to you a sac - ri - fice.
6. self be - stow; Dwell in me your love to know.
7. all a - bove, We send forth our hearts of love.

Text: 77 77; *Die parente temporum; Breviary of the Diocese of Le Mans,* 1748; tr. by Henry W. Baker, 1821–1877, alt.;
   Hymns Ancient and Modern, 1861.
Music: LÜBECK; Freylinghausen's *Geistreiches Gesangbuch,* 1704; adapt. by William H. Havergal, 1793–1870.

469

HOLY, HOLY, HOLY

1. Ho - ly, Ho - ly, Ho - ly! Lord ____ God Al - might - y!
2. Ho - ly, Ho - ly, Ho - ly! All the saints a - dore thee,
3. Ho - ly, Ho - ly, Ho - ly! Though the dark-ness hide thee,
4. Ho - ly, Ho - ly, Ho - ly! Lord ____ God Al - might - y!

1. Ear - ly in the morn - ing our song shall rise to thee:
2. Cast - ing down their gold - en crowns a - round the glass - y sea;
3. Though the eye made blind by sin thy glo - ry may not see,
4. All thy works shall praise thy Name, in earth, and sky, and sea;

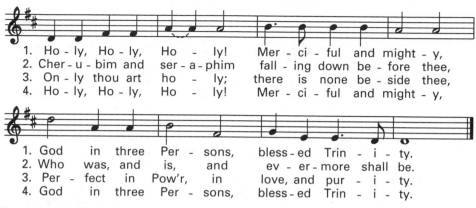

1. Ho - ly, Ho - ly, Ho - ly! Mer - ci - ful and might - y,
2. Cher - u - bim and ser - a - phim fall - ing down be - fore thee,
3. On - ly thou art ho - ly; there is none be - side thee,
4. Ho - ly, Ho - ly, Ho - ly! Mer - ci - ful and might - y,

1. God in three Per - sons, bless - ed Trin - i - ty.
2. Who was, and is, and ev - er - more shall be.
3. Per - fect in Pow'r, in love, and pur - i - ty.
4. God in three Per - sons, bless - ed Trin - i - ty.

Text: 11 12 12 10; Reginald Heber, 1783–1826, alt.
Music: NICAEA; John B. Dykes, 1823–1976.

HOW WONDERFUL THE THREE-IN-ONE 470

1. How won - der - ful the Three - in - One,
2. Be - fore the flow of dawn and dark,
3. The Lov - er's own Be - lov'd, in time,
4. Their E - qual Friend all life sus - tains
5. How won - der - ful the Liv - ing God:

1. Whose en - er - gies of danc - ing light
2. Cre - a - tion's Lov - er dreamed of earth,
3. Be - tween a cra - dle and a cross,
4. With green - ing pow'r and lov - ing care,
5. Di - vine Be - lov'd Em - pow'r - ing Friend,

1. Are un - di - vid - ed, pure and good,
2. And with a car - ing deep and wise,
3. At home in flesh, gave love and life
4. And calls us, born a - gain by grace,
5. E - ter - nal Lov - er, Three - in - One,

1. Com - mun - ing love in shared de - light.
2. All things con - ceived and brought to birth.
3. To heal our bro - ken - ness and loss.
4. In Love's com - mun - ing life to share.
5. Our hope's be - gin - ning, way and end.

Text: LM; Brian Wren, b. 1936, © 1989, Hope Publishing Co. All rights reserved. Used with permission.
Music: PROSPECT; William Walker's *The Southern Harmony*, 1854.

471   COME NOW, ALMIGHTY KING

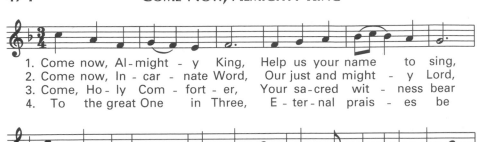

1. Come now, Al-might-y King,   Help us your name   to   sing,
2. Come now, In-car-nate Word,   Our just and might-y   Lord,
3. Come, Ho-ly Com-fort-er,   Your sa-cred wit-ness bear
4. To the great One   in Three,   E-ter-nal prais-es   be

1. Help us to praise: Fa-ther, all glo-ri-ous, Ev-er vic-
2. Our prayer at-tend: Come, and your peo-ple bless, And give your
3. In this glad hour: To us your grace im-part, And rule in
4. For-ev-er-more!   Your sov-'reign maj-es-ty May we in

1. to-ri-ous, Come, and reign o-ver us, An-cient of Days.
2. word suc-cess; Strength-en your righ-teous-ness, Sav-ior and Friend.
3. ev-'ry heart! Nev-er from us de-part, Spir-it of pow'r.
4. glo-ry see, And to e-ter-ni-ty Love and a-dore!

Text: 66 4 666 4; Anon., ca. 1757, alt.
Music: ITALIAN HYMN; Felice de Giardini, 1716–1796, alt.

472   DRAW NEAR AND TAKE THE BODY OF THE LORD

1. Draw near and take the bod-y of the Lord, Re-ceive the
2. Our lov-ing Sav-ior, Christ, the on-ly Son, Who by his
3. Let us ap-proach with thank-ful hearts sin-cere, And gain the
4. With heav'n-ly bread he makes the hun-gry whole, Gives liv-ing

1. ho-ly blood for you out-poured, Saved by that pre-cious bod-y
2. cross and blood the vic-t'ry won, Gave his own life for great-est
3. safe-guard of sal-va-tion here. God, who all faith-ful ser-vants
4. wa-ters to the thirst-y soul. The one e-ter-nal God, to

1. and that blood, Where-by re-freshed, we of-fer thanks to God.
2. and for least: Him-self the Vic-tim and him-self the Priest.
3. rules and shields, To all be-liev-ers life e-ter-nal yields.
4. whom shall bow All on the last day he is with us now.

Text: 10 10 10 10; Sancti, venite, Christi corpus sumite; Antiphonary of Bennchar, 7th cent.; tr. by John M. Neale, 1818–1866, alt.
Music: ANIMA CHRISTI; W.J. Maher, SJ, 1823–1877, alt.

LAUD, O ZION

Verses 1, 2

*1. Lo! the an-gel's food is giv-en To the
2. Truth the an-cient types ful-fill-ing, I-saac

1. pil-grim who has striv-en; See the chil-dren's bread from
2. bound, a vic-tim will-ing, Pas-chal lamb, its life-blood

1. heav-en, which on dogs may not be spent.
2. spill-ing, man-na to the fa-thers sent.

Verses 3, 4

3. Ver-y bread, good shep-herd, tend us,
4. You who all things can and know,

3. Je-su, of your love be-friend us,
4. Who on earth such food be-stow,

3. You re-fresh us, you de-fend us, Your e-ter-nal
4. Grant us with your saints, though low-est, Where the heav'n-ly

1
3. good-ness send us In the land of life to see.
4. feast you show,

2
3.
4. Fel-low heirs and guests to

4. be. A-men. Al-le-lu-ia.

*The shorter form of this sequence is given here. The long form is available in the octavo, *Laud O Zion,*
edition 11500, by Randall DeBruyn.

Text: Sequence for the *Solemnity of the Most Holy Body and Blood of Christ (Lauda Sion)*; fr. *The Roman Missal,*
© 1964, National Catholic Welfare Conference. All rights reserved. Administered by CCD. Used with permission.
Music: Randall DeBruyn, b. 1947, © 2000, 2001, Randall DeBruyn. Published by OCP Publications. All rights reserved.

474
JESUS, THE VERY THOUGHT OF YOU

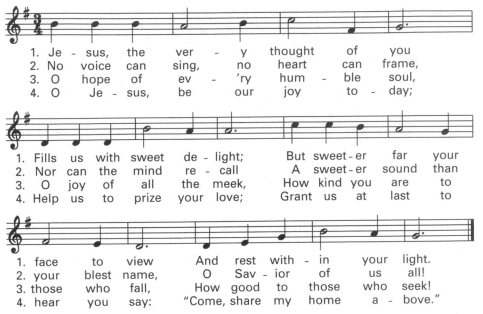

1. Je - sus, the ver - y thought of you
2. No voice can sing, no heart can frame,
3. O hope of ev - 'ry hum - ble soul,
4. O Je - sus, be our joy to - day;

1. Fills us with sweet de - light; But sweet-er far your
2. Nor can the mind re - call A sweet-er sound than
3. O joy of all the meek, How kind you are to
4. Help us to prize your love; Grant us at last to

1. face to view And rest with - in your light.
2. your blest name, O Sav - ior of us all!
3. those who fall, How good to those who seek!
4. hear you say: "Come, share my home a - bove."

Text: CM; *Jesu, dulcis memoria,* ca. 12th cent.; attr. to Bernard of Clairvaux, 1091–1153; tr. by Edward Caswall, 1814–1878, alt.
Music: ST. AGNES; John B. Dykes, 1823–1876.

475
O DEAREST LORD, YOUR SACRED HEAD

1. O dear - est Lord, your sa - cred head With
2. O dear - est Lord, your sa - cred hands With
3. O dear - est Lord, your sa - cred feet With
4. O dear - est Lord, your Sa - cred Heart With

1. thorns was pierced for me; O pour your bless - ing
2-3. nails were pierced for me; O pour your bless - ing
4. spear was pierced for me; O pour your bless - ing

1. on my head, That yours my thoughts may be.
2. on my hands That yours my works may be.
3. on my feet, That yours my path may be.
4. on my heart, That yours my life may be.

Text: CM; *Poems of Father Andrew,* 1918; Henry E. Hardy (Father Andrew, SDC), 1869–1946, © A.R. Mowbray and Co., Ltd.
All rights reserved. Used with permission.
Music: DETROIT; *A Supplement to the Kentucky Harmony,* 1820.

Heart of Jesus

1. Heart of Je - sus, ho - ly mys - t'ry, beat with-in our hearts, we
2. Heart of Je - sus, giv-en for us, may we love as we are
3. Heart of Je - sus, no __ strang - er to our dark - ness and our
4. Heart of Je - sus, ho - ly wis - dom, ev - er an - cient, ev - er

1. pray. May we mir - ror your com - pas - sion, let your
2. loved. May your Church be a good shep - herd, seek-ing
3. grief, how you wept for poor __ Laz - 'rus and a -
4. new, may your king - dom grow a - mong us in each

1. mind be ours to - day. Make us ves - sels of your glo - ry,
2. out those who are lost, break-ing bread with all who hun - ger,
3. woke him from his sleep. How you bore for us the spear-wound,
4. thing we say and do. May we fight the good fight glad - ly,

1. in our weak - ness show your strength. Make this Church a bold
2. giv - ing voice to the op - pressed: win-ning jus - tice and
3. great-er love there can - not be than to lay down one's
4. run the race our whole lives through, till at last with the

1. sign of your pow - er - ful grace.
2. peace for all those in dis - tress.
3. life to __ set oth - ers free.
4. saints we shall find rest in you.

ALLELUIA! SING TO JESUS

1. Al - le - lu - ia! sing to Je - sus! His the
2. Al - le - lu - ia! not as or - phans Are we
3. Al - le - lu - ia! Bread of An - gels, Here on
4. Al - le - lu - ia! King e - ter - nal, You the
5. Al - le - lu - ia! Al - le - lu - ia! Glo - ry

1. scep - ter, his the throne; Al - le - lu - ia!
2. left in sor - row now; Al - le - lu - ia!
3. earth our food, our stay! Al - le - lu - ia!
4. Lord of lords we own; Al - le - lu - ia!
5. be to God on high; Al - le - lu - ia

1. his the tri - umph, His the vic - to - ry a - lone;
2. he is near us, Faith be - lieves, nor ques - tions how:
3. here the sin - ful Flee to you from day to day:
4. born of Ma - ry, Earth your foot - stool, heav'n your throne:
5. to the Sav - ior Who has won the vic - to - ry;

1. Hark! the songs of peace - ful Zi - on Thun - der
2. Though the cloud from sight re - ceived him, When the
3. In - ter - ces - sor, friend of sin - ners, Earth's re -
4. You with - in the veil have en - tered, Robed in
5. Al - le - lu - ia to the Spir - it, Font of

1. like a might - y flood; Je - sus out of ev - 'ry
2. for - ty days were o'er, Shall our hearts for - get his
3. deem - er, plead for me, Where the songs of all the
4. flesh, our great high priest; Here on earth both priest and
5. love and sanc - ti - ty; Al - le - lu - ia! Al - le -

1. na - tion Has re - deemed us by his blood.
2. prom - ise? "I am with you ev - er - more!"
3. sin - less Sweep a - cross the crys - tal sea.
4. vic - tim In the Eu - cha - ris - tic feast.
5. lu - ia! To the tri - une maj - es - ty.

Text: 87 87 D; William C. Dix, 1837–1898, alt.
Music: HYFRYDOL; Rowland H. Prichard, 1811–1887.

REJOICE, THE LORD IS KING

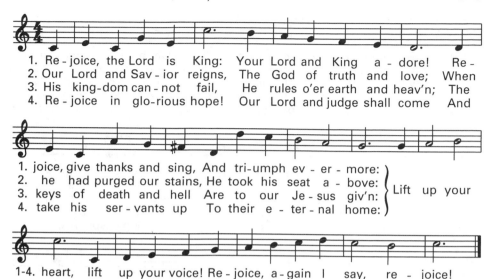

1. Re - joice, the Lord is King: Your Lord and King a - dore! Re -
2. Our Lord and Sav - ior reigns, The God of truth and love; When
3. His king - dom can - not fail, He rules o'er earth and heav'n; The
4. Re - joice in glo-rious hope! Our Lord and judge shall come And

1. joice, give thanks and sing, And tri-umph ev - er - more:
2. he had purged our stains, He took his seat a - bove:
3. keys of death and hell Are to our Je - sus giv'n:
4. take his ser - vants up To their e - ter - nal home: } Lift up your

1-4. heart, lift up your voice! Re - joice, a - gain I say, re - joice!

Text: 66 66 88; *Hymns for Our Lord's Resurrection*, 1746; Charles Wesley, 1707–1788.
Music: DARWALL'S 148TH; John Darwall, 1731–1789.

JESUS SHALL REIGN

1. Je - sus shall reign wher - e'er the sun Does its suc -
2. To him shall end - less prayer be made, And prais - es
3. Peo - ple and realms of ev - 'ry tongue Dwell on his
4. Bless-ings a - bound wher - e'er he reigns, The pris -'ners
5. Let ev - 'ry crea - ture rise and bring Their joy - ful

1. ces - sive jour - neys run; His king-dom stretch from
2. throng to crown his head; His name like sweet per -
3. love with sweet-est song, And chil-dren's voic - es
4. leap to lose their chains; The wea - ry find e -
5. prais - es to our King; An - gels de - scend with

1. shore to shore, Till moons shall wax and wane no more.
2. fume shall rise With ev - 'ry morn - ing sac - ri - fice.
3. shall pro - claim Their ear - ly bless - ings on his name.
4. ter - nal rest, And all who suf - fer want are blest.
5. songs a - gain, And earth re - peat the loud a - men!

Text: LM; based on Psalm 72; Isaac Watts, 1674–1748, alt.
Music: DUKE STREET; John Hatton, ca. 1710–1793.

480   CROWN HIM WITH MANY CROWNS

1. Crown him with man - y crowns, The Lamb up - on his
2. Crown him the Lord of life, Who tri - umphed o'er the
3. Crown him the Lord of love, Be - hold his hands and
4. Crown him the Lord of peace, Whose pow'r a scep - ter
5. Crown him the Lord of years, The ris - en Lord sub -

1. throne; Hark! how the heav'n - ly an - them drowns All
2. grave, And rose vic - to - rious in the strife For
3. side, Rich wounds yet vis - i - ble a - bove In
4. sways From pole to pole, that wars may cease, Ab -
5. lime, Cre - a - tor of the roll - ing spheres, The

1. mu - sic but its own. A - wake, my soul, and sing
2. those he came to save. His glo - ries now we sing,
3. beau - ty glo - ri - fied. No an - gel in the sky
4. sorbed in prayer and praise. His reign shall know no end,
5. Mas - ter of all time. All hail, Re - deem - er, hail!

1. Of him who set us free, And hail him as your
2. Who died and rose on high, Who died, e - ter - nal
3. Can ful - ly bear that sight, But down - ward bends his
4. And round his pierc - ed feet Fair flow'rs of Par - a -
5. For you have died for me; Your praise and glo - ry

1. heav'n - ly King Through all e - ter - ni - ty.
2. life to bring, And lives that death may die.
3. burn - ing eye At mys - ter - ies so bright.
4. dise ex - tend Their fra - grance ev - er sweet.
5. shall not fail Through - out e - ter - ni - ty.

Text: SMD; Revelation 19:12; verses 1, 3–5, Matthew Bridges, 1800–1894; verse 2, Godfrey Thring, 1823–1903, alt.
Music: DIADEMATA; George J. Elvey, 1816–1893.

481   HAIL, REDEEMER, KING DIVINE

Verses

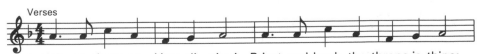

1. Hail, re - deem - er, king di - vine! Priest and lamb, the throne is thine;
2. King of ev - er - last - ing might! Be to us e - ter - nal light,

1. King whose reign shall nev - er cease, Prince of ev - er - last-ing peace.
2. Till in peace each na - tion rings With thy prais-es, king of kings.

Refrain

An - gels, saints and na-tions sing: "Praised be Je-sus Christ, our king;

Lord of earth and sky and sea, King of love on Cal - va - ry."

Text: 77 77 with refrain; Patrick Brennen, 1877–1951, © Burns & Oates, Ltd., England. All rights reserved. Used with permission.
Music: ST. GEORGE'S WINDSOR; George J. Elvey, 1816–1893.

ALL HAIL THE POWER OF JESUS' NAME 482

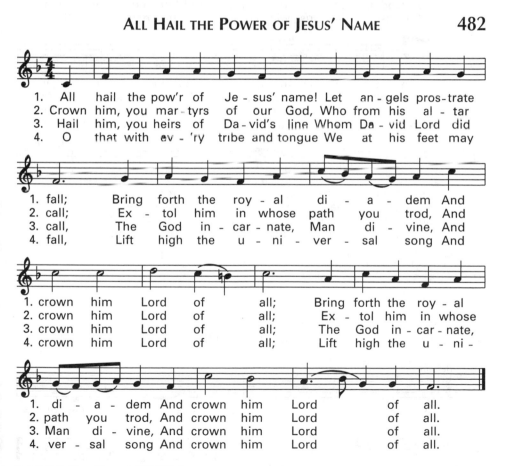

1. All hail the pow'r of Je - sus' name! Let an - gels pros-trate
2. Crown him, you mar - tyrs of our God, Who from his al - tar
3. Hail him, you heirs of Da-vid's line Whom Da - vid Lord did
4. O that with ev - 'ry tribe and tongue We at his feet may

1. fall; Bring forth the roy - al di - a - dem And
2. call; Ex - tol him in whose path you trod, And
3. call, The God in - car - nate, Man di - vine, And
4. fall, Lift high the u - ni - ver - sal song And

1. crown him Lord of all; Bring forth the roy - al
2. crown him Lord of all; Ex - tol him in whose
3. crown him Lord of all; The God in - car - nate,
4. crown him Lord of all; Lift high the u - ni -

1. di - a - dem And crown him Lord of all.
2. path you trod, And crown him Lord of all.
3. Man di - vine, And crown him Lord of all.
4. ver - sal song And crown him Lord of all.

Text: 86 86 86; Edward Perronet, 1726–1792, alt.
Music: CORONATION; *Union Harmony*, 1793; Oliver Holden, 1765–1844.

483

At the Name of Jesus

Refrain

At the name of Je-sus, ev-'ry knee shall bow, ev-'ry tongue con-fess him: King of glo-ry now. Je-sus is Lord, King of glo-ry now!

(last time only)

Verses

1. He ___ emp-tied him-self, as a slave, yet free,
2. He ___ hum-bled him-self, and o-beyed God's will.
3. God ex-alt-ed him, raised him up on high
4. Christ __ Je-sus will come at the end of time,

1. came in hu-man like-ness __ for you and for me; in
2. On a cross he died ___ on Cal-va-ry's hill; for
3. so a-bove all oth-ers __ his name will not die; that
4. come with ju-bi-la-tion __ to call __ us home. Un-

to Refrain

1. hu-man like-ness ___ for you and for me.
2. you and me he o-beyed __ God's will.
3. name we hon-or ___ and glo-ri-fy.
4. til that day you and I will pro-claim:

484

Jesus the Lord

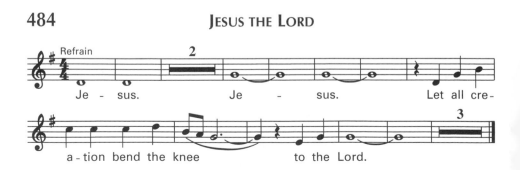

Refrain

Je-sus. Je-sus. Let all cre-a-tion bend the knee to the Lord.

1. In him we live, we move and have our be-ing; In him the Christ, in him the king! Je-sus, the Lord.

Verses 2, 3

2. Though Son, he did not cling to god-li-ness; but emp-tied him-self, be-came a slave! Je-sus, the Lord.
3. He lived o-be-dient-ly his Fa-ther's will ac-cept-ing his death, death on a tree! Je-sus, the Lord.

Text: Based on the Jesus Prayer, Philippians 2, Acts 17; Roc O'Connor, SJ, b. 1949.
Music: Roc O'Connor, SJ.
Text and music © 1981, Robert F. O'Connor, SJ, and New Dawn Music. Published by OCP Publications. All rights reserved.

TO JESUS CHRIST, OUR SOVEREIGN KING   485

1. To Je-sus Christ, our Sov-'reign King, Who is the world's sal-va-tion, All praise and hom-age do we bring And thanks and ad-o-ra-tion.
2. Thy reign ex-tend, O King be-nign, To ev-'ry land and na-tion; For in thy king-dom, Lord di-vine, A-lone we find sal-va-tion.
3. To thee and to thy Church, Great King, We pledge our hearts' ob-la-tion Un-til be-fore thy throne we sing In end-less ju-bi-la-tion.

Christ Je-sus, vic-tor!

1-3. Christ Je-sus, rul-er! Christ Je-sus, Lord and re-deem-er!

Text: 87 87 55 8; based on *Christus Vincit*, 8th cent.;
    Martin B. Hellriegel, 1891–1981, © 1941, assigned 1978 to Mrs. Irene C. Mueller. All rights reserved. Used with permission.
Music: ICH GLAUB AN GOTT; *Mainz Gesangbuch*, 1870.

486 THE KING OF KINGS, CHRIST JESUS REIGNS

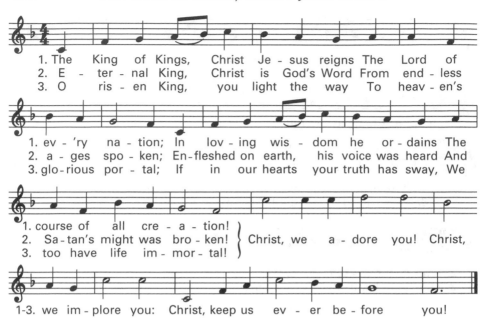

1. The King of Kings, Christ Je - sus reigns The Lord of
2. E - ter - nal King, Christ is God's Word From end - less
3. O ris - en King, you light the way To heav - en's

1. ev - 'ry na - tion; In lov - ing wis - dom he or - dains The
2. a - ges spo - ken; En-fleshed on earth, his voice was heard And
3. glo-rious por - tal; If in our hearts your truth has sway, We

1. course of all cre - a - tion!)
2. Sa - tan's might was bro - ken! } Christ, we a - dore you! Christ,
3. too have life im - mor - tal!)

1-3. we im - plore you: Christ, keep us ev - er be - fore you!

Text: 87 87 55 8; Melvin Farrell, SS, 1930–1986, © 1977, OCP Publications. All rights reserved.
Music: ICH GLAUB AN GOTT; *Mainz Gesangbuch*, 1870.

487 THE KING OF GLORY

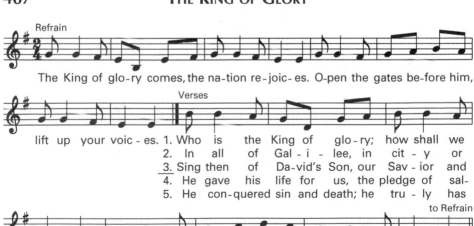

Refrain

The King of glo-ry comes, the na-tion re-joic-es. O-pen the gates be-fore him,

Verses

lift up your voic-es. 1. Who is the King of glo-ry; how shall we
2. In all of Gal - i - lee, in cit - y or
3. Sing then of Da-vid's Son, our Sav - ior and
4. He gave his life for us, the pledge of sal-
5. He con-quered sin and death; he tru - ly has

to Refrain

1. call him? He is Em - man - u - el, the prom-ised of a - ges.
2. vil - lage, He goes a - mong his peo-ple cur - ing their ill - ness.
3. broth - er; In all of Gal - i - lee was nev - er an - oth - er.
4. va - tion, He took up - on him-self the sins of the na - tion.
5. ris - en, And he will share with us his heav - en - ly vi - sion.

Text: 12 12 with refrain; Willard F. Jabusch, b. 1930, © 1967, Willard F. Jabusch.
    Administered by OCP Publications. All rights reserved.
Music: KING OF GLORY; Trad. Israeli Folk Song.

SOLEMNITIES AND FEASTS

ALMA REDEMPTORIS MATER

Al - ma Red - em - ptó - ris Ma - ter,
Lov - ing Moth - er of our Sav - ior;

quae pér - vi - a cae - li por - ta ma - nes,
thou o - pen gate lead - ing us to heav - en,

Et stel - la ma - ris, suc - cúr - re ca - dén - ti
and Star of the Sea, help thy fall - en peo - ple,

súr - ge - re qui cu - rat pó - pu - lo:
help all those who seek to rise a - gain.

Tu quae ge - nu - í - sti, na - tú - ra mi - rán - te,
Maid - en who didst give birth, all na - ture won - der - ing,

tu - um san - ctum Ge - ni - tó - rem:
to thy ho - ly Lord Cre - a - tor:

Vir - go pri - us ac po - sté - ri - us,
Vir - gin be - fore and vir - gin al - ways

Ga - bri - é - lis ab o - re su - mens il - lud A - ve,
who re - ceived from Ga - briel's mouth this mes-sage from heav - en,

pec - ca - tó - rum mi - se - ré - re.
take pit - y on us poor sin - ners.

Text: Ascr. to Hermannus Contractus, 1013–1054; adapt. by Theodore N. Marier, 1912–2001,
Music: Chant, Mode V.

489   HAIL MARY: GENTLE WOMAN

Introduction
Cantor

Hail Ma - ry,   full   of   grace,

the Lord   is with you.

Bless-ed are you a-mong wom-en   and   blest is the

fruit of your womb,   Je - sus.

Ho-ly Ma - ry,   Moth-er of God,

pray for us sin - ners now   and   at   the

hour   of death.   A - men.

Refrain
All

Gen-tle wom-an,   qui-et light,

morn-ing star,   so strong and bright,

gen-tle Moth-er,	peace-ful dove,

teach us wis-dom;	teach us love.

Verse 1

1. You were cho - sen	by the Fa-ther;

1. you were cho - sen	for the Son.

1. You were cho - sen	from all wom-en

to Refrain

1. and for wom-an,	shin-ing one.

Verse 2

2. Bless-ed are you	a-mong wom-en,

2. blest in turn	all wom-en, too.

2. Bless-ed they	with peace-ful spir-its.

to Refrain

2. Bless-ed they	with gen-tle hearts.

Text: Based on Luke 1:28; Carey Landry, b. 1944.
Music: Carey Landry.
Text and music © 1975, 1978, Carey Landry and NALR. Published by OCP Publications. All rights reserved.

490 SING OF MARY

1. Sing of Ma-ry, pure and low-ly, Vir-gin Moth-er un-de-
2. Sing of Je-sus, son of Ma-ry, In the home at Naz-a-
3. Glo-ry be to God the Fa-ther; Glo-ry be to God the

1. filed. Sing of God's own Son most ho-ly, Who be-came her
2. reth. Toil and la-bor can-not wea-ry Love en-dur-ing
3. Son; Glo-ry be to God the Spir-it; Glo-ry to the

1. lit-tle child. Fair-est child of fair-est moth-er,
2. un-to death. Con-stant was the love he gave her,
3. Three in One. From the heart of bless-ed Ma-ry,

1. God the Lord who came to earth, Word made flesh, our
2. Though he went forth from her side, Forth to preach and
3. From all saints the song as-cends, And the Church the

1. ver-y broth-er, Takes our na-ture by his birth.
2. heal and suf-fer, Till on Cal-va-ry he died.
3. strain re-ech-oes Un-to earth's re-mot-est ends.

Text: 87 87 D; Roland F. Palmer, SSJE, 1891–1985, © Estate of Roland F. Palmer. All rights reserved. Used with permission.
Music: PLEADING SAVIOR; *Christian Lyre*, 1830.

491 SING WE OF THE BLESSED MOTHER

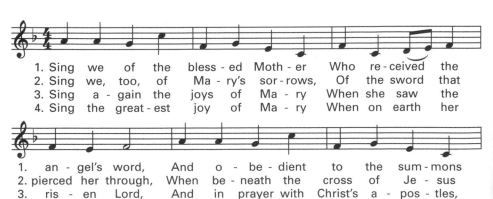

1. Sing we of the bless-ed Moth-er Who re-ceived the
2. Sing we, too, of Ma-ry's sor-rows, Of the sword that
3. Sing a-gain the joys of Ma-ry When she saw the
4. Sing the great-est joy of Ma-ry When on earth her

1. an-gel's word, And o-be-dient to the sum-mons
2. pierced her through, When be-neath the cross of Je-sus
3. ris-en Lord, And in prayer with Christ's a-pos-tles,
4. work was done, And the Lord of all cre-a-tion

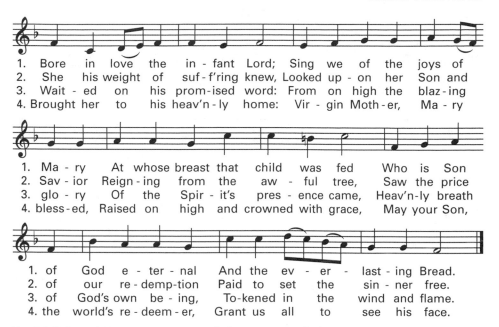

1. Bore in love the in - fant Lord; Sing we of the joys of
2. She his weight of suf - f'ring knew, Looked up - on her Son and
3. Wait - ed on his prom-ised word: From on high the blaz-ing
4. Brought her to his heav'n-ly home: Vir - gin Moth-er, Ma - ry

1. Ma - ry At whose breast that child was fed Who is Son
2. Sav - ior Reign - ing from the aw - ful tree, Saw the price
3. glo - ry Of the Spir - it's pres - ence came, Heav'n-ly breath
4. bless-ed, Raised on high and crowned with grace, May your Son,

1. of God e - ter - nal And the ev - er - last - ing Bread.
2. of our re - demp-tion Paid to set the sin - ner free.
3. of God's own be - ing, To-kened in the wind and flame.
4. the world's re - deem - er, Grant us all to see his face.

Text: 87 87 D; George B. Timms, 1910–1997, © 1975, Oxford University Press. All rights reserved. Used with permission.
Music: OMNI DIE DIC MARIAE; *Trier Gesängbuch*, 1695.

Daily, Daily Sing to Mary   492

1. Daily, daily sing to Mary;
Sing, my soul, her praises due.
All her glorious actions cherish,
With the heart's devotion true.
Lost in wond'ring contemplation,
Be her majesty confessed!
Call her Mother, call her Virgin,
Happy Mother, Virgin blest!

2. She is mighty to deliver;
Call her, trust her lovingly.
When the tempest rages 'round you,
She will calm the troubled sea.
Gifts of heaven she has given,
Noble Lady, to our race;
She, the Queen, who clothes her subjects
With the light of God's own grace.

3. Sing, my tongue, the Virgin's honors,
Who for us her Maker bore,
For the curse of old inflicted,
Peace and blessings to restore.

Sing in songs of praise unending,
Sing the world's majestic Queen;
Weary not nor faint in telling
All the gifts that earth has seen.

4. All my senses, heart, affections,
Strive to sound her glory forth.
Spread abroad the sweet memorials
Of the Virgin's priceless worth.
Where the voice of music thrilling,
Where the tongues of eloquence,
That can utter hymns befitting
All her matchless excellence?

5. All our joys do flow from Mary;
All then join her praise to sing.
Trembling, sing the Virgin Mother,
Mother of our Lord and King.
While we sing her awesome glory,
Far above our fancy's reach,
Let our hearts be quick to offer
Love the heart alone can teach.

Text: 87 87 D; Bernard of Morlaix, ca. 1140; tr. by Henry Bittleston, 1818–1886, alt.
Music: OMNI DIE DIC MARIAE; *Trier Gesängbuch*, 1695.

493

Ave María

A - ve, Ma - rí - a, grá - ti - a ple - na,
A - ve, Ma - rí - a: *Hail, Ma - ry, full of grace,*

Dó - mi - nus te - cum, be - ne - dí - cta tu
the Lord is with you. *O how blest are you*

in mu - li - é - ri - bus, et be - ne - dí -
a - mong all earth's wom - en. *And how tru - ly*

ctus fruc - tus ven - tris tu - i, Je - sus.
blest is the fruit of your womb, Je - sus.

San - cta Ma - rí - a, Ma - ter De - i,
O ho - ly Ma - ry, God's own moth - er,

o - ra pro no - bis pec - ca - tó - ri - bus,
pray for us, your chil - dren who stray from the way,

nunc et in ho - ra mor - tis no - strae. A - men.
now and in that fin - al hour when we come to die. *A - men.*

Text: Part one, Latin, based on Luke 1:28, 42; part two, Latin, 16th cent. English, Paul F. Ford, © 1995, Paul F. Ford.
Published by OCP Publications. All rights reserved.
Music: Chant, Mode I.

494

O Holy Mary

Refrain

O ho - ly Dwell-ing Place of God. O ho - ly Tem-ple of the

Word. O ho - ly Ma - ry, ho-ly Moth-er of God.

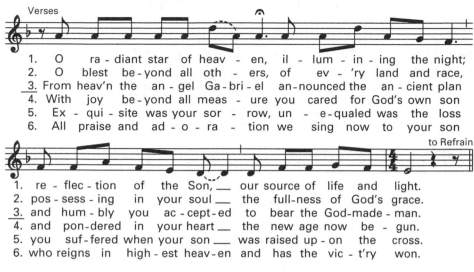

1. O ra-diant star of heav-en, il-lum-in-ing the night;
2. O blest be-yond all oth-ers, of ev-'ry land and race,
3. From heav'n the an-gel Ga-bri-el an-nounced the an-cient plan
4. With joy be-yond all meas-ure you cared for God's own son
5. Ex-qui-site was your sor-row, un-e-qualed was the loss
6. All praise and ad-o-ra-tion we sing now to your son

to Refrain

1. re-flec-tion of the Son, __ our source of life and light.
2. pos-sess-ing in your soul __ the full-ness of God's grace.
3. and hum-bly you ac-cept-ed to bear the God-made-man.
4. and pon-dered in your heart __ the new age now be-gun.
5. you suf-fered when your son __ was raised up-on the cross.
6. who reigns in high-est heav-en and has the vic-t'ry won.

Text: Owen Alstott, b. 1947.
Music: Owen Alstott.

Mary's Song
495

1. My soul doth glo-ry in your love, O Lord.
2. Great are you, God, and ho-ly is your name.
3. Ah, how you fill the hun-gry with your love.
4. My soul doth glo-ry in your love, O Lord.

1. My soul doth glo-ry in your love, O Lord. For you
2. Your mer-cy reach-es to the end of time. Ah, the
3. With emp-ty hands the rich are sent a-way. You will
4. My soul doth glo-ry in your love, O Lord. For you

1. gazed on your ser-vant __ with com-pas-sion, And you
2. low-ly you raise _____ to the heav-ens, And the
3. al-ways be mind-ful __ of your mer-cy, As you
4. smiled on your ser-vant __ with com-pas-sion, And you

1. reached out and took me by the hand.
2. proud-heart-ed have no part with you.
3. prom-ised your peo-ple long a-go.
4. reached out and took me by the hand.

Text: Luke 1:46–55; Millie Rieth.
Music: Millie Rieth.

496 MARY, WOMAN OF THE PROMISE

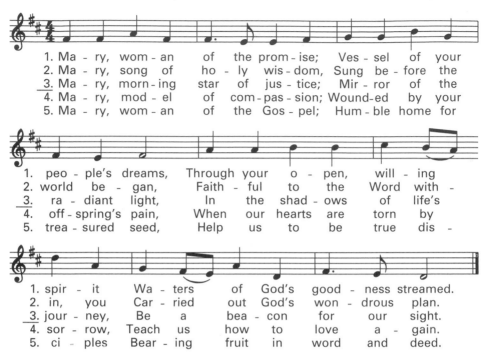

1. Ma - ry, wom - an of the prom - ise; Ves - sel of your
2. Ma - ry, song of ho - ly wis - dom, Sung be - fore the
3. Ma - ry, morn - ing star of jus - tice; Mir - ror of the
4. Ma - ry, mod - el of com - pas - sion; Wound-ed by your
5. Ma - ry, wom - an of the Gos - pel; Hum - ble home for

1. peo - ple's dreams, Through your o - pen, will - ing
2. world be - gan, Faith - ful to the Word with -
3. ra - diant light, In the shad - ows of life's
4. off - spring's pain, When our hearts are torn by
5. trea - sured seed, Help us to be true dis -

1. spir - it Wa - ters of God's good - ness streamed.
2. in, you Car - ried out God's won - drous plan.
3. jour - ney, Be a bea - con for our sight.
4. sor - row, Teach us how to love a - gain.
5. ci - ples Bear - ing fruit in word and deed.

Text: 87 87; Mary Frances Fleischaker, © 1988, Mary Frances Fleischaker. All rights reserved.
Used with permission of Selah Publishing Co., Inc., exclusive agent.
Music: DRAKES BROUGHTON; Edward Elgar, 1857–1934, © Burns & Oates, Ltd., England. All rights reserved.
Used with permission.

497 ON THIS DAY, O BEAUTIFUL MOTHER

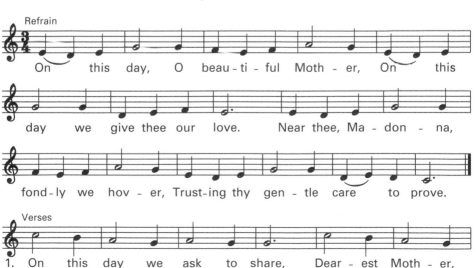

Refrain

On this day, O beau - ti - ful Moth - er, On this

day we give thee our love. Near thee, Ma - don - na,

fond - ly we hov - er, Trust-ing thy gen - tle care to prove.

Verses

1. On this day we ask to share, Dear - est Moth - er,
2. Queen of an - gels, deign to hear Lisp - ing chil - dren's

1. thy sweet care; Aid us ere our feet a -
2. hum - ble pray'r; Young hearts gain, O Vir - gin

to Refrain

1. stray Wan - der from thy guid - ing way.
2. pure, Sweet - ly to thy - self al - lure.

Text: 77 77 with refrain; Rohr's *Favorite Catholic Melodies*, 1857.
Music: BEAUTIFUL MOTHER; Louis Lambillotte, SJ, 1796–1855.

SONG OF MARY 498

1. Let us sing the prais - es of Ma - ry, daugh - ter of Da - vid's
2. Let us sing the prais - es of Ma - ry, cho - sen as bless - ed
3. Let us sing the prais - es of Ma - ry, wom - an of strong and
4. Let us sing the prais - es of Ma - ry, pierced by the sword of
5. Let us sing the prais - es of Ma - ry, friend of the poor in

1. ho - ly line, she who heard the voice of an an - gel
2. from the least, she who heard the song of the an - gels
3. stead - fast love. She who raised the Sav - ior of na - tions
4. sor - row's pain, she who saw the child of her lov - ing
5. ev - 'ry age, she who saw her Son and her Sav - ior

1. tell - ing the plan of God's de - sign, how in wis - dom's
2. fill - ing the night with heav - en's peace. When the prom - ised
3. held in her arms the Son of God. She who knew the
4. nailed on a cross to die in shame. Though his friends would
5. ris - en in glo - ry from the grave. Sin and death shall

1. ho - ly sight she would moth - er heav - en's Christ.
2. time had come she gave birth to God's own Son.
3. Fa - ther's grace taught her Son to know God's face.
4. flee in fear she re - mained for - ev - er near.
5. reign no more; Christ has o - pened heav - en's door.

1–5. Bless - ed be the name of Ma - ry, she who trust - ed the love of God.

Text: 98 98 77 88; Dan Schutte, b. 1947
Music: SONG OF MARY; Dan Schutte

SALVE, REGINA/HAIL, MARY

Sal - ve, Re - gí - na, ma - ter mi - se - ri - cór - di - ae: Vi - ta dul-
Hail, Ma - ry, moth- er and queen of ten- der mer - cy, our life, our

cé - do et spes no - stra, sal - ve. Ad te cla - má - mus,
com - fort, and our hope, we hail you. From this for- eign land

éx - su - les, fí - li - i He - vae. Ad te sus - pi - rá - mus,
Eve's sons and daugh- ters cry to you. So lost, so full of fear,

ge - mén - tes et flen - tes in hac la - cri - má - rum val - le.
we mourn, we grieve, we sigh from this tear- ful vale of ex - ile.

E - ia er - go, Ad - vo - cá - ta no - stra, il - los tu - os mi -
Ah, then, our help, our ad - vo- cate and guide, turn now to us the

se - ri - cór - des ó - cu - los ad nos con - vér - te.
gaze of your all - lov - ing eyes, so full of mer - cy.

Et Je - sum, be - ne - dí - ctum fruc - tum ven - tris tu - i,
And Je - sus— your Son, and Lord, your womb's most bless- ed fruit—

no - bis post hoc ex - sí - li - um os - tén - de.
show him to us when we com - plete our so - journ.

O cle - mens, O pi - a,
O gen - tle, O lov - ing,

O _____ dul - cis Vir - go Ma - rí - a.
O _____ be - lov - ed, O Vir - gin Ma - ry.

Text: Latin; attr. to Hermanus Contractus, 1013–1054; English, Paul F. Ford, b. 1947, © 1995, Paul F. Ford.
  Published by OCP Publications. All rights reserved.
Music: Chant, Mode V.

O Sanctissima/O Most Holy One

1. O san - ctís - si - ma, O pi - ís - si - ma,
2. Tu so - lá - ti - um Et re - fú - gi - um,
3. Ec - ce dé - bi - les, Per - quam flé - bi - les,
4. Vir - go ré - spi - ce, Ma - ter, ád - spi - ce,

1. O San - ctís - si - ma, Ho - ly Queen of Love,
2. O most beau - ti - ful, And most mer - ci - ful,
3. Ma - ry, Mys - tic Rose, Font that o - ver-flows,
4. Ma - ry, plead for us; In - ter - cede for us.

1. Dul - cis vir - go Ma - rí - a!
2. Vir - go ma - ter Ma - rí - a!
3. Sal - va nos, _____ Ma - rí - a!
4. Au - di nos, _____ Ma - rí - a!

1. Dear - est Vir - gin and Moth - er.
2. Gate of Heav - en, we hail you.
3. Seat of Wis - dom, we greet you.
4. Come and lead us to Je - sus.

1. Ma - ter a - má - ta, In - te - me - rá - ta,
2. Quid - quid op - tá - mus, Per _____ te spe - rá - mus,
3. Tol - le lan - guó - res, Sa - na do - ló - res,
4. Tu _____ me di - cí - nam, Por - tas di - ví - nam;

1. Blest by ev - 'ry na - tion, Ev - 'ry gen - er - a - tion:
2. Star of our sal - va - tion, Crown of all cre - a - tion:
3. Moth - er of our Sav - ior, Full of grace and fa - vor:
4. Moth - er in our sad - ness, Moth - er in our glad - ness:

1-4. O - ra, o - ra pro no - bis!
1-4. O - ra, o - ra pro no - bis!

Text: 55 7 D; Latin verse 1 fr. *Herder's Stimmen der Völker in Liedern*, 1807; verses 2–4 fr. *Arundel Hymnal*, 1905.
English tr. by Harry Hagan, OSB, b. 1947 © 2003, St. Meinrad Archabbey. Published by OCP Publications.
All rights reserved.
Music: O DU FRÖHLICHE; Tattersal's *Improved Psalmody*, 1794.

501

MARY'S SONG

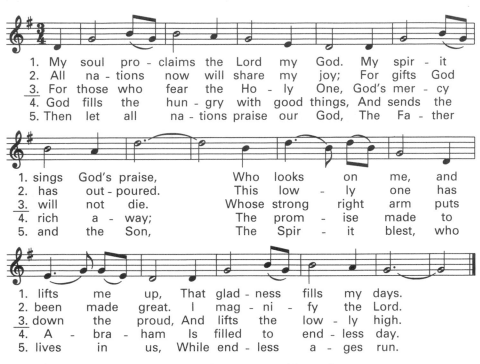

1. My soul pro-claims the Lord my God. My spir-it
2. All na-tions now will share my joy; For gifts God
3. For those who fear the Ho-ly One, God's mer-cy
4. God fills the hun-gry with good things, And sends the
5. Then let all na-tions praise our God, The Fa-ther

1. sings God's praise, Who looks on me, and
2. has out-poured. This low-ly one has
3. will not die. Whose strong right arm puts
4. rich a-way; The prom-ise made to
5. and the Son, The Spir-it blest, who

1. lifts me up, That glad-ness fills my days.
2. been made great. I mag-ni-fy the Lord.
3. down the proud, And lifts the low-ly high.
4. A-bra-ham Is filled to end-less day.
5. lives in us, While end-less a-ges run.

Text: CM; based on Luke 1:46–55; Anne Carter, 1944–1993, © 1988, Society of the Sacred Heart.
  All rights reserved. Used with permission.
Music: NEW BRITAIN; *Columbian Harmony,* 1829.

502

THERE IS NOTHING TOLD

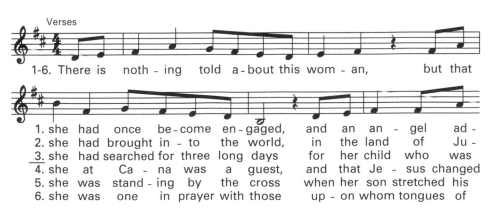

Verses

1-6. There is noth-ing told a-bout this wom-an, but that

1. she had once be-come en-gaged, and an an-gel ad-
2. she had brought in-to the world, in the land of Ju-
3. she had searched for three long days for her child who was
4. she at Ca-na was a guest, and that Je-sus changed
5. she was stand-ing by the cross when her son stretched his
6. she was one in prayer with those up-on whom tongues of

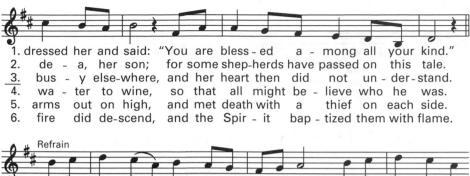

1. dressed her and said: "You are bless-ed a - mong all your kind."
2. de - a, her son; for some shep-herds have passed on this tale.
3. bus - y else-where, and her heart then did not un - der-stand.
4. wa - ter to wine, so that all might be - lieve who he was.
5. arms out on high, and met death with a thief on each side.
6. fire did de-scend, and the Spir - it bap - tized them with flame.

Refrain

On this day all earth and all par-a-dise join in nam-ing you

hap - py and blessed; Vir-gin Ma - ry, bless-ed are you.

Text: *Une femme dont on n'a rien dit*; Didier Rimaud, b. 1922; tr. by Christopher Willcock, b. 1947,
© 1988, Christopher Willcock, SJ. Published by OCP Publications. All rights reserved.
Music: Christopher Willcock, © 1988, Christopher Willcock, SJ. Published by OCP Publications. All rights reserved.

MY SOUL REJOICES 503

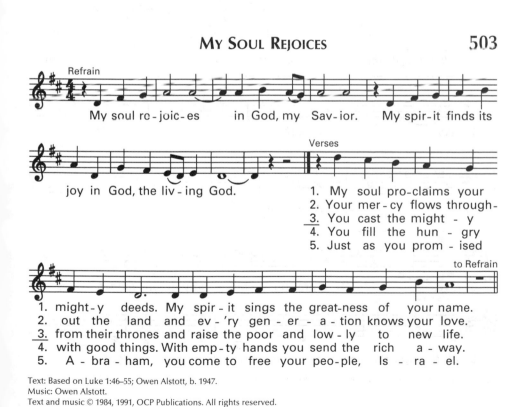

Refrain

My soul re-joic-es in God, my Sav-ior. My spir-it finds its

joy in God, the liv - ing God.

Verses

1. My soul pro-claims your
2. Your mer - cy flows through-
3. You cast the might - y
4. You fill the hun - gry
5. Just as you prom - ised

to Refrain

1. might-y deeds. My spir - it sings the great-ness of your name.
2. out the land and ev - 'ry gen - er - a - tion knows your love.
3. from their thrones and raise the poor and low - ly to new life.
4. with good things. With emp-ty hands you send the rich a - way.
5. A - bra - ham, you come to free your peo-ple, Is - ra - el.

Text: Based on Luke 1:46–55; Owen Alstott, b. 1947.
Music: Owen Alstott.
Text and music © 1984, 1991, OCP Publications. All rights reserved.

504

AVE MARIA

1. A - ve Ma - ri - a, gra - ti - a ple - na,
2. Be - ne - dic - ta, blest a - mong wom - en,
3. Sanc - ta Ma - ri - a, Ho - ly Ma - ry,

1. O ho - ly Ma - ry, ____ full ____ of grace;
2. be - ne - dic - tus, the child that you bore:
3. Ma - ter ____ De - i, ____ Moth - er of God:

1. Do - mi - nus te - cum, with you the Ho - ly One.
2. Je - sus the Sav - ior, God's love in - car - nate,
3. O - ra pro no - bis, pray for our faith - ful - ness

1. Such is your gift ____ to know ____ God in your
2. be - ne - dic - ta, deep wom - an of
3. all through the sea - sons of life with hope and with

1
1. heart. to Verse 2 **2** 2. faith. A - ve Ma - ri -

to Verse 3
2. a, A - ve, A - ve Ma - ri - a.

Final
3. love. O - ra pro no - bis, pray for our faith - ful - ness

3. all through the sea - sons of life with hope and with love.

HOLY IS HIS NAME

1. My soul __ pro-claims the great-ness of the Lord, __
2. He has mer - cy _____ in ev - 'ry gen - er - a - tion.

1. __ and my spir-it _____ ex-alts in God my Sav - ior.
2. He has __ re-vealed _____ his pow-er and his glo - ry.

1. For he has looked with mer - cy on my low-li - ness,
2. He has cast down the might - y in their ar - ro-gance,

1. and my name __ will be for - ev - er ex - alt - ed.
2. and has lift - ed up __ the meek and the low - ly.

1. For the might - y God has done great things for me,
2. He has come to help his ser - vant Is - ra - el;

1. and his mer-cy_____ will reach from age to age. __
2. he __ re-mem - bers __ his prom - ise to our fa-thers.

Refrain

And ho - ly, ho - ly,

ho - ly is his name.

Text: Based on Luke 1:46–55; John Michael Talbot, b. 1954.
Music: John Michael Talbot.
Text and music © 1980, Birdwing Music/BMG Songs. All rights reserved.
   Administered by EMI Christian Music Publishing. Used with permission.

506   IN HIS TEMPLE NOW BEHOLD HIM

1. In his tem-ple now be-hold him, See the long ex-
2. In the arms of her who bore him, Vir-gin pure, be-
3. Je-sus, by your pres-en-ta-tion, When they blest you,
4. Prince and au-thor of sal-va-tion, Be your bound-less

1. pect-ed Lord; An-cient proph-ets had fore-told him;
2. hold him lie, While his a-ged saints a-dore him
3. weak and poor, Make us see our great sal-va-tion,
4. love our theme! Je-sus, praise to you be giv-en,

1. God has now ful-filled his word, Now, to praise him,
2. Ere in faith and hope they die. Al-le-lu-ia!
3. Seal us with your prom-ise sure, And pre-sent us
4. By the world you did re-deem, With the Fa-ther

1. his re-deem-ed shall break forth with one ac-cord.
2. Al-le-lu-ia! Lo, th'in-car-nate God most high.
3. in your glo-ry to your Fa-ther, cleansed and pure.
4. and the Spir-it, Lord of maj-es-ty su-preme.

Text: 87 87 87; Luke 2:22–24; verses 1–3, Henry J. Pyle, 1825–1903; verse 4, William Cooke, 1821–1894.
Music: ST. THOMAS (TANTUM ERGO); John F. Wade, 1711–1786.

507   SONG OF SIMEON

Now, O God, let your ser-vant go.

Let me go in peace ac-cord-ing to your word.

For my eyes be-hold your sav-ing work:

a light for all the world, al - le - lu - ia.

Final

Al - le - lu - ia, al - le - lu - ia.

Text: Based on Luke 2:29–32; *Nunc dimittis;* Janèt Sullivan Whitaker, b. 1958.
Music: Janèt Sullivan Whitaker.

HOLY PATRON, THEE SALUTING 508

Verses

1. Ho - ly pa-tron, thee sa-lut-ing Here we meet, with
2. Thou who faith-ful - ly at-tend-ed Him whom heav'n and
3. May our fer-vent pray'rs as-cend-ing, Move thee for our
4. Through this life, O watch a-round us! Fill with love our

1. hearts sin - cere; Blest Saint Jo - seph, all u - nit - ing,
2. earth a - dore; Who with pi - ous care de - fend - ed
3. souls to plead; May thy smile of peace de - scend-ing,
4. ev - 'ry breath, And, when part - ing fear sur-rounds us,

Refrain

1. Call on thee to hear our prayer. Hap - py saint, in
2. Ma - ry, Vir - gin ev - er pure.
3. Ben - e - dic - tions on us shed.
4. Guide us through the toils of death.

bliss a - dor-ing Je-sus, Sav-ior of hu-man-kind, Hear thy

chil-dren thee im-plor-ing, May we thy pro - tec-tion find.

Text: 87 87 with refrain; American, ca. 1843; Anon.
Music: PLEADING SAVIOR; *Christian Lyre,* 1830.

THE HANDS THAT FIRST HELD MARY'S CHILD

1. The hands that first held Ma - ry's child Were
2. When Jo - seph mar - veled at the size Of
3. "This child shall be Em - man - u - el, Not
4. The tools which Jo - seph laid a - side A

1. hard from work - ing wood, From boards they
2. that small breath - ing frame, And gazed up -
3. God up - on the throne, But God with
4. mob would lat - er lift And use with

1. sawed and planed and filed And splint - ers they with -
2. on those bright new eyes And spoke the in - fant's
3. us, Em - man - u - el, As close as blood and
4. an - ger, fear, and pride To cru - ci - fy God's

1. stood. This day they gripped no tool of
2. name, The an - gel's words he once had
3. bone." The ti - ny form in Jo - seph's
4. gift. Let us, O Lord, not on - ly

1. steel, They drove no i - ron nail,
2. dreamed Poured down from heav - en's height,
3. palms Con - firmed what he had heard,
4. hold The Child who's born to - day,

1. But cra - dled from the head to
2. And like the host of stars that
3. And from his heart rose hymns and
4. But charged with faith may we be

1. heel Our Lord, new - born and frail.
2. beamed Bless'd earth with wel - come light.
3. psalms For heav - en's hu - man word.
4. bold To fol - low in his way.

Text: 86 86 D; Thomas H. Troeger, b. 1945, © 1985, Oxford University Press. All rights reserved. Used with permission.
Music: RESIGNATION; William Walker's *The Southern Harmony*, 1835.

A Just Man Honored from Above

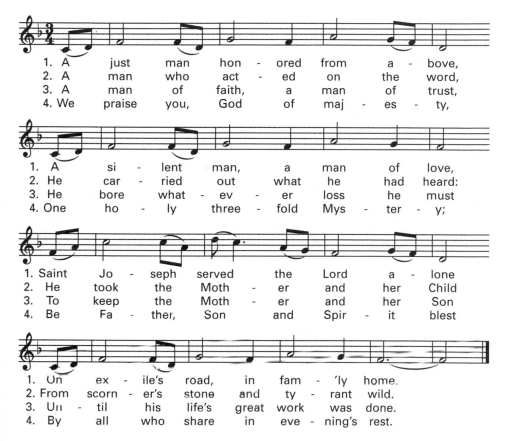

1. A just man hon - ored from a - bove,
2. A man who act - ed on the word,
3. A man of faith, a man of trust,
4. We praise you, God of maj - es - ty,

1. A si - lent man, a man of love,
2. He car - ried out what he had heard:
3. He bore what - ev - er loss he must
4. One ho - ly three - fold Mys - ter - y;

1. Saint Jo - seph served the Lord a - lone
2. He took the Moth - er and her Child
3. To keep the Moth - er and her Son
4. Be Fa - ther, Son and Spir - it blest

1. On ex - ile's road, in fam - 'ly home.
2. From scorn - er's stone and ty - rant wild.
3. Un - til his life's great work was done.
4. By all who share in eve - ning's rest.

Text: LM; Genevieve Glen, OSB, b. 1945, © 1998, The Benedictine Nuns of the Abbey of St. Walburga.
Published by OCP Publications. All rights reserved.
Music: PROSPECT; William Walker's *The Southern Harmony*, 1854.

511   COME NOW, AND PRAISE THE HUMBLE SAINT

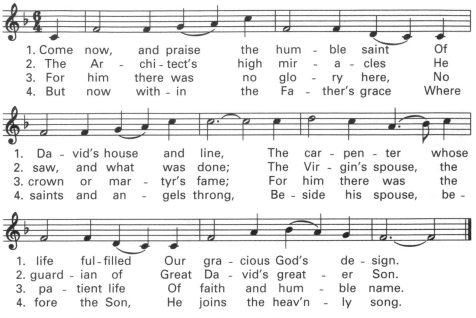

1. Come now, and praise the hum - ble saint Of
2. The Ar - chi - tect's high mir - a - cles He
3. For him there was no glo - ry here, No
4. But now with - in the Fa - ther's grace Where

1. Da - vid's house and line, The car - pen - ter whose
2. saw, and what was done; The Vir - gin's spouse, the
3. crown or mar - tyr's fame; For him there was the
4. saints and an - gels throng, Be - side his spouse, be -

1. life ful - filled Our gra - cious God's de - sign.
2. guard - ian of Great Da - vid's great - er Son.
3. pa - tient life Of faith and hum - ble name.
4. fore the Son, He joins the heav'n - ly song.

Text: CM; George W. Williams, b. 1922, © 1979, The Hymn Society. All rights reserved.
    Administered by Hope Publishing Co. Used with permission.
Music: LAND OF REST; Trad. American Melody.

512   PRAISE WE THE LORD THIS DAY

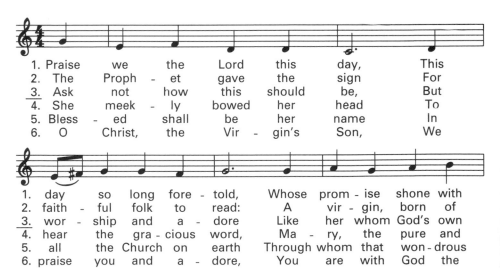

1. Praise we the Lord this day, This
2. The Proph - et gave the sign For
3. Ask not how this should be, But
4. She meek - ly bowed her head To
5. Bless - ed shall be her name In
6. O Christ, the Vir - gin's Son, We

1. day so long fore - told, Whose prom - ise shone with
2. faith - ful folk to read: A vir - gin, born of
3. wor - ship and a - dore Like her whom God's own
4. hear the gra - cious word, Ma - ry, the pure and
5. all the Church on earth Through whom that won - drous
6. praise you and a - dore, You are with God the

1. cheer - ing ray On wait - ing saints of old.
2. Da - vid's line, Shall bear the prom - ised Seed.
3. maj - es - ty Came down to shad - ow o'er.
4. low - ly maid, The fa - vored of the Lord.
5. mer - cy came, The in - car - nate Sav - ior's birth.
6. Fa - ther One And Spir - it ev - er - more.

Text: SM; Matthew 1:23; *Hymns for the Festivals and Saints' Days*, 1846.
Music: SWABIA; Johann M. Speiss, 1715–1772; adapt. by William H. Havergal, 1793–1870.

THE ANGEL GABRIEL FROM HEAVEN CAME   513

1. The an - gel Ga - bri - el from heav - en came, His
2. "For know a bless - ed Moth - er you shall be, All
3. Then gen - tle Ma - ry meek - ly bowed her head; "To
4. Of her, Em - man - u - el, the Christ, was born In

1. wings as drift - ed snow, his eyes as flame; "All
2. gen er - a - tions praise con - tin - ual - ly, Your
3. me be as it pleas - es God!" she said. "My
4. Beth - le - hem, all on a Christ - mas morn; And

1. hail," said he, "O low - ly maid - en Ma - ry,"
2. Son shall be Em - man - u - el, by seers fore - told."
3. soul shall laud and mag - ni - fy his ho - ly name." "Most
4. Chris - tian folk through - out the world will ev - er say:

1-4. high - ly fa - vored la - dy!" Glo - ri - a!

Text: 10 10 12 10; *Birjina gaztettobat zegoen*; Trad. Basque Carol; tr. by Sabine Baring-Gould, 1834–1924.
Music: GABRIEL'S MESSAGE; Trad. Basque Carol Melody.

514   THE GOD WHOM EARTH AND SEA AND SKY

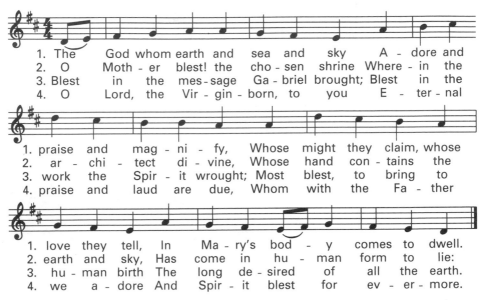

1. The God whom earth and sea and sky A - dore and
2. O Moth - er blest! the cho - sen shrine Where - in the
3. Blest in the mes - sage Ga - briel brought; Blest in the
4. O Lord, the Vir - gin - born, to you E - ter - nal

1. praise and mag - ni - fy, Whose might they claim, whose
2. ar - chi - tect di - vine, Whose hand con - tains the
3. work the Spir - it wrought; Most blest, to bring to
4. praise and laud are due, Whom with the Fa - ther

1. love they tell, In Ma - ry's bod - y comes to dwell.
2. earth and sky, Has come in hu - man form to lie:
3. hu - man birth The long de - sired of all the earth.
4. we a - dore And Spir - it blest for ev - er - more.

Text: LM; *Quem terra, pontus, aethera*; Venantius Honorius Fortunatus, ca. 530–609; tr. by John M. Neale, 1818–1866, alt.
Music: EISENACH; *Das ander Theil des andern newen Operis Geistlicher Deutscher Lieder*, 1605;
    adapt. by Johann Hermann Schein, 1586–1630.

515   THE GREAT FORERUNNER OF THE MORN

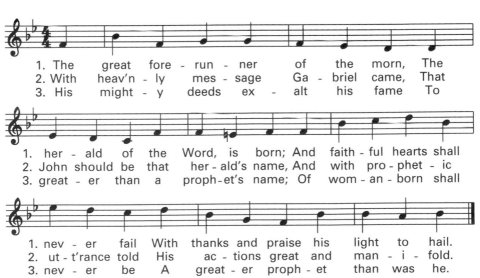

1. The great fore - run - ner of the morn, The
2. With heav'n - ly mes - sage Ga - briel came, That
3. His might - y deeds ex - alt his fame To

1. her - ald of the Word, is born; And faith - ful hearts shall
2. John should be that her - ald's name, And with pro - phet - ic
3. great - er than a proph - et's name; Of wom - an - born shall

1. nev - er fail With thanks and praise his light to hail.
2. ut - t'rance told His ac - tions great and man - i - fold.
3. nev - er be A great - er proph - et than was he.

Text: LM; *Praecursor altus luminis*; St. Bede the Venerable, 673–735; tr. by John M. Neale, 1818–1866, alt.
Music: WINCHESTER NEW; *Musikalisches Handbuch*, Hamburg, 1690; adapt. by William H. Havergal, 1793–1870.

THE ANGEL'S PROMISE

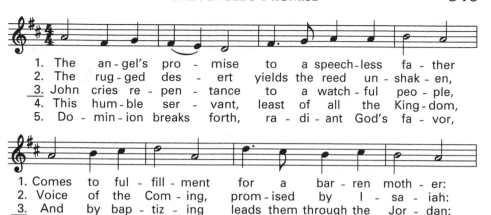

1. The an-gel's pro - mise to a speech-less fa - ther
2. The rug-ged des - ert yields the reed un - shak - en,
3. John cries re - pen - tance to a watch-ful peo - ple,
4. This hum-ble ser - vant, least of all the King-dom,
5. Do - min-ion breaks forth, ra - di - ant God's fa - vor,

1. Comes to ful - fill - ment for a bar - ren moth - er:
2. Voice of the Com - ing, prom-ised by I - sa - iah:
3. And by bap - tiz - ing leads them through the Jor - dan:
4. Strong with the pow - er prom-ised for E - li - jah,
5. Meet - ing of u - nion, Fa - ther, Son, and Spir - it.

1. John is the child's name, proph - et of the
2. "Fill ev - 'ry val - ley, lev - el ev - 'ry
3. Wa - ter of wait - ing, for the fire and
4. Pours out the Spir - it on the Son Be -
5. So let us praise God, Lab - y - rinth of

1. Most High, Hope of the King - dom.
2. moun - tain," Sound of the King - dom.
3. Spir - it Born of the King - dom.
4. lov - ed, Lamb of the King - dom.
5. Mys - t'ry, Lord of the King - dom.

Text: 11 11 11 5; Harry Hagan, OSB, b. 1947, © 1972, 2001, St. Meinrad Archabbey.
Published by OCP Publications. All rights reserved.
Music: CHRISTE SANCTORUM; *Antiphoner*, Paris, 1681.

517   TWO NOBLE SAINTS

1. Two no-ble saints both root - ed In faith and ho - ly love,
2. The words of Paul as - sure us Of Christ's re-deem-ing word;

1. By hope of God u - nit - ed They reach to heav'n a - bove.
2. The works of Pe - ter show us How we may serve the Lord.

1. One on a cross is mar - tyred, One by the sword is slain;
2. So praise we the Cre - a - tor, And praise we Christ the Son,

1. Both tri-umph in their dy - ing, Both glo - rious saint-hood gain.
2. Who with the Ho - ly Spir - it, Now reign, blest Three in One.

Text: 76 76 D; based on *Decora lux aeternitatis auream*; Anne K. LeCroy, b. 1930, © Anne K. LeCroy.
    All rights reserved. Used with permission.
Music: ELLACOMBE; *Gesangbuch der Herzogl, Wirtembergischen Katholischen Hofkapelle*, 1784, alt.;
    adapt. fr. Würth's *Katholisches Gesangbuch*, 1863.

518   'TIS GOOD, LORD, TO BE HERE

1. 'Tis good, Lord, to be here! Your
2. 'Tis good, Lord, to be here, Your
3. Ful - fill - er of the past! Prom -
4. Be - fore we taste of death, We
5. 'Tis good, Lord, to be here! Yet

1. glo - ry fills the night; Your face and gar - ments,
2. beau - ty to be - hold, Where Mo - ses and E -
3. ise of things to be! We hail your bod - y
4. see your king - dom come; We long to hold the
5. we may not re - main; But since you bid us

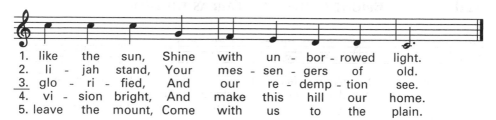

1. like the sun, Shine with un - bor - rowed light.
2. li - jah stand, Your mes - sen - gers of old.
3. glo - ri - fied, And our re - demp - tion see.
4. vi - sion bright, And make this hill our home.
5. leave the mount, Come with us to the plain.

Text: SM; based on Luke 9:32–33; Joseph A. Robinson, 1858–1933, alt., © Esme. D. E. Bird.
  All rights reserved. Used with permission.
Music: SWABIA; Johann M. Speiss, 1715–1772; adapt. by William H. Havergal, 1793–1870.

HAIL, HOLY QUEEN 519

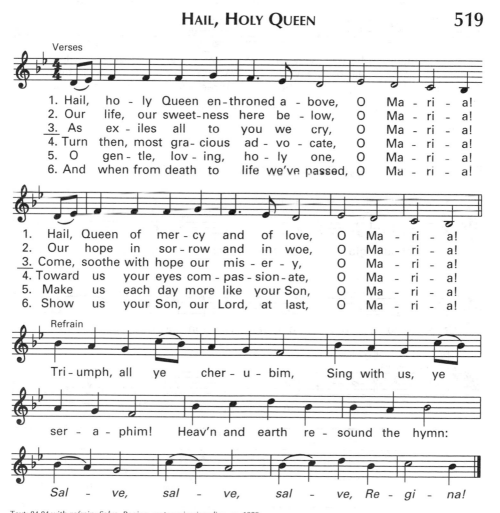

Verses

1. Hail, ho - ly Queen en - throned a - bove, O Ma - ri - a!
2. Our life, our sweet - ness here be - low, O Ma - ri - a!
3. As ex - iles all to you we cry, O Ma - ri - a!
4. Turn then, most gra - cious ad - vo - cate, O Ma - ri - a!
5. O gen - tle, lov - ing, ho - ly one, O Ma - ri - a!
6. And when from death to life we've passed, O Ma - ri - a!

1. Hail, Queen of mer - cy and of love, O Ma - ri - a!
2. Our hope in sor - row and in woe, O Ma - ri - a!
3. Come, soothe with hope our mis - er - y, O Ma - ri - a!
4. Toward us your eyes com - pas - sion - ate, O Ma - ri - a!
5. Make us each day more like your Son, O Ma - ri - a!
6. Show us your Son, our Lord, at last, O Ma - ri - a!

Refrain

Tri - umph, all ye cher - u - bim, Sing with us, ye
ser - a - phim! Heav'n and earth re - sound the hymn:
Sal - ve, sal - ve, sal - ve, Re - gi - na!

Text: 84 84 with refrain; Salve, Regina, mater misericordiae, ca. 1080;
  verses 1, 2, 5 and refrain tr. anon. in Roman Hymnal, 1884; verses 3, 4, 6, para.
Music: SALVE REGINA COELITUM; Melchior Ludwig Herold, 1753–1810; Choralmelodien zum Heiligen Gesänge, 1808.

520   BRIGHT AS THE SUN, FAIR AS THE MOON

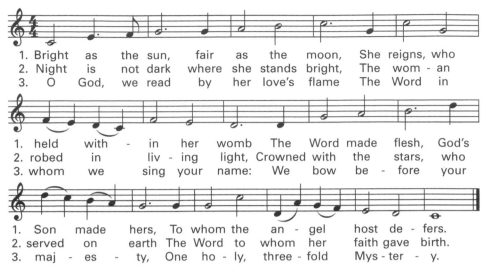

1. Bright as the sun, fair as the moon, She reigns, who
2. Night is not dark where she stands bright, The wom - an
3. O God, we read by her love's flame The Word in

1. held with - in her womb The Word made flesh, God's
2. robed in liv - ing light, Crowned with the stars, who
3. whom we sing your name: We bow be - fore your

1. Son made hers, To whom the an - gel host de - fers.
2. served on earth The Word to whom her faith gave birth.
3. maj - es - ty, One ho - ly, three - fold Mys - ter - y.

Text: LM; Genevieve Glen, OSB, b. 1945, © 1998, The Benedictine Nuns of the Abbey of St. Walburga.
Published by OCP Publications. All rights reserved.
Music: TRURO; William's *Psalmodia Evangelica, Part II,* 1789.

521   WE SHOULD GLORY IN THE CROSS

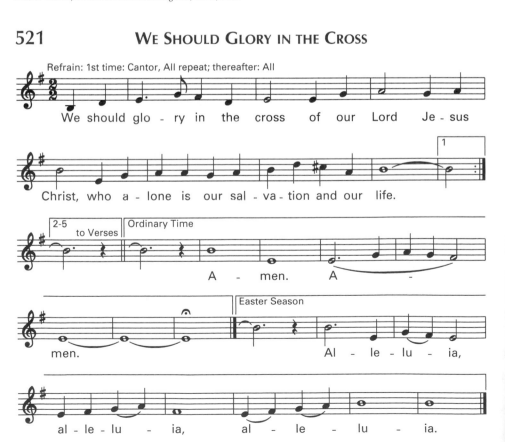

Refrain: 1st time: Cantor, All repeat; thereafter: All

We should glo - ry in the cross of our Lord Je - sus

Christ, who a - lone is our sal - va - tion and our life.

2-5 to Verses | Ordinary Time

A - men. A -

Easter Season

men. Al - le - lu - ia,

al - le - lu - ia, al - le - lu - ia.

Verses

Choir

1. Sing the song of tri-umph, of Sav - ior cru - ci - fied.
2. Raise the cross in tri-umph, so no - ble was the deed.
3. Praise, a - bove all oth - ers, the one and no - ble tree.
4. Bend your boughs in glo - ry, O Tree of glo - ry, bend.

1. Go pro-claim the sto - ry far and wide. Up -
2. By the flood from stain were we made free, that
3. None in blos-som, none in peer may be. The
4. That your birth be-stowed can now sus - pend the

1. on the cross a vic - tim, who in bat - tle con-quered
2. from the ho - ly bod - y, blood and wa - ter did pro -
3. fra - grance of the wood and i - ron, sweet the load can
4. Rul - er of the a - ges, on your bos - om gent - ly

1. death; in the cross our hope shall a - bide.
2. ceed. By the cross we've come to be - lieve.
3. be. Through the cross our lives are set free.
4. tend. With the cross all griev- ing shall end.

All   to Refrain

1. In the cross our hope shall a - bide.
2. By the cross we've come to be - lieve.
3. Through the cross our lives are set free.
4. With the cross all griev- ing shall end.

Text: Refrain based on Galatians 6:14; verses based on *Pange lingua gloriosi lauream certaminis;*
Venantius Honorius Fortunatus, ca. 530–609; tr. fr. *The Three Days,* adapt.; Ricky Manalo, CSP, b. 1965.
Music: Ricky Manalo, CSP.

522   LIFT HIGH THE CROSS

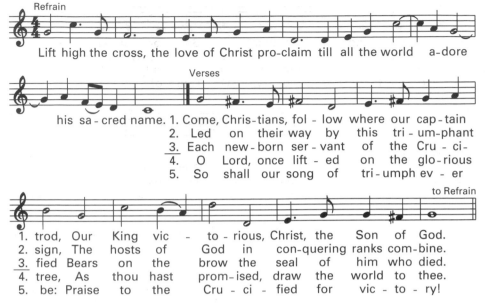

Refrain

Lift high the cross, the love of Christ pro-claim till all the world a-dore

Verses

his sa-cred name.
1. Come, Chris-tians, fol-low where our cap-tain
2. Led on their way by this tri-um-phant
3. Each new-born ser-vant of the Cru-ci-
4. O Lord, once lift-ed on the glo-rious
5. So shall our song of tri-umph ev-er

to Refrain

1. trod, Our King vic - to-rious, Christ, the Son of God.
2. sign, The hosts of God in con-quering ranks com-bine.
3. fied Bears on the brow the seal of him who died.
4. tree, As thou hast prom-ised, draw the world to thee.
5. be: Praise to the Cru - ci - fied for vic - to - ry!

Text: 10 10 with refrain; based on 1 Corinthians 1:18; George W. Kitchin, 1827–1912; alt. by Michael R. Newbolt, 1874–1956.
Music: CRUCIFER; Sydney H. Nicholson, 1875–1947.
Text and music © 1974, Hope Publishing Co. All rights reserved. Used with permission.

523   GLORY IN THE CROSS

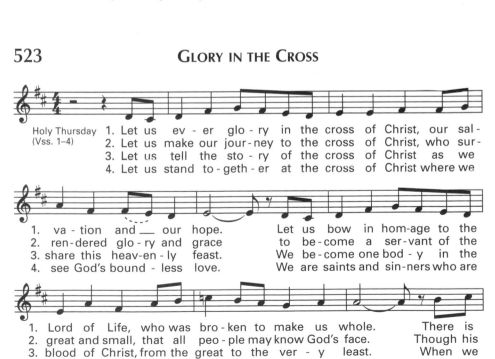

Holy Thursday
(Vss. 1–4)
1. Let us ev - er glo-ry in the cross of Christ, our sal-
2. Let us make our jour-ney to the cross of Christ, who sur-
3. Let us tell the sto-ry of the cross of Christ as we
4. Let us stand to-geth-er at the cross of Christ where we

1. va - tion and __ our hope.   Let us bow in hom-age to the
2. ren-dered glo-ry and grace   to be-come a ser-vant of the
3. share this heav-en - ly feast.   We be-come one bod - y in the
4. see God's bound - less love.   We are saints and sin-ners who are

1. Lord of Life, who was bro-ken to make us whole.   There is
2. great and small, that all peo-ple may know God's face.   Though his
3. blood of Christ, from the great to the ver - y least.   When we
4. joined by faith here on earth and in heav'n a - bove.   Nei-ther

1. no great-er love, as bless-ed as this: to lay down one's
2. birth was di-vine, he knelt as a slave, to wash com-mon
3. eat of this bread, and drink of this cup, we hon-or the
4. wom-an nor man, not ser-vant or free, but one in the

1. life for a friend.
2. dust from our feet.
3. death of the Lord.   Let us ev-er glo-ry in the cross of Christ and the
4. eyes of the Lord.

Fine

1-4. tri-umph of God's great love.

Good Friday

1. Let us ever glory in the cross of Christ
who redeems us with his blood.
Let us tell the story of the cross of Christ
and the pow'r of his saving love.
Like a lamb he was slain;
he carried our shame,
to show us the mercy of God.
Let us ever glory in the cross of Christ
and the triumph of God's great love.

2. Let us bring our burdens
to the cross of Christ
who has known our sorrow and tears.
In the great compassion of
the heart of Christ,
God has walked in our hopes and fears.
He was mocked and betrayed,
deserted by friends, and banished
to die among thieves.
Let us ever glory in the cross of Christ
and the triumph of God's great love.

3. Let us kneel in homage at
the cross of Christ
where we see God's human face.
We behold the Maker of the sun and stars
as he hangs on the throne of grace.
As we share in his pain,
his sorrow and shame,
our hearts will be tested in fire.
Let us ever glory in the cross of Christ
and the triumph of God's great love.

Easter

1. Let us ever glory in the cross of Christ,
our salvation and our hope.
Let us bow in homage to the Lord of Life,
who was broken to make us whole.
There is no greater love, as blessed as this:
to lay down one's life for a friend.
Let us ever glory in the cross of Christ
and the triumph of God's great love.

2. Let us ever glory in the cross of Christ
who is risen from the grave.
He will come in glory to receive our hearts
at the dawn of the lasting day.
For the trumpet will sound,
the dead shall be raised,
and death shall defeat us no more.
Let us ever glory in the cross of Christ
and the triumph of God's great love.

3. Let us raise our voices to the cross of Christ
where the earth and heaven unite.
God has wed creation on the tree of hope
where the darkness becomes our light.
Let us join in the dance of heaven and earth,
give thanks for the goodness of God.
Let us ever glory in the cross of Christ
and the triumph of God's great love.

524 TAKE UP YOUR CROSS

1. Take up your cross, the Sav - ior said, If
2. Take up your cross, be not a - shamed! Let
3. Take up your cross, which gives you strength, Which
4. Take up your cross, and fol - low Christ, Nor

1. you would my dis - ci - ple be; De - ny your - self, the
2. not dis - grace your spir - it fill! For God him - self en -
3. makes your trem-bling spir - it brave: 'Twill guide you to a
4. think till death to lay it down; For on - ly they who

1. world for - sake, And hum - bly fol - low af - ter me.
2. dured to die Up - on a cross, on Cal - vary's hill.
3. bet - ter home And lead to vic - t'ry o'er the grave.
4. bear the cross May hope to wear the glo - rious crown.

Text: LM; Charles W. Everest, 1814–1877, alt. © 1977, OCP Publications. All rights reserved.
Music: ERHALT UNS, HERR; J. Klug's *Geistliche Lieder*, Wittenberg, 1543; adapt. by Johann Sebastian Bach, 1685–1750, alt.

525 LITANY OF THE SAINTS

Repeat each invocation immediately after the priest or cantor:

Lord, have mer - cy. Christ, have mer - cy. Lord, have mer - cy.

(Saint Invocation) 1-4. Pray for us. ___ Pray for us. ___
("Lord, be merciful.") 5. Save your peo - ple. Save your peo - ple.
("Lord, give new life.") 6. Hear our prayer. ___ Hear our prayer. ___

1-4. Pray for us. ___ Pray for us. ___ Pray for us. ___
5. Save your peo - ple. Save your peo - ple. Save your peo - ple.
6. Hear our prayer. ___ Hear our prayer. ___ Hear our prayer. ___

D.S.

1-4. All you ho - ly men and wom - en, pray for us.
5-6. Christ, ___ hear us; Lord, ___ Je - sus, hear our prayer.

Text © 1973, ICEL. All rights reserved. Used with permission.
Music: John D. Becker, b. 1953, © 1987, John D. Becker. Published by OCP Publications. All rights reserved.

For All the Saints

1. For all the saints who from their la - bors
2. You were their rock, their for - tress and their
3. O may your sol - diers, faith - ful, true, and
4. O blest com - mun - ion, fam - i - ly di -
5. And when the strife is fierce, the war - fare
6. The gold - en eve - ning bright - ens in the
7. But then there breaks a yet more glo - rious
8. From earth's wide bounds, from o - cean's far - thest

1. rest, All who _____ by faith be - fore the
2. might; _____ You, Lord, their cap - tain in the
3. bold, _____ Fight as the saints who no - bly
4. vine! _____ We fee - bly strug - gle, they in
5. long, _____ Steals on the ear the dis - tant
6. west; _____ Soon, soon to faith - ful war - riors
7. day: The saints _____ tri - um - phant rise in
8. coast, Through gates _____ of pearl streams in the

1. world con - fessed Your name, O _____
2. well - fought fight; _____ You, in the
3. fought of old, And win, with _____
4. glo - ry shine; Yet all are _____
5. tri - umph song, And hearts are _____
6. comes their rest; _____ Sweet is the
7. bright ar - ray; The king of _____
8. count - less host, _____ Sing - ing to

1. Je - sus, be for - ev - er blest.
2. dark - ness drear, their one true light.
3. them, the vic - tor's crown of gold.
4. one with - in your great de - sign.
5. brave a - gain, and arms are strong.
6. calm of par - a - dise the blest.
7. glo - ry pass - es on his way.
8. Fa - ther, Son, and Ho - ly Ghost:

1-8. Al - le - lu - ia! Al - le - lu - ia!

Text: 10 10 10 with alleluias; William W. How, 1823–1897, alt.
Music: SINE NOMINE; *English Hymnal*, 1906; Ralph Vaughan Williams, 1872–1958.

527

REJOICE WITH ALL THE SAINTS

1. Re - joice with all the saints this day,
2. How blest are they, the Spir - it's poor;
3. How blest are those who fought the fight;
4. How blest are those who wrought the peace;
5. Come, ho - ly men and wom - en all;
6. Most blest the Fa - ther and the Son,

1. Who ran by faith the nar - row way.
2. Their king is Je - sus Christ the Lord,
3. God's jus - tice fills their thirst for right.
4. As heirs they share the Vic - tor's feast;
5. With heart and voice sing praise and call
6. Most blest the Spir - it, Three in One.

1. The great and low to - geth - er stand
2. And all who mourned have found new birth;
3. The pure of heart God's face be - hold;
4. And proph - ets by in - jus - tice slain
5. To Christ who rose tri - um - phant - ly
6. Your King - dom come, your will be done,

1. With glo - ry crowned at God's right hand.
2. The pa - tient meek a - wait the earth.
3. The mer - ci - ful have o - ver - flowed.
4. Have claimed the King - dom's righ - teous reign.
5. That we may join your com - pa - ny.
6. Your praise for - ev - er more be sung.

Text: LM; based on Matthew 5:3–10; Harry Hagan, OSB, b. 1947, © 1994, St. Meinrad Archabbey.
    Published by OCP Publications. All rights reserved.
Music: PROSPECT; William Walker's *The Southern Harmony*, 1854.

Ye Watchers and Ye Holy Ones

1. Ye watch-ers and ye ho-ly ones, Bright ser-aphs,
2. O high-er than the cher-u-bim, More glo-rious
3. Re-spond, ye souls in end-less rest, Ye pa-tri-
4. O friends, in glad-ness let us sing, Ce-les-tial

1. cher-u-bim, and thrones, Raise the glad strain, Al-le-lu-ia!
2. than the ser-a-phim, Lead their prais-es, Al-le-lu-ia!
3. archs and proph-ets blest, Al-le-lu-ia, Al-le-lu-ia!
4. an-thems ech-o-ing, Al-le-lu-ia, Al-le-lu-ia!

1. Cry out, do-min-ions, prince-doms, powers, Vir-tues, arch-
2. O bear-er of the e-ter-nal Word, Most gra-cious,
3. Ye ho-ly Twelve, ye mar-tyrs strong, All saints tri-
4. To God the Fa-ther, God the Son, And God the

1. an-gels, an-gels' choirs,
2. mag-ni-fy the Lord,
3. um-phant, raise in song,
4. Spir-it, Three-in-One,
Al-le-lu-ia, Al-le-lu-ia,

1-4. Al-le-lu-ia, Al-le-lu-ia, Al-le-lu-ia!

Text: LM with alleluias; *English Hymnal*, 1906; John A. Riley, 1858–1945.
Music: LASST UNS ERFREUEN; *Auserlesene Catholische Geistliche Kirchengesänge*, Cologne, 1623.

529   O LORD OF DARKNESS AND OF LIGHT

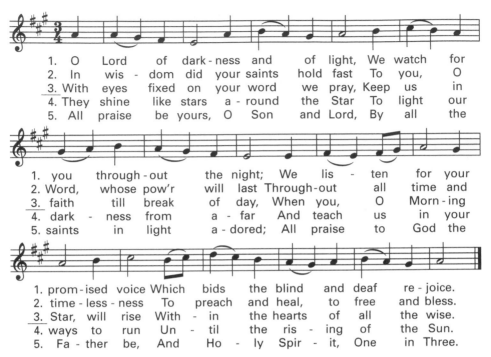

1. O Lord of dark-ness and of light, We watch for
2. In wis - dom did your saints hold fast To you, O
3. With eyes fixed on your word we pray, Keep us in
4. They shine like stars a - round the Star To light our
5. All praise be yours, O Son and Lord, By all the

1. you through - out the night; We lis - ten for your
2. Word, whose pow'r will last Through-out all time and
3. faith till break of day, When you, O Morn - ing
4. dark - ness from a - far And teach us in your
5. saints in light a - dored; All praise to God the

1. prom - ised voice Which bids the blind and deaf re - joice.
2. time - less - ness To preach and heal, to free and bless.
3. Star, will rise With - in the hearts of all the wise.
4. ways to run Un - til the ris - ing of the Sun.
5. Fa - ther be, And Ho - ly Spir - it, One in Three.

Text: LM; Genevieve Glen, OSB, b. 1945, © 1997, The Benedictine Nuns of the Abbey of St. Walburga.
    Published by OCP Publications. All rights reserved.
Music: WAREHAM; William Knapp, 1698–1768.

530   O LORD OF LIFE

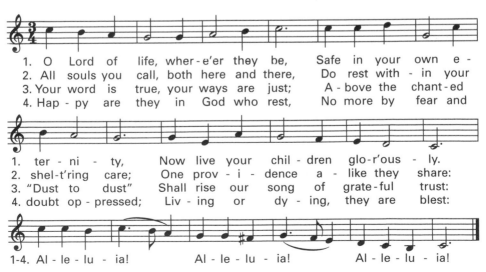

1. O Lord of life, wher - e'er they be, Safe in your own e -
2. All souls you call, both here and there, Do rest with - in your
3. Your word is true, your ways are just; A - bove the chant - ed
4. Hap - py are they in God who rest, No more by fear and

1. ter - ni - ty, Now live your chil - dren glo - r'ous - ly.
2. shel - t'ring care; One prov - i - dence a - like they share:
3. "Dust to dust" Shall rise our song of grate - ful trust:
4. doubt op - pressed; Liv - ing or dy - ing, they are blest:

1-4. Al - le - lu - ia!   Al - le - lu - ia!   Al - le - lu - ia!

Text: 888 with alleluias; Frederick Lucian Hosmer, 1840–1929, alt.
Music: GELOBT SEI GOTT; Melchior Vulpius, ca. 1560–1616.

Unless the Lord

1. Un - less the Lord shall build the house, The
2. You made us stew - ards of the earth To
3. Great God and all cre - a - tion's Lord, Un -

1. build - ers build in vain. And they who
2. bless and mul - ti - ply, And ev - 'ry -
3. fath - omed Depth and Height, O Mys - ter -

1. watch shall sure - ly fail Lest God their watch sus -
2. thing you made is good, As we must tes - ti -
3. y be - yond our grasp, O Love be - yond our

1. tain. In vain they rise and
2. fy: How won - drous ly you
3. might: We praise you, Fa - ther,

1. la - bor long To eat their bread of pain,
2. formed us all, An im - age of your face!
3. Source of Life, Re - vealed in Christ your Son,

1. For, while they slum - ber, God pours
2. How gra - cious - ly you bless us
3. With God the Spir - it, Font of

1. down Good gifts on them like rain.
2. still With your sur - pris - ing grace.
3. Love, E - ter - nal Three in One.

Text: 86 86 D; based on Psalm 127 and Genesis 1; Harry Hagan, OSB, b. 1947, © 1997, St. Meinrad Archabbey.
Published by OCP Publications. All rights reserved.
Music: RESIGNATION; William Walker's *The Southern Harmony*, 1835.

HOLY IS THE TEMPLE

Refrain

Ho - ly is the tem-ple of the LORD, it is the hand-i-work, the dwell-ing place of God.

Verses

1. How love - ly your dwell - ing place, LORD of hosts.
2. ⁊ Spar-rows and swal-lows ___ build their nests
3. How bless - ed are those who live in your house.
4. ⁊ As they go through the bar - ren val-ley
5. Our God is a ram - part ___ and a shield;

1. I long and I yearn for the courts of the
2. with - in ___ your house where they shel - ter their
3. In un - ceas - ing song ___ they of - fer you
4. the land is re - newed with ___ life - giv - ing
5. be-stow - er of grace, hold - ing back no good

1. LORD, My whole be - ing cries out to God,
2. young, ⁊ be - side ___ your al - tars, LORD,
3. praise. Hap - py those who find strength in you,
4. streams; ⁊ their strength grow - ing day by day,
5. thing ⁊ from those who walk righ-teous - ly;

to Refrain

1. ⁊ I sing out with joy to the liv - ing God. _
2. ⁊ your al - tars, my king ___ and my God. _
3. ⁊ who hold in their hearts ___ the way to Zi - on.
4. ⁊ they go ___ to see ___ God in Zi - on.
5. Hap-py those, ___ O LORD, ___ who trust in you. _

Text: Based on Psalm 84:2–8, 12–13; Bob Hurd, b. 1950.
Music: Bob Hurd.

CHURCH OF GOD, ELECT AND GLORIOUS

533

1. Church of God, e - lect and glo - rious, ho - ly na - tion,
2. God has called you out of dark - ness in - to his most
3. Once you were an al - ien peo - ple, strang-ers to God's
4. Church of God, e - lect and ho - ly, be the peo - ple

1. cho - sen race; called as God's own spe - cial
2. mar - v'lous light, brought his truth to life with -
3. heart of love; but he brought you home in
4. he in - tends; strong in faith and swift to

1. peo - ple, roy - al priests and heirs of grace: know the
2. in you, turned your blind - ness in - to sight. Let your
3. mer - cy, cit - i - zens of heav'n a - bove. Let his
4. an - swer each com - mand your mas - ter sends: roy - al

1. pur - pose of your call - ing, show to all God's
2. light so shine a - round you that God's name is
3. love flow out to oth - ers, let them feel a
4. priests, ful - fill your call - ing through your sac - ri -

1. might - y deeds; tell of love which knows no
2. glo - ri - fied; and all find fresh hope and
3. Fa - ther's care; that they too may know his
4. fice and prayer; give your lives in joy - ful

1. lim - its, grace which meets all hu - man needs.
2. pur - pose in Christ Je - sus cru - ci - fied.
3. wel - come and his count - less bless - ings share.
4. ser - vice, sing his praise, his love de - clare.

Text: 87 87 D; based on 1 Peter 2; J.E. Seddon, 1915–1983, © Mrs. M. Seddon, via Jubilee Hymns, Ltd.
All rights reserved. Used with permission.
Music: HYFRYDOL; Rowland H. Prichard, 1811–1887.

534   HOW BLESSED IS THIS PLACE

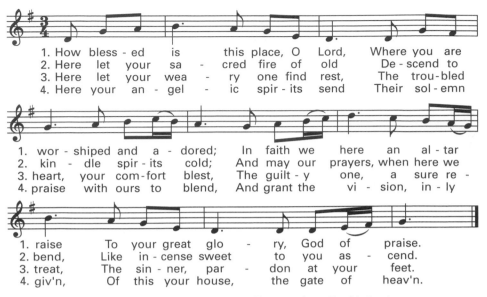

1. How bless-ed is this place, O Lord, Where you are
2. Here let your sa - cred fire of old De - scend to
3. Here let your wea - ry one find rest, The trou-bled
4. Here your an - gel - ic spir-its send Their sol-emn

1. wor - shiped and a - dored; In faith we here an al - tar
2. kin - dle spir - its cold; And may our prayers, when here we
3. heart, your com-fort blest, The guilt-y one, a sure re -
4. praise with ours to blend, And grant the vi - sion, in - ly

1. raise To your great glo - ry, God of praise.
2. bend, Like in - cense sweet to you as - cend.
3. treat, The sin - ner, par - don at your feet.
4. giv'n, Of this your house, the gate of heav'n.

Text: LM; Ernest E. Ryden, 1886–1981, alt. Verses 1–3 © Board of Publication, Lutheran Church in America;
    verse 4 © 1958, *Service Book and Hymnal*. All rights reserved. Reprinted by permission of Augsburg Fortress.
Music: O WALY WALY; Trad. English Melody.

535   IMMACULATE MARY

Verses

1. Im - mac - u - late Ma - ry, your prais-es we sing;
2. In heav - en the bless-ed your glo - ry pro - claim;
3. Your name is our pow - er, your vir - tues our light;
4. We pray for the Church, our true moth-er on earth,

1. You reign now with Je - sus, our Sav - ior and King.
2. On earth we, your chil-dren, in - voke your fair name.
3. Your love is our com-fort, your pray'rs are our might.
4. And ask you to watch o'er the land of our birth.

Refrain

A - ve, a - ve, a - ve, Ma - ri - a!

A - ve, a - ve, Ma - ri - a!

Text: 11 11 with refrain; anon. in *Parochial Hymn Book*, Boston, 1897;
    rev. of *Hail Virgin of virgins*, by Jeremiah Cummings, 1814–1866, alt.
Music: LOURDES HYMN; Trad. Pyrenean Melody; pub. Grenoble, 1882; alt. by Augustus Edmonds Tozer, 1857–1910.

THE PATH OF LIFE

536

Refrain: All

You will show me the path of life, the de-lights that a-wait me in your pres-ence. With-out you there is noth-ing; no joy can be com-plete un - til at last I sit by your side.

Verses 1, 2: Cantor

1. O God, you are my ref - uge, do not turn me a-way; I
2. I bless the Lord who guides me even in my sleep; my

1. say "You are my God." With-out you there can be no good.
2. face is turned to God. With the Lord at my side I shall stand firm.

to Refrain

Verse 3: Choir

3. My heart ex-ults, my spir-it sings, e - ven my
3. bod - y trusts in you; for you will not a-ban-don my
3. soul to death, nor let me sink in-to the grave.

to Refrain

Text: Psalm 16:11, 1–2, 7–10; Scott Soper, b. 1961.
Music: Scott Soper.

537
SIGNING OF THE SENSES

Verse 1: Priest

1. Receive the cross on your forehead. It is Christ himself who now strengthens you with this sign of his love. Learn to know and follow him.

Response

By this sign may you re-ceive Christ's love and al-ways fol-low him.

Verses 2-6: Priest

2. Receive the sign of the cross on your ears, that you may hear the voice of the Lord.

3. Receive the sign of the cross on your eyes, that you may see the glory of God.

4. Receive the sign of the cross on your lips, that you may respond to the word of God.

5. Receive the sign of the cross over your heart, that Christ may dwell there by faith.

6. Receive the sign of the cross on your shoulders that you may bear the gentle yoke of Christ.

Blessing: Priest

7. I sign you with the sign of eternal life in the name of the Father, and of the Son, and of the Holy Spirit.

Final Response

A - men. A - men. A - men.

Text © 1985, ICEL. All rights reserved. Used with permission.
Music: Randall DeBruyn, b. 1947, © 1987, OCP Publications. All rights reserved.

538
COME TO THE RIVER

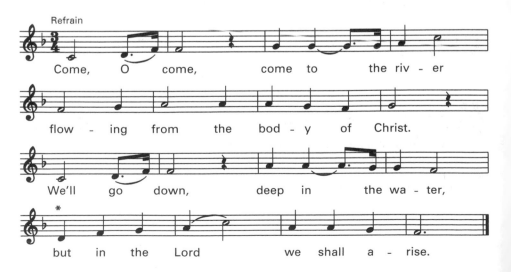

Refrain

Come, O come, come to the riv - er

flow - ing from the bod - y of Christ.

We'll go down, deep in the wa - ter,

but in the Lord we shall a - rise.

Verses

1. Washed in wa - ters of re-birth, we have put on Christ Je - sus.
2. Priest - ly peo - ple are ___ we, sealed and sent by the Spir - it.
3. Blest are those ___ who ___ thirst for the reign of God's jus - tice.
4. Let us walk ___ in the light of God's ho - ly prom - ise.
5. Those who sow ___ in ___ tears reap the har - vest re - joic - ing.

to Refrain

*Repeat last phrase final time.

Text and music: *Mass of Glory*; Bob Hurd, b. 1950, © 1994, 1999, Bob Hurd. Published by OCP Publications. All rights reserved.

WORD OF GOD 539

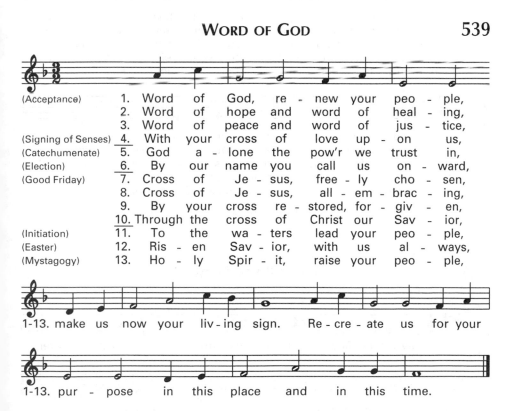

(Acceptance) 1. Word of God, re - new your peo - ple,
2. Word of hope and word of heal - ing,
3. Word of peace and word of jus - tice,
(Signing of Senses) 4. With your cross of love up - on us,
(Catechumenate) 5. God a - lone the pow'r we trust in,
(Election) 6. By our name you call us on - ward,
(Good Friday) 7. Cross of Je - sus, free - ly cho - sen,
8. Cross of Je - sus, all - em - brac - ing,
9. By your cross re - stored, for - giv - en,
10. Through the cross of Christ our Sav - ior,
(Initiation) 11. To the wa - ters lead your peo - ple,
(Easter) 12. Ris - en Sav - ior, with us al - ways,
(Mystagogy) 13. Ho - ly Spir - it, raise your peo - ple,

1-13. make us now your liv-ing sign. Re - cre - ate us for your

1-13. pur - pose in this place and in this time.

Text and music: Bernadette Farrell, b. 1957, © 2000, 2001, Bernadette Farrell.
Published by OCP Publications. All rights reserved.

540

YOU HAVE CALLED US

Refrain: 1st time: Cantor, All repeat; thereafter: All

You have called us by our name. We be - long to you.

You have called us by our name and we are yours.

Verses

1. You have cho - sen us to be mem - bers
2. You will lead us to your light, walk be -
3. You will hold us when we fall, give new
4. You will nour - ish, you will lead, giv - ing
5. Through our shar - ing here to - day may our

1. of your fam - i - ly. In your love you have cre -
2. fore us through the night. You will guide us on our
3. strength to hear your call. You will nev - er be be -
4. ev - 'ry gift we need, for your reign will be es -
5. faith and life con - vey Christ our light and Christ our

to Refrain

1. at - ed us to live in u - ni - ty.
2. jour - ney. You will keep our vi - sion bright.
3. yond us, for your love is all in all.
4. tab - lished from the small - est of all seeds.
5. vi - sion, Christ our pur - pose, Christ our way.

541

FLOW RIVER FLOW

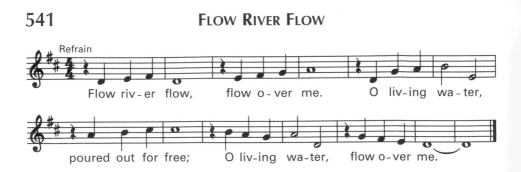

Refrain

Flow riv - er flow, flow o - ver me. O liv - ing wa - ter,

poured out for free; O liv - ing wa - ter, flow o - ver me.

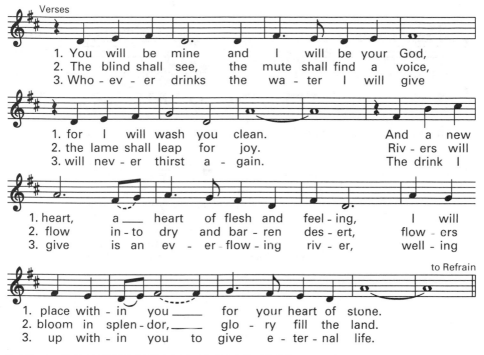

Verses

1. You will be mine and I will be your God,
2. The blind shall see, the mute shall find a voice,
3. Who - ev - er drinks the wa - ter I will give

1. for I will wash you clean. And a new
2. the lame shall leap for joy. Riv - ers will
3. will nev - er thirst a - gain. The drink I

1. heart, a __ heart of flesh and feel - ing, I will
2. flow in - to dry and bar - ren des - ert, flow - ers
3. give is an ev - er - flow - ing riv - er, well - ing

to Refrain

1. place with - in you __ for your heart of stone.
2. bloom in splen - dor, __ glo - ry fill the land.
3. up with - in you to give e - ter - nal life.

Text: Based on Ezekiel 11:19, 20; Isaiah 35: 1–6; John 4:7–15; Bob Hurd, b. 1950.
Music: Bob Hurd.

Baptized in Water
542

1. Bap - tized in wa - ter, Sealed by the Spir - it, Cleansed by the
2. Bap - tized in wa - ter, Sealed by the Spir - it, Dead in the
3. Bap - tized in wa - ter, Sealed by the Spir - it, Marked with the

1. blood of Christ our King: Heirs of sal - va - tion, Trust - ing his
2. tomb with Christ our King: One with his ris - ing, Freed and for -
3. sign of Christ our King: Born of one Fa - ther, We are his

1. prom - ise, Faith - ful - ly now God's praise we sing.
2. giv - en, Thank - ful - ly now God's praise we sing.
3. chil - dren, Joy - ful - ly now God's praise we sing.

Music: BUNESSAN; Trad. Gaelic Melody.

543   I SAW WATER FLOWING

Refrain

I saw wa-ter flow-ing, flow-ing from the side of the tem-ple; and where the wa-ter flowed there was new life.

Verses

1. When your hour had come and they pierced you, Lord,
2. Come to Christ the Lord, the ___ liv-ing stone, re-
3. Not to us, O Lord, but to you all praise,
4. May this house of prayer be a home to all.
5. May this church em-bod-y your pres-ence, Lord:

1. blood and wa-ter flowed forth ___ from your side.
2. ject-ed once but now ___ the cor-ner-stone.
3. for a-part from you ___ we build in vain.
4. May the love of Christ reign with-in these walls,
5. help for the op-pressed, Good News for the poor.

1. With great love you gave your-self for
2. Joined to him, we are God's dwell-ing
3. Help us live this ho-ly mys-ter-
4. so the ones who knock find wel-come
5. Use our hands to build your reign of

1. us! Who can tell the great love by which you
2. place, priest-ly peo-ple and in-stru-ments of
3. y: "It is no long-er I who live, but
4. here and all those who are thirst-ing re-ceive
5. peace; give us vi-sion to fash-ion a more

to Refrain

1. brought your Church to birth!
2. God's re-deem-ing grace.
3. Christ who lives in me."
4. liv-ing wa-ter here.
5. just so-ci-e-ty.

Text: Refrain based on Ezekiel 47:1-2, 9; verses based on John 16:21; 17:1; 19:34; 1 Peter 2:4-9; Psalm 127:1;
   Galatians 2:20; Bob Hurd, b. 1950.
Music: Bob Hurd.

WADE IN THE WATER

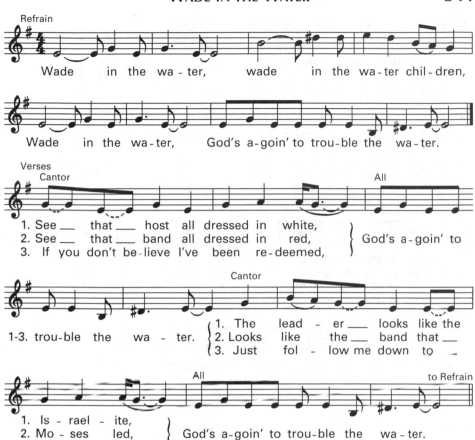

Refrain

Wade in the wa-ter, wade in the wa-ter chil-dren,

Wade in the wa-ter, God's a-goin' to trou-ble the wa-ter.

Verses

Cantor   *All*

1. See __ that __ host all dressed in white,
2. See __ that __ band all dressed in red,   God's a-goin' to
3. If you don't be-lieve I've been re-deemed,

Cantor

1-3. trou-ble the wa-ter.
1. The lead - er __ looks like the
2. Looks like the __ band that __
3. Just fol - low me down to __

All   *to Refrain*

1. Is - rael - ite,
2. Mo - ses led,   God's a-goin' to trou-ble the wa-ter.
3. Jor - dan's stream.

Text: Traditional.
Music: Spiritual.

YOU HAVE PUT ON CHRIST

You have put on Christ, al - le - lu - ia!

Bap - tized in Christ, al - le - lu - ia!

546   BATHED IN THE WATERS OF LIFE

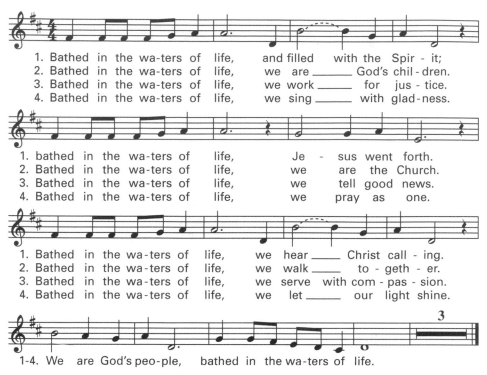

1. Bathed in the wa-ters of life, and filled with the Spir - it;
2. Bathed in the wa-ters of life, we are _____ God's chil - dren.
3. Bathed in the wa-ters of life, we work _____ for jus - tice.
4. Bathed in the wa-ters of life, we sing _____ with glad-ness.

1. bathed in the wa-ters of life, Je - sus went forth.
2. Bathed in the wa-ters of life, we are the Church.
3. Bathed in the wa-ters of life, we tell good news.
4. Bathed in the wa-ters of life, we pray as one.

1. Bathed in the wa-ters of life, we hear _____ Christ call - ing.
2. Bathed in the wa-ters of life, we walk _____ to - geth - er.
3. Bathed in the wa-ters of life, we serve with com - pas - sion.
4. Bathed in the wa-ters of life, we let _____ our light shine.

1-4. We are God's peo-ple, bathed in the wa-ters of life.

547   YOU HAVE PUT ON CHRIST

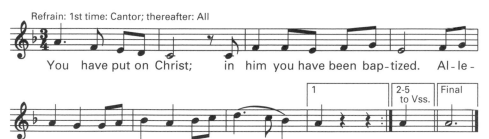

Refrain: 1st time: Cantor; thereafter: All

You have put on Christ; in him you have been bap-tized. Al - le -

lu - ia, al-le - lu - ia, al-le - lu - ia! | ia! | ia!

Verses: Cantor/Choir

1. We who were dead are now reborn.
We who were buried now are raised.
We who were dwelling in the dark
    now see light.

2. For though in Adam all have sinned,
in Jesus Christ are all made clean.
The grace abounding of his death
    sets us free.

3. One Lord we serve, who died for us;
one faith we hold in life to come;
one God and Father of us all
    we proclaim.

4. And this we know, that nothing ill,
no prince nor pow'r, nor death nor sin,
can separate us from God's love,
    shown in Christ.

RIVER OF GLORY

Refrain

Riv - er of glo - ry, springs of our birth, flood of God's
rich - es poured on the earth. We are born from the dark-ness
and clothed in the light! We are bathed in the glo - ry of

1-4 / to Verses   Final
God!   God, bathed in the glo - ry of God!

Verses

1. Foun - tain of mer - cy, grace flow - ing free, streams of sal -
2. Here there is ha - ven, heal - ing and health, joy for the
3. Bread for our jour - ney God will pro - vide. Hope for all
4. Dark - ness is ban-ished, night turned a - way. Christ is our

to Refrain

1. va - tion, spill - ing with love from a tree!
2. ask - ing, love in a - bun - dance of wealth!
3. a - ges, Je - sus, com - pan - ion and guide!
4. sun - light, lift - ing and lead - ing our way!

YOU ARE CHOSEN

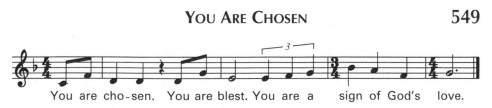

You are cho - sen. You are blest. You are a sign of God's love.

550 MAY WE SEE YOU

Refrain

May we see you in faith, may we know you in faith. Lord of life, may we love you in faith.

Verses

1. May our eyes be o-pened to see _____ those in need.
2. May our hearts be o-pened to love _____ those in need.
3. May our ears be o-pened to hear your ho - ly Word.
4. May our minds be o-pened, im - plant your Word, O Lord.

to Refrain

1. May your Spir - it _____ guide us to tend to all in need.
2. May your pre - sence _____ guide us to give to all in need.
3. May your Word give us cour-age to bring your love to all.
4. May your love bring us peace, _____ your peace to com-fort all.

Text: Based on John 9:1–12; Gerard Chiusano, b. 1953.
Music: Gerard Chiusano.
Text and music © 1999, Gerard Chiusano. Published by OCP Publications. All rights reserved.

551 O BREATHE ON ME, O BREATH OF GOD

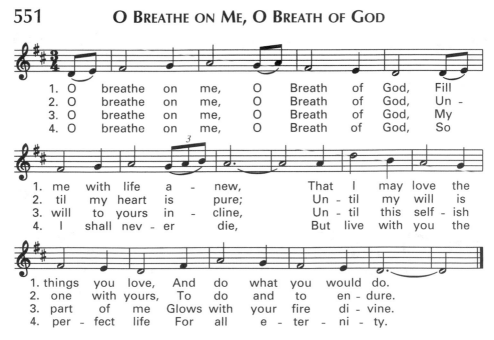

1. O breathe on me, O Breath of God, Fill
2. O breathe on me, O Breath of God, Un -
3. O breathe on me, O Breath of God, My
4. O breathe on me, O Breath of God, So

1. me with life a - new, That I may love the
2. til my heart is pure; Un - til my will is
3. will to yours in - cline, Un - til this self - ish
4. I shall nev - er die, But live with you the

1. things you love, And do what you would do.
2. one with yours, To do and to en - dure.
3. part of me Glows with your fire di - vine.
4. per - fect life For all e - ter - ni - ty.

Text: CM; Edwin Hatch, 1835–1889, alt.
Music: ST. COLUMBA; Trad. Irish Melody.

We Will Journey in Faith

Refrain

We will jour-ney in faith by the light of Christ and will
(Dismissal) *May you jour-ney in faith by the light of Christ. May you*

live by his gos-pel in spir - it and truth.
live by his gos-pel in spir - it and truth.

Verses

1. Let us seek with our minds the truth of Christ,
2. Let us speak with our lips the peace of Christ,
3. We a - wait with our ears the voice of Christ,
4. We be - hold with our eyes the face of Christ,
5. Let us bear in our hearts the love of Christ,
6. We pre - pare with our hands the work of Christ,
7. Let us walk ev - er - more as friends of Christ,

to Refrain

1. who taught us the wis - dom of God.
2. the heal - ing and hope of our God.
3. who calls us the chil - dren of God.
4. who shows us the mer - cy of God.
5. the ten - der com - pas - sion of God.
6. in build - ing the king - dom of God.
7. the ho - ly be - lov - ed of God.

Text and music: Dan Schutte, b. 1947, © 2000, Daniel L. Schutte. Published by OCP Publications. All rights reserved.

Litany of Forgiveness

553

*Ostinato Refrain: All

Lord, have mer - cy. Lord, have mer - cy.

Lord, have mer - cy on us.

*Verses available in accompaniment books.

Text: Based on the *Rite of Penance*; Peter Rubalcava, b. 1958.
Music: Peter Rubalcava.
Text and music © 1997, Peter Rubalcava. Published by OCP Publications. All rights reserved.

554 OUR FATHER, WE HAVE WANDERED

1. Our Fa-ther, we have wan-dered And hid-den from your face;
2. And now at length dis-cern-ing The e-vil that we do,
3. O Lord of all the liv-ing, Both ban-ished and re-stored,

1. In fool-ish-ness have squan-dered Your leg-a-cy of grace.
2. Be-hold us, Lord, re-turn-ing With hope and trust to you.
3. Com-pas-sion-ate, for-giv-ing And ev-er car-ing Lord,

1. But now, in ex-ile dwell-ing, We rise with fear and shame,
2. In haste you come to meet us And home re-joic-ing bring,
3. Grant now that our trans-gress-ing, Our faith-less-ness may cease.

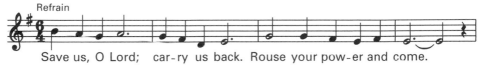

1. As dis-tant but com-pell-ing, We hear you call our name.
2. In glad-ness there to greet us With calf and robe and ring.
3. Stretch out your hand in bless-ing, In par-don and in peace.

Text: 76 76 D; Kevin Nichols, b. 1929, © 1981, ICEL. All rights reserved. Used with permission.
Music: PASSION CHORALE; Hans Leo Hassler, 1564–1612; adapt. by Johann Sebastian Bach, 1685–1750.

555 SAVE US, O LORD

Refrain

Save us, O Lord; car-ry us back. Rouse your pow-er and come.

Res-cue your peo-ple; show us your face. Bring us back.

Verse 1

1. O Shep-herd of Is-ra-el, hear us. Re-turn and we shall be

to Refrain

1. saved. A-rise, O Lord; hear our cries, O Lord: bring us back!

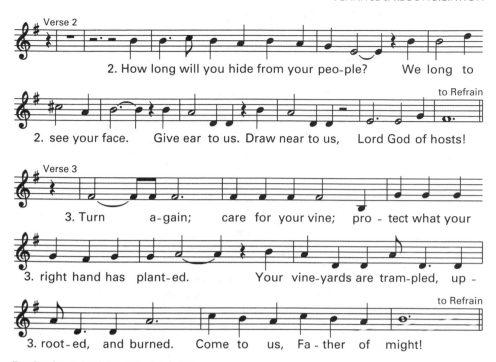

2. How long will you hide from your peo-ple? We long to

2. see your face. Give ear to us. Draw near to us, Lord God of hosts!

3. Turn a-gain; care for your vine; pro - tect what your

3. right hand has plant-ed. Your vine-yards are tram-pled, up -

3. root-ed, and burned. Come to us, Fa-ther of might!

Text: Based on Psalm 80; Bob Dufford, SJ, b. 1943.
Music: Bob Dufford, SJ.
Text and music © 1981, 1983, Robert J. Dufford, SJ, and New Dawn Music. Published by OCP Publications. All rights reserved.

FORGIVE OUR SINS 556

1. "For - give our sins as we for - give," You
2. How can your par - don reach and bless The
3. In blaz - ing light your Cross re - veals The
4. Lord, cleanse the depths with - in our souls And

1. taught us, Lord, to pray, But you a - lone can
2. un - for - giv - ing heart That broods on wrongs and
3. truth we dim - ly knew: What triv - ial debts are
4. bid re - sent - ment cease. Then, bound to all in

1. grant us grace To live the words we say.
2. will not let Old bit - ter - ness de - part?
3. owed to us, How great our debt to you!
4. bonds of love, Our lives will spread your peace.

Text: CM; Rosamond E. Herklots, 1905–1987, © Oxford University Press, London. All rights reserved. Used with permission.
Music: DETROIT; A Supplement to the Kentucky Harmony, 1820.

557   SOFTLY AND TENDERLY JESUS IS CALLING

Verses

1. Soft - ly and ten - der - ly Je - sus is call - ing, call - ing for
2. Why should we tar - ry when Je - sus is plead - ing, plead - ing for
3. O for the won - der - ful love he has prom - ised, prom - ised for

1. you and for me; see, on the por - tals he's
2. you and for me? Why should we lin - ger and
3. you and for me! Though we have sinned, he has

1. wait - ing and watch - ing, watch - ing for you and for me.
2. heed not his mer - cies, mer - cies for you and for me?
3. mer - cy and par - don, par - don for you and for me.

Refrain

Come home, come home, you who are

wea - ry, come home; ear - nest - ly, ten - der - ly,

Je - sus is call - ing, call - ing for you to come home!

Text: 11 7 11 7 with refrain; Will L. Thompson, 1847–1909, alt.
Music: THOMPSON; Will I. Thompson, 1847–1909.

558   SEEK THE LORD

Refrain

Seek the Lord while he may be found;

call to him while he is still near.

1. To-day is the day ___ and now the prop-er hour to for-
2. As high as the sky ___ is a-bove the earth, so
3. Find-ing the Lord, ___ let us cling to him. His

1. sake our sin - ful lives ___ and turn to the Lord.
2. high a-bove our ways, ___ the ways of the Lord.
3. words, his ways ___ lead us to life.

Verse 4

4. Some-day we'll live in the house of God;

to Refrain

4. gaze on his face and praise his name.

Text: Based on Isaiah 55:6–9; Roc O'Connor, SJ, b. 1949.
Music: Roc O'Connor, SJ.
Text and music © 1975, 1996, Robert F. O'Connor, SJ and New Dawn Music.
  Published by OCP Publications. All rights reserved.

HOSEA   559

Verses

1. Come back to me with all your heart. Don't let
   Trees do bend, though straight and tall; so must
2. The wil-der-ness will lead ___ you to your
   In-teg-ri-ty and jus - tice with ten-der-
3. You shall sleep se - cure with peace; faith-ful-

Refrain

1. fear keep us a - part. Long have I wait-ed for your
   we to oth-ers' call.
2. heart where I will speak.
   ness you shall know.
3. ness will be your joy.

com-ing home to me and liv-ing deep-ly our new life.

Text and music: Weston Priory, Gregory Norbet, OSB, b. 1940,
  © 1972, The Benedictine Foundation of the State of Vermont, Inc. All rights reserved. Used with permission.

560 LOVING AND FORGIVING

Refrain: 1st time: Cantor, All repeat; thereafter: All

Lov-ing and for - giv-ing are you, O Lord; slow to an - ger,
rich in kind-ness, lov-ing and for - giv - ing are you.

Verses: Cantor/Choir

1. All my be - ing, bless the Lord, ___ bless the ho - ly
2. God for-gives us all our sins, ___ heal-ing those who
3. Good and gra - cious is the Lord, ___ slow to an - ger,
4. As heav-en soars a - bove the earth, so great the love of

1. name of God. ___ All my be - ing, bless the Lord, re -
2. live in pain, ___ sav - ing us from fi - nal death. God
3. rich in love. ___ God re-mem - bers not our sins; for -
4. God for us. As far as east is from the west, the

to Refrain

1. mem - b'ring the good - ness of God.
2. fills us with good - ness and love.
3. giv - ing and lov - ing is God.
4. Lord takes our sins ___ from us.

Text: Psalm 103:8, 1–2, 3–4, 8–10, 11–12; Scott Soper, b. 1961.
Music: Scott Soper.

561 REMEMBER YOUR LOVE

Refrain

Re - mem-ber your love and your faith-ful-ness, O Lord. Re -
mem - ber your peo-ple and have mer - cy on us, Lord.

Verses

1. The Lord is my light and my sal - va - tion,
2. If you dwelt, ___ O Lord, up - on our sin - ful - ness,
3. O Lord, hear the sound ___ of my call ___
4. As sen - ti - nels wait up - on the day - light,
5. Be - fore all the moun-tains were be - got - ten

1. whom should I fear? The Lord is my
2. then who could stand? But with you there is
3. and an - swer me. My heart cries ___
4. wait for the Lord. I trust in your
5. and earth took shape, e - ven then, ___ O

to Refrain

1. life ___ and my ref - uge, when I call God hears.
2. mer - cy and for - give - ness and a guid - ing hand.
3. out ___ for your pres - ence; it is you I seek.
4. kind-ness and re - demp-tion; and your faith - ful word.
5. Lord, you were our ref - uge through-out ev - 'ry age.

Text: Based on Psalms 25, 27, 90, 130; Mike Balhoff, b. 1946.
Music: Darryl Ducote, b. 1945, and Gary Daigle, b. 1957.
Text and music © 1973, 1978, Damean Music. All rights reserved. Used with permission.

CREATE IN ME 562

Refrain *Fine*

Cre - ate in me a clean heart.

Verses

1. Have mer - cy on me God, in your com - pas-sion.
2. O pu - ri - fy my heart and teach me wis-dom;
3. O give me back the joy of your sal - va - tion;

to Refrain

1. Re-move my sin. Wash me ___ from my guilt.
2. then I shall be clean - er ___ than the snow.
3. a will - ing spir - it sus-tain in me.

Text: Based on Psalm 51:12, 3–4, 8–9, 14; Bob Hurd, b. 1950.
Music: Bob Hurd.
Text and music © 1986, Bob Hurd. Published by OCP Publications. All rights reserved.

563   SHOW US YOUR MERCY

Refrain

In times of trou-ble, God, come to our aid.

Show us your mer - cy, come save! In times of

trou-ble, God, come to our aid. Show us your

1-3 to Verses | *Final*

mer - cy, come save!   save!   Show us your

Verses

mer - cy, come save!

1. We live se - cure in the
2. Lost and a - fraid, we're _
3. All of our lives we __

1. shel - ter of God, safe in the fold of God's
2. nev - er a - lone, God watch - es o - ver our
3. look to our God. We will lie safe in God's

1. wings. We will pro - claim the great - ness of
2. lives. Walk - ing our path and light - ing our
3. care. God is our rock. In God we can

to Refrain

1. God, the rock of sal - va - tion God brings.
2. way, __ guard - ing us day and by night.
3. trust __ all of our trou - bles to bear.

MAY LOVE BE OURS

Verses

1. Not for tongues of heav-en's an-gels, Not for wis-dom to
2. Love is hum-ble, love is gen-tle, Love is ten-der, true
3. Nev-er jeal-ous, nev-er self-ish, Love will not re-joice
4. In the day this world is fad-ing, Faith and hope will play

1. dis-cern, Not for faith that mas-ters moun-tains, For this bet-ter
2. and kind; Love is gra-cious, ev-er pa-tient, Gen-er-ous of
3. in wrong; Nev-er boast-ful nor re-sent-ful, Love be-lieves and
4. their part: But when Christ is seen in glo-ry, Love shall reign in

Refrain

1. gift we yearn: May love be ours, O Lord; may love be ours.
2. heart and mind.
3. suf-fers long.
4. ev-'ry heart.

*Cue note is an alternative lower note.

LOVE IS THE SUNLIGHT

565

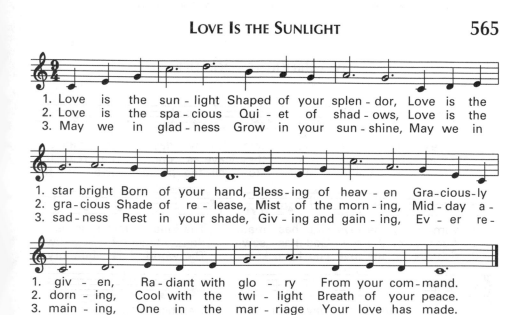

1. Love is the sun-light Shaped of your splen-dor, Love is the
2. Love is the spa-cious Qui-et of shad-ows, Love is the
3. May we in glad-ness Grow in your sun-shine, May we in

1. star bright Born of your hand, Bless-ing of heav-en Gra-cious-ly
2. gra-cious Shade of re-lease, Mist of the morn-ing, Mid-day a-
3. sad-ness Rest in your shade, Giv-ing and gain-ing, Ev-er re-

1. giv-en, Ra-diant with glo-ry From your com-mand.
2. dorn-ing, Cool with the twi-light Breath of your peace.
3. main-ing, One in the mar-riage Your love has made.

566

MAY GOD BLESS YOU

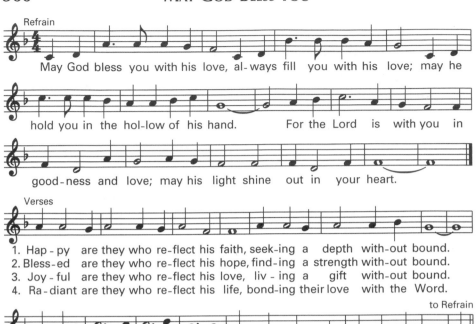

Refrain

May God bless you with his love, al-ways fill you with his love; may he hold you in the hol-low of his hand. For the Lord is with you in good-ness and love; may his light shine out in your heart.

Verses

1. Hap - py are they who re-flect his faith, seek-ing a depth with-out bound.
2. Bless-ed are they who re-flect his hope, find-ing a strength with-out bound.
3. Joy - ful are they who re-flect his love, liv - ing a gift with-out bound.
4. Ra - diant are they who re-flect his life, bond-ing their love with the Word.

to Refrain

1. Lord, it is good that we are here to see that faith which oth-ers have found.
2. Lord, it is good that we are here to see that hope which oth-ers have found.
3. Lord, it is good that we are here to see that love which oth-ers have found.
4. Lord, it is good that we are here to share that life with one __ ac - cord.

Text and music: George Van Grieken, FSC, b. 1952, © 1984, OCP Publications. All rights reserved.

567

LIVES BROUGHT TOGETHER

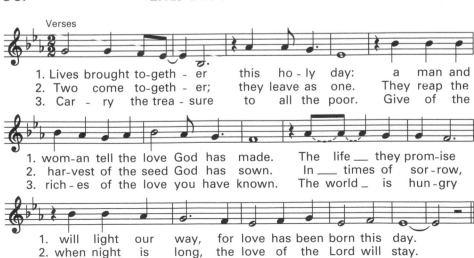

Verses

1. Lives brought to-geth - er this ho - ly day: a man and
2. Two come to-geth - er; they leave as one. They reap the
3. Car - ry the trea - sure to all the poor. Give of the

1. wom-an tell the love God has made. The life __ they prom-ise
2. har-vest of the seed God has sown. In __ times of sor-row,
3. rich - es of the love you have known. The world __ is hun-gry

1. will light our way, for love has been born this day.
2. when night is long, the love of the Lord will stay.
3. for what you've known: the love of our God this day.

Refrain

Lord, may your love be the mel - o-dy we sing, be the har - mo-ny we bring

1, 2 to our days, and the strength of our ways.

Final and the strength of our ways.

WHEN LOVE IS FOUND 568

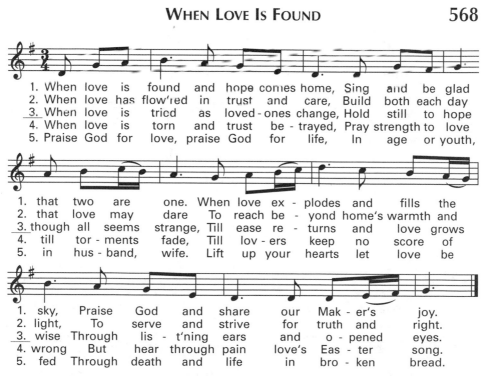

1. When love is found and hope comes home, Sing and be glad
2. When love has flow'red in trust and care, Build both each day
3. When love is tried as loved - ones change, Hold still to hope
4. When love is torn and trust be - trayed, Pray strength to love
5. Praise God for love, praise God for life, In age or youth,

1. that two are one. When love ex - plodes and fills the
2. that love may dare To reach be - yond home's warmth and
3. though all seems strange, Till ease re - turns and love grows
4. till tor - ments fade, Till lov - ers keep no score of
5. in hus - band, wife. Lift up your hearts let love be

1. sky, Praise God and share our Mak - er's joy.
2. light, To serve and strive for truth and right.
3. wise Through lis - t'ning ears and o - pened eyes.
4. wrong But hear through pain love's Eas - ter song.
5. fed Through death and life in bro - ken bread.

569

WHERE THERE IS LOVE

Refrain

Where there is love, there is God. The love of God has gath-ered us to - geth-er; Al - le - lu - ia.

Verses 1, 3

1. Love is pa - tient, love is kind, nev - er jeal-ous, nev - er proud,
3. Man-y things will pass a - way. There are but three things that last:

1. nev-er seek-ing for one's self. ___ Love nev-er leads to an-ger. ___
3. Faith, Hope, and Love;___ the great-est of these is Love. ___

Verse 2

2. Love is gra-cious and for-giv-ing, tak-ing no de-light in wrong;

to Refrain

2. Love re-joic-es in the truth; Love will en - dure.

Text: Based on 1 John 4:16; 1 Corinthians 13:4–7, 10, 13; David Haas, b. 1957.
Music: David Haas.
Text and music © 1985, David Haas. Published by OCP Publications. All rights reserved.

570

WHEREVER YOU GO

Verse 1

1. Wher-ev-er you go I shall go. Wher-ev-er you live

1. so shall I live. Your peo-ple will be my peo -

1. ple, and your God will be my God too.

Verse 2

2. Wher-ev-er you die I shall die, and there shall

2. I be bur-ied be-side you. We will be to-geth-er for-

2. ev - er, and our love will be the gift of our life.

Text: Based on Ruth 1:16, 17; Weston Priory, Gregory Norbet, OSB, b. 1940.
Music: Weston Priory, Gregory Norbet, OSB.
Text and music © 1972, The Benedictine Foundation of the State of Vermont, Inc. All rights reserved. Used with permission.

GOD, WHO CREATED HEARTS TO LOVE 571

1. God who cre - at - ed hearts to love, Show-'ring all bless-ings
2. Je - sus at Ca - na gave a sign, Turn - ing the wa - ter
3. Spir - it of God, be at their side: Wis - dom and com - fort,
4. Sing, friends and fam-'ly gath-ered here, Voic - es in wit - ness
5. God, let our joy-ful sing - ing be Sign of our faith com -

1. from a - bove, Al-le - lu - ia! Al-le - lu-ia! Give these, who come to
2. in - to wine: Al-le - lu - ia! Al-le - lu-ia! Sign that con - tin - ues
3. guard-ian, guide. Al-le - lu - ia! Al-le - lu-ia! Make of their hearts a
4. ring - ing clear; Al-le - lu - ia! Al-le - lu-ia! Here is the mys-ter -
5. mu - ni - ty. Al-le - lu - ia! Al-le - lu-ia! Bap - tized in wa - ter,

1. you with praise, Peace, love and laugh-ter all their days.
2. as he said— Love, liv - ing, ris - en from the dead.
3. rest - ing place; In ev - 'ry tri - al, gen - tle grace. } Al-le - lu-ia!
4. y be - gun: Wo - man and man be-com-ing one.
5. we are fed, Shar - ing the liv - ing wine and bread.

1-5. Al-le - lu - ia! Al-le - lu - ia! Al-le - lu - ia! Al-le - lu - ia!

Text: LM with alleluias; M.D. Ridge, © 1992, M.D. Ridge. Published by OCP Publications. All rights reserved.
Music: LASST UNS ERFREUEN; *Auserlesene Catholische Geistliche Kirchengesänge*, Cologne, 1623.

WHERE LOVE IS FOUND

Refrain

Where char-i-ty and love are found, there will the face of God be seen. The love of Christ will bind our hearts; as one bod-y we will be.

Verses

1. Love is pa-tient, love is kind,
2. Love is stead-fast to the end,
3. Though I speak with an-gel's tongue,
4. There are three things that will last:

1. nev-er boast-ful, nev-er proud. Love is hope-ful in its
2. ev-er read-y to en-dure. Love is gra-cious in its
3. I am noth-ing more than sound. I am but a cym-bal
4. there is faith, hope and ___ love. But the great-est of all

to Refrain

1. wait-ing, ev-er trust-ing in God's light.
2. kind-ness, ev-er read-y to for-give.
3. clang-ing if I sing with-out God's love.
4. bless-ings is the faith-ful-ness of love.

Text: Based on the Latin chant *Ubi Caritas;* I Corinthians 13:1–7, 13; Dan Schutte, b. 1947.
Music: Dan Schutte.
Text and music © 2001, Daniel L. Schutte. Published by OCP Publications. All rights reserved.

573   LOVE WHICH NEVER ENDS

Refrain: All

God of ten-der mer-cy, God of love, God of glo-rious light from heav'n a-bove; in your light we see light, in your love we feel love: light e-ter-nal, love which nev-er ends.

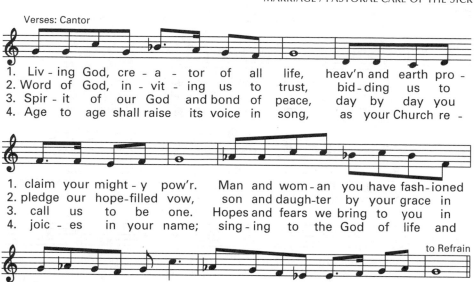

Verses: Cantor

1. Liv - ing God, cre - a - tor of all life, heav'n and earth pro -
2. Word of God, in - vit - ing us to trust, bid - ding us to
3. Spir - it of our God and bond of peace, day by day you
4. Age to age shall raise its voice in song, as your Church re -

1. claim your might - y pow'r. Man and wom - an you have fash-ioned
2. pledge our hope-filled vow, son and daugh-ter by your grace in
3. call us to be one. Hopes and fears we bring to you in
4. joic - es in your name; sing - ing to the God of life and

to Refrain

1. in your lov-ing kind-ness, set - ting them to pros - per and to grow.
2. one flesh now u - nit - ed, called to live the sac - ra - ment of love.
3. sor - row and re - joic - ing, strength-ened by the prom - ise of your love.
4. source of ev - 'ry bless - ing: praise and glo - ry now and ev - er - more!

TALL STANDS THE TREE BESIDE THE STREAM 574

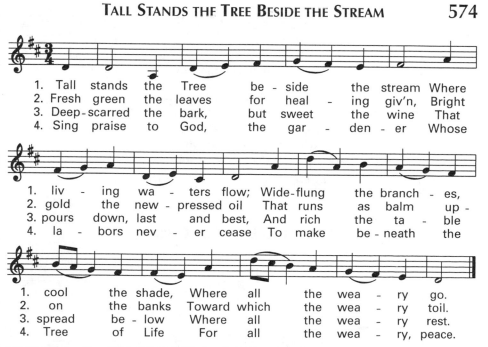

1. Tall stands the Tree be - side the stream Where
2. Fresh green the leaves for heal - ing giv'n, Bright
3. Deep-scarred the bark, but sweet the wine That
4. Sing praise to God, the gar - den - er Whose

1. liv - ing wa - ters flow; Wide-flung the branch - es,
2. gold the new - pressed oil That runs as balm up -
3. pours down, last and best, And rich the ta - ble
4. la - bors nev - er cease To make be - neath the

1. cool the shade, Where all the wea - ry go.
2. on the banks Toward which the wea - ry toil.
3. spread be - low Where all the wea - ry rest.
4. Tree of Life For all the wea - ry, peace.

575   BE STILL MY SOUL

1. Be still, my soul— the Lord is on thy side!
2. Be still, my soul— thy God doth un - der - take
3. Be still, my soul— the hour is has - t'ning on

1. Bear pa - tient - ly the cross of grief or pain;
2. To guide the fu - ture as he has the past;
3. When we shall be for - ev - er with the Lord,

1. Leave to thy God to or - der and pro - vide—
2. Thy hope, thy con - fi - dence let noth - ing shake—
3. When dis - ap - point - ment, grief, and fear are gone,

1. In ev - 'ry change he faith - ful will re - main.
2. All now mys - te - rious shall be bright at last.
3. Sor - row for - got, love's pur - est joys re - stored.

1. Be still, my soul— thy best, thy heav'n - ly friend
2. Be still, my soul— the waves and winds still know
3. Be still, my soul— when change and tears are past,

1. Through thorn - y ways leads to a joy - ful end.
2. His voice who ruled them while he dwelt be - low.
3. All safe and bless - ed we shall meet at last.

Text: 10 10 10 10 10 10; Katharina von Schlegel; in *Neue Sammlung Geislicher Lieder*, 1752; tr. by Jane Borthwick, 1813–1897.
Music: FINLANDIA; Jean Sibelius, 1865–1957.

576   O HEALING LIGHT OF CHRIST

Refrain

O heal-ing light of Christ, trans-form us, life-giv-ing source of hope.

O heal-ing light of Christ, trans - form us; heal your peo - ple,

Christ our light.

1. Ra - diant the light that strengthens the body,
2. You light the way for hearts of compassion;
3. Your light gives life to all of creation,

1. eases and comforts the troubled mind. Ra - diant the light that __
2. your light is guide for __ hands that heal. You light the pathways of
3. colors the flower and warms the heart. Yours is the light that __

to Refrain

1. soothes our ____ spirits; ra - diant your healing light.
2. all our ____ caring; you are our healing light.
3. breaks through the darkness; you are our healing light.

O CHRIST, THE HEALER 577

1. O Christ, the heal - er, we have come To
2. From ev - 'ry ail - ment flesh en - dures Our
3. How strong, O Lord, are our de - sires, How
4. In con - flicts that de - stroy our health We
5. Grant that we all, made one in faith, In

1. pray for health, to plead for friends. How can we fail to
2. bod - ies clam - or to be freed; Yet in our hearts we
3. weak our knowl - edge of our - selves! Re - lease in us those
4. rec - og - nize the world's dis - ease; Our com - mon life de -
5. your com - mun - i - ty may find The whole - ness that, en -

1. be re - stored, When reached by love that nev - er ends?
2. would con - fess That whole - ness is our deep - est need.
3. heal - ing truths Un - con - scious pride re - sists or shelves.
4. clares our ills: Is there no cure, O Christ, for these?
5. rich - ing us, Shall reach the whole of hu - man - kind.

578
Holy Darkness

Refrain

Ho - ly dark - ness, bless - ed night, heav - en's an - swer hid - den from our sight. As we a - wait you, O God of si - lence, we em - brace your ho - ly night.

Verses 1-3

1. I have tried you in fires of af - flic - tion; I have
2. I have taught you the price of com - pas - sion; you have
3. Were you there when I raised up the moun - tains? Can you

1. taught your soul to grieve. In the bar - ren soil of your
2. stood be - fore the grave. Though my love can seem like a
3. guide the morn - ing star? Does the hawk take flight when you

1. lone - li - ness, there I will plant my seed.
2. rag - ing storm, this is the love that saves.
3. give com - mand? Why do you doubt my pow'r?

to Refrain

Verses 4, 5

4. In your deep - est hour of dark - ness I will
5. As the watch - man waits for morn - ing, and the

4. give you wealth un - told. When the si - lence stills your
5. bride a - waits her groom, so we wait to hear your

4. spir - it, will my rich - es fill your soul.
5. foot - steps as we rest be - neath your moon.

to Refrain

Your Hands, O Lord, in Days of Old

579

1. Your hands, O Lord, in days of old Were strong to
2. And then your touch brought life and health, Gave hear - ing,
3. O be our might - y heal - er still, Great Lord of

1. heal and save; They tri - umphed o'er dis -
2. speech, and sight; While strength re - newed and
3. life and death; Re - store and strength - en,

1. ease and death, O'er dark - ness and the grave. To
2. health re - stored Ac - claimed you Lord of light; And
3. soothe and bless, With your al - might - y breath; On

1. you they went, the blind, the deaf, The pal - sied,
2. so, O Lord, be near to bless, With all your
3. hands that work and eyes that see, Your heal - ing

1. and the lame, The lep - er set a -
2. heal - ing pow'r, In trou - bled home, in
3. wis - dom pour, That whole and sick, and

1. part and shunned, The sick and those in shame.
2. crowd - ed street, In sor - row's sad - dest hour.
3. weak and strong, May praise you ev - er - more.

Text: CMD; Edward Plumptre, 1821–1891, alt.
Music: Attr. to Wolfgang Amadeus Mozart, 1756–1791.

580
SONG OF FAREWELL

Refrain: 1st time: Cantor, All repeat; thereafter: All

May the choirs of an-gels come to greet you. May they speed you to par-a-dise. May the Lord en-fold you in his mer-cy. May you find e-ter-nal life.

Verses

1. The __ Lord is my light and my help; _____ it is he who pro-tects me from harm. _____ The __ Lord is the strength of my days; ____ be-fore whom should I trem-ble with fear? _____
2. There is one thing I ask of the Lord; _____ that he grant me my heart-felt de-sire. _____ To __ dwell in the courts of our God _____ ev-'ry day of my life in his pres-ence. __
3. O __ Lord, hear my voice when I cry; _____ have __ mer-cy on me and give an-swer. __ Do not cast me a-way in your an-ger, __ for __ you are the God of my help. _____
4. I am sure I shall see the Lord's good-ness; _ I shall dwell in the land of the liv-ing. __ Hope in God, __ stand firm and take heart, _____ place all your trust in the Lord. _____

to Refrain

Text: Refrain, *In Paradisum*; verses, based on Psalm 27; Ernest Sands, b. 1949.
Music: Ernest Sands.
Text and music © 1990, Ernest Sands. Published by OCP Publications. All rights reserved.

581
HOW LOVELY IS YOUR DWELLING PLACE

Refrain

O how love-ly is your dwell-ing place, dwell-ing of the Lord of hosts! How we long for your house, O Lord, sing-ing out a song of joy to the liv-ing God!

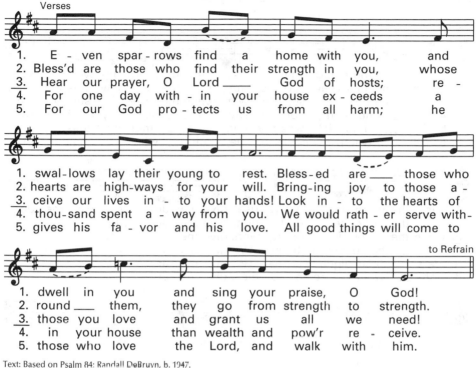

Verses

1. E - ven spar - rows find a home with you, and
2. Bless'd are those who find their strength in you, whose
3. Hear our prayer, O Lord ___ God of hosts; re -
4. For one day with - in your house ex - ceeds a
5. For our God pro - tects us from all harm; he

1. swal - lows lay their young to rest. Bless - ed are ___ those who
2. hearts are high - ways for your will. Bring - ing joy to those a -
3. ceive our lives in - to your hands! Look in - to the hearts of
4. thou - sand spent a - way from you. We would rath - er serve with-
5. gives his fa - vor and his love. All good things will come to

to Refrain

1. dwell in you and sing your praise, O God!
2. round ___ them, they go from strength to strength.
3. those you love and grant us all we need!
4. in your house than wealth and pow'r re - ceive.
5. those who love the Lord, and walk with him.

Text: Based on Psalm 84; Randall DeBruyn, b. 1947.
Music: Randall DeBruyn.

INTO YOUR HANDS   582

Refrain

In - to your hands, Lord, I com - mend my soul.

In - to your hands, Lord, I com - mend my soul.

Verses

1. Whoever goes to the Most High for safety,
whoever remains
under the protection of the Lord
can say to the Lord:
You are my protector;
you are my God, in you I trust.

2. He will surely keep you safe
from all dangers;
he will cover you with his wings.

You will be safe under his care.
His faithfulness will protect
and defend you.

3. Because you have made the Lord
your defender,
the Most High your protector,
God will put his angels in charge of you
to protect you wherever you go.

Text: Based on Psalm 91; Grayson Warren Brown, b. 1948.
Music: Grayson Warren Brown.

583

GIVE ME JESUS

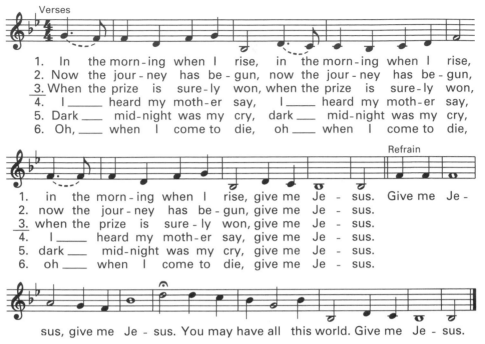

Verses

1. In the morn-ing when I rise, in the morn-ing when I rise,
2. Now the jour-ney has be-gun, now the jour-ney has be-gun,
3. When the prize is sure-ly won, when the prize is sure-ly won,
4. I ___ heard my moth-er say, I ___ heard my moth-er say,
5. Dark ___ mid-night was my cry, dark ___ mid-night was my cry,
6. Oh, ___ when I come to die, oh ___ when I come to die,

Refrain

1. in the morn-ing when I rise, give me Je - sus. Give me Je-
2. now the jour-ney has be-gun, give me Je - sus.
3. when the prize is sure-ly won, give me Je - sus.
4. I ___ heard my moth-er say, give me Je - sus.
5. dark ___ mid-night was my cry, give me Je - sus.
6. oh ___ when I come to die, give me Je - sus.

sus, give me Je - sus. You may have all this world. Give me Je - sus.

Text: 77 74 with refrain; verses 1, 4–6 and refrain, Spiritual.
Verses 2–3, James Hansen, b. 1937, © 1992, James Hansen. Published by OCP Publications. All rights reserved.
Music: Spiritual.

584

I, THE LORD

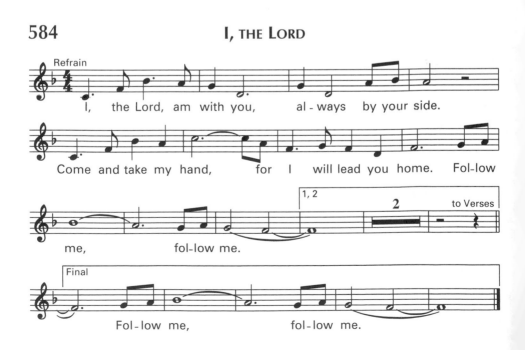

Refrain

I, the Lord, am with you, al - ways by your side.

Come and take my hand, for I will lead you home. Fol-low

1, 2 | 2 | to Verses

me, fol-low me.

Final

Fol-low me, fol-low me.

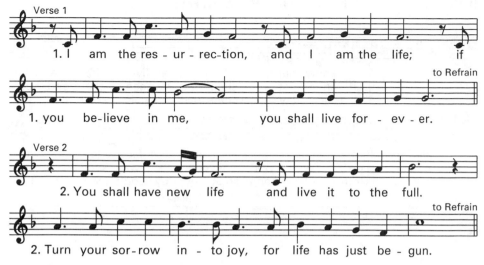

Verse 1

1. I am the res - ur - rec-tion, and I am the life; if

1. you be-lieve in me, you shall live for - ev - er.

to Refrain

Verse 2

2. You shall have new life and live it to the full.

2. Turn your sor-row in - to joy, for life has just be - gun.

to Refrain

Text: Based on John 6:35–58; Tom Kendzia, b. 1954.
Music: Tom Kendzia.

SONG OF FAREWELL 585

Ostinato Refrain: 1st time: Cantor, All repeat; thereafter: All

Go now in peace, faith-ful friend of God, as you

take our love in - to par - a - dise.

God's ho - ly an - gels will lead you home to the

wide wait - ing arms of the Lord.

Verses: Cantor

1. I know my Savior lives!
   His voice will bid me rise again!
   And on that final day
   I shall rejoice with the Lord.

2. My shepherd is the Lord.
   My spirit wants for nothing more.
   In valleys fresh and green
   I shall rejoice with the Lord.

Text: Based on *In Paradisum*; Dan Schutte, b. 1947.
Music: Dan Schutte.

586   I KNOW THAT MY REDEEMER LIVES

1. I know that my Re-deem-er lives, the One who
2. I know that I shall one day see the good-ness
3. The last day I shall rise a-gain, shall be re-

1. calls me home. I long to see God face - to - face, to
2. of the Lord, when God will wipe a - way our tears, and
3. made like God. My home shall be by God's own side, the

Refrain

1. see with my own eyes. I know that my Re-
2. death will be no more.
3. dy - ing, ris - ing Lord.

1. deem-er lives, that I shall rise a - gain. gain.

Text: Based on Job 19, Psalm 27, Isaiah 25; Scott Soper, b. 1961.
Music: Scott Soper.
Text and music © 1990, Scott Soper. Published by OCP Publications. All rights reserved.

587   THE LORD IS MY LIGHT

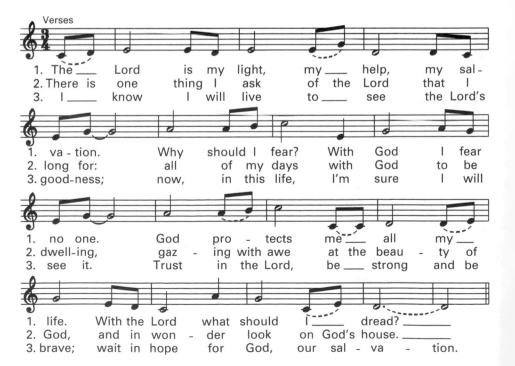

Verses

1. The___ Lord is my light, my ___ help, my sal-
2. There is one thing I ask of the Lord that I
3. I___ know I will live to ___ see the Lord's

1. va - tion. Why should I fear? With God I fear
2. long for: all of my days with God to be
3. good-ness; now, in this life, I'm sure I will

1. no one. God pro - tects me___ all my ___
2. dwell-ing, gaz - ing with awe at the beau - ty of
3. see it. Trust in the Lord, be ___ strong and be

1. life. With the Lord what should I___ dread? _____
2. God, and in won - der look on God's house. _____
3. brave; wait in hope for God, our sal - va - tion.

The Lord is my light, the Lord is my help, the Lord is my sal - va - tion.

Text: Based on Psalm 27; Christopher Walker, b. 1947.
Music: Christopher Walker.

PARABLE

588

1-4. To ev-'ry thing there is a sea-son; a time to be born

1-4. and a time to die. 1, 4. A time to plant and a time for har-vest;
2. A time to speak and a time for si - lence;
3. A time for joy and a time for griev-ing;

1, 4. a time to meet and a time to part. 4. part. 1. A sow - er went
2. a time to wound and a time to heal. 2. Noth-ing can
3. a time to seek and a time to lose. 3. God's word is

1. out to sow the seed. Some of it fell up - on the path, some fell on
2. grow in bar - ren soil; bri - ars and ra - vens take their toll; still there is
3. like the far-mer's seed, root-ed in joy - ful, lov-ing hearts, grow-ing like

1. shal - low, rock - y soil, and some a - mong chok-ing thorns.
2. grain a hun-dred - fold, from seed that took root and grew.
3. grain in fer - tile ground, a har-vest that o - ver - flows.

Text: Based on Ecclesiastes 3:1–9, Matthew 13:4–8; M.D. Ridge.
Music: M.D. Ridge.

589

KEEP IN MIND

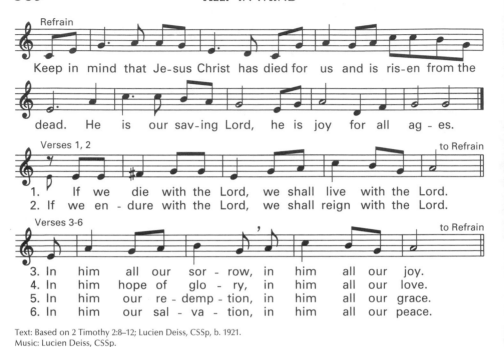

Refrain

Keep in mind that Je-sus Christ has died for us and is ris-en from the dead. He is our sav-ing Lord, he is joy for all ag-es.

Verses 1, 2   *to Refrain*

1. If we die with the Lord, we shall live with the Lord.
2. If we en-dure with the Lord, we shall reign with the Lord.

Verses 3-6   *to Refrain*

3. In him all our sor-row, in him all our joy.
4. In him hope of glo-ry, in him all our love.
5. In him our re-demp-tion, in him all our grace.
6. In him our sal-va-tion, in him all our peace.

Text: Based on 2 Timothy 2:8–12; Lucien Deiss, CSSp, b. 1921.
Music: Lucien Deiss, CSSp.

590

YES, I SHALL ARISE

Refrain

Yes, I shall a-rise! I shall gaze up-on the love-li-ness of God for-ev-er-more.

Verses

1. One thing I ask of the Lord, this I seek: to
2. Day af-ter day I seek the house of the Lord.
3. Yearn-ing and pin-ing for the courts of the Lord, my
4. Thus will I go in-to the al-tar of God, the
5. Hap-py are they who place their trust in the Lord, for

to Refrain

1. dwell in the house of the Lord all the days of my life.
2. When shall I en-ter and see, see the face of my God?
3. flesh and my spir-it cry out for the God of my life.
4. God of my glad-ness and joy, giv-ing thanks on the harp.
5. they shall in-her-it the prize; theirs is life with-out end!

Text: Based on Psalms 27, 43; Owen Alstott, b. 1947.
Music: Owen Alstott.

Jesus, Lord, Have Mercy

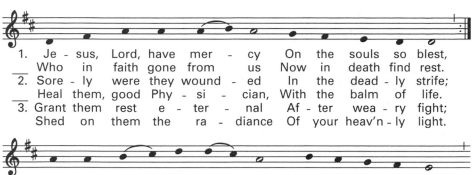

1. Je - sus, Lord, have mer - cy On the souls so blest,
   Who in faith gone from us Now in death find rest.
2. Sore - ly were they wound - ed In the dead - ly strife;
   Heal them, good Phy - si - cian, With the balm of life.
3. Grant them rest e - ter - nal Af - ter wea - ry fight;
   Shed on them the ra - diance Of your heav'n - ly light.

1. Here 'mid stress and con - flict Toils can nev - er cease;
2. Ev - 'ry taint of e - vil, Frail - ty and de - cay,
3. Lead them on - ward, up - ward, To the ho - ly place

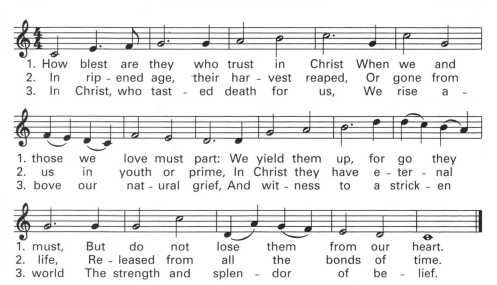

1. There the war - fare end - ed, Bid them rest in peace.
2. Good and gra - cious Sav - ior, Cleanse and purge a - way.
3. Where your saints, made per - fect, Gaze up - on your face.

Text: 65 65 D; Swahili; tr. by Edmund S. Palmer, 1856–1931, alt.
Music: ADORO TE DEVOTE; Chant, Mode V; *Paris Processional,* 1697.

How Blest Are They

592

1. How blest are they who trust in Christ When we and
2. In rip - ened age, their har - vest reaped, Or gone from
3. In Christ, who tast - ed death for us, We rise a -

1. those we love must part: We yield them up, for go they
2. us in youth or prime, In Christ they have e - ter - nal
3. bove our nat - ural grief, And wit - ness to a strick - en

1. must, But do not lose them from our heart.
2. life, Re - leased from all the bonds of time.
3. world The strength and splen - dor of be - lief.

Text: LM; Fred Pratt Green, 1903–2000, © 1972, The Hymn Society. All rights reserved.
   Administered by Hope Publishing Co. Used with permission.
Music: TRURO; Williams' *Psalmodia Evangelica, Part II,* 1789.

593   HOLY GOD, WE PRAISE THY NAME

1. Ho - ly God, we praise thy name; Lord of all, we
2. Hark! the loud ce - les - tial hymn An - gel choirs a -
3. Lo! the ap - os - tol - ic train Join, the sa - cred
4. Ho - ly Fa - ther, Ho - ly Son, Ho - ly Spir - it,

1. bow be - fore thee! All on earth thy scep - tre claim,
2. bove are rais - ing; Cher - u - bim and Ser - a - phim,
3. Name to hal - low; Proph - ets swell the loud re - frain,
4. Three we name thee; While in es - sence on - ly One,

1. All in heav'n a - bove a - dore thee; In - fi -
2. In un - ceas - ing cho - rus prais - ing; Fill the
3. And the white - robed mar - tyrs fol - low; And from
4. Un - di - vid - ed God we claim thee; And a -

1. nite, thy vast do - main, Ev - er - last - ing
2. heav'ns with sweet ac - cord: "Ho - ly, ho - ly,
3. morn to set of sun, Through the Church the
4. dor - ing, bend the knee, While we own the

1. is thy reign. In - fi - nite, thy vast do -
2. ho - ly Lord!" Fill the heav'ns with sweet ac -
3. song goes on. And from morn to set of
4. mys - ter - y. And a - dor - ing, bend the

1. main, Ev - er - last - ing is thy reign.
2. cord: "Ho - ly, ho - ly, ho - ly Lord!"
3. sun, Through the Church the song goes on.
4. knee, While we own the mys - ter - y.

Text: 78 78 77 with repeat; *Te Deum laudamus*; attr. to St. Nicetas, ca. 335–414; *Grosser Gott, wir loben dich*;
    tr. ascr. to Ignaz Franz, 1719–1790; tr. by Clarence A. Walworth, 1820–1900.
Music: GROSSER GOTT; *Allgemeines Katholisches Gesangbuch*, Vienna, ca. 1774.

GOD, WE PRAISE YOU

1. God, we praise you! God, we bless you! God, we
2. True a-pos-tles, faith-ful proph-ets, Saints who
3. Je-sus Christ, the King of glo-ry, Ev-er-
4. Christ, at God's right hand vic-to-rious, You will

1. name you sov-'reign Lord! Might-y King whom an-gels
2. set their world a-blaze, Mar-tyrs, once un-known, un-
3. last-ing Son of God, Hum-ble was your vir-gin
4. judge the world you made; Lord, in mer-cy help your

1. wor-ship, Fa-ther, by your Church a-dored:
2. heed-ed, Join one grow-ing song of praise,
3. moth-er, Hard the lone-ly path you trod:
4. ser-vants For whose free-dom you have paid:

1. All cre-a-tion shows your glo-ry, Heav'n and
2. While your Church on earth con-fess-es One ma-
3. By your cross is sin de-feat-ed, Hell con-
4. Raise us up from dust to glo-ry, Guard us

1. earth draw near your throne, Sing-ing "Ho-ly, ho-ly,
2. jes-tic Trin-i-ty: Fa-ther, Son, and Ho-ly
3. front-ed face to face, Heav-en o-pened to be-
4. from all sin to-day; King en-throned a-bove all

1. ho-ly," Lord of hosts and God a-lone!
2. Spir-it, God, our hope e-ter-nal-ly.
3. liev-ers, Sin-ners jus-ti-fied by grace.
4. prais-es, Save your peo-ple, God, we pray.

Text: 87 87 D; *Te Deum laudamus*; attr. to St. Nicetas, ca. 335–414; tr. by Christopher Idle, b. 1938, © 1982, Jubilate Hymns, Ltd.
All rights reserved. Administered by Hope Publishing Co. Used with permission.
Music: NETTLETON; J. Wyeth's *Repository of Sacred Music, Part II*, 1813.

ALL THE ENDS OF THE EARTH

Refrain

All the ends of the earth, all you crea-tures of the sea, lift up your eyes to the won - ders of the Lord. For the Lord of the earth, the mas-ter of the sea, has come with jus-tice for the world.

Verses 1, 2

1. Break in - to song at the deeds of the Lord,
2. Heav - en and earth shall re - joice in his might;

1. the won-ders God has _ done in ev -'ry age.
2. ev -'ry heart, _____ ev -'ry na - tion call him Lord.

Verse 3

3. The Lord has made sal - va - tion known, faith-ful to the prom-

3. - is - es of old. Let the ends of the earth, let the

to Refrain

3. sea and all it holds make mu - sic be - fore our King!

Text: Based on Psalm 98; Bob Dufford, SJ, b. 1943.
Music: Bob Dufford, SJ.

GLORY AND PRAISE TO OUR GOD

Refrain

Glo - ry and praise to our God, who a - lone gives light to our days.

Man - y are the bless-ings he bears to those who trust in his

ways.

Verses 1-3

1. We the daugh-ters and sons of him who
2. In his wis - dom he strength-ens us, like
3. Ev - 'ry mo - ment of ev - 'ry day our

1. built the val-leys and plains, praise the won-ders our
2. gold that's test-ed in fire. Though the pow - er of
3. God is wait-ing to save, al - ways read - y to

to Refrain

1. God has done in ev - 'ry heart that sings.
2. sin pre-vails, our God is there to save.
3. seek the lost, to an - swer those who pray.

Verse 4

4. God has wa-tered our bar-ren land and spent his mer-ci-ful rain.

to Refrain

4. Now the riv-ers of life run full for an - y - one to drink.

Text: Based on Psalms 65, 66; Dan Schutte, b. 1947.
Music: Dan Schutte.

597   PRAISE TO THE LORD

1. Praise to the Lord, the Al - might - y, the King of cre -
2. Praise to the Lord, a - bove all things so won - drous - ly
3. Praise to the Lord, who will pros - per your work and de -
4. Praise to the Lord! O let all that is in me a -

1. a - tion! O my soul, praise him, for
2. reign - ing, Shel - t'ring you un - der his
3. fend you; Sure - ly his good - ness and
4. dore him! All that has life and breath,

1. he is your health and sal - va - tion!
2. wings, and so gent - ly sus - tain - ing.
3. mer - cy shall dai - ly at - tend you.
4. come now with prais - es be - fore him!

1. Come, all who hear: Now to his al - tar draw
2. Have you not seen All that is need - ful has
3. Pon - der a - new What the Al - might - y can
4. Let the "A - men!" Sound from his peo - ple a -

1. near, Join - ing in glad ad - o - ra - tion!
2. been Sent by his gra - cious or - dain - ing?
3. do As with his love he be - friends you.
4. gain, Glad - ly with praise we a - dore him!

Text: 14 14 4 7 8; Joachim Neander, 1650–1680; tr. by Catherine Winkworth, 1827–1878, alt.
Music: LOBE DEN HERREN; *Erneuerten Gesangbuch,* Stralsund, 1665.

598   LAUDATE, LAUDATE DOMINUM

Refrain

Lau - da - te, lau - da - te Do - mi - num, om - nes gen - tes, lau -
We praise you, we praise your ho - ly name, God of jus - tice, e -

da - te Do - mi - num. Ex - sul - ta - te, ju - bi - la - te per
ter - nal - ly the same. May our liv - ing be thanks - giv - ing, re -

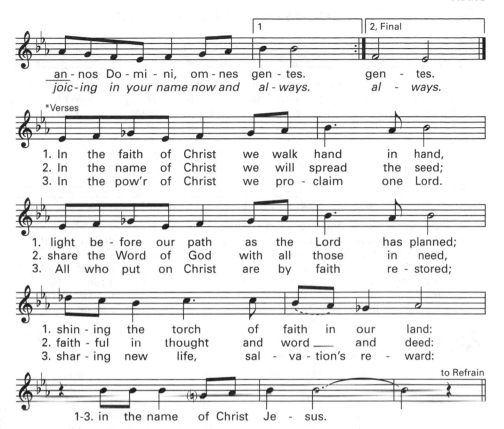

an - nos Do - mi - ni, om - nes gen - tes. gen - tes.
joic - ing in your name now and al - ways. al - ways.

*Verses

1. In the faith of Christ we walk hand in hand,
2. In the name of Christ we will spread the seed;
3. In the pow'r of Christ we pro - claim one Lord.

1. light be - fore our path as the Lord has planned;
2. share the Word of God with all those in need,
3. All who put on Christ are by faith re - stored;

1. shin - ing the torch of faith in our land:
2. faith - ful in thought and word and deed:
3. shar - ing new life, sal - va - tion's re - ward:

to Refrain

1-3. in the name of Christ Je - sus.

*Additional verses available in accompaniment books.

Text and music: Christopher Walker, b. 1947, © 1997, Christopher Walker. Published by OCP Publications. All rights reserved.

O Bless the Lord, My Soul　599

1. O bless the Lord, my soul! His grace to thee pro - claim!
2. O bless the Lord, my soul! His mer - cies bear in mind!
3. He clothes us with his love; Up - holds us with his truth;
4. Then bless his ho - ly name, Whose grace hath made us whole,

1. And all that is with - in me join To bless his ho - ly name!
2. For - get not all his ben - e - fits! The Lord to thee is kind.
3. He heals all our in - fir - mi - ties And ran - soms us from death.
4. Whose lov - ing kind - ness crowns our days! O bless the Lord, my soul!

Text: SM; para. of Psalm 103:1–5; James Montgomery, 1771–1854, alt.
Music: ST. THOMAS (WILLIAMS); *New Universal Psalmodist*, 1770; Aaron Williams, 1731–1776, alt.

600 ALL CREATURES OF OUR GOD AND KING

1. All crea-tures of our God and King, Lift
2. Great rush-ing winds that are so strong, White
3. Swift flow-ing wa-ter, pure and clear, Make
4. Dear moth-er earth, who day by day Un-
5. All you that are of ten-der heart, For-
6. And you, most kind and gen-tle death, Wait-
7. Let all things their Cre - a - tor bless And

1. up your voice and let us sing; Al - le - lu - ia!
2. clouds a - bove that sail a - long, O___ praise him!
3. mu - sic for your Lord to hear, Al - le - lu - ia!
4. folds rich bless-ings on our way, O___ praise him!
5. giv - ing oth - ers, take your part. Sing his prais - es!
6. ing to hush our fi - nal breath, O___ praise him!
7. wor-ship him in hum-ble - ness! O___ praise him!

1. Al - le - lu - ia! Bright burn-ing sun with gold-en
2. Al - le - lu - ia! Fair ris - ing morn, in praise re-
3. Al - le - lu - ia! Fierce fire so mas-ter-ful and
4. Al - le - lu - ia! The flow'rs and fruits that in you
5. Al - le - lu - ia! All you that pain and sor-row
6. Al - le - lu - ia! You lead back home the child of
7. Al - le - lu - ia! Praise God the Fa - ther, praise the

1. beam, Pale sil - ver moon with soft - er gleam,
2. joice; O stars of eve - ning, find a voice!
3. bright, Pro - vid - ing us both warmth and light,
4. grow, Let them his glo - ry al - so show!
5. bear, Praise God, and on him cast your care!
6. God, Where Christ our Lord the way has trod:
7. Son, And praise the Spir - it, Three - in - One:

1-7. O praise him! O praise him! Al - le - lu - ia!

1-7. Al - le - lu - ia! Al - le - lu - ia!

Text: LM with additions; St. Francis of Assisi, 1182–1226; *Laudato sia Deo mio Signore*; tr. by William H. Draper, 1855–1933, alt.,
© 1923, renewed, J. Curwen & Sons. International copyright secured.
Used by permission of G. Schirmer, Inc., U.S./Canadian agent.
Music: LASST UNS ERFREUEN; *Auserlesene Catholische Geistliche Kirchengesänge*, Cologne, 1623.

SING TO THE MOUNTAINS

Refrain

Sing to the moun-tains, sing to the sea. Raise your voic - es, lift your hearts. This is the day the Lord has made. Let all the earth re - joice.

to Verses

Last time

Let all the earth re - joice.

Verse 1

1. I will give thanks to you, my Lord. You have an-swered my plea. You have saved my soul from death. You are my strength and my song.

to Refrain

Verse 2

2. Ho - ly, ho - ly, ho - ly Lord. Heav - en and earth are full of your glo - ry.

to Refrain

Verse 3

3. This is the day that the Lord has made. Let us be glad and re-joice. Death has lost and all is life. Sing of the glo-ry of God.

to Refrain

Text: Based on Psalm 118; Bob Dufford, SJ, b. 1943.
Music: Bob Dufford, SJ.
Text and music © 1975, Robert J. Dufford, SJ and New Dawn Music. Published by OCP Publications. All rights reserved.

602 THE GOD OF ABRAHAM PRAISE

1. The God of A-braham praise, Who reigns en-throned a-
2. He by him-self hath sworn: We on his oath de-
3. There dwells the Lord, our King, The Lord, our Righ-teous-
4. The God who reigns on high The great arch-an-gels
5. The whole tri-um-phant host give thanks to God on

1. bove; An-cient of ev-er-last-ing days, And God of
2. pend; We shall, on ea-gle-wings up-borne, To heav'n a-
3. ness, Tri-um-phant o'er the world and sin, The Prince of
4. sing, And "Ho-ly, ho-ly, ho-ly," cry, "Al-might-y
5. high; "Hail, Fa-ther, Son, and Ho-ly Ghost!" They ev-er

1. love; The Lord, the great I AM, By earth and heav'n con-
2. scend: We shall be-hold his face, We shall his pow'r a-
3. Peace; On Zi-on's sa-cred height His king-dom he main-
4. King! Who was, and is, the same, And ev-er-more shall
5. cry; Hail, A-braham's Lord di-vine! With heav'n our songs we

1. fessed: We bow and bless the sa-cred Name For ev-er blest.
2. dore, And sing the won-ders of his grace For ev-er-more.
3. tains, And, glo-rious with his saints in light, For ev-er reigns.
4. be: E-ter-nal Fa-ther, great I AM, We wor-ship thee."
5. raise; All might and maj-es-ty are thine, And end-less praise.

Text: 66 84 D; Thomas Olivers, 1725–1799, alt.
Music: LEONI; Hebrew Melody.

603 FROM ALL THAT DWELL BELOW THE SKIES/ PRAISE GOD FROM WHOM ALL BLESSINGS FLOW

1. From all that dwell be-low the skies,
2. E - ter - nal are your mer - cies, Lord;
3. Your loft - y themes, all mor - tals, bring;
4. In ev - 'ry land be - gin the song;

Doxology Praise God, from whom all bless - ings flow;

1. Let the Cre - a - tor's praise a - rise;
2. E - ter - nal truth at - tends your word:
3. In songs of praise di - vine - ly sing;
4. To ev - 'ry land the strains be - long;
   Praise him, all crea - tures here be - low;

1. Let the Re - deem - er's name be sung,
2. Your praise shall sound from shore to shore,
3. The great sal - va - tion loud pro - claim,
4. In cheer - ful sounds all voic - es raise,
   Praise him a - bove, you heav'n - ly host:

1. Through ev - 'ry land by ev - 'ry tongue.
2. Till suns shall rise and set no more.
3. And shout for joy the Sav - ior's name.
4. And fill the world with loud - est praise.
   Praise Fa - ther, Son and Ho - ly Ghost.

Text: LM; based on Psalm 117; verses 1–2, Isaac Watts, 1674–1748, alt; verses 3–4, anon., ca. 1781;
Doxology, Thomas Ken, 1637–1711.
Music: OLD HUNDREDTH, *Genevan Psalter*, 1551; attr. to Louis Bourgeois, ca. 1510–1561, alt.

ALL PEOPLE THAT ON EARTH DO DWELL   604

1. All people that on earth do dwell,
   Sing to the Lord with cheerful voice;
   Him serve with mirth, his praise forth tell,
   Come we before him, and rejoice.

2. Know that the Lord is God indeed;
   Without our aid he did us make;
   We are his folk, he does us feed,
   And for his sheep he does us take.

3. O enter then his gates with praise;
   Approach with joy his courts unto;

Praise, laud, and bless his Name always,
For it is seemly so to do.

4. For why? the Lord our God is good:
   His mercy is for ever sure;
   His truth at all times firmly stood,
   And shall from age to age endure.

5. To Father, Son, and Holy Ghost,
   The God whom heav'n and earth adore,
   From us and from the angel host
   Be praise and glory evermore.

Text: LM; based on Psalm 100; William Kethe, d. ca. 1594, alt.
Music: OLD HUNDREDTH; *Genevan Psalter*, 1551; attr. to Louis Bourgeois, ca. 1510–1561, alt.

605

SING OF THE LORD'S GOODNESS

Verses

1. Sing of the Lord's good-ness, Fa-ther of all wis-dom,
2. Pow-er he has wield-ed, hon-or is his gar-ment,
3. Cour-age in our dark-ness, com-fort in our sor-row,
4. Praise him with your sing-ing, praise him with the trum-pet,

1. come to him and bless his name. Mer-cy he has shown us,
2. ris-en from the snares of death. His word he has spo-ken,
3. Spir-it of our God most high; so-lace for the wear-y,
4. praise God with the lute and harp; praise him with the cym-bals,

1. his love is for-ev-er, faith-ful to the end of days.
2. one bread he has bro-ken, new life he now gives to all.
3. par-don for the sin-ner, splen-dor of the liv-ing God.
4. praise him with your danc-ing, praise God till the end of days.

Refrain

Come, then, all you na-tions, sing of your Lord's good-ness, mel-o-dies of praise and thanks to God. Ring out the Lord's glo-ry, praise him with your mu-sic, wor-ship him and bless his name.

Text and music: Ernest Sands, b. 1949, © 1981, Ernest Sands. Published by OCP Publications. All rights reserved.

606

HE IS THE LORD

Refrain

Sing to the Lord with shouts of joy, let all cre-a-tion re-joice! Come join the song of praise to our God! He is the Lord! He is the Lord!

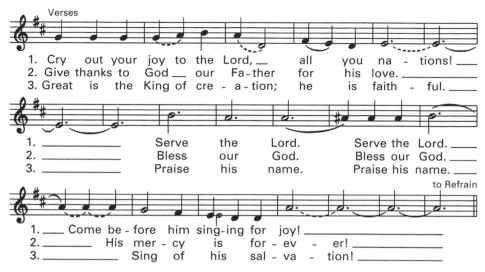

1. Cry out your joy to the Lord, — all you na - tions! —
2. Give thanks to God — our Fa - ther for his love. _____
3. Great is the King of cre - a - tion; he is faith - ful. ____

1. _____ Serve the Lord. Serve the Lord. ____
2. _____ Bless our God. Bless our God. ____
3. _____ Praise his name. Praise his name. ____

to Refrain

1. ___ Come be - fore him sing-ing for joy! _____
2. _____ His mer - cy is for - ev - er! _____
3. _____ Sing of his sal - va - tion! _____

SING A NEW SONG 607

Sing a new song un - to the Lord; let your song be sung from

moun - tains high. Sing a new song un - to the Lord, sing-ing

al - le - lu - ia.

Verses

1. Yah-weh's peo - ple dance for joy.
2. Rise, O chil - dren, from your sleep;
3. Glad my soul for I have seen

1. O come be - fore the Lord. And play for him on
2. your Sav - ior now has come. He has turned your
3. the glo - ry of the Lord. The trum - pet sounds; the

to Refrain

1. glad tam - bou - rines, and let your trum - pet sound.
2. sor - row to joy, and filled your soul with song.
3. dead shall be raised. I know my Sav - ior lives.

608

COME, CHRISTIANS, JOIN TO SING

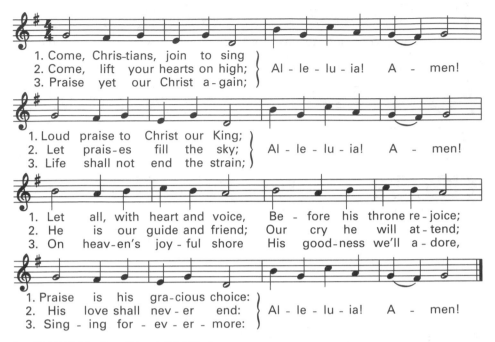

1. Come, Chris-tians, join to sing
2. Come, lift your hearts on high;
3. Praise yet our Christ a-gain;
} Al - le - lu - ia! A - men!

1. Loud praise to Christ our King;
2. Let prais-es fill the sky;
3. Life shall not end the strain;
} Al - le - lu - ia! A - men!

1. Let all, with heart and voice, Be - fore his throne re - joice;
2. He is our guide and friend; Our cry he will at - tend;
3. On heav-en's joy - ful shore His good-ness we'll a - dore,

1. Praise is his gra-cious choice:
2. His love shall nev - er end:
3. Sing - ing for - ev - er - more:
} Al - le - lu - ia! A - men!

Text: 66 66 D; Christian Henry Bateman, 1813–1889, alt.
Music: MADRID; anon. melody, Philadelphia, 1826.

609

BLESSED ASSURANCE

Verses

1. Bless-ed as - sur - ance, Je - sus is mine!
2. Per - fect sub - mis - sion, per - fect de - light,
3. Per - fect sub - mis - sion, all is at rest,

1. Oh, what a fore - taste of glo - ry di - vine!
2. Vi-sions of rap - ture now burst on my sight;
3. I, in my Sav - ior, am hap - py and blest;

1. Heirs of sal - va - tion, chil - dren of God,
2. An - gels de - scend - ing, bring from a - bove
3. Watch-ing and wait - ing, look - ing a - bove,

1. Born of one Spir - it, washed in his blood.
2. Ech - oes of mer - cy, whis-pers of love.
3. Filled with his good - ness, lost in his love.

This is my sto - ry, this is my song, Prais-ing my
Sav - ior all the day long; This is my sto - ry, this is my
song, Prais-ing my Sav - ior all the day long.

Text: 9 10 9 9 with refrain; Fanny J. Crosby, 1820–1915, alt.
Music: ASSURANCE; Phoebe P. Knapp, 1839–1908.

SING PRAISE TO GOD WHO REIGNS ABOVE 610

1. Sing praise to God who reigns a - bove, The God of all
2. What God's al - might - y power has made, His gra-cious mer -
3. Then all my glad - some way a - long, I sing a - loud
4. Let all who name Christ's ho - ly name, Give God all praise

1. cre - a - tion, The God of power, the God of love, The
2. cy keep-ing; By morn-ing glow or eve - ning shade His
3. your prais-es, That all may hear the grate - ful song My
4. and glo - ry; All you who own his power, pro - claim A -

1. God of our sal - va - tion; With heal - ing balm my
2. watch-ful eye ne'er sleep-ing; With - in the king-dom
3. voice un - wea - ried rais - es; Be joy - ful in the
4. loud the won - drous sto - ry! Cast each false i - dol

1. soul he fills, And ev - 'ry faith - less mur - mur stills:
2. of his might, Lo! all is just and all is right:
3. Lord, my heart, Both soul and bod - y sing your part:
4. from its throne, The Lord is God, and he a - lone:

1-4. To God all praise and glo - ry.

Text: 87 87 88 7; *Sei Lob und Ehr' dem höchsten Gut*; Johann J. Schütz, 1640–1690; tr. by Frances E. Cox, 1812–1897.
Music: MIT FREUDEN ZART; *Bohemian Brethren's Kirchengesänge*, 1566.

611   LET ALL MORTAL FLESH KEEP SILENCE

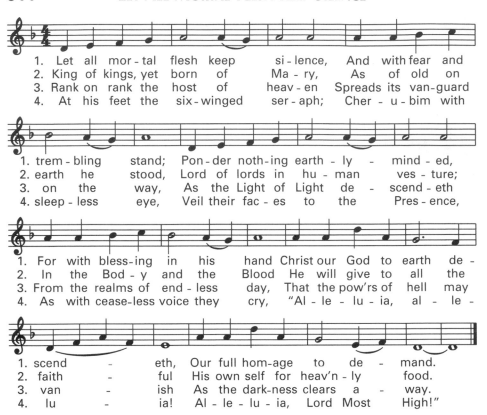

1. Let all mor-tal flesh keep si-lence, And with fear and
2. King of kings, yet born of Ma-ry, As of old on
3. Rank on rank the host of heav-en Spreads its van-guard
4. At his feet the six-winged ser-aph; Cher-u-bim with

1. trem-bling stand; Pon-der noth-ing earth-ly mind-ed,
2. earth he stood, Lord of lords in hu-man ves-ture;
3. on the way, As the Light of Light de-scend-eth
4. sleep-less eye, Veil their fac-es to the Pres-ence,

1. For with bless-ing in his hand Christ our God to earth de-
2. In the Bod-y and the Blood He will give to all the
3. From the realms of end-less day, That the pow'rs of hell may
4. As with cease-less voice they cry, "Al-le-lu-ia, al-le-

1. scend - eth, Our full hom-age to de-mand.
2. faith - ful His own self for heav'n-ly food.
3. van - ish As the dark-ness clears a-way.
4. lu - ia! Al-le-lu-ia, Lord Most High!"

Text: 87 87 87; Liturgy of St. James, 4th cent.; para. by Gerard Moultrie, 1829–1885, alt.
Music: PICARDY; French, 17th cent.; *Chansons populaires des Provinces de France*, 1860.

612   PRAISE, MY SOUL, THE KING OF HEAVEN

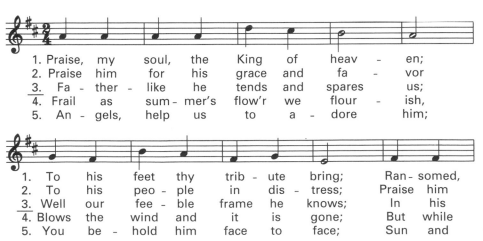

1. Praise, my soul, the King of heav - en;
2. Praise him for his grace and fa - vor
3. Fa - ther - like he tends and spares us;
4. Frail as sum-mer's flow'r we flour - ish,
5. An - gels, help us to a - dore him;

1. To his feet thy trib - ute bring; Ran-somed,
2. To his peo - ple in dis - tress; Praise him
3. Well our fee - ble frame he knows; In his
4. Blows the wind and it is gone; But while
5. You be - hold him face to face; Sun and

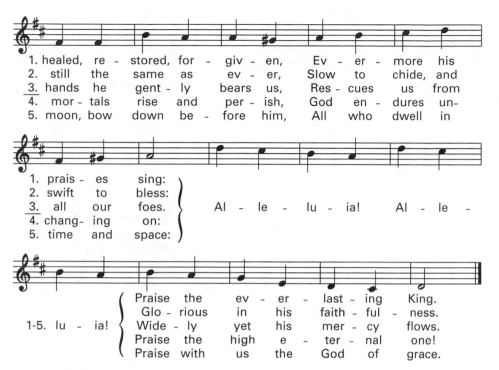

1. healed, re - stored, for - giv - en, Ev - er - more his
2. still the same as ev - er, Slow to chide, and
3. hands he gent - ly bears us, Res - cues us from
4. mor - tals rise and per - ish, God en - dures un-
5. moon, bow down be - fore him, All who dwell in

1. prais - es sing:
2. swift to bless:
3. all our foes. } Al - le - lu - ia! Al - le -
4. chang- ing on:
5. time and space:

1-5. lu - ia! {
Praise the ev - er - last - ing King.
Glo - rious in his faith - ful - ness.
Wide - ly yet his mer - cy flows.
Praise the high e - ter - nal one!
Praise with us the God of grace.
}

Text: 87 87 87; based on Psalm 103; Henry F. Lyte, 1793–1847, alt.
Music: LAUDA ANIMA; John Goss, 1800–1880,

GOD, WHOSE LOVE IS REIGNING O'ER US   613

1. God, whose love is reigning o'er us,
   Source of all, the ending true;
   Hear the universal chorus
   Raised in joyful praise to you:
   Alleluia, Alleluia,
   Worship ancient, worship new.

2. Word of God from nature bringing
   Springtime green and autumn gold;
   Mountain streams like children singing,
   Ocean waves like thunder bold:
   Alleluia, Alleluia,
   As creation's tale is told.

3. Holy God of ancient glory,
   Choosing man and woman, too;
   Abr'am's faith and Sarah's story

Formed a people bound to you.
Alleluia, Alleluia,
To your cov'nant keep us true.

4. Cov'nant, new again in Jesus,
   Starchild born to set us free;
   Sent to heal us, sent to teach us
   How love's children we might be.
   Alleluia, Alleluia,
   Risen Christ, our Savior he!

5. Lift we then our human voices
   In the songs that faith would bring;
   Live we then in human choices
   Lives that, like our music, sing:
   Alleluia, Alleluia,
   Joined in love our praises ring!

Text: 87 87 87; William Boyd Grove, © 1980, William Boyd Grove. All rights reserved. Used with permission.
Music: LAUDA ANIMA; John Goss, 1800–1880.

O GOD BEYOND ALL PRAISING

1. O God be-yond all prais - ing, We wor-ship you to - day
2. Then hear, O gra-cious Sav - ior, Ac - cept the love we bring,

1. And sing the love a - maz - ing That songs can-not re - pay;
2. That we who know your fa - vor May serve you as our King;

1. For we can on - ly won - der At ev - 'ry gift you send,
2. And wheth - er our to - mor-rows Be filled with good or ill,

1. At bless-ings with - out num - ber And mer-cies with-out end:
2. We'll tri - umph through our sor - rows And rise to bless you still:

1. We lift our hearts be - fore you And wait up-on your word,
2. To mar - vel at your beau - ty And glo - ry in your ways,

1. We hon - or and a-dore you, Our great and might-y Lord.
2. And make a joy - ful du - ty Our sac - ri - fice of praise.

Text: 76 76 76 D; Michael Perry, 1942–1996, © 1982, 1987, Jubilate Hymns, Ltd. All rights reserved.
   Administered by Hope Publishing Co. Used with permission.
Music: THAXTED; Gustav T. Holst, 1874–1934.

615   ABBA, FATHER

Refrain   Ab - ba,   Ab - ba, Fa -
Verses 1. Mold   us,   mold us and fash - ion
      2. Fa - ther,   may we be one in
      3. Glo - ry,   glo - ry and praise to

    ther.   You are the pot - ter;
1. us   in - to the im - age   of
2. you.   May we be one in you   as
3. you.   Glo - ry and praise to you   for-

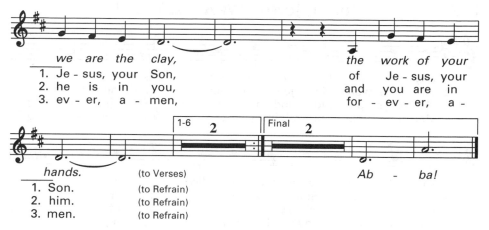

we are the clay, the work of your
1. Je - sus, your Son, of Je - sus, your
2. he is in you, and you are in
3. ev - er, a - men, for - ev - er, a -

1-6 | Final

hands. (to Verses) Ab - ba!
1. Son. (to Refrain)
2. him. (to Refrain)
3. men. (to Refrain)

Text: Refrain based on Jeremiah 18:6, Romans 8:15; verse 1 based on Romans 8:28;
verse 2 based on John 17:21; Carey Landry, b. 1944.
Music: Carey Landry.
Text and music © 1977, NALR. Published by OCP Publications. All rights reserved.

SING A JOYFUL SONG 616

Refrain

Sing a joy - ful song to the Lord! Al - le - lu - ia!

Let the heav - ens and earth re - joice! Al - le - lu - ia!

Al - le - lu - ia!

Verses

1. The heav - ens pro -
2. Our God is a
3. Sing praise, O Je -
4. Sing praise to the

1. claim God's name, and earth in re - ply ech - oes
2. might - y God, un - e - qualled in pow'r, yet with
3. ru - sa - lem! Sing praise to your King, rul - ing
4. God of gods, the An - cient of Days! Ho - ly,

to Refrain

1. back with joy - ful songs __ of praise!
2. gen - tle mer - cy cov - ers the earth.
3. earth with jus - tice age af - ter age.
4. ho - ly, ho - ly Lord __ of all!

Text: Based on Psalm 145; Jim Farrell, b. 1947.
Music: Jim Farrell.
Text and music © 1984, OCP Publications. All rights reserved.

617
JOYFUL, JOYFUL, WE ADORE YOU

1. Joy - ful, joy - ful, we a - dore you, God of glo - ry,
2. All your works with joy sur-round you, Earth and heav'n re -
3. Al - ways giv - ing and for - giv - ing, Ev - er bless-ing,
4. Mor - tals, join the might - y cho - rus Which the morn-ing

1. Lord of love; Hearts un - fold like flow'rs be - fore you,
2. flect your rays, Stars and an - gels sing a - round you,
3. ev - er blest, Well-spring of the joy of liv - ing,
4. stars be - gan; Love di - vine is reign - ing o'er us,

1. O - p'ning to the sun a - bove. Melt the clouds of
2. Cen - ter of un - bro - ken praise; Field and for - est,
3. O - cean depth of hap - py rest! Lov - ing Fa - ther,
4. Bind - ing all with - in its span. Ev - er sing - ing,

1. sin and sad - ness; Drive the dark of doubt a - way;
2. vale and moun-tain, Flow - 'ry mead - ow, flash - ing sea,
3. Christ our broth - er, Let your light up - on us shine;
4. march we on - ward, Vic - tors in the midst of strife;

1. Giv - er of im - mor - tal glad-ness, Fill us with the light of day!
2. Chant-ing bird and flow-ing foun-tain, Prais-ing you e - ter - nal-ly!
3. Teach us how to love each oth - er, Lift us to the joy di-vine.
4. Joy - ful mu - sic leads us sun-ward, In the tri-umph song of life.

Text: 87 87 D; Henry van Dyke, 1852–1933, alt.
Music: HYMN TO JOY; Ludwig van Beethoven, 1770–1827; adapt. by Edward Hodges, 1796–1867.

618
LET ALL THE PEOPLES

Refrain

Let all the peo - ples praise you, O Lord, let

all the peo - ples praise you. you.

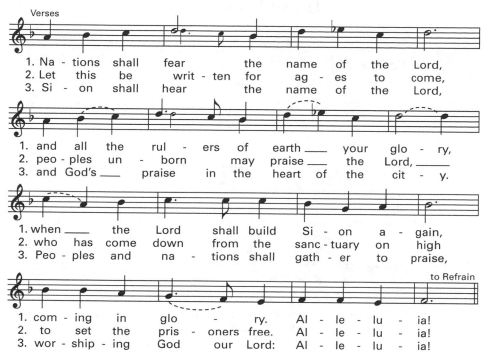

Verses

1. Na - tions shall fear the name of the Lord,
2. Let this be writ - ten for ag - es to come,
3. Si - on shall hear the name of the Lord,

1. and all the rul - ers of earth ___ your glo - ry,
2. peo - ples un - born may praise ___ the Lord, ___
3. and God's ___ praise in the heart of the cit - y.

1. when ___ the Lord shall build Si - on a - gain,
2. who has come down from the sanc - tuary on high
3. Peo - ples and na - tions shall gath - er to praise,

to Refrain

1. com - ing in glo - ry. Al - le - lu - ia!
2. to set the pris - oners free. Al - le - lu - ia!
3. wor - ship - ing God our Lord: Al - le - lu - ia!

Text: Based on Psalm 102:16–17, 19–21, 22–23; Christopher Willcock, b. 1947.
Refrain © 1991, Christopher Willcock, SJ. Published by OCP Publications. All rights reserved.
Verses © 1963, The Grail (England). All rights reserved. Used with permission of A.P. Watt, Ltd.
Music: Christopher Willcock, © 1991, Christopher Willcock, SJ. Published by OCP Publications. All rights reserved.

BLESSED BY YOUR SACRIFICE 619

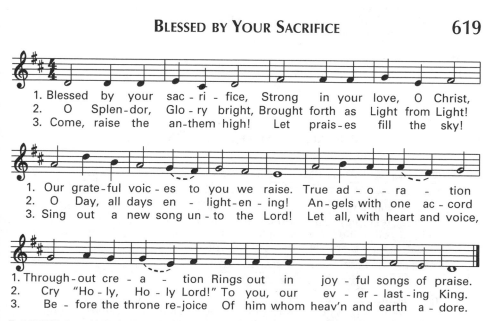

1. Blessed by your sac - ri - fice, Strong in your love, O Christ,
2. O Splen-dor, Glo - ry bright, Brought forth as Light from Light!
3. Come, raise the an-them high! Let prais-es fill the sky!

1. Our grate-ful voic - es to you we raise. True ad - o - ra - tion
2. O Day, all days en - light-en - ing! An-gels with one ac - cord
3. Sing out a new song un - to the Lord! Let all, with heart and voice,

1. Through-out cre - a - tion Rings out in joy - ful songs of praise.
2. Cry "Ho - ly, Ho - ly Lord!" To you, our ev - er - last-ing King.
3. Be - fore the throne re-joice Of him whom heav'n and earth a - dore.

Text: 66 9 55 8; Owen Alstott, b. 1947, and Jeanne Frolick, SFCC, © 1979, 1982, OCP Publications. All rights reserved.
Music: ST. ELIZABETH; Trad. Silesian Melody; Hoffman and Richter's *Schlesische Volkslieder*, Leipzig, 1842.

LIFT UP YOUR HEARTS

Refrain

Lift up your hearts to the Lord, praise God's gra-cious mer-cy!

Sing out your joy to the Lord, whose love is en-dur-ing.

Verses

1. Shout with joy to the Lord, all the earth!
2. Let the earth wor-ship, sing-ing your praise.
3. God's right hand made a path through the night,
4. Lis-ten now, all you ser-vants of God,

1. Praise the name a-bove all names! Say to God, "How
2. Praise the glo-ry of your name! Come and see the
3. split the wa-ters of the sea. All cre-a-tion,
4. as I tell of these great works. Bless-ed be the

to Refrain

1. won-drous your works, how glo-rious your name!"
2. deeds of the Lord; bless God's ho-ly name!
3. lift up your voice: "Our God set us free!"
4. Lord of my life, whose love shall en-dure!

Text: Based on Psalm 66; Roc O'Connor, SJ, b. 1949.
Music: Roc O'Connor, SJ.
Text and music © 1981, 1993, Robert F. O'Connor, SJ and New Dawn Music.
Published by OCP Publications. All rights reserved.

621   IMMORTAL, INVISIBLE, GOD ONLY WISE

1. Im - mor - tal, in - vis - i - ble, God on - ly wise,
2. Un - rest - ing, un - hast - ing, and si - lent as light,
3. Life - giv - ing Cre - a - tor, of both great and small;
4. Great Fa - ther of glo - ry, pure Fa - ther of light,

1. In light in - ac - ces - si - ble hid from our eyes,
2. Nor want - ing, nor wast - ing, you rule day and night;
3. Of all life the mak - er, the true life of all;
4. Your an - gels a - dor - ing, all veil - ing their sight;

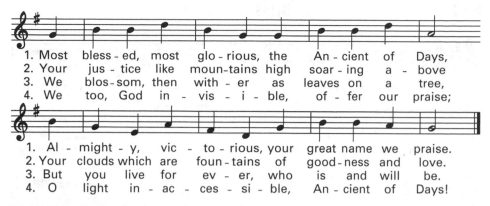

1. Most bless-ed, most glo-rious, the An-cient of Days,
2. Your jus-tice like moun-tains high soar-ing a - bove,
3. We blos-som, then with-er as leaves on a tree,
4. We too, God in-vis-i-ble, of-fer our praise;

1. Al - might-y, vic - to-rious, your great name we praise.
2. Your clouds which are foun-tains of good-ness and love.
3. But you live for ev - er, who is and will be.
4. O light in-ac-ces-si-ble, An-cient of Days!

Text: 11 11 11 11; 1 Timothy 1:17; Walter C. Smith, 1824–1908, alt.
Music: ST. DENIO; Roberts' *Canaidau y Cyssegr*, 1839.

WE PRAISE YOU, O GOD 622

1. We praise you, O God; ___ ac - claim you as Lord.
2. A - pos - tles and proph-ets, the mar - tyrs for Christ,
3. Lord Je - sus the Christ, ___ your death brings us life.
4. Lord, grant us sal - va - tion, pro - tect us from harm.

1. All of cre - a - tion re - sounds to the voice of the
2. sing of your good - ness while bathed in the beams of your
3. Come with your judg - ment and grant us a place in the
4. Free us from e - vil and bless us with mer - cy as

1. heav - en - ly host u - nit - ed in song,
2. in - fi - nite love, your splen - dor and light,
3. King - dom of God, at one with your saints,
4. dai - ly in you we trust and we hope,

prais - ing your

1-4. maj - es - ty, prais-ing your glo - ry. Al - le-lu - ia, al - le -

1-4. lu - ia. Ho-ly is God, ho-ly and strong. Al - le-lu -

1-4. ia, al-le - lu - ia. Ho-ly Im-mor-tal One.

Text: Based on the *Te Deum laudamus*; attr. to St. Nicetas, ca. 335–414; Peter Jones, b. 1951.
Music: Peter Jones.

623

O BLESS THE LORD

Refrain

O bless the Lord, the God of our sal - va - tion, Rock of

strength and a ref - uge sure! O bless the Lord, the God of ev - 'ry

na - tion, o - ver all the earth!

Verses

1. O bless the Lord,
2. Let all the earth
3. Let all the na -
4. Let all the peo -

1. high - est heav - ens a - bove! Bless the Lord!
2. sing with joy to the Lord, all the seas,
3. - tions on earth bless the Lord, for the Lord
4. - ple on earth bless the Lord! Young and old,

1. Glo - ri - fy his name! Sun in the day, moon and
2. crea - tures of the deep! Moun - tains and hills, birds and
3. gov - erns all the world! Let all the rul - ers on
4. glo - ri - fy his name! Let ev - 'ry voice sing with

to Refrain

1. stars in the night, wor - ship and praise!
2. beasts in the fields, wor - ship and praise!
3. earth bless the Lord! Wor - ship and praise!
4. joy to the Lord: "Glo - ry and praise!"

Text: Based on Psalm 148; John Michaels, b. 1947.
Music: John Michaels.

624

WHEN IN OUR MUSIC

1. When in our mu - sic God is glo - ri - fied, And a - do -
2. How of - ten, mak - ing mu - sic, we have found A new di -
3. So has the Church, in lit - ur - gy and song, In faith and
4. And did not Je - sus sing a psalm that night When ut - most
5. Let ev - 'ry in - stru - ment be tuned for praise! Let all re -

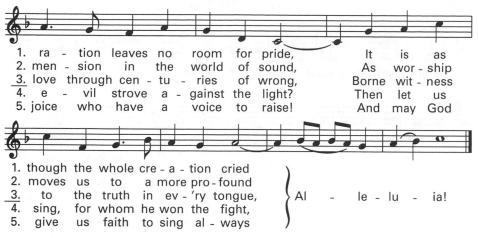

1. ra - tion leaves no room for pride, It is as
2. men - sion in the world of sound, As wor - ship
3. love through cen - tu - ries of wrong, Borne wit - ness
4. e - vil strove a - gainst the light? Then let us
5. joice who have a voice to raise! And may God

1. though the whole cre - a - tion cried
2. moves us to a more pro - found
3. to the truth in ev - 'ry tongue,   } Al - le - lu - ia!
4. sing, for whom he won the fight,
5. give us faith to sing al - ways

Text: 10 10 10 with alleluia; Fred Pratt Green, 1903–2000, © 1972, Hope Publishing Co.
  All rights reserved. Used with permission.
Music: ENGELBERG; Charles Villiers Stanford, 1852–1924, alt.

SING PRAISE TO THE LORD   625

1. Sing praise to the Lord! praise God in the height;
2. Sing praise to the Lord! praise God up - on earth,
3. Sing praise to the Lord, all things that give sound;
4. Sing praise to the Lord! thanks - giv - ing and song

1. Re - joice in his word, you an - gels of light;
2. In tune - ful ac - cord, all you of new birth;
3. Each ju - bi - lant chord re - ech - o a - round;
4. To him be out - poured all a - ges a - long;

1. O heav - ens, a - dore him by whom you were made,
2. Praise him who has brought you his grace from a - bove,
3. Loud or - gans, his glo - ry tell forth in deep tone,
4. For love in cre - a - tion, for heav - en re - stored,

1. And wor - ship be - fore him in bright-ness ar - rayed.
2. Praise him who has taught you to sing of his love.
3. And trum-pets, the sto - ry of what God has done.
4. For grace of sal - va - tion, sing praise to the Lord!

Text: 10 10 11 11; based on Psalms 148 and 150; Henry W. Baker, 1821–1877, alt.
Music: LAUDATE DOMINUM; Charles H. H. Parry, 1840–1918.

WE PRAISE YOU

Refrain

We praise you, O Lord, for all your works are won-der-ful. We praise

you, O Lord, for ev-er is your love.

Verses

1. Your wis-dom made the
2. ⅞ You have cho - sen
3. You led us out of
4. The na - tions fash-ioned
5. O house of Is - ra-
*6. ⅞ Hap - py is the
*7. ⅞ May the Lord give

1. heav-ens and the earth, O Lord;   you formed the land, then
2. Ja - cob for your-self, O Lord;   so ten - der - ly you
3. E - gypt with a guid-ing hand.   You raised your arm to
4. sil - ver i - dols, gol - den gods;   but none have hear-ing,
5. el, now come to bless the Lord,   O house of Aar - on,
6. home of you that fear the Lord;   so fruit - ful shall your
7. you his bless-ings all your days.   ⅞ May you see him

1. set the lights;   and like your love the sun will
2. spoke his name;   then called a ho - ly na - tion,
3. set us free.   And like a ten - der vine you
4. speech or sight.   Their mak - ers shall be like their
5. bless his name.   O bless the Lord, all you who
6. love be - come.   Your chil - dren flour-ish like the
7. fill your land   un - til your chil-dren bring their

to Refrain

1. rule the day,   and stars will grace the night.
2. Is - ra - el,   to make them yours, you came.
3. plant-ed us   to grow un - to the sea.
4. emp - ty gods,   the Lord a - lone brings life.
5. hon - or him,   and praise his ho - ly name.
6. ol - ive plants,   for ev - er are you one.
7. chil-dren home   to show his love a - gain.

*Wedding verses.

Text: Verses 1–5 based on Psalms 135, 136; verses 6–7 based on Psalm 128; Mike Balhoff, b. 1946.
Music: Darryl Ducote, b. 1945, and Gary Daigle, b. 1957.
Text and music © 1973, 1978, Damean Music. All rights reserved. Used with permission.

ALLE, ALLE, ALLELUIA

Refrain Al - le, al - le, al - le - lu - ia,

Verses 1. Fa - ther, Fa - ther, mak - er of the world.
2. Je - sus, Je - sus, Je - sus is the way.
3. Spir - it, Spir - it, come down on us, Lord.

al - le, al - le, al - le - lu - ia.
1. Fa - ther, Fa - ther, cre - a - tor of the earth.
2. Je - sus, Je - sus, Je - sus is the truth.
3. Spir - it, Spir - it, rain down on us, Lord.

Al - le, al - le, al - le - lu - ia.
1. Fa - ther, Fa - ther, speak - er of the word.
2. Je - sus, Je - sus, Je - sus is the life.
3. Spir - it, Spir - it, flood us with your pow'r.

Al - le, al - le, al - le, al - le - lu - ia.
1. Make us, Fa - ther, break us, Fa - ther, mold us in your ways.
2. Je - sus is the way, he is the truth, he is the life.
3. Fill us with the light of God, oh, fill us with your pow'r.

1-6

Al - le, al - le, al - le, al - le - lu - ia. (to Verses)
1. Make us, Fa - ther, break us, Fa - ther, mold us in your ways. (to Refrain)
2. Je - sus is the way, he is the truth, he is the life. (to Refrain)
3. Fill us with the light of God, oh, fill us with your pow'r. (to Refrain)

Final

ia. Al - le, al - le, al - le - lu - ia.

Al - le, al - le, al - le - lu - ia. Al - le!

628

HOW GREAT THOU ART

Verses

1. O Lord my God! When I in awe-some won-der Con - si - der
2. When through the woods and for-est glades I wan-der, And hear the
3. And when I think that God, his Son not spar - ing, Sent him to
4. When Christ shall come with shout of ac - cla - ma - tion And take me

1. all the *worlds thy hands have made, I see the stars, I
2. birds sing sweet - ly in the trees; When I look down from
3. die, I scarce can take it in, That on the cross, my
4. home, what joy shall fill my heart! Then I shall bow in

1. hear the *roll - ing thun - der, Thy pow'r through-out the
2. lof - ty moun-tain gran - deur And hear the brook, and
3. bur - den glad - ly bear - ing, He bled and died to
4. hum - ble ad - o - ra - tion, And there pro - claim, my

Refrain

1. u - ni - verse dis-played; Then sings my soul, my Sav-ior God to
2. feel the gen - tle breeze;
3. take a - way my sin;
4. God, how great thou art!

thee; How great thou art, how great thou art! Then sings my soul, my

Sav-ior God to thee; How great thou art, how great thou art!

*Author's original words are "works" and "mighty."

Text: 11 10 11 10 with refrain; Carl Boberg, 1850–1940; tr. by Stuart K. Hine, 1899–1989.
Music: O STORE GUD; Swedish Folk Melody; adapt. by Stuart K. Hine.
Text and music © 1953, Stuart K. Hine, renewed 1981, assigned to Manna Music, Inc. All rights reserved. Used with permission.

629

FOR THE FRUITS OF THIS CREATION

1. For the fruits of this cre - a - tion, Thanks be to God;
2. In the just re - ward of la - bor, God's will be done;
3. For the har-vests of the Spir - it, Thanks be to God;

1. For the gifts of ev - 'ry na - tion, Thanks be to God;
2. In the help we give our neigh-bor, God's will be done;
3. For the good we all in - her - it, Thanks be to God;

1. For the plow - ing, sow-ing, reap-ing, Si - lent growth while we are
2. In the world-wide task of car - ing For the hun - gry and de-
3. For the won - ders that as-tound us, For the truths that will con -

1. sleep-ing, Fu - ture needs in earth's safe-keep-ing, Thanks be to God.
2. spair-ing, In the har-vests we are shar-ing, God's will be done.
3. found us, Most of all, that love has found us, Thanks be to God.

Text: 84 84 88 84; Fred Pratt Green, 1903–2000, © 1970, Hope Publishing Co. All rights reserved. Used with permission.
Music: AR HYD Y NOS; Trad. Welsh Melody.

MANY AND GREAT 630

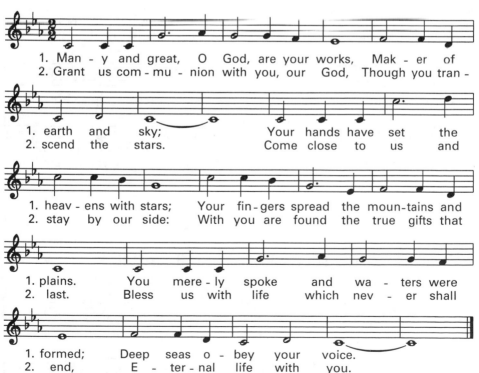

1. Man - y and great, O God, are your works, Mak - er of
2. Grant us com - mu - nion with you, our God, Though you tran -

1. earth and sky; Your hands have set the
2. scend the stars. Come close to us and

1. heav - ens with stars; Your fin - gers spread the moun-tains and
2. stay by our side: With you are found the true gifts that

1. plains. You mere - ly spoke and wa - ters were
2. last. Bless us with life which nev - er shall

1. formed; Deep seas o - bey your voice.
2. end, E - ter - nal life with you.

Text: 96 99 96; *Wakantanka tuki nitawa*; Dakota Hymn; para. by Phillip Frazier, 1892–1964.
Music: LAQUIPARLE; *Dakota Odowan*, 1879.

631
IN PRAISE OF HIS NAME

Refrain

Bless the Lord,   O my soul;   bless the Lord, praise his name!

Bless the Lord,   O my soul;   let all cre-a-tion praise his name!

Verse 1

1. Sun and the moon, bless the Lord!   Bless him, all of the earth! Sea and its

1. waves,   glo-ry in your pow'r. Let your thun-der ech-o his name!

Verse 2

2. Let all cre-a-tion a-rise   and give praise   to our God   for Yah-weh a-

2. lone is   God.   He   made us,   we be-long   to   him!

Verse 3

3. Wom-en and men,   praise our God, and chil-dren lift up your hearts.

3. En-ter his gates with songs of joy;   with glad-ness serve you the Lord!

Text: Based on Psalms 100, 148; Roc O'Connor, SJ, b. 1949.
Music: Roc O'Connor, SJ.
Text and music © 1976, Robert F. O'Connor, SJ and New Dawn Music. Published by OCP Publications. All rights reserved.

632
ALL THINGS BRIGHT AND BEAUTIFUL

Refrain

All things bright and beau - ti - ful, All   crea-tures great and   small,

All things wise and   won - der - ful, The   Lord God made them   all.

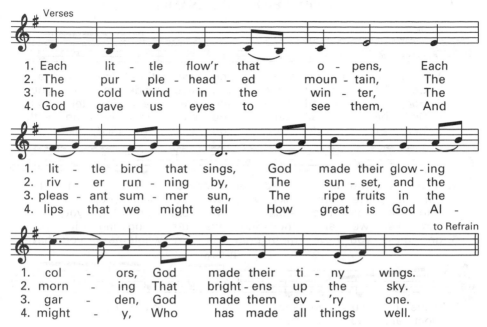

1. Each lit - tle flow'r that o - pens, Each
2. The pur - ple - head - ed moun - tain, The
3. The cold wind in the win - ter, The
4. God gave us eyes to see them, And

1. lit - tle bird that sings, God made their glow - ing
2. riv - er run - ning by, The sun - set, and the
3. pleas - ant sum - mer sun, The ripe fruits in the
4. lips that we might tell How great is God Al -

to Refrain

1. col - ors, God made their ti - ny wings.
2. morn - ing That bright - ens up the sky.
3. gar - den, God made them ev - 'ry one.
4. might - y, Who has made all things well.

Text: 76 76 with refrain; Cecil Francis H. Alexander, 1818–1895, alt.
Music: ROYAL OAK; Trad. English Melody; adapt. by Martin Shaw, 1875–1958.

Oh, Who Can Know the Mind of God 633

1. Oh, who can know the mind of God, Or
2. Who else has cupped the seas in hand, Or
3. Who else sur - rounds in bound - less deeps The
4. Too high for us, O Lord, your ways, Too

1. who dare call his name, Whose glo - ry is the
2. set the skies a - light? Who else could carve from
3. is - land of the mind? Who else in clouds of
4. vast your works: to them We reach with trem - bling

1. ris - ing sun, Whose ev - 'ry word is flame?
2. stone the land, Or sum - mon day from night?
3. si - lence keeps Long watch for all our kind?
4. words of praise To touch your gar - ment's hem.

Text: CM; Genevieve Glen, OSB, b. 1945, © 1998, The Benedictine Nuns of the Abbey of St. Walburga.
   Published by OCP Publications. All rights reserved.
Music: MORNING SONG; *Sixteen Tune Settings*, Philadelphia, 1812; *Kentucky Harmony*, 1816.

634   GOD, BEYOND ALL NAMES

Verses

1. God, be - yond our dreams, you have stirred in us a
2. God, be - yond all names, you have made us in your
3. God, be - yond all words, all cre - a - tion tells your
4. God, be - yond all time, you are la - bor - ing with -
5. God of ten - der care, you have cra - dled us in

1. mem - 'ry; you have placed your pow'r - ful spir - it in the
2. im - age; we are like you, we re - flect you; we are
3. sto - ry; you have shak - en with our laugh - ter, you have
4. in us; we are mov - ing, we are chang - ing in your
5. good-ness, you have moth-ered us in whole-ness, you have

Refrain

1. hearts of hu - man-kind. All a - round us we have
2. wom - an, we are man.
3. trem - bled with our tears.
4. spir - it ev - er new.
5. loved us in - to birth.

known you, all cre - a - tion lives to hold you. In our

liv - ing and our dy - ing we are bring-ing you to birth.

635   I SING THE MIGHTY POWER OF GOD

1. I sing the might - y pow'r of God That made the
2. I sing the good-ness of the Lord That filled the
3. There's not a plant or flow'r be - low, But makes thy

1. moun-tains rise, That spread the flow-ing seas a - broad, And
2. earth with food; He formed the crea-tures with his word, And
3. glo - ries known; And clouds a - rise, and tem-pests blow By

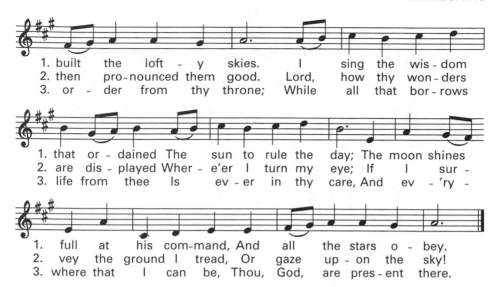

1. built the loft - y skies. I sing the wis - dom
2. then pro-nounced them good. Lord, how thy won - ders
3. or - der from thy throne; While all that bor - rows

1. that or - dained The sun to rule the day; The moon shines
2. are dis - played Wher - e'er I turn my eye; If I sur -
3. life from thee Is ev - er in thy care, And ev - 'ry -

1. full at his com-mand, And all the stars o - bey.
2. vey the ground I tread, Or gaze up - on the sky!
3. where that I can be, Thou, God, are pres - ent there.

Text: CMD; Isaac Watts, 1674–1748, alt.
Music: ELLACOMBE; *Gesangbuch der Herzogl, Wirtembergischen Katholischen Hofkapelle,* 1784, alt.;
   adapt. fr. Würth's *Katholisches Gesangbuch,* 1863.

Now Thank We All Our God   636

1. Now thank we all our God With heart, and hands, and
2. O may this gra-cious God Through all our life be
3. All praise and thanks to God The Fa - ther now be

1. voic - es, Who won-drous things has done, In whom his world re-
2. near us, With ev - er joy - ful hearts And bless - ed peace to
3. giv - en, The Son, and Spir - it blest, Who reigns in high-est

1. joic - es; Who, from our moth-er's arms Has blessed us on our
2. cheer us; Pre-serve us in his grace, And guide us in dis -
3. heav - en, E - ter-nal, Tri - une God, Whom earth and heav'n a -

1. way With count-less gifts of love, And still is ours to - day.
2. tress, And free us from all sin, Till heav-en we pos-sess.
3. dore; For thus it was, is now, And shall be, ev - er-more.

Text: 67 67 66 66; Sirach 50:22–24; Martin Rinkart, 1586–1649; tr. by Catherine Winkworth, 1827–1878, alt.
Music: NUN DANKET; Johann Crüger, 1598–1662; adapt. by Felix Mendelssohn, 1809–1847, alt.

637 ALL MY DAYS

Refrain

Till the end of my days, O Lord, I will bless your name,

sing your praise, give you thanks, all my days.

Verses

1. You have made me lit - tle less than a god, _____
2. You have blessed _ me with good things and plen-ty ____
3. Your sun ___ and your moon give me light, _____
4. How great ___ is your love, O _____ Fa-ther, ___

1. and have lav - ished my heart with your love. With dig - ni - ty and
2. and sur - round - ed my ta - ble with friends. Their love _ and their
3. and your stars show the way through the night. Your riv - ers and
4. that you sent us your Sav - ior Son. His death _ and his

to Refrain

1. hon - or you've clothed me, giv - en me rule o - ver all.
2. laugh - ter en - rich me; to - geth - er we sing your _ praise.
3. streams have re - freshed me. I ____ will sing your _ praise.
4. ris - ing will heal us, and draw us ___ all un - to you.

Text: Based on Psalm 8; adapt. by J-Glenn Murray, SJ.
Music: Dan Schutte, b. 1947.

638 THANKS BE TO GOD

1. Thanks be to God whose love has gath - ered us this day;
2. Thanks be to God for all the gifts of life and light;
3. Thanks be to God who knows our se - cret joys and fears;
4. Thanks be to God who nev - er turns his face a - way;
5. Thanks be to God who made our world and all we see;

1. thanks be to God who helps and guides us on our way.
2. thanks be to God whose care pro - tects us day and night.
3. thanks be to God who when we call him al - ways hears.
4. thanks be to God who heals and par - dons all who stray.
5. thanks be to God who gave his Son to set us free.

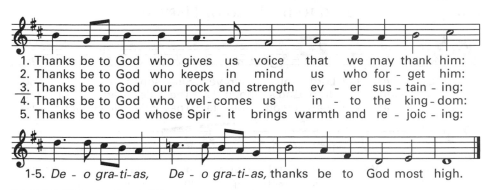

1. Thanks be to God who gives us voice that we may thank him:
2. Thanks be to God who keeps in mind us who for - get him:
3. Thanks be to God our rock and strength ev - er sus - tain - ing:
4. Thanks be to God who wel - comes us in - to the king - dom:
5. Thanks be to God whose Spir - it brings warmth and re - joic - ing:

1-5. *De - o gra-ti-as, De - o gra-ti-as,* thanks be to God most high.

Text: 12 12 13 55 6; Stephen Dean, b. 1948.
Music: CHARIS; Stephen Dean.
Text and music © 1994, Stephen Dean. Published by OCP Publications. All rights reserved.

COME, YE THANKFUL PEOPLE, COME 639

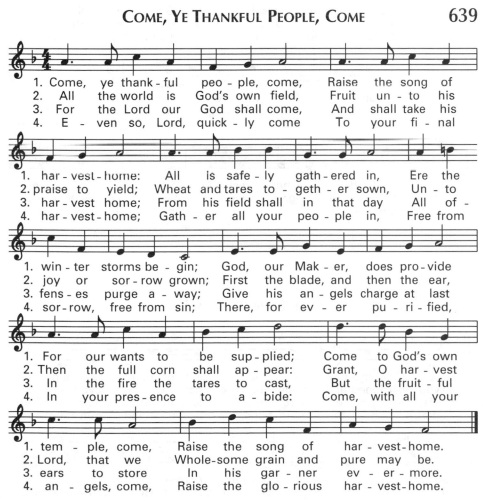

1. Come, ye thank - ful peo - ple, come, Raise the song of
2. All the world is God's own field, Fruit un - to his
3. For the Lord our God shall come, And shall take his
4. E - ven so, Lord, quick - ly come To your fi - nal

1. har - vest - home: All is safe - ly gath - ered in, Ere the
2. praise to yield; Wheat and tares to - geth - er sown, Un - to
3. har - vest home; From his field shall in that day All of -
4. har - vest - home; Gath - er all your peo - ple in, Free from

1. win - ter storms be - gin; God, our Mak - er, does pro - vide
2. joy or sor - row grown; First the blade, and then the ear,
3. fens - es purge a - way; Give his an - gels charge at last
4. sor - row, free from sin; There, for ev - er pu - ri - fied,

1. For our wants to be sup - plied; Come to God's own
2. Then the full corn shall ap - pear: Grant, O har - vest
3. In the fire the tares to cast, But the fruit - ful
4. In your pres - ence to a - bide: Come, with all your

1. tem - ple, come, Raise the song of har - vest - home.
2. Lord, that we Whole-some grain and pure may be.
3. ears to store In his gar - ner ev - er - more.
4. an - gels, come, Raise the glo - rious har - vest - home.

Text: 77 77 D; Henry Alford, 1810–1871, alt.
Music: ST. GEORGE'S WINDSOR; George J. Elvey, 1816–1893.

640   SING TO THE LORD OF HARVEST

1. Sing to the Lord of har-vest, Sing songs of love and
2. The clouds all drop God's boun-ty, The des-erts bloom and
3. Place at the sa-cred al-tar The gifts which good-ness

1. praise; With joy-ful hearts and voic-es Your
2. spring; The hills leap up in glad-ness, The
3. gave, The gold-en sheaves of har-vest, The

1. al-le-lu-ias raise! By God the roll-ing
2. val-leys laugh and sing. God gifts the earth in
3. souls Christ came to save; Your hearts lay down in

1. sea-sons In fruit-ful or-der move; Sing
2. full-ness, All things with large in-crease, And
3. hom-age, At ho-ly feet now fall, Through

1. to the Lord of har-vest A joy-ful song of love.
2. crowns the year with good-ness, With plen-ty and with peace.
3. all your life a-dor-ing The One who died for all.

Text: 76 76 D; John S.B. Monsell, 1811–1875, alt.
Music: WIE LIEBLICH IST DER MAIEN; Johann Steuerlein, 1546–1613.

641   LET ALL THINGS NOW LIVING

1. Let all things now liv-ing A song of thanks-giv-ing To
   Who fash-ioned and made us, Pro-tect-ed and stayed us, By
2. His law he en-forc-es, The stars in their cours-es, The
   The hills and the moun-tains, The riv-ers and foun-tains, The

1. God our Cre-a-tor tri-um-phant-ly raise;
   guid-ing us on to the end of our days. God's ban-ners are
2. sun in its or-bit o-be-dient-ly shine,
   depths of the o-cean pro-claim God di-vine. We, too, should be

1. o'er us, Pure light goes be - fore us, A pil - lar of fire shin-ing
2. voic-ing Our love and re - joic-ing With glad ad - o - ra-tion, a

1. forth in the night: Till shad-ows have van-ished And dark-ness is
2. song let us raise: Till all things now liv - ing U - nite in thanks-

1. ban-ished, As for-ward we trav - el from light in - to Light.
2. giv - ing, To God in the high - est, ho - san - na and praise.

Text: 66 11 66 11 D; Katherine K. Davis, 1892–1980, © 1939, E.C. Schirmer Music Co. All rights reserved. Used with permission.
Music: ASH GROVE; Trad. Welsh Melody.

FOR THE BEAUTY OF THE EARTH 642

1. For the beau - ty of the earth, For the beau - ty
2. For the beau - ty of each hour Of the day and
3. For the joy of ear and eye, For the heart and
4. For the joy of hu - man love, Broth - er, sis - ter,
5. For the Church, who ev - er - more Lifts her ho - ly
6. For each per - fect gift di - vine To our world so

1. of the skies, For the love which from our birth
2. of the night, Hill and vale, and tree and flow'r,
3. mind's de - light, For the mys - tic har - mo - ny
4. par - ent, child, Friends on earth and friends a - bove;
5. hands a - bove, Of - f'ring up on ev - 'ry shore
6. free - ly giv'n, Joys be - stowed by love's de - sign,

1. O - ver and a - round us lies:
2. Sun and moon, and stars of light:
3. Link - ing sense to sound and sight:
4. For all gen - tle thoughts and mild:
5. Her pure sac - ri - fice of love:
6. Flow'rs of earth and fruits of heav'n:

Lord of all to

1-6. you we raise This our gift of grate - ful praise.

Text: 77 77 77; Folliot S. Pierpoint, 1835–1917, alt.
Music: DIX; Conrad Kocher, 1786–1872; adapt. by William H. Monk, 1823–1889.

GIVE THANKS TO THE LORD

Verses 1 & 2, 4 & 5, 7 & 8, 10

1. Give thanks to the Lord who does won-drous deeds, who
2. Give thanks to the God who has blessed our land, who
4. Give thanks to the God of the sum-mer rains, who
5. Give thanks to the Lord who is mer-ci-ful, whose
7. Give thanks to the Lord for the blaz-ing sun, for
8. Give thanks to the Lord for the crim-son skies, for
10. Give thanks to the God who has set us free, who

1. mas-ters the winds and the rag-ing seas,
2. guards ev-'ry step with a might-y hand,
4. spreads out the hills and the gold-en plains,
5. kind-ness is wide and love boun-ti-ful, whose
7. great, roll-ing waves where the dol-phins run,
8. wild, wind-y heights where the ea-gle flies,
10. raised us to life on a bless-ed tree,

love is for ev-er, whose love is for ev-er, whose love is for

1, 4, 7, Final   Fine   2, 5, 8

ev-er more!   more!

Verses 3, 6, 9

3. O, bless the Lord for ev-'ry gift that comes to grace our way. And
6. O, bless the Lord with mu-sic, ev-'ry crea-ture great and small. And
9. O, bless the Lord all peo-ple, for the mu-sic of the skies. And

3. praise the God of faith-ful-ness, who comes to light our day. (to Vss 4 & 5)
6. sing through all the a-ges of God's fa-vor to us all. (to Vss 7 & 8)
9. tell the won-drous sto-ry of a love that nev-er dies. (to Vs 10)

All Good Gifts

1. We plow the fields and scat - ter the good seed on the
2. You on - ly are the mak - er of all things near and
3. We thank you, then, Cre - a - tor, for all things bright and

1. land, but it is fed and wa - tered by God's al - might - y
2. far, you paint the way-side flow - er, you light the eve - ning
3. good, the seed-time and the har - vest, our life, our health, our

1. hand. God sends the snow in win - ter, the warmth to swell the
2. star. The winds and waves o - bey you, by you the birds are
3. food. And all that we can of - fer, your bound-less love im-

1. grain, the breez-es and the sun-shine, and soft, re-fresh-ing rain.
2. fed; much more, to us, your chil - dren, you give our dai - ly bread.
3. parts; the gifts to you most pleas - ing are hum-ble, thank-ful hearts.

Refrain

All good gifts a-round us are sent from heav-en a-bove;

thank you, Lord, O thank you for all your love.

Text: 76 76 D with refrain; Matthias Claudius, 1740–1815; tr. by Jane M. Campbell, 1817–1878, alt.
Music: HEISLMAN; Kevin Keil, ASCAP, b. 1956, © 1993, Kevin Keil. Published by OCP Publications. All rights reserved.

645

LORD OF GLORY

Refrain

Leap-ing the moun - tains, bound-ing the hills,

see how our God has come to meet us. His voice is lift-ed;

his face is joy. Now is the sea - son to sing our

1, 3 to Vss. 1, 3 | **2** to Vs. 2 | **Final**

song on high.

Verses 1, 2

1. Come, then, O Lord of glo - ry, show us your face. ____
2. He pas - tures his flock a - mong the wild ____ flow'rs ___ and

to Refrain

1. Speak, ___ for we know your words are life.
2. leads them to the moun-tain of his love.

Verse 3

3. All through the day, all through the night,

to Refrain

3. seek for the Lord and sing his love.

Text: Based on Song of Songs 2; Tim Manion, b. 1951.
Music: Tim Manion.

646

I WILL LIFT UP MY EYES

Refrain

3

I will lift up my eyes at the name of the one who knows me well.

647

IF GOD IS FOR US

1. If God is for us, who can be a-gainst us?
2. If God is for us, who then can con-demn us?
3. If God is for us, who can stand a-gainst us?

1. If God is on our side, what can we be de-
2. Sure-ly not Christ our Lord, who a-rose from the
3. If Christ did set us free, who can make us a

1. nied? In all these things we are more than
2. dead. There's noth-ing in this world that can
3. slave? Can pain or suf - fer-ing keep us

1. con-quer-ors in Je - sus.
2. sep-a-rate us from his love.   If God is
3. from the love of Je - sus?

1-3. on our side, what can we be de-nied?

Text: Based on Romans 8:31–39; Grayson Warren Brown, b. 1948.
Music: Grayson Warren Brown.
Text and music © 1995, Grayson Warren Brown. Published by OCP Publications. All rights reserved.

648

LIKE A SHEPHERD

Refrain

Like a shep-herd he feeds his flock and gath-ers the lambs in his

arms, hold-ing them care-ful-ly close to his heart,

1-3 to Verses | Final

lead-ing them home.   home,   lead-ing them home.

1. Say to the cit-ies of Ju - dah: Pre-pare __ the
2. I __ my - self __ will shep-herd them, for oth-ers have

1. way of the Lord. Go to the moun-tain-top,
2. led them a - stray. The lost I will res - cue and

1. lift your voice: Je - ru - sa - lem, here is your God.
2. heal their wounds and pas-ture them, giv-ing them rest.

Verse 3

3. Come un-to me if you are heav-i-ly bur-dened, and

3. take my yoke up-on your shoul-ders. I will give you rest.

Text: Based on Isaiah 40:9ff; Ezekiel 34:11ff; Matthew 12:28ff; Bob Dufford, SJ, b. 1943.
Music: Bob Dufford, SJ.
Text and music © 1976, Robert J. Dufford, SJ and New Dawn Music. Published by OCP Publications. All rights reserved.

I HAVE LOVED YOU
649

I have loved you with an ev-er-last-ing love, I have called you

and you are mine; I have loved you with an ev-er-last-ing love,

I have called you and you are mine. 1-3. Seek the face of the Lord and

Verses

1. long for him: he will bring you his light and his peace.
2. long for him: he will bring you his joy and his hope.
3. long for him: he will bring you his care and his love.

Text: Based on Jeremiah 31:3; Psalm 24:3; Michael Joncas, b. 1951.
Music: Michael Joncas.
Text and music © 1979, New Dawn Music. Published by OCP Publications. All rights reserved.

COME TO THE WATER

1. O let all who thirst, let them come to the
2. And let all who seek, let them come to the
3. And let all who toil, let them come to the
4. And let all the poor, let them come to the

1. wa - ter. And let all who have noth-ing,
2. wa - ter. And let all who have noth-ing,
3. wa - ter. And let all who are wea - ry,
4. wa - ter. Bring the ones who are lad - en,

1. let them come to the Lord: with-out
2. let them come to the Lord: with-out
3. let them come to the Lord: all who
4. bring them all to the Lord: bring the

1. mon-ey, with-out price. Why should you pay the
2. mon-ey, with-out strife. Why should you spend your
3. la - bor, with-out rest. How can your soul find
4. chil-dren with-out might. Eas - y the load and

1. price, ex-cept for the Lord?
2. life, ex-cept for the Lord?
3. rest, ex-cept for the Lord?
4. light: come to the Lord.

Text: Based on Isaiah 55:1, 2; Matthew 11:28–30; John Foley, S.J., b. 1939.
Music: John Foley, S.J.
Text and music © 1978, John B. Foley, S.J. and New Dawn Music. Published by OCP Publications. All rights reserved.

651   # RAIN DOWN

Refrain

Rain down, rain down, rain down your

1. love on your peo - ple.
2. love, God of life.

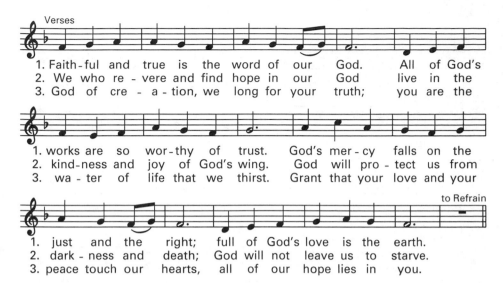

1. Faith-ful and true is the word of our God. All of God's
2. We who re - vere and find hope in our God live in the
3. God of cre - a - tion, we long for your truth; you are the

1. works are so wor-thy of trust. God's mer-cy falls on the
2. kind-ness and joy of God's wing. God will pro - tect us from
3. wa - ter of life that we thirst. Grant that your love and your

to Refrain

1. just and the right; full of God's love is the earth.
2. dark - ness and death; God will not leave us to starve.
3. peace touch our hearts, all of our hope lies in you.

Text: Based on Psalm 33; Jaime Cortez, b. 1963.
Music: Jaime Cortez.
Text and music © 1991, Jaime Cortez. Published by OCP Publications. All rights reserved.

OUR GOD PROVIDES 652

1. Our God pro vides for us and knows us each by name,
2. Who spared this on - ly Son no sor - row, grief nor shame,
3. Who shall then sev - er us from God, our life, our blood?

1. Who calls us to this life, and res-cues us from shame,
2. Who o - pened wide his soul, laid bare to love and pain.
3. No fu - ture and no death can spoil the pow'r of good.

1. Has cho - sen us to be the like - ness of the Son
2. If God stands firm for us, then who may cause us ill?
3. God's faith - ful ways and love shall al - ways be my peace,

1. Who walked with us on earth, who shared our blood and bone.
2. All things are from God's hands, from whom all have their fill.
3. For none can hin - der God, whose days shall nev - er cease.

Text: 12 12 12 12 12; Huub Oosterhuis, b. 1933; tr. by Tony Barr, © 1972, 1990, TEAM publications.
Published by OCP Publications. All rights reserved.
Music: GELUKKIG IS HET LAND; Trad. Dutch Melody.

653

ISAIAH 49

Verse 1

1. I will nev-er for-get you, my peo-ple; I have carved you
1. on the palm of my hand. I will nev-er for-get you; I will
1. not leave you or-phaned. I will nev-er for-get my own.

Verse 2

2. Does a moth-er for-get her ba-by? Or a
2. wom-an the child with-in her womb? Yet e-ven if these for-
2. get, yes, e-ven if these for-get, I will nev-er for-get my own. *(Repeat Vs 1)*

Text: Based on Isaiah 49:15; Carey Landry, b. 1944.
Music: Carey Landry.

654

JESUS DIED UPON THE CROSS

Je - sus died up-on the cross, Christ a-rose
from the dead; and just as sure as the sun will
rise, Je-sus Christ, my Lord and Sav-ior, will come a-gain!

GOD, WHOSE GLORY REIGNS ETERNAL

1. God, whose glo-ry reigns e-ter-nal, Span-ning space as
2. In Christ's heal-ing touch and teach-ing We see life as
3. Now we pon-der life's great mys-t'ry Suf-f'ring sav-ior,

1. well as time, Show us signs in seed and ker-nel, Life po-
2. you in-tend, Self-less love to oth-ers reach-ing, Pain and
3. cross en-throned, Past and fu-ture in one his-t'ry Our mor-

1. ten-tial, hope sub-lime. Grant us in-sight, all dis-cern-ing,
2. bro-ken-ness to end. And when hun-gry folk are nour-ished,
3. tal-i-ty Christ owned. And as res-ur-rec-tion's glo-ry

1. See-ing truth be-yond bare fact, Love trans-lat-ing
2. Filled by hope and word and bread, These are signs your
3. Shines in-to the emp-ty tomb, We, too, tell the

1. all our learn-ing In-to pow'r to be and act.
2. reign has flour-ished And from bond-age we are led.
3. an-cient sto-ry, Joy dis-pel-ling all the gloom.

Text: 87 87 D; based on Matthew 13:31–32; 9:10–11; 14:13–20; 27; 28; Jane Parker Huber; fr. *A Singing Faith*,
© 1982, Jane Parker Huber. All rights reserved. Used by permission of Westminster/John Knox Press.
Music: BEACH SPRING; *The Sacred Harp*, 1844.

656

THERE IS A RIVER

Refrain

There is a riv-er, a great flow-ing riv-er, and it makes glad the cit-y of God. Broad are its wa-ters, and deep are its voic-es. Its songs are of peace in the house of the Lord.

Verses

1. What shall we fear, though na-tions may trem-ble,
2. What shall we fear? The bow shall be bro-ken,

1. and dark-ness may rise to trou-ble the sun?
2. the spear shall be shat-tered, and war-ring shall cease.

1. The king-dom is near, the rem-nants as-sem-ble,
2. The king-dom is near, the word has been spo-ken,

to Refrain

1. and lift up their eyes to a day just be-gun.
2. and though we lie bat-tered, we are called to the feast.

Text and music: Tim Manion, b. 1951, © 1985, OCP Publications. All rights reserved.

657

BEATITUDES

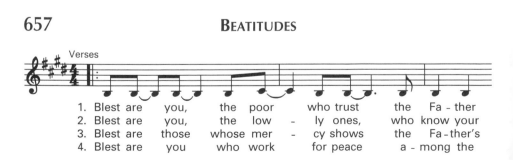

Verses

1. Blest are you, the poor who trust the Fa-ther
2. Blest are you, the low-ly ones, who know your
3. Blest are those whose mer-cy shows the Fa-ther's
4. Blest are you who work for peace a-mong the

1. with your lives,
2. need to share,
3. love to all,
4. Fa-ther's own,

For with-in your heart is born the

1-4. King-dom of the Lord.

1. Blest are you, the sor - row - ing,
2. Blest are you whose search-ing souls
3. Blest are you, the pure in heart,
4. Blest are you who suf - fer hate

1. _____ who know your Fa - ther wise,
2. _____ will draw you to God's care,
3. _____ who live the Fa-ther's call,
4. _____ to pre - pare the day to come,

For with-in your heart

1, 3   2, 4

1-4. is born the King-dom of the Lord.

Refrain

Let your light shine for all the world to see: the bright-ness of

your life with-in, the peace that sets you free. Let your

light shine to fill your nights and days; all will see the deeds

1   to Verse 3   Final
      3

you do and give your Fa - ther praise.

Text: Based on the Beatitudes; Mike Balhoff, b. 1946.
Music: Darryl Ducote, b. 1945.

I WILL NOT DIE

Verses

1. I will not die be-fore I've lived to see that land;
2. I will not rest un - til your dawn is in my eyes;
3. And I will breathe _ in that might - y wind of jus - tice;
4. You will stand up ____ for the poor and the need - y;

1. firm as the earth, your own prom - ise.
2. that frag - ile light, new like morn - ing.
3. I'll know my name and rise up sing - ing.
4. you'll break the chains that bind your peo - ple.

1. I'll not let go un - til I've held it in my hand;
2. I will not sleep be-fore I've wak - ened to that sun-rise;
3. And I will call un - til my words bring on the thun - der;
4. For you are home ____ for the lost ____ and the des-p'rate;

Fine

1. that word of hope, and gen - tle laugh-ter. __ (to Vs. 2)
2. and all the world knows your glo - ry. __ (to Refrain)
3. washed in that rain, then I'll know you. __ (to Vs. 4)
4. your strong right hand goes be - fore us. __ (to Refrain)

Refrain

For your right hand has de - liv-ered us from death; you have re-

1st time: to Vs. 3
2nd time: to Vs. 1 & *Fine*

gard - ed our tears, you who are good-ness and grace.

Text and music: Tom Conry, b. 1951, © 1984, 1990, TEAM publications. Published by OCP Publications. All rights reserved.

LEAD ME, LORD

Verses

1. Bless - ed are the poor in spir - it, long - ing for their
2. Bless - ed are the mer - ci - ful, for mer - cy shall be
3. Blest are they who through their life-times sow the seeds of

1. Lord, for God's com - ing king - dom shall be theirs.
2. theirs, and the pure in heart shall see their God.
3. peace, all will call them chil - dren of the Lord.

1. Bless - ed are the sor - row - ing, for they shall be con -
2. Blest are they whose hun - ger on - ly ho - li - ness can
3. Blest are you, though per - se - cu - ted in your ho - ly

1. soled, and the meek shall come to rule the world.
2. fill, for I say they shall be sat - is - fied.
3. life, for in heav - en, great is your re - ward.

Refrain

Lead me, Lord, lead me, Lord, by the light of truth to

seek and to find the nar-row way. Be my way;

be my truth; be my life, my Lord, and lead me, Lord, to-

1-2 to Verses	Final

day. day. And lead me, Lord, to-day.

Text: Based on the Beatitudes; Matthew 5:3–12; 7:7, 13; John 14:6; John D. Becker, b. 1953.
Music: John D. Becker.

WE ARE THE LIGHT OF THE WORLD

Verses

1. Bless - ed are they who are poor in spir - it,
2. Bless - ed are they who are meek and hum - ble,
3. Bless - ed are they who will mourn in sor - row,
4. Bless those who hun - ger and thirst for jus - tice,
5. Bless - ed are they who show oth - ers mer - cy,
6. Bless - ed are hearts that are clean and ho - ly,
7. Bless - ed are they who bring peace a - mong us,
8. Bless those who suf - fer from per - se - cu - tion,

1. Theirs is the king-dom of God. Bless us, O Lord, make us
2. They will in - her - it the earth. Bless us, O Lord, make us
3. They will be com - fort - ed. Bless us, O Lord, when we
4. They will be sat - is - fied. Bless us, O Lord, hear our
5. They will know mer - cy too. Bless us, O Lord, hear our
6. They will be - hold the Lord. Bless us, O Lord, make us
7. They are the chil - dren of God. Bless us, O Lord, may your
8. Theirs is the king-dom of God. Bless us, O Lord, when they

1. poor in spir - it; Bless us, O Lord, our God.
2. meek and hum - ble; Bless us, O Lord, our God.
3. share their sor - row; Bless us, O Lord, our God.
4. cry for jus - tice; Bless us, O Lord, our God.
5. cry for mer - cy; Bless us, O Lord, our God.
6. pure and ho - ly; Bless us, O Lord, our God.
7. peace be with us; Bless us, O Lord, our God.
8. per - se - cute us; Bless us, O Lord, our God.

Refrain

We are the light of the world, may our light shine be-fore all,

That they may see the good that we do, and give glo - ry to God.

Text: 10 6 10 6 with refrain; the Beatitudes; adapt. by Jean Anthony Greif, 1898–1981, alt.
Music: GREIF; Jean Anthony Greif.

CHRIST BE OUR LIGHT

Verses

1. Long-ing for light, __ we wait in dark - ness. Long-ing for
2. Long-ing for peace, __ our world is trou - bled. Long-ing for
3. Long-ing for food, __ man - y are hun - gry. Long-ing for
4. Long-ing for shel-ter, man - y are home-less. Long-ing for
5. Man - y the gifts, __ man - y the peo - ple, man - y the

1. truth, _____ we turn to you. Make us your own, _____
2. hope, _____ man - y de - spair. Your word a - lone _____
3. wa - ter, man - y still thirst. Make us your bread, _____
4. warmth, __ man - y are cold. Make us your build - ing,
5. hearts that yearn to be - long. Let us be ser - vants

1. your ho - ly peo-ple, light for the world to see.
2. has pow'r to save us. Make us your liv - ing voice.
3. bro - ken for oth-ers, shared un - til all are fed.
4. shel - ter - ing oth-ers, walls made of liv - ing stone.
5. to one an - oth - er, mak - ing your king - dom come.

Refrain

Christ, be our light! Shine in our hearts. Shine through the dark - ness.

Christ, be our light! Shine in your church gath-ered to-day.

Easter Vigil Verses

1. This is the night of new beginnings.
   This is the night when heaven meets earth.
   This is the night filled with God's glory,
   promise of our new birth!

2. This is the night Christ our redeemer
   rose from the grave triumphant and free,
   leaving the tomb of evil and darkness,
   empty for all to see.

3. Now will the fire kindled in darkness
   burn to dispel the shadows of night.
   Star of the morning, Jesus our Savior,
   you are the world's true light!

4. Sing of the hope deeper than dying.
   Sing of the pow'r stronger than death.
   Sing of the love endless as heaven,
   dawning throughout the earth.

5. Into this world morning is breaking.
   All of God's people, lift up your voice.
   Cry out with joy, tell out the story,
   all of the earth rejoice.

662 MOST SPLENDID AND RESPLENDENT LIGHT

1. Most splen-did and re-splen-dent Light, O
2. True Light and bear-er of the Light, True
3. More glo-rious than the sun's bright light, And
4. May our de-sire with love u-nite; Our
5. O Christ, the un-cre-a-ted Light, To

1. Bril-liance o-ver-whelm-ing night, You bring to light all
2. gal-a-xy be-yond all sight, O Morn-ing Star an-
3. more mys-te-rious than the night, You shine with-in the
4. love re-veal your pur-est light. Make us glad tem-ples
5. you be glo-ry, praise, and might; The Fa-ther's sole be-

1. things con-cealed; In you is all the world re-vealed.
2. nounc-ing day, Re-veal-ing all in just one ray.
3. in-most heart, Re-veal-ing all its se-cret parts.
4. of your praise, Our lives a mir-ror of your ways.
5. got-ten Son, The Spir-it's Word: God, Three in One.

Text: LM; *Lucis Largitor*, anon., 10th cent.; tr. by Harry Hagan, OSB, b. 1947, © 1999, St. Meinrad Archabbey.
  Published by OCP Publications. All rights reserved.
Music: EISENACH; *Das ander Theil des andern newen Operis Geistlicher Deutscher Lieder*, 1605;
  adapt. by Johann Hermann Schein, 1586–1630.

663 OUT OF DARKNESS

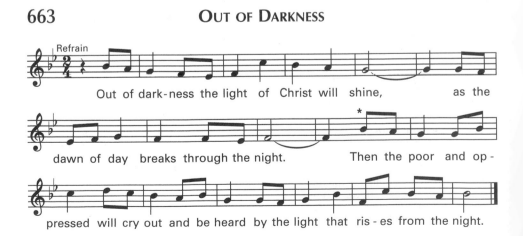

Refrain

Out of dark-ness the light of Christ will shine, as the

dawn of day breaks through the night. Then the poor and op-

pressed will cry out and be heard by the light that ris-es from the night.

Verses

1. Let the darkness flee from here.
   Put an end to sadness and fear.
   The hungry will eat, the sick will dance,
   the dead will live again.

2. This is the night, O holy of nights,
   the chains of death are destroyed.

This is the light;
the glory of God is raised to life again.

3. A single flame,
   a flicker of hope spreads like a sea of fire.
   Open the door, shout to the night:
   We will live again.

*Last time repeat final phrase.

I AM THE LIGHT OF THE WORLD   664

"I am the Light of the world," says the Lord,
"They who fol-low me will have the light of life."

Verses 1, 2

1. "A - rise," says the Lord, "Have no fear with-
2. "Walk in the light, there is no cause to

1. in you; for in my pres-ence there will be no
2. stum - ble; I have come to light the path be -

1. dark - ness. I am the Light of the world."
2. fore you. I am the Light of the world."

to Refrain

Verse 3

3. "Lis-ten to my words; they are from the One who
3. sent me: For you, my friends, are called to share God's

3. glo - ry. You are the Light of the world."

to Refrain

WE ARE MARCHING/SIYAHAMBA

We are march - ing in the light of God, we are
Si - ya - hamb' e - ku - kha - nyen' kwen - khos', si - ya -

march-ing in the light of God. We are march - ing in the
hamb' e - ku - kha-nyen' kwen-khos'. Si - ya - hamb' e - ku-kha-

light of God, we are march-ing in the light of God.
nyen' kwen-khos', si - ya - hamb' e - ku - kha-nyen' kwen - khos'.

We are march-ing, Oo we are
Si - ya - ham - ba, Oo si - ya -

march-ing in the light of God. We are march-ing,
hamb' e - ku - kha-nyen' kwen - khos'. Si - ya - ham - ba,

Oo we are march-ing in the light of God.
Oo si - ya - hamb' e - ku - kha-nyen' kwen-khos'.

666   JESUS CHRIST, INNER LIGHT

Ostinato Refrain: All

Je - sus Christ, in - ner light, let not our own dark-ness con-quer us.

Je - sus Christ, in - ner light, en - a-ble us to wel-come your love.

Verses: (Sung over Refrain)

1. Jesus Christ, source of light,
in you we discover a radiance.
To whom shall we go,
to whom shall we go
to see the face of God?

2. Risen Christ, you go down to the depths,
to the depths of our human condition.

You burden yourself with what burdens us.
You take on our darkness.

3. Jesus Christ, in our search for you,
bring us into the warmth of your light,
Jesus Christ, embrace us with your love.

4. Jesus Christ, help us to face our darkness.
Help us to find its hidden treasure.

YOUR LIGHT WILL COME, JERUSALEM 667

Refrain
Your light will come, Je-ru-sa-lem; for on you will dawn the glo-ry of the Lord, and all na-tions will walk in your light, al-le-lu-ia, al-le-lu - ia.

Verses
1. Christ is the light of the world, a light dis-pel-ling the dark-ness. May we, his bod-y, re-flect that ho-ly light.
2. His light is mer-cy and peace, a peace sur-pass-ing all tell-ing. May we, his bod-y, be in-stru-ments of peace.
3. His light is jus-tice and truth, and love which casts out all ha-tred. May we, his bod-y, pre-pare the reign of God.

668   O CHRIST, YOU SPEAK THE NAMES OF GOD

1. O Christ, you speak the names of God In
2. You are the pre - sence of our God, Not
3. You are the wis - dom of our God, Whose
4. You are the pow - er of our God, You
5. You are the glo - ry of our God In
6. You are the jus - tice of our God, Whose
7. You are the mer - cy of our God, Soft
8. O Christ, you are the voice of God; To

1. tongues we un - der - stand To touch and heal the
2. hid in cloud or flame But clothed in liv - ing
3. fol - ly is the cross On which you flung your
4. roll the stone a - way From ev - 'ry tomb that
5. earth - en lan - tern borne To light the way that
6. mer - cy tem - pers might: In you is ev - 'ry
7. fall - en as the rain, To pen - e - trate the
8. hear you, clam - ors cease, The rag - ing of our

1. deaf - ened ear With love's al - might - y hand.
2. flesh of earth Called by a hu - man name.
3. life a - way— And count us worth the loss.
4. seals us in Where sin and death hold sway.
5. we must walk, The path your feet have worn.
6. soul set free And ev - 'ry wrong set right.
7. hard - ened heart And wash a - way our pain.
8. seas falls still, Your ev - 'ry word our peace.

Text: CM; Genevieve Glen, OSB, b. 1945, © 2001, The Benedictine Nuns of the Abbey of St. Walburga.
    Published by OCP Publications. All rights reserved.
Music: MORNING SONG; *Sixteen Tune Settings,* Philadelphia, 1812; *Kentucky Harmony,* 1816.

669   JESU, JOY OF OUR DESIRING

1. Je - su, joy of our de - sir - ing, Ho - ly wis - dom,
2. Through the way where hope is guid-ing, Hear what peace - ful

1. love most bright, Drawn by you, our souls as - pir - ing,
2. mu - sic rings; Where the flocks in you con - fid-ing,

1. Soar to un-cre-at-ed Light. Word of God, our flesh that
2. Drink of joy from death-less springs! Theirs is beau-ty's fair-est

1. fash-ioned With the fire of life im-pas-sioned, Striv-ing
2. plea-sure; Theirs is wis-dom's ho-liest trea-sure; You do

1. still to truth un-known, Soar-ing, dy-ing, 'round your throne.
2. ev-er lead your own, In the love of joys un-known.

Text: 87 87 88 77; *Christlich Herzens Andacht,* 1665; Martin Jahn, ca. 1620–1682; tr. by Robert S. Bridges, 1844–1930, rev.
Music: WERDE MUNTER; *Himmlische Lieder, Vol. 3,* Lüneberg, 1642; Johann P. Schop, ca. 1590–1664.

O Christ, Our Teacher 670

1. O Christ, our Teach-er and our Way, Teach us to
2. O Christ, our Teach-er and our Light, Il-lu-mine
3. O Christ, our Teach-er and our Life, Teach us to
4. All praise to you, O Christ, our Way, Our Truth and

1. fol-low you this day, And as our hearts with love
2. us with truth and right That we may see but you
3. rec-on-cile all strife, To break down each di-vid-
4. Life, our on-ly Day! All praise to you, O Christ,

1. ex-pand To run the way of your com-mands.
2. a-lone, And by your light and truth be known.
3. ing wall And live this day in peace with all.
4. the Son With Fa-ther and the Spir-it: One! A-men.

Text: LM; Harry Hagan, OSB, b. 1947, © 1999, St. Meinrad Archabbey. Published by OCP Publications. All rights reserved.
Music: HERR JESU CHRIST, DICH ZU UNS WEND; *Cantionale Germanicum,* 1628; adapt. by Johann Sebastian Bach, 1685–1750.

671

WE HAVE NO GLORY

Refrain

We have no glo-ry, we have no name. We are as grains of sand up-on the shore. Our on-ly glo-ry, our on-ly name, is Je-sus Christ.

Verses

1. Our source of life is Christ the Lord. In him we
2. How great the love which caused to be the u - ni -
3. But we a - lone are not the name, for we are
4. Your Name is ours, O Je - sus Christ! Your cross we

1. live and move and have our be - ing. It is
2. ty we share now with each oth - er. To - geth -
3. but a part of God's cre - a - tion. Should we
4. bear, the glo - ry of our jour - ney. What more

to Refrain

1. not we who live; it is Christ who lives in us.
2. er we be-come Name-of - Christ up - on the earth.
3. be si - lent now, then the stones them-selves would shout:
4. can we re-quest, than a name which is the Name?

Text and music: Owen Alstott, b. 1947, © 1988, OCP Publications. All rights reserved.

672

EARTHEN VESSELS

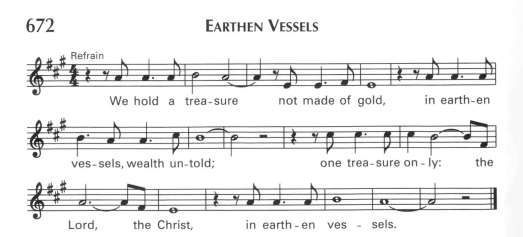

Refrain

We hold a trea-sure not made of gold, in earth-en ves-sels, wealth un-told; one trea-sure on - ly: the Lord, the Christ, in earth-en ves - sels.

Verses

1. Light has shone in our dark-ness: God has shone in our heart
2. God has cho-sen the low-ly who are small in this world;

to Refrain

1. with the light of the glo-ry of Je-sus, the Lord.
2. in this weak-ness is glo-ry in Je-sus, the Lord.

Text: Based on 2 Corinthians 4:6–7; 1 Corinthians 1:27–29, alt.; John Foley, S.J., b. 1939.
Music: John Foley, S.J.

HAIL SOV'REIGN LOVE 673

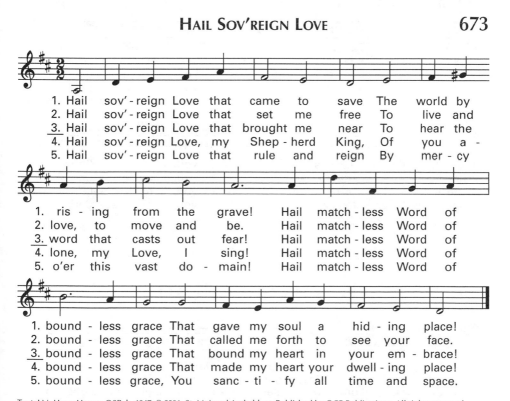

1. Hail sov'-reign Love that came to save The world by
2. Hail sov'-reign Love that set me free To live and
3. Hail sov'-reign Love that brought me near To hear the
4. Hail sov'-reign Love, my Shep-herd King, Of you a-
5. Hail sov'-reign Love that rule and reign By mer-cy

1. ris-ing from the grave! Hail match-less Word of
2. love, to move and be. Hail match-less Word of
3. word that casts out fear! Hail match-less Word of
4. lone, my Love, I sing! Hail match-less Word of
5. o'er this vast do-main! Hail match-less Word of

1. bound-less grace That gave my soul a hid-ing place!
2. bound-less grace That called me forth to see your face.
3. bound-less grace That bound my heart in your em-brace!
4. bound-less grace That made my heart your dwell-ing place!
5. bound-less grace, You sanc-ti-fy all time and space.

Text: LM; Harry Hagan, OSB, b. 1947, © 2001, St. Meinrad Archabbey. Published by OCP Publications. All rights reserved.
Music: SOV'REIGN LOVE; Randall DeBruyn, b. 1947, © 2002, Randall DeBruyn.

674 PRAISE TO YOU, O CHRIST OUR SAVIOR

Refrain

Praise to you, O Christ, our Sav-ior, Word of the Fa-ther, call-ing us to life;

Son of God who leads us to free-dom: glo-ry to you, Lord Je-sus Christ!

Verses

1. You are the Word who calls us out of dark-ness; you are the
2. You are the one whom proph-ets hoped and longed for; you are the
3. You are the Word who calls us to be ser-vants; you are the
4. You are the Word who binds us and u-nites us; you are the

1. Word who leads us in-to light; you are the Word who
2. one who speaks to us to-day; you are the one who
3. Word whose on-ly law is love; you are the Word - made-
4. Word who calls us to be one; you are the Word who

to Refrain

1. brings us through the des-ert: glo-ry to you, Lord Je-sus Christ!
2. leads us to our fu-ture: glo-ry to you, Lord Je-sus Christ!
3. flesh who lives a-mong us: glo-ry to you, Lord Je-sus Christ!
4. teach-es us for-give-ness: glo-ry to you, Lord Je-sus Christ!

Text and music: Bernadette Farrell, b. 1957, © 1986, Bernadette Farrell. Published by OCP Publications. All rights reserved.

675 BLESSED JESUS, AT YOUR WORD

1. Bless-ed Je-sus, at your word we are gath-ered
2. All our knowl-edge, sense, and sight lie in deep-est
3. Glor-ious Lord, your-self im-part! Light of Light, from

1. all to hear you; let our hearts and minds be stirred
2. dark-ness shroud-ed, till your Spir-it breaks our night
3. God pro-ceed-ing, o-pen now each mind and heart,

1. now to seek and love and fear you; by your teach-ings
2. with the beams of truth un-cloud - ed; you a - lone to
3. help us by your Spir - it's plead - ing. Hear the cry your

1. true and ho - ly, drawn from earth to love you sole - ly.
2. God can win us; you must work all good with - in us.
3. Church now rais-es; Lord, ac - cept our prayers and prais - es.

Text: 78 78 88; Tobias Clausnitzer, 1619–1684; tr. by Catherine Winkworth, 1827–1878, alt.
Music: LIEBSTER JESU; Johann R. Ahle, 1625–1673, alt.

WORD OF GOD, YOU SPOKE CREATION 676

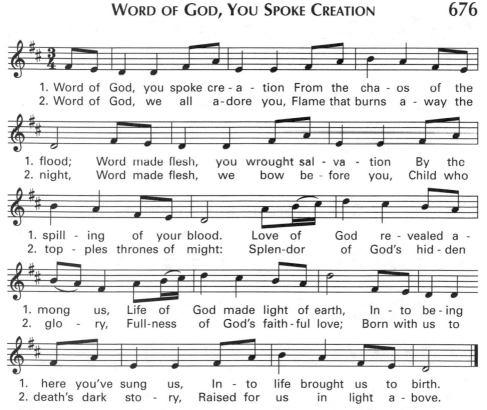

1. Word of God, you spoke cre - a - tion From the cha - os of the
2. Word of God, we all a-dore you, Flame that burns a - way the

1. flood; Word made flesh, you wrought sal - va - tion By the
2. night, Word made flesh, we bow be - fore you, Child who

1. spill - ing of your blood. Love of God re - vealed a -
2. top - ples thrones of might: Splen-dor of God's hid - den

1. mong us, Life of God made light of earth, In - to be - ing
2. glo - ry, Full-ness of God's faith-ful love; Born with us to

1. here you've sung us, In - to life brought us to birth.
2. death's dark sto - ry, Raised for us in light a - bove.

Text: 87 87 D; Jennifer Glen, CCVI, b. 1945, © 1987, 2001, The Sisters of Charity of the Incarnate Word.
Published by OCP Publications. All rights reserved.
Music: NETTLETON; J. Wyeth's *Repository of Sacred Music, Part II,* 1813.

677   THE WORD OF GOD WAS FROM THE START

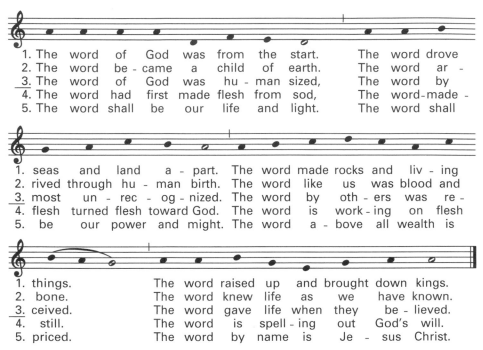

1. The word of God was from the start. The word drove
2. The word be-came a child of earth. The word ar -
3. The word of God was hu - man sized, The word by
4. The word had first made flesh from sod, The word-made -
5. The word shall be our life and light. The word shall

1. seas and land a - part. The word made rocks and liv - ing
2. rived through hu - man birth. The word like us was blood and
3. most un - rec - og - nized. The word by oth - ers was re -
4. flesh turned flesh toward God. The word is work - ing on flesh
5. be our power and might. The word a - bove all wealth is

1. things. The word raised up and brought down kings.
2. bone. The word knew life as we have known.
3. ceived. The word gave life when they be - lieved.
4. still. The word is spell - ing out God's will.
5. priced. The word by name is Je - sus Christ.

Text: LM; based on John 1:1–14; Thomas H. Troeger, b. 1945; fr. *Borrowed Light,* © 1994, Oxford University Press, Inc.
   All rights reserved. Used with permission.
Music: JESU DULCIS MEMORIA; Chant, Mode I.

678   GOD HAS SPOKEN BY HIS PROPHETS

1. God has spo-ken by his proph-ets, Spo-ken his un-chang-ing Word;
2. God has spo-ken by Christ Je - sus, Christ, the ev - er - last-ing Son,
3. God is speak-ing by his Spir - it, Speak-ing to the hearts of all,

1. Each from age to age pro-claim-ing God, the one the righ-teous, Lord.
2. Bright-ness of the Fa-ther's glo - ry, With the Fa - ther ev - er one;
3. In the age-less Word ex-pound-ing God's own mes-sage for us all.

1. In the world's de - spair and tur - moil, One firm an - chor holds us fast;
2. Spo - ken by the Word In - car - nate, God of God, be - fore time was;
3. Through the rise and fall of na - tions One sure faith yet stand - ing fast;

1. God is king, his throne e - ter - nal; God the first, and God the last.
2. Light of Light, to earth de - scend - ing, He re - veals our God to us.
3. God a - bides, his Word un - chang - ing; God the first, and God the last.

Text: 87 87 D; George W. Briggs, 1875–1959, alt., © 1953, 1981, The Hymn Society. All rights reserved.
 Administered by Hope Publishing Co. Used with permission.
Music: RUSTINGTON; Charles H. H. Parry, 1848–1918.

The Bearers of the Living Word — 679

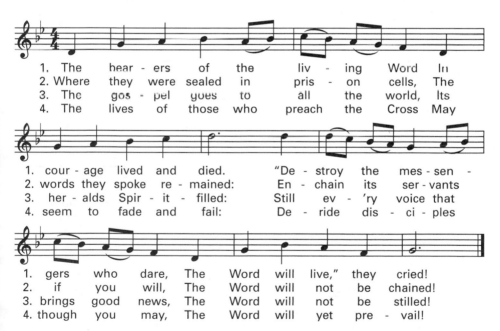

1. The bear - ers of the liv - ing Word In
2. Where they were sealed in pris - on cells, The
3. The gos - pel goes to all the world, Its
4. The lives of those who preach the Cross May

1. cour - age lived and died. "De - stroy the mes - sen -
2. words they spoke re - mained: En - chain its ser - vants
3. her - alds Spir - it - filled: Still ev - 'ry voice that
4. seem to fade and fail: De - ride dis - ci - ples

1. gers who dare, The Word will live," they cried!
2. if you will, The Word will not be chained!
3. brings good news, The Word will not be stilled!
4. though you may, The Word will yet pre - vail!

Text: CM; Genevieve Glen, OSB, b. 1945, © 2000, The Benedictine Nuns of the Abbey of St. Walburga.
 Published by OCP Publications. All rights reserved.
Music: HIDING PLACE; Joshua Leavitt, 1794–1837; *Christian Lyre*, 1831.

YOUR WORDS ARE SPIRIT AND LIFE

Refrain

Your words are spir-it and life, O Lord: rich-er than gold, strong-er than death. Your words are spir-it and life, O Lord; life ev-er-last-ing.

Verses

1. God's law is per-fect, re-fresh-ing the soul, re-viv-ing the wea-ry spir-it. God's rule can be trust-ed: bring-ing us wis-dom, bring-ing God's wis-dom to birth.
2. God's pre-cepts keep us; their pur-pose is right. They glad-den the hearts of peo-ple. God's com-mand is so clear it brings us new vi-sion; bring-ing God's light to our eyes.
3. Liv-ing by God's truth is ho-ly and sure; God's pres-ence is ev-er-last-ing. God's truth is e-ter-nal, bring-ing us jus-tice; bring-ing God's jus-tice to earth.
4. God's word is pre-cious, de-sired more than gold; worth more than we dare i-mag-ine and, sweet-er than hon-ey, this word will feed us, bring-ing ful-fill-ment and joy.

to Refrain

Text: Based on Psalm 19:8–11; Bernadette Farrell, b. 1957.
Music: Bernadette Farrell.
Text and music © 1993, Bernadette Farrell. Published by OCP Publications. All rights reserved.

MINE EYES HAVE SEEN THE GLORY

Verses

1. Mine eyes have seen the glo - ry of the com - ing
2. I have seen him in the watch - fires of a hun - dred
3. He has sound - ed forth the trum - pet that shall nev - er
4. In the beau - ty of the lil - ies Christ was born a -

1. of the Lord; He is tram - pling out the vin - tage where the
2. cir - cling camps; They have build - ed him an al - tar in the
3. call re - treat; He is sift - ing out the hearts of all be -
4. cross the sea, With a glo - ry in his bos - om that trans -

1. grapes of wrath are stored; He hath loosed the fate - ful light - ning
2. eve - ning dews and damps; I can read his righ - teous sen - tence
3. fore his judg - ment seat; O be swift, my soul, to an - swer
4. fig - ures you and me; As he died to make us ho - ly,

1. of his ter - ri - ble swift sword: His truth is march - ing on.
2. by the dim and flar - ing lamps; His day is march - ing on.
3. him; be ju - bi - lant, my feet! Our God is march - ing on.
4. let us die that all be free! While God is march - ing on.

Refrain

Glo - ry! Glo - ry! Hal - le - lu - jah! Glo - ry!

Glo - ry! Hal - le - lu - jah! Glo - ry! Glo - ry! Hal - le -

lu - jah! His truth is march - ing on.

Text: 15 15 15 6 with refrain; Julia W. Howe, 1819–1910.
Music: BATTLE HYMN OF THE REPUBLIC; Trad. American Melody; attr. to William Steffe, ca. 1830–1911.

682

WORTHY IS THE LAMB

Refrain

Wor-thy is the Lamb that was slain to re - ceive
hon - or and glo - ry. Wor-thy are the ones who be - lieve
to re - ceive the good-ness of God. *Fine*

Verses

1. Wor - thy are you, O Pas - chal Lamb.
2. Wor - thy are you, O Bread of Life. Sal -
3. Wor - thy are you, O Ris - en Christ.

1. Wis - dom and strength be - long now to you. You
2. va - tion and joy be - long now to us. By
3. Won - ders and signs, re - veal - ing your might. Your

1. laid down your life and died up - on the cross: we've be -
2. con - quer - ing death and ris - ing to new life, we've be -
3. pow - er and glo - ry shines up - on our lives: we've be -

2 to Refrain

1. come a peo - ple of hope.
2. come a peo - ple of praise.
3. come a light for the world.

Text: Based on Revelation 5:9–14; Ricky Manalo, CSP, b. 1965.
Music: Ricky Manalo, CSP.
Text and music © 1997, Ricky Manalo, CSP. Published by OCP Publications. All rights reserved.

683

SOON AND VERY SOON

1. Soon and ver - y soon, We are going to see the King;
2. No more cry - ing there, We are going to see the King;
3. No more dy - ing there, We are going to see the King;

1. Soon and ver-y soon, We are going to see the King;
2. No more cry-ing there, We are going to see the King;
3. No more dy-ing there, We are going to see the King;

1. Soon and ver-y soon, We are going to see the King; ⎫
2. No more cry-ing there, We are going to see the King; ⎬ Hal-le-
3. No more dy-ing there, We are going to see the King; ⎭

1-3. lu - jah! Hal-le-lu - jah! We're going to see the King.

Text: 57 57 57 86; Andraé Crouch, b. 1945.
Music: SOON AND VERY SOON; Andraé Crouch; adapt. by William F. Smith, b. 1941.

LET THE HEAVENS BE GLAD — 684

Refrain

Let the heav-ens be glad and the earth re - joice, the

sea and what fills it re - sound. Let the plains and the fields be

filled with joy, for the Lord comes to rule the land.

Verses

1. Then shall the trees, the trees of the for-est ex - ult
2. The Lord shall rule with jus-tice for all of the earth.

to Refrain

1. be-fore the Lord, who comes now to rule the earth.
2. In con-stant love he comes now to rule the earth.

Text: Based on Psalm 96:11–13; Dan Feiten.
Music: Dan Feiten.

685

IN THE DAY OF THE LORD

Refrain

In the day of the Lord, the sun will shine like the dawn of e-ter-nal day. All cre-a-tion will rise to dance and sing the glo-ry of the Lord!

Verses

1. And on that day will jus-tice tri-umph, on that
2. Then shall the na-tions throng to-geth-er to the
3. And they shall beat their swords to plow-shares; there will
4. For Is-ra-el shall be de-liv-ered, and the
5. And on that day of Christ in glo-ry, God will
6. O give us eyes to see your glo-ry, give us

1. day will all be free: free from want, free from
2. moun-tain of the Lord: they shall walk in the
3. be an end to war: one in peace, one in
4. des-ert lands will bloom. Say to all, "Do not
5. wipe a-way our tears, and the dead shall rise
6. hearts to un-der-stand. Let our ears hear your

to Refrain

1. fear, _____ free to live!
2. light _____ of the Lord!
3. love, _____ one in God!
4. fear. Here is your God!"
5. up _____ from their graves!
6. voice _____ 'til you come!

Text: Based on Isaiah 2, 25, 41; M.D. Ridge.
Music: M.D. Ridge.

GOD BE IN MY HEAD

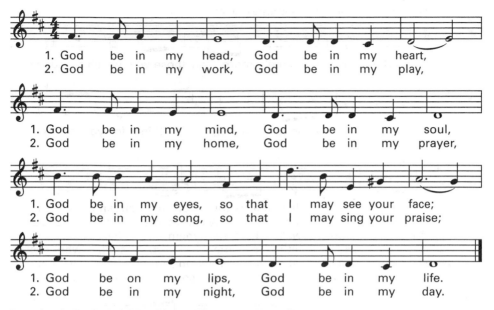

1. God be in my head, God be in my heart,
2. God be in my work, God be in my play,

1. God be in my mind, God be in my soul,
2. God be in my home, God be in my prayer,

1. God be in my eyes, so that I may see your face;
2. God be in my song, so that I may sing your praise;

1. God be on my lips, God be in my life.
2. God be in my night, God be in my day.

Text and music: Grayson Warren Brown, b. 1948, © 1999, Grayson Warren Brown.
Published by OCP Publications. All rights reserved.

CHRIST BE BESIDE ME

1. Christ be be - side me, Christ be be - fore me, Christ be be -
2. Christ on my right hand, Christ on my left hand, Christ all a -
3. Christ be in all hearts think - ing a - bout me; Christ be on

1. hind me, King of my heart. Christ be with - in me,
2. round me, shield in the strife. Christ in my sleep - ing,
3. all tongues tell - ing of me. Christ be the vi - sion

1. Christ be be - low me, Christ be a - bove me, nev - er to part.
2. Christ in my sit - ting, Christ in my ris - ing, light of my life.
3. in eyes that see me; In ears that hear me, Christ ev - er be.

Text: 55 54 D; New Hymns for All Seasons; St. Patrick's Breastplate, para.; tr. by James D. Quinn, SJ, b. 1919,
© 1969, James D. Quinn, SJ. All rights reserved. Used with permission of Selah Publishing Co.
Music: ST. ROSE; Laura Wasson, b. 1952, © 1993, OCP Publications. All rights reserved.

688 O GOD, FOR YOU I LONG

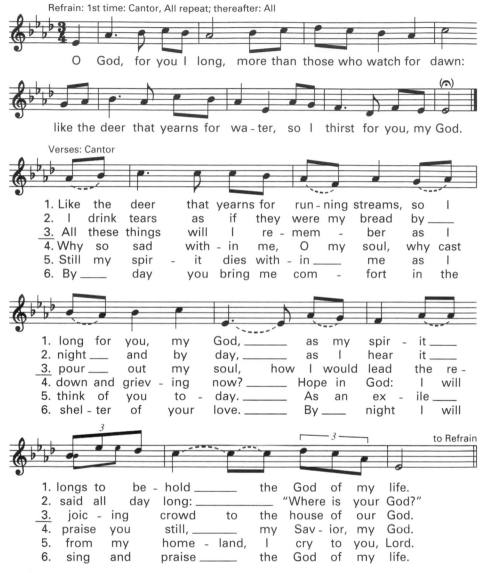

Refrain: 1st time: Cantor, All repeat; thereafter: All

O God, for you I long, more than those who watch for dawn:

like the deer that yearns for wa-ter, so I thirst for you, my God.

Verses: Cantor

1. Like the deer that yearns for run-ning streams, so I
2. I drink tears as if they were my bread by ___
3. All these things will I re-mem - ber as I
4. Why so sad with-in me, O my soul, why cast
5. Still my spir - it dies with-in ___ me as I
6. By ___ day you bring me com - fort in the

1. long for you, my God, ___ as my spir - it ___
2. night ___ and by day, ___ as I hear it ___
3. pour ___ out my soul, how I would lead the re -
4. down and griev - ing now? ___ Hope in God: I will
5. think of you to - day. ___ As an ex - ile ___
6. shel - ter of your love. ___ By ___ night I will

to Refrain

1. longs to be - hold ___ the God of my life.
2. said all day long: ___ "Where is your God?"
3. joic - ing crowd to the house of our God.
4. praise you still, ___ my Sav - ior, my God.
5. from my home - land, I cry to you, Lord.
6. sing and praise ___ the God of my life.

Text: Psalm 42:2–7, 9; Bernadette Farrell, b. 1957.
Music: Bernadette Farrell.

THIS ALONE

Refrain

One thing I ask, this a-lone I seek, to dwell in the house of the Lord all my days. For one day with-in your tem-ple heals ev - 'ry day a - lone. O Lord, bring me to your dwell - ing.

Verses 1, 3

1. Hear, __ O __ Lord, ____ the sound of my call - ing.
3. Wait on __ the Lord, and __ hope in his mer - cy.

to Refrain

1. Hear, __ O __ Lord, and show me your way.
3. Wait on ____ the Lord, and live in his love.

Verse 2

2. The Lord is my light and hope of sal - va - tion. The

to Refrain

2. Lord is my ref-uge; whom should I fear?

Text: Based on Psalm 27; Tim Manion, b. 1951.
Music: Tim Manion.

690

LORD OF ALL HOPEFULNESS

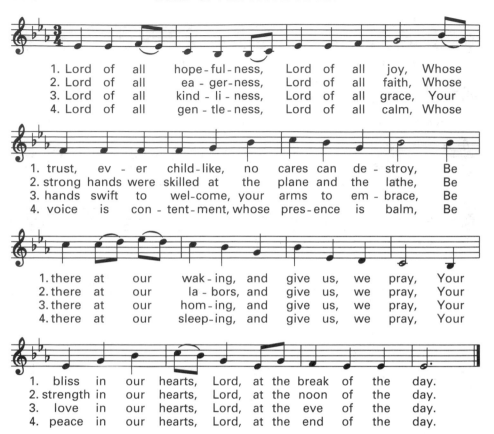

1. Lord of all hope-ful-ness, Lord of all joy, Whose
2. Lord of all ea-ger-ness, Lord of all faith, Whose
3. Lord of all kind-li-ness, Lord of all grace, Your
4. Lord of all gen-tle-ness, Lord of all calm, Whose

1. trust, ev-er child-like, no cares can de-stroy, Be
2. strong hands were skilled at the plane and the lathe, Be
3. hands swift to wel-come, your arms to em-brace, Be
4. voice is con-tent-ment, whose pres-ence is balm, Be

1. there at our wak-ing, and give us, we pray, Your
2. there at our la-bors, and give us, we pray, Your
3. there at our hom-ing, and give us, we pray, Your
4. there at our sleep-ing, and give us, we pray, Your

1. bliss in our hearts, Lord, at the break of the day.
2. strength in our hearts, Lord, at the noon of the day.
3. love in our hearts, Lord, at the eve of the day.
4. peace in our hearts, Lord, at the end of the day.

Text: 10 11 11 12; *Enlarged Songs of Praise*, 1931; Jan Struther, 1901–1953, © Oxford University Press, London.
All rights reserved. Used with permission.
Music: SLANE; Trad. Irish Melody.

691

TO YOU, O GOD, I LIFT UP MY SOUL

Refrain: 1st time: Cantor, All repeat; thereafter: All

To you, O God, I lift up my soul; lift up my spir-it

to my Lord. To you I lift up my soul.

To you I lift up my soul. To you I lift up my soul.

1. Make me to know your ways, O God; teach me your
2. Good and up-right our gra-cious God, show-ing the
3. Stead-fast and kind your ways, O God; all who re-

1. paths, guide me. You are my Sav-ior.
2. way, guid-ing the hum-ble to jus-tice.
3. vere your cov-e-nant know your friend-ship.

Text: Based on Psalm 25:1, 4–5, 8–9, 10, 14; Bob Hurd, b. 1950.
Music: Bob Hurd.
Text and music © 1991, Bob Hurd. Published by OCP Publications. All rights reserved.

THERE IS A LONGING 692

There is a long-ing in our hearts, O Lord, for you to re-veal your-self to us. There is a long-ing in our hearts for love we on-ly find in you, our God.

Verses

1. For jus-tice, for free-dom, for mer-cy: hear our prayer. In
2. For wis-dom, for cour-age, for com-fort: hear our prayer. In
3. For heal-ing, for whole-ness, for new life: hear our prayer. In
4. Lord save us, take pit-y, light in our dark-ness. We

1. sor-row, in grief:
2. weak-ness, in fear:
3. sick-ness, in death:
4. call you, we wait:

be near, hear our prayer, O God.

Text and music: Anne Quigley, © 1992, Anne Quigley. Published by OCP Publications. All rights reserved.

693 COME, MY WAY, MY TRUTH, MY LIFE

1. Come, my Way, my Truth, my Life: Such a
2. Come, my Light, my Feast, my Strength: Such a
3. Come, my Joy, my Love, my Heart: Such a

1. way as gives us breath; Such a truth as ends all
2. light as shows a feast; Such a feast as mends in
3. joy as none can move; Such a love as none can

1. strife; Such a life as kill - eth death.
2. length; Such a strength as makes his guest.
3. part; Such a heart as joys in love.

Text: 77 77; George Herbert, 1593–1632.
Music: THE CALL; *Five Mystical Songs*; Ralph Vaughan Williams, 1872–1958.

694 JESUS, COME TO US

Refrain

Je - sus, come to us, lead us to your light. Je - sus, be with us,

for we need you.

Verses

1. Lord, we come be - fore you, _____ lis - ten
2. Lord, we come to praise you for your faith - ful -
3. Lord, you give us won - ders, _ your glo -

to Refrain

1. to our prayer. Fill us all with hope and your love.
2. ness through night. You will be with us, this we know.
3. ry to all. We be-lieve in you, come to us.

OPEN MY EYES

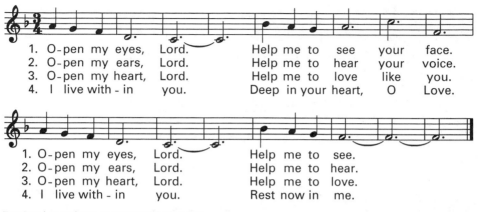

1. O-pen my eyes, Lord. Help me to see your face.
2. O-pen my ears, Lord. Help me to hear your voice.
3. O-pen my heart, Lord. Help me to love like you.
4. I live with-in you. Deep in your heart, O Love.

1. O-pen my eyes, Lord. Help me to see.
2. O-pen my ears, Lord. Help me to hear.
3. O-pen my heart, Lord. Help me to love.
4. I live with-in you. Rest now in me.

Text: Based on Mark 8:22–25; Jesse Manibusan, b. 1958.
Music: Jesse Manibusan.
Text and music © 1988, 1999, Jesse Manibusan. Published by OCP Publications. All rights reserved.

PSALM 42: AS THE DEER LONGS

696

1. As the deer longs for flow-ing streams, so longs my
2. My tears have fed me day and night, while some have
3. Why do I mourn and toil with-in, when it is

1. soul for you, O God. My soul does thirst
2. said "Where is your God?" But I re-call,
3. mine to hope in God? I shall a-gain

1. for the liv-ing God, when shall I come to see your
2. as my soul pours dry, the days of praise with-in your
3. sing praise to him, he is my help, he is my

1, 2   2 D.C. || Final

1. face?   3. God.   He is my God.
2. house.

Text: Irregular; based on Psalm 42; Donna Harkin, © 1975, Word Music, Inc. All rights reserved. Used with permission.
Music: O WALY WALY, alt.; Trad. English Melody.

CENTER OF MY LIFE

Refrain: Repeat 1st time

O Lord, you are the cen-ter of my life: I will al-ways praise you,

I will al-ways serve you, I will al-ways keep you in my sight. 1. sight.
2.
3. And

1-5 (to Verses) | Final

Verses 1-3

1. Keep me safe, O God, __ I take ref- uge in you._ I say to the
2. I will bless the Lord who gives me coun - sel, ____ who e - ven at
3. so my heart re - joic - es, my soul is glad;____ e - ven in

1. Lord, "You are my God. My hap - pi - ness ____ lies in you a-
2. night di - rects my heart. I keep __ the Lord ____ ev - er in my
3. safe - ty shall my bod-y rest. For you will not leave my soul a-mong the

to Refrain

1. lone; my hap-pi-ness _____ lies in you a - lone."___
2. sight: since he is at my right _ hand, _ I shall stand firm.
3. dead, nor let __ your be-lov-ed know de - cay. _____

Verse 4

4. You will show me the path of life, the full - ness of

4. joy in your pres - ence, at your right hand,

to Refrain

4. at your right hand hap-pi-ness for- ev - er.

FAITH OF OUR FATHERS

1. Faith of our fa - thers! Liv - ing still
2. The mar - tyrs, chained in pris - ons dark,
3. Faith of our moth - ers! Ma - ry's pray'rs
4. Faith of our fa - thers! We will love

1. In spite of dun - geon, fire and sword:
2. Were still in heart and con - science free:
3. Shall win all na - tions un - to thee;
4. Both friend and foe in all our strife:

1. O how our hearts beat high with joy,
2. And tru - ly blest would be our fate,
3. And through the truth that comes from God,
4. And preach thee, too, as love knows how,

1. When - e'er we hear that glo - rious word:
2. If we, like them, should die for thee.
3. We all shall then in - deed be free.
4. By kind - ly words and vir - tuous life.

1. Faith of our fa - thers, ho - ly faith!
2. Faith of the mar - tyrs, ho - ly faith!
3. Faith of our moth - ers, ho - ly faith!
4. Faith of our fa - thers, ho - ly faith!

1-4. We will be true to thee till death.

Text: 88 88 88; Frederick W. Faber, 1814–1863, alt.
Music: ST. CATHERINE; Henri F. Hemy, 1818–1888; adapt. by James G. Walton, 1821–1905.

699

THERE IS ONE LORD

Refrain

There is one Lord. There is one faith. There is one foun-tain flow - ing with the wa-ters of re - birth.

Verses

1. As the dew from heav-en falls up - on the earth,
2. See the wa - ter flow-ing from the tem - ple wall,
3. Like a thirst - y deer that longs for run - ning streams,
4. In the roar of wa - ters deep calls out to deep.
5. Blest be - yond all meas-ure by the love of God,

to Refrain

1. so the love of God de-scends up - on ___ us.
2. from the side of Christ, re - new-ing all the earth.
3. so my spir - it longs for God, the liv - ing God.
4. In the surg-ing waves the voice of God is heard.
5. all cre - a - tion sings the glo - ry of his name.

Text: cf. Ephesians 4:5; Owen Alstott, b. 1947.
Music: Owen Alstott.
Text and music © 1984, OCP Publications. All rights reserved.

700

WE WALK BY FAITH

1, 5. We walk by faith, and not by sight: No gra-cious words we hear
2. We may not touch his hands and side, Nor fol - low where he trod;
3. Help then, O Lord, our un - be - lief, And may our faith a-bound;
4. That when our life of faith is done In realms of clear - er light

1, 5. Of him who spoke as none e'er spoke, But we be - lieve him near.
2. Yet in his prom-ise we re - joice And cry, "My Lord and God!"
3. To call on you when you are near, And seek where you are found:
4. We may be - hold you as you are In full and end-less sight.

Text: CM; Henry Alford, alt., 1810–1871.
Music: ST. ANNE; attr. to William Croft, 1678–1727.

Jesus, Lord

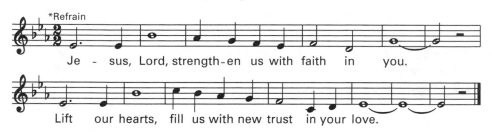

Je - sus, Lord, strength-en us with faith in you.

Lift our hearts, fill us with new trust in your love.

Verses

1. God so loved the world he gave his on - ly Son,
2. God sent his Son in - to a bro - ken world,
3. Je - sus is the light by which we see the truth;

to Refrain

1. With our faith in him we shall have e - ter - nal life.
2. Not to con - demn, but that we might be saved.
3. If we fol - low him we are blest in all we do.

*Opening Refrain is sung twice before proceeding to Verse 1.

Text: Based on John 3:16–21; Randall DeBruyn, b. 1947.
Music: Randall DeBruyn.
Text and music © 1984, OCP Publications. All rights reserved.

Hold Me in Life

702

Refrain

Hold me in life for you are my safe - ty, al-ways my eyes are

Verses

look-ing for you.
1. Be-cause you are just who you are, don't pass me
2. Are you the one who is to come, or must we
3. You gave your word to this our world: you are my

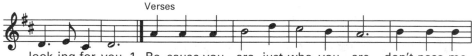

to Refrain

1. by, but show me your mer - cy; I will wait for you all my life.
2. wait and fol - low some oth - er? Lord, my God, I am cer-tain of you.
3. song, the God of my glad-ness; my de - sire goes out to you.

Text: Based on Psalm 25; Huub Oosterhuis, b. 1933; tr. by David Smith, b. 1933, and Forrest Ingram, b. 1938.
Music: Bernard Huijbers, b. 1922.
Text and music © 1967, Gooi en Sticht, bv., Baarn, The Netherlands. All rights reserved.
    Exclusive agent for English-language countries: OCP Publications.

703

AGE TO AGE

Refrain: 1st time: Cantor, All repeat; thereafter: All

Age to age we will love you. Dawn-ing light we will
wake with you. In-to night we will fol-low you. We will
love you age to age.

Verses

1. As the ea - gle
2. As the lil - ies of the
3. Come, all you
4. Lord, let my

1. flies to the heav'ns a - bove, on wings of
2. field nei-ther toil nor spin, what splen - dor we
3. wea - ry, for you are blessed. God will light - en your
4. faith in you be re - vealed. On - ly say the

2 to Refrain

1. faith God will bear you up.
2. find in the love God gives.
3. bur - den and give you rest.
4. word and I shall be healed.

Text: Based on Isaiah 40:31; Matthew 6:28, 11:28–30; Janet Vogt, b. 1953.
Music: Janet Vogt.
Text and music © 1996, 1997, Janet Vogt. Published by OCP Publications. All rights reserved.

704

ON EAGLE'S WINGS

Verse 1

1. You who dwell in the shel-ter of the Lord, who a - bide in his

to Refrain

1. shad-ow for life, say to the Lord: "My ref-uge, my rock in whom I trust!"

Refrain

And he will raise you up on ea-gle's wings, bear you on the breath of dawn, make you to shine like the sun, and hold you in the palm of his hand.

Coda

And hold you, hold you in the palm of his hand.

Verse 2

2. The snare of the fowl-er will nev-er cap-ture you, and fam-ine will bring

2. you no fear: un-der his wings your ref-uge, his faith-ful-ness your shield.

to Refrain

Verse 3

3. You need not fear the ter-ror of the night, nor the ar-row that flies by

3. day; though thou-sands fall a-bout you, near you it shall not come.

to Refrain

Verse 4

4. For to his an-gels he's giv-en a com-mand to

4. guard you in all of your ways; up-on their hands they will

4. bear you up, lest you dash your foot a-gainst a stone.

to Refrain

Text: Based on Psalm 91; Michael Joncas, b. 1951.
Music: Michael Joncas.

O GOD, OUR HELP IN AGES PAST

1. O God, our help in a - ges past, Our
2. Be - neath the shad - ow of your throne Your
3. Be - fore the hills in or - der stood, Or
4. A thou - sand a - ges in your sight Are
5. Time, like an ev - er - roll - ing stream, Bears
6. O God, our help in a - ges past, Our

1. hope for years to come, Our shel - ter from the
2. saints have dwelt se - cure; Suf - fi - cient is your
3. earth re - ceived her frame, From ev - er - last - ing
4. like an eve - ning gone; Short as the watch that
5. all our years a - way; They fly for - got - ten,
6. hope for years to come, Still be our guard while

1. storm - y blast, And our e - ter - nal home.
2. arm a - lone, And our de - fense is sure.
3. you are God, To end - less years the same.
4. ends the night Be - fore the ris - ing sun.
5. as a dream Dies at the o - p'ning day.
6. trou - bles last, And our e - ter - nal home.

Text: CM; based on Psalm 90; Isaac Watts, 1674–1748, alt.
Music: ST. ANNE; attr. to William Croft, 1678–1727.

706 BE NOT AFRAID

Verse 1

1. You shall cross the bar - ren des - ert, but you shall not die of

1. thirst. You shall wan - der far in safe - ty though you do not know the

1. way. You shall speak your words in for - eign lands and all will un - der-

to Refrain

1. stand. You shall see the face of God and live.

Refrain

Be not a-fraid. I go be-fore you al-ways. Come fol-low me, and I will give you rest.

1, 2 to Vss 2, 3 | Final 2

Verse 2

2. If you pass through rag-ing wa-ters in the sea, you shall not drown. If you walk a-mid the burn-ing flames, you shall not be harmed. If you stand be-fore the pow'r of hell and death is at your side, know that I am with you through it all.

to Refrain

Verse 3

3. Bless-ed are your poor, for the king-dom shall be theirs. Blest are you that weep and mourn, for one day you shall laugh. And if wick-ed tongues in-sult and hate you all be-cause of me, bless-ed, bless-ed are you!

to Refrain

Text: Based on Isaiah 43:2–3; Luke 6:20ff; Bob Dufford, SJ, b. 1943.
Music: Bob Dufford, SJ.
Text and music © 1975, 1978, Robert J. Dufford, SJ, and New Dawn Music. Published by OCP Publications. All rights reserved.

ONLY A SHADOW

Verses

1. The love we have for you, O Lord, is __
2. The bread we take and eat, O Lord, is __
3. Our own be - lief in you, O Lord, ᵧ is
4. The dreams we share to - day, O Lord, ᵧ are
5. The joy we share to - day, O Lord, ᵧ is

1. on - ly a __ shad-ow of your love for us;
2. your bod - y __ bro - ken and shared with us;
3. on - ly __ a shad-ow of your faith in us;
4. on - ly __ a shad-ow of your dreams for us;
5. on - ly __ a shad-ow of your joys for us;

1. on - ly a shad-ow of your love for us, your
2. your bod - y bro - ken and shared with us, the
3. on - ly a shad-ow of your faith in us; your
4. on - ly a shad-ow of your dreams for us; if
5. on - ly a shad-ow of your joys for us; when

1. deep a - bid - ing love. (to Verse 2)
2. gift of your great love. (to Refrain)
3. deep and last - ing faith. (to Verse 4)
4. we but fol - low you. (to Refrain)
5. we meet face to face. (to Refrain)

Refrain

Our lives are in your hands, our lives
are in your hands. Our love for you will
grow, O Lord; your light in us will shine.

Blest Be the Lord

Refrain

Blest be the Lord; blest be the Lord, the God of mer - cy, the God who saves. I shall not fear the dark of night, nor the ar - row that flies by day.

Verses

1. He will re-lease me from the nets of all my foes.
2. I need not shrink be - fore the ter-rors of the night,
3. Al-though a thou - sand strong have fall - en at my side,

1. He will pro - tect me from their wick-ed hands.
2. nor stand a-lone be - fore the light of day.
3. I'll not be shak-en with the Lord at hand.

1. Be - neath the shad-ow of his wings I
2. No harm shall come to me, no ar - row
3. His faith - ful love is all the ar - mor

to Refrain

1. will re - joice to find a dwell-ing place se-cure.
2. strike me down, no e - vil set - tle in my soul.
3. that I need to wage my bat- tle with the foe.

Text: Based on Psalm 91; Dan Schutte, b. 1947.
Music: Dan Schutte.

A MIGHTY FORTRESS

1. A might-y for-tress is our God, A
2. No strength of ours can match his might! We
3. Though hordes of dev-ils fill the land All
4. God's Word for-ev-er shall a-bide, No

1. sword and shield vic-to-rious; He breaks the
2. would be lost, re-ject-ed. But now a
3. threat-n'ing to de-vour us, We trem-ble
4. thanks to foes, who fear it; For God him-

1. cruel op-pres-sor's rod And wins sal-va-tion
2. cham-pion comes to fight, Whom God him-self e-
3. not, un-moved we stand; They can-not o-ver-
4. self fights by our side With weap-ons of the

1. glo-rious. The old sa-tan-ic foe
2. lect-ed. You ask who this may be?
3. pow'r us. Let this world's ty-rant rage;
4. Spir-it. Were they to take our house,

1. Has sworn to work us woe! With craft and
2. The Lord of hosts is he! Christ Je-sus,
3. In bat-tle we'll en-gage! His might is
4. Goods, hon-or, child, or spouse, Though life be

1. dread-ful might He arms him-self to fight.
2. might-y Lord, God's on-ly Son, a-dored.
3. doomed to fail; God's judg-ment must pre-vail!
4. wrenched a-way, They can-not win the day.

1. On earth he has no e - qual.
2. He holds the field vic - to - rious.
3. One lit - tle word sub - dues him.
4. The King - dom's ours for - ev - er!

Text: 87 87 66 66 7; based on Psalm 46; Martin Luther, 1483–1546; tr. © 1978, *Lutheran Book of Worship*.
All rights reserved. Reprinted by permission of Augsburg Fortress.
Music: EIN' FESTE BURG; Martin Luther.

FOR YOU ARE MY GOD
710

Refrain

For you are my God; you a - lone are my joy. De-

fend me, O Lord.

Verses

1. You give mar - vel - ous
2. — You are my
3. — Glad are my
4. ⸭ You show me the

1. com - rades __ to me: the faith - ful who dwell in your
2. por - tion __ and cup; it is you __ that I claim for my
3. heart __ and my soul; se - cure - ly my bod - y shall
4. path __ for my life; in your pres - ence _ the full - ness of

1. land. Those _ who choose a - li - en gods ____
2. prize. Your her - i - tage ____ is my de - light, ____
3. rest. For you __ will not leave me _ for dead, ____
4. joy. To be __ at your right hand _ for - ev - er __

to Refrain

1. ____ have cho - sen an a - li - en band. _____
2. ____ the lot you have giv - en to me. _____
3. ____ nor lead your be - lov - ed a - stray. _____
4. ____ for me would be hap - pi - ness al - ways. _____

Text: Based on Psalm 16; John Foley, S.J., b. 1939.
Music: John Foley, S.J.
Text and music © 1970, John B. Foley, S.J. Published by OCP Publications. All rights reserved.

O GOD, YOU SEARCH ME

1. O God, you search me and you know me.
2. You know my rest-ing and my ris-ing.
3. Be-fore a word is on my tongue, Lord,
4. Al-though your Spir-it is up-on me,
5. For you cre-at-ed me and shaped me,

1. All my thoughts lie o-pen to your gaze.
2. You dis-cern my pur-pose from a-far,
3. You have known its mean-ing through and through.
4. Still I search for shel-ter from your light.
5. Gave me life with-in my moth-er's womb.

1. When I walk or lie down you are be-fore me:
2. And with love ev-er-last-ing you be-siege me:
3. You are with me be-yond my un-der-stand-ing:
4. There is no-where on earth I can es-cape you:
5. For the won-der of who I am, I praise you:

1. Ev-er the mak-er and keep-er of my days.
2. In ev-'ry mo-ment of life or death, you are.
3. God of my pres-ent, my past and fu-ture, too.
4. E-ven the dark-ness is ra-diant in your sight.
5. Safe in your hands, all cre-a-tion is made new.

Text: Psalm 139; Bernadette Farrell, b. 1957.
Music: Bernadette Farrell.
Text and music © 1992, Bernadette Farrell. Published by OCP Publications. All rights reserved.

712

ONLY IN GOD

Verses

1. On-ly in God is my soul at_ rest, in ___ him comes my sal-
2. On-ly in God is found safe-ty when my en-e-my pur-

1. va-tion. He, ___ on-ly, ___ is my_ rock, my strength_ and
2. sues me. On-ly in God is found glo-ry when I am found

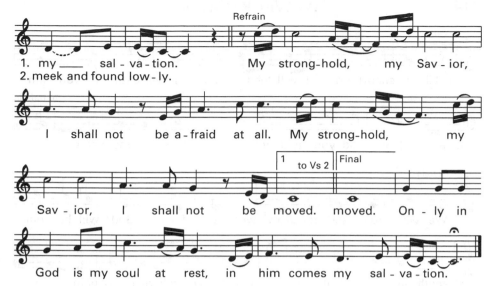

1. my ___ sal - va - tion.   My strong-hold,   my Sav - ior,
2. meek and found low - ly.

I   shall not   be a - fraid   at all.   My strong-hold,   my

Sav - ior,   I   shall not   be   moved.   moved.   On - ly in

God   is my soul   at   rest,   in   him comes my   sal - va - tion.

Text: Based on Psalm 62; John Michael Talbot, b. 1954.
Music: John Michael Talbot.
Text and music © 1980, Birdwing Music/Cherry Lane Music Publishing Co., Inc. All rights reserved.
   Administered by EMI Christian Publishing. Used with permission.

AMAZING GRACE   713

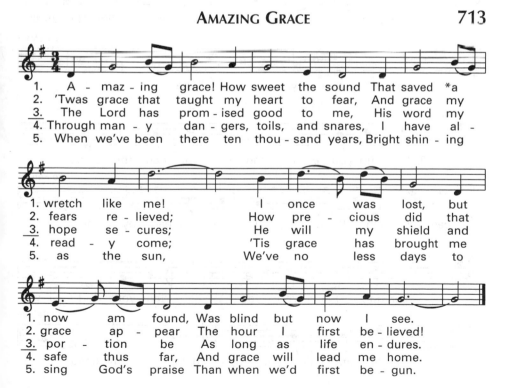

1. A - maz - ing   grace! How sweet   the sound That saved   *a
2. 'Twas grace that   taught my heart   to   fear, And grace   my
3. The   Lord has   prom - ised good   to   me,   His word   my
4. Through man - y   dan - gers, toils,   and snares,   I   have   al -
5. When we've been   there   ten   thou - sand years, Bright shin - ing

1. wretch   like   me!   I   once   was   lost,   but
2. fears   re - lieved;   How   pre -   cious   did   that
3. hope   se - cures;   He   will   my   shield   and
4. read - y   come;   'Tis   grace   has   brought me
5. as   the   sun,   We've   no   less   days   to

1. now   am   found, Was   blind   but   now   I   see.
2. grace   ap - pear The   hour   I   first   be - lieved!
3. por - tion   be   As   long   as   life   en - dures.
4. safe   thus   far,   And grace   will   lead   me home.
5. sing   God's   praise Than when we'd   first   be - gun.

*Alternate text: "and set me free!"

Text: CM; verses 1–4, John Newton, 1725–1807; verse 5, anon.; fr. *A Collection of Sacred Ballads,* 1790.
Music: NEW BRITAIN; *Columbian Harmony,* 1829.

We Will Rise Again

Verse 1
1. Like a shep-herd I will feed you; I will gath - er you with
1. care. I will lead you and hold you close to my heart.

Refrain
We will run and not grow wea - ry, for our God will be our
strength, and we will fly like the ea - gle, we will rise a - gain.

Verse 2
2. I am strength to the wea - ry; to the weak I am new life. Though the
2. young may grow wea - ry, I will be their hope.

Verse 3
3. Lift up your eyes, and see who made the stars. I
3. lead you, and I know you, I call you each by name.

Verse 4
4. Fear not, I am with you; I am your God. I will
4. strength-en you and help you; up - hold you with my hand.

Text: Based on Isaiah 40:11, 26, 29–30; 41:10; David Haas, b. 1957.
Music: David Haas.

THOUGH THE MOUNTAINS MAY FALL

Refrain

Though the moun - tains may fall and the hills turn to dust,

yet the love of the Lord will stand

as a shel - ter for all who will call on his name.

Sing the praise and the glo - ry of God.

Verses

1. Could the Lord ev - er leave you? Could the Lord for -
2. Should you turn and for - sake him, he will gent - ly
3. Go to him when you're wea - ry; he will give you
4. As he swore to your fa - thers, when the flood de -

1. get his love? Though a moth - er for -
2. call your name. Should you wan - der a -
3. ea - gle's wings. You will run, nev - er
4. stroyed the land, he will nev - er for -

to Refrain

1. sake her child, he will not a - ban - don you.
2. way from him, he will al - ways take you back.
3. tire, _____ for your God will be your strength.
4. sake you; _____ he will swear to you a - gain.

Text: Based on Isaiah 54:6–10; 49:15; 40:31–32; Dan Schutte, b. 1947.
Music: Dan Schutte.
Text and music © 1975, 1979, Daniel L. Schutte and New Dawn Music. Published by OCP Publications. All rights reserved.

How Firm a Foundation

1. How firm a foundation, you saints of the Lord,
2. "Fear not, I am with you, O be not dis-mayed,
3. "When through the deep wa-ters I call you to go,
4. "The soul that on Je-sus still leans for re-pose,

1. Is laid for your faith in his ex-cel-lent Word!
2. For I am your God, and will still give you aid;
3. The riv-ers of woe shall not you o-ver-flow;
4. I will not, I will not de-sert to its foes;

1. What more can he say than to you he has said,
2. I'll strength-en you, help you, and cause you to stand,
3. For I will be with you, your trou-bles to bless,
4. That soul, though all hell should en-deav-or to shake,

1. To you who for ref-uge to Je-sus have fled?
2. Up-held by my righ-teous, om-nip-o-tent hand."
3. And sanc-ti-fy to you, your deep-est dis-tress."
4. I'll nev-er, no nev-er, no nev-er for-sake!"

Text: 11 11 11 11; "K" in Rippon's *A Selection of Hymns*, 1787.
Music: FOUNDATION; Funk's *A Compilation of Genuine Church Music*, 1832.

717   HERE I AM

Refrain

Here I am, stand-ing right be-side you. Here I am;

do not be a-fraid. Here I am, wait-ing like a lov-er.

1-3 to Vss. | Final

I am here; here I am. am. I am here; here I am.

1. Do not fear when the tempt-er calls you. Do not
1. fear e-ven though you fall. Do not fear, I have con-quered
1. e-vil. Do not fear, nev-er be a-fraid.

2. I am here in the face of ev-'ry child.
2. I am here in ev-'ry warm em-brace. I am here with
2. ten-der-ness and mer-cy. Here I am, I am here.

3. I am here in the midst of ev-'ry tri-al. I am
3. here in the face of de-spair. I am here when
3. par-don-ing your broth-er. Here I am, I am here.

718   To You, O Lord

Refrain

To you, O Lord, I lift my soul. To you, O Lord, I lift up my prayer.

Verses

1. I will fol - low your ways, O Lord; I will
2. Of my weak-ness and sin - ful - ness be not
3. Put an end to my suf - fer - ing; bring me
4. I will place all my trust in you; I will

to Refrain

1. walk in your paths, for you are my Sav - ior and my God.
2. mind - ful, O Lord. In your kind - ness, Lord, re - mem - ber me.
3. out of dis - tress and re - lieve the trou - bles of my heart.
4. not be a - shamed, for I know that you, O Lord, are near.

Text: Based on Psalm 25; Owen Alstott, b. 1947.
Music: Owen Alstott.

719   The Lord Is Near

Refrain/Alternate Refrain: All

O the Lord is near to all who call on him; he is
*Alt. May the an - gels lead you in - to par - a - dise; may the

close to all who seek his face, slow to an - ger and
mar - tyrs come to wel - come you, and take you

full of com - pas - sion and a - bound - ing in mer - ci - ful
to the ho - ly cit - y, the new and e - ter - nal Je -

1-3 *to Verses* | **Final**

love.
ru - sa - lem.

love. A - men.
ru - sa - lem.

1. The Lord is my light and my sal-va-tion, there is noth-ing at all I fear;
1. the Lord is the ref-uge of my life; of whom should I be a-fraid?

Verses 2, 3: Cantor

2. One thing I ask___ of the Lord; there is on-ly one
3. For God will___ hide me in his house and con-ceal me in the

2. thing___ I seek: to dwell in the house___ of the
3. shel-ter of his tent. E-ven now___ my head is held___

2. Lord all the days of my life.
3. high o-ver those who would see me fall.

*Alternate refrain for funerals.

Text: Based on Psalm 27; alt. refrain based on *In Paradisum*; Michael Joncas, b. 1951.
Music: Michael Joncas.
Text and music © 1979, New Dawn Music. Published by OCP Publications. All rights reserved.

SEEK YE FIRST 720

1. Seek ye___ first the king-dom of God and his
2. Ask and it shall be giv-en un-to you; seek, and
3. You do not live by bread___ a-lone, but by

1. righ-teous-ness, And all these things shall be
2. ye shall___ find; Knock, and it shall be___
3. ev-'ry___ word That pro-ceeds from the

1. add-ed un-to you.
2. o-pened un-to you. Al-le-lu, al-le-lu-ia.
3. mouth___ of___ God.

Text: Based on Matthew 6:33; Karen Lafferty, b. 1948.
Music: Karen Lafferty.
Text and music © 1972, Maranatha! Music (Administered by The Copyright Company, Nashville, TN)/CCCM Music
(Administered by Maranatha! Music c/o The Copyright Company, Nashville, TN). All rights reserved.
International copyright secured. Used with permission.

721 HOW CAN I KEEP FROM SINGING

Verses

1. My life flows on in end - less song; A-
2. Through all the tu - mult and the strife, I
3. What though the tem - pest 'round me roar, I
4. When ty - rants trem - ble, sick with fear, And
5. The peace of Christ makes fresh my heart, A

1. bove earth's lam - en - ta - tion. I hear the real though
2. hear that mu - sic ring-ing; It sounds and ech - oes
3. hear the truth it liv - eth. What though the dark - ness
4. hear their death knells ring - ing; When friends re - joice both
5. foun - tain ev - er spring-ing. All things are mine since

1. far - off hymn That hails a new cre - a - tion.
2. in my soul; How can I keep from sing-ing?
3. 'round me close, Songs in the night it giv-eth.
4. far and near, How can I keep from sing-ing?
5. I am his; How can I keep from sing-ing?

Refrain

No storm can shake my in-most calm, While to that rock I'm

cling-ing. Since Love is Lord of heav-en and earth,

How can I keep from sing-ing?

Text: 87 87 with refrain; attr. to Robert Lowry, 1826–1899, alt.; verse 3, Doris Plenn.
Music: ENDLESS SONG; Quaker Hymn; attr. to Robert Lowry.

722 YOU ARE NEAR

Refrain

Yah-weh, I know you are near, stand-ing al-ways at my side. You

guard me from the foe, and you lead me in ways ev-er-last-ing.

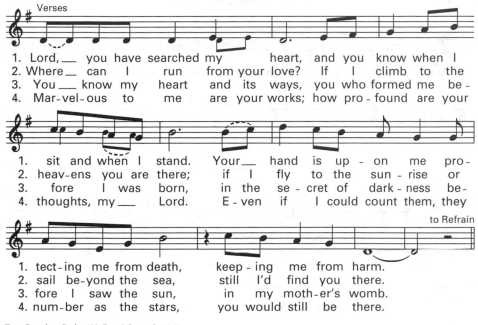

1. Lord, __ you have searched my heart, and you know when I
2. Where __ can I run from your love? If I climb to the
3. You __ know my heart and its ways, you who formed me be-
4. Mar-vel-ous to me are your works; how pro-found are your

1. sit and when I stand. Your __ hand is up-on me pro-
2. heav-ens you are there; if I fly to the sun-rise or
3. fore I was born, in the se-cret of dark-ness be-
4. thoughts, my __ Lord. E-ven if I could count them, they

to Refrain

1. tect-ing me from death, keep-ing me from harm.
2. sail be-yond the sea, still I'd find you there.
3. fore I saw the sun, in my moth-er's womb.
4. num-ber as the stars, you would still be there.

Text: Based on Psalm 139; Dan Schutte, b. 1947.
Music: Dan Schutte.
Text and music © 1971, Daniel L. Schutte. Published by OCP Publications. All rights reserved.

THERE IS A BALM IN GILEAD 723

Refrain

There is a balm in Gil-e-ad to make the wound-ed whole,

there is a balm in Gil-e-ad to heal the sin-sick soul.

Verses

1. Some-times I feel dis-cour-aged, And __ think my work's in vain,
2. If you can-not preach like Pe-ter, If you can-not pray like Paul,
3. Don't __ ev-er feel dis-cour-aged, For __ Je-sus is your friend;

to Refrain

1. but __ then the Ho-ly Spir-it Re-vives my soul a-gain.
2. you can tell the love of Je-sus, And say, "He died for all."
3. and __ if you lack for knowl-edge, He'll ne'er re-fuse to lend.

Text: 76 76 with refrain; based on Jeremiah 8:22.
Music: BALM IN GILEAD; Spiritual.

SHELTER ME, O GOD

Shel-ter me, O God; hide me in the shad-ow of your wings. You a-lone

are my hope.

1. When my foes sur-round me, set me
2. As a moth-er gath-ers her ____
3. Though I walk in dark-ness, through the

1. high a-bove their reach. Hear me when I call your name.
2. young be-neath her care, gath-er me in-to your arms.
3. nee-dle's eye of death, you will nev-er leave my side.

Text: Based on Psalm 16; Psalm 61; Luke 13:34; Bob Hurd, b. 1950.
Music: Bob Hurd.

725 BECAUSE THE LORD IS MY SHEPHERD

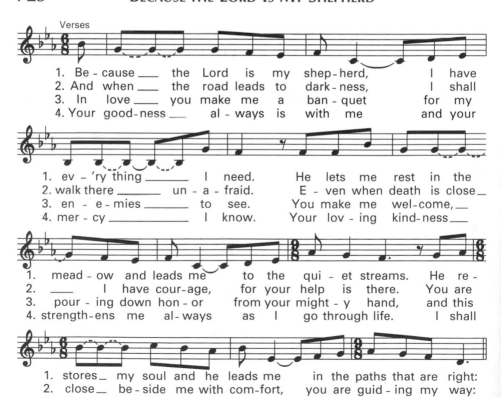

Verses

1. Be-cause ____ the Lord is my shep-herd, I have
2. And when ____ the road leads to dark-ness, I shall
3. In love ____ you make me a ban-quet for my
4. Your good-ness ____ al-ways is with me and your

1. ev-'ry thing ____ I need. He lets me rest in the
2. walk there ____ un-a-fraid. E-ven when death is close ____
3. en-e-mies ____ to see. You make me wel-come, ____
4. mer-cy ____ I know. Your lov-ing kind-ness ____

1. mead-ow and leads me to the qui-et streams. He re-
2. ____ I have cour-age, for your help is there. You are
3. pour-ing down hon-or from your might-y hand, and this
4. strength-ens me al-ways as I go through life. I shall

1. stores ____ my soul and he leads me in the paths that are right:
2. close ____ be-side me with com-fort, you are guid-ing my way:
3. joy ____ fills me with glad-ness; it is too much to bear:
4. dwell in your pres-ence for-ev-er, giv-ing praise to your name:

Lord, you are my shep-herd, you are my friend.

I want to fol-low you al - ways, just to fol-low my friend.

Text: Based on Psalm 23; Christopher Walker, b. 1947.
Music: Christopher Walker.
Text and music © 1985, Christopher Walker. Published by OCP Publications. All rights reserved.

CHRIST IN THE RUBBLE 726

1. O Christ, be - neath the fall - en stones, Nailed
2. O Christ, a - mong the wreck - age shorn Of
3. O Christ, with - in a world at war, Where

1. fast to twist - ed bars of steel, And slain in flesh
2. hope for those who lie there dead, Yet bathed in sweat
3. love and hate fight for the soul, And all sights trained

1. and blood and bones, Pierced by the fear all mor - tals
2. of la - bors borne To free the griev - ing from their
3. on death see far, But on - ly Love can see the

1. feel: A - rise from ash and dust and death,
2. dread: A - rise from our de - spair's long night,
3. whole: A - rise from un - for - giv - ing pain,

1. And breathe in - to crushed hearts new Breath.
2. And pour up - on us liv - ing Light.
3. And teach us how to love a - gain.

Text: 88 88 88; Genevieve Glen, OSB, b. 1945, © 2001, The Benedictine Nuns of the Abbey of St. Walburga.
    Published by OCP Publications. All rights reserved.
Music: SEPTEMBER HOPE; Tobias Colgan, OSB, b. 1950, © 2001, St. Meinrad Archabbey.
    Published by OCP Publications. All rights reserved.

IN EVERY AGE

Verses

1. Long be-fore the moun - tains came to be
2. Des - ti - ny is cast, and at your si-lent word
3. Teach us to make use of the time we have.

1. and the land and sea and stars of the night,
2. we re-turn to dust and scat - ter to the wind. A
3. Teach us to be pa - tient e - ven as we wait.

1. through the end-less sea - sons of all time, you have
2. thou-sand years are like a sin - gle mo-ment gone, as the
3. Teach us to em-brace our ev - 'ry joy and pain. To sleep

1. al - ways been, you will al - ways be.
2. light that fades at the end of day.
3. peace - ful - ly, and to rise up strong.

Refrain

In ev-'ry age, O God, you have been our ref-uge.

1, 2 — *to Verses 2, 3*

In ev-'ry age, O God, you have been our hope.

Final

God, you have been our hope,

you have been our ref - uge, you have been our hope.

Text: Based on Psalm 90: 1–4, 12; Janèt Sullivan Whitaker, b. 1958.
Music: Janèt Sullivan Whitaker.

COME TO ME

Refrain

Come to me, all who la-bor and are heav-y bur - dened, and
I shall give you rest. Take up my yoke and learn from
me, for I am meek and hum - ble of heart,
and you'll find rest for your souls. Yes, my
yoke is eas - y and my bur - den is
light.

Verses

1. You, God, are my shep-herd.
2. Be - side peace-ful wa - ters
3. Should I be sur-round-ed
4. Be - fore my deep hun - ger
5. Pur - sue me, O God, ___

1. I shall nev - er be in need. Fresh and green are the
2. you re - store ___ my true self; There you lead me to
3. by the shad - ows of death, I will not fear, for
4. you spread out ___ your ___ feast. My ___ skin you a -
5. with your fath - om - less love. In your tent let me

to Refrain

1. mead - ows where you give me ___ rest.
2. walk ___ in the path of new life.
3. you are stead - fast in your ___ love.
4. noint ___ with the rich - est of oil.
5. dwell ___ all the days of my life.

Text: Matthew 11:28–30; Psalm 23; original text, Weston Priory, Gregory Norbet, OSB, b. 1940.
Music: Weston Priory, Gregory Norbet, OSB.
Text and music © 1971, 1994 (revised text), The Benedictine Foundation of the State of Vermont, Inc.
All rights reserved. Used with permission.

729
I HEARD THE VOICE OF JESUS

1. I heard the voice of Je-sus say, "Come un-to me and
2. I heard the voice of Je-sus say, "Be-hold, I free-ly
3. I heard the voice of Je-sus say, "I am this dark world's

1. rest; Lay down, thou wea-ry one, lay down Thy head up-
2. give The liv-ing wa-ter; thirst-y one, Stoop down, and
3. light; Look un-to me, thy morn shall rise, And all thy

1. on my breast." I came to Je-sus as I was, So
2. drink, and live." I came to Je-sus, and I drank Of
3. day be bright." I looked to Je-sus, and I found In

1. wea-ry, worn and sad; I found in him a
2. that life-giv-ing stream; My thirst was quenched, my
3. him my star, my sun; And in that light of

1. rest-ing place, And he has made me glad.
2. soul re-vived, And now I live in him.
3. life I'll walk Till trav-'ling days are done.

Text: CMD; Horatius Bonar, 1808–1889, alt.
Music: KINGSFOLD; Trad. English Melody; *English Country Songs*, 1893; adapt. by Ralph Vaughan Williams, 1872–1958.

730
THE LORD IS MY HOPE

Refrain

The Lord is my hope and my glo-ry. The Lord is the song that I

sing: so ten-der and lov-ing a shep-herd, so root-ed in

jus-tice, a king. When shad-ow con-fus-es my vi-sion,

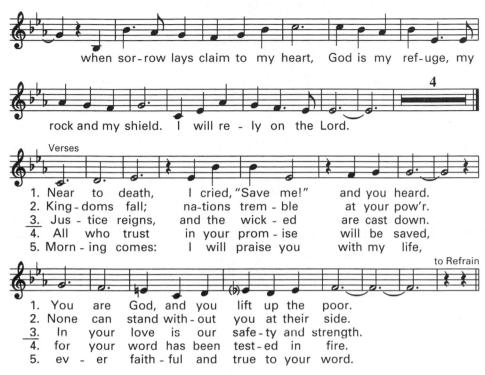

when sor-row lays claim to my heart, God is my ref-uge, my

rock and my shield. I will re-ly on the Lord.

Verses

1. Near to death, I cried, "Save me!" and you heard.
2. King-doms fall; na-tions trem-ble at your pow'r.
3. Jus-tice reigns, and the wick-ed are cast down.
4. All who trust in your prom-ise will be saved,
5. Morn-ing comes: I will praise you with my life,

to Refrain

1. You are God, and you lift up the poor.
2. None can stand with-out you at their side.
3. In your love is our safe-ty and strength.
4. for your word has been test-ed in fire.
5. ev-er faith-ful and true to your word.

Text: Based on 2 Samuel 22; M.D. Ridge.
Music: M.D. Ridge.
Text and music © 1989, M.D. Ridge. Published by OCP Publications. All rights reserved.

Do Not Be Afraid 731

Ostinato Refrain: All

Do not be a-fraid, do not be a-fraid.

Have cour-age! It is I.

Verses: (Sung over Refrain)

1. Let not your hearts be troubled.
   I am with you.

2. Peace I leave you, my peace I give you.
   Peace is my gift to you.

3. You, O God, will guard us.
   You will not slumber nor sleep,
   for you are our help and our shield.

4. You are our peace.
   You are our shelter.
   You are at our right hand forever.

5. Sun shall not harm us by day,
   nor the moon by night.
   You guard us from all evil, O God.

Text: Based on Matthew 14:27; John 14:27; Psalm 121:3; Suzanne Toolan, RSM, b. 1927.
Music: Suzanne Toolan, RSM.
Text and music © 1996, Suzanne Toolan, RSM. Published by OCP Publications. All rights reserved.

MY SHEPHERD WILL SUPPLY MY NEED

1. My Shep-herd will sup-ply my need; The
2. When I walk through the shades of death, Your
3. The sure pro-vi-sions of my God At-

1. Lord God is his name. In pas-tures
2. pres-ence is my stay; One word of
3. tend me all my days; O may your

1. green he makes me feed, Be-side the liv-ing
2. your sup-port-ing breath Drives all my fears a-
3. house be my a-bode, And all my work be

1. stream. He brings my wan-d'ring
2. way. Your hand, in sight of
3. praise! There would I find a

1. spir-it back, When I for-sake his ways;
2. all my foes, Does still my ta-ble spread;
3. set-tled rest, While oth-ers go and come,

1. And leads me for his mer-cy's
2. My cup with bless-ings o-ver-
3. No more a stran-ger nor a

1. sake, In paths of truth and grace.
2. flows, Your oil a-noints my head.
3. guest; But like a child at home.

Text: 86 86 D; based on Psalm 23; Isaac Watts, 1674–1748.
Music: RESIGNATION; William Walker's *The Southern Harmony*, 1835.

THE KING OF LOVE MY SHEPHERD IS

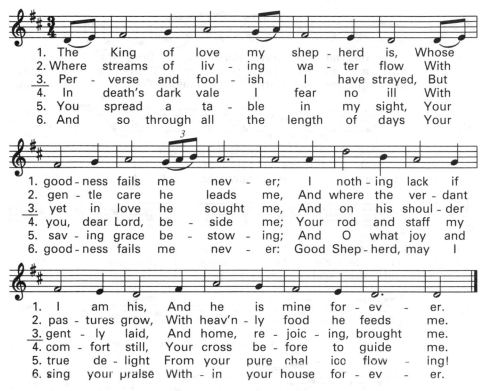

1. The King of love my shep - herd is, Whose
2. Where streams of liv - ing wa - ter flow With
3. Per - verse and fool - ish I have strayed, But
4. In death's dark vale I fear no ill With
5. You spread a ta - ble in my sight, Your
6. And so through all the length of days Your

1. good - ness fails me nev - er; I noth - ing lack if
2. gen - tle care he leads me, And where the ver - dant
3. yet in love he sought me, And on his shoul - der
4. you, dear Lord, be - side me; Your rod and staff my
5. sav - ing grace be - stow - ing; And O what joy and
6. good - ness fails me nev - er: Good Shep - herd, may I

1. I am his, And he is mine for - ev - er.
2. pas - tures grow, With heav'n - ly food he feeds me.
3. gent - ly laid, And home, re - joic - ing, brought me.
4. com - fort still, Your cross be - fore to guide me.
5. true de - light From your pure chal - ice flow - ing!
6. sing your praise With - in your house for - ev - er.

Text: 87 87; based on Psalm 23; Matthew 18; John 10; Henry Williams Baker, 1821–1877, alt.
Music: ST. COLUMBA; Trad. Irish Melody.

LIKE A CHILD RESTS

Refrain

Like a child rests in its moth-er's arms, so will I rest in

you. Like a so will I rest in you.

Verses   to Refrain

1. My God, I am not proud. I do not look for things too great.
2. My God, I trust in you. You care for me, you give me peace.
3. O Is - rael, trust in God, ___ now and al - ways trust in God.

Text: Based on Psalm 131; Christopher Walker, b. 1947.
Music: Christopher Walker.

735
COME TO ME

1. Come to me, all pil-grims thirst-y, Drink the wa-ter
2. Come to me, all trav-'lers wea-ry, Come that I may
3. Come to me, be-liev-ers bur-dened, Find re-fresh-ment

1. I will give. If you knew what gift I of-fer,
2. give you rest. Drink the cup of life I of-fer;
3. in this place. If you knew the gift I of-fer,

1. You would come to me and live.
2. At this ta-ble be my guest. } Je-sus, ev-er-
3. You would turn and seek my face.

1-3. flow-ing foun-tain, Give us wa-ter from your well. In the

1-3. gra-cious gift you of-fer There is joy no tongue can tell.

Text: 87 87 D; based on Matthew 11:28–30; Isaiah 55:1–2; Delores Dufner, OSB, b. 1939, © 1992, The Sisters of St. Benedict.
    All rights reserved. Used with permission.
Music: HOLY MANNA; William Moore's *The Columbian Harmony*, 1825.

736
PSALM 23

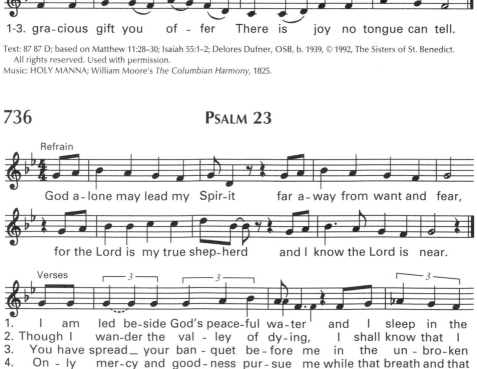

Refrain

God a-lone may lead my Spir-it far a-way from want and fear,

for the Lord is my true shep-herd and I know the Lord is near.

Verses

1. I am led be-side God's peace-ful wa-ter and I sleep in the
2. Though I wan-der the val-ley of dy-ing, I shall know that I
3. You have spread_ your ban-quet be-fore me in the un-bro-ken
4. On-ly mer-cy and good-ness pur-sue me while that breath and that

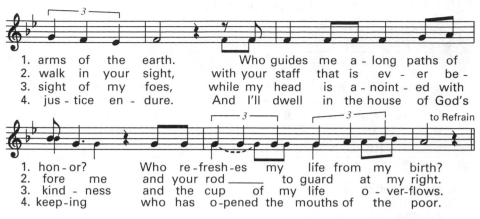

1. arms of the earth. Who guides me a - long paths of
2. walk in your sight, with your staff that is ev - er be -
3. sight of my foes, while my head is a - noint - ed with
4. jus - tice en - dure. And I'll dwell in the house of God's

1. hon - or? Who re - fresh - es my life from my birth?
2. fore me and your rod _____ to guard at my right.
3. kind - ness and the cup of my life o - ver - flows.
4. keep - ing who has o - pened the mouths of the poor.

Text and music: Tom Conry, b. 1951, © 1988, TEAM publications. Published by OCP Publications. All rights reserved.

GENTLE SHEPHERD   737

Refrain: 1st time: Cantor, All repeat; thereafter: All

O Je - sus, gen - tle shep - herd and liv - ing bread,

feed us, guide us to the land of ev - er - last - ing life.

Verses

1. The Lord is my shep - herd; there is noth - ing I shall
2. You have pre - pared me a ban - quet in the sight _ of my
3. Sure - ly good - ness and kind - ness shall fol - low me _ all my

1. want. _____ Fresh _____ and _ green are the pas -
2. foes. _____ My head _ you have a - noint - ed with pre -
3. days. _____ In the Lord's _____ own _ house shall I dwell _

to Refrain

1. - tures where he gives _____ me re - pose. _
2. - cious oil, and my cup is o - ver - flow - ing.
3. _____ for - ev - er and ev - er.

Text: Psalm 23:1–2, 5, 6; Tobias Colgan, OSB, b. 1950.
Music: Tobias Colgan, OSB.
Text and music © 1979, 1983, 1988, St. Meinrad Archabbey. Published by OCP Publications. All rights reserved.

PRAYER OF ST. FRANCIS

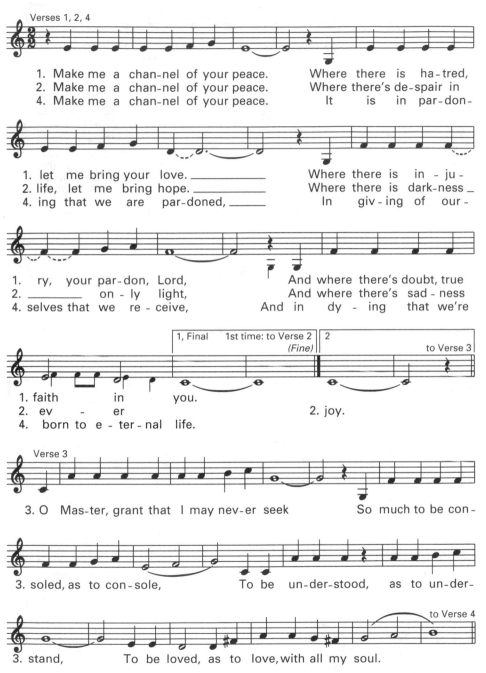

Verses 1, 2, 4

1. Make me a chan-nel of your peace. Where there is ha-tred,
2. Make me a chan-nel of your peace. Where there's de-spair in
4. Make me a chan-nel of your peace. It is in par-don-

1. let me bring your love. _____ Where there is in - ju-
2. life, let me bring hope. _____ Where there is dark-ness _
4. ing that we are par-doned, ____ In giv-ing of our-

1. ry, your par-don, Lord, And where there's doubt, true
2. _____ on - ly light, And where there's sad - ness
4. selves that we re - ceive, And in dy - ing that we're

1, Final   1st time: to Verse 2 | 2
                    (Fine)   to Verse 3

1. faith in you.
2. ev - er   2. joy.
4. born to e - ter - nal life.

Verse 3

3. O Mas-ter, grant that I may nev-er seek   So much to be con-

3. soled, as to con-sole, To be un-der-stood, as to un-der-

to Verse 4

3. stand, To be loved, as to love, with all my soul.

Text: Based on the prayer traditionally ascr. to St. Francis of Assisi, 1182–1226; Sebastian Temple, 1928–1997.
Music: Sebastian Temple.
Text and music © 1967, OCP Publications. All rights reserved. Dedicated to Mrs. Frances Tracy.

LET THERE BE PEACE ON EARTH

Let there be peace on earth and let it be-gin with me.

Let there be peace on earth, the peace that was meant to

be. With God as our Fa-ther, broth-ers
(optional text) we are

all are we; Let me walk with my broth-er in
fam - i - ly. Let us walk with each oth - er

per - fect har - mo - ny. Let peace be-gin with me, let

this be the mo-ment now. With ev - 'ry step I take, let

this be my sol - emn vow: To take each mo-ment and live each

mo-ment in peace e - ter - nal - ly. Let there be peace on earth and

1
let it be-gin with me.

Final
let it be-gin with me.

O DAY OF PEACE THAT DIMLY SHINES

1. O day of peace that dim-ly shines through all our
2. Then shall the wolf dwell with the lamb, nor shall the

1. hopes and prayers and dreams, guide us to jus - tice, truth, and
2. fierce de - vour the small; as beasts and cat - tle calm-ly

1. love, de-liv-ered from our self - ish schemes. May swords of
2. graze, a lit-tle child shall lead them all. Then en - e-

1. hate fall from our hands, our hearts from en - vy find re-
2. mies shall learn to love, all crea-tures find their true ac-

1. lease, till by God's grace our war - ring world shall see Christ's
2. cord; the hope of peace shall be ful - filled, for all the

1. prom-ised reign of peace.
2. earth shall know the   Lord.

741   PEACE

Refrain

Peace I leave with you, my friends, peace the world can-not give.

(Repeat Final time)

Peace I leave with you, my friends, so that your joy be ev-er full.

Verses

	1.	The	Fa - ther's	love	I	came	to	give,
	2.	Take	his	gift	and	be	at	peace;
	3.	By	this	love	which	you	should	have,
	4.	Take	my	words	of	life	to	heart,
	5.	All	I	have	I	give	to	you;
	6.	I	came	so	that	you	may	have	life,
	7.	If	you	love	me,	keep	my	word,

to Refrain

	1.	to	be	the	hope	for	all	who	live.
	2.	the	Spir - it	of	our	love	I	bring.
	3.	all	will	know	you	are	my	friends.
	4.	and	you	will	live	with	hope	and	joy.
	5.	I	share	with	you	the	Fa - ther's	love.
	6.	and	have	it	to	the	full.
	7.	and	our	home	we'll	make	with	you.

Text: Based on John 14:27ff; Weston Priory, Gregory Norbet, OSB, b. 1940.
Music: Weston Priory, Gregory Norbet, OSB.
Text and music © 1971, 1986, The Benedictine Foundation of the State of Vermont, Inc. All rights reserved. Used with permission.

DONA NOBIS PACEM   742

Do - na no - bis pa - cem, pa - cem. Do - na no - bis pa -

cem. Do - na no - bis pa - cem. Do - na no - bis pa - cem.

Do - na no - bis pa - cem. Do - na no - bis pa - cem.

Text and music: Traditional.

BEARERS OF PEACE

1. Peo - ple of Je - sus, trust - ed to be bear - ers of
2. Feel for the ones who have no more bread, feel for the
3. Feel for the ones whose homes are de - stroyed, feel for the
4. Stand with the ones who see a new way: peo - ple of
5. Pray for the day our chil - dren will see war strange and
6. Why spend your tears on what can - not heal? Why spend your
7. Chil - dren of peace, go forth through the earth, heal - ing our

1. peace from God's liv - ing tree, peace that the world it - self can-not
2. ones with chil - dren un - fed. Long - ing for food, they find in our
3. lives now shat-tered and void. Wait - ing for loved ones no - bod - y
4. faith who strug - gle and pray, giv - en the call to shape and re -
5. dis - tant as slav - er - y. Work for a world where new ways a -
6. rage on what you con-ceal? God's liv - ing Word cries out to re -
7. world and bring - ing to birth vi - sion to build and fash - ion a

1. know, the peace that is giv - en to plant and to grow.
2. hands a moun-tain of weap-ons more sa - cred than land.
3. saw: the in - no-cent peo - ple who suf - fer in war.
4. build our ac - tions, our con-scienc-es, our bro - ken world.
5. bound to meet and to di - a - logue till peace is found.
6. veal a love that will sat - is - fy, hope that is real.
7. way: the full - ness of life for God's peo - ple to - day.

Text and music: Bernadette Farrell, b. 1957, © 1999, Bernadette Farrell. Published by OCP Publications. All rights reserved.

744   DONA NOBIS PACEM

Refrain

Do - na no - bis pa - cem. Do - na no -

1-6 to Verses | Final

bis pa - cem. cem. Do - na no -

- bis pa - cem. Do - na no - bis pa-cem.

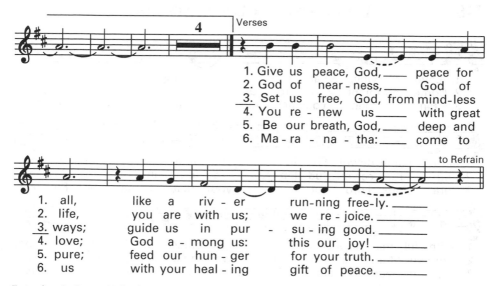

1. Give us peace, God, ____ peace for
2. God of near - ness, ____ God of
3. Set us free, God, from mind-less
4. You re - new us ____ with great
5. Be our breath, God, ____ deep and
6. Ma - ra - na - tha: ____ come to

1. all, like a riv - er run-ning free-ly. ____
2. life, you are with us; we re - joice. ____
3. ways; guide us in pur - su - ing good. ____
4. love; God a - mong us: this our joy! ____
5. pure; feed our hun - ger for your truth. ____
6. us with your heal - ing gift of peace. ____

PEACE IS FLOWING LIKE A RIVER 745

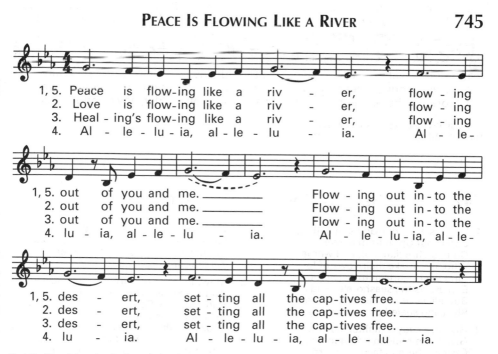

1, 5. Peace is flow-ing like a riv - er, flow - ing
2. Love is flow-ing like a riv - er, flow - ing
3. Heal - ing's flow-ing like a riv - er, flow - ing
4. Al - le - lu - ia, al - le - lu - ia. Al - le -

1, 5. out of you and me. ____ Flow - ing out in - to the
2. out of you and me. ____ Flow - ing out in - to the
3. out of you and me. ____ Flow - ing out in - to the
4. lu - ia, al - le - lu - ia. Al - le - lu - ia, al - le -

1, 5. des - ert, set - ting all the cap-tives free. ____
2. des - ert, set - ting all the cap-tives free. ____
3. des - ert, set - ting all the cap-tives free. ____
4. lu - ia. Al - le - lu - ia, al - le - lu - ia.

746   LOVE DIVINE, ALL LOVES EXCELLING

1. Love di-vine, all loves ex-cel-ling, Joy of heav'n, to
2. Come, al-might-y to de-liv-er; Let us all your
3. Fin-ish then your new cre-a-tion, Pure and spot-less,

1. earth come down! Fix in us your hum-ble dwell-ing; All your
2. life re-ceive; Sud-den-ly re-turn and nev-er, Nev-er-
3. gra-cious Lord; Let us see your great sal-va-tion Per-fect-

1. faith-ful mer-cies crown. Je-sus, source of all com-pas-sion,
2. more your tem-ples leave. Lord, we would be al-ways bless-ing,
3. ly in you re-stored. Changed from glo-ry in-to glo-ry,

1. Love un-bound-ed, love all pure; Vis-it us with
2. Serve you as your hosts a-bove, Pray, and praise you
3. Till in heav'n we take our place, Till we sing be-

1. your sal-va-tion, Let your love in us en-dure.
2. with-out ceas-ing, Glo-ry in your pre-cious love.
3. fore the al-might-y, Lost in won-der, love and praise.

Text: 87 87 D; Charles Wesley, 1707–1788, alt.
Music: HYFRYDOL; Rowland H. Prichard, 1811–1887.

747   HEAR US NOW, OUR GOD AND FATHER

1. Hear us now, our God and Father,
Send your Spirit from above
On this Christian man and woman
Who here make their vows of love!
Bind their hearts in true devotion
Endless as the seashore's sands,
Boundless as the deepest oceans,
Blest and sealed by your own hands.

2. Give them joy to lighten sorrow!
Give them hope to brighten life!
Go with them to face the morrow,
Stay with them in ev'ry strife.

As your Word has promised, ever
Fill them with your strength and grace,
So that each may serve the other
Till they see you face to face.

3. May the grace of Christ, our Savior,
And the Father's boundless love,
With the Holy Spirit's favor
Rest upon them from above.
Thus may they abide in union
With each other and the Lord,
And possess in sweet communion
Joys which earth cannot afford.

Text: 87 87 D; verses 1–2, Harry N. Huxhold, b. 1922, © 1978, *Lutheran Book of Worship*. All rights reserved.
   Reprinted by permission of Augsburg Fortress. Verse 3, John Newton, 1725–1807, alt.
Music: HYFRYDOL; Rowland H. Prichard, 1811–1887.

THERE'S A WIDENESS IN GOD'S MERCY

1. There's a wide-ness in God's mer-cy Like the wide-ness
2. For the love of God is broad-er Than the mea-sures
3. Trou-bled souls, why will you scat-ter Like a crowd of

1. of the sea: There's a kind-ness in God's
2. of our mind; And the heart of the E -
3. fright - ened sheep? Fool - ish hearts! why will you

1. jus - tice Which is more than lib - er - ty.
2. ter - nal Is most won - der - ful - ly kind.
3. wan - der From a love so true and deep?

1. There is plen - ti - ful re - demp - tion In the
2. If our love were but more sim - ple We should
3. There is wel - come for the sin - ner And more

1. blood that has been shed; There is joy for
2. take him at his word; And our lives would
3. grac - es for the good; There is mer - cy

1. all the mem-bers In the sor - rows of the Head.
2. be il - lu - mined By the pres-ence of our Lord.
3. with the Sav - ior, There is heal - ing in his blood.

Text: 87 87 D; Frederick W. Faber, 1814–1863, alt.
Music: IN BABILONE; *Oude en Nieuwe Hollantse Boerenlities en Contradanseu*, ca. 1710.

749

GOD IS LOVE

1. God is Love, let heav'n a - dore him; God is Love, let
2. God is Love; and love en - folds us, All the world in
3. God is Love; and though with blind - ness Sin af - flicts all

1. earth re - joice; Let cre - a - tion sing be - fore him And ex-
2. one em - brace: With un - fail - ing grasp God holds us, Ev - 'ry
3. hu - man life, God's e - ter - nal lov - ing kind - ness Guides us

1. alt him with one voice. God who laid the earth's foun - da - tion,
2. child of ev - 'ry race. And when hu - man hearts are break - ing
3. through our earth - ly strife. Sin and death and hell shall nev - er

1. God who spread the heav'ns a - bove, God who breathes through
2. Un - der sor - row's i - ron rod, Then we find that
3. O'er us fi - nal tri - umph gain; God is Love, so

1. all cre - a - tion: God is Love, e - ter - nal Love.
2. self - same ach - ing Deep with - in the heart of God.
3. Love for ev - er O'er the u - ni - verse must reign.

Text: 87 87 D; Timothy Rees, 1874–1939, alt.
Music: ABBOT'S LEIGH; Cyril Vincent Taylor, 1907–1991, © 1942, renewed 1970, Hope Publishing Co.
   All rights reserved. Used with permission.

750

THE WILL OF YOUR LOVE/TU VOLUNTAD

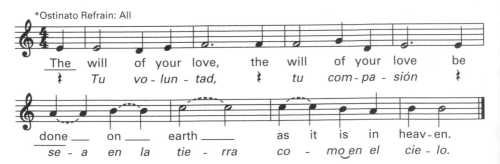

*Ostinato Refrain: All

The will of your love, the will of your love be
Tu vo - lun - tad, tu com - pa - sión

done on earth as it is in heav - en.
se - a en la tie - rra co - mo en el cie - lo.

*Verses available in accompaniment books.

Text: Suggested by Brother Roger, Taizé Community; Suzanne Toolan, RSM, b. 1927;
   Spanish tr. by Pia Moriarty, b. 1948, and Bob Hurd, b. 1950.
Music: Suzanne Toolan, RSM.
Text and music © 1995, Suzanne Toolan, RSM. Published by OCP Publications. All rights reserved.

CHRISTIANS, LET US LOVE ONE ANOTHER

1. Chris-tians, let us love one an-oth-er, As we share the
2. We who break this bread are one bod-y, We who share this
3. We who eat and drink at this ta-ble Die and rise a-
4. On the path of life we may fal-ter, Earth-ly food a-
5. Wheat and grape in-car-nate a mys-t'ry: Je-sus is the
6. Je-sus is the vine, we the branch-es; We are grains of

1. true liv-ing bread. Je-sus is our God and our
2. cup are all one. Chil-dren of our Fa-ther in
3. gain with our Lord. Draw-ing from our Rock liv-ing
4. lone leaves us weak; Al-ways you in-vite from the
5. true liv-ing bread. Let us eat with joy and thanks-
6. wheat, Christ the bread. Those who eat this bread live for-

1. broth-er; With his flesh and blood we are fed.
2. heav-en, We are heirs with God's on-ly son.
3. wa-ter Giv'n to all who thirst for ac-cord.
4. al-tar, "Hun-gry souls their food here must seek."
5. giv-ing, Trust-ing in the word he has said.
6. ev-er, One with Christ, our Lord and our Head.

Ev-'ry-one who

1-6. loves is born of God. Je-sus is our life. God is love.

Text: 98 98 98; Claudia Foltz, SNJM, and Armand Nigro, SJ, b. 1928, © 1973, Claudia Foltz, SNJM, and Armand Nigro, SJ.
Published by OCP Publications. All rights reserved.
Music: PICARDY; French Carol, 17th cent.; *Chansons populaires des Provinces de France*, 1860.

LOVE ONE ANOTHER

*Refrain
Love one an-oth-er as I have loved you. Care for each
oth-er. I have cared for you. Bear each oth-er's bur-dens.
Bind each oth-er's wounds; and so you will know my re-turn.

*Verses available in accompaniment books.

Text: Based on John 14–16, I Corinthians 13; Bob Dufford, SJ, b. 1943.
Music: Bob Dufford, SJ.
Text and music © 1987, Robert J. Dufford, SJ. Published by OCP Publications. All rights reserved.

UBI CARITAS/
WHERE TRUE CHARITY AND LOVE DWELL

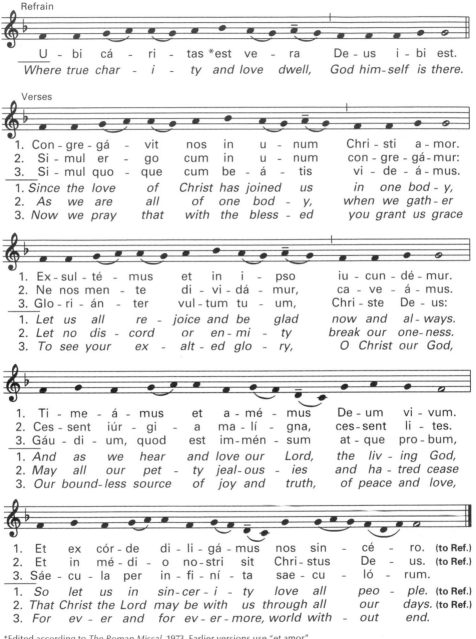

Refrain

1. U - bi cá - ri - tas *est ve - ra De - us i - bi est.
Where true char - i - ty and love dwell, God him-self is there.

Verses

1. Con - gre - gá - vit nos in u - num Chri - sti a - mor.
2. Si - mul er - go cum in u - num con - gre - gá-mur:
3. Si - mul quo - que cum be - á - tis vi - de - á - mus.
1. *Since the love of Christ has joined us in one bod - y,*
2. *As we are all of one bod - y, when we gath - er*
3. *Now we pray that with the bless - ed you grant us grace*

1. Ex - sul - té - mus et in i - pso iu - cun - dé - mur.
2. Ne nos men - te di - vi - dá - mur, ca - ve - á - mus.
3. Glo - ri - án - ter vul - tum tu - um, Chri - ste De - us:
1. *Let us all re - joice and be glad now and al - ways.*
2. *Let no dis - cord or en - mi - ty break our one-ness.*
3. *To see your ex - alt - ed glo - ry, O Christ our God,*

1. Ti - me - á - mus et a - mé - mus De - um vi - vum.
2. Ces - sent iúr - gi - a ma - lí - gna, ces-sent li - tes.
3. Gáu - di - um, quod est im-mén - sum at - que pro - bum,
1. *And as we hear and love our Lord, the liv - ing God,*
2. *May all our pet - ty jeal-ous - ies and ha - tred cease*
3. *Our bound-less source of joy and truth, of peace and love,*

1. Et ex cór - de di - li - gá - mus nos sin - cé - ro. **(to Ref.)**
2. Et in mé - di - o no-stri sit Chri - stus De - us. **(to Ref.)**
3. Sáe - cu - la per in - fi - ní - ta sae - cu - ló - rum.
1. *So let us in sin-cer - i - ty love all peo - ple.* **(to Ref.)**
2. *That Christ the Lord may be with us through all our days.* **(to Ref.)**
3. *For ev - er and for ev - er - more, world with - out end.*

*Edited according to *The Roman Missal*, 1973. Earlier versions use "et amor".

Text: 12 12 12 12 with refrain; Latin, 9th cent.; tr. by Joyce MacDonald Glover, b. 1923, © 1982, Joyce M. Glover.
All rights reserved. Used with permission.
Music: UBI CARITAS; Chant, Mode VI.

Ubi Caritas

Refrain

U - bi ca - ri - tas et a - mor, De - us i - bi est. est.

Verses 1, 3

1. We gath - er to - geth - er
Our God is a - live, the
3. Then, joined with the bless - ed,
Our joy none can mea - sure,

1. in the love of Christ;
God of love is near;
3. filled with hope and grace,
joy that knows no end,

let each one be
so love one an -
dear Lord, in great
re - sound-ing from

1. glad in him _____ and re - joice.
oth - er with a heart sin - cere. (to Refrain)
3. glo - ry may we see your face.
end - less age to age. A - men. (to Refrain)

Verse 2

2. We, the man - y, be - come one bod - y
Let all quar - rels, all di - vi - sion,

2. as the Spir - it binds,
all our con - flict cease;

and we seek to be
then will Christ tru - ly

2. one in Christ and one in heart and mind.
dwell a - mong us as our Lord of Peace. (to Refrain)

Text: Adapt. fr. *Holy Thursday Liturgy;* Laurence Rosania, b. 1957.
Music: Laurence Rosania.
Text and music © 1992, Laurence Rosania. Published by OCP Publications. All rights reserved.

755   WHAT WONDROUS LOVE IS THIS

1. What won-drous love is this, O my soul, O my
2. What won-drous love is this, O my soul, O my
3. To God and to the Lamb I will sing, I will
4. And when from death I'm free, I'll sing on, I'll sing

1. soul? What won-drous love is this, O my soul? What
2. soul? What won-drous love is this, O my soul? What
3. sing; To God and to the Lamb, I will sing; To
4. on; And when from death I'm free, I'll sing on; And

1. won-drous love is this that caused the Lord of
2. won-drous love is this that caused the Lord of
3. God and to the Lamb, who is the great I
4. when from death I'm free, I'll sing and joy - ful

1. bliss To bear the dread-ful curse for my soul, for my
2. bliss To send this pre-cious peace to my soul, to my
3. AM, While mil - lions join the theme, I will sing, I will
4. be, And through e - ter - ni - ty, I'll sing on, I'll sing

1. soul, To bear the dread-ful curse for my soul?
2. soul, To send this pre-cious peace to my soul?
3. sing; While mil - lions join the theme, I will sing.
4. on! And through e - ter - ni - ty, I'll sing on.

Text: 12 9 12 12 9; anon.; first appeared in *A General Selection of the Newest and Most Admired Hymns and Spiritual Songs*, 1811, adapt.
Music: WONDROUS LOVE; William Walker's *The Southern Harmony*, 1835.

756   WHERE CHARITY AND LOVE PREVAIL

1. Where char - i - ty and love pre - vail, There God is ev - er found;
2. With grate-ful joy and ho - ly fear God's char - i - ty we learn;
3. For - give we now each oth-er's faults As we our faults con - fess;
4. Let strife a - mong us be un-known, Let all con - ten - tion cease;
5. Let us re - call that in our midst Dwells God's be - got - ten Son;
6. No race nor creed can love ex - clude, If hon - ored be God's name;

1. Brought here to-geth-er by Christ's love, By love are we thus bound.
2. Let us with heart and mind and soul Now love God in re-turn.
3. And let us love each oth-er well In Chris-tian ho-li-ness.
4. Be God's the glo-ry that we seek, Be ours God's ho-ly peace.
5. As mem-bers of his bod-y joined, We are in Christ made one.
6. Our fam-i-ly em-brac-es all Whose Fa-ther is the same.

Text: CM; *Ubi Caritas,* 9th cent.; tr. by Omer Westendorf, 1916–1997.
Music: CHRISTIAN LOVE; Paul Benoit, OSB, 1893–1979.

IN PERFECT CHARITY 757

1. O most high and glo-rious God, cast your light in-to
2. O most high and glo-rious God, o-pen wide the door
3. Then most high and thank-ful praise I will sing un-to

1. the dark-ness of my heart. Give me right faith, and cer-tain
2. that leads me to your love. Give me your firm, yet gen-tle
3. the glo-ry of your name: To Fa-ther, Son, and Spir-it

1. hope, and perfect, perfect char-i-ty. Give me true
2. strength; may I live that per-fect char-i-ty. Lord, may your
3. bright, Liv-ing Pres-ence, Per-fect Char-i-ty. Praise to the

1. in-sight, Lord, and wis-dom, that I may al-ways live with-
2. peace be ev-er in me, that I may al-ways seek to
3. Love that shines in splen-dor, that lights the path-ways of my

1. in your ev-er ho-ly will. Lord, may your light with-
2. serve your chil-dren here on earth; that I may find my
3. heart, and brings me close to you. O Ho-ly One, in-

1. in me burn, shin-ing out in per-fect char-i-ty.
2. home with you, and live in per-fect char-i-ty.
3. vite me in, where you live in per-fect char-i-ty.

Text: Verse 1 based on a prayer of St. Francis of Assisi, 1182–1226; verses 2–3, Randall DeBruyn, b. 1947.
Music: Randall DeBruyn.

758   THOSE WHO LOVE AND THOSE WHO LABOR

1. Those who love and those who la - bor Fol - low
2. Where the man - y work to - geth - er, They with
3. Let the seek - er nev - er fal - ter Till the

1. in the way of Christ; Thus the first dis - ci - ples
2. Christ him - self a - bide, But the lone - ly work - ers
3. truth is found a - far With the wis - dom of the

1. found him, Thus the gift of love suf - ficed.
2. al - so Find him ev - er at their side.
3. a - ges Un - der - neath a gi - ant star,

1. Je - sus says to those who seek him, I will
2. Lo, the Prince of com - mon wel - fare Dwells with -
3. With the rich - est and the poor - est, Of the

1. nev - er pass you by; Raise the stone and you shall
2. in the mar - ket strife; Lo, the bread of heav'n is
3. sum of things pos - sessed, Like a child at first to

1. find me; Cleave the wood, and there am I.
2. bro - ken In the sac - ra - ment of life.
3. won - der, Like a king at last to rest.

Text: 87 87 D; *Songs of Praise*, 1931, 1959; Geoffrey Dearmer, 1893–1996, © Oxford University Press.
All rights reserved. Used with permission.
Music: NETTLETON; J. Wyeth's *Repository of Sacred Music*, Part II, 1813.

759   JOURNEYSONG

*1. On this new day may we be gath - ered In the
2. Com - pan - ions on our pil - grim jour - ney, Spir - it -
3. Do not our hearts burn deep with - in us As we
4. From strength to strength, from cross to glo - ry, Lead us,

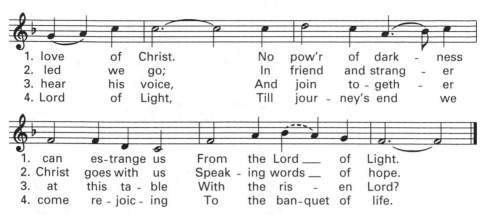

1. love of Christ. No pow'r of dark - ness
2. led we go; In friend and strang - er
3. hear his voice, And join to - geth - er
4. Lord of Light, Till jour - ney's end we

1. can es-trange us From the Lord ___ of Light.
2. Christ goes with us Speak - ing words ___ of hope.
3. at this ta - ble With the ris - en Lord?
4. come re - joic - ing To the ban-quet of life.

*Alternate text for use at Evening Prayer/Mass: *As evening falls may we be gathered....* (at Evening Prayer omit verse 3).

Text: 95 95; based on Luke 24; Bob Hurd, b. 1950, © 1996, Bob Hurd. Published by OCP Publications. All rights reserved.
Music: LAND OF REST; Trad. American Melody.

UNLESS A GRAIN OF WHEAT   760

Refrain

Un-less a grain of wheat shall fall up-on the ground and die,

it re-mains but a sin-gle grain with no life.

Verses

1. If we have died with him, then we shall live with him;
2. If an - y one serves ___ me, then they must fol - low me;
3. Make your home in me as I make mine in you;
4. If you re - main in me and my word lives in you,
5. Those who love me are loved by my Fa - ther;
6. Peace I leave with you, my peace I give to you;

to Refrain

1. if we hold firm, we shall reign with him. ___
2. wher - ev - er I am, my ser - vants will be.
3. those who re - main in me bear much fruit. ___
4. then you will be my dis - ci - ples. ___
5. we shall be with them and dwell in them. ___
6. peace which the world can - not give is my gift.

Text: Based on Psalm 12:24; Bernadette Farrell, b. 1957.
Music: Bernadette Farrell.
Text and music © 1983, Bernadette Farrell. Published by OCP Publications. All rights reserved.

ANTHEM

Refrain

We are called, we are cho-sen. We are Christ for one an-oth-er. We are

prom-ised to to-mor-row, while we are for him to-day. We are

sign, we are won-der. We are sow-er, we are seed. We are

har-vest, we are hun-ger. We are ques-tion, we are creed.

Verses

1. Then where can we stand jus-ti-fied?_ In what can we be-lieve? In no one
2. Then how are we to stand at all,_ this world of bend-ed knee? In noth-ing
3. Then shall we not stand emp-ty_ at the al-tar of our dreams:_ When he

1. else but he who suf-fered, noth-ing more than he who rose.
2. more than bar-ren shad-ows. No one else but he could save us.
3. prom-ised us our-selves. _ Who mark time a-gainst to-mor-row.

1, 2. Who was jus-tice for the poor. Who was rage a-gainst the night.
3. Who are jus-tice for the poor. Who are rage a-gainst the night.

to Refrain

1, 2. Who was hope for peace-ful peo-ple. Who was light.
3. Who are hope for peace-ful peo-ple. Who are light.

ALL THAT IS HIDDEN

1. If you would fol-low me, fol-low where life will lead: ___
2. If you would hon-or me, hon-or the least of these: ___
3. If you would speak of me, live all your life in me: ___
4. If you would rise with me, rise through your des-ti-ny: ___

1. ___ do not look for me a-mong the dead, for I am
2. ___ you will not find me dressed in fin-er-y. My Word cries
3. ___ my ways are not the ways that you would choose; my thoughts are
4. ___ do not re-fuse the death which brings you life, for as the

1. hid-den in pain, ___ ris-en in love; there is no
2. out to be heard; ___ breaks through the world: my Word is
3. far be-yond yours, ___ as heav-en from earth: if you be-
4. grain in the earth ___ must die for re-birth, so I have

Refrain

1. har-vest with-out sow-ing of grain. All that is hid-den
2. on your lips and lives in your heart.
3. lieve in me my voice will be heard.
4. plant-ed your life deep with-in mine.

will be made clear. All that is dark now will be re-vealed.

What you have heard in the dark pro-claim in the light; what you

hear in whis-pers pro-claim from the house-tops.

Text: Refrain based on Luke 12:2–3; Bernadette Farrell, b. 1957.
Music: Bernadette Farrell.

763 PESCADOR DE HOMBRES/LORD, YOU HAVE COME

Estrofas/Verses

1. Tú has ve-ni-do a la o-ri-lla, no has bus-ca-do
2. Tú sa-bes bien lo que ten-go; en mi bar-ca
3. Tú ne-ce-si-tas mis ma-nos, mi can-san-cio
4. Tú, pes-ca-dor de o-tros la-gos, an-sia e-ter-na

1. *Lord, you have come to the sea-shore, nei-ther search-ing for*
2. *Lord, see my goods, my pos-ses-sions; in my boat you find*
3. *Lord, take my hands and di-rect them. Help me spend my-self*
4. *Lord, as I drift on the wa-ters, be the rest-ing place*

1. ni a sa-bios ni a ri-cos; _____ tan só-lo quie-res
2. no hay o-ro ni es-pa-das, _____ tan só-lo re-des
3. que a o-tros des-can-se, _____ a-mor que quie-ra
4. de al-mas que es-pe-ran, _____ a-mi-go bue-no,

1. *the rich nor the wise, _____ de-sir-ing on-ly*
2. *no pow-er, no wealth. _____ Will you ac-cept, then,*
3. *in seek-ing the lost, _____ re-turn-ing love for*
4. *of my rest-less heart, _____ my life's com-pan-ion,*

Estribillo/Refrain

1. que yo te si-ga.
2. y mi tra-ba-jo.
3. se-guir a-man-do.
4. que a-sí me lla-mas.

1. *that I should fol-low.*
2. *my nets and la-bor?*
3. *the love you gave me.*
4. *my friend and ref-uge.*

Se-ñor, me has mi-ra-do a los

O Lord, with your eyes set up-

_____ o-jos, son-ri-en-do _____ has di-cho mi

on me, gent-ly smil-ing, _____ you have spo-ken my

nom-bre, _____ en la a-re-na he de-ja-do mi bar-ca,

name; _____ all I longed for I have found by the wa-ter,

jun-to a ti bus-ca-ré o-tro mar.

at your side, I will seek oth-er shores.

LORD OF THE DANCE

Verses

1. I danced in the morn-ing when the world was be-gun, And I
2. I danced for the scribe _ and the Phar - i - see, But they
3. I danced on the Sab-bath and I cured the _ lame, The _
4. I danced on a Fri-day when the sky turned _ black; It's _
5. They cut me _ down _ and I leapt up _ high, _____

1. danced in the moon and the stars _ and the sun, And I
2. would not _ dance and they would-n't fol - low me; I _
3. ho - ly _ peo - ple, they said it was a shame; They _
4. hard to _ dance with the dev - il on your back; They _
5. I am the life that - 'll nev - er, nev - er die, I'll _

1. came down from heav-en and I danced on the earth, ___ At
2. danced for the fish - er-men, for James and for John; ___ They
3. whipped and they stripped _ and they hung me _ high, And they
4. bur - ied my bod-y and they thought I'd _ gone, ___ But
5. live in ____ you _ if you'll live in _ me; _____

Refrain

1. Beth - le - hem I _ had my birth. "Dance, then wher-
2. came with _ me and the dance went on.
3. left me _ there on a cross to die.
4. I am the dance and I still go on.
5. "I am the Lord of the Dance," said he.

ev - er you may be. I am the Lord of the Dance," said he. "I'll

lead you all wher-ev-er you may be, I will lead you all in the

1-4 | **to Verses** | **Final**

Dance," said he. Dance," said he.

Text: Irregular with refrain; adapt. by Sydney B. Carter, 1915–1982.
Music: LORD OF THE DANCE; Shaker Melody, 19th cent.; adapt. by Sydney B. Carter.

OUT OF DARKNESS

Refrain

Out of dark-ness God has called us, claimed by Christ as God's own peo-ple. Ho-ly na-tion, roy-al priest-hood, walk-ing in God's

1. mar-v'lous light.
2-4. mar-v'lous light.
to Verses 2
Final mar-v'lous light. A - men.

Verses

1. Let us take the words you give. Strong and faith-ful words to live.
2. Let us take the Christ you give. Bro - ken Bod - y, Christ we live.
3. Let us take the love you give, that the way of love we live.

to Refrain

1. Words that in our hearts are sown; words that bind us as your own.
2. Christ the ris - en from the tomb; Christ, who calls us as your own.
3. Love to bring your peo - ple home; love to make us all your own.

Text and music: Christopher Walker, b. 1947, © 1989, Christopher Walker. Published by OCP Publications. All rights reserved.

766 ONLY THIS I WANT

Refrain

On-ly this I want: but to know the Lord,

and to bear his cross, so to wear the crown he wore.

Verses

1. All but this is loss, worth-less ref - use to me,
2. I will run the race; I will fight the good fight,
3. Let your heart be glad, al - ways glad in the Lord,

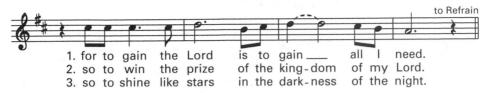

1. for to gain the Lord is to gain___ all I need.
2. so to win the prize of the king-dom of my Lord.
3. so to shine like stars in the dark-ness of the night.

Text: Based on Philippians 3:7–16; 2:15, 18; Dan Schutte, b. 1947.
Music: Dan Schutte.
Text and music © 1981, Daniel L. Schutte and New Dawn Music. Published by OCP Publications. All rights reserved.

Now Is the Time

767

Refrain

Come to us, you who say, "I will not for-get you." Be with us, you who say, "Do not be a-fraid." Take hold of us, our hearts, our minds, our whole be - ing. Make us your own, now is the time.

Verses

Cantor   All
1. Spir - it of love, crush the pain of ha - tred.
2. Spir - it of peace, si - lence tongues of an - ger.
3. Spir - it of faith, rise a - bove our doubt-ing.

Cantor   All   Cantor
1. Spir-it of hope, stand be - fore our eyes. Spir-it of light,
2. Spir-it of life, break the chains of death. Spir-it of joy,
3. Spir-it of truth, save us from our lies. Spir-it of God,

All   to Refrain
1. dance with-in our dark-ness. Make us your own, now is the time.
2.   o - ver-come our sad-ness. Make us your own, now is the time.
3. walk a-mong your peo - ple. Make us your own, now is the time.

*Last time, repeat final phrase twice.

Text and music: Tom Kendzia, b. 1954, © 1998, Tom Kendzia. Published by OCP Publications. All rights reserved.

768

SENT FORTH BY GOD'S BLESSING

1. Sent forth by God's bless-ing, our true faith con - fess-ing, The
2. With praise and thanks - giv - ing, to God who is liv - ing, The

_ God's sac - ri - fice end - ed, O now be ex - tend-ed The
Our faith ev - er shar-ing, in love ev - er car-ing, We

1. peo-ple of God from his dwell-ing take leave.
_ fruits of this Mass in all hearts who be - lieve. The seed of his
2. tasks of our ev - 'ry-day life we em-brace.
claim as our neigh-bor all those of each race. One bread that has

1. teach-ing our in - ner souls reach-ing, Shall blos-som in ac-tion for
2. fed us, one light that has led us U - nite us as one in his

1. God and for all. His grace shall in - cite us, his love shall u -
2. life that we share. Then may all the liv-ing with praise and thanks-

1. nite us To fur-ther God's king-dom and an-swer his call.
2. giv-ing Give hon - or to Christ and his name that we bear.

769

JESUS, OUR DIVINE COMPANION

1. Je - sus, our di - vine com-pan-ion, By your low - ly hu - man
2. All who tread the path of la - bor Fol-low where your feet have
3. Ev - 'ry task, how - ev - er hum-ble, Fills the soul with grace a -

1. birth You have come to join all work-ers, Bur-den-bear-ers
2. trod; All who work with - out com-plain-ing Do the ho - ly
3. new; Ev - 'ry deed of love and kind-ness Done in faith is

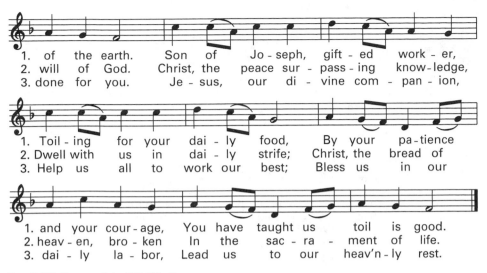

1. of the earth. Son of Jo-seph, gift-ed work-er,
2. will of God. Christ, the peace sur-pass-ing know-ledge,
3. done for you. Je-sus, our di-vine com-pan-ion,

1. Toil-ing for your dai-ly food, By your pa-tience
2. Dwell with us in dai-ly strife; Christ, the bread of
3. Help us all to work our best; Bless us in our

1. and your cour-age, You have taught us toil is good.
2. heav-en, bro-ken In the sac-ra-ment of life.
3. dai-ly la-bor, Lead us to our heav'n-ly rest.

Text: 87 87 D; Henry van Dyke, 1852–1933, alt.
Music: PLEADING SAVIOR; *Christian Lyre*, 1830.

Come Unto Me 770

Refrain

Come, come un-to me; I will make you a jew-el.

Pre-cious and rare the glo-ry you'll bear in the crown of

Verses

God. 1. There are deeds you a-lone must do; there are
2. From the dawn of cre-a-tion, from the

1. words on-ly you can say. Trust in me, and do not trem-
2. tree on __ Cal-va-ry, I chose you and gave my life __

to Refrain

1. ble, for I go with you to show you the way.
2. __ to be my own, __ to be my de-light.

Text: Based on Isaiah 62 and Matthew 11:28–30; Bob Hurd, b. 1950.
Music: Bob Hurd.

771 WHERE TWO OR THREE HAVE GATHERED

1. Where ___ two or three have gath - ered, You have prom-ised
2. By the life you lived a - mong us, You have taught us
3. Through the clear bap - tis - mal wa - ters, You have claimed us
4. As the dark - ness falls a - round us With the com - ing
5. As the blaz - ing sky at sun - rise Speaks the glo - ry

1. to be there. In your prom-ise, we have gath - ered, Trust-ing
2. how to live. By your mer - cy and com - pas - sion, You have
3. as your own. We are one in you for - ev - er, Nev - er
4. of the night, On - ly dim - ly can we see the path And we
5. of your name, Let our lives de - clare your glo - ry And the

1. in your love and care. You have called us in - to your
2. taught us to for - give. By your jus - tice, Lord, you have
3. strang-ers or a - lone. In your love and truth we are
4. hun - ger for your light. You have set the stars in the
5. cov - e - nant we claim. Make us brave and faith - ful a -

1. pres-ence; Turn our hearts and minds to you That to - geth - er
2. shown us What the reign of God must be. By your cross and
3. nur - tured As a seed-ling grows and thrives. From our wak - ing
4. heav - ens And the ra - diant moon as sign. You will guide us
5. pos - tles; Give us vi - sion clear and true. Pour us out like

1. we may gath-er strength For what you would have us do.
2. res - ur - rec - tion, You have set your peo - ple free.
3. to our sleep - ing, We will praise you with our lives.
4. through our dark - ness. We will see your glo - ry shine.
5. liv - ing wa - ter Un - til all are one in you.

Text: 87 87 97 87; M.D. Ridge.
Music: MEADOWBROOK; M.D. Ridge.
Text and music © 1994, 1997, M.D. Ridge. Published by OCP Publications. All rights reserved.

'TIS THE GIFT TO BE SIMPLE

1. 'Tis the gift to be sim-ple, 'tis the gift to be free, 'Tis the gift to
2. 'Tis the gift to be gen-tle, 'tis the gift to be fair, 'Tis the gift to
3. 'Tis the gift to be lov-ing, 'tis the gift best of all, Like a qui-et

1. come down where you ought to be, And when we find our-selves in the
2. wake and breathe the morn-ing air; And ev-'ry day to walk in the
3. rain, it bless-es where it falls; And if we have the gift, we will

1. place just __ right __ 'Twill be in the val-ley of love and de-light.
2. path we __ choose, 'Tis the gift that we pray we may ne'er come to lose.
3. tru-ly be-lieve __ 'Tis bet-ter to give than it is to re-ceive.

Refrain

When true sim-plic-i-ty is gained, To bow and to bend we

shan't be a-shamed; To turn, turn will be our de-light, Till by

turn-ing, turn-ing we come 'round right.

Text: Irregular with refrain; Shaker Song, 18th cent. Verses 2–3, Joyce Merman, © 1975 (renewed), Shawnee Press, Inc.
   All rights reserved. Used with permission.
Music: SIMPLE GIFTS; Shaker Melody, 18th cent.

WE LIVE NOT FOR OURSELVES

773

We live not for our-selves. We die not for our-selves. We live and we

die for our God and Lord, to whom a-lone we be-long.

Text: Based on Romans 14:7–8; Huub Oosterhuis, b. 1933; tr. by Tony Barr, b. 1945 and James Hansen, b. 1937.
Music: Floris van der Putt, 1915–1990; adapt. by Bernard Huijbers, b. 1922.
Text and music © 1967, 1996, Gooi en Sticht, bv., Baarn, The Netherlands. All rights reserved.
   Exclusive agent for English language countries: OCP Publications.

HOLY WISDOM, LAMP OF LEARNING

1. Ho-ly Wis-dom, lamp of learn-ing, Bless the light that
2. Vine of truth, in you we flour-ish; By your grace we
3. Ho-ly God, the hope of na-tions, Tune us toward your

1. rea-son lends. Teach us judg-ment as we kin-dle Sparks of
2. learn and grow. May the word of Christ a-mong us Shape our
3. righ-teous will, As the sym-pho-ny of a-ges Claims our

1. thought your Spir-it sends. Sanc-ti-fy our search for knowl-edge
2. life, our search to know. Joined to Christ in liv-ing, dy-ing,
3. best, our fin-est skill. Shape our search for peace and jus-tice

1. And the truth that sets us free. Come, il-lu-mine
2. May we help the church con-vey Wit-ness to the
3. Through pro-phet-ic deed and word. Christ, con-duct us,

1. mind and spir-it Joined in deep-est u-ni-ty.
2. sav-ing gos-pel, Bear-ing fruit of faith to-day.
3. set our rhy-thm, That God's praise be ev-er heard.

Text: 87 87 D; Ruth C. Duck, b. 1947, © 1996, The Pilgrim Press. All rights reserved. Used with permission.
Music: BEACH SPRING; *The Sacred Harp*, 1844.

775

I WILL CHOOSE CHRIST

Refrain

I will choose Christ, I will choose love, I choose to serve.

I give my heart, I give my life, I give my all

1-3 to Verses | Final

to you.   to you.   I give my all to you.

1. How man-y times must he call my name and show to
1. me that he is God? And as a ser-vant he
to Refrain
1. calls to me, you must serve too.

Verse 2
2. Christ, my teach - er and heal - er, teach my
2. heart and heal my soul. And as I walk this
to Refrain
2. road with you, teach me to love.

Verse 3
3. As I look up-on your cross, so too
3. must I die with you. And with the death of my
to Refrain
3. own de - sires, I'll rise with you.

GREAT IS THE POWER WE PROCLAIM

Refrain

Great is the pow-er we pro-claim, now, as we wor-ship and
praise God's name. For the glo-ry of God is re-vealed when we pray:
"Come Lord!" Come Lord, and live in us to-day.

Verses

1. God's peo-ple, called to serve as dis-
2. God's peo-ple, called to bring to the
3. God's peo-ple, called to pray for the
4. God's peo-ple, called to - day to make
5. God's peo-ple, called to share in the

1. ci - ples of the Lord. Gifts of the
2. world the peace of Christ. Love for our
3. church to be made one: one ho - ly
4. known the love of God. Seeds we are
5. bless - ing cup of Christ: bread that is

1. Spir - it are gifts we in - her - it to
2. neigh - bor, and jus - tice in our la - bor, com -
3. na - tion in hope of sal - va - tion,
4. sow - ing with faith that is grow - ing
5. bro - ken, and word that is spo - ken,

to Refrain

1. build up the bod - y of Christ.
2. pelled by the love of Christ.
3. broth - ers and sis - ters in Christ.
4. strong in the pow - er of Christ.
5. one in the bod - y of Christ.

GATHER AND REMEMBER

1. Now is the time to gath-er and re-mem-ber
2. This was our call, so clear and so in - vit - ing:
3. And so a - rose from ev - 'ry town and vil - lage
4. Al-might-y God, re - vis - it your cre - a - tion.

1. Our si - lent past, in church a voice - less throng,
2. "Come and cre - ate a new and liv - ing voice.
3. Wom - en and men in won-drous har - mo - ny
4. In - still new life in hearts both old and young.

1. Fro - zen in time as in a cold De-cem - ber,
2. Be not a - fraid! God's spir - it is en-light-'ning
3. Sing-ing the song with long-lost hope and cour - age,
4. O Je - sus Christ, re - new in us the vis - ion:

1. Un - til that won - drous shep-herd came a - long,
2. All that you do, your ev - 'ry fal - t'ring choice.
3. Rais - ing a - gain the cross for all to see,
4. A world where peace and jus - tice can be - long.

1. Who said, "A - rise! Come, fan the dy - ing em - ber
2. Your song will be trans-form-ing and u - nit - ing.
3. Sign of new hope, new life and new be - gin-nings,
4. O Spir - it Blest, fill ev - 'ry land and na - tion.

1. And bring to life my peo-ple's prayer and song!"
2. You are God's gift— in you we all re - joice!"
3. Sign of the Christ who came to set us free.
4. Come, re - cre - ate in us God's liv - ing song!

Text: 11 10 11 10 11 10; Owen Alstott, b. 1947, © 2001, Owen Alstott. Published by OCP Publications. All rights reserved.
Music: FINLANDIA; Jean Sibelius, 1865–1957.

ONE SPIRIT, ONE CHURCH

Refrain

We are a pil-grim peo-ple, we are the Church of God. A fam-'ly of be-liev-ers, dis-ci-ples of the Lord. U-nit-ed in one spir-it, ig-nit-ed by the fire. Still burn-ing through the a-ges, still pres-ent in our lives. lives. A - men!

1, 2 to Vss | Final | Verses

1. Come, Ho-ly Ghost, Cre-a-tor
2. O Com-fort-er, to thee we

1. blest, and in our hearts take up thy rest; come with thy
2. cry, thou gift of God sent from on high. Thou font of

to Refrain

1. grace and heav'n-ly aid to fill the hearts which thou hast made.
2. life and fire of love, the soul's a-noint-ing from a-bove.

Text: Refrain, Maryanne Quinlivan, OSU, © 1990, Ursuline Academy of Cleveland. Published by OCP Publications.
All rights reserved. Verses fr. *Veni, Creator Spiritus*; attr. to Rabanus Maurus, 776–856; tr. by Edward Caswall, 1814–1878, alt.
Music: Refrain, Kevin Keil, ASCAP, b. 1956; verses based on LAMBILLOTTE, © 1990, Kevin Keil.
Published by OCP Publications. All rights reserved.

779 THE CHURCH'S ONE FOUNDATION

1. The Chur-ch's one foun-da-tion Is Je-sus Christ her Lord;
2. E-lect from ev-'ry na-tion, Yet one o'er all the earth,
3. 'Mid toil and trib-u-la-tion, And tu-mult of her war,
4. Yet she on earth hath un-ion With God, the Three-in-One,

1. She is his new cre-a-tion By wa-ter and the word:
2. Her char-ter of sal-va-tion, "One Lord, one faith, one birth!"
3. She waits the con-sum-ma-tion Of peace for-ev-er-more,
4. And with the saints, com-mun-ion With those whose rest is won.

1. From heav'n he came and sought her To be his ho - ly bride;
2. One ho - ly Name she bless - es, Par - takes one ho - ly food,
3. Till with the vi - sion glo - rious Her long - ing eyes are blest,
4. O hap - py ones and ho - ly! Lord, give us grace that we

1. With his own blood he bought her, And for her life he died.
2. And to one hope she press - es With ev - 'ry grace en - dued.
3. And the great Church vic - to - rious Shall be the Church at rest.
4. Like them, the meek and low - ly, On high may dwell with thee.

Text: 76 76 D; Samuel J. Stone, 1839–1900.
Music: AURELIA; Samuel S. Wesley, 1810–1876.

CHRIST IS MADE THE SURE FOUNDATION 780

1. Christ is made the sure foun - da - tion, Christ, the head and
2. To this tem - ple, where we call you, Come, O Lord of
3. Grant, we pray, to all your peo - ple, All the grace they
4. Praise and hon - or to the Fa - ther, Praise and hon - or

1. cor - ner - stone; Cho - sen of the Lord, and pre - cious,
2. hosts, to - day; With your wont - ed lov - ing kind - ness,
3. ask to gain; What they gain from you for ev - er
4. to the Son, Praise and hon - or to the Spir - it,

1. Bind - ing all the Church in one, Ho - ly Si - on's
2. Hear your ser - vants as they pray, And your ful - lest
3. With the bless - ed to re - tain, And here - af - ter
4. Ev - er three and ev - er one, One in might and

1. help for ev - er, And her con - fi - dence a - lone.
2. ben - e - dic - tion, Shed in all its bright - est ray.
3. in your glo - ry, Ev - er-more with you to reign.
4. one in glo - ry, While un - end - ing a - ges run.

Text: 87 87 87; *Angularis fundamentum*, 11th cent.; tr. by John M. Neale, 1818–1866, alt.
Music: WESTMINSTER ABBEY; Henry Purcell, 1659–1695.

SINGING SONGS OF EXPECTATION

1. Sing-ing songs of ex - pec - ta - tion, On-ward goes the
2. One the light of God's own pres - ence, O'er his ran-somed
3. One the strain the lips of thou - sands Lift as from the

1. pil - grim band, Through the night of doubt and sor - row,
2. peo - ple shed, Chas - ing far the gloom and ter - ror,
3. heart of one; One the con - flict, one the per - il,

1. March - ing to the prom-ised land. Clear be - fore us through the
2. Bright-'ning all the path we tread: One the ob - ject of our
3. One the march in God be - gun: One the glad-ness of re -

1. dark-ness Gleams and burns the guid - ing light: Trust-ing God we
2. jour - ney, One the faith which nev - er tires, One the ear-nest
3. joic - ing On the far e - ter - nal shore, Where the one al -

1. march to - geth - er Step-ping fear - less through the night.
2. look - ing for - ward, One the hope our God in - spires.
3. might - y Fa - ther Reigns in love for ev - er-more.

Text: 87 87 D; Bernard Severin Ingeman, 1798–1862; tr. Sabin Baring-Gould, 1834–1924, alt.
Music: HOLY MANNA; William Moore's *The Columbian Harmony,* 1825.

BLESSED FEASTS OF BLESSED MARTYRS 782

1. Bless - ed feasts of bless-ed mar-tyrs, Ho - ly wom - en,
2. Faith pre - vail-ing, hope un - fail-ing, Lov - ing Christ with
3. There-fore, all that reign in glo - ry, Faith-ful heirs with

1. ho - ly men, With our love and ad - mi - ra-tion, Greet we
2. sin - gle heart, Thus they, glo-rious and vic - to-rious, Brave-ly
3. Christ on high, Join to ours your sup-pli - ca-tion When be -

1. your re - turn a - gain. Wor-thy deeds they wrought, and won-ders,
2. bore the mar - tyr's part, By con-tempt of ev - 'ry an-guish,
3. fore Christ we draw nigh, Pray-ing that, this life com-plet - ed,

1. Wor - thy of the name they bore; We, with joy - ful
2. By un - yield-ing bat - tle done; Vic - tors at the
3. All its fleet-ing mo-ments past, By Christ's grace we

1. praise and sing - ing, Hon - or them for ev - er - more.
2. last, they tri - umph, With the host of an - gels one.
3. may be wor - thy Of e - ter - nal bliss at last.

Text: 87 87 D; *O beata beatorum*, 11th cent.; tr. by John M. Neale, 1818–1866, alt.
Music: IN BABILONE; *Oude en Nieuwe Hollanste Boerenlities*, ca. 1710.

SING WE NOW THE GLORIOUS MARTYRS 783

1. Sing we now the glorious martyrs,
Faithful, fallen, raised on high.
Strong they stood, in ranks of courage,
Loath to live if truth must die.
Grant to us, O God, their wisdom
That could dare to choose the cross,
Christ their one and only treasure,
All else, even life, no loss.

2. Keep alight upon our hilltops
Lamps like these, set high apart,
Flames of faith no night can vanquish,
Beacons for the faint of heart.
Let them burn with such an ardor
That the very dark must quail.
Before love so all-consuming
Death itself cannot prevail.

Text: 87 87 D; Genevieve Glen, OSB, b. 1945, © 1999, 2001, The Benedictine Nuns of the Abbey of St. Walburga.
Published by OCP Publications. All rights reserved.
Music: IN BABILONE; *Oude en Nieuwe Hollanste Boerenlities*, ca. 1710.

784   BY ALL YOUR SAINTS STILL STRIVING

1. By all your saints still striv - ing, For all your saints at rest,
*2. A - pos - tles, proph-ets, mar - tyrs, And all the no - ble throng
3. Then let us praise the Fa - ther And wor-ship God the Son

1. Your ho - ly Name, O Je - sus, For ev - er - more be blessed.
2. Who wear the spot-less rai - ment And raise the cease-less song:
3. And sing to God the Spir - it, E - ter - nal Three in One,

1. You rose, our King vic - to - rious, That they might wear the crown
2. For them and those whose wit - ness Is on - ly known to you
3. Till all the ran - somed num - ber Who stand be - fore the throne,

1. And ev - er shine in splen - dor Re - flect - ed from your throne.
2. By walk - ing in their foot - steps We give you praise a - new.
3. A - scribe all pow'r and glo - ry And praise to God a - lone.

Alternate Verses

Conversion of St. Paul (January 25)
4. Praise for the light from heaven
   And for the voice of awe:
Praise for the glorious vision
   The persecutor saw.
O Lord, for Paul's conversion,
   We bless your Name today.
Come shine within our darkness
   And guide us in the Way.

Chair of St. Peter (February 22)
5. We praise you, Lord, for Peter,
   So eager and so bold:
Thrice falling, yet repentant,
   Thrice charged to feed your fold.
Lord, make your pastors faithful
   To guard your flock from harm
And hold them when they waver
   With your almighty arm.

**St. Joseph, husband of
the Blessed Virgin Mary (March 19)**
6. All praise, O God, for Joseph,
   The guardian of your Son,
Who saved him from King Herod,
   When safety there was none.
He taught the trade of builder,
   When they to Naz'reth came,
And Joseph's love made "Father"
   To be, for Christ, God's name.

Annunciation of the Lord (March 25)
7. We sing with joy of Mary
   Whose heart with awe was stirred
When, youthful and unready,
   She heard the angel's word;
Yet she her voice upraises
   God's glory to proclaim,
As once for our salvation
   Your mother she became.

St. Mark (April 25)
8. For Mark, O Lord, we praise you,
   The weak by grace made strong:
His witness in his Gospel
   Becomes victorious song.
May we, in all our weakness,
   Receive your power divine,
And all, as faithful branches,
   Grow strong in you, the Vine.

Ss. Philip and James (May 3)
9. We praise you, Lord, for Philip,
   Blest guide to Greek and Jew,
And for young James the faithful,
   Who heard and followed you,
O grant us grace to know you,
   The victor in the strife,
That we with all your servants
   May wear the crown of life.

*This verse may be replaced by an appropriate Alternate Verse.

St. Matthias (May 13)

10. For one in place of Judas,
    The apostles sought God's choice:
    The lot fell to Matthias
    For whom we now rejoice.
    May we like true apostles
    Your holy Church defend,
    And not betray our calling
    But serve you to the end.

St. Barnabas (June 11)

11. For Barnabas we praise you,
    Who kept your law of love
    And, leaving earthly treasures,
    Sought riches from above.
    O Christ, our Lord and Savior,
    Let gifts of grace descend,
    That your true consolation
    May through the world extend.

Nativity of St. John the Baptist (June 24)

12. All praise for John the Baptist,
    Forerunner of the Word,
    Our true Elijah, making
    A highway for the Lord.
    The last and greatest prophet,
    He saw the dawning ray
    Of light that grows in splendor
    Until the perfect day.

Ss. Peter and Paul (June 29)

13. We praise you for Saint Peter;
    We praise you for Saint Paul.
    They taught both Jew and Gentile
    that Christ is all in all.
    To cross and sword they yielded
    And saw the kingdom come:
    O God, your two apostles
    Won life through martyrdom.

St. Thomas (July 3)

14. All praise, O Lord, for Thomas
    Whose short-lived doubtings prove
    Your perfect twofold nature,
    The depth of your true love.
    To all who live with questions
    A steadfast faith afford;
    And grant us grace to know you,
    Made flesh, yet God and Lord.

St. Mary Magdalene (July 22)

15. All praise for Mary Magd'lene,
    Whose wholeness was restored
    By you, her faithful Master,
    Her Savior and her Lord.
    On Easter morning early,
    A word from you sufficed:
    Her faith was first to see you,
    Her Lord, the risen Christ.

St. James (July 25)

16. O Lord, for James, we praise you,
    Who fell to Herod's sword.
    He drank the cup of suff'ring
    And thus fulfilled your word.
    Lord, curb our vain impatience
    For glory and for fame,
    Equip us for such suff'rings
    As glorify your Name.

St. Bartholomew (August 24)

17. Praised for your blest apostle
    Surnamed Bartholomew;
    We know not his achievements
    But know that he was true,
    For he at the Ascension
    Was an apostle still.
    May we discern your presence
    And seek, like him, your will.

St. Matthew (September 21)

18. We praise you, Lord, for Matthew,
    Whose gospel words declare
    That, wordly gain forsaking,
    Your path of life we share.
    From all unrighteous mammon,
    O raise our eyes anew,
    That we, whate'er our station
    May rise and follow you.

St. Luke (October 18)

19. For Luke, beloved physician,
    All praise; whose Gospel shows
    The healer of the nations,
    The one who shares our woes.
    Your wine and oil, O Savior,
    Upon our spirits pour,
    And with true balm of Gilead
    Anoint us evermore.

Ss. Simon and Jude (October 28)

20. Praise, Lord, for your apostles,
    Saint Simon and Saint Jude.
    One love, one hope impelled them
    To tread the way, renewed.
    May we with zeal as earnest
    The faith of Christ maintain,
    Be bound in love together,
    And life eternal gain.

St. Andrew (November 30)

21. All praise, O Lord, for Andrew,
    The first to follow you;
    He witnessed to his brother,
    "This is Messiah true."
    You called him from his fishing
    Upon Lake Galilee;
    He rose to meet your challenge,
    "Leave all and follow me."

("By All Your Saints Still Striving" continued on the following page)

St. Stephen (December 26)

22. All praise, O Lord, for Stephen
    Who, martyred, saw you stand
    To help in time of torment,
    To plead at God's right hand.
    Like you, our suff'ring Savior,
    His enemies he blessed,
    With "Lord, receive my spirit,"
    His faith, in death, confessed.

St. John (December 27)

23. For John, your loved disciple,
    Exiled to Patmos' shore,
    And for his faithful record,
    We praise you evermore;
    Praise for the mystic vision
    His words to us unfold.
    Instill in us his longing,
    Your glory to behold.

Holy Innocents (December 28)

24. Praise for your infant martyrs,
    Whom your mysterious love
    Called early from life's conflicts
    To share your peace above.
    O Rachel, cease your weeping;
    They're free from pain and cares.
    Lord, grant us crowns as brilliant
    And lives as pure as theirs.

Text: 76 76 D; based on *From All Thy Saints in Warfare* by Horatio Bolton Nelson, 1823–1913; Jerry D. Godwin, b. 1944.
© 1985, The Church Pension Fund. All rights reserved. Used with permission.
Music: ST. THEODULPH; Melchior Teschner, 1584–1635.

785　　LORD GOD TRIUMPHANT

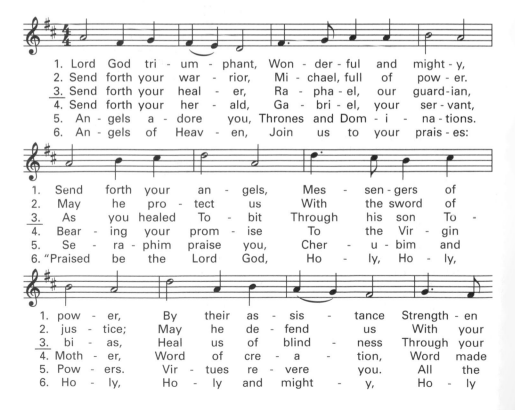

1. Lord God triumphant, Wonderful and mighty,
   Send forth your angels, Messengers of power,
   By their assistance Strengthen us
2. Send forth your warrior, Michael, full of power.
   May he protect us With the sword of justice;
   May he defend us With your
3. Send forth your healer, Raphael, our guardian,
   As you healed Tobit Through his son To
   bias, Heal us of blindness Through your
4. Send forth your herald, Gabriel, your servant,
   Bearing your promise To the Virgin
   Mother, Word of creation, Word made
5. Angels adore you, Thrones and Dominations.
   Seraphim praise you, Cherubim and Powers.
   Virtues revere you. All the
6. Angels of Heaven, Join us to your praises:
   "Praised be the Lord God, Holy, Holy,
   Holy, Holy and mighty, Holy

1. and up - hold us: Lord God tri - um - phant.
2. peace and mer - cy: Shield of the king - dom.
3. Son's re - demp - tion, Christ Je - sus, Sa - vior.
4. flesh a - mong us, Word of the gos - pel.
5. choirs are sing - ing: "Ho - ly, Most Ho - ly."
6. and im - mor - tal: Mer - cy, have mer - cy."

Text: 11 11 11 5; Harry Hagan, OSB, b. 1947, © 2001, St. Meinrad Archabbey.
Published by OCP Publications. All rights reserved.
Music: CHRISTE SANCTORUM; *Antiphoner*, Paris, 1681.

SHALL WE GATHER AT THE RIVER 786

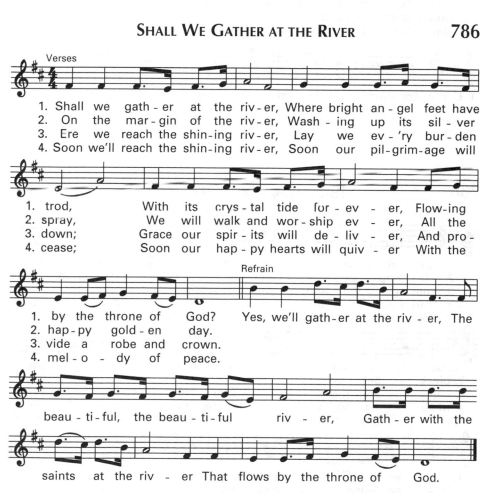

Verses

1. Shall we gath - er at the riv - er, Where bright an - gel feet have
2. On the mar - gin of the riv - er, Wash - ing up its sil - ver
3. Ere we reach the shin-ing riv-er, Lay we ev - 'ry bur - den
4. Soon we'll reach the shin-ing riv-er, Soon our pil-grim-age will

1. trod, With its crys - tal tide for - ev - er, Flow-ing
2. spray, We will walk and wor-ship ev - er, All the
3. down; Grace our spir - its will de - liv - er, And pro -
4. cease; Soon our hap - py hearts will quiv - er With the

Refrain

1. by the throne of God? Yes, we'll gath-er at the riv - er, The
2. hap-py gold - en day.
3. vide a robe and crown.
4. mel - o - dy of peace.

beau - ti - ful, the beau - ti - ful riv - er, Gath - er with the

saints at the riv - er That flows by the throne of God.

Text: 87 87 with refrain; Revelation 22:1–5; Robert Lowry, 1826–1899.
Music: HANSON PLACE; Robert Lowry.

787 — STEAL AWAY TO JESUS

Refrain

Steal a-way, steal a-way, steal a-way to Je - sus!

Steal a-way, steal a-way home, I ain't got long to stay here.

Verses

1. My Lord, he calls me, He calls me by the thun-der; The
2. Green trees are bend-ing, Poor sin-ners stand a-trem-bling; The
3. My Lord, he calls me, He calls me by the light-ning; The

to Refrain

1-3. trum-pet sounds with-in my soul; I ain't got long to stay here.

Text: Traditional.
Music: Spiritual.

788 — JERUSALEM, MY HAPPY HOME

1. Je - ru - sa - lem, my hap - py home, When shall I
2. O hap - py har - bor of the saints, O sweet and
3. Your gar - dens and your gal - lant walks Con - tin - ual -
4. There trees for - ev - er - more bear fruit And ev - er -
5. Je - ru - sa - lem, Je - ru - sa - lem, God grant that

1. come to thee? When shall my sor - rows
2. pleas - ant soil! In you no sor - row
3. ly are green; There grow such sweet and
4. more do spring; There ev - er - more the
5. I may see Your end - less joy, and

1. have an end? Your joys when shall I see?
2. may be found, No grief, no care, no toil.
3. pleas - ant flow'rs As no - where else are seen.
4. an - gels sit And ev - er - more do sing!
5. of the same Par - tak - er ev - er be!

Text: CM; F. B. P., London, ca. 16th cent., alt.
Music: LAND OF REST; Trad. American Melody.

SING WITH ALL THE SAINTS IN GLORY

1. Sing with all the saints in glo - ry, Sing the res - ur -
2. Oh, what glo - ry, far ex - ceed - ing All that eye has
3. Life e - ter - nal! heav'n re - joic - es: Je - sus lives who
4. Life e - ter - nal! O what won - ders Crowd on faith; what

1. rec - tion song! Death and sor - row, earth's dark sto - ry,
2. yet per - ceived! Ho - liest hearts for a - ges plead - ing,
3. once was dead; Join with all the heav'n - ly voic - es;
4. joy un - known, When, a - mid earth's clos - ing thun - ders,

1. To the form - er days be - long. All a - round the
2. Nev - er that full joy con - ceived. God has prom - ised,
3. Child of God, lift up your head! Pa - tri - archs from
4. Saints shall stand be - fore the throne! Oh, to en - ter

1. clouds are break ing, Soon the storms of time shall cease; In God's
2. Christ pre - pares it, There on high our wel-come waits; Ev - 'ry
3. dis - tant a - ges, Saints all long - ing for their heav'n, Proph-ets,
4. that bright por - tal, See that glow - ing fir - ma - ment, Know, with

1. like - ness, peo - ple wak - ing, Know the ev - er - last - ing peace.
2. hum - ble spir - it shares it, Christ has passed th'e - ter - nal gates.
3. psalm-ists, seers, and sa - ges, All a - wait the glo - ry giv'n.
4. you, O God im-mor - tal, Je - sus Christ whom you have sent!

Text: 87 87 D; 1 Corinthians 15:20; William J. Irons, 1812–1993; fr. *Psalms and Hymns*, 1873, alt.
Music: HYMN TO JOY; Ludwig van Beethoven, 1770–1827; adapt. by Edward Hodges, 1796–1867.

COME, WORSHIP THE LORD

Come, and wor-ship the Lord, for we are his peo - ple, the
flock that he shep-herds. Al - le - lu - ia.

Verses 1, 2

1. Come, let us sing to the Lord, and shout with joy ___ to the
2. Come, let us bow down and wor-ship, bend-ing the knee be-fore the

1. rock who saves us. Let us come with thanks-giv-ing,
2. Lord our ma - ker. For we are his peo - ple,

1. and sing joy - ful songs to the Lord. ___
2. we are the flock that he shep-herds. ___

Verse 3

3. The Lord is God, the might-y God, the great king o'er

3. all oth-er gods. He holds in his hands the depths of the earth and the

3. high - est moun-tains as well. He made the sea, it be-longs now to

3. him; the dry land, too, was formed by his hand.

LET US GO REJOICING

1a. Let us go re - joic-ing, re - joic-ing to the house of God.
2a. Now our feet are stand-ing with - in your gates, Je - ru - sa - lem.
3a. Peace reign in this cit - y, the peace of God with - in these walls.
4a. Let us go re - joic-ing, re - joic-ing to the house of God.
*1b. Let us go re - joic-ing, re - joic-ing from the house of God,
2b. Washed in liv-ing wa - ter, we bear the name of Christ the Lord.
3b. Stand - ing with the out-cast, the pow-er - less, the ref - u - gee,

1a. Let us join to - geth - er, who come from near and far,
2a. Gath - ered as one peo - ple, we of - fer thanks and praise
3a. May this peace em - pow'r us to put an end to war,
4a. Let us sit at ta - ble with Christ the ris - en Lord.
1b. strength-ened by this eu-ch'rist to live the gos - pel call,
2b. We re - ceive the mis-sion to take Christ to the world,
3b. with the bruised and bro - ken the Church must ev - er be,

1a. who seek the ho - ly cit - y, the new Je - ru - sa - lem,
2a. be - fore the throne of jus - tice, com - pas - sion and all grace,
3a. to seek the reign of jus - tice with dig - ni - ty for all,
4a. Then guid-ed by his Spir - it as ser-vants we'll go forth,
1b. to be a ho - ly peo-ple, a sac - ra - ment to all,
2b. to be his heal - ing pres-ence, to share his sav - ing word,
3b. a sign of hope and jus - tice for all the world to see,

1-3

1-4. re - joic - ing be - fore the liv - ing God.

Final

4. God, re - joic-ing be - fore the liv-ing God.

*Alternate verses for use as a sending forth song.

Text: 68 66 76 9; based on Psalm 122:1–9; Bob Hurd, b. 1950.
Music: POINT HILL; Bob Hurd.

AS WE GATHER AT YOUR TABLE

1. As we gath-er at your Ta-ble, As we lis-ten to your
2. Turn our wor-ship in-to wit-ness In the sac-ra-ment of
3. Gra-cious Spir-it, help us sum-mon Oth-er guests to share that

1. Word, Help us know, O God, your pres-ence: Let our
2. life; Send us forth to love and serve you, Bring-ing
3. feast Where tri-um-phant Love will wel-come Those who

1. hearts and minds be stirred. Nour-ish us with sa-cred
2. peace where there is strife. Give us, Christ, your great com-
3. had been last and least. There no more will en-vy

1. sto - ry Till we claim it as our own; Teach us
2. pas - sion To for - give as you for-gave; May we
3. blind us Nor will pride our peace de-stroy, As we

1. through this ho - ly ban-quet How to make Love's vic - t'ry known.
2. still be - hold your im-age In the world you died to save.
3. join with saints and an - gels To re - peat the sound-ing joy.

Text: 87 87 D; Carl P. Daw, Jr., © 1989, Hope Publishing Co. All rights reserved. Used with permission.
Music: NETTLETON; J. Wyeth's *Repository of Sacred Music, Part II*, 1813.

TABLE OF PLENTY

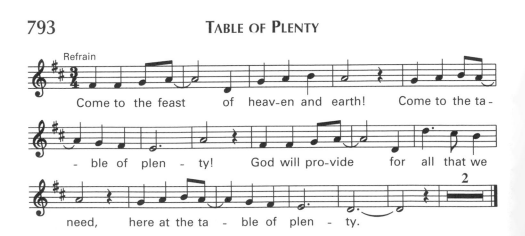

Refrain

Come to the feast of heav-en and earth! Come to the ta-

- ble of plen - ty! God will pro-vide for all that we

need, here at the ta - ble of plen - ty.

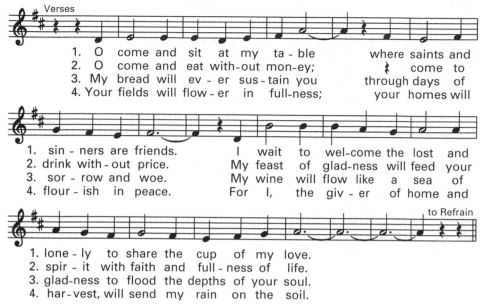

Verses

1. O come and sit at my ta-ble where saints and
2. O come and eat with-out mon-ey; come to
3. My bread will ev-er sus-tain you through days of
4. Your fields will flow-er in full-ness; your homes will

1. sin-ners are friends. I wait to wel-come the lost and
2. drink with-out price. My feast of glad-ness will feed your
3. sor-row and woe. My wine will flow like a sea of
4. flour-ish in peace. For I, the giv-er of home and

to Refrain

1. lone-ly to share the cup of my love.
2. spir-it with faith and full-ness of life.
3. glad-ness to flood the depths of your soul.
4. har-vest, will send my rain on the soil.

Text and music: Dan Schutte, b. 1947, © 1992, Daniel L. Schutte. Published by OCP Publications. All rights reserved.

WE GATHER TOGETHER 794

1. We gath-er to-geth-er to ask the Lord's bless-ing; He
2. Be-side us to guide us, our God with us join-ing, Whose
3. We all do ex-tol you, our lead-er tri-um-phant, And

1. chas-tens and has-tens his will to make known; The
2. king-dom calls all to the love which en-dures. So
3. pray that you still our de-fend-er will be. Let

1. wick-ed op-press-ing now cease from dis-tress-ing: Sing
2. from the be-gin-ning the fight we were win-ning: You,
3. your con-gre-ga-tion es-cape trib-u-la-tion: Your

1. prais-es to his name; he for-gets not his own.
2. Lord, were at our side; all __ glo-ry be yours!
3. name be ev-er praised! O __ Lord, make us free!

Text: 12 11 12 11; *Wilt heden nu treden*; tr. by Theodore Baker, 1851–1934, alt.
Music: KREMSER; Valerius' *Nederlandtsch Gedenckclanck*, Haarlam, 1626.

VEN AL BANQUETE/COME TO THE FEAST

Refrain/Estribillo

(Bilingual) Ven, ven al ban-que-te. Ven a la fies-ta de Dios.
(Español) Ven, ven al ban-que-te. Ven a la fies-ta de Dios.
(English) Come, come to the ban-quet. Come, __ come to the feast.

Here the hun-gry find plen-ty, here the thirst-y shall drink. __
Los que tie-nen ham-bre y sed se-rán __ sa-cia-dos.
Here the hun-gry find plen-ty, here the thirst-y shall drink, __

Ven a la ce-na de Cris-to, come __ to __ the feast.
Ven a la ce-na de Cris-to, ven a la fies-ta de Dios.
here at the sup-per of Je-sus, come __ to __ the feast.

Verses/Estrofas

1. Like the child whose fish-es and loaves fed the mul-ti-
   __ ¿Quién le pue-de dar de co-mer a la mul-ti-
2. 'Til the seed is giv-en to earth, it is just one
   Hay que dar-se a __ mo-rir pa-ra co-se-
3. In the strang-er by __ our side, in the least and
   Los des-am-pa-ra-dos ven-drán a par-tir el

1. tude, in the Lord the lit-tle we have,
   tud? Con Je-sús, al com-par-tir lo
2. grain; but once sown its death brings new birth, the
   char, las se-mi-llas de li-ber-tad y
3. last, in the thirst for jus-tice we share,
   pan y ve-rán su dig-ni-dad de

to Refrain/al Estribillo

1. bro-ken and shared, be-comes a-bun-dant food.
   po-co que hay, re-ci-bi-mos ple-ni-tud.
2. har-vest is rich; what's lost is raised a-gain.
   re-su-rrec-ción, la pro-me-sa de vi-vir.
3. Christ __ is here in the break-ing of the bread.
   nue-vo en Je-sús, Sal-va-dor y Buen Pas-tor.

*Last time, repeat final phrase.

Text: Bob Hurd, b. 1950, Pia Moriarty, b. 1948, and Jaime Cortez, b. 1963.
Music: Bob Hurd.

GOD IS HERE! AS WE HIS PEOPLE

1. God is here! As we his peo-ple, Meet to of-fer
2. Here are sym-bols to re-mind us Of our life-long
3. Here our chil-dren find a wel-come In the Shep-herd's
4. Lord of all, of church and king-dom, In an age of

1. praise and prayer, May we find in full-er mea-sure
2. need of grace; Here are ta-ble, font and pul-pit,
3. flock and fold; Here, as bread and wine are tak-en,
4. change and doubt, Keep us faith-ful to the gos-pel,

1. What it is in Christ we share: Here, as in the world a-
2. Here the cross has cen-tral place: Here in hon-es-ty of
3. Christ sus-tains us as of old: Here the ser-vants of the
4. Help us work your pur-pose out: Here, in this day's ded-i-

1. round us, All our var-ied skills and arts Wait the com-ing
2. preach-ing, Here in si-lence as in speech, Here in new-ness
3. Ser-vant Seek in wor-ship to ex-plore What it means in
4. ca-tion, All we have to give, re-ceive; We who can-not

1. of his Spir-it In-to o-pen minds and hearts.
2. and re-new-al God the Spir-it comes to each.
3. dai-ly liv-ing To be-lieve and to a-dore.
4. live with-out you, We a-dore you! We be-lieve!

797 DRAW US IN THE SPIRIT'S TETHER

1. Draw us in the Spir-it's teth-er, For when hum-bly
2. As dis-ci-ples used to gath-er In the name of
3. All our meals and all our liv-ing Make as sac-ra-

1. in your name, Two or three are met to-
2. Christ to sup, Then with thanks to God the
3. ments of you, That by car-ing, help-ing,

1. geth-er, You are in the midst of
2. Fa-ther Break the bread and bless the
3. giv-ing, We may be dis-ci-ples

1. them; Al-le-lu-ia! Al-le-lu-ia!
2. cup, Al-le-lu-ia! Al-le-lu-ia!
3. true. Al-le-lu-ia! Al-le-lu-ia!

1. Touch we now your gar-ment's hem.
2. So now bind our friend-ship up.
3. We will serve with faith a-new.

798 GATHER YOUR PEOPLE

Refrain

Gath-er your peo-ple, O Lord. Gath-er your

peo-ple, O Lord. One bread, one bod-y, one

spir-it of love. Gath-er your peo-ple, O Lord.

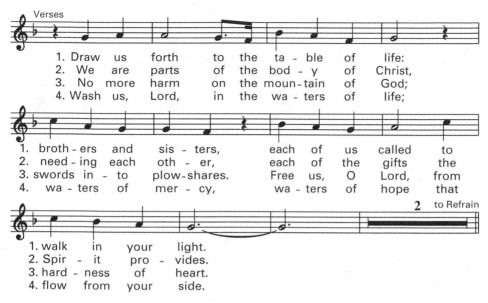

Verses

1. Draw us forth to the ta - ble of life:
2. We are parts of the bod - y of Christ,
3. No more harm on the moun - tain of God;
4. Wash us, Lord, in the wa - ters of life;

1. broth - ers and sis - ters, each of us called to
2. need - ing each oth - er, each of the gifts the
3. swords in - to plow-shares. Free us, O Lord, from
4. wa - ters of mer - cy, wa - ters of hope that

2 to Refrain

1. walk in your light.
2. Spir - it pro - vides.
3. hard - ness of heart.
4. flow from your side.

WHAT IS THIS PLACE 799

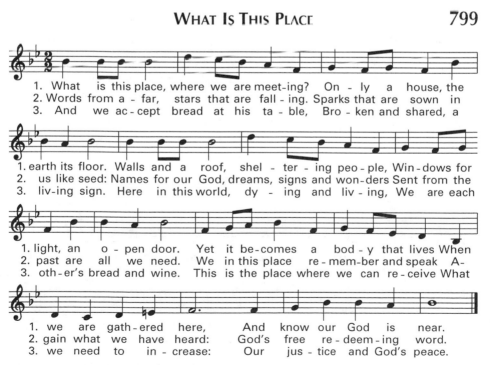

1. What is this place, where we are meet-ing? On - ly a house, the
2. Words from a - far, stars that are fall - ing. Sparks that are sown in
3. And we ac - cept bread at his ta - ble, Bro - ken and shared, a

1. earth its floor. Walls and a roof, shel - ter - ing peo - ple, Win - dows for
2. us like seed: Names for our God, dreams, signs and won - ders Sent from the
3. liv-ing sign. Here in this world, dy - ing and liv - ing, We are each

1. light, an o - pen door. Yet it be-comes a bod - y that lives When
2. past are all we need. We in this place re - mem-ber and speak A-
3. oth - er's bread and wine. This is the place where we can re - ceive What

1. we are gath-ered here, And know our God is near.
2. gain what we have heard: God's free re - deem - ing word.
3. we need to in - crease: Our jus - tice and God's peace.

800

LET US GO TO THE ALTAR

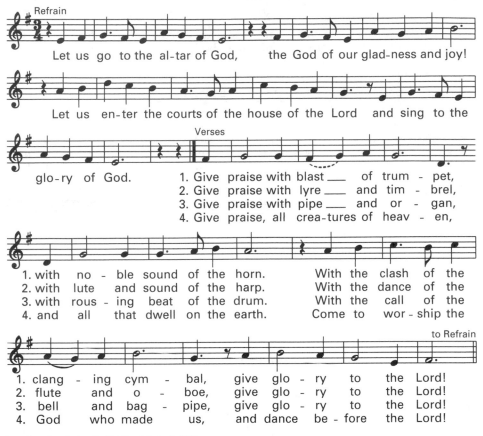

Refrain

Let us go to the al-tar of God, the God of our glad-ness and joy!

Let us en-ter the courts of the house of the Lord and sing to the

Verses

glo-ry of God.

1. Give praise with blast ___ of trum - pet,
2. Give praise with lyre ___ and tim - brel,
3. Give praise with pipe ___ and or - gan,
4. Give praise, all crea-tures of heav - en,

1. with no - ble sound of the horn. With the clash of the
2. with lute and sound of the harp. With the dance of the
3. with rous - ing beat of the drum. With the call of the
4. and all that dwell on the earth. Come to wor - ship the

to Refrain

1. clang - ing cym - bal, give glo - ry to the Lord!
2. flute and o - boe, give glo - ry to the Lord!
3. bell and bag - pipe, give glo - ry to the Lord!
4. God who made us, and dance be - fore the Lord!

Text: Based on Psalms 42, 150; Dan Schutte, b. 1947.
Music: Dan Schutte.

801

GATHER US TOGETHER

Refrain

Lord, Je-sus Christ, gath-er us to-geth-er. Make us one bread, one

Verses

bod-y in your love.

1. Gath-er your peo - ple, who long
2. We do pro - claim you the Sav-
3. For-give our fail - ings, cre - ate
4. In - to your hands, Lord, we place
5. With-in your tem - ple your prais-

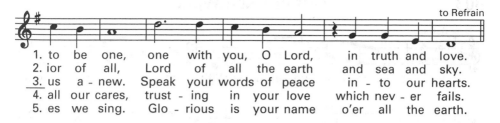

1. to be one, one with you, O Lord, in truth and love.
2. ior of all, Lord of all the earth and sea and sky.
3. us a-new. Speak your words of peace in-to our hearts.
4. all our cares, trust-ing in your love which nev-er fails.
5. es we sing. Glo-rious is your name o'er all the earth.

UNLESS A GRAIN OF WHEAT   802

Refrain

Un-less a grain of wheat fall to the ground and die, it remains a sin-gle grain. But if it die
it will yield a rich har-vest.

Verses

1. In his own bod-
2. Do not draw back

1. y, by his own wounds, he brought your
2. now, do not be shy. Turn not a-

1. sins to the cross, and suf-fer'd for you;
2. way _ from him who paid the price.

1. pour'd out his life - blood up-on the tree,
2. Come to his ta - ble, sit by his side.

to Refrain

1. pour'd out his life - blood for you and for me.
2. There he a-waits you: the Lord _ of Life.

803

GIFT OF FINEST WHEAT

Refrain

You sat-is-fy the hun-gry heart With gift of fin-est wheat, Come

give to us, O sav-ing Lord, The bread of life to eat.

Verses

1. As when the
2. With joy - ful
3. Is not the
4. The mys - t'ry
5. You give your-

1. shep - herd calls his sheep, They know and heed his voice; So
2. lips we sing to you Our praise and grat - i - tude, That
3. cup we bless and share The blood of Christ out-poured? Do
4. of your pres-ence, Lord, No mor - tal tongue can tell: Whom
5. self to us, O Lord; Then self - less let us be, To

to Refrain

1. when you call your fam-'ly, Lord, We fol - low and re-joice.
2. you should count us wor-thy, Lord, To share this heav'n-ly food.
3. not one cup, one loaf, de - clare Our one-ness in the Lord?
4. all the world can-not con-tain Comes in our hearts to dwell.
5. serve each oth - er in your name In truth and char - i - ty.

Text: CM with refrain; Omer Westendorf, 1916–1997.
Music: BICENTENNIAL; Robert Kreutz, 1922–1996.

804

JESUS, LAMB OF GOD

Verses: Cantor/Choir

1. Je - sus, Lamb of God, bear - er of our sin;
2. Je - sus, Lamb of God, bear - er of our pain;
3. Je - sus, Lamb of God, bro - ken as our bread,
4. Je - sus, Lamb of God, poured out as our wine,
5. Je - sus, Word of God, dwell - ing with the poor;
6. Je - sus, Word of God, dwell - ing in our midst;
7. Je - sus, Word of God, speak - ing in our hearts
8. Je - sus, Word made flesh, touch - ing each one's need;
9. Kneel - ing by your friends, wash - ing each one's feet;
10. Hope be - yond de - spair, dawn of frag - ile light;
11. Tomb of se - cret hope, o - pen to the dawn;

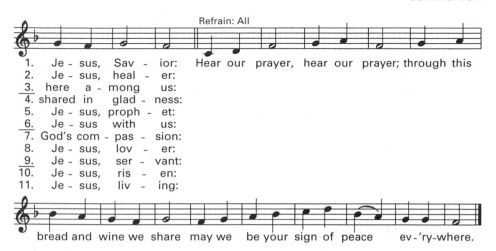

1. Je - sus, Sav - ior: Hear our prayer, hear our prayer; through this
2. Je - sus, heal - er:
3. here a - mong us:
4. shared in glad - ness:
5. Je - sus, proph - et:
6. Je - sus with us:
7. God's com - pas - sion:
8. Je - sus, lov - er:
9. Je - sus, ser - vant:
10. Je - sus, ris - en:
11. Je - sus, liv - ing:

bread and wine we share may we be your sign of peace ev - 'ry - where.

Text and music: *Mass of Hope*; Bernadette Farrell, b. 1957, © 1991, Bernadette Farrell.
Published by OCP Publications. All rights reserved.

UBI CARITAS 805

*U - bi ca - ri - tas est ve - ra, est ve - ra: De - us i - bi

est, De - us i - bi est.

Verses. Cantor/Choir

1. The love of Christ joins us to-
2. In true com - mu - nion let us
3. May we who gath - er at this
4. For those in need make us your
5. May we one day be - hold your

1. geth - er. Let us re - joice in him, and in our love and
2. gath - er. May all di - vi - sions cease and in their place be
3. ta - ble to share the bread of life be - come a sac - ra-
4. mer - cy, for those op - pressed, your might. Make us, your Church, a
5. glo - ry and see you face to face, re - joic - ing with the

to Refrain

1. care for all now love God in re - turn.
2. Christ the Lord, our ris - en Prince of Peace.
3. ment of love, your heal - ing touch, O Christ.
4. ho - ly sign of jus - tice and new life.
5. saints of God to sing e - ter - nal praise.

*"Where there is true charity, God is present."

Text: Refrain and verses 1, 2 and 5 based on the Latin Chant text from the *Liturgy of Holy Thursday*;
verses 3 and 4, Bob Hurd, b. 1950.
Music: Bob Hurd.
Text and music © 1996, Bob Hurd. Published by OCP Publications. All rights reserved.

806

LET US BREAK BREAD TOGETHER

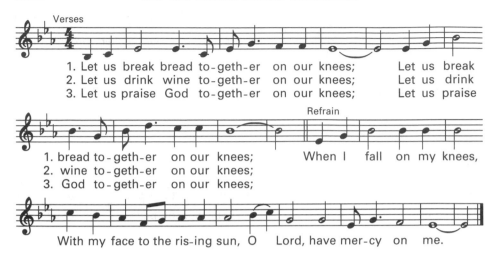

1. Let us break bread to-geth-er on our knees; Let us break
2. Let us drink wine to-geth-er on our knees; Let us drink
3. Let us praise God to-geth-er on our knees; Let us praise

Refrain

1. bread to-geth-er on our knees;
2. wine to-geth-er on our knees;
3. God to-geth-er on our knees;

When I fall on my knees,

With my face to the ris-ing sun, O Lord, have mer-cy on me.

Text: 10 10 with refrain; Spiritual.
Music: LET US BREAK BREAD; Spiritual.

807

HERE AT THIS TABLE

Refrain

Come and be filled here at this ta-ble.

Food for all who hun-ger and drink for all who thirst.

Drink of his love, wine of sal - va - tion.

You shall live for - ev - er in Je - sus Christ the

1-5 *to Verses* *Final*

Lord. Lord. You shall live for -

ev - er in Je - sus Christ the Lord.

Verses 1, 2, 4

1. You who la-bor for jus-tice, you who la-bor for
2. You with lives full of pain, you who sor-row and
4. You, the a-ged a-mong us, ho-ly, faith-ful and

1. peace, you who stead-y the plow in the
2. weep, you, be-lov-ed of Christ, come to
4. wise, may the wis-dom you share form our

to Refrain

1. field of the Lord,
2. him, come to him!
4. lives and our world!

Verses 3, 5

3. Chil-dren of ev-'ry col-or in ev-'ry land,
5. Let each wom-an and man learn from the strang-er;

3. you are his own, he gath-ers you gent-ly.
5. we're not so dif-f'rent and so much u-nites us.

3. Don't you grow wea-ry, for when you
5. For we are one, blest with the

to Refrain

3. run, you run with the Lord!
5. Spir-it and the pow-er of love!

Text and music: Janèt Sullivan Whitaker, b. 1958, and Max Whitaker, b. 1986,

IN THE BREAKING OF THE BREAD/
CUANDO PARTIMOS EL PAN DEL SEÑOR

Refrain In ___ the break - ing ___ of ___ the
Verses 1. Bread for the jour - ney, ___ ⁊ strength for our
2. Bread of the prom - ise, ___ ⁊ peo - ple of
Estribillo Cuan-do par - ti - mos ___ el pan del Se -
Estrofas 1. Pan pa - ra el via - je, ___ ⁊ pan de la
2. Pan de pro - me - sa, ___ ⁊ pan de es-pe -

bread ___ we ___ have known him;
1. years, ___ man - na of ag - es, of
2. hope, ___ wine of com - pas - sion, ___
___ ñor, ___ lo co - no - ce - mos, nos
1. vi - da, pan de los si - glos de
2. ran - za, vi - no de vi - da, de

we have been fed. ___ Je - sus the ___
1. strug-gle and tears. ___ Cup of sal -
2. life for the world. ___ Gath-ered at ___
da de co - mer. ___ ⁊ Je - sús des - co - no -
1. lu - cha y do - lor, ___ y es - te ___
2. su com - pa - sión. ___ En es - ta ___

strang - er, ___ Je - sus the Lord, ___
1. va - tion, ___ fruit of the land, ___
2. ta - ble, ___ joined as his bod - y, ___
ci - do, ___ ⁊ Je - sús ___ Se - ñor, ___
1. vi - no, ___ ⁊ fru - to de la tie - rra, ___
2. me - sa, ___ un so - lo cuer - po, ___

___ be our com - pan - ion; ___
1. ___ bless and re - ceive ___ now, ___
2. ___ sealed in the ___ Spir - it, ___
___ nues - tro com-pa - ñe - ro ___
1. ___ ⁊ ben - dí - ce - lo ___ Pa - dre, ___
2. ___ en un es - pí - ri - tu, ___

	be ___	our	hope.	(to Verses)
1. ___ 𝄽 the	work of	our	hands.	(to Refrain)
2. ___	sent by	the	Word.	(to Refrain)
___ 𝄽 y	fuen - te	de	fe.	(a las Estrofas)
1. ___ 𝄽 es	tu - yo	mi	Dios.	(al Estribillo)
2. ___ 𝄽 con	u - na	mi -	sión.	(al Estribillo)

Text: Luke 24:13–35; Acts 2:42. English text, Bob Hurd, b. 1950. Revised English text © 1987, Bob Hurd and Michael Downey.
Spanish text, Stephen Dean, b. 1948, and Kathleen Orozco, b. 1945.
Music: Bob Hurd.
Text and music © 1984, 1987, 1989, Bob Hurd. Published by OCP Publications. All rights reserved.

BEHOLD THE LAMB 809

Verses

1. Those who were in the dark are thank-ful for the
2. Peace-ful now, those whose hearts are blessed with un-der-
3. Gen-tle one, Child of God, join with us at this
4. Lord of all, give us light. De-liv-er us from

1. sun-light; we who live, we who die are grate-ful for his
2. stand-ing of the wheat, of the wine u-nit-ed with his
3. ta-ble. Bless our lives; nour-ish all who hun-ger for this
4. e-vil. Make us one; be our shield. Make still the winds that

Refrain

1. gift, thank-ful for his love. Be-hold, be-hold the Lamb of
2. word and the love we share.
3. feast; shel-ter them with peace.
4. blow; cra-dle us with love.

God. All who eat, all who drink shall live; and all,

all who dwell in God shall come to know his glo-ry.

Text: Based on John 1:29; Martin Willett, b. 1960.
Music: Martin Willet.
Text and music © 1984, OCP Publications. All rights reserved.

810
BREAD FOR THE WORLD

Refrain: All

Bread for the world: a world of hun-ger. Wine for all
peo-ples: peo-ple who thirst. May we who eat
be bread for oth-ers. May we who drink pour out our love.

Verses: Cantor

1. Lord Je-sus Christ, you are the bread of life, bro-ken to
2. Lord Je-sus Christ, you are the wine of peace, poured in-to
3. Lord Je-sus Christ, you call us to your feast, at which the

1. reach and heal the wounds of hu-man pain. Where we di-
2. hearts once bro-ken and where dry-ness sleeps. Where we are
3. rich and pow'r-ful have be-come the least. Where we sur-

1. vide your peo-ple you are wait-ing there
2. tired and wea-ry, you are wait-ing there
3. vive on oth-ers in our hu-man greed,

to Refrain

1. on bend-ed knee to wash our feet with end-less care.
2. to be the way which beck-ons us be-yond de-spair.
3. you walk a-mong us beg-ging for your ev-'ry need.

811
SEED, SCATTERED AND SOWN

Refrain

Seed, scat-tered and sown, wheat, gath-ered and grown,
bread, bro-ken and shared as one, the liv-ing bread of God.

Vine, fruit of the land, wine, work of our hands, one cup that is
shared by all; the liv-ing cup, the liv-ing bread of God.

Verses

1. Is not the bread we break a shar-ing in our Lord?
2. The seed which falls on rock will with-er and will die.
3. As wheat up-on the hills was gath-ered and was grown,

to Refrain

1. Is not the cup we bless the blood of Christ out-poured?
2. The seed with-in good ground will flow-er and have life.
3. so may the church of God be gath-ered in-to one.

Text: Based on Didache 9; 1 Corinthians 10:16–17; Mark 4:3–6; Dan Feiten.
Music: Dan Feiten.
Text and music © 1987, EKKLESIA MUSIC, INC. All rights reserved. Used with permission.

THIS BODY 812

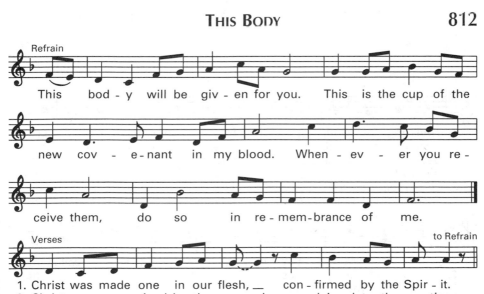

Refrain

This bod-y will be giv-en for you. This is the cup of the
new cov-e-nant in my blood. When-ev-er you receive them, do so in re-mem-brance of me.

Verses
to Refrain

1. Christ was made one in our flesh, __ con-firmed by the Spir-it.
2. Christ was per-ceived by the an-gels, pro-claimed to the na-tions.
3. Christ is the hope of us all, __ and rules now in glo-ry.

Text: Based on 1 Corinthians 11:24–25; 1 Timothy 3:16. Refrain © 1973, ICEL. All rights reserved. Used with permission.
Verses, Christopher Willcock, b. 1947, © 1970, Christopher Willcock, SJ. Published by OCP Publications. All rights reserved.
Music: Christopher Willcock, © 1970, Christopher Willcock, SJ. Published by OCP Publications. All rights reserved.

PAN DE VIDA

(Bilingual) *Pan de Vi - da, cuer-po del Se - ñor,
(Spanish) Pan de Vi - da, cuer-po del Se - ñor,

cup of bless - ing, blood of Christ the Lord.
san-ta co - pa, Cris - to Re - den-tor.

At this ta - ble the last shall be first.
Su jus - ti - cia nos con-ver-ti - rá.

**Po - der es ser-vir, por-que Dios es a - mor.
Po - der es ser-vir, por-que Dios es a - mor.

1-3 to Verses/a las Estrofas   4   Final 3   Verses/Estrofas

Po -
Po -

1. We are the
2. You call me
3. There is no
1. So-mos el
2. Us - te - des me
3. No hay es -

1. dwell-ing of God, _____ fra-gile and wound-ed and weak. __
2. Teach-er and Lord; _____ I, who have washed __ your feet. __
3. Jew __ or Greek; _____ there is no slave __ or free;
1. tem-plo de Dios, frá - gi - les se - res hu - ma -
2. lla - man "Se - ñor". _____ Me in-cli-no a la - var - les los pies. __
3. cla - vos ni li - bres, no hay mu - je - res ni hom -

1. _____ We are the bod - y of Christ, called to
2. _____ So you must do as I do, so the
3. _____ there is no wom-an or man; on - ly
1. nos. So-mos el cuer-po de Cris - to, lla -
2. _____ Ha - gan lo mis-mo, hu - mil - des, sir -
3. bres, só - lo a - que-llos que he-re - dan el

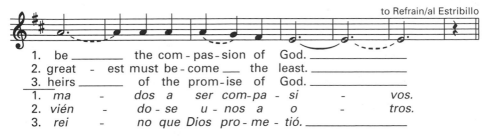

to Refrain/al Estribillo

1. be _____ the com - pas - sion of God. _____
2. great - est must be - come __ the least. _____
3. heirs _____ of the prom - ise of God. _____
1. ma - dos a ser com - pa - si - vos.
2. vién - do - se u - nos a o - tros.
3. rei - no que Dios pro - me - tió. _____

*Bread of Life, body of the Lord,
**Power is for service, because God is love.

Text: Based on John 13:1–15; Galatians 3:28–29; Bob Hurd, b. 1950, and Pia Moriarty, b. 1948;
   Spanish adapt. by Jaime Cortez, b. 1963, Magali Jerez, Elena García and Gustavo Castillo.
Music: Bob Hurd.
Text and music © 1988, 1995, 1999, Bob Hurd and Pia Moriarty. Published by OCP Publications. All rights reserved.

ONE LOVE RELEASED   814

Refrain

One bread, one bod - y, one cup, one call,

one faith, one Spir - it pres - ent in us all.

One prayer, one bless - ing, one hope, one peace,

one church, one peo - ple, one love re - leased.

Verses

1. Is not this bread we share, the bod - y of our Lord?
2. I am the bread of life, eat and you shall live.
3. I am the liv - ing bread, as man - na from the sky.
4. No one will come to me, un - less our God has led.

to Refrain

1. Is not this wine we drink, the blood of Christ out - poured?
2. To those who share this meal, my strength I'll al - ways give.
3. This bread I give to you, that you may nev - er die.
4. And I shall raise them up, _____ raise them from the dead!

Text: Bob Frenzel, b. 1953, and Kevin Keil, ASCAP, b. 1956.
Music: Based on O WALY WALY; Bob Frenzel and Kevin Keil, ASCAP, © 1999, 2000, Robert H. Frenzel and Kevin Keil.
   Published by OCP Publications. All rights reserved.

815

I RECEIVED THE LIVING GOD

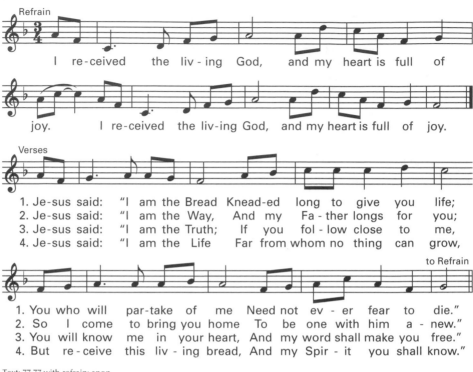

Refrain

I re-ceived the liv-ing God, and my heart is full of joy. I re-ceived the liv-ing God, and my heart is full of joy.

Verses

1. Je-sus said: "I am the Bread Knead-ed long to give you life;
2. Je-sus said: "I am the Way, And my Fa - ther longs for you;
3. Je-sus said: "I am the Truth; If you fol - low close to me,
4. Je-sus said: "I am the Life Far from whom no thing can grow,

to Refrain

1. You who will par-take of me Need not ev - er fear to die."
2. So I come to bring you home To be one with him a - new."
3. You will know me in your heart, And my word shall make you free."
4. But re - ceive this liv - ing bread, And my Spir - it you shall know."

Text: 77 77 with refrain; anon.
Music: LIVING GOD; anon.

816

TO BE YOUR BREAD

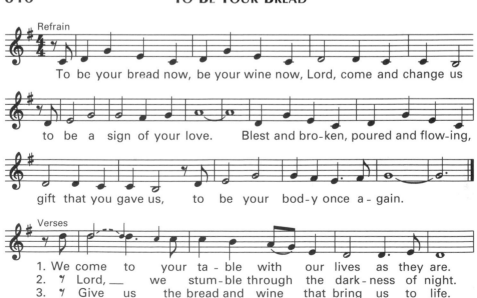

Refrain

To be your bread now, be your wine now, Lord, come and change us to be a sign of your love. Blest and bro-ken, poured and flow-ing, gift that you gave us, to be your bod-y once a - gain.

Verses

1. We come to your ta - ble with our lives as they are.
2. ⅞ Lord, __ we stum-ble through the dark-ness of night.
3. ⅞ Give us the bread and wine that bring us to life.

to Refrain

1. Heal us, Lord, _ for we are bro-ken; make us one a-gain.
2. Lead us, now, _ O Lord, we fol-low; bring us home to you.
3. Feed us, ___ and we'll nev-er hun-ger, nev-er thirst a-gain.

JESUS, THE BREAD OF LIFE 817

Refrain

Je - sus, the Bread of life, Je - sus, the
Bread of life. All who eat and drink of him will nev -
- er die, will nev - er die.

Verses: Cantor

1. I am the Bread that came down from
2. All who come to me will not
3. All who love and keep my com-

1. heav - en. I will be ____ your food. ____
2. hun - ger nor will they ev - er thirst. ____
3. mand-ments will be loved by my Fa -

1. ___ All who put their trust in
2. ___ If you turn to me in
3. ther. And we shall both com - fort

to Refrain

1. me will nev - er die.
2. faith I'll nev - er turn a - way.
3. them and make our home in them.

COME, TASTE AND SEE

Refrain

All you who are thirst-y, come to the wa-ter!

Though you have no mon-ey, come, eat and drink!

Why spend your mon-ey for what is not food, your wa-ges for

what fails to sat-is-fy you? Hear me and heed me, and you shall eat

well; lis-ten, and your souls will live. Come, taste and

Verses

see!

1. I have come bring-ing you new life,
2. I am the vine; come, be my branch-es.
3. From me shall flow life-giv-ing wa-ter,

1. life o-ver-flow-ing a-bun-dant-ly. I am the Good
2. Come to me, live in me, draw life from me. Cut off __ from
3. quench-ing your thirst __ e-ter-nal-ly. I give __ my

1. Shep-herd; I know my sheep. __ Come to my
2. me, __ you can do noth-ing. With me, your
3. bod-y, I pour my life-blood. Here is real

to Refrain

1. pas-ture; come, taste and see!
2. lives will bear fruit; taste and see!
3. food and drink; come, taste and see!

Text: Refrain based on Isaiah 55; verses based on John 10:10, 14; 7:37–38; 6:55–57; John D. Becker, b. 1953.
Music: John D. Becker.

BREAD OF LIFE

Refrain

Bread of life, hope of the world, Je-sus Christ, our broth-er:
feed us now, give us life, lead us to one an-oth-er.

Verses

1. As we pro-claim your death, as we re-call your life, we re-
2. The bread we break and share was scat-tered once as grain: just as
3. We eat this liv-ing bread, we drink this sav-ing cup: sign of
4. Hold us in u-ni-ty, in love for all to see; that the
5. You are the bread of peace, you are the wine of joy, bro-ken

to Refrain

1. mem-ber your prom-ise to re-turn a-gain.
2. now it is gath-ered, make your peo-ple one.
3. hope in our bro-ken world, source of last-ing love.
4. world may be-lieve in you, God of all who live.
5. now for your peo-ple, poured in end-less love.

Alternate Verses: for Advent/Christmas

Adv. 1. Be with your peo-ple, Lord, send us your sav-ing Word: Je-sus
Adv. 2. Bring to our world of fear the truth we long to hear: Je-sus
Chr. 1. A child is born for us, a son is giv'n to us, In our
Chr. 2. With our own eyes we see, with our own ears we hear The sal-
Chr. 3. You are the hope of all, our prom-ise and our call, Ra-diant

to Refrain

1. Christ, light of glad-ness, come a-mong us now.
2. Christ, hope of a-ges, come to save us now.
1. midst, Christ, our Lord and God comes as one who serves.
2. va-tion of all the world, God's in-car-nate Word.
3. light in our dark-ness, truth to set us free.

820

ONE BREAD, ONE BODY

Refrain

One bread, one bod-y, one Lord of all, one cup of bless-ing which we bless. And we, though man-y, through-out the earth, we are one bod-y in this one Lord.

Verses

1. Gen-tile or Jew, ser-vant or
2. Man-y the gifts, man-y the
3. Grain for the fields, scat-tered and

to Refrain

1. free, wom-an or man, no more.
2. works, one in the Lord of all.
3. grown, gath-ered to one, for all.

Text: Based on 1 Corinthians 10:16–17; Galatians 3:28; Ephesians 4:4–6; Didache 9; John Foley, S.J., b. 1939.
Music: John Foley, S.J.

821

TASTE AND SEE

Refrain

Taste and see, O taste and see, taste and see the good-ness of God.

Verses 1, 2

1. Glo-ry, glo-ry to God most high,
2. Who has fash-ioned the earth and sky,

1. glo-ry, bless-ing and praise. With one voice, O peo-ple, re-
2. who cre-a-ted the deep, who ex-alts the low-ly and

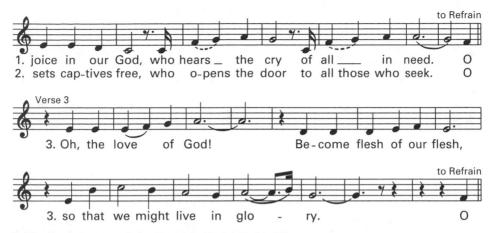

1. joice in our God, who hears the cry of all in need. O
2. sets cap-tives free, who o-pens the door to all those who seek. O

Verse 3

3. Oh, the love of God! Be-come flesh of our flesh,

to Refrain

3. so that we might live in glo - ry. O

Text: Based on Psalm 34:9, 2–4; Psalm 136:5–6; Luke 1:52; Bob Hurd, b. 1950.
Music: Bob Hurd.

I Am the Living Bread

822

Refrain

See this bread; take and eat and live in me. See this cup;

take and drink, re-mem-ber me.

Verses

1. I am the liv - ing
2. I am the liv - ing
3. I am the liv - ing
4. You are the liv - ing

1. bread come down from heav - en. All who eat my
2. bread; you shall not hun - ger. If you be - lieve in
3. bread ris - en a - mong you. If you be - lieve in
4. bread; life for the world. O Lord, to

to Refrain

1. flesh and drink my blood will live, will live for - ev - er.
2. me you shall not thirst, but live, but live for - ev - er.
3. me, though you die, you will live; you will live for - ev - er.
4. whom shall we go? Your words, they live for - ev - er.

Text: Based on John 6; David Haas, b. 1957.
Music: David Haas.

WHEN WE EAT THIS BREAD

Refrain

When we eat this bread and we drink this cup, we pro-claim your

death un - til you come.

Verses

1. Where two or three __ are __
2. Come, you __ bless - ed __
3. I saw the cit - y __ Je-
4. There will be no __ more __
5. All praise to the Fa-ther, __ Cre-

1. gath-ered to - geth - er in my name,   where two or
2. of my __ Fa - ther, come to me.   En - ter __
3. ru - sa - lem __ come from God,   all clothed and a-
4. weep-ing or mourn-ing, nev - er-more: and God will __
5. a - tor most ho - ly, praise to him.   All praise to the

1. three __ are __ gath-ered to - geth - er, there am I.   How
2. in - to __ God's ho - ly __ king-dom, full of joy.   How
3. dorned __ as a bride for her hus-band, filled with love.   How
4. dwell __ with his ho - ly __ peo - ple ev - er-more.   How
5. Son, __ our __ Sav - ior and broth-er, praise to him;   All

to Refrain

1-4. bless-ed are they who are called to the ban-quet of the Lord.
5. glo - ry and praise to the Spir - it of God who makes us one.

824 AMÉN. EL CUERPO DE CRISTO

Refrain: All

A - mén. El Cuer - po de Cris - to. A -

mén. La San - gre del Se - ñor.   *Eat - ing your bod - y,*

drink - ing your blood, we be - come what we re - ceive. A -

mén. A - mén.

Verses: Cantor

1. A - mén. We re -
2. A - mén. Now we
3. A - mén. Lord, you
4. A - mén. We find
5. A - mén. We look

1. mem - ber your dy - ing and your ris - ing. A - mén.
2. of - fer the sac - ri - fice you gave us. A - mén.
3. make us one bod - y and one spir - it. A - mén.
4. you when we serve the poor and low - ly. A - mén.
5. for - ward to your re - turn in glo - ry. A - mén.

to Refrain

1. Y con - ti - go, Se - ñor, re - su - ci - ta - mos. A - mén.
2. Te o - fre - ce - mos, Se - ñor, to - do lo que so - mos. A - mén.
3. En tu cuer - po, Se - ñor, un __ pue - blo san - to. A - mén.
4. A ti mis - mo ser - vi - mos __ en los po - bres. A - mén.
5. Es - pe - ra - mos el día de __ tu ve - ni - da. A - mén.

Text and music: John Schiavone, b. 1947, © 1995, John Schiavone. Published by OCP Publications. All rights reserved.

SHEPHERD OF SOULS   825

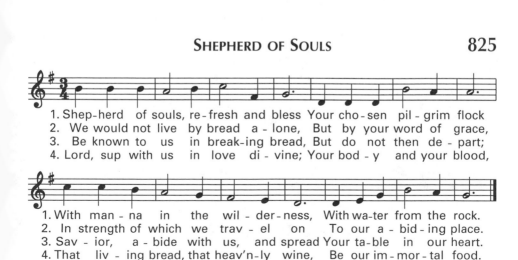

1. Shep - herd of souls, re - fresh and bless Your cho - sen pil - grim flock
2. We would not live by bread a - lone, But by your word of grace,
3. Be known to us in break - ing bread, But do not then de - part;
4. Lord, sup with us in love di - vine; Your bod - y and your blood,

1. With man - na in the wil - der - ness, With wa - ter from the rock.
2. In strength of which we trav - el on To our a - bid - ing place.
3. Sav - ior, a - bide with us, and spread Your ta - ble in our heart.
4. That liv - ing bread, that heav'n - ly wine, Be our im - mor - tal food.

Text: CM; verses 1–2, James Montgomery, 1771–1854; verses 3–4, anon.
Music: ST. AGNES; John B. Dykes, 1823–1876.

826   LORD, WHO AT THY FIRST EUCHARIST

1. Lord, who at thy first Eu - cha - rist did pray That
*1. *At that first Eu - cha - rist be - fore you died,* O
2. For all thy Church, O Lord, we in - ter - cede; Make
3. We pray thee, too, for wan - d'rers from thy fold; O
4. So, Lord, at length when sac - ra - ments shall cease, May

1. all thy Church might be for - ev - er one, Grant us at
1. *Lord, you prayed that all be one in you;* At this our
2. thou our sad di - vi - sions soon to cease; Draw us the
3. bring them back, Good Shep - herd of the sheep, Back to the
4. we be one with all thy Church a - bove, One with thy

1. ev - 'ry Eu - cha - rist to say With long - ing heart and
1. *Eu - cha - rist a - gain pre - side,* And in our hearts your
2. near - er each, to each we plead, By draw - ing all to
3. faith which saints be - lieved of old, Back to the Church which
4. saints in one un - bro - ken peace, One with thy saints in

1. soul, "Thy will be done." O may we all one bread, one
1. *law of love re - new.* O may we all one bread, one
2. thee, O Prince of Peace; Thus may we all one bread, one
3. still that faith doth keep; Soon may we all one bread, one
4. one un - bound - ed love; More bless - ed still in peace and

1. bod - y be, Through this blest Sac - ra - ment of U - ni - ty.
1. *bod - y be, Through this blest Sac - ra - ment of U - ni - ty.*
2. bod - y be, Through this blest Sac - ra - ment of U - ni - ty.
3. bod - y be, Through this blest Sac - ra - ment of U - ni - ty.
4. love to be One with the Trin - i - ty in U - ni - ty.

*Alternate verse.

Text: 10 10 10 10 10 10; William H. Turton, 1859–1938.
Music: UNDE ET MEMORES; William H. Monk, 1823–1889, alt.

827   MAY GOD BLESS AND KEEP YOU

May God bless and keep you, may God's face shine on you:

may God be kind to you and give you peace.

Text: Based on Numbers 6:22–27; Christopher Walker, b. 1947.
Music: Christopher Walker.

Go Make of All Disciples

828

1. "Go make of all dis - ci - ples:" We hear the call, O Lord, That comes from you, our Fa - ther, In your e - ter - nal Word. In - spire our ways of learn - ing Through earn-est, fer-vent prayer, And let our dai - ly liv - ing Re - veal you ev - 'ry - where.

2. "Go make of all dis - ci - ples:" Bap - tiz - ing in the name Of Fa - ther, Son, and Spir - it— From age to age the same. We call each new dis - ci - ple To fol - low you, O Lord, Re - deem - ing soul and bod - y By wa - ter and the Word.

3. "Go make of all dis - ci - ples:" We at your feet would stay Un - til each life's vo - ca - tion Ac - cents your ho - ly way. We cul - ti - vate the na - ture God plants in ev - 'ry heart, Re - veal - ing in our wit - ness The Mas - ter Teach-er's art.

4. "Go make of all dis - ci - ples:" We wel - come your com - mand; "Lo, I am with you al - ways:" We take your guid - ing hand. The task looms large be - fore us— We fol - low with-out fear. In heav'n and earth your pow - er Shall bring God's king - dom here.

Music: ELLACOMBE; *Gesangbuch der Herzogl, Wirtembergischen Katholischen Hofkapelle,* 1784, alt.; adapt. fr. Würth's *Katholisches Gesangbuch,* 1863.

829
THE SERVANT SONG

1, 6. Will you let me be your ser-vant, Let me be as
2. We are pil-grims on a jour-ney, We are trav-'lers
3. I will hold the Christ-light for you In the night-time
4. I will weep when you are weep-ing; When you laugh I'll
5. When we sing to God in heav-en We shall find such

1, 6. Christ to you; Pray that I may have the grace to
2. on the road; We are here to help each oth-er
3. of your fear; I will hold my hand out to you,
4. laugh with you. I will share your joy and sor-row
5. har-mo-ny, Born of all we've known to-geth-er

1, 6. Let you be my ser - vant, too.
2. Walk the mile and bear the load.
3. Speak the peace you long to hear.
4. 'Til we've seen this jour - ney through.
5. Of Christ's love and ag - o - ny.

Text: 87 87; Richard Gillard, b. 1953.
Music: SERVANT SONG; Richard Gillard.
Text and music © 1977, Scripture in Song (a div. of Integrity Music, Inc.). All rights reserved. Used with permission.

830
CITY OF GOD

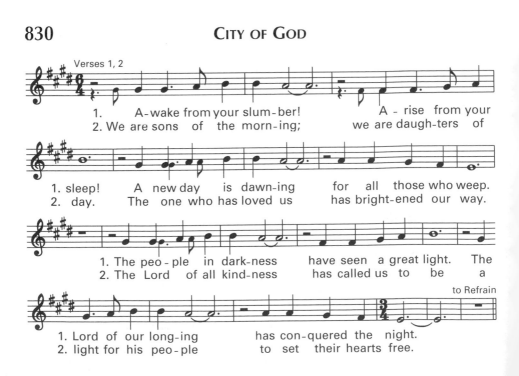

Verses 1, 2

1. A-wake from your slum-ber! A - rise from your
2. We are sons of the morn-ing; we are daugh-ters of

1. sleep! A new day is dawn-ing for all those who weep.
2. day. The one who has loved us has bright-ened our way.

1. The peo-ple in dark-ness have seen a great light. The
2. The Lord of all kind-ness has called us to be a

to Refrain

1. Lord of our long-ing has con-quered the night.
2. light for his peo-ple to set their hearts free.

Refrain

Let us build the cit-y of God. May our tears be turned in-to danc-ing! For the Lord, our light and our love, has turned the night in-to day!

Verse 3

3. God is light; in him there is no dark-ness.
3. Let us walk in his light, his chil-dren,
3. one and all. O com-fort my
3. peo-ple; make gen-tle your words. Pro-claim to my
3. cit-y the day of her birth.

Verse 4

4. O cit-y of glad-ness, now lift up your voice!
4. Pro-claim the good tid-ings that all may re-joice!

to Refrain

Text: Based on Isaiah 9; 1 John 1; Dan Schutte, b. 1947.
Music: Dan Schutte.

831

GOD HAS CHOSEN ME

Verses

1. God has cho-sen me, God has cho-sen me to bring good news
2. God has cho-sen me, God has cho-sen me to set a - light
3. God is call - ing me, God is call - ing me in all whose cry

1. to the poor. God has cho-sen me, God has cho-sen me to
2. a new fire. God has cho-sen me, God has cho-sen me to
3. is un - heard. God is call - ing me, God is call - ing me to

1. bring __ new sight to those search-ing for light: God has
2. bring __ to birth a new king - dom on earth: God has
3. raise up the voice with no pow - er or choice: God is

Refrain

1. cho - sen me, cho - sen me: And to tell the world
2. cho - sen me, cho - sen me:
3. call - ing me, call - ing me:

that God's king-dom is near, to re - move op-pres - sion and

break down fear, yes, God's time is near, God's time is near,

God's time is near, God's time is near.

Text and music: Bernadette Farrell, b. 1957, © 1990, Bernadette Farrell. Published by OCP Publications. All rights reserved.

HERE I AM, LORD

Verses

1. I, the Lord of sea and sky, I have heard my peo-ple cry.
2. I, the Lord of snow and rain, I have borne my peo-ple's pain.
3. I, the Lord of wind and flame, I will tend the poor and lame.

1. All who dwell in dark and sin My hand will save. I, who
2. I have wept for love of them. They turn a-way. I will
3. I will set a feast for them. My hand will save. Fin-est

1. made the stars of night, I will make their dark-ness bright.
2. break their hearts of stone, Give them hearts for love a-lone.
3. bread I will pro-vide Till their hearts be sat-is-fied.

1. Who will bear my light to them? Whom shall I send?
2. I will speak my word to them. Whom shall I send?
3. I will give my life to them. Whom shall I send?

Refrain

Here I am, Lord. Is it I, Lord? I have heard you

call-ing in the night. I will go, Lord, if you lead me.

I will hold your peo-ple in my heart.

Text: Based on Isaiah 6; Dan Schutte, b. 1947.
Music: Dan Schutte.

GO FORTH

Refrain

Go forth, spread-ing good news to the world; proclaim it in ev - 'ry land: Vic-t'ry and glo - ry belong to the Lamb that was slain. Go forth in Je - sus'

1-4
name!

2 to Verses
name!

Final
Go

forth in Je - sus' name!

Verses

1. Go to all na - tions, tell them the signs you've seen.
2. Go to all na - tions, preach-ing the Word of God,
3. Go to all na - tions, cur - ing the blind and lame,
4. Go to all na - tions, bap - tiz - ing all who be - lieve.

2

1. Tell them the Sav - ior is ris - en, con - quer-ing
2. spread-ing the sto - ry of Christ, __ who came a-
3. cur - ing the ones most in need, __ giv - ing them
4. Go make dis - ci - ples of Christ; __ go to all

to Refrain

1. death up - on __ the Tree of Life! __
2. mong us bear - ing the Light of God! __
3. hope and free - dom from ev - 'ry ill! __
4. na - tions, preach-ing the ho - ly Word __ of God! __

Text and music: Ricky Manalo, CSP, b. 1965, © 1997, Ricky Manalo, CSP. Published by OCP Publications. All rights reserved.

CELTIC ALLELUIA: SENDING FORTH

834

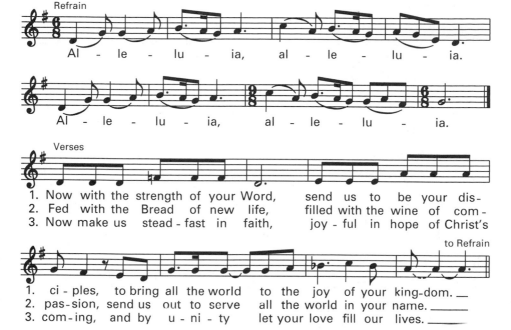

Refrain

Al - le - lu - ia, al - le - lu - ia.
Al - le - lu - ia, al - le - lu - ia.

Verses

1. Now with the strength of your Word, send us to be your dis-
2. Fed with the Bread of new life, filled with the wine of com-
3. Now make us stead-fast in faith, joy-ful in hope of Christ's

to Refrain

1. ci - ples, to bring all the world to the joy of your king-dom. __
2. pas-sion, send us out to serve all the world in your name. ____
3. com-ing, and by u - ni - ty let your love fill our lives. ____

Text and music: *Celtic Mass*; Fintan O'Carroll, d. 1977, and Christopher Walker, b. 1947,
    © 1985, 1996, Fintan O'Carroll and Christopher Walker. Published by OCP Publications. All rights reserved.

THE SPIRIT SENDS US FORTH

835

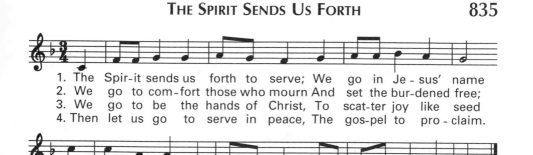

1. The Spir-it sends us forth to serve; We go in Je - sus' name
2. We go to com-fort those who mourn And set the bur-dened free;
3. We go to be the hands of Christ, To scat-ter joy like seed
4. Then let us go to serve in peace, The gos-pel to pro - claim.

1. To bring glad ti - dings to the poor, God's fa - vor to pro-claim.
2. Where hope is dim, to share a dream And help the blind to see.
3. And, all our days, to cher-ish life, To do the lov-ing deed.
4. God's Spir - it has em-pow-er'd us; We go in Je - sus' name.

Text: CM; Delores Dufner, OSB, b. 1939, © 1993, The Sisters of St. Benedict, St. Joseph, MN.
    Published by OCP Publications. All rights reserved.
Music: AZMON; Carl Gotthilf Gläser, 1784–1829.

836
TAKE CHRIST TO THE WORLD

Refrain: 1st time: Cantor(s), All repeat; thereafter: All

Take Christ to the world, cel-e-brate our faith, man-i-fest his love to all:

take Christ to the world, show that we are his in the way we live.

Verses 1-3: Cantor(s)

1. We are the bod - y of Christ made in - car - nate
2. When we gath - er to - geth - er to pray
3. We are called to be hear - ers and bear - ers

1. in this time and place. Let us o - pen our-
2. in his ho - ly name, he is our strength and the
3. of the word of Christ: may it flour - ish and

to Refrain

1. selves to be tru - ly path-ways of his grace.
2. song on our lips, he is pres-ent in our midst.
3. grow in our hearts, bring-ing oth - ers to his light.

Verses 4, 5: Cantor(s)

4. When we of - fer our-selves ___ to join more com-
5. Go - ing forth, we can be for the world liv - ing

4. plete - ly in his life, we are the al - tar,
5. wit - ness - es of love in our ser - vice to

4. we are the meal, we be-come his sac - ri - fice. (to Refrain)
5. all those we meet as we jour - ney on in faith. (to Final Refrain)

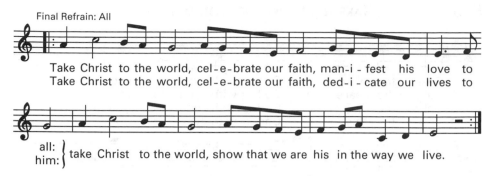

Final Refrain: All

Take Christ to the world, cel-e-brate our faith, man-i-fest his love to
Take Christ to the world, cel-e-brate our faith, ded-i-cate our lives to

all: } take Christ to the world, show that we are his in the way we live.
him: }

SERVANT SONG 837

Verses

1. What do you want of me, Lord? Where do you
2. I hear you call my name, Lord, and I am
3. A-bove, be-low, and a-round me, be-fore, be-
4. You are the light in my dark-ness. You are my
5. I am your song and ser-vant, sing-ing your

1. want me to serve you? Where can I sing your
2. moved with-in me. Your Spir-it stirs my
3. hind, and all through me, your Spir-it burns deep with-
4. strength when I'm wea-ry. You give me sight when I'm
5. praise like Ma-ry. Sur-ren-dered to your

1. prais - es? I am your song.
2. deep - est self. Sing your songs in me.
3. in me. Fire my life with your love.
4. blind - ed. Come, see for me.
5. Spir - it, "Let it be done to me."

Refrain

1. Je - sus, Je - sus, you are the Lord.
2. Je - sus, Je - sus, you are my Lord.
3. Je - sus, Je - sus, be the warmth of my heart.
4. Je - sus, Je - sus, you are my Light.
5. Je - sus, Je - sus, "Let it be done to me."

1-5. Je - sus, Je - sus, you are the way.

838   TAKE THE WORD OF GOD WITH YOU

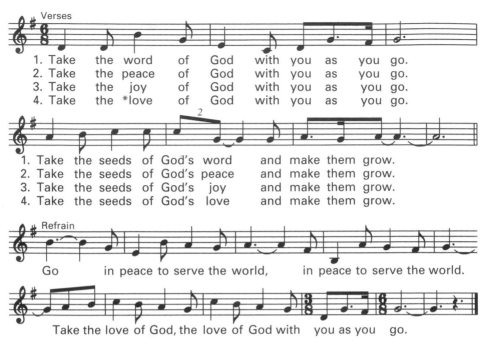

Verses

1. Take the word of God with you as you go.
2. Take the peace of God with you as you go.
3. Take the joy of God with you as you go.
4. Take the *love of God with you as you go.

1. Take the seeds of God's word and make them grow.
2. Take the seeds of God's peace and make them grow.
3. Take the seeds of God's joy and make them grow.
4. Take the seeds of God's love and make them grow.

Refrain

Go in peace to serve the world, in peace to serve the world.

Take the love of God, the love of God with you as you go.

*Add other words if needed, such as "faith," "hope," etc.

839   IF YOU BELIEVE AND I BELIEVE

If you be-lieve and I be-lieve and we to-geth-er pray,

the Ho-ly Spir-it must come down and set God's peo-ple free,

and set God's peo-ple free, and set God's peo-ple free;

the Ho-ly Spir-it must come down and set God's peo-ple free.

LORD, WHOSE LOVE IN HUMBLE SERVICE

840

1. Lord, whose love in hum-ble ser - vice Bore the
2. Still your chil - dren wan-der home - less; Still the
3. As we wor - ship, grant us vi - sion, Till your
4. Called from wor - ship in - to ser - vice Forth in

1. weight of hu - man need, Who up - on the cross, for -
2. hun - gry cry for bread; Still the cap - tives long for
3. love's re - veal-ing light, Till the height and depth and
4. your great name we go, To the child, the youth, the

1. sak - en, Of-fered mer - cy's per - fect deed; We, your
2. free - dom; Still in grief we mourn our dead. As, O
3. great - ness Dawns up - on our hu - man sight: Mak - ing
4. a - ged, Love in liv - ing deeds to show; Hope and

1. ser - vants, bring the wor - ship Not of voice a -
2. Lord, your deep com - pas - sion Healed the sick and
3. known the needs and bur - dens Your com - pas - sion
4. health, good - will and com - fort, Coun - sel, aid, and

1. lone, but heart: Con - se - crat - ing to your
2. freed the soul, Use the love your Spir - it
3. bids us bear, Stir - ring us to tire - less
4. peace we give, That your chil - dren, Lord, in

1. pur - pose Ev - 'ry gift which you im - part.
2. kin - dles Still to save and make us whole.
3. striv - ing, Your a - bun - dant life to share.
4. free - dom, May your mer - cy know, and live.

Text: 87 87 D; Albert F. Bayly, 1901–1984, alt., © Oxford University Press, London. All rights reserved. Used with permission.
Music: BEACH SPRING; *The Sacred Harp*, 1844.

841   YOUR LOVE, O GOD, HAS ALL THE WORLD CREATED

1. Your love, O God, has all the world cre - a - ted,
2. We bring you, Lord, in fer - vent in - ter - ces - sion
3. From out the dark - ness of our hope's frus - tra - tion,
4. In pit - y look up - on your chil - dren's striv - ing
5. In - spire your church, mid earth's dis - cord - ant voic - es,

1. And led your peo - ple to this pre - sent hour;
2. The chil - dren of your world - wide fam - i - ly:
3. From all the bro - ken i - dols of our pride,
4. In dai - ly strug - gles to be un - der - stood,
5. To preach the gos - pel of its Lord a - bove,

1. In Christ we see life's glo - ry con - sum - mat - ed;
2. With con - trite hearts we of - fer our con - fes - sion,
3. We turn to seek your truth's il - lu - mi - na - tion,
4. Till at the full - ness of your truth ar - riv - ing,
5. Un - til the day this war - ring world re - joic - es

1. Your Spir - it man - i - fests his liv - ing pow'r.
2. For we have sinned a - gainst your char - i - ty.
3. And find your mer - cy wait - ing at our side.
4. We find in Christ the crown of ev - 'ry good.
5. To hear the might - y har - mo - nies of love.

Text: 11 10 11 10; Albert F. Bayly, 1901–1984, alt.
Music: NORTHBROOK; Reginald S. Thatcher, 1888–1957, © Oxford University Press. All rights reserved. Used with permission.

842   WE SHALL OVERCOME

1. We shall o - ver - come, we shall o - ver - come,
2. We'll walk hand in hand, we'll walk hand in hand,
3. We shall all be free, we shall all be free,
4. We are not a - fraid, we are not a - fraid,
5. We shall live in peace, we shall live in peace,

1. we shall o - ver-come some - day; Oh, deep in my heart
2. we'll walk hand in hand some - day; Oh, deep in my heart
3. we shall all be free some - day; Oh, deep in my heart
4. we are not a - fraid to - day; Oh, deep in my heart
5. we shall live in peace some-day; Oh, deep in my heart

1. I do be - lieve, we shall o - ver - come some - day.
2. I do be - lieve, we'll walk hand in hand some - day.
3. I do be - lieve, we shall all be free some - day.
4. I do be - lieve, we are not a - fraid to - day.
5. I do be - lieve, we shall live in peace some - day.

Text: Traditional.
Music: Traditional.

THE CHURCH OF CHRIST IN EVERY AGE 843

1. The Church of Christ in ev - 'ry age Be - set by
2. A - cross the world, a - cross the street, The vic - tims
3. Then let the ser - vant Church a - rise, A car - ing
4. For he a - lone, whose blood was shed, Can cure the
5. We have no mis - sion but to serve In full o -

1. change but Spir - it led, Must claim and test its her - i -
2. of in - jus - tice cry For shel - ter and for bread to
3. Church that longs to be A part - ner in Christ's sac - ri -
4. fe - ver in our blood, And teach us how to share our
5. be - dience to our Lord: To care for all, with - out re -

1. tage And keep on ris - ing from the dead.
2. eat, And nev - er live un - til they die.
3. fice, And clothed in Christ's hu - man - i - ty.
4. bread And feed the starv - ing mul - ti - tude.
5. serve, And spread his lib - er - at - ing Word.

CHRIST'S PEACE

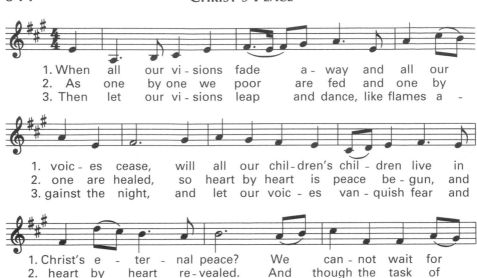

1. When all our vi-sions fade a-way and all our
2. As one by one we poor are fed and one by
3. Then let our vi-sions leap and dance, like flames a -

1. voic-es cease, will all our chil-dren's chil-dren live in
2. one are healed, so heart by heart is peace be-gun, and
3. gainst the night, and let our voic-es van-quish fear and

1. Christ's e - ter - nal peace? We can-not wait for
2. heart by heart re-vealed. And though the task of
3. claim the prom-ised light. Our God will keep our

1. bet-ter times, but now must dream and dare to bring Christ's
2. peace is great, and dai-ly do we fail, yet Christ shall
3. vi-sions bright when all our voic-es cease, and ev-'ry

1. peace to wound-ed earth with Christ's own lov-ing care.
2. come to ev-'ry heart, the reign of God pre-vail.
3. child will live in love and Christ's e - ter - nal peace.

Text: CMD; M.D. Ridge.
Music: TIDEWATER; M.D. Ridge.
Text and music © 1989, M.D. Ridge. Published by OCP Publications. All rights reserved.

845   # GO DOWN, MOSES

Verses

1. When Is - rael was in E - gypt's land,
2. The Lord told Mo - ses what to do,
3. They jour-neyed on at God's com-mand,
4. Oh, let us all from bond-age flee,

Let my peo-ple go;

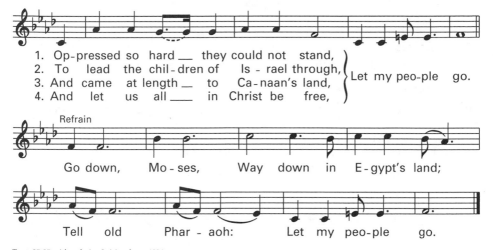

1. Op-pressed so hard __ they could not stand,
2. To lead the chil-dren of Is - rael through,
3. And came at length __ to Ca-naan's land,
4. And let us all __ in Christ be free,

Let my peo-ple go.

Refrain

Go down, Mo - ses, Way down in E-gypt's land;

Tell old Phar - aoh: Let my peo-ple go.

Text: 85 85 with refrain; Spiritual, ca. 1831.
Music: GO DOWN, MOSES; Spiritual, ca. 1831.

WHATSOEVER YOU DO   846

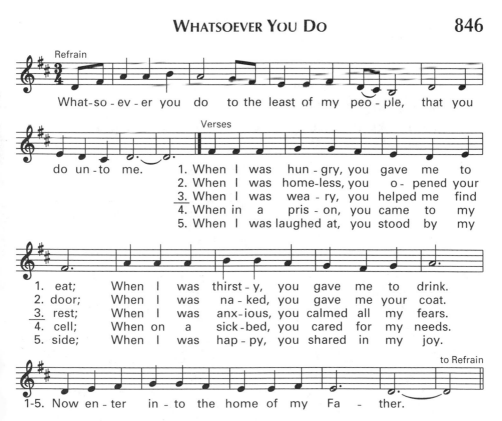

Refrain

What-so-ev-er you do to the least of my peo-ple, that you

Verses

do un-to me.
1. When I was hun-gry, you gave me to
2. When I was home-less, you o-pened your
3. When I was wea-ry, you helped me find
4. When in a pris-on, you came to my
5. When I was laughed at, you stood by my

1. eat; When I was thirst-y, you gave me to drink.
2. door; When I was na-ked, you gave me your coat.
3. rest; When I was anx-ious, you calmed all my fears.
4. cell; When on a sick-bed, you cared for my needs.
5. side; When I was hap-py, you shared in my joy.

to Refrain

1-5. Now en-ter in-to the home of my Fa - ther.

Text and music: Willard F. Jabusch, b. 1930, © 1967, Willard F. Jabusch. All rights reserved. Administered by OCP Publications.

847 THE CRY OF THE POOR

Refrain

The Lord hears the cry of the poor. Bless-ed be the Lord.

Verses: Slightly faster

1. I will bless the Lord at all times, with praise
2. Let the low - ly hear and be glad: the Lord
3. Ev - 'ry spir - it crushed, God will save; will be
4. We pro-claim your great - ness, O God, your praise

1. ev - er in my mouth. Let my soul glo - ry in the
2. lis - tens to their pleas; and to hearts bro - ken, God is
3. ran-som for their lives; will be safe shel - ter for their
4. ev - er in our mouth; ev - 'ry face bright-ened in your

to Refrain

1. Lord, who will hear the cry of the poor.
2. near, who will hear the cry of the poor.
3. fears, and will hear the cry of the poor.
4. light, for you hear the cry of the poor.

Text: Based on Psalm 34:1–2, 17–18, 19, 22; John Foley, S.J., b. 1939.
Music: John Foley, S.J.
Text and music © 1978, 1991, John B. Foley, S.J., and New Dawn Music. Published by OCP Publications. All rights reserved.

848 CHRIST IS THE KING

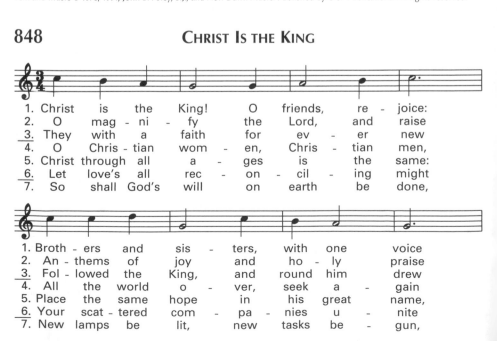

1. Christ is the King! O friends, re - joice:
2. O mag - ni - fy the Lord, and raise
3. They with a faith for ev - er new
4. O Chris - tian wom - en, Chris - tian men,
5. Christ through all a - ges is the same:
6. Let love's all rec - on - cil - ing might
7. So shall God's will on earth be done,

1. Broth - ers and sis - ters, with one voice
2. An - thems of joy and ho - ly praise
3. Fol - lowed the King, and round him drew
4. All the world o - ver, seek a - gain
5. Place the same hope in his great name,
6. Your scat - tered com - pa - nies u - nite
7. New lamps be lit, new tasks be - gun,

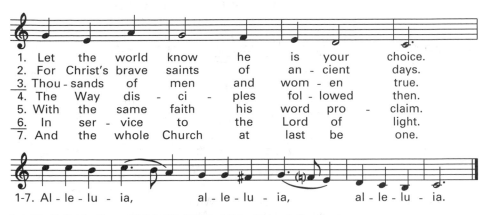

1. Let the world know he is your choice.
2. For Christ's brave saints of an - cient days.
3. Thou - sands of men and wom - en true.
4. The Way dis - ci - ples fol - lowed then.
5. With the same faith his word pro - claim.
6. In ser - vice to the Lord of light.
7. And the whole Church at last be one.

1-7. Al - le - lu - ia, al - le - lu - ia, al - le - lu - ia.

Text: 888 with alleluias; George K.A. Bell, 1883–1958, alt., © Oxford University Press, London.
  All rights reserved. Used with permission.
Music: GELOBT SEI GOTT; Melchior Vulpius, ca. 1560–1616.

THEY'LL KNOW WE ARE CHRISTIANS 849

Verses

1. We are one in the Spir - it, we are one in the Lord,
2. We will walk with each oth - er, we will walk hand in hand,
3. We will work with each oth - er, we will work side by side,
4. All ___ praise to the Fa - ther, from ___ whom all things come,

1. We are one in the Spir - it, we are one in the Lord,
2. We will walk with each oth - er, we will walk hand in hand,
3. We will work with each oth - er, we will work side by side,
4. And all praise to Christ Je - sus, his ___ on - ly ___ Son,

1. And we pray that all u - ni - ty may one day be re - stored.
2. And to - geth - er we'll spread the news that God is in our land.
3. And we'll guard each one's dig - ni - ty and save ___ each one's pride.
4. And all praise to the Spir - it, who ___ makes ___ us ___ one.

Refrain

And they'll know we are Chris-tians by our love, by our love, Yes they'll know we are Chris-tians by our love.

Text: 13 13 14 with refrain; Peter Scholtes, b. 1938.
Music: ST. BRENDAN'S; Peter Scholtes.
Text and music © 1966, 1967, F.E.L. Church Publications, Ltd., assigned 1991 to the Lorenz Corporation.
  All rights reserved. Used with permission.

850

In Christ There Is No East or West

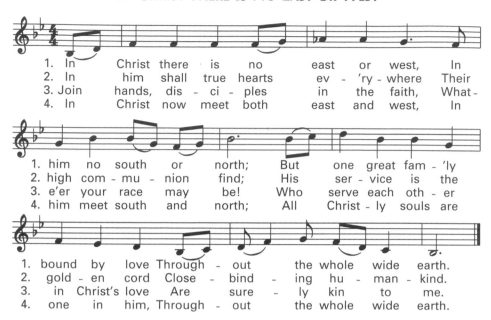

1. In Christ there is no east or west, In
2. In him shall true hearts ev - 'ry - where Their
3. Join hands, dis - ci - ples in the faith, What-
4. In Christ now meet both east and west, In

1. him no south or north; But one great fam - 'ly
2. high com - mu - nion find; His ser - vice is the
3. e'er your race may be! Who serve each oth - er
4. him meet south and north; All Christ - ly souls are

1. bound by love Through - out the whole wide earth.
2. gold - en cord Close - bind - ing hu - man - kind.
3. in Christ's love Are sure - ly kin to me.
4. one in him, Through - out the whole wide earth.

Text: CM; Galatians 3:28; John Oxenham, 1852–1941, alt.
Music: McKEE; Spiritual; adapt. by Harry T. Burleigh, 1866–1949.

851

Companions on the Journey

Refrain

We are com-pan-ions on the jour - ney, break-ing bread and

shar-ing life; and in the love we bear is the hope we share for we be-

lieve in the love of our God, we be-lieve in the love of our God.

Verse 1

1. No long-er strang-ers to each oth - er; no long-er

1. strang-ers in God's house; we are fed and we are nour-ished by the

to Refrain

1. strength of those who care, by the strength of those who care.

Verse 2

2. We have been gift-ed with each oth - er, and we are called by the

2. Word of the Lord: to act with jus-tice, to love ten-der - ly, and to walk

to Refrain

2. hum-bly with our God, to walk hum-bly with our God.

Verse 3

3. We will seek and we shall find; we will knock and the door will be

3. o-pened; we will ask and it shall be giv-en, for we be-lieve in the

to Refrain

3. love of our God, we be-lieve in the love of our God.

Verse 4

4. We are made for the glo-ry of our God, for ser-vice in the name of

4. Je-sus; to walk side by side with hope in our hearts, for we be-

to Refrain

4. lieve in the love of our God, we be-lieve in the love of our God.

Text: Based on Micah 6:8; Matthew 7:7; Carey Landry, b. 1944.
Music: Carey Landry.

SOMOS EL CUERPO DE CRISTO/ WE ARE THE BODY OF CHRIST

Refrain: All

So-mos el cuer-po de Cris-to. We are the bod-y of
So-mos el cuer-po de Cris-to. We are the bod-y of

Christ. ℣ He-mos o - í - do el lla - ma-do; we've an-swered
Christ. Tra - e - mos su san - to men - sa - je. We come to

1
"Yes," to the call of the Lord.
bring the good news to the

2 to Verses Cantor
world. 3. Que

Final
world.

Verses
Cantor

1. Dios vie-ne al mun-do a tra - vés de no-so-tros.
   _ mun-do a cum-plir la mi - sión de la I-gle-sia,
2. Ca - da per - so - na es par-te del rei-no;
   _ To - das las ra - zas que ha-bi-tan la tie-rra,
3. nues-tras ac - cio-nes re - fle-jen jus-ti - cia;
   Va - mos al mun-do a cui - dar su re-ba-ño.

So-mos el cuer-po de

Cantor

Cris-to.

1. God is re-vealed when we love one an-oth - er.
   _ Bring-ing the light of God's mer-cy to oth-ers,
2. Put - ting a stop to all dis-crim-i - na - tion,
   _ All are in-vit - ed to feast in the ban-quet.
3. Stop-ping a - buse and re - liev-ing the hun-gry,
   Serv-ing each oth - er we build up the king-dom;

All

We are the bod-y of Christ.

1, 3, 5

Cantor 2, 4, 6
to Refrain

1. Al
2. ℟ Christ.
3. ℟

FATHER, LORD OF ALL CREATION

1. Fa-ther, Lord of all cre - a-tion, Ground of be-ing,
2. Je-sus Christ, the man for oth-ers, We, your peo-ple,
3. Ho-ly Spir-it, rush-ing, burn-ing Wind and flame of

1. life and love; Height and depth be - yond de - scrip-tion
2. make our prayer: Give us grace to love all oth - ers,
3. Pen - te - cost, Fire our hearts a - fresh with yearn-ing

1. On - ly life in you can prove: You are mor - tal
2. Those whose bur-dens we can share. Where your name binds
3. To re - gain what we have lost. May your love u -

1. life's de - pen - dence: Thought, speech, sight are
2. us to - geth - er You, Lord Christ, will
3. nite our ac - tion, Nev - er - more to

1. ours by grace; Yours is ev - 'ry hour's ex -
2. sure - ly be; Where no self - ish - ness can
3. speak a - lone: God, in us a - bol - ish

1. ist - ence, Sov - 'reign Lord of time and space.
2. sev - er, There your love we all may see.
3. fac - tion. God, through us your love make known.

854 PANIS ANGELICUS/HOLY AND LIVING BREAD

1. Pa - nis an - gé - li - cus, fit ___ pa - nis hó - mi - num,
2. Te, tri - na Dé - i - tas ú - na - que, pó - sci - mus,
1. Ho - ly and liv - ing bread, won - drous food from heav - en sent,
2. God, ho - ly Three - In - One, through this off - 'ring of your Son

1. Dat pa - nis cáe - li - cus fi - gú - ris tér - mi - num.
2. Sic nos tu ví - si - ta, sic - ut te có - li - mus;
1. God's sac - ri - fice fore - told—now in our hands we hold.
2. All now on earth can see what we are called to be:

1. O res mi - rá - bi - lis man - dú - cat Dó - mi - num,
2. Per tu - as sé - mi - tas duc nos quo tén - di - mus,
1. Sign and re - al - i - ty, chal - lenge for us to be
2. Hope for a world in need, signs that love can suc - ceed

1. Pau - per, ser - vus, et hú - mi - lis.
2. Ad lu - cem quam in - há - bi - tas.
1. Hum - ble ser - vants to all the poor.
2. Where true jus - tice and peace en - dure.

Text: 12 12 12 8; Latin; St. Thomas Aquinas, 1227–1274; English, Owen Alstott, b. 1947;
© 2001, OCP Publications. All rights reserved.
Music: SACRIS SOLEMNIIS; Louis Lambillotte, SJ, 1796–1855.

855 O LORD, I AM NOT WORTHY

1. O Lord, I am not wor - thy That thou should'st come to me;
2. And hum - bly I'll re - ceive thee, The Bride - groom of my soul,
3. E - ter - nal Ho - ly Spir - it, Un - wor - thy though I be,
4. In - crease my faith, dear Je - sus, In thy real pres - ence here,

1. But speak the word of com - fort, My spir - it healed shall be.
2. No more by sin to grieve thee Or fly thy sweet con - trol.
3. Pre - pare me to re - ceive him And trust the Word to me.
4. And make me feel most deep - ly That thou to me art near.

Text: 76 76; based on Matthew 8:8; O Herr, ich bin nicht würdig; Landshuter Gesangbuch, 1777; tr. anon.
Music: NON DIGNUS; anon.; Catholic Youth Hymnal, 1871.

O SACRAMENT MOST HOLY

Verses

1. O Je - sus, we a - dore you, Who, in your love di - vine,
2. O Je - sus, we a - dore you, Our vic - tim and our priest,
3. O Je - sus, we a - dore you, Our Sav - ior and our King,
4. O Je - sus, we a - dore you; Come, live in us we pray,
5. O come, all you who la - bor In sor-row and in pain;

1. Con - ceal your might - y God-head In forms of bread and wine.
2. Whose pre-cious blood and bod - y Be - come our sa - cred feast.
3. And with the saints and an - gels Our hum - ble hom - age bring.
4. That all our thoughts and ac - tions Be yours a - lone to - day.
5. Come, eat this bread from heav - en; Your peace and strength re - gain.

Refrain

O sac - ra-ment most ho - ly, O sac - ra-ment di - vine,

All praise and all thanks-giv - ing Be ev - 'ry mo-ment thine!

Text: 76 76 with refrain; refrain from the *Raccolta*, Rome, 19th cent.; tr. unknown; verses by Irvin Udulutsch, OFM, Cap.,
© 1958, The Basilian Fathers c/o The Willis Music Company. All rights reserved. Used with permission.
Music: FULDA; *Gebet-und Gesangbuch*, Fulda, 1891.

SOUL OF MY SAVIOR

857

1. Soul of my Sav - ior, sanc - ti - fy my breast; Bod - y of
2. Strength and pro - tec - tion may thy Pas-sion be; O Bless-ed
3. Hear me, Lord Je - sus, lis - ten as I pray; "Lead me from

1. Christ, be thou my sav-ing guest; Blood of my Sav - ior, bathe me
2. Je - sus, hear and an-swer me; Deep in thy wounds, Lord, hide and
3. night to nev - er end-ing day. Fill all the world with love and

1. in thy tide; Wash me with wa - ter flow-ing from his side.
2. shel-ter me; So shall I nev - er, nev - er part from thee.
3. grace di - vine, And glo - ry, laud, and praise be ev - er thine."

Text: 10 10 10 10; verses 1–2 attr. to Pope John XXII, 1249–1334; tr. by Edward Caswall, 1814–1878, alt.;
verse 3, composite, based on *God of Our Fathers*; Daniel C. Roberts, 1841–1907.
Music: ANIMA CHRISTI; W.J. Maher, SJ, 1823–1877, alt.

858 ADORO TE DEVOTE/GODHEAD HERE IN HIDING

Verses 1-7: Latin

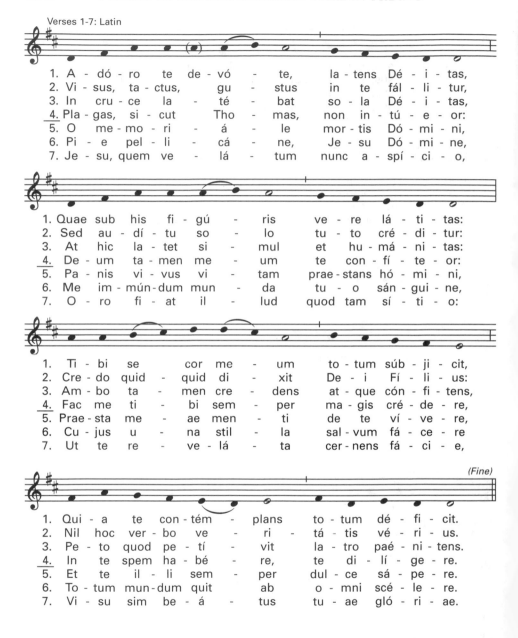

1. A - dó - ro te de - vó - te, la - tens Dé - i - tas,
2. Vi - sus, ta - ctus, gu - stus in te fál - li - tur,
3. In cru - ce la - té - bat so - la Dé - i - tas,
4. Pla - gas, si - cut Tho - mas, non in - tú - e - or:
5. O me - mo - ri - á - le mor - tis Dó - mi - ni,
6. Pi - e pel - li - cá - ne, Je - su Dó - mi - ne,
7. Je - su, quem ve - lá - tum nunc a - spí - ci - o,

1. Quae sub his fi - gú - ris ve - re lá - ti - tas:
2. Sed au - dí - tu so - lo tu - to cré - di - tur:
3. At hic la - tet si - mul et hu - má - ni - tas:
4. De - um ta - men me - um te con - fí - te - or:
5. Pa - nis vi - vus vi - tam prae - stans hó - mi - ni,
6. Me im - mún - dum mun - da tu - o sán - gui - ne,
7. O - ro fi - at il - lud quod tam sí - ti - o:

1. Ti - bi se cor me - um to - tum súb - ji - cit,
2. Cre - do quid - quid di - xit De - i Fí - li - us:
3. Am - bo ta - men cre - dens at - que cón - fi - tens,
4. Fac me ti - bi sem - per ma - gis cré - de - re,
5. Prae - sta me - ae men - ti de te ví - ve - re,
6. Cu - jus u - na stil - la sal - vum fá - ce - re
7. Ut te re - ve - lá - ta cer - nens fá - ci - e,

(Fine)

1. Qui - a te con - tém - plans to - tum dé - fi - cit.
2. Nil hoc ver - bo ve - ri - tá - tis vé - ri - us.
3. Pe - to quod pe - tí - vit la - tro paé - ni - tens.
4. In te spem ha - bé - re, te di - lí - ge - re.
5. Et te il - li sem - per dul - ce sá - pe - re.
6. To - tum mun - dum quit ab o - mni scé - le - re.
7. Vi - su sim be - á - tus tu - ae gló - ri - ae.

Verses 1-7: English

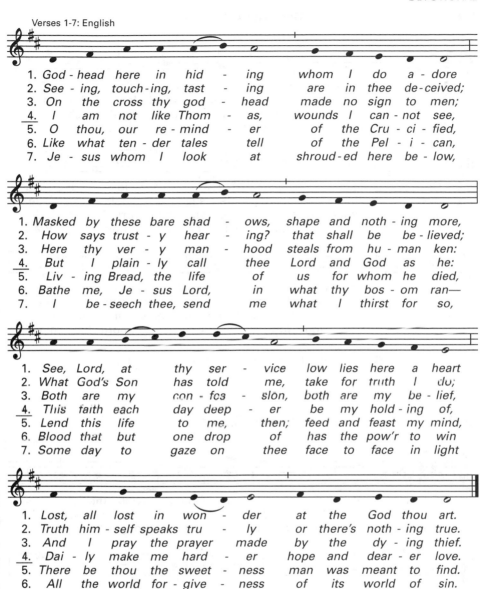

1. God - head here in hid - ing whom I do a - dore
2. See - ing, touch-ing, tast - ing are in thee de-ceived;
3. On the cross thy god - head made no sign to men;
4. I am not like Thom - as, wounds I can-not see,
5. O thou, our re - mind - er of the Cru - ci - fied,
6. Like what ten - der tales tell of the Pel - i - can,
7. Je - sus whom I look at shroud-ed here be - low,

1. Masked by these bare shad - ows, shape and noth - ing more,
2. How says trust - y hear - ing? that shall be be - lieved;
3. Here thy ver - y man - hood steals from hu - man ken:
4. But I plain - ly call thee Lord and God as he:
5. Liv - ing Bread, the life of us for whom he died,
6. Bathe me, Je - sus Lord, in what thy bos - om ran—
7. I be - seech thee, send me what I thirst for so,

1. See, Lord, at thy ser - vice low lies here a heart
2. What God's Son has told me, take for truth I do;
3. Both are my con - fes - sion, both are my be - lief,
4. This faith each day deep - er be my hold - ing of,
5. Lend this life to me, then; feed and feast my mind,
6. Blood that but one drop of has the pow'r to win
7. Some day to gaze on thee face to face in light

1. Lost, all lost in won - der at the God thou art.
2. Truth him - self speaks tru - ly or there's noth - ing true.
3. And I pray the prayer made by the dy - ing thief.
4. Dai - ly make me hard - er hope and dear - er love.
5. There be thou the sweet - ness man was meant to find.
6. All the world for - give - ness of its world of sin.
7. And be blest for - ev - er with thy glo - ry's sight.

Text: 11 11 11 11; St. Thomas Aquinas, ca. 1224–1274, alt.; tr. by Gerard Manley Hopkins, SJ, 1844–1899, alt.
Music: ADORO TE DEVOTE; Chant, Mode V; *Paris Processional*, 1697.

859   BEAUTIFUL SAVIOR

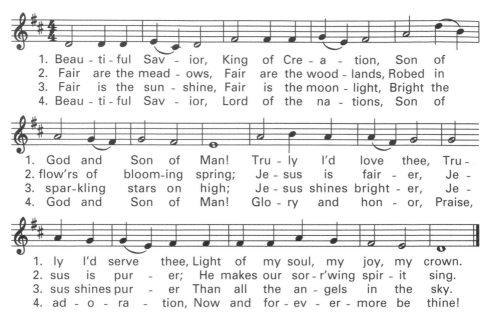

1. Beau-ti-ful Sav - ior, King of Cre-a - tion, Son of
2. Fair are the mead-ows, Fair are the wood-lands, Robed in
3. Fair is the sun-shine, Fair is the moon-light, Bright the
4. Beau-ti-ful Sav - ior, Lord of the na - tions, Son of

1. God and Son of Man! Tru-ly I'd love thee, Tru-
2. flow'rs of bloom-ing spring; Je-sus is fair - er, Je-
3. spar-kling stars on high; Je-sus shines bright-er, Je-
4. God and Son of Man! Glo-ry and hon - or, Praise,

1. ly I'd serve thee, Light of my soul, my joy, my crown.
2. sus is pur - er; He makes our sor-r'wing spir-it sing.
3. sus shines pur - er Than all the an-gels in the sky.
4. ad - o - ra - tion, Now and for-ev-er-more be thine!

Text: 55 7 55 8; Psalm 45:3; *Schönster Herr Jesu*, in *Münster Gesangbuch*, 1677; tr. by Joseph A. Seiss, 1823–1904.
Music: ST. ELIZABETH; Trad. Silesian Melody; Hoffman and Richter's *Schlesische Volkslieder*, Leipzig, 1842.

860   IN THE GARDEN

Verses

1. I come to the gar-den a - lone, while the dew is
2. He speaks, and the sound of his voice is so sweet the
3. I'd stay in the gar-den with him though the night a-

1. still on the ros - es; and the voice I hear, fall-ing
2. birds hush their sing - ing, and the mel - o - dy that he
3. round me be fall - ing, but he bids me go; through the

1. on my ear, the Son of God dis-clos - es.
2. gave to me with-in my heart is ring - ing.
3. voice of woe his voice to me is call - ing.

And he walks with me, and he talks with me, and he tells me I am his own, and the joy we share, as we tar - ry there, none oth - er has ev - er known.

Text: 89 55 7 with refrain; C. Austin Miles, 1868–1946.
Music: GARDEN; C. Austin Miles.

NEARER, MY GOD TO THEE   861

1. Near - er, my God, to thee, Near - er to thee!
2. Though like the wan - der - er, The sun gone down,
3. There let the way ap - pear, Steps un - to heav'n;
4. Then, with my wak - ing thoughts Bright with thy praise,
5. Or if, on joy - ful wing Cleav - ing the sky,

1. E'en though it be a cross That rais - eth me,
2. Dark - ness be o - ver me, My rest a stone;
3. All that thou send - est me, In mer - cy given;
4. Out of my ston - y griefs Beth - el I'll raise;
5. Sun, moon, and stars for - got, Up - ward I fly,

1. Still all my song shall be, Near - er, my God, to thee;
2. Yet in my dreams I'd be Near - er, my God, to thee;
3. An - gels to beck - on me Near - er, my God, to thee;
4. So by my woes to be Near - er, my God, to thee;
5. Still all my song shall be, Near - er, my God, to thee;

1-5. Near - er, my God, to thee, Near - er to thee!

Text: 64 64 66 64; based on Genesis 28:10–22; Sarah F. Adams, 1805–1848.
Music: BETHANY; Lowell Mason, 1792–1872.

862 AMERICA THE BEAUTIFUL

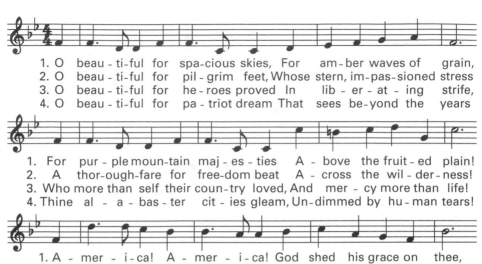

1. O beau-ti-ful for spa-cious skies, For am-ber waves of grain,
2. O beau-ti-ful for pil-grim feet, Whose stern, im-pas-sioned stress
3. O beau-ti-ful for he-roes proved In lib-er-at-ing strife,
4. O beau-ti-ful for pa-triot dream That sees be-yond the years

1. For pur-ple moun-tain maj-es-ties A-bove the fruit-ed plain!
2. A thor-ough-fare for free-dom beat A-cross the wil-der-ness!
3. Who more than self their coun-try loved, And mer-cy more than life!
4. Thine al-a-bas-ter cit-ies gleam, Un-dimmed by hu-man tears!

1. A-mer-i-ca! A-mer-i-ca! God shed his grace on thee,
2. A-mer-i-ca! A-mer-i-ca! God mend thine ev-'ry flaw,
3. A-mer-i-ca! A-mer-i-ca! May God thy gold re-fine,
4. A-mer-i-ca! A-mer-i-ca! God shed his grace on thee,

1. And crown thy good with broth-er-hood From sea to shin-ing sea.
2. Con-firm thy soul in self-con-trol, Thy lib-er-ty in law.
3. Till all suc-cess be no-ble-ness, And ev-'ry gain di-vine.
4. And crown thy good with broth-er-hood From sea to shin-ing sea.

Text: CMD; Katherine L. Bates, 1859–1929.
Music: MATERNA; Samuel A. Ward, 1848–1903.

863 THIS IS MY SONG

1. This is my song, O God of all the na-tions,
2. My coun-try's skies are blu-er than the o-cean,
3. This is my prayer, O Lord of all earth's king-doms:

1. A song of peace for lands a-far and mine.
2. And sun-light beams on clo-ver-leaf and pine;
3. Thy king-dom come; on earth thy will be done.

1. This is my home, the coun-try where my heart is;
2. But oth-er lands have sun-light too, and clo-ver,
3. Let Christ be lift-ed up till all shall serve him,

1. Here are my hopes, my dreams, my ho - ly shrine;
2. And skies are ev - ery - where as blue as mine.
3. And hearts u - nit - ed learn to live as one.

1. But oth - er hearts in oth - er lands are beat-ing
2. O hear my song, thou God of all the na-tions,
3. O hear my prayer, thou God of all the na-tions;

1. With hopes and dreams as true and high as mine.
2. A song of peace for their land and for mine.
3. My - self I give thee; let thy will be done.

Text: 11 10 11 10 11 10; verses 1, 2, Lloyd Stone, © 1934, 1962, Lorenz Publishing Co. All rights reserved. Used with permission.
Verse 3, Georgia Harkness, © 1964, Lorenz Publishing Co. All rights reserved. Used with permission.
Music: FINLANDIA; Jean Sibelius, 1865–1957.

AMERICA 864

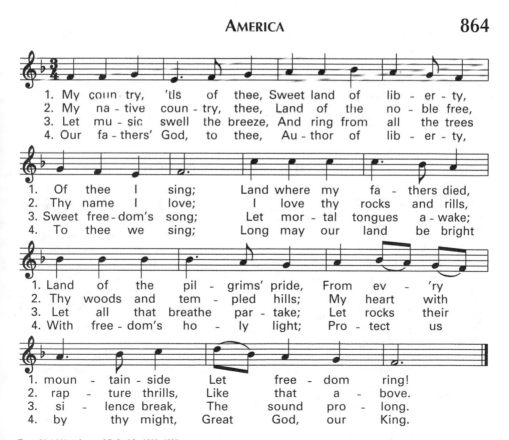

1. My coun - try, 'tis of thee, Sweet land of lib - er - ty,
2. My na - tive coun - try, thee, Land of the no - ble free,
3. Let mu - sic swell the breeze, And ring from all the trees
4. Our fa - thers' God, to thee, Au - thor of lib - er - ty,

1. Of thee I sing; Land where my fa - thers died,
2. Thy name I love; I love thy rocks and rills,
3. Sweet free-dom's song; Let mor - tal tongues a - wake;
4. To thee we sing; Long may our land be bright

1. Land of the pil - grims' pride, From ev - 'ry
2. Thy woods and tem - pled hills; My heart with
3. Let all that breathe par - take; Let rocks their
4. With free - dom's ho - ly light; Pro - tect us

1. moun - tain - side Let free - dom ring!
2. rap - ture thrills, Like that a - bove.
3. si - lence break, The sound pro - long.
4. by thy might, Great God, our King.

Text: 66 4 666 4; Samuel F. Smith, 1808–1895.
Music: AMERICA; *Thesaurus Musicus*, 1744.

865   ETERNAL FATHER, STRONG TO SAVE

1. E - ter - nal Fa - ther, strong to save, Whose arm has bound the
2. O Christ, the Lord of hill and plain O'er which our traf - fic
3. O Spir - it, whom the Fa - ther sent To spread a - broad the
4. O Trin - i - ty of love and pow'r, Your chil - dren shield in

1. rest - less wave, Who bids the might - y o - cean deep Its
2. runs a - main By moun - tain pass or val - ley low; Where-
3. fir - ma - ment; O Wind of heav - en, by your might Save
4. dan - ger's hour; From rock and tem - pest, fire and foe, Pro -

1. own ap - point - ed lim - its keep: O hear us when we
2. ev - er, Lord, your loved ones go, Pro - tect them by your
3. all who dare the ea - gle's flight, And keep them by your
4. tect them where - so - e'er they go; And then shall rise with

1. raise our plea For those in per - il on the sea.
2. guard - ing hand From ev - 'ry per - il on the land.
3. watch - ful care From ev - 'ry per - il in the air.
4. voic - es free Glad praise from air and land and sea.

Text: 88 88 88; verses 1, 4, William Whiting, 1825–1878, alt.; verses 2, 3, Robert N. Spencer, 1877–1961, alt.
Music: MELITA; John B. Dykes, 1823–1876.

866   FOR THE HEALING OF THE NATIONS

1. For the heal - ing of the na - tions, Lord, we pray with
2. Lead us for - ward in - to free - dom; From de - spair your
3. All that kills a - bun - dant liv - ing, Let it from the
4. You, Cre - a - tor God, have writ - ten Your great name on

1. one ac - cord; For a just and e - qual shar - ing
2. world re - lease, That, re - deemed from war and ha - tred,
3. earth be banned; Pride of sta - tus, race, or school - ing,
4. hu - man - kind; For our grow - ing in your like - ness

1. Of the things that earth af - fords; To a life of
2. All may come and go in peace. Show us how through
3. Dog - mas that ob - scure your plan. In our com - mon
4. Bring the life of Christ to mind, That by our re -

1. love in ac - tion Help us rise and pledge our
2. care and good - ness Fear will die and hope in -
3. quest for jus - tice May we hal - low life's brief
4. sponse and ser - vice Earth its des - ti - ny may

1. word, Help us rise and pledge our word.
2. crease, Fear will die and hope in - crease.
3. span, May we hal - low life's brief span.
4. find, Earth its des - ti - ny may find.

Text: 87 87 87 7; Revelation 21:1–27; 22:1–5; Fred Kaan, b. 1929, © 1968, Hope Publishing Co.
   All rights reserved. Used with permission.
Music: CWM RHONDDA; John Hughes, 1873–1932.

GOD OF OUR FATHERS   867

1. God of our fa - thers, whose al - might - y hand
2. Thy love di - vine hath led us in the past,
3. From war's a - larms, from dead - ly pes - ti - lence,
4. Re - fresh thy peo - ple on their toil - some way,

1. Leads forth in beau - ty all the star - ry band
2. In this free land by thee our lot is cast;
3. Be thy strong arm our ev - er sure de - fense;
4. Lead us from night to nev - er - end - ing day;

1. Of shin - ing worlds in splen - dor through the skies,
2. Be thou our rul - er, guard - ian, guide, and stay,
3. Thy true re - li - gion in our hearts in - crease,
4. Fill all our lives with love and grace di - vine,

1. Our grate - ful songs be - fore thy throne a - rise.
2. Thy word our law, thy paths our cho - sen way.
3. Thy boun - teous good - ness nour - ish us in peace.
4. And glo - ry, laud, and praise be ev - er thine.

Text: 10 10 10 10; Daniel Crane Roberts, 1841–1907.
Music: NATIONAL HYMN; George William Warren, 1828–1902.

868   LORD, AS THE DAY BEGINS

1. Lord, as the day be - gins   Lift up our hearts in
2. Christ be in work and skill,   Serv - ing each oth - er's
3. Grant us the Spir - it's strength,   Teach us to walk his
4. Now as the day be - gins   Make it the best of

1. praise;   Take from us all our sins,   Guard us in
2. need;   Christ be in thought and will,   Christ be in
3. way;   So bring us all at length   Safe to the
4. days;   Take from us all our sins,   Guard us in

1. all our ways. Our ev - 'ry step di - rect and
2. word and deed. Our minds be set on things a -
3. close of day. From hour to hour sus - tain and
4. all our ways. Our ev - 'ry step di - rect and

1. guide That Christ in all be glo - ri - fied.
2. bove In joy and peace, in faith and love.
3. bless, And let our song be thank - ful - ness.
4. guide That Christ in all be glo - ri - fied.

Text: 66 66 88; Timothy Dudley-Smith, b. 1926, © 1984, Hope Publishing Co. All rights reserved. Used with permission.
Music: HOLY VINE; Stephen Dean, b. 1948, © 1993, Stephen Dean. Published by OCP Publications. All rights reserved.

869   AS MORNING BREAKS FROM NIGHT

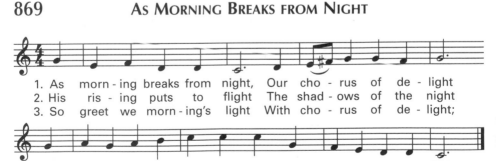

1. As morn - ing breaks from night, Our cho - rus of de - light
2. His ris - ing puts to flight The shad - ows of the night
3. So greet we morn - ing's light With cho - rus of de - light;

1. Sings prais - es to the glo - rious Son, The ris - en Ho - ly One.
2. That fell a-cross the ban - ished world When blight of death un-furled.
3. Sing prais - es to the glo - rious Son, The ris - en Ho - ly One.

Text: SM; Jennifer Glen, CCVI, b. 1945, © 1984, The Sisters of Charity of the Incarnate Word.
    Published by OCP Publications. All rights reserved.
Music: SWABIA; Johann J. Speiss, 1715–1772; adapt. by William H. Havergal, 1793–1870.

O Splendor of God's Glory

1. O Splen-dor of God's glo-ry bright, O Day-star
2. O Christ, true Sun, up-on us shine, En-light-en
3. May pru-dence be a lamp and guide, And jus-tice
4. O Christ, be food to make us whole, And faith a
5. As day from ear-ly dawn is born Come forth, O

1. bring - ing light from light, O Light of Light, light's
2. us with light di-vine. Send forth the Spir-it's
3. burn a-way all pride. Let com-mon sense like
4. cup that o-ver-flows That we by drink-ing
5. Christ, our per-fect morn: The Word in God the

1. liv-ing Spring, O Day, all days il-lu-min-ing.
2. pierc-ing rays To sanc-ti-fy us for your praise.
3. light a-bound And cour-age shine as vir-tue's crown.
4. deep may feel The Spir-it's calm, con-sum-ing zeal.
5. Fa-ther one, The Fa-ther per-fect in the Son.

Text: LM; verses 1 and 5, *Splendor paternae gloriae*; St. Ambrose, 340–397; tr. by Robert S. Bridges, 1844–1930;
Yattendon Hymnal, 1899. Verses 2–4, Harry Hagan, OSB, b. 1947, © 2000, St. Meinrad Archabbey.
Published by OCP Publications. All rights reserved.
Music: PUER NOBIS; Trier MS, 15th cent.; adapt. by Michael Praetorius, 1571–1621.

Morning Has Broken

871

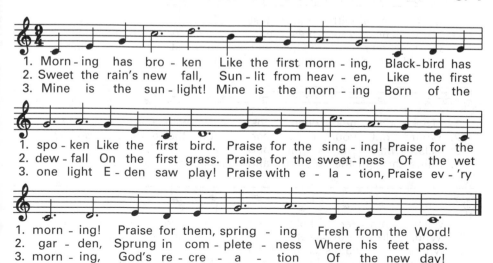

1. Morn-ing has bro-ken Like the first morn-ing, Black-bird has
2. Sweet the rain's new fall, Sun-lit from heav-en, Like the first
3. Mine is the sun-light! Mine is the morn-ing Born of the

1. spo-ken Like the first bird. Praise for the sing-ing! Praise for the
2. dew-fall On the first grass. Praise for the sweet-ness Of the wet
3. one light E-den saw play! Praise with e-la-tion, Praise ev-'ry

1. morn-ing! Praise for them, spring-ing Fresh from the Word!
2. gar-den, Sprung in com-plete-ness Where his feet pass.
3. morn-ing, God's re-cre-a-tion Of the new day!

Text: 55 54 D; Eleanor Farjeon, 1881–1965, © 1957, Eleanor Farjeon. All rights reserved.
Reprinted by permission of Harold Ober Assoc., Inc.
Music: BUNESSAN; Trad. Gaelic Melody.

872   THE SUN NO MORE

1. The sun no more our star by day, Nor
2. Such love and mer-cy nev-er set, Nor
3. All praise to you, who give the day And

1. moon our guide by night, The Lord in glo-ry
2. jus-tice ev-er wanes: From north to south and
3. turn our work to prayer. Re-ceive this noon-day

1. like the sun, Our ev-er-last-ing light.
2. east to west E-ter-nal-ly the same.
3. song of praise And bless us with your care.

Text: CM; based on Isaiah 60:19–20; Harry Hagan, OSB, b. 1947, © 1995, St. Meinrad Archabbey.
   Published by OCP Publications. All rights reserved.
Music: MEAR; American Psalm Tune, 18th cent.

873   ABIDE WITH ME

1. A-bide with me! fast falls the e-ven-tide;
2. I need your pres-ence ev-'ry pass-ing hour:
3. I fear no foe, with you at hand to bless;
4. Hold then your cross be-fore my clos-ing eyes;

1. The dark-ness deep-ens; Lord, with me a-bide;
2. What but your grace can foil the tempt-er's pow'r?
3. Ills have no weight, and tears no bit-ter-ness:
4. Shine through the gloom and point me to the skies!

1. When oth-er help-ers fail and com-forts flee,
2. Who, like your-self, my guide and strength can be?
3. Where is death's sting? Where, grave, your vic-to-ry?
4. Heav'n's morn-ing breaks and earth's vain shad-ows flee:

1. Help of the help-less, O a - bide with me!
2. Through cloud and sun-shine, Lord, a - bide with me!
3. I tri - umph still, if you a - bide with me!
4. In life, in death, O Lord, a - bide with me!

Text: 10 10 10 10; Henry Francis Lyte, 1793–1847, alt.; *Remains,* 1850, alt.
Music: EVENTIDE; William Henry Monk, 1823–1889; *Hymns Ancient and Modern,* 1861.

THE DAY YOU GAVE US, LORD, IS ENDED   874

1. The day you gave us, Lord is end-ed, The
2. We thank you that your Church, un - sleep-ing While
3. A - cross each con - ti - nent and is - land As
4. The sun that bids us rest is wak-ing Your
5. So be it, Lord; your realm shall nev - er, Like

1. dark - ness falls at your be hest, To
2. earth rolls on ward in - to light, Through
3. dawn leads on an - oth - er day, The
4. chil - dren un - der west - ern skies And
5. earth's proud em - pires, pass a - way: Your

1. you our morn - ing hymns as - cend-ed, Your
2. all the world its watch is keep-ing, And
3. voice of prayer is nev - er si - lent, Nor
4. hour by hour as day is break-ing, Fresh
5. king - dom stands, and grows for - ev - er, Till

1. praise shall sanc - ti - fy our rest.
2. nev - er rests by day or night.
3. do the prais - es die a - way.
4. hymns of thank - ful praise a - rise.
5. all your crea - tures own your sway.

Text: 98 98; John Ellerton, 1826–1893, alt.
Music: ST. CLEMENT; Clement C. Scholefield, 1839–1904.

875 **DAY IS DONE**

1. Day is done, but Love un-fail-ing Dwells ev-er here;
2. Dark de-scends, but Light un-end-ing Shines through our night;
3. Eyes will close, but you un-sleep-ing Watch by our side;

1. Shad-ows fall, but hope, pre-vail-ing, Calms ev-'ry fear.
2. You are with us, ev-er lend-ing New strength to sight.
3. Death may come, in Love's safe-keep-ing Still we a-bide.

1. God, our Mak-er, none for-sak-ing, Take our hearts, of Love's own
2. One in love, your truth con-fess-ing, One in hope of heav-en's
3. God of love, all e-vil quell-ing, Sin for-giv-ing, fear dis-

1. mak-ing; Watch our sleep-ing, guard our wak-ing, Be al-ways near.
2. bless-ing, May we see, in love's pos-sess-ing, Love's end-less light!
3. pel-ling: Stay with us, our hearts in-dwell-ing, This e-ven-tide.

Text: 84 84 88 84; James D. Quinn, SJ, b. 1919, © 1969, James D. Quinn, SJ. All rights reserved.
Used with permission of Selah Publishing Co.
Music: AR HYD Y NOS; Trad. Welsh Melody.

876 **LORD, BID YOUR SERVANT GO IN PEACE**

1. Lord, bid your ser-vant go in peace, Your
2. This is the Sav-ior of the world, The
3. This child shall see the rise, the fall, Of
4. His moth-er's soul a sword shall pierce, Of
5. Blest be the Fa-ther, who has giv'n His

1. word is now ful-filled. These eyes have seen sal-
2. gen-tiles' prom-ised light, God's glo-ry dwell-ing
3. those in Is-ra-el, God's sign raised high for
4. sor-row keen and deep; And se-cret thoughts of
5. Son to be our Lord, Blest too that Son, and

1. va-tion's dawn, This child so long fore-told.
2. in our midst, The joy of Is-ra-el.
3. all to see, Whom some shall yet de-ny.
4. man-y hearts Through him shall be re-vealed.
5. with them both The Spir-it of their love.

Text: CM; based on Luke 2:29–32, 34–35; *Nunc dimittis*; James D. Quinn, SJ, b. 1919, alt., © 1969, 1989, James D. Quinn, SJ.
All rights reserved. Used with permission of Selah Publishing Co., Inc., North American agent.
Music: MORNING SONG; *Sixteen Tune Settings*, Philadelphia, 1812; *Kentucky Harmony*, 1816.

Tradition holds that Jesus walked from Pilate's praetorium to Golgatha (the Place of the Skull). The devotion known as "the way" or Stations of the Cross (Via Crucis) originated with pilgrims who walked the Via Dolorosa (the "way of tears") in the city of Jerusalem. In 2001 the Congregation for the Discipline of the Sacraments issued the document, Directory on Popular Piety and the Liturgy (DPPL). In referring to this devotion, this document states the following: "In the Via Crucis, various strands of Christian piety coalesce: the idea of life as being journey or pilgrimage; as a passage from earthly exile to our true home in Heaven; the deep desire to be conformed to the Passion of Christ, which imply that his disciples must follow behind their Master, daily carrying their own crosses (cf. Luke 9, 23)." (133 DPPL) For music, please see no. 398, 408.

1. **JESUS IS CONDEMNED TO DEATH.**
   Christ, help us to lead a better life and to seek your will.

2. **JESUS BEARS HIS CROSS.**
   Lord, we join you in your journey of suffering.

3. **JESUS FALLS FOR THE FIRST TIME.**
   Christ, help us who fall into sinful ways; teach us to rise with you.

4. **JESUS MEETS HIS MOTHER.**
   Lord, we implore your mother to console us who mourn.

5. **JESUS IS HELPED BY SIMON.**
   Christ, help as we try to do your work in our world.

6. **VERONICA WIPES HIS FACE.**
   Lord, help us as we help others.

7. **JESUS FALLS THE SECOND TIME.**
   Christ, teach us the healing power of penance.

8. **JESUS SPEAKS TO THE WOMEN.**
   Lord, help us to comfort those who have no one to help them.

9. **JESUS FALLS A THIRD TIME.**
   Christ, teach us the joy of obedience.

10. **JESUS IS STRIPPED OF HIS GARMENTS.**
    Lord, help us to model your life of holiness.

11. **JESUS IS NAILED TO THE CROSS.**
    Christ, draw us closer to you from this day forward.

12. **JESUS DIES ON THE CROSS.**
    Lord, we pray that you will be with us at our hour of death.

13. **HE IS TAKEN FROM THE CROSS.**
    Christ, open our hearts to the beauty of your love for us.

14. **HE IS LAID IN THE TOMB.**
    Lord, help us to walk in your ways all the days of our lives.

LECTIONARY READINGS

The word of God proclaimed in worship makes Christ present through the power of the Holy Spirit. In the liturgy of the Church the Sacred Scriptures find their true home, for here both creation and redemption are crowned in mystery. God's word and the liturgy quench the thirst of all who seek the way, the truth and the life. We pray that the word of God be etched indelibly in our heart and on our lips that we may faithfully conform to it and boldly proclaim its love to all. (Additional music for the Responsorial Psalm may be found in #15–124; music for the Gospel Acclamation is also found in #151, 152, 195, 207, 208, 229, 240, 241, 268–280.)

SEASON OF ADVENT

878   FIRST SUNDAY OF ADVENT — A

FIRST READING   *Isaiah 2:1–5*

This is what Isaiah, son of Amoz, saw
concerning Judah and Jerusalem.
   In days to come,
   the mountain of the LORD's house
     shall be established as the
       highest mountain
   and raised above the hills.
All nations shall stream toward it;
   many peoples shall come and say:
"Come, let us climb the
     LORD's mountain,
   to the house of the God of Jacob,
that he may instruct us in his ways,
   and we may walk in his paths."

For from Zion shall go forth instruction,
   and the word of the LORD
     from Jerusalem.
He shall judge between the nations,
   and impose terms on many peoples.
They shall beat their swords
     into plowshares
   and their spears into pruning hooks;
one nation shall not raise the sword
     against another,
   nor shall they train for war again.
O house of Jacob, come,
   let us walk in the light of the LORD!

RESPONSORIAL PSALM   *Psalm 122: 1–2, 3–4, 4–5, 6–7, 8–9*

℟. Let us go rejoicing to the house of the Lord.

Music: John Schiavone, b. 1947, © 2001, OCP Publications.

▶ I rejoiced because they said to me,
"We will go up to the house of
the LORD."
And now we have set foot
within your gates, O Jerusalem. ℟.

▶ Jerusalem, built as a city
with compact unity.
To it the tribes go up,
the tribes of the LORD. ℟.

▶ According to the decree for Israel,
to give thanks to the name of
the LORD.

In it are set up judgment seats,
seats for the house of David. ℟.

▶ Pray for the peace of Jerusalem!
May those who love you prosper!
May peace be within your walls,
prosperity in your buildings. ℟.

▶ Because of my brothers and friends
I will say, "Peace be within you!"
Because of the house of the LORD,
our God,
I will pray for your good. ℟.

SECOND READING

Romans 13:11–14

Brothers and sisters: You know the time; it is the hour now for you to awake from sleep. For our salvation is nearer now than when we first believed; the night is advanced, the day is at hand. Let us then throw off the works of darkness and put on the armor of light; let us conduct ourselves properly as in the day, not in orgies and drunkenness, not in promiscuity and lust, not in rivalry and jealousy. But put on the Lord Jesus Christ, and make no provision for the desires of the flesh.

GOSPEL ACCLAMATION

cf. Psalm 85:8

℟. Al - le - lu - ia, al - le - lu - ia, al - le - lu - ia.

Music: John Schiavone, b. 1947, © 2001, OCP Publications.

▶ Show us, Lord, your love;
and grant us your salvation. ℟.

GOSPEL READING

Matthew 24:37–44

Jesus said to his disciples: "As it was in the days of Noah, so it will be at the coming of the Son of Man. In those days before the flood, they were eating and drinking, marrying and giving in marriage, up to the day that Noah entered the ark. They did not know until the flood came and carried them all away. So will it be also at the coming of the Son of Man. Two men will be out in the field; one will be taken, and one will be left. Two women will be grinding at the mill; one will be taken, and one will be left. Therefore, stay awake! For you do not know on which day your Lord will come. Be sure of this: if the master of the house had known the hour of night when the thief was coming, he would have stayed awake and not let his house be broken into. So too, you also must be prepared, for at an hour you do not expect, the Son of Man will come."

879   FIRST SUNDAY OF ADVENT — B

FIRST READING   *Isaiah 63:16b–17, 19b; 64:2–7*

You, LORD, are our father,
  our redeemer you are named forever.
Why do you let us wander, O LORD,
    from your ways,
  and harden our hearts so that we fear
    you not?
Return for the sake of your servants,
  the tribes of your heritage.
Oh, that you would rend the heavens
    and come down,
  with the mountains quaking
    before you,
while you wrought awesome deeds we
    could not hope for,
  such as they had not heard of from
    of old.
No ear has ever heard, no eye ever
    seen, any God but you
  doing such deeds for those who wait
    for him.
Would that you might meet us

doing right,
  that we were mindful of you in
    our ways!
Behold, you are angry, and we
    are sinful;
  all of us have become like
    unclean people,
  all our good deeds are like
    polluted rags;
we have all withered like leaves,
  and our guilt carries us away like
    the wind.
There is none who calls upon
    your name,
  who rouses himself to cling to you;
for you have hidden your face from us
  and have delivered us up to our guilt.
Yet, O LORD, you are our father;
  we are the clay and you the potter:
  we are all the work of your hands.

RESPONSORIAL PSALM   *Psalm 80:2–3, 15–16, 18–19*

℟. Lord, make us turn to you; let us see your face and we shall be saved.

Music: John Schiavone, b. 1947, © 2001, OCP Publications.

▶ O shepherd of Israel, hearken,
  from your throne upon the
    cherubim, shine forth.
Rouse your power,
  and come to save us. ℟.

▶ Once again, O LORD of hosts,
  look down from heaven, and see;
take care of this vine,
  and protect what your right hand
    has planted,
  the son of man whom you yourself
    made strong. ℟.

▶ May your help be with the man of
  your right hand,
  with the son of man whom you
    yourself made strong.
Then we will no more withdraw
    from you;
  give us new life, and we will call
    upon your name. ℟.

SECOND READING   *1 Corinthians 1:3–9*

Brothers and sisters: Grace to you and
peace from God our Father and the
Lord Jesus Christ.

I give thanks to my God always on
your account for the grace of God
bestowed on you in Christ Jesus, that in

him you were enriched in every way, with all discourse and all knowledge, as the testimony to Christ was confirmed among you, so that you are not lacking in any spiritual gift as you wait for the revelation of our Lord Jesus Christ.

He will keep you firm to the end, irreproachable on the day of our Lord Jesus Christ. God is faithful, and by him you were called to fellowship with his Son, Jesus Christ our Lord.

GOSPEL ACCLAMATION

Psalm 85:8

℟. Al - le - lu - ia, al - le - lu - ia, al - le - lu - ia.

Music: John Schiavone, b. 1947, © 2001, OCP Publications.

▶ Show us, Lord, your love;
and grant us your salvation. ℟.

GOSPEL READING

Mark 13:33–37

Jesus said to his disciples: "Be watchful! Be alert! You do not know when the time will come. It is like a man traveling abroad. He leaves home and places his servants in charge, each with his own work, and orders the gatekeeper to be on the watch. Watch, therefore; you do not know when the lord of the house is coming, whether in the evening, or at midnight, or at cockcrow, or in the morning. May he not come suddenly and find you sleeping. What I say to you, I say to all: 'Watch!' "

FIRST SUNDAY OF ADVENT — C 880

FIRST READING

Jeremiah 33:14–16

The days are coming, says the LORD, when I will fulfill the promise I made to the house of Israel and Judah. In those days, in that time, I will raise up for David a just shoot; he shall do what is right and just in the land. In those days Judah shall be safe and Jerusalem shall dwell secure; this is what they shall call her: "The LORD our justice."

RESPONSORIAL PSALM

Psalm 25:4–5, 8–9, 10, 14

℟. To you, O Lord, I lift my soul, [I lift my soul.]

Music: John Schiavone, b. 1947, © 2001, OCP Publications.

▶ Your ways, O LORD, make known to me;
teach me your paths,
guide me in your truth and teach me,
for you are God my savior,
and for you I wait all the day. ℟.

▶ Good and upright is the LORD;
thus he shows sinners the way.
He guides the humble to justice,
and teaches the humble his way. ℟.

℟. **To you, O Lord, I lift my soul.**

▶ All the paths of the LORD are kindness and constancy
toward those who keep his covenant and his decrees.

The friendship of the LORD is with those who fear him,
and his covenant, for their instruction. ℟.

SECOND READING

1 Thessalonians 3:12—4:2

Brothers and sisters: May the Lord make you increase and abound in love for one another and for all, just as we have for you, so as to strengthen your hearts, to be blameless in holiness before our God and Father at the coming of our Lord Jesus with all his holy ones. Amen.

Finally, brothers and sisters, we earnestly ask and exhort you in the Lord Jesus that, as you received from us how you should conduct yourselves to please God — and as you are conducting yourselves — you do so even more. For you know what instructions we gave you through the Lord Jesus.

GOSPEL ACCLAMATION

Psalm 85:8

℟. Al - le - lu - ia, al - le - lu - ia, al - le - lu - ia.

Music: John Schiavone, b. 1947, © 2001, OCP Publications.

▶ Show us, Lord, your love;
and grant us your salvation. ℟.

GOSPEL READING

Luke 21:25–28, 34–36

Jesus said to his disciples: "There will be signs in the sun, the moon, and the stars, and on earth nations will be in dismay, perplexed by the roaring of the sea and the waves. People will die of fright in anticipation of what is coming upon the world, for the powers of the heavens will be shaken. And then they will see the Son of Man coming in a cloud with power and great glory. But when these signs begin to happen, stand erect and raise your heads because your redemption is at hand.

"Beware that your hearts do not become drowsy from carousing and drunkenness and the anxieties of daily life, and that day catch you by surprise like a trap. For that day will assault everyone who lives on the face of the earth. Be vigilant at all times and pray that you have the strength to escape the tribulations that are imminent and to stand before the Son of Man."

---

881   SECOND SUNDAY OF ADVENT — A

FIRST READING

Isaiah 11:1–10

On that day, a shoot shall sprout from the stump of Jesse,
and from his roots a bud shall blossom.
The spirit of the Lord shall rest upon him:
a spirit of wisdom and of understanding,
a spirit of counsel and of strength,
a spirit of knowledge and of fear of the LORD,

and his delight shall be the fear of
the LORD.
Not by appearance shall he judge,
nor by hearsay shall he decide,
but he shall judge the poor with justice,
and decide aright for the land's
afflicted.
He shall strike the ruthless with the rod
of his mouth,
and with the breath of his lips he
shall slay the wicked.
Justice shall be the band around
his waist,
and faithfulness a belt upon his hips.
Then the wolf shall be a guest of
the lamb,
and the leopard shall lie down with
the kid;

the calf and the young lion shall
browse together,
with a little child to guide them.
The cow and the bear shall be neighbors,
together their young shall rest;
the lion shall eat hay like the ox.
The baby shall play by the cobra's den,
and the child lay his hand on the
adder's lair.
There shall be no harm or ruin on all
my holy mountain;
for the earth shall be filled with
knowledge of the LORD,
as water covers the sea.
On that day, the root of Jesse,
set up as a signal for the nations,
the Gentiles shall seek out,
for his dwelling shall be glorious.

RESPONSORIAL PSALM

Psalm 72:1–2, 7–8, 12–13, 17

℟. Jus - tice shall flour - ish in his time, and full - ness of peace for ev - er.

Music: John Schiavone, b. 1947, © 2001, OCP Publications.

▶ O God, with your judgment endow
the king,
and with your justice, the king's son;
he shall govern your people with justice
and your afflicted ones with
judgment. ℟.

▶ Justice shall flower in his days,
and profound peace, till the moon
be no more.
May he rule from sea to sea,
and from the River to the ends of
the earth. ℟.

▶ For he shall rescue the poor when he
cries out,
and the afflicted when he has no
one to help him.
He shall have pity for the lowly and
the poor;
the lives of the poor he shall save. ℟.

▶ May his name be blessed forever;
as long as the sun his name
shall remain.
In him shall all the tribes of the earth
be blessed;
all the nations shall proclaim his
happiness. ℟.

SECOND READING

Romans 15:4–9

Brothers and sisters: Whatever was
written previously was written for our
instruction, that by endurance and by
the encouragement of the Scriptures
we might have hope. May the God of
endurance and encouragement grant
you to think in harmony with one
another, in keeping with Christ Jesus,

that with one accord you may with one
voice glorify the God and Father of our
Lord Jesus Christ.
Welcome one another, then, as Christ
welcomed you, for the glory of God.
For I say that Christ became a minister
of the circumcised to show God's
truthfulness, to confirm the promises to

the patriarchs, but so that the Gentiles might glorify God for his mercy. As it is written:

Therefore, I will praise you among the Gentiles and sing praises to your name.

GOSPEL ACCLAMATION

Luke 3:4, 6

℟. Al - le - lu - ia, al - le - lu - ia, al - le - lu - ia.

Music: John Schiavone, b. 1947, © 2001, OCP Publications.

▶ Prepare the way of the Lord, make straight his paths: all flesh shall see the salvation of God. ℟.

GOSPEL READING

Matthew 3:1–12

John the Baptist appeared, preaching in the desert of Judea and saying, "Repent, for the kingdom of heaven is at hand!" It was of him that the prophet Isaiah had spoken when he said:
A voice of one crying out in the desert,
Prepare the way of the Lord,
make straight his paths.
John wore clothing made of camel's hair and had a leather belt around his waist. His food was locusts and wild honey. At that time Jerusalem, all Judea, and the whole region around the Jordan were going out to him and were being baptized by him in the Jordan River as they acknowledged their sins.

When he saw many of the Pharisees and Sadducees coming to his baptism, he said to them, "You brood of vipers! Who warned you to flee from the coming wrath? Produce good fruit as evidence of your repentance. And do not presume to say to yourselves, 'We have Abraham as our father.' For I tell you, God can raise up children to Abraham from these stones. Even now the ax lies at the root of the trees. Therefore every tree that does not bear good fruit will be cut down and thrown into the fire. I am baptizing you with water, for repentance, but the one who is coming after me is mightier than I. I am not worthy to carry his sandals. He will baptize you with the Holy Spirit and fire. His winnowing fan is in his hand. He will clear his threshing floor and gather his wheat into his barn, but the chaff he will burn with unquenchable fire."

---

882   SECOND SUNDAY OF ADVENT — B

FIRST READING

Isaiah 40:1–5, 9–11

Comfort, give comfort to my people, says your God.
Speak tenderly to Jerusalem, and proclaim to her
that her service is at an end, her guilt is expiated;
indeed, she has received from the hand of the LORD
double for all her sins.

A voice cries out:
In the desert prepare the way of the LORD!
Make straight in the wasteland a highway for our God!
Every valley shall be filled in, every mountain and hill shall be made low;
the rugged land shall be made a plain, the rough country, a broad valley.

Then the glory of the LORD shall
   be revealed,
   and all people shall see it together;
for the mouth of the LORD has spoken.

Go up onto a high mountain,
   Zion, herald of glad tidings;
cry out at the top of your voice,
   Jerusalem, herald of good news!
Fear not to cry out
   and say to the cities of Judah:

Here is your God!
Here comes with power
   the Lord GOD,
   who rules by his strong arm;
here is his reward with him,
   his recompense before him.
Like a shepherd he feeds his flock;
   in his arms he gathers the lambs,
carrying them in his bosom,
   and leading the ewes with care.

RESPONSORIAL PSALM

Psalm 85:9–10, 11–12, 13–14

℟. **Lord, let us see your kind-ness, and grant us your sal-va-tion.**

Music: John Schiavone, b. 1947, © 2001, OCP Publications.

▶ I will hear what God proclaims;
   the LORD — for he proclaims peace
     to his people.
Near indeed is his salvation to those
   who fear him,
   glory dwelling in our land. ℟.

▶ Kindness and truth shall meet;
   justice and peace shall kiss.

Truth shall spring out of the earth,
   and justice shall look down from
     heaven. ℟.

▶ The LORD himself will give
   his benefits;
   our land shall yield its increase.
Justice shall walk before him,
   and prepare the way of his steps. ℟.

SECOND READING

2 Peter 3:8–14

Do not ignore this one fact, beloved, that with the Lord one day is like a thousand years and a thousand years like one day. The Lord does not delay his promise, as some regard "delay," but he is patient with you, not wishing that any should perish but that all should come to repentance. But the day of the Lord will come like a thief, and then the heavens will pass away with a mighty roar and the elements will be dissolved by fire, and the earth and everything done on it will be found out.

   Since everything is to be dissolved in this way, what sort of persons ought you to be, conducting yourselves in holiness and devotion, waiting for and hastening the coming of the day of God, because of which the heavens will be dissolved in flames and the elements melted by fire. But according to his promise we await new heavens and a new earth in which righteousness dwells. Therefore, beloved, since you await these things, be eager to be found without spot or blemish before him, at peace.

GOSPEL ACCLAMATION

Luke 3:4, 6

℟. Al - le - lu - ia, al - le - lu - ia, al - le - lu - ia.

Music: John Schiavone, b. 1947, © 2001, OCP Publications.

▶ Prepare the way of the Lord, make straight his paths:
all flesh shall see the salvation of God. ℟.

GOSPEL READING

Mark 1:1–8

The beginning of the gospel of Jesus Christ the Son of God.
  As it is written in Isaiah the prophet:
Behold, I am sending my messenger
  ahead of you;
he will prepare your way.
A voice of one crying out in
  the desert:
  "Prepare the way of the Lord,
  make straight his paths."
John the Baptist appeared in the desert proclaiming a baptism of repentance for the forgiveness of sins. People of the whole Judean countryside and all the inhabitants of Jerusalem were going out to him and were being baptized by him in the Jordan River as they acknowledged their sins. John was clothed in camel's hair, with a leather belt around his waist. He fed on locusts and wild honey. And this is what he proclaimed: "One mightier than I is coming after me. I am not worthy to stoop and loosen the thongs of his sandals. I have baptized you with water; he will baptize you with the Holy Spirit."

---

883   SECOND SUNDAY OF ADVENT — C

FIRST READING

Baruch 5:1–9

Jerusalem, take off your robe of
    mourning and misery;
  put on the splendor of glory from
    God forever:
wrapped in the cloak of justice from God,
  bear on your head the mitre
  that displays the glory of the
    eternal name.
For God will show all the earth
    your splendor:
  you will be named by God forever
  the peace of justice, the glory of
    God's worship.

Up, Jerusalem! stand upon the heights;
  look to the east and see your children
gathered from the east and the west
  at the word of the Holy One,
  rejoicing that they are remembered
    by God.

Led away on foot by their enemies they
    left you:
  but God will bring them back to you
  borne aloft in glory as on royal thrones.
For God has commanded
  that every lofty mountain be made low,
and that the age-old depths and gorges
  be filled to level ground,
  that Israel may advance secure in the
    glory of God.
The forests and every fragrant kind
    of tree
  have overshadowed Israel at
    God's command;
for God is leading Israel in joy
  by the light of his glory,
  with his mercy and justice for company.

RESPONSORIAL PSALM

Psalm 126:1–2, 2–3, 4–5, 6

℟. The Lord has done great things for us; we are filled with joy.

Music: John Schiavone, b. 1947, © 2001, OCP Publications.

▶ When the LORD brought back the
captives of Zion,
we were like men dreaming.
Then our mouth was filled
with laughter,
and our tongue with rejoicing. ℟.

▶ Then they said among the nations,
"The LORD has done great things
for them."
The LORD has done great things for us;
we are glad indeed. ℟.

▶ Restore our fortunes, O LORD,
like the torrents in the
southern desert.
Those who sow in tears
shall reap rejoicing. ℟.

▶ Although they go forth weeping,
carrying the seed to be sown,
they shall come back rejoicing,
carrying their sheaves. ℟.

SECOND READING

Philippians 1:4–6, 8–11

Brothers and sisters: I pray always with joy in my every prayer for all of you, because of your partnership for the gospel from the first day until now. I am confident of this, that the one who began a good work in you will continue to complete it until the day of Christ Jesus. God is my witness, how I long for all of you with the affection of Christ Jesus. And this is my prayer: that your love may increase ever more and more in knowledge and every kind of perception, to discern what is of value, so that you may be pure and blameless for the day of Christ, filled with the fruit of righteousness that comes through Jesus Christ for the glory and praise of God.

GOSPEL ACCLAMATION

Luke 3:4, 6

℟. Al - le - lu - ia, al - le - lu - ia, al - le - lu - ia.

Music: John Schiavone, b. 1947, © 2001, OCP Publications.

▶ Prepare the way of the Lord, make straight his paths:
all flesh shall see the salvation of God. ℟.

GOSPEL READING

Luke 3:1–6

In the fifteenth year of the reign of Tiberius Caesar, when Pontius Pilate was governor of Judea, and Herod was tetrarch of Galilee, and his brother Philip tetrarch of the region of Ituraea and Trachonitis, and Lysanias was tetrarch of Abilene, during the high priesthood of Annas and Caiaphas, the word of God came to John the son of Zechariah in the desert. John went throughout the whole region of the Jordan, proclaiming a baptism of repentance for the forgiveness of sins, as it is written in the book of the words of the prophet Isaiah:

*A voice of one crying out in
the desert:
"Prepare the way of the Lord,
make straight his paths.
Every valley shall be filled
and every mountain and hill shall
be made low.*

*The winding roads shall be
made straight,
and the rough ways made smooth,
and all flesh shall see the salvation
of God."*

884   THIRD SUNDAY OF ADVENT — A

FIRST READING
Isaiah 35:1–6a, 10

The desert and the parched land
　　will exult;
　　the steppe will rejoice and bloom.
They will bloom with abundant flowers,
　　and rejoice with joyful song.
The glory of Lebanon will be given
　　to them,
　　the splendor of Carmel and Sharon;
they will see the glory of the LORD,
　　the splendor of our God.
Strengthen the hands that are feeble,
　　make firm the knees that are weak,
say to those whose hearts are
　　frightened:
Be strong, fear not!

Here is your God,
　　he comes with vindication;
with divine recompense
　　he comes to save you.
Then will the eyes of the blind
　　be opened,
　　the ears of the deaf be cleared;
then will the lame leap like a stag,
　　then the tongue of the mute will sing.

Those whom the LORD has ransomed
　　will return
　　and enter Zion singing,
　　crowned with everlasting joy;
they will meet with joy and gladness,
　　sorrow and mourning will flee.

RESPONSORIAL PSALM
Psalm 146:6–7, 8–9, 9–10

℞. [Lord,]   Lord,   come and save us, [come and save us.]

Music: John Schiavone, b. 1947, © 2001, OCP Publications.

or: **Alleluia.**

▶ The LORD God keeps faith forever,
　　secures justice for the oppressed,
　　gives food to the hungry.
The LORD sets captives free. ℞.

▶ The LORD gives sight to the blind;
　　the LORD raises up those who were
　　bowed down.
The LORD loves the just;
　　the LORD protects strangers. ℞.

▶ The fatherless and the widow
　　he sustains,
　　but the way of the wicked
　　he thwarts.
The LORD shall reign forever;
　　your God, O Zion, through all
　　generations. ℞.

SECOND READING
James 5:7–10

Be patient, brothers and sisters, until the coming of the Lord. See how the farmer waits for the precious fruit of the earth, being patient with it until it receives the early and the late rains. You too must be patient. Make your hearts firm, because the coming of the Lord is at hand. Do not complain, brothers and sisters, about one another, that you may not be judged. Behold, the Judge is standing before the gates. Take as an example of hardship and patience, brothers and sisters, the prophets who spoke in the name of the Lord.

GOSPEL ACCLAMATION
Isaiah 61:1 (cited in Luke 4:18)

℟. Al - le - lu - ia, al - le - lu - ia, al - le - lu - ia.

Music: John Schiavone, b. 1947, © 2001, OCP Publications.

▶ The Spirit of the Lord is upon me,
because he has anointed me
to bring glad tidings to the poor. ℟.

GOSPEL READING
Matthew 11:2–11

When John the Baptist heard in prison of the works of the Christ, he sent his disciples to Jesus with this question, "Are you the one who is to come, or should we look for another?" Jesus said to them in reply, "Go and tell John what you hear and see: the blind regain their sight, the lame walk, lepers are cleansed, the deaf hear, the dead are raised, and the poor have the good news proclaimed to them. And blessed is the one who takes no offense at me."

As they were going off, Jesus began to speak to the crowds about John, "What did you go out to the desert to see? A reed swayed by the wind? Then what did you go out to see? Someone dressed in fine clothing? Those who wear fine clothing are in royal palaces. Then why did you go out? To see a prophet? Yes, I tell you, and more than a prophet. This is the one about whom it is written:
Behold, I am sending my messenger
ahead of you;
he will prepare your way
before you.
Amen, I say to you, among those born of women there has been none greater than John the Baptist; yet the least in the kingdom of heaven is greater than he."

THIRD SUNDAY OF ADVENT — B   885

FIRST READING
Isaiah 61:1–2a, 10–11

The spirit of the Lord GOD is upon me,
because the LORD has anointed me;
he has sent me to bring glad tidings to
the poor,
to heal the brokenhearted,
to proclaim liberty to the captives
and release to the prisoners,
to announce a year of favor from
the LORD
and a day of vindication by our God.

I rejoice heartily in the LORD,
in my God is the joy of my soul;

for he has clothed me with a robe
   of salvation
and wrapped me in a mantle
   of justice,
like a bridegroom adorned with
   a diadem,
   like a bride bedecked with her jewels.

As the earth brings forth its plants,
   and a garden makes its growth
   spring up,
so will the Lord GOD make justice
   and praise
   spring up before all the nations.

RESPONSORIAL PSALM

Luke 1:46–48, 49–50, 53–54

℞. My soul re - joic - es in my God.

Music: John Schiavone, b. 1947, © 2001, OCP Publications.

▶ My soul proclaims the greatness of
   the Lord;
   my spirit rejoices in God my Savior,
for he has looked upon his
   lowly servant.
   From this day all generations will
   call me blessed: ℞.

▶ The Almighty has done great things
   for me,
   and holy is his Name.

He has mercy on those who fear him
   in every generation. ℞.

▶ He has filled the hungry with
   good things,
   and the rich he has sent away empty.
He has come to the help of his
   servant Israel
   for he has remembered his promise
   of mercy. ℞.

SECOND READING

1 Thessalonians 5:16–24

Brothers and sisters: Rejoice always.
Pray without ceasing. In all circumstances
give thanks, for this is the will of God
for you in Christ Jesus. Do not quench
the Spirit. Do not despise prophetic
utterances. Test everything; retain what
is good. Refrain from every kind of evil.

May the God of peace make you
perfectly holy and may you entirely,
spirit, soul, and body, be preserved
blameless for the coming of our Lord
Jesus Christ. The one who calls you is
faithful, and he will also accomplish it.

GOSPEL ACCLAMATION

Isaiah 61:1 (cited in Luke 4:18)

℞. Al - le - lu - ia, al - le - lu - ia, al - le - lu - ia.

Music: John Schiavone, b. 1947, © 2001, OCP Publications.

▶ The Spirit of the Lord is upon me,
   because he has anointed me
   to bring glad tidings to the poor. ℞.

GOSPEL READING *John 1:6–8, 19–28*

A man named John was sent from God. He came for testimony, to testify to the light, so that all might believe through him. He was not the light, but came to testify to the light.

And this is the testimony of John. When the Jews from Jerusalem sent priests and Levites to him to ask him, "Who are you?" he admitted and did not deny it, but admitted, "I am not the Christ."

So they asked him, "What are you then? Are you Elijah?" And he said, "I am not." "Are you the Prophet?" He answered, "No." So they said to him, "Who are you, so we can give an answer to those who sent us? What do you have to say for yourself?" He said:

"I am *the voice of one crying out in the desert,*
make straight the way of the Lord,
as Isaiah the prophet said." Some Pharisees were also sent. They asked him, "Why then do you baptize if you are not the Christ or Elijah or the Prophet?" John answered them, "I baptize with water; but there is one among you whom you do not recognize, the one who is coming after me, whose sandal strap I am not worthy to untie." This happened in Bethany across the Jordan, where John was baptizing.

THIRD SUNDAY OF ADVENT — C **886**

FIRST READING *Zephaniah 3:14–18a*

Shout for joy, O daughter Zion!
  Sing joyfully, O Israel!
Be glad and exult with all your heart,
  O daughter Jerusalem!
The LORD has removed the judgment
    against you
  he has turned away your enemies;
the King of Israel, the LORD, is in
    your midst,

you have no further misfortune to fear.
On that day, it shall be said to Jerusalem·
  Fear not, O Zion, be not discouraged!
The LORD, your God, is in your midst,
  a mighty savior;
he will rejoice over you with gladness,
  and renew you in his love,
he will sing joyfully because of you,
  as one sings at festivals.

RESPONSORIAL PSALM *Isaiah 12:2–3, 4, 5–6*

℟. Cry out with joy and glad-ness: for a-mong you is the great and Ho-ly One of Is-ra-el.

Music: John Schiavone, b. 1947, © 2001, OCP Publications.

▶ God indeed is my savior;
  I am confident and unafraid.
My strength and my courage is
    the LORD,

and he has been my savior.
With joy you will draw water
  at the fountain of salvation. ℟.

℟. Cry out with joy and gladness: for among you is the great and Holy One of Israel.

▶ Give thanks to the LORD, acclaim
his name;
among the nations make known
his deeds,
proclaim how exalted is his name. ℟.

▶ Sing praise to the LORD for his glorious
achievement;

let this be known throughout all
the earth.
Shout with exultation, O city of Zion,
for great in your midst
is the Holy One of Israel! ℟.

SECOND READING
Philippians 4:4–7

Brothers and sisters: Rejoice in the Lord always. I shall say it again: rejoice! Your kindness should be known to all. The Lord is near. Have no anxiety at all, but in everything, by prayer and petition, with thanksgiving, make your requests known to God. Then the peace of God that surpasses all understanding will guard your hearts and minds in Christ Jesus.

GOSPEL ACCLAMATION
Isaiah 61:1 (cited in Luke 4:18)

℟. Al - le - lu - ia, al - le - lu - ia, al - le - lu - ia.

Music: John Schiavone, b. 1947, © 2001, OCP Publications.

▶ The Spirit of the Lord is upon me,
because he has anointed me
to bring glad tidings to the poor. ℟.

GOSPEL READING
Luke 3:10–18

The crowds asked John the Baptist, "What should we do?" He said to them in reply, "Whoever has two cloaks should share with the person who has none. And whoever has food should do likewise." Even tax collectors came to be baptized and they said to him, "Teacher, what should we do?" He answered them, "Stop collecting more than what is prescribed." Soldiers also asked him, "And what is it that we should do?" He told them, "Do not practice extortion, do not falsely accuse anyone, and be satisfied with your wages."

Now the people were filled with expectation, and all were asking in their hearts whether John might be the Christ. John answered them all, saying, "I am baptizing you with water, but one mightier than I is coming. I am not worthy to loosen the thongs of his sandals. He will baptize you with the Holy Spirit and fire. His winnowing fan is in his hand to clear his threshing floor and to gather the wheat into his barn, but the chaff he will burn with unquenchable fire." Exhorting them in many other ways, he preached good news to the people.

FOURTH SUNDAY OF ADVENT — A   887

FIRST READING   *Isaiah 7:10–14*

The LORD spoke to Ahaz, saying: Ask for a sign from the LORD, your God; let it be deep as the netherworld, or high as the sky! But Ahaz answered, "I will not ask! I will not tempt the LORD!" Then Isaiah said: Listen, O house of David! Is it not enough for you to weary people, must you also weary my God? Therefore the LORD himself will give you this sign: the virgin shall conceive, and bear a son, and shall name him Emmanuel.

RESPONSORIAL PSALM   *Psalm 24:1–2, 3–4, 5–6*

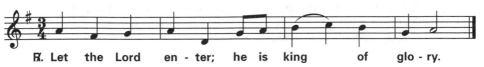

℞. Let the Lord en - ter; he is king of glo - ry.

Music: John Schiavone, b. 1947, © 2001, OCP Publications.

▶ The LORD's are the earth and its fullness;
   the world and those who dwell in it.
For he founded it upon the seas
   and established it upon the rivers. ℞.

▶ Who can ascend the mountain of
   the LORD?
   or who may stand in his holy place?
One whose hands are sinless, whose
   heart is clean,
   who desires not what is vain. ℞.

▶ He shall receive a blessing from
   the LORD,
   a reward from God his savior.
Such is the race that seeks for him,
   that seeks the face of the God
   of Jacob. ℞.

SECOND READING   *Romans 1:1–7*

Paul, a slave of Christ Jesus, called to be an apostle and set apart for the gospel of God, which he promised previously through his prophets in the holy Scriptures, the gospel about his Son, descended from David according to the flesh, but established as Son of God in power according to the Spirit of holiness through resurrection from the dead, Jesus Christ our Lord. Through him we have received the grace of apostleship, to bring about the obedience of faith, for the sake of his name, among all the Gentiles, among whom are you also, who are called to belong to Jesus Christ; to all the beloved of God in Rome, called to be holy. Grace to you and peace from God our Father and the Lord Jesus Christ.

GOSPEL ACCLAMATION   *Matthew 1:23*

℞. Al - le - lu - ia, al - le - lu - ia, al - le - lu - ia.

Music: John Schiavone, b. 1947, © 2001, OCP Publications.

▶ The virgin shall conceive, and bear a son,
   and they shall name him Emmanuel. ℞.

GOSPEL READING

Matthew 1:18–24

This is how the birth of Jesus Christ came about. When his mother Mary was betrothed to Joseph, but before they lived together, she was found with child through the Holy Spirit. Joseph her husband, since he was a righteous man, yet unwilling to expose her to shame, decided to divorce her quietly. Such was his intention when, behold, the angel of the Lord appeared to him in a dream and said, "Joseph, son of David, do not be afraid to take Mary your wife into your home. For it is through the Holy Spirit that this child has been conceived in her. She will bear a son and you are to name him Jesus, because he will save his people from their sins." All this took place to fulfill what the Lord had said through the prophet:

Behold, the virgin shall conceive and
bear a son,
and they shall name him Emmanuel,

which means "God is with us." When Joseph awoke, he did as the angel of the Lord had commanded him and took his wife into his home.

---

888   FOURTH SUNDAY OF ADVENT — B

FIRST READING

2 Samuel 7:1–5, 8b–12, 14a, 16

When King David was settled in his palace, and the LORD had given him rest from his enemies on every side, he said to Nathan the prophet, "Here I am living in a house of cedar, while the ark of God dwells in a tent!" Nathan answered the king, "Go, do whatever you have in mind, for the LORD is with you." But that night the LORD spoke to Nathan and said: "Go, tell my servant David, 'Thus says the LORD: Should you build me a house to dwell in?

" 'It was I who took you from the pasture and from the care of the flock to be commander of my people Israel. I have been with you wherever you went, and I have destroyed all your enemies before you. And I will make you famous like the great ones of the earth. I will fix a place for my people Israel; I will plant them so that they may dwell in their place without further disturbance. Neither shall the wicked continue to afflict them as they did of old, since the time I first appointed judges over my people Israel. I will give you rest from all your enemies. The LORD also reveals to you that he will establish a house for you. And when your time comes and you rest with your ancestors, I will raise up your heir after you, sprung from your loins, and I will make his kingdom firm. I will be a father to him, and he shall be a son to me. Your house and your kingdom shall endure forever before me; your throne shall stand firm forever.' "

RESPONSORIAL PSALM

Psalm 89:2–3, 4–5, 27, 29

℟. For ev - er I will sing the good - ness of the Lord.

Music: John Schiavone, b. 1947, © 2001, OCP Publications.

▶ The promises of the LORD I will
    sing forever;
      through all generations my mouth
      shall proclaim your faithfulness.

For you have said, "My kindness is
    established forever";
      in heaven you have confirmed your
      faithfulness. ℟.

▶ "I have made a covenant with my
    chosen one,
  I have sworn to David my servant:

forever will I confirm your posterity
and establish your throne for
  all generations." ℟.

▶ "He shall say of me, 'You are
    my father,
  my God, the Rock, my savior.'
Forever I will maintain my kindness
  toward him,
  and my covenant with him
    stands firm." ℟.

SECOND READING
Romans 16:25–27

Brothers and sisters: To him who can strengthen you, according to my gospel and the proclamation of Jesus Christ, according to the revelation of the mystery kept secret for long ages but now manifested through the prophetic writings and, according to the command of the eternal God, made known to all nations to bring about the obedience of faith, to the only wise God, through Jesus Christ be glory forever and ever. Amen.

GOSPEL ACCLAMATION
Luke 1:38

℟. Al - le - lu - ia, al - le - lu - ia, al - le - lu - ia.

Music: John Schiavone, b. 1947, © 2001, OCP Publications.

▶ Behold, I am the handmaid of the Lord.
  May it be done to me according to your word. ℟.

GOSPEL READING
Luke 1:26–38

The angel Gabriel was sent from God to a town of Galilee called Nazareth, to a virgin betrothed to a man named Joseph, of the house of David, and the virgin's name was Mary. And coming to her, he said, "Hail, full of grace! The Lord is with you." But she was greatly troubled at what was said and pondered what sort of greeting this might be. Then the angel said to her, "Do not be afraid, Mary, for you have found favor with God.

  "Behold, you will conceive in your womb and bear a son, and you shall name him Jesus. He will be great and will be called Son of the Most High, and the Lord God will give him the throne of David his father, and he will rule over the house of Jacob forever, and of his kingdom there will be no end." But Mary said to the angel, "How can this be, since I have no relations with a man?" And the angel said to her in reply, "The Holy Spirit will come upon you, and the power of the Most High will overshadow you. Therefore the child to be born will be called holy, the Son of God. And behold, Elizabeth, your relative, has also conceived a son in her old age, and this is the sixth month for her who was called barren; for nothing will be impossible for God." Mary said, "Behold, I am the handmaid of the Lord. May it be done to me according to your word." Then the angel departed from her.

889   FOURTH SUNDAY OF ADVENT — C

FIRST READING   *Micah 5:1–4a*

Thus says the LORD:
You, Bethlehem-Ephrathah,
   too small to be among the clans
      of Judah,
from you shall come forth for me
   one who is to be ruler in Israel;
whose origin is from of old,
   from ancient times.
Therefore the Lord will give them up,
   until the time
      when she who is to give birth
      has borne,

and the rest of his kindred shall return
   to the children of Israel.
He shall stand firm and shepherd
   his flock
   by the strength of the LORD,
in the majestic name of the LORD,
   his God;
and they shall remain, for now
   his greatness
   shall reach to the ends of the earth;
he shall be peace.

RESPONSORIAL PSALM   *Psalm 80:2–3, 15–16, 18–19*

℟. Lord, make us turn to you; let us see your face and we shall be saved.

Music: John Schiavone, b. 1947, © 2001, OCP Publications.

▶ O shepherd of Israel, hearken,
   from your throne upon the
      cherubim, shine forth.
Rouse your power,
   and come to save us. ℟.

▶ Once again, O LORD of hosts,
   look down from heaven, and see;
take care of this vine,
   and protect what your right hand
      has planted,

the son of man whom you yourself
   made strong. ℟.

▶ May your help be with the man of
   your right hand,
with the son of man whom you
   yourself made strong.
Then we will no more withdraw
   from you;
give us new life, and we will call
   upon your name. ℟.

SECOND READING   *Hebrews 10:5–10*

Brothers and sisters: When Christ came into the world, he said:
   "Sacrifice and offering you did
      not desire,
   but a body you prepared for me;
in holocausts and sin offerings you
      took no delight.
Then I said, 'As is written of me in
   the scroll,
behold, I come to do your will,
   O God.'"

First he says, "Sacrifices and offerings, holocausts and sin offerings, you neither desired nor delighted in." These are offered according to the law. Then he says, "Behold, I come to do your will." He takes away the first to establish the second. By this "will," we have been consecrated through the offering of the body of Jesus Christ once for all.

GOSPEL ACCLAMATION
Luke 1:38

℟. Al - le - lu - ia, al - le - lu - ia, al - le - lu - ia.

Music: John Schiavone, b. 1947, © 2001, OCP Publications.

▶ Behold, I am the handmaid of the Lord.
  May it be done to me according to your word. ℟.

GOSPEL READING
Luke 1:39–45

Mary set out and traveled to the hill country in haste to a town of Judah, where she entered the house of Zechariah and greeted Elizabeth. When Elizabeth heard Mary's greeting, the infant leaped in her womb, and Elizabeth, filled with the Holy Spirit, cried out in a loud voice and said, "Blessed are you among women, and blessed is the fruit of your womb. And how does this happen to me, that the mother of my Lord should come to me? For at the moment the sound of your greeting reached my ears, the infant in my womb leaped for joy. Blessed are you who believed that what was spoken to you by the Lord would be fulfilled."

SEASON OF CHRISTMAS

NATIVITY OF THE LORD (CHRISTMAS): VIGIL MASS — ABC
890

FIRST READING
Isaiah 62:1–5

For Zion's sake I will not be silent,
  for Jerusalem's sake I will not be quiet,
until her vindication shines forth like
    the dawn
  and her victory like a burning torch.

Nations shall behold your vindication,
  and all the kings your glory;
you shall be called by a new name
  pronounced by the mouth of the LORD.
You shall be a glorious crown in the
    hand of the LORD,
a royal diadem held by your God.
No more shall people call you "Forsaken,"
  or your land "Desolate,"
but you shall be called "My Delight,"
  and your land "Espoused."
For the LORD delights in you
  and makes your land his spouse.
As a young man marries a virgin,
  your Builder shall marry you;
and as a bridegroom rejoices in his bride
  so shall your God rejoice in you.

RESPONSORIAL PSALM
Psalm 89:4–5, 16–17, 27, 29

℟. For ev - er I will sing the good - ness of the Lord.

Music: John Schiavone, b. 1947, © 2001, OCP Publications.

℟. For ever I will sing the goodness of the Lord.

▶ I have made a covenant with my
    chosen one,
  I have sworn to David my servant:
  forever will I confirm your posterity
    and establish your throne for
    all generations. ℟.

▶ Blessed the people who know the
    joyful shout;
  in the light of your countenance,
    O LORD, they walk.

At your name they rejoice all the day,
  and through your justice they are
  exalted. ℟.

▶ He shall say of me, "You are my father,
  my God, the rock, my savior."
  Forever I will maintain my kindness
    toward him,
  and my covenant with him stands
    firm. ℟.

SECOND READING
Acts of the Apostles 13:16–17, 22–25

When Paul reached Antioch in Pisidia and entered the synagogue, he stood up, motioned with his hand, and said, "Fellow Israelites and you others who are God-fearing, listen. The God of this people Israel chose our ancestors and exalted the people during their sojourn in the land of Egypt. With uplifted arm he led them out of it. Then he removed Saul and raised up David as king; of him he testified, 'I have found David, son of Jesse, a man after my own heart; he will carry out my every wish.' From this man's descendants God, according to his promise, has brought to Israel a savior, Jesus. John heralded his coming by proclaiming a baptism of repentance to all the people of Israel; and as John was completing his course, he would say, 'What do you suppose that I am? I am not he. Behold, one is coming after me; I am not worthy to unfasten the sandals of his feet.'"

GOSPEL ACCLAMATION

℟. Al - le - lu - ia, al - le - lu - ia, al - le - lu - ia.

Music: John Schiavone, b. 1947, © 2001, OCP Publications.

▶ Tomorrow the wickedness of the earth will be destroyed:
  the Savior of the world will reign over us. ℟.

GOSPEL READING
Matthew 1:1–25 or 1:18–25

(Include bracketed text for Long Form)

[The book of the genealogy of Jesus Christ, the son of David, the son of Abraham.

  Abraham became the father of Isaac, Isaac the father of Jacob, Jacob the father of Judah and his brothers. Judah became the father of Perez and Zerah, whose mother was Tamar. Perez became the father of Hezron, Hezron the father of Ram, Ram the father of Amminadab.

Amminadab became the father of Nahshon, Nahshon the father of Salmon, Salmon the father of Boaz, whose mother was Rahab. Boaz became the father of Obed, whose mother was Ruth. Obed became the father of Jesse, Jesse the father of David the king.

  David became the father of Solomon, whose mother had been the wife of Uriah. Solomon became the father of

Rehoboam, Rehoboam the father of Abijah, Abijah the father of Asaph. Asaph became the father of Jehoshaphat, Jehoshaphat the father of Joram, Joram the father of Uzziah. Uzziah became the father of Jotham, Jotham the father of Ahaz, Ahaz the father of Hezekiah. Hezekiah became the father of Manasseh, Manasseh the father of Amos, Amos the father of Josiah. Josiah became the father of Jechoniah and his brothers at the time of the Babylonian exile.

After the Babylonian exile, Jechoniah became the father of Shealtiel, Shealtiel the father of Zerubbabel, Zerubbabel the father of Abiud. Abiud became the father of Eliakim, Eliakim the father of Azor, Azor the father of Zadok. Zadok became the father of Achim, Achim the father of Eliud, Eliud the father of Eleazar. Eleazar became the father of Matthan, Matthan the father of Jacob, Jacob the father of Joseph, the husband of Mary. Of her was born Jesus who is called the Christ.

Thus the total number of generations from Abraham to David is fourteen generations; from David to the Babylonian exile, fourteen generations; from the Babylonian exile to the Christ, fourteen generations.

Now] this is how the birth of Jesus Christ came about. When his mother Mary was betrothed to Joseph, but before they lived together, she was found with child through the Holy Spirit. Joseph her husband, since he was a righteous man, yet unwilling to expose her to shame, decided to divorce her quietly. Such was his intention when, behold, the angel of the Lord appeared to him in a dream and said, "Joseph, son of David, do not be afraid to take Mary your wife into your home. For it is through the Holy Spirit that this child has been conceived in her. She will bear a son and you are to name him Jesus, because he will save his people from their sins." All this took place to fulfill what the Lord had said through the prophet:

Behold, the virgin shall conceive and bear a son,
and they shall name him Emmanuel,

which means "God is with us." When Joseph awoke, he did as the angel of the Lord had commanded him and took his wife into his home. He had no relations with her until she bore a son, and he named him Jesus.

NATIVITY OF THE LORD (CHRISTMAS): MASS AT MIDNIGHT — ABC   891

The Proclamation of the Birth of Christ may be sung or proclaimed after the Greeting and Introduction.

FIRST READING   *Isaiah 9:1–6*

The people who walked in darkness have seen a great light; upon those who dwelt in the land of gloom a light has shone. You have brought them abundant joy and great rejoicing, as they rejoice before you as at the harvest, as people make merry when dividing spoils.

For the yoke that burdened them, the pole on their shoulder, and the rod of their taskmaster you have smashed, as on the day of Midian. For every boot that tramped in battle, every cloak rolled in blood, will be burned as fuel for flames. For a child is born to us, a son is given us; upon his shoulder dominion rests. They name him Wonder-Counselor,

God-Hero,
Father-Forever, Prince of Peace.
His dominion is vast
and forever peaceful,
from David's throne, and over
his kingdom,

which he confirms and sustains
by judgment and justice,
both now and forever.
The zeal of the LORD of hosts will
do this!

RESPONSORIAL PSALM
Psalm 96: 1–2, 2–3, 11–12, 13

℟. [To - day,] to - day is born our Sav - ior, Christ the Lord.

Music: John Schiavone, b. 1947, © 2001, OCP Publications.

▶ Sing to the LORD a new song;
sing to the LORD, all you lands.
Sing to the LORD; bless his name. ℟.

▶ Announce his salvation, day after day.
Tell his glory among the nations;
among all peoples, his wondrous
deeds. ℟.

▶ Let the heavens be glad and the
earth rejoice;
let the sea and what fills it resound;

let the plains be joyful and all that is
in them!
Then shall all the trees of the
forest exult. ℟.

▶ They shall exult before the LORD, for
he comes;
for he comes to rule the earth.
He shall rule the world with justice
and the peoples with his constancy. ℟.

SECOND READING
Titus 2:11–14

Beloved: The grace of God has
appeared, saving all and training us to
reject godless ways and worldly desires
and to live temperately, justly, and
devoutly in this age, as we await the
blessed hope, the appearance of the
glory of our great God and savior Jesus
Christ, who gave himself for us to
deliver us from all lawlessness and to
cleanse for himself a people as his own,
eager to do what is good.

GOSPEL ACCLAMATION
Luke 2:10–11

℟. Al - le - lu - ia, al - le - lu - ia, al - le - lu - ia.

Music: John Schiavone, b. 1947, © 2001, OCP Publications.

▶ I proclaim to you good news of great joy:
today a Savior is born for us,
Christ the Lord. ℟.

GOSPEL READING
Luke 2:1–14

In those days a decree went out from
Caesar Augustus that the whole world
should be enrolled. This was the first
enrollment, when Quirinius was
governor of Syria. So all went to be
enrolled, each to his own town. And
Joseph too went up from Galilee from
the town of Nazareth to Judea, to the

city of David that is called Bethlehem, because he was of the house and family of David, to be enrolled with Mary, his betrothed, who was with child. While they were there, the time came for her to have her child, and she gave birth to her firstborn son. She wrapped him in swaddling clothes and laid him in a manger, because there was no room for them in the inn.

Now there were shepherds in that region living in the fields and keeping the night watch over their flock. The angel of the Lord appeared to them and the glory of the Lord shone around them, and they were struck with great fear. The angel said to them, "Do not be afraid; for behold, I proclaim to you good news of great joy that will be for all the people. For today in the city of David a savior has been born for you who is Christ and Lord. And this will be a sign for you: you will find an infant wrapped in swaddling clothes and lying in a manger." And suddenly there was a multitude of the heavenly host with the angel, praising God and saying:
"Glory to God in the highest
and on earth peace to those on
whom his favor rests."

NATIVITY OF THE LORD (CHRISTMAS): 892
MASS AT DAWN — ABC

FIRST READING
Isaiah 62:11–12

See, the LORD proclaims
  to the ends of the earth:
say to daughter Zion,
  your savior comes!
Here is his reward with him,

his recompense before him.
They shall be called the holy people,
  the redeemed of the LORD,
and you shall be called "Frequented,"
  a city that is not forsaken.

RESPONSORIAL PSALM
Psalm 97:1, 6, 11–12

℞. A light will shine on us this day: the Lord is born for us.

Music: John Schiavone, b. 1947, © 2001, OCP Publications.

▶ The LORD is king; let the earth rejoice;
  let the many islands be glad.
The heavens proclaim his justice,
  and all peoples see his glory. ℞.

▶ Light dawns for the just;
  and gladness, for the upright
  of heart.
Be glad in the LORD, you just,
  and give thanks to his holy name. ℞.

SECOND READING
Titus 3:4–7

Beloved:
When the kindness and generous love
  of God our savior appeared,
not because of any righteous deeds we
    had done
  but because of his mercy,
he saved us through the bath of rebirth

and renewal by the Holy Spirit,
  whom he richly poured out on us
    through Jesus Christ our savior,
so that we might be justified by
    his grace
  and become heirs in hope of
    eternal life.

GOSPEL ACCLAMATION *Luke 2:14*

℟. Al - le - lu - ia, al - le - lu - ia, al - le - lu - ia.

Music: John Schiavone, b. 1947, © 2001, OCP Publications.

▸ Glory to God in the highest,
and on earth peace to those
on whom his favor rests. ℟.

GOSPEL READING *Luke 2:15–20*

When the angels went away from them to heaven, the shepherds said to one another, "Let us go, then, to Bethlehem to see this thing that has taken place, which the Lord has made known to us." So they went in haste and found Mary and Joseph, and the infant lying in the manger. When they saw this, they made known the message that had been told them about this child. All who heard it were amazed by what had been told them by the shepherds. And Mary kept all these things, reflecting on them in her heart. Then the shepherds returned, glorifying and praising God for all they had heard and seen, just as it had been told to them.

---

893   NATIVITY OF THE LORD (CHRISTMAS): MASS DURING THE DAY — ABC

FIRST READING *Isaiah 52:7–10*

How beautiful upon the mountains
  are the feet of him who brings
    glad tidings,
announcing peace, bearing good news,
  announcing salvation, and saying
    to Zion,
  "Your God is King!"

Hark! Your sentinels raise a cry,
  together they shout for joy,
for they see directly, before their eyes,
the LORD restoring Zion.
Break out together in song,
  O ruins of Jerusalem!
For the LORD comforts his people,
  he redeems Jerusalem.
The LORD has bared his holy arm
  in the sight of all the nations;
all the ends of the earth will behold
  the salvation of our God.

RESPONSORIAL PSALM *Psalm 98:1, 2–3, 3–4, 5–6*

℟. All the ends of the earth have seen the sav - ing pow - er of God.

Music: John Schiavone, b. 1947, © 2001, OCP Publications.

▸ Sing to the LORD a new song,
  for he has done wondrous deeds;
his right hand has won victory for him,
  his holy arm. ℟.

▸ The LORD has made his salvation
  known:
  in the sight of the nations he has
  revealed his justice.

He has remembered his kindness and
his faithfulness
toward the house of Israel. ℟.

▶ All the ends of the earth have seen
the salvation by our God.
Sing joyfully to the LORD, all you lands;
break into song; sing praise. ℟.

▶ Sing praise to the LORD with the harp,
with the harp and melodious song.
With trumpets and the sound of
the horn
sing joyfully before the King,
the LORD. ℟.

SECOND READING

Hebrews 1:1–6

Brothers and sisters: In times past, God
spoke in partial and various ways to our
ancestors through the prophets; in
these last days, he has spoken to us
through the Son, whom he made heir
of all things and through whom he
created the universe,
who is the refulgence of his glory,
the very imprint of his being,
and who sustains all things by his
mighty word.
When he had accomplished
purification from sins,
he took his seat at the right hand of

the Majesty on high,
as far superior to the angels
as the name he has inherited is more
excellent than theirs.

For to which of the angels did God
ever say:
*You are my son; this day I have
begotten you?*
Or again:
*I will be a father to him, and he shall
be a son to me?*
And again, when he leads the firstborn
into the world, he says:
Let all the angels of God worship him.

GOSPEL ACCLAMATION

℟. Al - le - lu - ia, al - le - lu - ia, al - le - lu - ia.

Music: John Schiavone, b. 1947, © 2001, OCP Publications.

▶ A holy day has dawned upon us.
Come, you nations, and adore the Lord.
For today a great light has come upon the earth. ℟.

GOSPEL READING

John 1:1–18 or 1:1–5, 9–14

(Include bracketed text for Long Form)

In the beginning was the Word,
and the Word was with God,
and the Word was God.
He was in the beginning with God.
All things came to be through him,
and without him nothing came
to be.
What came to be through him
was life,
and this life was the light of the
human race;

the light shines in the darkness,
and the darkness has not
overcome it.
[A man named John was sent from God.
He came for testimony, to testify to the
light, so that all might believe through
him. He was not the light, but came
to testify to the light.] The true light,
which enlightens everyone, was coming
into the world.

He was in the world,
and the world came to be
through him,
but the world did not know him.
He came to what was his own,
but his own people did not
accept him.
But to those who did accept him he
gave power to become children of God,
to those who believe in his name, who
were born not by natural generation
nor by human choice nor by a man's
decision but of God.
And the Word became flesh
and made his dwelling among us,

and we saw his glory,
the glory as of the Father's
only Son,
full of grace and truth.
[John testified to him and cried out,
saying, "This was he of whom I said,
'The one who is coming after me ranks
ahead of me because he existed before
me.'" From his fullness we have all
received, grace in place of grace,
because while the law was given
through Moses, grace and truth came
through Jesus Christ. No one has ever
seen God. The only Son, God, who is at
the Father's side, has revealed him.]

---

894 HOLY FAMILY OF JESUS, MARY AND JOSEPH — ABC

FIRST READING

Sirach 3:2–6, 12–14

God sets a father in honor over
his children;
a mother's authority he confirms over
her sons.
Whoever honors his father atones
for sins,
and preserves himself from them.
When he prays, he is heard;
he stores up riches who reveres
his mother.
Whoever honors his father is gladdened
by children,
and, when he prays, is heard.
Whoever reveres his father will live a

long life;
he who obeys his father brings
comfort to his mother.
My son, take care of your father when
he is old;
grieve him not as long as he lives.
Even if his mind fail, be considerate
of him;
revile him not all the days of his life;
kindness to a father will not be forgotten,
firmly planted against the debt of
your sins
— a house raised in justice to you.

RESPONSORIAL PSALM

Psalm 128:1–2, 3, 4–5

℟. Bless-ed are those who fear the Lord and walk in his ways.

Music: John Schiavone, b. 1947, © 2001, OCP Publications.

▶ Blessed is everyone who fears
the LORD,
who walks in his ways!
For you shall eat the fruit of
your handiwork;
blessed shall you be, and favored. ℟.

▶ Your wife shall be like a fruitful vine
in the recesses of your home;

your children like olive plants
around your table. ℟.

▶ Behold, thus is the man blessed
who fears the LORD.
The LORD bless you from Zion:
may you see the prosperity
of Jerusalem
all the days of your life. ℟.

SECOND READING

Colossians 3:12–21 or 3:12–17

(Include bracketed text for Long Form)

Brothers and sisters: Put on, as God's chosen ones, holy and beloved, heartfelt compassion, kindness, humility, gentleness, and patience, bearing with one another and forgiving one another, if one has a grievance against another; as the Lord has forgiven you, so must you also do. And over all these put on love, that is, the bond of perfection. And let the peace of Christ control your hearts, the peace into which you were also called in one body. And be thankful. Let the word of Christ dwell in you richly, as in all wisdom you teach and admonish one another, singing psalms, hymns, and spiritual songs with gratitude in your hearts to God. And whatever you do, in word or in deed, do everything in the name of the Lord Jesus, giving thanks to God the Father through him.

[Wives, be subordinate to your husbands, as is proper in the Lord. Husbands, love your wives, and avoid any bitterness toward them. Children, obey your parents in everything, for this is pleasing to the Lord. Fathers, do not provoke your children, so they may not become discouraged.]

GOSPEL ACCLAMATION

Colossians 3:15a, 16a

℟. Al - le - lu - ia, al - le - lu - ia, al - le - lu - ia.

Music: John Schiavone, b. 1947, © 2001, OCP Publications.

▶ Let the peace of Christ control your hearts; let the word of Christ dwell in you richly. ℟.

GOSPEL READING — A

Matthew 2:13–15, 19–23

When the magi had departed, behold, the angel of the Lord appeared to Joseph in a dream and said, "Rise, take the child and his mother, flee to Egypt, and stay there until I tell you. Herod is going to search for the child to destroy him." Joseph rose and took the child and his mother by night and departed for Egypt. He stayed there until the death of Herod, that what the Lord had said through the prophet might be fulfilled, *Out of Egypt I called my son.*

When Herod had died, behold, the angel of the Lord appeared in a dream to Joseph in Egypt and said, "Rise, take the child and his mother and go to the land of Israel, for those who sought the child's life are dead." He rose, took the child and his mother, and went to the land of Israel. But when he heard that Archelaus was ruling over Judea in place of his father Herod, he was afraid to go back there. And because he had been warned in a dream, he departed for the region of Galilee. He went and dwelt in a town called Nazareth, so that what had been spoken through the prophets might be fulfilled, *He shall be called a Nazorean.*

GOSPEL READING — B
Luke 2:22–40 or 2:22, 39–40

(Include bracketed text for Long Form)

When the days were completed for their purification according to the law of Moses, they took him up to Jerusalem to present him to the Lord, [just as it is written in the law of the Lord, *Every male that opens the womb shall be consecrated to the Lord,* and to offer the sacrifice of *a pair of turtledoves or two young pigeons,* in accordance with the dictate in the law of the Lord.

Now there was a man in Jerusalem whose name was Simeon. This man was righteous and devout, awaiting the consolation of Israel, and the Holy Spirit was upon him. It had been revealed to him by the Holy Spirit that he should not see death before he had seen the Christ of the Lord. He came in the Spirit into the temple; and when the parents brought in the child Jesus to perform the custom of the law in regard to him, he took him into his arms and blessed God, saying:

"Now, Master, you may let your
    servant go
  in peace, according to your word,
for my eyes have seen your salvation,
  which you prepared in sight of all
    the peoples,
a light for revelation to the Gentiles,
  and glory for your people Israel."

The child's father and mother were amazed at what was said about him; and Simeon blessed them and said to Mary his mother, "Behold, this child is destined for the fall and rise of many in Israel, and to be a sign that will be contradicted — and you yourself a sword will pierce — so that the thoughts of many hearts may be revealed." There was also a prophetess, Anna, the daughter of Phanuel, of the tribe of Asher. She was advanced in years, having lived seven years with her husband after her marriage, and then as a widow until she was eighty-four. She never left the temple, but worshiped night and day with fasting and prayer. And coming forward at that very time, she gave thanks to God and spoke about the child to all who were awaiting the redemption of Jerusalem.]

When they had fulfilled all the prescriptions of the law of the Lord, they returned to Galilee, to their own town of Nazareth. The child grew and became strong, filled with wisdom; and the favor of God was upon him.

GOSPEL READING — C
Luke 2:41–52

Each year Jesus' parents went to Jerusalem for the feast of Passover, and when he was twelve years old, they went up according to festival custom. After they had completed its days, as they were returning, the boy Jesus remained behind in Jerusalem, but his parents did not know it. Thinking that he was in the caravan, they journeyed for a day and looked for him among their relatives and acquaintances, but not finding him, they returned to Jerusalem to look for him. After three days they found him in the temple, sitting in the midst of the teachers, listening to them and asking them questions, and all who heard him were astounded at his understanding and his answers. When his parents saw him, they were astonished, and his mother said to him, "Son, why have you done this to us? Your father and I have been looking for you with great anxiety." And he said to them, "Why were you looking for me? Did you not know that I must be in my Father's house?" But they did not understand what he said to them. He went down with them and came to Nazareth, and was obedient to them; and his mother kept all these things in her heart. And Jesus advanced in wisdom and age and favor before God and man.

HOLY FAMILY OF JESUS, MARY AND JOSEPH   **895**
OPTIONAL READINGS — B

FIRST READING   *Genesis 15:1–6; 21:1–3*

The word of the LORD came to Abram in a vision, saying:
"Fear not, Abram!
     I am your shield;
     I will make your reward very great."
But Abram said, "O Lord GOD, what good will your gifts be, if I keep on being childless and have as my heir the steward of my house, Eliezer?" Abram continued, "See, you have given me no offspring, and so one of my servants will be my heir." Then the word of the LORD came to him: "No, that one shall not be your heir; your own issue shall be your heir." The Lord took Abram outside and said, "Look up at the sky and count the stars, if you can. Just so," he added, "shall your descendants be." Abram put his faith in the LORD, who credited it to him as an act of righteousness.

The LORD took note of Sarah as he had said he would; he did for her as he had promised. Sarah became pregnant and bore Abraham a son in his old age, at the set time that God had stated. Abraham gave the name Isaac to this son of his whom Sarah bore him.

RESPONSORIAL PSALM   *Psalm 105:1–2, 3–4, 5–6, 8–9*

℟. The Lord re - mem - bers his cov - e - nant for ev - er.

Music: John Schiavone, b. 1947, © 2001, OCP Publications.

▶ Give thanks to the LORD, invoke
          his name;
     make known among the nations
          his deeds.
Sing to him, sing his praise,
     proclaim all his wondrous deeds. ℟.

▶ Glory in his holy name;
     rejoice, O hearts that seek
          the LORD!
Look to the LORD in his strength;
     constantly seek his face. ℟.

▶ You descendants of Abraham,
          his servants,
     sons of Jacob, his chosen ones!
He, the LORD, is our God;
     throughout the earth his judgments
          prevail. ℟.

▶ He remembers forever his covenant
     which he made binding for a
          thousand generations
which he entered into with Abraham
     and by his oath to Isaac. ℟.

SECOND READING   *Hebrews 11:8, 11–12, 17–19*

Brothers and sisters: By faith Abraham obeyed when he was called to go out to a place that he was to receive as an inheritance; he went out, not knowing where he was to go. By faith he received power to generate, even though he was past the normal age — and Sarah herself was sterile — for he thought that the one who had made the promise was trustworthy. So it was that there came forth from one man, himself as good as dead, descendants as numerous as the stars in the sky and as countless as the sands on the seashore.

By faith Abraham, when put to the test,

offered up Isaac, and he who had received the promises was ready to offer his only son, of whom it was said, "Through Isaac descendants shall bear your name." He reasoned that God was able to raise even from the dead, and he received Isaac back as a symbol.

GOSPEL ACCLAMATION
Hebrews 1:1-2

℟. Al - le - lu - ia, al - le - lu - ia, al - le - lu - ia.

Music: John Schiavone, b. 1947, © 2001, OCP Publications.

▶ In the past God spoke to our ancestors through the prophets; in these last days, he has spoken to us through the Son. ℟.

Use Gospel Reading for Year B, number 894.

---

896   HOLY FAMILY OF JESUS, MARY AND JOSEPH
OPTIONAL READINGS — C

FIRST READING
1 Samuel 1:20–22, 24–28

In those days Hannah conceived, and at the end of her term bore a son whom she called Samuel, since she had asked the LORD for him. The next time her husband Elkanah was going up with the rest of his household to offer the customary sacrifice to the LORD and to fulfill his vows, Hannah did not go, explaining to her husband, "Once the child is weaned, I will take him to appear before the LORD and to remain there forever; I will offer him as a perpetual nazirite."

Once Samuel was weaned, Hannah brought him up with her, along with a three-year-old bull, an ephah of flour, and a skin of wine, and presented him at the temple of the LORD in Shiloh. After the boy's father had sacrificed the young bull, Hannah, his mother, approached Eli and said: "Pardon, my lord! As you live, my lord, I am the woman who stood near you here, praying to the LORD. I prayed for this child, and the LORD granted my request. Now I, in turn, give him to the LORD; as long as he lives, he shall be dedicated to the LORD." Hannah left Samuel there.

RESPONSORIAL PSALM
Psalm 84:2–3, 5–6, 9–10

℟. Bless - ed are they who dwell in your house, O Lord.

Music: John Schiavone, b. 1947, © 2001, OCP Publications.

▶ How lovely is your dwelling place,
   O LORD of hosts!
My soul yearns and pines for the
   courts of the LORD.
My heart and my flesh cry out for the
   living God. ℟.

▶ Happy they who dwell in your house!
   Continually they praise you.
Happy the men whose strength
   you are!
Their hearts are set upon the
   pilgrimage. ℟.

▶ O LORD of hosts, hear our prayer;
hearken, O God of Jacob!

O God, behold our shield,
and look upon the face of your
anointed. ℟.

SECOND READING

1 John 3:1–2, 21–24

Beloved: See what love the Father has bestowed on us that we may be called the children of God. And so we are. The reason the world does not know us is that it did not know him. Beloved, we are God's children now; what we shall be has not yet been revealed. We do know that when it is revealed we shall be like him, for we shall see him as he is.

Beloved, if our hearts do not condemn us, we have confidence in God and receive from him whatever we ask, because we keep his commandments and do what pleases him. And his commandment is this: we should believe in the name of his Son, Jesus Christ, and love one another just as he commanded us. Those who keep his commandments remain in him, and he in them, and the way we know that he remains in us is from the Spirit he gave us.

GOSPEL ACCLAMATION

cf. Acts of the Apostles 16:14b

℟. Al - le - lu - ia, al - le - lu - ia, al - le - lu - ia.

Music: John Schiavone, b. 1947, © 2001, OCP Publications.

▶ Open our hearts, O Lord,
to listen to the words of your Son. ℟.

Use Gospel Reading for Year C, number 894.

BLESSED VIRGIN MARY, MOTHER OF GOD — ABC 897

FIRST READING

Numbers 6:22–27

The LORD said to Moses: "Speak to Aaron and his sons and tell them: This is how you shall bless the Israelites. Say to them:
The LORD bless you and keep you!
The LORD let his face shine upon

you, and be gracious to you!
The LORD look upon you kindly and give you peace!
So shall they invoke my name upon the Israelites, and I will bless them."

RESPONSORIAL PSALM

Psalm 67:2–3, 5, 6, 8

℟. May God bless us in his mer - cy.

Music: John Schiavone, b. 1947, © 2001, OCP Publications.

℟. **May God bless us in his mercy.**

▶ May God have pity on us and bless us;
   may he let his face shine upon us.
So may your way be known upon earth;
   among all nations, your salvation. ℟.

▶ May the nations be glad and exult
   because you rule the peoples
   in equity;
   the nations on the earth you guide. ℟.

▶ May the peoples praise you, O God;
   may all the peoples praise you!
May God bless us,
   and may all the ends of the earth
   fear him! ℟.

SECOND READING
Galatians 4:4–7

Brothers and sisters: When the fullness of time had come, God sent his Son, born of a woman, born under the law, to ransom those under the law, so that we might receive adoption as sons. As proof that you are sons, God sent the Spirit of his Son into our hearts, crying out, "Abba, Father!" So you are no longer a slave but a son, and if a son then also an heir, through God.

GOSPEL ACCLAMATION
Hebrews 1:1–2

℟. Al - le - lu - ia, al - le - lu - ia, al - le - lu - ia.

Music: John Schiavone, b. 1947, © 2001, OCP Publications.

▶ In the past God spoke to our ancestors through the prophets;
   in these last days, he has spoken to us through the Son. ℟.

GOSPEL READING
Luke 2:16–21

The shepherds went in haste to Bethlehem and found Mary and Joseph, and the infant lying in the manger. When they saw this, they made known the message that had been told them about this child. All who heard it were amazed by what had been told them by the shepherds. And Mary kept all these things, reflecting on them in her heart. Then the shepherds returned, glorifying and praising God for all they had heard and seen, just as it had been told to them.

   When eight days were completed for his circumcision, he was named Jesus, the name given him by the angel before he was conceived in the womb.

---

898 EPIPHANY OF THE LORD — ABC

FIRST READING
Isaiah 60:1–6

Rise up in splendor, Jerusalem! Your
   light has come,
   the glory of the Lord shines upon you.
See, darkness covers the earth,
   and thick clouds cover the peoples;
but upon you the LORD shines,
   and over you appears his glory.

Nations shall walk by your light,
   and kings by your shining radiance.
Raise your eyes and look about;
   they all gather and come to you:
your sons come from afar,
   and your daughters in the arms of
   their nurses.

Then you shall be radiant at what you see,
  your heart shall throb and overflow,
for the riches of the sea shall be
    emptied out before you,
  the wealth of nations shall be brought
    to you.

Caravans of camels shall fill you,
  dromedaries from Midian and Ephah;
all from Sheba shall come
  bearing gold and frankincense,
  and proclaiming the praises of
    the LORD.

RESPONSORIAL PSALM

Psalm 72:1–2, 7–8, 10–11, 12–13

℟. Lord, ev-'ry na-tion on earth will a-dore you,   [will a-dore   you.]

Music: John Schiavone, b. 1947, © 2001, OCP Publications.

▶ O God, with your judgment endow
    the king,
  and with your justice, the king's son;
  he shall govern your people
    with justice
  and your afflicted ones with
    judgment. ℟.

▶ Justice shall flower in his days,
  and profound peace, till the moon
    be no more.
  May he rule from sea to sea,
    and from the River to the ends of
    the earth. ℟.

▶ The kings of Tarshish and the Isles
    shall offer gifts;
  the kings of Arabia and Seba shall
    bring tribute.
  All kings shall pay him homage,
    all nations shall serve him. ℟.

▶ For he shall rescue the poor when he
    cries out,
  and the afflicted when he has no
    one to help him.
  He shall have pity for the lowly and
    the poor;
  the lives of the poor he shall save. ℟.

SECOND READING

Ephesians 3:2–3a, 5–6

Brothers and sisters: You have heard of the stewardship of God's grace that was given to me for your benefit, namely, that the mystery was made known to me by revelation. It was not made known to people in other generations as it has now been revealed to his holy apostles and prophets by the Spirit: that the Gentiles are coheirs, members of the same body, and copartners in the promise in Christ Jesus through the gospel.

GOSPEL ACCLAMATION

Matthew 2:2

℟. Al-le - lu - ia, al-le - lu - ia, al-le - lu - ia.

Music: John Schiavone, b. 1947, © 2001, OCP Publications.

▶ We saw his star at its rising
  and have come to do him homage. ℟.

GOSPEL READING

Matthew 2:1–12

When Jesus was born in Bethlehem of Judea, in the days of King Herod, behold, magi from the east arrived in Jerusalem, saying, "Where is the newborn king of the Jews? We saw his star at its rising and have come to do him homage." When King Herod heard this, he was greatly troubled, and all Jerusalem with him. Assembling all the chief priests and the scribes of the people, he inquired of them where the Christ was to be born. They said to him, "In Bethlehem of Judea, for thus it has been written through the prophet:

And you, Bethlehem, land of Judah,
    are by no means least among the
        rulers of Judah;
since from you shall come a ruler,
    who is to shepherd my people
        Israel."

Then Herod called the magi secretly and ascertained from them the time of the star's appearance. He sent them to Bethlehem and said, "Go and search diligently for the child. When you have found him, bring me word, that I too may go and do him homage." After their audience with the king they set out. And behold, the star that they had seen at its rising preceded them, until it came and stopped over the place where the child was. They were overjoyed at seeing the star, and on entering the house they saw the child with Mary his mother. They prostrated themselves and did him homage. Then they opened their treasures and offered him gifts of gold, frankincense, and myrrh. And having been warned in a dream not to return to Herod, they departed for their country by another way.

The Proclamation of the date of Easter may be sung or proclaimed after the Gospel or following the Prayer after Communion.

---

899   BAPTISM OF THE LORD — ABC

FIRST READING

Isaiah 42:1–4, 6–7

Thus says the LORD:
Here is my servant whom I uphold,
    my chosen one with whom I
        am pleased,
upon whom I have put my spirit;
    he shall bring forth justice to
        the nations,
not crying out, not shouting,
    not making his voice heard in
        the street.
A bruised reed he shall not break,
    and a smoldering wick he shall
        not quench,
until he establishes justice on the earth;

the coastlands will wait for
    his teaching.

I, the LORD, have called you for the
        victory of justice,
    I have grasped you by the hand;
I formed you, and set you
    as a covenant of the people,
    a light for the nations,
to open the eyes of the blind,
    to bring out prisoners from
        confinement,
    and from the dungeon, those who
        live in darkness.

RESPONSORIAL PSALM

Psalm 29:1–2, 3–4, 3, 9–10

℟. The Lord will bless his peo - ple with peace.

Music: John Schiavone, b. 1947, © 2001, OCP Publications.

▶ Give to the LORD, you sons of God,
   give to the LORD glory and praise,
   give to the LORD the glory due his name;
   adore the LORD in holy attire. ℟.

▶ The voice of the LORD is over the waters,
   the LORD, over vast waters.
   The voice of the LORD is mighty;
   the voice of the LORD is majestic. ℟.

▶ The God of glory thunders,
   and in his temple all say, "Glory!"
   The LORD is enthroned above the flood;
   the LORD is enthroned as king
   forever. ℟.

SECOND READING

Acts of the Apostles 10:34–38

Peter proceeded to speak to those gathered in the house of Cornelius, saying: "In truth, I see that God shows no partiality. Rather, in every nation whoever fears him and acts uprightly is acceptable to him. You know the word that he sent to the Israelites as he proclaimed peace through Jesus Christ, who is Lord of all, what has happened all over Judea, beginning in Galilee after the baptism that John preached, how God anointed Jesus of Nazareth with the Holy Spirit and power. He went about doing good and healing all those oppressed by the devil, for God was with him."

GOSPEL ACCLAMATION

cf. Mark 9:7

℟. Al - le - lu - ia, al - le - lu - ia, al - le - lu - ia.

Music: John Schiavone, b. 1947, © 2001, OCP Publications.

▶ The heavens were opened and the voice of the Father thundered:
   This is my beloved Son, listen to him. ℟.

GOSPEL READING — A

Matthew 3:13–17

Jesus came from Galilee to John at the Jordan to be baptized by him. John tried to prevent him, saying, "I need to be baptized by you, and yet you are coming to me?" Jesus said to him in reply, "Allow it now, for thus it is fitting for us to fulfill all righteousness." Then he allowed him. After Jesus was baptized, he came up from the water and behold, the heavens were opened for him, and he saw the Spirit of God descending like a dove and coming upon him. And a voice came from the heavens, saying, "This is my beloved Son, with whom I am well pleased."

GOSPEL READING — B

Mark 1:7–11

This is what John the Baptist proclaimed: "One mightier than I is coming after me. I am not worthy to stoop and loosen the thongs of his sandals. I have baptized you with water; he will baptize you with the Holy Spirit."

It happened in those days that Jesus came from Nazareth of Galilee and was baptized in the Jordan by John. On coming up out of the water he saw the heavens being torn open and the Spirit, like a dove, descending upon him. And a voice came from the heavens, "You are my beloved Son; with you I am well pleased."

GOSPEL READING — C

Luke 3:15–16, 21–22

The people were filled with expectation, and all were asking in their hearts whether John might be the Christ. John answered them all, saying, "I am baptizing you with water, but one mightier than I is coming. I am not worthy to loosen the thongs of his sandals. He will baptize you with the Holy Spirit and fire."

After all the people had been baptized and Jesus also had been baptized and was praying, heaven was opened and the Holy Spirit descended upon him in bodily form like a dove. And a voice came from heaven, "You are my beloved Son; with you I am well pleased."

---

900   BAPTISM OF THE LORD
OPTIONAL READINGS — B

FIRST READING

Isaiah 55:1–11

Thus says the LORD:
All you who are thirsty,
   come to the water!
You who have no money,
   come, receive grain and eat;
come, without paying and without cost,
   drink wine and milk!
Why spend your money for what is
    not bread,
   your wages for what fails to satisfy?
Heed me, and you shall eat well,
   you shall delight in rich fare.
Come to me heedfully,
   listen, that you may have life.
I will renew with you the everlasting
    covenant,
   the benefits assured to David.
As I made him a witness to the peoples,
   a leader and commander of nations,
so shall you summon a nation you
    knew not,
   and nations that knew you not shall
    run to you,

because of the LORD, your God,
   the Holy One of Israel, who has
    glorified you.

Seek the LORD while he may be found,
   call him while he is near.
Let the scoundrel forsake his way,
   and the wicked man his thoughts;
let him turn to the LORD for mercy;
   to our God, who is generous
    in forgiving.
For my thoughts are not your thoughts,
   nor are your ways my ways, says
    the LORD.
As high as the heavens are above
    the earth
   so high are my ways above your ways
   and my thoughts above your thoughts.

For just as from the heavens
   the rain and snow come down
and do not return there
   till they have watered the earth,
   making it fertile and fruitful,

giving seed to the one who sows
and bread to the one who eats,
so shall my word be
that goes forth from my mouth;

my word shall not return to me void,
but shall do my will,
achieving the end for which I sent it.

RESPONSORIAL PSALM

Isaiah 12:2–3, 4bcd, 5–6

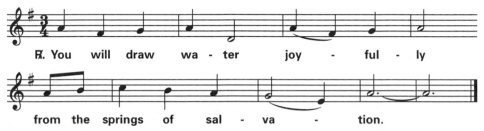

℟. You will draw wa - ter joy - ful - ly from the springs of sal - va - tion.

Music: John Schiavone, b. 1947, © 2001, OCP Publications.

▶ God indeed is my savior;
I am confident and unafraid.
My strength and my courage is
the LORD,
and he has been my savior.
With joy you will draw water
at the fountain of salvation. ℟.

▶ Give thanks to the LORD, acclaim
his name;
among the nations make known
his deeds,
proclaim how exalted is his name. ℟.

▶ Sing praise to the LORD for his
glorious achievement;
let this be known throughout all
the earth.
Shout with exultation, O city of Zion,
for great in your midst
is the Holy One of Israel! ℟.

SECOND READING

1 John 5:1–9

Beloved: Everyone who believes that Jesus is the Christ is begotten by God, and everyone who loves the Father loves also the one begotten by him. In this way we know that we love the children of God when we love God and obey his commandments. For the love of God is this, that we keep his commandments. And his commandments are not burdensome, for whoever is begotten by God conquers the world. And the victory that conquers the world is our faith. Who indeed is the victor over the world but the one who believes that Jesus is the Son of God?

This is the one who came through water and blood, Jesus Christ, not by water alone, but by water and blood. The Spirit is the one who testifies, and the Spirit is truth. So there are three that testify, the Spirit, the water, and the blood, and the three are of one accord. If we accept human testimony, the testimony of God is surely greater. Now the testimony of God is this, that he has testified on behalf of his Son.

GOSPEL ACCLAMATION

cf. John 1:29

℞. Al - le - lu - ia, al - le - lu - ia, al - le - lu - ia.

Music: John Schiavone, b. 1947, © 2001, OCP Publications.

▶ John saw Jesus approaching him, and said:
Behold the Lamb of God who takes away the sin of the world. ℞.

Use Gospel Reading for Year B, number 899.

---

901   BAPTISM OF THE LORD
OPTIONAL READINGS — C

FIRST READING

Isaiah 40:1–5, 9–11

Comfort, give comfort to my people,
    says your God.
Speak tenderly to Jerusalem, and
    proclaim to her
    that her service is at an end,
    her guilt is expiated;
indeed, she has received from the hand
    of the LORD
    double for all her sins.

    A voice cries out:
In the desert prepare the way of
    the LORD!
    Make straight in the wasteland a
    highway for our God!
Every valley shall be filled in,
    every mountain and hill shall be
    made low;
the rugged land shall be made a plain,
    the rough country, a broad valley.
Then the glory of the LORD shall

be revealed,
    and all people shall see it together;
    for the mouth of the LORD has spoken.

Go up onto a high mountain,
    Zion, herald of glad tidings;
cry out at the top of your voice,
    Jerusalem, herald of good news!
Fear not to cry out
    and say to the cities of Judah:
    Here is your God!
Here comes with power
    the Lord GOD,
    who rules by a strong arm;
here is his reward with him,
    his recompense before him.
Like a shepherd he feeds his flock;
    in his arms he gathers the lambs,
carrying them in his bosom,
    and leading the ewes with care.

RESPONSORIAL PSALM

Psalm 104:1b–2, 3–4, 24–25, 27–28, 29–30

℞. [O bless the Lord, O bless the Lord,] O bless the Lord, my soul.

Music: John Schiavone, b. 1947, © 2001, OCP Publications.

▶ O LORD, my God, you are great indeed!
    you are clothed with majesty
        and glory,
    robed in light as with a cloak.
    You have spread out the heavens
        like a tent-cloth. ℞.

▶ You have constructed your palace
    upon the waters.
    You make the clouds your chariot;
    you travel on the wings of the wind.
    You make the winds your messengers,
    and flaming fire your ministers. ℞.

▶ How manifold are your works, O LORD!
In wisdom you have wrought
them all —
the earth is full of your creatures;
the sea also, great and wide,
in which are schools without number
of living things both small
and great. ℟.

▶ They look to you to give them food in
due time.
When you give it to them, they
gather it;
when you open your hand, they are
filled with good things. ℟.

▶ If you take away their breath, they
perish and return to the dust.
When you send forth your spirit,
they are created,
and you renew the face of the earth. ℟.

SECOND READING

Titus 2:11–14; 3:4–7

Beloved: The grace of God has appeared,
saving all and training us to reject
godless ways and worldly desires and
to live temperately, justly, and devoutly
in this age, as we await the blessed
hope, the appearance of the glory of
our great God and savior Jesus Christ,
who gave himself for us to deliver us
from all lawlessness and to cleanse for
himself a people as his own, eager to
do what is good.

When the kindness and generous love
of God our savior appeared,

not because of any righteous deeds
we had done
but because of his mercy,
he saved us through the bath of rebirth
and renewal by the Holy Spirit,
whom he richly poured out on us
through Jesus Christ our savior,
so that we might be justified by
his grace
and become heirs in hope of
eternal life.

GOSPEL ACCLAMATION

cf. Luke 3:16

℟. Al - le - lu - ia, al - le - lu - ia, al - le - lu - ia.

Music: John Schiavone, b. 1947, © 2001, OCP Publications.

▶ John said: One mightier than I is coming;
he will baptize you with the Holy Spirit and with fire. ℟.

Use Gospel Reading for Year C, number 899.

SEASON OF LENT

ASH WEDNESDAY — ABC

FIRST READING

Joel 2:12–18 (219)

Even now, says the LORD,
  return to me with your whole heart,
  with fasting, and weeping,
    and mourning;
Rend your hearts, not your garments,
  and return to the LORD, your God.
For gracious and merciful is he,
  slow to anger, rich in kindness,
  and relenting in punishment.
Perhaps he will again relent
  and leave behind him a blessing,
Offerings and libations
  for the LORD, your God.

Blow the trumpet in Zion!
  proclaim a fast,
  call an assembly;

Gather the people,
  notify the congregation;
Assemble the elders,
  gather the children
  and the infants at the breast;
Let the bridegroom quit his room
  and the bride her chamber.
Between the porch and the altar
  let the priests, the ministers of the
    LORD , weep,
And say, "Spare, O LORD, your people,
  and make not your heritage a reproach,
  with the nations ruling over them!
Why should they say among the peoples,
  'Where is their God?' "
Then the LORD was stirred to concern
for his land and took pity on his people.

RESPONSORIAL PSALM

Psalm 51:3–4, 5–6ab, 12–13, 14 & 17

℞. Be mer - ci - ful, O Lord, for we have sinned.

Music: John Schiavone, b. 1947, © 2001, OCP Publications.

▶ Have mercy on me, O God, in
    your goodness;
  in the greatness of your compassion
    wipe out my offense.
Thoroughly wash me from my guilt
  and of my sin cleanse me. ℞.

▶ For I acknowledge my offense,
    and my sin is before me always:
  "Against you only have I sinned,
    and done what is evil in
    your sight." ℞.

▶ A clean heart create for me, O God,
    and a steadfast spirit renew
    within me.
Cast me not out from your presence,
  and your Holy Spirit take not
    from me. ℞.

▶ Give me back the joy of
    your salvation,
  and a willing spirit sustain in me.
O Lord, open my lips,
  and my mouth shall proclaim
    your praise. ℞.

SECOND READING

2 Corinthians 5:20—6:2

Brothers and sisters: We are ambassadors
for Christ, as if God were appealing
through us. We implore you on behalf
of Christ, be reconciled to God. For our

sake he made him to be sin who did not
know sin, so that we might become the
righteousness of God in him.
  Working together, then, we appeal to

you not to receive the grace of God in vain. For he says:
> In an acceptable time I heard you,
> and on the day of salvation
> I helped you.

Behold, now is a very acceptable time; behold, now is the day of salvation.

GOSPEL ACCLAMATION

See Psalm 95:8

℟. Praise to you, Lord Je - sus Christ, King of end - less glo - ry!

Music: John Schiavone, b. 1947, © 2001, OCP Publications.

▶ If today you hear his voice,
harden not your hearts. ℟.

GOSPEL READING

Matthew 6:1–6, 16–18

Jesus said to his disciples: "Take care not to perform righteous deeds in order that people may see them; otherwise, you will have no recompense from your heavenly Father. When you give alms, do not blow a trumpet before you, as the hypocrites do in the synagogues and in the streets to win the praise of others. Amen, I say to you, they have received their reward. But when you give alms, do not let your left hand know what your right is doing, so that your almsgiving may be secret. And your Father who sees in secret will repay you.

"When you pray, do not be like the hypocrites, who love to stand and pray in the synagogues and on street corners so that others may see them. Amen, I say to you, they have received their reward. But when you pray, go to your inner room, close the door, and pray to your Father in secret. And your Father who sees in secret will repay you.

"When you fast, do not look gloomy like the hypocrites. They neglect their appearance, so that they may appear to others to be fasting. Amen, I say to you, they have received their reward. But when you fast, anoint your head and wash your face, so that you may not appear to be fasting, except to your Father who is hidden. And your Father who sees what is hidden will repay you."

BLESSING AND IMPOSITION OF ASHES

After the homily, the priest blesses ashes from the branches blessed the preceding year for Palm Sunday of the Lord's Passion.

After sprinkling the ashes with holy water, the priest, deacon or other ministers then place the ashes on those who come forward, saying to each, "Turn away from sin and be faithful to the gospel," or "Remember, man, you are dust and to dust you will return."

Meanwhile an appropriate song may be sung (for music see #374, 375).

After the giving of ashes the priest or other ministers wash their hands; the rite concludes with the General Intercessions. The Profession of Faith is not said.

903   First Sunday of Lent — A

FIRST READING   *Genesis 2:7–9; 3:1–7*

The LORD God formed man out of the clay of the ground and blew into his nostrils the breath of life, and so man became a living being.

Then the LORD God planted a garden in Eden, in the east, and placed there the man whom he had formed. Out of the ground the LORD God made various trees grow that were delightful to look at and good for food, with the tree of life in the middle of the garden and the tree of the knowledge of good and evil.

Now the serpent was the most cunning of all the animals that the LORD God had made. The serpent asked the woman, "Did God really tell you not to eat from any of the trees in the garden?" The woman answered the serpent: "We may eat of the fruit of the trees in the garden; it is only about the fruit of the tree in the middle of the garden that God said, 'You shall not eat it or even touch it, lest you die.' " But the serpent said to the woman: "You certainly will not die! No, God knows well that the moment you eat of it your eyes will be opened and you will be like gods who know what is good and what is evil." The woman saw that the tree was good for food, pleasing to the eyes, and desirable for gaining wisdom. So she took some of its fruit and ate it; and she also gave some to her husband, who was with her, and he ate it. Then the eyes of both of them were opened, and they realized that they were naked; so they sewed fig leaves together and made loincloths for themselves.

RESPONSORIAL PSALM   *Psalm 51:3–4, 5–6, 12–13, 17*

℟. Be mer - ci - ful, O Lord, for we have sinned.

Music: John Schiavone, b. 1947, © 2001, OCP Publications.

▶ Have mercy on me, O God, in
    your goodness;
  in the greatness of your compassion
    wipe out my offense.
Thoroughly wash me from my guilt
  and of my sin cleanse me. ℟.

▶ For I acknowledge my offense,
  and my sin is before me always:
"Against you only have I sinned,
  and done what is evil in your sight." ℟.

▶ A clean heart create for me, O God,
  and a steadfast spirit renew
    within me.
Cast me not out from your presence,
  and your Holy Spirit take not
    from me. ℟.

▶ Give me back the joy of your salvation,
  and a willing spirit sustain in me.
O Lord, open my lips,
  and my mouth shall proclaim
    your praise. ℟.

SECOND READING   *Romans 5:12–19 or 5:12, 17–19*

(Include bracketed text for Long Form)

Brothers and sisters: Through one man sin entered the world, and through sin, death, and thus death came to all men, inasmuch as all sinned — [for up to the time of the law, sin was in the world, though sin is not accounted when there is no law. But death reigned from Adam to Moses, even over those who did not sin after the pattern of the trespass of Adam, who is the type of the one who was to come.

But the gift is not like the transgression. For if by the transgression of the one, the many died, how much more did the grace of God and the gracious gift of the one man Jesus Christ overflow for the many. And the gift is not like the result of the one who sinned. For after one sin there was the judgment that brought condemnation; but the gift, after many transgressions, brought acquittal.] For if, by the transgression of the one, death came to reign through that one, how much more will those who receive the abundance of grace and of the gift of justification come to reign in life through the one Jesus Christ. In conclusion, just as through one transgression condemnation came upon all, so, through one righteous act, acquittal and life came to all. For just as through the disobedience of the one man the many were made sinners, so, through the obedience of the one, the many will be made righteous.

GOSPEL ACCLAMATION

Matthew 4:4b

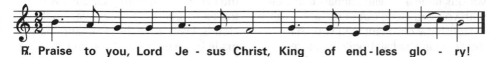

℟. Praise to you, Lord Je - sus Christ, King of end - less glo - ry!

Music: John Schiavone, b. 1947, © 2001, OCP Publications.

▶ One does not live on bread alone,
but on every word that comes forth from the mouth of God. ℟.

GOSPEL READING

Matthew 4:1–11

At that time Jesus was led by the Spirit into the desert to be tempted by the devil. He fasted for forty days and forty nights, and afterwards he was hungry. The tempter approached and said to him, "If you are the Son of God, command that these stones become loaves of bread." He said in reply, "It is written:

*One does not live on bread alone,
but on every word that comes forth
from the mouth of God."*

Then the devil took him to the holy city, and made him stand on the parapet of the temple, and said to him, "If you are the Son of God, throw yourself down. For it is written:

*He will command his angels
concerning you*

*and with their hands they will
support you,
lest you dash your foot against
a stone."*

Jesus answered him, "Again it is written, *You shall not put the Lord, your God, to the test."* Then the devil took him up to a very high mountain, and showed him all the kingdoms of the world in their magnificence, and he said to him, "All these I shall give to you, if you will prostrate yourself and worship me." At this, Jesus said to him, "Get away, Satan! It is written:

*The Lord, your God, shall you worship
and him alone shall you serve."*

Then the devil left him and, behold, angels came and ministered to him.

SENDING TO RITE OF ELECTION OR ENROLLMENT OF NAMES

At the beginning of Lent each faith community sends catechumens to the bishop, who declares in the presence of the community the Church's approval of these candidates. After the godparents testify to their state of formation, the catechumens are called out by God to prepare for the Easter sacraments of initiation. These elect receive the affirmation of the whole community; all the faithful encircle them with prayer and lead them to meet Christ.

---

904   FIRST SUNDAY OF LENT — B

FIRST READING
Genesis 9:8–15

God said to Noah and to his sons with him: "See, I am now establishing my covenant with you and your descendants after you and with every living creature that was with you: all the birds, and the various tame and wild animals that were with you and came out of the ark. I will establish my covenant with you, that never again shall all bodily creatures be destroyed by the waters of a flood; there shall not be another flood to devastate the earth." God added: "This is the sign that I am giving for all ages to come, of the covenant between me and you and every living creature with you: I set my bow in the clouds to serve as a sign of the covenant between me and the earth. When I bring clouds over the earth, and the bow appears in the clouds, I will recall the covenant I have made between me and you and all living beings, so that the waters shall never again become a flood to destroy all mortal beings."

RESPONSORIAL PSALM
Psalm 25:4–5, 6–7, 8–9

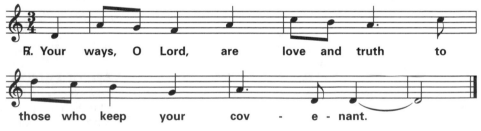

℟. Your ways, O Lord, are love and truth to those who keep your cov - e - nant.

Music: John Schiavone, b. 1947, © 2001, OCP Publications.

▸ Your ways, O LORD, make known to me;
    teach me your paths.
Guide me in your truth and teach me,
    for you are God my savior. ℟.

▸ Remember that your compassion,
    O LORD,
    and your love are from of old.

In your kindness remember me,
    because of your goodness,
    O LORD. ℟.

▸ Good and upright is the LORD,
    thus he shows sinners the way.
He guides the humble to justice,
    and he teaches the humble
    his way. ℟.

SECOND READING
1 Peter 3:18–22

Beloved: Christ suffered for sins once, the righteous for the sake of the unrighteous, that he might lead you to God. Put to death in the flesh, he was brought to life in the Spirit. In it he also went to preach to the spirits in prison, who had once been disobedient while God patiently waited in the days of

Noah during the building of the ark, in which a few persons, eight in all, were saved through water. This prefigured baptism, which saves you now. It is not a removal of dirt from the body but an appeal to God for a clear conscience, through the resurrection of Jesus Christ, who has gone into heaven and is at the right hand of God, with angels, authorities, and powers subject to him.

GOSPEL ACCLAMATION

Matthew 4:4b

℟. Praise to you, Lord Je - sus Christ, King of end - less glo - ry!

Music: John Schiavone, b. 1947, © 2001, OCP Publications.

▶ One does not live on bread alone,
but on every word that comes forth from the mouth of God. ℟.

GOSPEL READING

Mark 1:12–15

The Spirit drove Jesus out into the desert, and he remained in the desert for forty days, tempted by Satan. He was among wild beasts, and the angels ministered to him.

After John had been arrested, Jesus came to Galilee proclaiming the gospel of God: "This is the time of fulfillment. The kingdom of God is at hand. Repent, and believe in the gospel."

SENDING TO RITE OF ELECTION OR ENROLLMENT OF NAMES

See number 903.

FIRST SUNDAY OF LENT — C   905

FIRST READING

Deuteronomy 26:4–10

Moses spoke to the people, saying: "The priest shall receive the basket from you and shall set it in front of the altar of the LORD, your God. Then you shall declare before the LORD, your God, 'My father was a wandering Aramean who went down to Egypt with a small household and lived there as an alien. But there he became a nation great, strong, and numerous. When the Egyptians maltreated and oppressed us, imposing hard labor upon us, we cried to the LORD, the God of our fathers, and he heard our cry and saw our affliction, our toil, and our oppression. He brought us out of Egypt with his strong hand and outstretched arm, with terrifying power, with signs and wonders; and bringing us into this country, he gave us this land flowing with milk and honey. Therefore, I have now brought you the firstfruits of the products of the soil which you, O LORD, have given me.' And having set them before the Lord, your God, you shall bow down in his presence."

RESPONSORIAL PSALM

Psalm 91:1–2, 10–11, 12–13, 14–15

℟. Be with me, Lord, when I am in trou - ble.

Music: John Schiavone, b. 1947, © 2001, OCP Publications.

▶ You who dwell in the shelter of the
    Most High,
  who abide in the shadow of
    the Almighty,
  say to the LORD, "My refuge and fortress,
    my God in whom I trust." ℟.

▶ No evil shall befall you,
    nor shall affliction come near
    your tent,
  for to his angels he has given
    command about you,
    that they guard you in all
    your ways. ℟.

▶ Upon their hands they shall bear
    you up,

lest you dash your foot against
  a stone.
You shall tread upon the asp and
  the viper;
  you shall trample down the lion and
  the dragon. ℟.

▶ Because he clings to me, I will
    deliver him;
  I will set him on high because he
    acknowledges my name.
He shall call upon me, and I will
  answer him;
  I will be with him in distress;
  I will deliver him and glorify him. ℟.

SECOND READING

Romans 10:8–13

Brothers and sisters: What does Scripture say?
  The word is near you,
    in your mouth and in your heart
— that is, the word of faith that we preach —, for, if you confess with your mouth that Jesus is Lord and believe in your heart that God raised him from the dead, you will be saved. For one believes with the heart and so is justified, and one confesses with the mouth and so is saved. For the Scripture says, *No one who believes in him will be put to shame.* For there is no distinction between Jew and Greek; the same Lord is Lord of all, enriching all who call upon him. For "everyone who calls on the name of the Lord will be saved."

GOSPEL ACCLAMATION

Matthew 4:4b

℟. Praise to you, Lord Je - sus Christ, King of end - less glo - ry!

Music: John Schiavone, b. 1947, © 2001, OCP Publications.

▶ One does not live on bread alone,
    but on every word that comes forth from the mouth of God. ℟.

GOSPEL READING

Luke 4:1–13

Filled with the Holy Spirit, Jesus returned from the Jordan and was led by the Spirit into the desert for forty days, to be tempted by the devil. He ate nothing during those days, and when they were over he was hungry. The devil said to him, "If you are the Son of God, command this stone to become bread." Jesus answered him, "It is written, *One does not live on bread alone.*" Then he took him up and

showed him all the kingdoms of the world in a single instant. The devil said to him, "I shall give to you all this power and glory; for it has been handed over to me, and I may give it to whomever I wish. All this will be yours, if you worship me." Jesus said to him in reply, "It is written:
> You shall worship the Lord, your God,
>   and him alone shall you serve."

Then he led him to Jerusalem, made him stand on the parapet of the temple, and said to him, "If you are the Son of God, throw yourself down from here,

for it is written:
> He will command his angels
>   concerning you, to guard you,

and:
> With their hands they will support you,
>   lest you dash your foot against
>   a stone."

Jesus said to him in reply, "It also says, *You shall not put the Lord, your God, to the test.*" When the devil had finished every temptation, he departed from him for a time.

SENDING TO RITE OF ELECTION OR ENROLLMENT OF NAMES

See number 903.

SECOND SUNDAY OF LENT — A   906

FIRST READING   *Genesis 12:1–4a*

The LORD said to Abram: "Go forth from the land of your kinsfolk and from your father's house to a land that I will show you.
> "I will make of you a great nation,
>   and I will bless you;
> I will make your name great,

so that you will be a blessing.
> I will bless those who bless you
>   and curse those who curse you.
> All the communities of the earth
>   shall find blessing in you."

Abram went as the LORD directed him.

RESPONSORIAL PSALM   *Psalm 33:4–5, 18–19, 20, 22*

℟. **Lord, let your mer-cy be on us,   as we place our trust in you.**

Music: John Schiavone, b. 1947, © 2001, OCP Publications.

▸ Upright is the word of the LORD,
    and all his works are trustworthy.
He loves justice and right;
    of the kindness of the LORD the
    earth is full. ℟.

▸ See, the eyes of the LORD are upon
    those who fear him,
    upon those who hope for
    his kindness,

to deliver them from death
    and preserve them in spite of
    famine. ℟.

▸ Our soul waits for the LORD,
    who is our help and our shield.
May your kindness, O LORD, be
    upon us
    who have put our hope in you. ℟.

SECOND READING

2 Timothy 1:8b–10

Beloved: Bear your share of hardship for the gospel with the strength that comes from God.

He saved us and called us to a holy life, not according to our works but according to his own design and the grace bestowed on us in Christ Jesus before time began, but now made manifest through the appearance of our savior Christ Jesus, who destroyed death and brought life and immortality to light through the gospel.

GOSPEL ACCLAMATION

cf. Matthew 17:5

℟. **Praise to you, Lord Je - sus Christ, King of end - less glo - ry!**

Music: John Schiavone, b. 1947, © 2001, OCP Publications.

▶ From the shining cloud the Father's voice is heard:
  This is my beloved Son, hear him. ℟.

GOSPEL READING

Matthew 17:1–9

Jesus took Peter, James, and John his brother, and led them up a high mountain by themselves. And he was transfigured before them; his face shone like the sun and his clothes became white as light. And behold, Moses and Elijah appeared to them, conversing with him. Then Peter said to Jesus in reply, "Lord, it is good that we are here. If you wish, I will make three tents here, one for you, one for Moses, and one for Elijah." While he was still speaking, behold, a bright cloud cast a shadow over them, then from the cloud came a voice that said, "This is my beloved Son, with whom I am well pleased; listen to him." When the disciples heard this, they fell prostrate and were very much afraid. But Jesus came and touched them, saying, "Rise, and do not be afraid." And when the disciples raised their eyes, they saw no one else but Jesus alone.

As they were coming down from the mountain, Jesus charged them, "Do not tell the vision to anyone until the Son of Man has been raised from the dead."

---

907   SECOND SUNDAY OF LENT — B

FIRST READING

Genesis 22:1–2, 9a, 10–13, 15–18

God put Abraham to the test. He called to him, "Abraham!" "Here I am!" he replied. Then God said: "Take your son Isaac, your only one, whom you love, and go to the land of Moriah. There you shall offer him up as a holocaust on a height that I will point out to you."

When they came to the place of which God had told him, Abraham built an altar there and arranged the wood on it. Then he reached out and took the knife to slaughter his son. But the LORD's messenger called to him from heaven, "Abraham, Abraham!" "Here I am!" he answered. "Do not lay your hand on the boy," said the messenger. "Do not do the least thing to him. I know now how devoted you are to God, since you did not withhold from me your own beloved son." As Abraham looked about, he spied a ram caught by its horns in the thicket. So he went and took the ram and offered it up as a holocaust in place of his son.

Again the LORD's messenger called to Abraham from heaven and said: "I swear by myself, declares the LORD, that because you acted as you did in not withholding from me your beloved son, I will bless you abundantly and make your descendants as countless as the stars of the sky and the sands of the seashore; your descendants shall take possession of the gates of their enemies, and in your descendants all the nations of the earth shall find blessing — all this because you obeyed my command."

RESPONSORIAL PSALM   *Psalm 116:10, 15, 16–17, 18–19*

℟. I will walk be - fore the Lord, in the land of the liv - ing.

Music: John Schiavone, b. 1947, © 2001, OCP Publications.

▸ I believed, even when I said,
  "I am greatly afflicted."
Precious in the eyes of the LORD
  is the death of his faithful ones. ℟.

▸ O LORD, I am your servant;
  I am your servant, the son of
    your handmaid;
  you have loosed my bonds.

To you will I offer sacrifice of
    thanksgiving,
  and I will call upon the name of
    the LORD. ℟.

▸ My vows to the LORD I will pay
  in the presence of all his people,
in the courts of the house of the LORD,
  in your midst, O Jerusalem. ℟.

SECOND READING   *Romans 8:31b–34*

Brothers and sisters: If God is for us, who can be against us? He who did not spare his own Son but handed him over for us all, how will he not also give us everything else along with him?
   Who will bring a charge against God's chosen ones? It is God who acquits us. Who will condemn? Christ Jesus it is who died — or, rather, was raised — who also is at the right hand of God, who indeed intercedes for us.

GOSPEL ACCLAMATION   *cf. Matthew 17:5*

℟. Praise to you, Lord Je - sus Christ, King of end - less glo - ry!

Music: John Schiavone, b. 1947, © 2001, OCP Publications.

▸ From the shining cloud the Father's voice is heard:
  This is my beloved Son, listen to him. ℟.

GOSPEL READING   *Mark 9:2–10*

Jesus took Peter, James, and John and led them up a high mountain apart by themselves. And he was transfigured before them, and his clothes became dazzling white, such as no fuller on earth could bleach them. Then Elijah appeared to them along with Moses, and they were conversing with Jesus. Then Peter said to Jesus in reply, "Rabbi, it is good that we are here! Let us make three tents: one for you, one for Moses, and one for Elijah." He hardly knew what to say, they were so terrified. Then a cloud came, casting a shadow over them; from the cloud came a voice, "This is my beloved Son. Listen to him." Suddenly, looking around, they no longer saw anyone but Jesus alone with them.

As they were coming down from the mountain, he charged them not to relate what they had seen to anyone, except when the Son of Man had risen from the dead. So they kept the matter to themselves, questioning what rising from the dead meant.

---

908   SECOND SUNDAY OF LENT — C

FIRST READING   *Genesis 15:5–12, 17–18*

The Lord God took Abram outside and said, "Look up at the sky and count the stars, if you can. Just so," he added, "shall your descendants be." Abram put his faith in the LORD, who credited it to him as an act of righteousness.

He then said to him, "I am the LORD who brought you from Ur of the Chaldeans to give you this land as a possession." "O Lord GOD," he asked, "how am I to know that I shall possess it?" He answered him, "Bring me a three-year-old heifer, a three-year-old she-goat, a three-year-old ram, a turtledove, and a young pigeon." Abram brought him all these, split them in two,

and placed each half opposite the other; but the birds he did not cut up. Birds of prey swooped down on the carcasses, but Abram stayed with them. As the sun was about to set, a trance fell upon Abram, and a deep, terrifying darkness enveloped him.

When the sun had set and it was dark, there appeared a smoking fire pot and a flaming torch, which passed between those pieces. It was on that occasion that the LORD made a covenant with Abram, saying: "To your descendants I give this land, from the Wadi of Egypt to the Great River, the Euphrates."

RESPONSORIAL PSALM   *Psalm 27:1, 7–8, 8–9, 13–14*

℟. The Lord is my light and my sal - va - tion.

Music: John Schiavone, b. 1947, © 2001, OCP Publications.

▶ The LORD is my light and my salvation;
   whom should I fear?
The LORD is my life's refuge;
   of whom should I be afraid? ℟.

▶ Hear, O LORD, the sound of my call;
   have pity on me, and answer me.
Of you my heart speaks; you my
   glance seeks. ℟.

▶ Your presence, O LORD, I seek.
   Hide not your face from me;
do not in anger repel your servant.
   You are my helper: cast me not off. ℟.

▶ I believe that I shall see the bounty of
   the LORD
in the land of the living.
Wait for the LORD with courage;
   be stouthearted, and wait for
   the LORD. ℟.

SECOND READING
Philippians 3:17—4:1 or 3:20—4:1

(Include bracketed text for Long Form and text in parentheses for short form)

[Join with others in being imitators of me,] brothers and sisters, [and observe those who thus conduct themselves according to the model you have in us. For many, as I have often told you and now tell you even in tears, conduct themselves as enemies of the cross of Christ. Their end is destruction. Their God is their stomach; their glory is in their "shame." Their minds are occupied with earthly things. But] our citizenship is in heaven, and from it we also await a savior, the Lord Jesus Christ. He will change our lowly body to conform with his glorified body by the power that enables him also to bring all things into subjection to himself.

Therefore, my brothers and sisters, whom I love and long for, my joy and crown, in this way stand firm in the Lord, *(beloved)*.

GOSPEL ACCLAMATION
cf. Matthew 17:5

℟. Praise to you, Lord Je - sus Christ, King of end - less glo - ry!

Music: John Schiavone, b. 1947, © 2001, OCP Publications.

▶ From the shining cloud the Father's voice is heard:
This is my beloved Son, hear him. ℟.

GOSPEL READING
Luke 9:28b–36

Jesus took Peter, John, and James and went up the mountain to pray. While he was praying his face changed in appearance and his clothing became dazzling white. And behold, two men were conversing with him, Moses and Elijah, who appeared in glory and spoke of his exodus that he was going to accomplish in Jerusalem. Peter and his companions had been overcome by sleep, but becoming fully awake, they saw his glory and the two men standing with him. As they were about to part from him, Peter said to Jesus, "Master, it is good that we are here; let us make three tents, one for you, one for Moses, and one for Elijah." But he did not know what he was saying. While he was still speaking, a cloud came and cast a shadow over them, and they became frightened when they entered the cloud. Then from the cloud came a voice that said, "This is my chosen Son; listen to him." After the voice had spoken, Jesus was found alone. They fell silent and did not at that time tell anyone what they had seen.

THIRD SUNDAY OF LENT — A   909

FIRST READING
Exodus 17:3–7

In those days, in their thirst for water, the people grumbled against Moses, saying, "Why did you ever make us leave Egypt? Was it just to have us die here of thirst with our children and our livestock?" So Moses cried out to the LORD, "What shall I do with this people? A little more and they will stone me!" The LORD answered Moses, "Go over there in front of the people, along with some of the elders of Israel, holding in your hand, as you go, the staff with which you struck the river. I will be standing there in front of you on the rock in Horeb. Strike the rock, and the water will flow from it for the people to drink." This Moses did, in the presence of the elders of Israel. The place was called Massah and Meribah, because the Israelites quarreled there and tested the LORD, saying, "Is the LORD in our midst or not?"

RESPONSORIAL PSALM
Psalm 95:1–2, 6–7, 8–9

℟. If to - day you hear his voice, hard - en not your hearts.

Music: John Schiavone, b. 1947, © 2001, OCP Publications.

▸ Come, let us sing joyfully to the LORD;
 let us acclaim the Rock of
  our salvation.
 Let us come into his presence
  with thanksgiving;
  let us joyfully sing psalms to him. ℟.

▸ Come, let us bow down in worship;
 let us kneel before the LORD who
  made us.
 For he is our God,
  and we are the people he
   shepherds, the flock he guides. ℟.

▸ Oh, that today you would hear
 his voice:
 "Harden not your hearts as
  at Meribah,
 as in the day of Massah in the desert,
 where your fathers tempted me;
  they tested me though they had
   seen my works." ℟.

SECOND READING
Romans 5:1–2, 5–8

Brothers and sisters: Since we have been justified by faith, we have peace with God through our Lord Jesus Christ, through whom we have gained access by faith to this grace in which we stand, and we boast in hope of the glory of God. And hope does not disappoint, because the love of God has been poured out into our hearts through the Holy Spirit who has been given to us. For Christ, while we were still helpless, died at the appointed time for the ungodly. Indeed, only with difficulty does one die for a just person, though perhaps for a good person one might even find courage to die. But God proves his love for us in that while we were still sinners Christ died for us.

GOSPEL ACCLAMATION
cf. John 4:42, 15

℟. Praise to you, Lord Je - sus Christ, King of end - less glo - ry!

Music: John Schiavone, b. 1947, © 2001, OCP Publications.

▸ Lord, you are truly the Savior of the world;
 give me living water, that I may never thirst again. ℟.

GOSPEL READING

John 4:5–42 or 4:5–15, 19b–26, 39a, 40–42

(Include bracketed text for Long Form)

Jesus came to a town of Samaria called Sychar, near the plot of land that Jacob had given to his son Joseph. Jacob's well was there. Jesus, tired from his journey, sat down there at the well. It was about noon.

A woman of Samaria came to draw water. Jesus said to her, "Give me a drink." His disciples had gone into the town to buy food. The Samaritan woman said to him, "How can you, a Jew, ask me, a Samaritan woman, for a drink?" — For Jews use nothing in common with Samaritans. — Jesus answered and said to her, "If you knew the gift of God and who is saying to you, 'Give me a drink,' you would have asked him and he would have given you living water." The woman said to him, "Sir, you do not even have a bucket and the cistern is deep; where then can you get this living water? Are you greater than our father Jacob, who gave us this cistern and drank from it himself with his children and his flocks?" Jesus answered and said to her, "Everyone who drinks this water will be thirsty again; but whoever drinks the water I shall give will never thirst; the water I shall give will become in him a spring of water welling up to eternal life." The woman said to him, "Sir, give me this water, so that I may not be thirsty or have to keep coming here to draw water."

[Jesus said to her, "Go call your husband and come back." The woman answered and said to him, "I do not have a husband." Jesus answered her, "You are right in saying, 'I do not have a husband.' For you have had five husbands, and the one you have now is not your husband. What you have said is true." The woman said to him, "Sir,] I can see that you are a prophet. Our ancestors worshiped on this mountain; but you people say that the place to worship is in Jerusalem." Jesus said to her, "Believe me, woman, the hour is coming when you will worship the Father neither on this mountain nor in Jerusalem. You people worship what you do not understand; we worship what we understand, because salvation is from the Jews. But the hour is coming, and is now here, when true worshipers will worship the Father in Spirit and truth; and indeed the Father seeks such people to worship him. God is Spirit, and those who worship him must worship in Spirit and truth." The woman said to him, "I know that the Messiah is coming, the one called the Christ; when he comes, he will tell us everything." Jesus said to her, "I am he, the one speaking with you."

[At that moment his disciples returned, and were amazed that he was talking with a woman, but still no one said, "What are you looking for?" or "Why are you talking with her?" The woman left her water jar and went into the town and said to the people, "Come see a man who told me everything I have done. Could he possibly be the Christ?" They went out of the town and came to him. Meanwhile, the disciples urged him, "Rabbi, eat." But he said to them, "I have food to eat of which you do not know." So the disciples said to one another, "Could someone have brought him something to eat?" Jesus said to them, "My food is to do the will of the one who sent me and to finish his work. Do you not say, 'In four months the harvest will be here'? I tell you, look up and see the fields ripe for the harvest. The reaper is already receiving payment and gathering crops for eternal life, so that the sower and reaper can rejoice together. For here the saying is verified that 'One sows and another reaps.' I sent you to reap what you have not worked for; others have done the work, and you are sharing the fruits of their work."]

Many of the Samaritans of that town began to believe in him [because of the word of the woman who testified, "He told me everything I have done."] When the Samaritans came to him, they invited him to stay with them; and he stayed there two days. Many more began to believe in him because of his word, and they said to the woman, "We no longer believe because of your word; for we have heard for ourselves, and we know that this is truly the savior of the world."

FIRST SCRUTINY

After the homily the elect come before the community for exorcisms and prayers. Like the woman at the well, they seek Christ's merciful wisdom and long to worship the Father in Spirit and in truth. For musical settings, see #127.

---

910   THIRD SUNDAY OF LENT — B

When celebrating the Scrutinies, the readings given for Year A, number 909, may be used in place of these.

FIRST READING

Exodus 20:1–17 or 20:1–3, 7–8, 12–17

(Include bracketed text for Long Form)

In those days, God delivered all these commandments:

"I, the LORD, am your God, who brought you out of the land of Egypt, that place of slavery. You shall not have other gods besides me. [You shall not carve idols for yourselves in the shape of anything in the sky above or on the earth below or in the waters beneath the earth; you shall not bow down before them or worship them. For I, the LORD, your God, am a jealous God, inflicting punishment for their fathers' wickedness on the children of those who hate me, down to the third and fourth generation; but bestowing mercy down to the thousandth generation on the children of those who love me and keep my commandments.]

"You shall not take the name of the LORD, your God, in vain. For the LORD will not leave unpunished the one who takes his name in vain.

"Remember to keep holy the sabbath day. [Six days you may labor and do all your work, but the seventh day is the sabbath of the LORD, your God. No work may be done then either by you, or your son or daughter, or your male or female slave, or your beast, or by the alien who lives with you. In six days the LORD made the heavens and the earth, the sea and all that is in them; but on the seventh day he rested. That is why the LORD has blessed the sabbath day and made it holy.]

"Honor your father and your mother, that you may have a long life in the land which the LORD, your God, is giving you.
You shall not kill.
You shall not commit adultery.
You shall not steal.
You shall not bear false witness against your neighbor.
You shall not covet your neighbor's house.
You shall not covet your neighbor's wife, nor his male or female slave, nor his ox or ass, nor anything else that belongs to him."

RESPONSORIAL PSALM

Psalm 19:8, 9, 10, 11

℟. Lord, you have the words of ev - er - last - ing life.

Music: John Schiavone, b. 1947, © 2001, OCP Publications.

▸ The law of the LORD is perfect,
refreshing the soul;
the decree of the LORD is trustworthy,
giving wisdom to the simple. ℟.

▸ The precepts of the LORD are right,
rejoicing the heart;
the command of the LORD is clear,
enlightening the eye. ℟.

▸ The fear of the LORD is pure,
enduring forever;
the ordinances of the LORD are true,
all of them just. ℟.

▸ They are more precious than gold,
than a heap of purest gold;
sweeter also than syrup
or honey from the comb. ℟.

SECOND READING

1 Corinthians 1:22–25

Brothers and sisters: Jews demand signs and Greeks look for wisdom, but we proclaim Christ crucified, a stumbling block to Jews and foolishness to Gentiles, but to those who are called, Jews and Greeks alike, Christ the power of God and the wisdom of God. For the foolishness of God is wiser than human wisdom, and the weakness of God is stronger than human strength.

GOSPEL ACCLAMATION

John 3:16

℟. Praise to you, Lord Je - sus Christ, King of end - less glo - ry!

Music: John Schiavone, b. 1947, © 2001, OCP Publications.

▸ God so loved the world that he gave his only Son,
so that everyone who believes in him might have eternal life. ℟.

GOSPEL READING

John 2:13–25

Since the Passover of the Jews was near, Jesus went up to Jerusalem. He found in the temple area those who sold oxen, sheep, and doves, as well as the money changers seated there. He made a whip out of cords and drove them all out of the temple area, with the sheep and oxen, and spilled the coins of the money changers and overturned their tables, and to those who sold doves he said, "Take these out of here, and stop making my Father's house a marketplace." His disciples recalled the words of Scripture, *Zeal for your house will consume me.* At this the Jews answered and said to him, "What sign can you show us for doing this?" Jesus answered and said to them, "Destroy this temple and in three days I will raise it up." The Jews said, "This temple has been under construction for forty-six years, and you will raise it up in three days?" But he was speaking about the temple of his body. Therefore, when he was raised from the dead, his disciples remembered that he had said this, and they came to believe the Scripture and the word Jesus had spoken.

While he was in Jerusalem for the feast of Passover, many began to believe in his name when they saw the signs he was doing. But Jesus would not trust himself to them because he knew them all, and did not need anyone to testify about human nature. He himself understood it well.

---

911   THIRD SUNDAY OF LENT — C

When celebrating the Scrutinies, the readings given for Year A, number 909, may be used in place of these.

FIRST READING

Exodus 3:1–8a, 13–15

Moses was tending the flock of his father-in-law Jethro, the priest of Midian. Leading the flock across the desert, he came to Horeb, the mountain of God. There an angel of the LORD appeared to Moses in fire flaming out of a bush. As he looked on, he was surprised to see that the bush, though on fire, was not consumed. So Moses decided, "I must go over to look at this remarkable sight, and see why the bush is not burned."

When the LORD saw him coming over to look at it more closely, God called out to him from the bush, "Moses! Moses!" He answered, "Here I am." God said, "Come no nearer! Remove the sandals from your feet, for the place where you stand is holy ground. I am the God of your fathers," he continued, "the God of Abraham, the God of Isaac, the God of Jacob." Moses hid his face, for he was afraid to look at God. But the LORD said, "I have witnessed the affliction of my people in Egypt and have heard their cry of complaint against their slave drivers, so I know well what they are suffering. Therefore I have come down to rescue them from the hands of the Egyptians and lead them out of that land into a good and spacious land, a land flowing with milk and honey."

Moses said to God, "But when I go to the Israelites and say to them, 'The God of your fathers has sent me to you,' if they ask me, 'What is his name?' what am I to tell them?" God replied, "I am who am." Then he added, "This is what you shall tell the Israelites: I AM sent me to you."

God spoke further to Moses, "Thus shall you say to the Israelites: The LORD, the God of your fathers, the God of Abraham, the God of Isaac, the God of Jacob, has sent me to you.

"This is my name forever;
   thus am I to be remembered
      through all generations."

RESPONSORIAL PSALM

Psalm 103: 1–2, 3–4, 6–7, 8, 11

℟. The Lord is kind and mer-ci-ful, [kind and mer-ci-ful.]

Music: John Schiavone, b. 1947, © 2001, OCP Publications.

▶ Bless the LORD, O my soul;
   and all my being, bless his holy name.
Bless the LORD, O my soul,
   and forget not all his benefits. ℟.

▶ He pardons all your iniquities,
   he heals all your ills.

He redeems your life from destruction,
   he crowns you with kindness and
      compassion. ℟.

▶ The LORD secures justice
   and the rights of all the oppressed.
He has made known his ways to Moses,
   and his deeds to the children
      of Israel. ℟.

▶ Merciful and gracious is the LORD,
  slow to anger and abounding
  in kindness.

For as the heavens are high above
  the earth,
  so surpassing is his kindness toward
  those who fear him. ℟.

SECOND READING

1 Corinthians 10:1–6, 10–12

I do not want you to be unaware, brothers and sisters, that our ancestors were all under the cloud and all passed through the sea, and all of them were baptized into Moses in the cloud and in the sea. All ate the same spiritual food, and all drank the same spiritual drink, for they drank from a spiritual rock that followed them, and the rock was the Christ. Yet God was not pleased with most of them, for they were struck down in the desert.

These things happened as examples for us, so that we might not desire evil things, as they did. Do not grumble as some of them did, and suffered death by the destroyer. These things happened to them as an example, and they have been written down as a warning to us, upon whom the end of the ages has come. Therefore, whoever thinks he is standing secure should take care not to fall.

GOSPEL ACCLAMATION

Matthew 4:17

℟. Praise to you, Lord Je - sus Christ, King of end - less glo - ry!

Music: John Schiavone, b. 1947, © 2001, OCP Publications.

▶ Repent, says the Lord;
  the kingdom of heaven is at hand. ℟.

GOSPEL READING

Luke 13:1–9

Some people told Jesus about the Galileans whose blood Pilate had mingled with the blood of their sacrifices. Jesus said to them in reply, "Do you think that because these Galileans suffered in this way they were greater sinners than all other Galileans? By no means! But I tell you, if you do not repent, you will all perish as they did! Or those eighteen people who were killed when the tower at Siloam fell on them— do you think they were more guilty than everyone else who lived in Jerusalem? By no means! But I tell you, if you do not repent, you will all perish as they did!"

And he told them this parable: "There once was a person who had a fig tree planted in his orchard, and when he came in search of fruit on it but found none, he said to the gardener, 'For three years now I have come in search of fruit on this fig tree but have found none. So cut it down. Why should it exhaust the soil?' He said to him in reply, 'Sir, leave it for this year also, and I shall cultivate the ground around it and fertilize it; it may bear fruit in the future. If not you can cut it down.'"

912   FOURTH SUNDAY OF LENT — A

FIRST READING

1 Samuel 16:1b, 6–7, 10–13a

The LORD said to Samuel: "Fill your horn with oil, and be on your way. I am sending you to Jesse of Bethlehem, for I have chosen my king from among his sons."

As Jesse and his sons came to the sacrifice, Samuel looked at Eliab and thought, "Surely the Lord's anointed is here before him." But the LORD said to Samuel: "Do not judge from his appearance or from his lofty stature, because I have rejected him. Not as man sees does God see, because man sees the appearance but the LORD looks into the heart." In the same way Jesse presented seven sons before Samuel, but Samuel said to Jesse, "The LORD has not chosen any one of these." Then Samuel asked Jesse, "Are these all the sons you have?" Jesse replied, "There is still the youngest, who is tending the sheep." Samuel said to Jesse, "Send for him; we will not begin the sacrificial banquet until he arrives here." Jesse sent and had the young man brought to them. He was ruddy, a youth handsome to behold and making a splendid appearance. The LORD said, "There — anoint him, for this is the one!" Then Samuel, with the horn of oil in hand, anointed David in the presence of his brothers; and from that day on, the spirit of the LORD rushed upon David.

RESPONSORIAL PSALM

Psalm 23: 1–3a, 3b–4, 5, 6

℞. **The Lord is my shep-herd; there is noth-ing I shall want.**

Music: John Schiavone, b. 1947, © 2001, OCP Publications.

▶ The LORD is my shepherd; I shall
    not want.
  In verdant pastures he gives
    me repose;
beside restful waters he leads me;
  he refreshes my soul. ℞.

▶ He guides me in right paths
    for his name's sake.
Even though I walk in the dark valley
    I fear no evil; for you are at my side
with your rod and your staff
    that give me courage. ℞.

▶ You spread the table before me
    in the sight of my foes;
you anoint my head with oil;
    my cup overflows. ℞.

▶ Only goodness and kindness
    follow me
  all the days of my life;
and I shall dwell in the house of
    the LORD
    for years to come. ℞.

SECOND READING

Ephesians 5:8–14

Brothers and sisters: You were once darkness, but now you are light in the Lord. Live as children of light, for light produces every kind of goodness and righteousness and truth. Try to learn what is pleasing to the Lord. Take no part in the fruitless works of darkness; rather expose them, for it is shameful even to mention the things done by them in secret; but everything exposed by the light becomes visible, for everything that becomes visible is light. Therefore, it says:

"Awake, O sleeper,
  and arise from the dead,
  and Christ will give you light."

GOSPEL ACCLAMATION   *John 8:12*

℟. Praise to you, Lord Je - sus Christ, King of end - less glo - ry!

Music: John Schiavone, b. 1947, © 2001, OCP Publications.

▶ I am the light of the world, says the Lord;
whoever follows me will have the light of life. ℟.

GOSPEL READING   *John 9:1–41 or 9:1, 6–9, 13–17, 34–38*

(Include bracketed text for Long Form)

As Jesus passed by he saw a man blind from birth. [His disciples asked him, "Rabbi, who sinned, this man or his parents, that he was born blind?" Jesus answered, "Neither he nor his parents sinned; it is so that the works of God might be made visible through him. We have to do the works of the one who sent me while it is day. Night is coming when no one can work. While I am in the world, I am the light of the world." When he had said this,] he spat on the ground and made clay with the saliva, and smeared the clay on his eyes, and said to him, "Go wash in the Pool of Siloam" — which means Sent —. So he went and washed, and came back able to see.

His neighbors and those who had seen him earlier as a beggar said, "Isn't this the one who used to sit and beg?" Some said, "It is," but others said, "No, he just looks like him." He said, "I am." [So they said to him, "How were your eyes opened?" He replied, "The man called Jesus made clay and anointed my eyes and told me, 'Go to Siloam and wash.' So I went there and washed and was able to see." And they said to him, "Where is he?" He said, "I don't know."]

They brought the one who was once blind to the Pharisees. Now Jesus had made clay and opened his eyes on a sabbath. So then the Pharisees also asked him how he was able to see. He said to them, "He put clay on my eyes, and I washed, and now I can see." So some of the Pharisees said, "This man is not from God, because he does not keep the sabbath." But others said, "How can a sinful man do such signs?" And there was a division among them. So they said to the blind man again, "What do you have to say about him, since he opened your eyes?" He said, "He is a prophet."

[Now the Jews did not believe that he had been blind and gained his sight until they summoned the parents of the one who had gained his sight. They asked them, "Is this your son, who you say was born blind? How does he now see?" His parents answered and said, "We know that this is our son and that he was born blind. We do not know how he sees now, nor do we know who opened his eyes. Ask him, he is of age; he can speak for himself." His parents said this because they were afraid of the Jews, for the Jews had already agreed that if anyone acknowledged him as the Christ, he would be expelled from the synagogue. For this reason his parents said, "He is of age; question him."

So a second time they called the man who had been blind and said to him, "Give God the praise! We know that this man is a sinner." He replied, "If he is a sinner, I do not know. One thing I do know is that I was blind and now I see." So they said to him, "What did he do to you? How did he open your eyes?" He answered them, "I told you already and you did not listen. Why do you want to hear it again? Do you want to become his disciples, too?"

They ridiculed him and said, "You are that man's disciple; we are disciples of Moses! We know that God spoke to Moses, but we do not know where this one is from." The man answered and said to them, "This is what is so amazing, that you do not know where he is from, yet he opened my eyes. We know that God does not listen to sinners, but if one is devout and does his will, he listens to him. It is unheard of that anyone ever opened the eyes of a person born blind. If this man were not from God, he would not be able to do anything."] They answered and said to him, "You were born totally in sin, and are you trying to teach us?" Then they threw him out.

When Jesus heard that they had thrown him out, he found him and said, "Do you believe in the Son of Man?" He answered and said, "Who is he, sir, that I may believe in him?" Jesus said to him, "You have seen him, and the one speaking with you is he." He said, "I do believe, Lord," and he worshiped him. [Then Jesus said, "I came into this world for judgment, so that those who do not see might see, and those who do see might become blind."

Some of the Pharisees who were with him heard this and said to him, "Surely we are not also blind, are we?" Jesus said to them, "If you were blind, you would have no sin; but now you are saying, 'We see,' so your sin remains."]

SECOND SCRUTINY

After the readings and the homily, the elect come forward with their godparents. With the faithful they pray to God, who led the man born blind to the kingdom of light, to be their light in darkness as well. For musical settings, see #127.

---

913   FOURTH SUNDAY OF LENT — B

When celebrating the Scrutinies, the readings given for Year A, number 912, may be used in place of these.

FIRST READING   *2 Chronicles 36:14–16, 19–23*

In those days, all the princes of Judah, the priests, and the people added infidelity to infidelity, practicing all the abominations of the nations and polluting the LORD's temple which he had consecrated in Jerusalem.

Early and often did the LORD, the God of their fathers, send his messengers to them, for he had compassion on his people and his dwelling place. But they mocked the messengers of God, despised his warnings, and scoffed at his prophets, until the anger of the LORD against his people was so inflamed that there was no remedy. Their enemies burnt the house of God, tore down the walls of Jerusalem, set all its palaces afire, and destroyed all its precious objects. Those who escaped the sword were carried captive to Babylon, where they became servants of the king of the Chaldeans and his

sons until the kingdom of the Persians came to power. All this was to fulfill the word of the LORD spoken by Jeremiah: "Until the land has retrieved its lost sabbaths, during all the time it lies waste it shall have rest while seventy years are fulfilled."

In the first year of Cyrus, king of Persia, in order to fulfill the word of the LORD spoken by Jeremiah, the LORD inspired King Cyrus of Persia to issue this proclamation throughout his kingdom, both by word of mouth and in writing: "Thus says Cyrus, king of Persia: All the kingdoms of the earth the LORD, the God of heaven, has given to me, and he has also charged me to build him a house in Jerusalem, which is in Judah. Whoever, therefore, among you belongs to any part of his people, let him go up, and may his God be with him!"

RESPONSORIAL PSALM

Psalm 137:1–2, 3, 4–5, 6

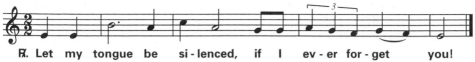

℟. Let my tongue be si - lenced, if I ev - er for - get you!

Music: John Schiavone, b. 1947, © 2001, OCP Publications.

▸ By the streams of Babylon
  we sat and wept
  when we remembered Zion.
On the aspens of that land
  we hung up our harps. ℟.

▸ For there our captors asked of us
  the lyrics of our songs,
and our despoilers urged us to
  be joyous:
  "Sing for us the songs of Zion!" ℟.

▸ How could we sing a song of the LORD
  in a foreign land?
If I forget you, Jerusalem,
  may my right hand be forgotten! ℟.

▸ May my tongue cleave to my palate
  if I remember you not,
if I place not Jerusalem
  ahead of my joy. ℟.

SECOND READING

Ephesians 2:4–10

Brothers and sisters: God, who is rich in mercy, because of the great love he had for us, even when we were dead in our transgressions, brought us to life with Christ — by grace you have been saved —, raised us up with him, and seated us with him in the heavens in Christ Jesus, that in the ages to come he might show the immeasurable riches of his grace in his kindness to us in Christ Jesus. For by grace you have been saved through faith, and this is not from you; it is the gift of God; it is not from works, so no one may boast. For we are his handiwork, created in Christ Jesus for the good works that God has prepared in advance, that we should live in them.

GOSPEL ACCLAMATION

John 3:16

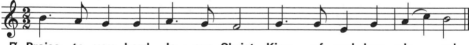

℟. Praise to you, Lord Je - sus Christ, King of end - less glo - ry!

Music: John Schiavone, b. 1947, © 2001, OCP Publications.

▸ God so loved the world that he gave his only Son,
  so everyone who believes in him might have eternal life. ℟.

GOSPEL READING

John 3:14–21

Jesus said to Nicodemus: "Just as Moses lifted up the serpent in the desert, so must the Son of Man be lifted up, so that everyone who believes in him may have eternal life."

For God so loved the world that he gave his only Son, so that everyone who believes in him might not perish but might have eternal life. For God did not send his Son into the world to condemn the world, but that the world might be saved through him. Whoever believes in him will not be condemned, but whoever does not believe has already been condemned, because he has not believed in the name of the only Son of God. And this is the verdict, that the light came into the world, but people preferred darkness to light, because their works were evil. For everyone who does wicked things hates the light and does not come toward the light, so that his works might not be exposed. But whoever lives the truth comes to the light, so that his works may be clearly seen as done in God.

---

914 FOURTH SUNDAY OF LENT — C

When celebrating the Scrutinies, the readings given for Year A, number 912, may be used in place of these.

FIRST READING

Joshua 5:9a, 10–12

The LORD said to Joshua, "Today I have removed the reproach of Egypt from you."

While the Israelites were encamped at Gilgal on the plains of Jericho, they celebrated the Passover on the evening of the fourteenth of the month. On the day after the Passover, they ate of the produce of the land in the form of unleavened cakes and parched grain. On that same day after the Passover, on which they ate of the produce of the land, the manna ceased. No longer was there manna for the Israelites, who that year ate of the yield of the land of Canaan.

RESPONSORIAL PSALM

Psalm 34:2–3, 4–5, 6–7

℟. [Taste and see,] taste and see the good-ness of the Lord.

Music: John Schiavone, b. 1947, © 2001, OCP Publications.

▶ I will bless the LORD at all times;
  his praise shall be ever in my mouth.
Let my soul glory in the LORD;
  the lowly will hear me and be glad. ℟.

▶ Glorify the LORD with me,
  let us together extol his name.
I sought the LORD, and he answered me
  and delivered me from all my fears. ℟.

▶ Look to him that you may be radiant
  with joy,
  and your faces may not blush
  with shame.
When the poor one called out,
  the LORD heard,
  and from all his distress he saved
  him. ℟.

SECOND READING

2 Corinthians 5:17–21

Brothers and sisters: Whoever is in Christ is a new creation: the old things have passed away; behold, new things have come. And all this is from God, who has reconciled us to himself through Christ and given us the ministry of reconciliation, namely, God was reconciling the world to himself in Christ, not counting their trespasses against them and entrusting to us the message of reconciliation. So we are ambassadors for Christ, as if God were appealing through us. We implore you on behalf of Christ, be reconciled to God. For our sake he made him to be sin who did not know sin, so that we might become the righteousness of God in him.

GOSPEL ACCLAMATION

Luke 15:18

℟. Praise to you, Lord Je - sus Christ, King of end - less glo - ry!

Music: John Schiavone, b. 1947, © 2001, OCP Publications.

▶ I will get up and go to my Father and shall say to him:
Father, I have sinned against heaven and against you. ℟.

GOSPEL READING

Luke 15:1–3, 11–32

Tax collectors and sinners were all drawing near to listen to Jesus, but the Pharisees and scribes began to complain, saying, "This man welcomes sinners and eats with them." So to them Jesus addressed this parable: "A man had two sons, and the younger son said to his father, 'Father, give me the share of your estate that should come to me.' So the father divided the property between them. After a few days, the younger son collected all his belongings and set off to a distant country where he squandered his inheritance on a life of dissipation. When he had freely spent everything, a severe famine struck that country, and he found himself in dire need. So he hired himself out to one of the local citizens who sent him to his farm to tend the swine. And he longed to eat his fill of the pods on which the swine fed, but nobody gave him any. Coming to his senses he thought, 'How many of my father's hired workers have more than enough food to eat, but here am I, dying from hunger. I shall get up and go to my father and I shall say to him, "Father, I have sinned against heaven and against you. I no longer deserve to be called your son; treat me as you would treat one of your hired workers." ' So he got up and went back to his father. While he was still a long way off, his father caught sight of him, and was filled with compassion. He ran to his son, embraced him and kissed him. His son said to him, 'Father, I have sinned against heaven and against you; I no longer deserve to be called your son.' But his father ordered his servants, 'Quickly bring the finest robe and put it on him; put a ring on his finger and sandals on his feet. Take the fattened calf and slaughter it. Then let us celebrate with a feast, because this son of mine was dead, and has come to life again; he was lost, and has been found.' Then the celebration began. Now the older son had been out in the field and, on his way back, as he neared the house, he heard the sound of music and dancing. He called one of the servants and asked what this might mean. The servant said to him, 'Your brother has returned and your father has slaughtered the fattened calf because he has him back safe and sound.' He became angry, and when he refused to enter the house, his father came out and pleaded with him. He said to his father in reply, 'Look, all these years I served you and not once did I disobey your orders; yet you never gave me even a young goat to feast on with my friends. But when your son returns who swallowed up your property with prostitutes, for him you slaughter the fattened calf.' He said to him, 'My son, you are here with me always; everything I have is yours. But now we must celebrate and rejoice, because your brother was dead and has come to life again; he was lost and has been found.' "

915   FIFTH SUNDAY OF LENT — A

FIRST READING
Ezekiel 37:12–14

Thus says the LORD GOD: O my people, I will open your graves and have you rise from them, and bring you back to the land of Israel. Then you shall know that I am the LORD, when I open your graves and have you rise from them, O my people! I will put my spirit in you that you may live, and I will settle you upon your land; thus you shall know that I am the LORD. I have promised, and I will do it, says the LORD.

RESPONSORIAL PSALM
Psalm 130:1–2, 3–4, 5–6, 7–8

Music: John Schiavone, b. 1947, © 2001, OCP Publications.

▶ Out of the depths I cry to you, O LORD;
    LORD, hear my voice!
Let your ears be attentive
    to my voice in supplication. ℟.

▶ If you, O LORD, mark iniquities,
    LORD, who can stand?
But with you is forgiveness,
    that you may be revered. ℟.

▶ I trust in the LORD;
    my soul trusts in his word.
More than sentinels wait for the dawn,
    let Israel wait for the LORD. ℟.

▶ For with the LORD is kindness
    and with him is plenteous
    redemption;
and he will redeem Israel
    from all their iniquities. ℟.

SECOND READING
Romans 8:8–11

Brothers and sisters: Those who are in the flesh cannot please God. But you are not in the flesh; on the contrary, you are in the spirit, if only the Spirit of God dwells in you. Whoever does not have the Spirit of Christ does not belong to him. But if Christ is in you, although the body is dead because of sin, the spirit is alive because of righteousness. If the Spirit of the one who raised Jesus from the dead dwells in you, the one who raised Christ from the dead will give life to your mortal bodies also, through his Spirit dwelling in you.

GOSPEL ACCLAMATION
John 11:25a, 26

Music: John Schiavone, b. 1947, © 2001, OCP Publications.

▶ I am the resurrection and the life, says the Lord;
    whoever believes in me, even if he dies, will never die. ℟.

GOSPEL READING

John 11:1–45 or 11:3–7, 17, 20–27, 33b–45

(Include bracketed text for Long Form)

[Now a man was ill, Lazarus from Bethany, the village of Mary and her sister Martha. Mary was the one who had anointed the Lord with perfumed oil and dried his feet with her hair; it was her brother Lazarus who was ill. So] the sisters of Lazarus sent word to Jesus saying, "Master, the one you love is ill." When Jesus heard this he said, "This illness is not to end in death, but is for the glory of God, that the Son of God may be glorified through it." Now Jesus loved Martha and her sister and Lazarus. So when he heard that he was ill, he remained for two days in the place where he was. Then after this he said to his disciples, "Let us go back to Judea." [The disciples said to him, "Rabbi, the Jews were just trying to stone you, and you want to go back there?" Jesus answered, "Are there not twelve hours in a day? If one walks during the day, he does not stumble, because he sees the light of this world. But if one walks at night, he stumbles, because the light is not in him." He said this, and then told them, "Our friend Lazarus is asleep, but I am going to awaken him." So the disciples said to him, "Master, if he is asleep, he will be saved." But Jesus was talking about his death, while they thought that he meant ordinary sleep. So then Jesus said to them clearly, "Lazarus has died. And I am glad for you that I was not there, that you may believe. Let us go to him." So Thomas, called Didymus, said to his fellow disciples, "Let us also go to die with him."]

When Jesus arrived, he found that Lazarus had already been in the tomb for four days. [Now Bethany was near Jerusalem, only about two miles away. And many of the Jews had come to Martha and Mary to comfort them about their brother.] When Martha heard that Jesus was coming, she went to meet him; but Mary sat at home.

Martha said to Jesus, "Lord, if you had been here, my brother would not have died. But even now I know that whatever you ask of God, God will give you." Jesus said to her, "Your brother will rise." Martha said to him, "I know he will rise, in the resurrection on the last day." Jesus told her, "I am the resurrection and the life; whoever believes in me, even if he dies, will live, and everyone who lives and believes in me will never die. Do you believe this?" She said to him, "Yes, Lord. I have come to believe that you are the Christ, the Son of God, the one who is coming into the world."

[When she had said this, she went and called her sister Mary secretly, saying, "The teacher is here and is asking for you." As soon as she heard this, she rose quickly and went to him. For Jesus had not yet come into the village, but was still where Martha had met him. So when the Jews who were with her in the house comforting her saw Mary get up quickly and go out, they followed her, presuming that she was going to the tomb to weep there. When Mary came to where Jesus was and saw him, she fell at his feet and said to him, "Lord, if you had been here, my brother would not have died." When Jesus saw her weeping and the Jews who had come with her weeping,] he became perturbed and deeply troubled, and said, "Where have you laid him?" They said to him, "Sir, come and see." And Jesus wept. So the Jews said, "See how he loved him." But some of them said, "Could not the one who opened the eyes of the blind man have done something so that this man would not have died?"

So Jesus, perturbed again, came to the tomb. It was a cave, and a stone lay across it. Jesus said, "Take away the stone." Martha, the dead man's sister, said to him, "Lord, by now there will be a stench; he has been dead for four days." Jesus said to her, "Did I not tell you that if you believe you will see the glory of God?" So they took away the stone. And Jesus raised his eyes and said, "Father, I thank you for hearing me. I know that you always hear me; but because of the crowd here I have said this, that they may believe that you sent me." And when he had said this, he cried out in a loud voice, "Lazarus, come out!" The dead man came out, tied hand and foot with burial bands, and his face was wrapped in a cloth. So Jesus said to them, "Untie him and let him go."

Now many of the Jews who had come to Mary and seen what he had done began to believe in him.

THIRD SCRUTINY

The community prays for the elect with the presiding minister who says with hands outstretched, "God of the living, as your Son Jesus raised Lazarus from the dead, save us too on the last day." For musical settings, see #127.

916 FIFTH SUNDAY OF LENT — B

When celebrating the Scrutinies, the readings given for Year A, number 915, may be used in place of these.

FIRST READING

Jeremiah 31:31–34

The days are coming, says the LORD, when I will make a new covenant with the house of Israel and the house of Judah. It will not be like the covenant I made with their fathers the day I took them by the hand to lead them forth from the land of Egypt; for they broke my covenant, and I had to show myself their master, says the LORD. But this is the covenant that I will make with the house of Israel after those days, says the LORD. I will place my law within them and write it upon their hearts; I will be their God, and they shall be my people. No longer will they have need to teach their friends and relatives how to know the LORD. All, from least to greatest, shall know me, says the LORD, for I will forgive their evildoing and remember their sin no more.

RESPONSORIAL PSALM

Psalm 51:3–4, 12–13, 14–15

℟. Cre - ate a clean heart in me, O God.

Music: John Schiavone, b. 1947, © 2001, OCP Publications.

▶ Have mercy on me, O God, in
   your goodness;
   in the greatness of your compassion
      wipe out my offense.
   Thoroughly wash me from my guilt
   and of my sin cleanse me. ℟.

▶ A clean heart create for me, O God,
   and a steadfast spirit renew
      within me.

Cast me not out from your presence,
   and your Holy Spirit take not
      from me. ℟.

▶ Give me back the joy of your salvation,
   and a willing spirit sustain in me.
   I will teach transgressors your ways,
   and sinners shall return to you. ℟.

SECOND READING
Hebrews 5:7–9

In the days when Christ Jesus was in the flesh, he offered prayers and supplications with loud cries and tears to the one who was able to save him from death, and he was heard because of his reverence. Son though he was, he learned obedience from what he suffered; and when he was made perfect, he became the source of eternal salvation for all who obey him.

GOSPEL ACCLAMATION
John 12:26

℟. Praise to you, Lord Je - sus Christ, King of end - less glo - ry!

Music: John Schiavone, b. 1947, © 2001, OCP Publications.

▶ Whoever serves me must follow me, says the Lord; and where I am, there also will my servant be. ℟.

GOSPEL READING
John 12:20–33

Some Greeks who had come to worship at the Passover Feast came to Philip, who was from Bethsaida in Galilee, and asked him, "Sir, we would like to see Jesus." Philip went and told Andrew; then Andrew and Philip went and told Jesus. Jesus answered them, "The hour has come for the Son of Man to be glorified. Amen, amen, I say to you, unless a grain of wheat falls to the ground and dies, it remains just a grain of wheat; but if it dies, it produces much fruit. Whoever loves his life loses it, and whoever hates his life in this world will preserve it for eternal life. Whoever serves me must follow me, and where I am, there also will my servant be. The Father will honor whoever serves me.

"I am troubled now. Yet what should I say? 'Father, save me from this hour'? But it was for this purpose that I came to this hour. Father, glorify your name." Then a voice came from heaven, "I have glorified it and will glorify it again." The crowd there heard it and said it was thunder; but others said, "An angel has spoken to him." Jesus answered and said, "This voice did not come for my sake but for yours. Now is the time of judgment on this world; now the ruler of this world will be driven out. And when I am lifted up from the earth, I will draw everyone to myself." He said this indicating the kind of death he would die.

FIFTH SUNDAY OF LENT — C 917

When celebrating the Scrutinies, the readings given for Year A, number 915, may be used in place of these.

FIRST READING
Isaiah 43:16–21

Thus says the LORD,
who opens a way in the sea
and a path in the mighty waters,
who leads out chariots and horsemen,
a powerful army,
till they lie prostrate together, never
to rise,
snuffed out and quenched like a wick.
Remember not the events of the past,
the things of long ago consider not;
see, I am doing something new!
Now it springs forth, do you not
perceive it?

In the desert I make a way,
  in the wasteland, rivers.
Wild beasts honor me,
  jackals and ostriches,
for I put water in the desert

and rivers in the wasteland
  for my chosen people to drink,
the people whom I formed for myself,
  that they might announce my praise.

RESPONSORIAL PSALM

Psalm 126:1–2, 2–3, 4–5, 6

℟. **The Lord has done great things for us; we are filled with joy.**

Music: John Schiavone, b. 1947, © 2001, OCP Publications.

▶ When the LORD brought back the
  captives of Zion,
  we were like men dreaming.
Then our mouth was filled
  with laughter,
  and our tongue with rejoicing. ℟.

▶ Then they said among the nations,
  "The LORD has done great things
  for them."
The LORD has done great things for us;
  we are glad indeed. ℟.

▶ Restore our fortunes, O LORD,
  like the torrents in the
  southern desert.
Those that sow in tears
  shall reap rejoicing. ℟.

▶ Although they go forth weeping,
  carrying the seed to be sown,
they shall come back rejoicing,
  carrying their sheaves. ℟.

SECOND READING

Philippians 3:8–14

Brothers and sisters: I consider everything as a loss because of the supreme good of knowing Christ Jesus my Lord. For his sake I have accepted the loss of all things and I consider them so much rubbish, that I may gain Christ and be found in him, not having any righteousness of my own based on the law but that which comes through faith in Christ, the righteousness from God, depending on faith to know him and the power of his resurrection and the sharing of his sufferings by being conformed to his death, if somehow I may attain the resurrection from the dead.

It is not that I have already taken hold of it or have already attained perfect maturity, but I continue my pursuit in hope that I may possess it, since I have indeed been taken possession of by Christ Jesus. Brothers and sisters, I for my part do not consider myself to have taken possession. Just one thing: forgetting what lies behind but straining forward to what lies ahead, I continue my pursuit toward the goal, the prize of God's upward calling, in Christ Jesus.

GOSPEL ACCLAMATION

Joel 2:12–13

℟. **Praise to you, Lord Je - sus Christ, King of end - less glo - ry!**

Music: John Schiavone, b. 1947, © 2001, OCP Publications.

▶ Even now, says the Lord,
  return to me with your whole heart;
  for I am gracious and merciful. ℟.

GOSPEL READING

John 8:1–11

Jesus went to the Mount of Olives. But early in the morning he arrived again in the temple area, and all the people started coming to him, and he sat down and taught them. Then the scribes and the Pharisees brought a woman who had been caught in adultery and made her stand in the middle. They said to him, "Teacher, this woman was caught in the very act of committing adultery. Now in the law, Moses commanded us to stone such women. So what do you say?" They said this to test him, so that they could have some charge to bring against him. Jesus bent down and began to write on the ground with his finger. But when they continued asking him, he straightened up and said to them, "Let the one among you who is without sin be the first to throw a stone at her." Again he bent down and wrote on the ground. And in response, they went away one by one, beginning with the elders. So he was left alone with the woman before him. Then Jesus straightened up and said to her, "Woman, where are they? Has no one condemned you?" She replied, "No one, sir." Then Jesus said, "Neither do I condemn you. Go, and from now on do not sin any more."

PALM SUNDAY OF THE LORD'S PASSION — ABC   **918**

COMMEMORATION OF THE LORD'S ENTRANCE INTO JERUSALEM

On this day the Church celebrates Christ's entrance into Jerusalem to accomplish the Paschal Mystery of his death and resurrection. Accordingly, the memorial of this event is included in every Mass, with the procession or the solemn entrance before the principal Mass, with the simple entrance before the other Masses. The solemn entrance may be repeated before other Masses.

FIRST FORM: THE PROCESSION

At the scheduled time, the assembly gathers in a suitable place distinct from the church to which the procession will move. The faithful carry palm or other branches. The priest and ministers put on red vestments for Mass and go to the place where the people have assembled. Meanwhile, an appropriate song is sung (see #396, 397).

The priest sprinkles the branches with holy water in silence. Then the account of the Lord's entrance is proclaimed from one of the four gospels. This is done by a deacon or, if there is no deacon, by the priest.

GOSPEL READING — A

Matthew 21:1–11

When Jesus and the disciples drew near Jerusalem and came to Bethphage on the Mount of Olives, Jesus sent two disciples, saying to them, "Go into the village opposite you, and immediately you will find an ass tethered, and a colt with her. Untie them and bring them here to me. And if anyone should say anything to you, reply, 'The master has need of them.' Then he will send them at once." This happened so that what had been spoken through the prophet might be fulfilled:

> Say to daughter Zion,
> "Behold, your king comes to you,
> meek and riding on an ass,
> and on a colt, the foal of a beast
> of burden."

The disciples went and did as Jesus had ordered them. They brought the ass and the colt and laid their cloaks over them, and he sat upon them.

The very large crowd spread their cloaks on the road, while others cut branches from the trees and strewed them on the road. The crowds preceding him and those following kept crying out and saying:
"Hosanna to the Son of David;
blessed is he who comes in the name of the Lord;
hosanna in the highest."
And when he entered Jerusalem the whole city was shaken and asked, "Who is this?" And the crowds replied, "This is Jesus the prophet, from Nazareth in Galilee."

GOSPEL READING — B

Mark 11:1–10

When Jesus and his disciples drew near to Jerusalem, to Bethphage and Bethany at the Mount of Olives, he sent two of his disciples and said to them, "Go into the village opposite you, and immediately on entering it, you will find a colt tethered on which no one has ever sat. Untie it and bring it here. If anyone should say to you, 'Why are you doing this?' reply, 'The Master has need of it and will send it back here at once.'" So they went off and found a colt tethered at a gate outside on the street, and they untied it. Some of the bystanders said to them, "What are you doing, untying the colt?" They answered them just as Jesus had told them to, and they permitted them to do it. So they brought the colt to Jesus and put their cloaks over it. And he sat on it. Many people spread their cloaks on the road, and others spread leafy branches that they had cut from the fields. Those preceding him as well as those following kept crying out:
"Hosanna!
Blessed is he who comes in the name of the Lord!
Blessed is the kingdom of our father David that is to come!
Hosanna in the highest!"

OR

GOSPEL READING — B

John 12:12–16

When the great crowd that had come to the feast heard that Jesus was coming to Jerusalem, they took palm branches and went out to meet him, and cried out:
"Hosanna!
Blessed is he who comes in the name of the Lord,
the king of Israel."
Jesus found an ass and sat upon it, as is written:
*Fear no more, O daughter Zion;
see, your king comes, seated upon an ass's colt.*
His disciples did not understand this at first, but when Jesus had been glorified they remembered that these things were written about him and that they had done this for him.

GOSPEL READING — C

Luke 19:28–40

Jesus proceeded on his journey up to Jerusalem. As he drew near to Bethphage and Bethany at the place called the Mount of Olives, he sent two of his disciples. He said, "Go into the village opposite you, and as you enter it you will find a colt tethered on which no one has ever sat. Untie it and bring it here. And if anyone should ask you, 'Why are you untying it?' you will answer, 'The Master has need of it.'" So those who had been sent went off and found everything just as he had told them. And as they were untying the colt, its owners said to them, "Why are you untying this colt?" They answered, "The Master has need of it." So they brought it to Jesus, threw their cloaks over the colt, and helped Jesus to mount. As he rode along, the people were spreading their cloaks on the road; and now as he was approaching the slope of the Mount of Olives, the whole multitude of his disciples began to praise God aloud with joy for all the mighty deeds they had seen. They proclaimed:

"Blessed is the king who comes
in the name of the Lord.
Peace in heaven
and glory in the highest."
Some of the Pharisees in the crowd said to him, "Teacher, rebuke your disciples." He said in reply, "I tell you, if they keep silent, the stones will cry out!"

After the gospel, a brief homily may be given. The procession to the church where the Mass will be celebrated then begins. During the procession, the people sing an appropriate hymn or song (see #399).

When the priest comes to the altar he venerates it. Then he goes to his chair and prays the opening prayer of Mass, which concludes the procession. Mass then continues, omitting the Greeting and Penitential Rite, with the Opening Prayer, followed by the Liturgy of the Word (below).

SECOND FORM: THE SOLEMN ENTRANCE

If the procession cannot be held outside the church, the commemoration of the Lord's entrance may be celebrated before the principal Mass with the solemn entrance, which takes place within the church. This form may also be used at other Masses.

The faithful, holding the branches, assemble either in front of the church door or inside the church. The priest and ministers, with a representative group of the faithful, go to a suitable place in the church outside the sanctuary, so that most of the people will be able to see the rite.

While the priest goes to the appointed place, the rite proceeds according to the First Form but abbreviated to fit the occasion. Mass then continues, omitting the Greeting and Penitential Rite, with the Opening Prayer, followed by the Liturgy of the Word (below).

THIRD FORM: THE SIMPLE ENTRANCE

While the priest goes to the altar, the Entrance Antiphon or a suitable hymn with the same theme is sung. After the priest venerates the altar, he goes to his chair and greets the people. Mass continues in the usual way, with the Introductory Rites (see #143).

LITURGY OF THE WORD

FIRST READING   *Isaiah 50:4–7*

The Lord GOD has given me
    a well-trained tongue,
that I might know how to speak to
        the weary
    a word that will rouse them.
Morning after morning
    he opens my ear that I may hear;
and I have not rebelled,
    have not turned back.
I gave my back to those who beat me,

my cheeks to those who plucked
    my beard;
my face I did not shield
    from buffets and spitting.

The Lord God is my help,
    therefore I am not disgraced;
I have set my face like flint,
    knowing that I shall not be put
        to shame.

RESPONSORIAL PSALM

Psalm 22:8–9, 17–18, 19–20, 23–24

℞. My God, my God, why have you a-ban-doned me?

Music: John Schiavone, b. 1947, © 2001, OCP Publications.

▶ All who see me scoff at me;
   they mock me with parted lips, they
     wag their heads:
  "He relied on the LORD; let him
    deliver him,
   let him rescue him, if he loves him." ℞.

▶ Indeed, many dogs surround me,
   a pack of evildoers closes in upon me;
  they have pierced my hands and
    my feet;
   I can count all my bones. ℞.

▶ They divide my garments among them,
   and for my vesture they cast lots.
  But you, O LORD, be not far from me;
   O my help, hasten to aid me. ℞.

▶ I will proclaim your name to
    my brethren;
   in the midst of the assembly I will
    praise you:
  "You who fear the LORD, praise him;
   all you descendants of Jacob, give
    glory to him;
   revere him, all you descendants
    of Israel!" ℞.

SECOND READING

Philippians 2:6–11

Christ Jesus, though he was in the form
   of God,
  did not regard equality with God
  something to be grasped.
Rather, he emptied himself,
  taking the form of a slave,
  coming in human likeness;
  and found human in appearance,
  he humbled himself,
  becoming obedient to the point
   of death,

even death on a cross.
Because of this, God greatly exalted him
  and bestowed on him the name
  which is above every name,
  that at the name of Jesus
  every knee should bend,
  of those in heaven and on earth and
   under the earth,
  and every tongue confess that
  Jesus Christ is Lord,
  to the glory of God the Father.

GOSPEL ACCLAMATION

Philippians 2:8–9

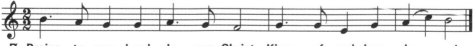

℞. Praise to you, Lord Je-sus Christ, King of end-less glo-ry!

Music: John Schiavone, b. 1947, © 2001, OCP Publications.

▶ Christ became obedient to the point of death,
  even death on a cross.
  Because of this, God greatly exalted him
  and bestowed on him the name which is above every name. ℞.

THE PASSION OF THE LORD — A

Matthew 26:14—27:66 or 27:11–54

The priest and/or readers read the Passion according to St. Matthew. Speakers in Passion Narrative are represented by these abbreviations:

N. – Narrator   V. – Voice

† – Christ   **C. – Crowd**

(Include bracketed text for Long Form)

N. The Passion of our Lord Jesus Christ according to Matthew

[One of the Twelve, who was called Judas Iscariot, went to the chief priests and said,

V. "What are you willing to give me if I hand him over to you?"

N. They paid him thirty pieces of silver, and from that time on he looked for an opportunity to hand him over.

On the first day of the Feast of Unleavened Bread, the disciples approached Jesus and said,

V. "Where do you want us to prepare for you to eat the Passover?"

N. He said,

† "Go into the city to a certain man and tell him, 'The teacher says, "My appointed time draws near; in your house I shall celebrate the Passover with my disciples."'"

N. The disciples then did as Jesus had ordered, and prepared the Passover.

When it was evening, he reclined at table with the Twelve. And while they were eating, he said,

† "Amen, I say to you, one of you will betray me."

N. Deeply distressed at this, they began to say to him one after another,

V. "Surely it is not I, Lord?"

N. He said in reply,

† "He who has dipped his hand into the dish with me is the one who will betray me. The Son of Man indeed goes, as it is written of him, but woe to that man by whom the Son of Man is betrayed. It would be better for that man if he had never been born."

N. Then Judas, his betrayer, said in reply,

V. "Surely it is not I, Rabbi?"

N. He answered,

† "You have said so."

N. While they were eating, Jesus took bread, said the blessing, broke it, and giving it to his disciples said,

† "Take and eat; this is my body."

N. Then he took a cup, gave thanks, and gave it to them, saying,

† "Drink from it, all of you, for this is my blood of the covenant, which will be shed on behalf of many for the forgiveness of sins. I tell you, from now on I shall not drink this fruit of the vine until the day when I drink it with you new in the kingdom of my Father."

N. Then, after singing a hymn, they went out to the Mount of Olives.

Then Jesus said to them,

† "This night all of you will have your faith in me shaken, for it is written:
*I will strike the shepherd,
    and the sheep of the flock will
        be dispersed;*
but after I have been raised up, I shall go before you to Galilee."

N. Peter said to him in reply,

V. "Though all may have their faith in you shaken, mine will never be."

N. Jesus said to him,

† "Amen, I say to you, this very night before the cock crows, you will deny me three times."

N. Peter said to him,

V. "Even though I should have to die with you, I will not deny you."

N. And all the disciples spoke likewise.

Then Jesus came with them to a place called Gethsemane, and he said to his disciples,

† "Sit here while I go over there and pray."

N. He took along Peter and the two sons of Zebedee, and began to feel sorrow and distress. Then he said to them,

† "My soul is sorrowful even to death. Remain here and keep watch with me."

N. He advanced a little and fell prostrate in prayer, saying,

† "My Father, if it is possible, let this cup pass from me; yet, not as I will, but as you will."

N. When he returned to his disciples he found them asleep. He said to Peter,

† "So you could not keep watch with me for one hour? Watch and pray that you may not undergo the test. The spirit is willing, but the flesh is weak."

N. Withdrawing a second time, he prayed again,

† "My Father, if it is not possible that this cup pass without my drinking it, your will be done!"

N. Then he returned once more and found them asleep, for they could not keep their eyes open. He left them and withdrew again and prayed a third time, saying the same thing again. Then he returned to his disciples and said to them,

† "Are you still sleeping and taking your rest? Behold, the hour is at hand when the Son of Man is to be handed over to sinners. Get up, let us go. Look, my betrayer is at hand."

N. While he was still speaking, Judas, one of the Twelve, arrived, accompanied by a large crowd, with swords and clubs, who had come from the chief priests and the elders of the people. His betrayer had arranged a sign with them, saying,

V. "The man I shall kiss is the one; arrest him."

N. Immediately he went over to Jesus and said,

V. "Hail, Rabbi!"

N. and he kissed him. Jesus answered him,

† "Friend, do what you have come for."

N. Then stepping forward they laid hands on Jesus and arrested him. And behold, one of those who accompanied Jesus put his hand to his sword, drew it, and struck the high priest's servant, cutting off his ear.

Then Jesus said to him,

† "Put your sword back into its sheath, for all who take the sword will perish by the sword. Do you think that I cannot call upon my Father and he will not provide me at this moment with more than twelve legions of angels? But then how would the Scriptures be fulfilled which say that it must come to pass in this way?"

N. At that hour Jesus said to the crowds,

† "Have you come out as against a robber, with swords and clubs to seize me? Day after day I sat teaching in the temple area, yet you did not arrest me. But all this has come to pass that the writings of the prophets may be fulfilled."

N. Then all the disciples left him and fled.

Those who had arrested Jesus led him away to Caiaphas the high priest, where the scribes and the elders were assembled. Peter was following him at a distance as far as the high priest's courtyard, and going inside he sat down with the servants to see the outcome. The chief priests and the entire Sanhedrin kept trying to obtain false testimony against Jesus in order to put him to death, but they found none, though many false witnesses came forward. Finally two came forward who stated,

C. **"This man said, 'I can destroy the temple of God and within three days rebuild it.'"**

N. The high priest rose and addressed him,

V. "Have you no answer? What are these men testifying against you?"

N. But Jesus was silent. Then the high priest said to him,

V. "I order you to tell us under oath before the living God whether you are the Christ, the Son of God."

N. Jesus said to him in reply,

† "You have said so. But I tell you:
From now on you will see the Son of Man
seated at the right hand of

the Power'
and 'coming on the clouds
of heaven.'"

N. Then the high priest tore his robes and said,

V. "He has blasphemed! What further need have we of witnesses? You have now heard the blasphemy; what is your opinion?"

N. They said in reply,

C. **"He deserves to die!"**

N. Then they spat in his face and struck him, while some slapped him, saying,

C. **"Prophesy for us, Christ: who is it that struck you?"**

N. Now Peter was sitting outside in the courtyard. One of the maids came over to him and said,

C. **"You too were with Jesus the Galilean."**

N. But he denied it in front of everyone, saying,

V. "I do not know what you are talking about!"

N. As he went out to the gate, another girl saw him and said to those who were there,

C. **"This man was with Jesus the Nazorean."**

N. Again he denied it with an oath,

V. "I do not know the man!"

N. A little later the bystanders came over and said to Peter,

C. **"Surely you too are one of them; even your speech gives you away."**

N. At that he began to curse and to swear,

V. "I do not know the man."

N. And immediately a cock crowed. Then Peter remembered the word that Jesus had spoken: "Before the cock crows you will deny me three times." He went out and began to weep bitterly.

When it was morning, all the chief priests and the elders of the people took counsel against Jesus to put him to death. They bound him, led him away, and handed him over to Pilate, the governor.

Then Judas, his betrayer, seeing that Jesus had been condemned, deeply regretted what he had done. He returned the thirty pieces of silver to the chief priests and elders, saying,

V. "I have sinned in betraying innocent blood."

N. They said,

C. **"What is that to us? Look to it yourself."**

N. Flinging the money into the temple, he departed and went off and hanged himself. The chief priests gathered up the money, but said,

C. **"It is not lawful to deposit this in the temple treasury, for it is the price of blood."**

N. After consultation, they used it to buy the potter's field as a burial place for foreigners. That is why that field even today is called the Field of Blood. Then was fulfilled what had been said through Jeremiah the prophet, *And they took the thirty pieces of silver, the value of a man with a price on his head, a price set by some of the Israelites, and they paid it out for the potter's field just as the Lord had commanded me.*

Now] Jesus stood before the governor, (Pontius Pilate,) who questioned him,

V. "Are you the king of the Jews?"

N. Jesus said,

† "You say so."

N. And when he was accused by the chief priests and elders, he made no answer. Then Pilate said to him,

V. "Do you not hear how many things they are testifying against you?"

N. But he did not answer him one word, so that the governor was greatly amazed.

Now on the occasion of the feast the governor was accustomed to release to the crowd one prisoner whom they wished. And at that time they had a notorious prisoner called Barabbas. So when they had assembled, Pilate said to them,

V. "Which one do you want me to release to you, Barabbas, or Jesus called Christ?"

N. For he knew that it was out of envy that they had handed him over. While he was still seated on the bench, his wife sent him a message, "Have nothing to do with that righteous man. I suffered much in a dream today because of him." The chief priests and the elders persuaded the crowds to ask for Barabbas but to destroy Jesus. The governor said to them in reply,

V. "Which of the two do you want me to release to you?"

N. They answered,

C. **"Barabbas!"**

N. Pilate said to them,

V. "Then what shall I do with Jesus called Christ?"

N. They all said,

C. **"Let him be crucified!"**

N. But he said,

V. "Why? What evil has he done?"

N. They only shouted the louder,

C. **"Let him be crucified!"**

N. When Pilate saw that he was not succeeding at all, but that a riot was breaking out instead, he took water and washed his hands in the sight of the crowd, saying,

V. "I am innocent of this man's blood. Look to it yourselves."

N. And the whole people said in reply,

C. **"His blood be upon us and upon our children."**

N. Then he released Barabbas to them, but after he had Jesus scourged, he handed him over to be crucified.

Then the soldiers of the governor took Jesus inside the praetorium and gathered the whole cohort around him. They stripped off his clothes and threw a scarlet military cloak about him. Weaving a crown out of thorns, they placed it on his head, and a reed in his right hand. And kneeling before him, they mocked him, saying,

C. **"Hail, King of the Jews!"**

N. They spat upon him and took the reed and kept striking him on the head. And when they had mocked him, they stripped him of the cloak, dressed him in his own clothes, and led him off to crucify him.

As they were going out, they met a Cyrenian named Simon; this man they pressed into service to carry his cross.

And when they came to a place called Golgotha — which means Place of the Skull —, they gave Jesus wine to drink mixed with gall. But when he had tasted it, he refused to drink. After they had crucified him, they divided his garments by casting lots; then they sat down and kept watch over him there. And they placed over his head the written charge against him: This is Jesus, the King of the Jews. Two revolutionaries were crucified with him, one on his right and the other on his left. Those passing by reviled him, shaking their heads and saying,

C. **"You who would destroy the temple and rebuild it in three days, save yourself, if you are the Son of God, and come down from the cross!"**

N. Likewise the chief priests with the scribes and elders mocked him and said,

C. **"He saved others; he cannot save himself. So he is the king of Israel! Let him come down from the cross now, and we will believe in him. He trusted in God; let him deliver him now if he wants him. For he said, 'I am the Son of God.'"**

N. The revolutionaries who were crucified with him also kept abusing him in the same way.

From noon onward, darkness came over the whole land until three in the afternoon. And about three o'clock Jesus cried out in a loud voice,

† *"Eli, Eli, lema sabachthani?"*

N. which means,

† "My God, my God, why have you forsaken me?"

N. Some of the bystanders who heard it said,

C. **"This one is calling for Elijah."**

N. Immediately one of them ran to get a sponge; he soaked it in wine, and putting it on a reed, gave it to him to drink. But the rest said,

C. **"Wait, let us see if Elijah comes to save him."**

N. But Jesus cried out again in a loud voice, and gave up his spirit.

Here all kneel and pause for a short time.

N. And behold, the veil of the sanctuary was torn in two from top to bottom. The earth quaked, rocks were split, tombs were opened, and the bodies of many saints who had fallen asleep were raised. And coming forth from their tombs after his resurrection, they entered the holy city and appeared to many. The centurion and the men with him who were keeping watch over Jesus feared greatly when they saw the earthquake and all that was happening, and they said,

C. **"Truly, this was the Son of God!"**

N. [There were many women there, looking on from a distance, who had followed Jesus from Galilee, ministering to him. Among them were Mary Magdalene and Mary the mother of James and Joseph, and the mother of the sons of Zebedee.

When it was evening, there came a rich man from Arimathea named Joseph, who was himself a disciple of Jesus. He went to Pilate and asked for the body of Jesus; then Pilate ordered it to be handed over. Taking the body, Joseph wrapped it in clean linen and laid it in his new tomb that he had hewn in the rock. Then he rolled a huge stone across the entrance to the tomb and departed. But Mary Magdalene and the other Mary remained sitting there, facing the tomb. The next day, the one following the day of preparation, the chief priests and the Pharisees gathered before Pilate and said,

C. **"Sir, we remember that this impostor while still alive said, 'After three days I will be raised up.' Give orders, then, that the grave be secured until the third day, lest his disciples come and steal him and say to the people, 'He has been raised from the dead.' This last imposture would be worse than the first."**

N. Pilate said to them,

V. "The guard is yours; go, secure it as best you can."

N. So they went and secured the tomb by fixing a seal to the stone and setting the guard.]

THE PASSION OF THE LORD — B

Mark 14:1—15:47 or 15:1–39

The priest and/or readers read the Passion according to St. Mark. Speakers in Passion Narrative are represented by these abbreviations:

N. – Narrator	V. – Voice
† – Christ	**C. – Crowd**

(Include bracketed text for Long Form)

N. The Passion of our Lord Jesus Christ according to Mark

[The Passover and the Feast of Unleavened Bread were to take place in two days' time. So the chief priests and the scribes were seeking a way to arrest him by treachery and put him to death. They said,

C. **"Not during the festival, for fear that there may be a riot among the people."**

N. When he was in Bethany reclining at table in the house of Simon the leper, a woman came with an alabaster jar of perfumed oil, costly genuine spikenard. She broke the alabaster jar and poured it on his head. There were some who were indignant.

C. **"Why has there been this waste of perfumed oil? It could have been sold for more than three hundred days' wages and the money given to the poor."**

N. They were infuriated with her. Jesus said,

† "Let her alone. Why do you make trouble for her? She has done a good thing for me. The poor you will always have with you, and whenever you wish you can do good to them, but you will not always have me. She has done what she could. She has anticipated anointing my body for burial. Amen, I say to you, wherever the gospel is proclaimed to the whole world, what she has done will be told in memory of her."

N. Then Judas Iscariot, one of the Twelve, went off to the chief priests to hand him over to them. When they heard him they were pleased and promised to pay him money. Then he looked for an opportunity to hand him over.

On the first day of the Feast of Unleavened Bread, when they sacrificed the Passover lamb, his disciples said to him,

C. **"Where do you want us to go and prepare for you to eat the Passover?"**

N. He sent two of his disciples and said to them,

† "Go into the city and a man will meet you, carrying a jar of water. Follow him. Wherever he enters, say to the master of the house, 'The Teacher says, "Where is my guest room where I may eat the Passover with my disciples?"' Then he will show you a large upper room furnished and ready. Make the preparations for us there."

N. The disciples then went off, entered the city, and found it just as he had told them; and they prepared the Passover.

When it was evening, he came with the Twelve. And as they reclined at table and were eating, Jesus said,

† "Amen, I say to you, one of you will betray me, one who is eating with me."

N. They began to be distressed and to say to him, one by one,

V. "Surely it is not I?"

N. He said to them,

† "One of the Twelve, the one who dips with me into the dish. For the Son of Man indeed goes, as it is written of him, but woe to that man by whom the Son of Man is betrayed. It would be better for that man if he had never been born."

N. While they were eating, he took bread, said the blessing, broke it, and gave it to them, and said,

† "Take it; this is my body."

N. Then he took a cup, gave thanks, and gave it to them, and they all drank from it. He said to them,

† "This is my blood of the covenant, which will be shed for many. Amen, I say to you, I shall not drink again the fruit of the vine until the day when I drink it new in the kingdom of God."

N. Then, after singing a hymn, they went out to the Mount of Olives.

Then Jesus said to them,

† "All of you will have your faith shaken, for it is written:
'I will strike the shepherd,
and the sheep will
be dispersed.'
But after I have been raised up, I shall go before you to Galilee."

N. Peter said to him,

V. "Even though all should have their faith shaken, mine will not be."

N. Then Jesus said to him,

† "Amen, I say to you, this very night before the cock crows twice you will deny me three times."

N. But he vehemently replied,

V. "Even though I should have to die with you, I will not deny you."

N. And they all spoke similarly.

Then they came to a place named Gethsemane, and he said to his disciples,

† "Sit here while I pray."

N. He took with him Peter, James, and John, and began to be troubled and distressed. Then he said to them,

† "My soul is sorrowful even to death. Remain here and keep watch."

N. He advanced a little and fell to the ground and prayed that if it were possible the hour might pass by him; he said,

† "Abba, Father, all things are possible to you. Take this cup away from me, but not what I will but what you will."

N. When he returned he found them asleep. He said to Peter,

† "Simon, are you asleep? Could you not keep watch for one hour? Watch and pray that you may not undergo the test. The spirit is willing but the flesh is weak."

N. Withdrawing again, he prayed, saying the same thing. Then he returned once more and found them asleep, for they could not keep their eyes open and did not know what to answer him. He returned a third time and said to them,

† "Are you still sleeping and taking your rest? It is enough. The hour has come. Behold, the Son of Man is to be handed over to sinners. Get up, let us go. See, my betrayer is at hand."

N. Then, while he was still speaking, Judas, one of the Twelve, arrived, accompanied by a crowd with swords and clubs who had come from the chief priests, the scribes, and the elders. His betrayer had arranged a signal with them, saying,

V. "The man I shall kiss is the one; arrest him and lead him away securely."

N. He came and immediately went over to him and said,

V. "Rabbi."

N. And he kissed him. At this they laid hands on him and arrested him. One of the bystanders drew his sword, struck the high priest's servant, and cut off his ear. Jesus said to them in reply,

† "Have you come out as against a robber, with swords and clubs, to seize me? Day after day I was with you teaching in the temple area, yet you did not arrest me; but that the Scriptures may be fulfilled."

N. And they all left him and fled. Now a young man followed him wearing nothing but a linen cloth about his body. They seized him, but he left the cloth behind and ran off naked.

They led Jesus away to the high priest, and all the chief priests and the elders and the scribes came together. Peter followed him at a distance into the high priest's courtyard and was seated with the guards, warming himself at the fire. The chief priests and the entire Sanhedrin kept trying to obtain testimony against Jesus in order to put him to death, but they found none.

Many gave false witness against him, but their testimony did not agree. Some took the stand and testified falsely against him, alleging,

C. **"We heard him say, 'I will destroy this temple made with hands and within three days I will build another not made with hands.'"**

N. Even so their testimony did not agree. The high priest rose before the assembly and questioned Jesus, saying,

V. "Have you no answer? What are these men testifying against you?"

N. But he was silent and answered nothing. Again the high priest asked him and said to him,

V. "Are you the Christ, the son of the Blessed One?"

N. Then Jesus answered,

† "I am;

and 'you will see the
Son of Man
seated at the right hand
of the Power
and coming with the clouds
of heaven.'"

N. At that the high priest tore his garments and said,

V. "What further need have we of witnesses? You have heard the blasphemy. What do you think?"

N. They all condemned him as deserving to die. Some began to spit on him. They blindfolded him and struck him and said to him,

C. **"Prophesy!"**

N. And the guards greeted him with blows.

While Peter was below in the courtyard, one of the high priest's maids came along. Seeing Peter warming himself, she looked intently at him and said,

C. **"You too were with the Nazarene, Jesus."**

N. But he denied it saying,

V. "I neither know nor understand what you are talking about."

N. So he went out into the outer court. Then the cock crowed. The maid saw him and began again to say to the bystanders,

C. **"This man is one of them."**

N. Once again he denied it. A little later the bystanders said to Peter once more,

C. **"Surely you are one of them; for you too are a Galilean."**

N. He began to curse and to swear,

V. "I do not know this man about whom you are talking."

N. And immediately a cock crowed a second time. Then Peter remembered the word that Jesus had said to him, "Before the cock crows twice you will deny me three times." He broke down and wept.]

As soon as morning came, the chief priests with the elders and the scribes, that is, the whole Sanhedrin, held a council. They bound Jesus, led him away, and handed him over to Pilate. Pilate questioned him,

V. "Are you the king of the Jews?"

N. He said to him in reply,

† "You say so."

N. The chief priests accused him of many things. Again Pilate questioned him,

V. "Have you no answer? See how many things they accuse you of."

N. Jesus gave him no further answer, so that Pilate was amazed.

Now on the occasion of the feast he used to release to them one prisoner whom they requested. A man called Barabbas was then in prison along with the rebels who had committed murder in a rebellion. The crowd came forward and began to ask him to do for them as he was accustomed. Pilate answered,

V. "Do you want me to release to you the king of the Jews?"

N. For he knew that it was out of envy that the chief priests had handed him over. But the chief priests stirred up the crowd to have him release Barabbas for them instead. Pilate again said to them in reply,

V. "Then what do you want me to do with the man you call the king of the Jews?"

N. They shouted again,

C. **"Crucify him."**

N. Pilate said to them,

V. "Why? What evil has he done?"

N. They only shouted the louder,

C. **"Crucify him."**

N. So Pilate, wishing to satisfy the crowd, released Barabbas to them and, after he had Jesus scourged, handed him over to be crucified.

The soldiers led him away inside the palace, that is, the praetorium, and assembled the whole cohort. They clothed him in purple and, weaving a crown of thorns, placed it on him. They began to salute him with,

C. **"Hail, King of the Jews!"**

N. and kept striking his head with a reed and spitting upon him. They knelt before him in homage. And when they had mocked him, they stripped him of the purple cloak, dressed him in his own clothes, and led him out to crucify him.

They pressed into service a passer-by, Simon, a Cyrenian, who was coming in from the country, the father of Alexander and Rufus, to carry his cross.

They brought him to the place of Golgotha — which is translated Place of the Skull —. They gave him wine drugged with myrrh, but he did not take it. Then they crucified him and divided his garments by casting lots for them to see what each should take. It was nine o'clock in the morning when they crucified him. The inscription of the charge against him read, "The King of the Jews." With him they crucified two revolutionaries, one on his right and one on his left. Those passing by reviled him, shaking their heads and saying,

C. **"Aha! You who would destroy the temple and rebuild it in three days, save yourself by coming down from the cross."**

N. Likewise the chief priests, with the scribes, mocked him among themselves and said,

C. **"He saved others; he cannot save himself. Let the Christ, the King of Israel, come down now from the cross that we may see and believe."**

N. Those who were crucified with him also kept abusing him.

At noon darkness came over the whole land until three in the afternoon. And at three o'clock Jesus cried out in a loud voice,

† *"Eloi, Eloi, lema sabachthani?"*

N. which is translated,

† *"My God, my God, why have you forsaken me?"*

N. Some of the bystanders who heard it said,

C. **"Look, he is calling Elijah."**

N. One of them ran, soaked a sponge with wine, put it on a reed and gave it to him to drink, saying,

V. "Wait, let us see if Elijah comes to take him down."

N. Jesus gave a loud cry and breathed his last.

Here all kneel and pause for a short time.

N. The veil of the sanctuary was torn in two from top to bottom. When the centurion who stood facing him saw how he breathed his last he said,

V. "Truly this man was the Son of God!"

N. [There were also women looking on from a distance. Among them were Mary Magdalene, Mary the mother of the younger James and of Joses, and Salome. These women had followed him when he was in Galilee and ministered to him. There were also many other women who had come up with him to Jerusalem.

When it was already evening, since it was the day of preparation, the day before the sabbath, Joseph of Arimathea, a distinguished member of the council, who was himself awaiting the kingdom of God, came and courageously went to Pilate and asked for the body of Jesus. Pilate was amazed that he was already dead. He summoned the centurion and asked him if Jesus had already died. And when he learned of it from the centurion, he gave the body to Joseph. Having bought a linen cloth, he took him down, wrapped him in the linen cloth, and laid him in a tomb that had been hewn out of the rock. Then he rolled a stone against the entrance to the tomb. Mary Magdalene and Mary the mother of Joses watched where he was laid.]

THE PASSION OF THE LORD — C

Luke 22:14—23:56 or 23:1–49

The priest and/or readers read the Passion according to St. Luke. Speakers in Passion Narrative are represented by these abbreviations:

N. – Narrator	V. – Voice
† – Christ	**C. – Crowd**

(Include bracketed text for Long Form)

N. The Passion of our Lord Jesus Christ according to Luke

[When the hour came, Jesus took his place at table with the apostles. He said to them,

† "I have eagerly desired to eat this Passover with you before I suffer, for, I tell you, I shall not eat it again until there is fulfillment in the kingdom of God."

N. Then he took a cup, gave thanks, and said,

† "Take this and share it among yourselves; for I tell you that from this time on I shall not drink of the fruit of the vine until the kingdom of God comes."

N. Then he took the bread, said the blessing, broke it, and gave it to them, saying,

† "This is my body, which will be given for you; do this in memory of me."

N. And likewise the cup after they had eaten, saying,

† "This cup is the new covenant in my blood, which will be shed for you.

"And yet behold, the hand of the one who is to betray me is with me on the table; for the Son of Man indeed goes as it has been determined; but woe to that man by whom he is betrayed."

N. And they began to debate among themselves who among them would do such a deed.

Then an argument broke out among them about which of them should be regarded as the greatest. He said to them,

† "The kings of the Gentiles lord it over them and those in authority over them are addressed as 'Benefactors'; but among you it shall not be so. Rather, let the greatest among you be as the youngest, and the leader as the servant. For who is greater: the one seated at table or the one who serves? Is it not the one seated at table? I am among you as the one who serves. It is you who have stood by me in my trials; and I confer a kingdom on you, just as my Father has conferred one on me, that you may eat and drink at my table in my kingdom; and you will sit on thrones judging the twelve tribes of Israel.

"Simon, Simon, behold Satan has demanded to sift all of you like wheat, but I have prayed that your own faith may not fail; and once you have turned back, you must strengthen your brothers."

N. He said to him,

V. "Lord, I am prepared to go to prison and to die with you."

N. But he replied,

† "I tell you, Peter, before the cock crows this day, you will deny three times that you know me."

N. He said to them,

† "When I sent you forth without a money bag or a sack or sandals, were you in need of anything?"

C. **"No, nothing,"**

N. they replied. He said to them,

† "But now one who has a money bag should take it, and likewise a sack, and one who does not have a sword should sell his cloak and buy one. For I tell you that this Scripture must be fulfilled in me, namely, *He was counted among the wicked*; and indeed what is written about me is coming to fulfillment."

N. Then they said,

C. **"Lord, look, there are two swords here."**

N. But he replied,

† "It is enough!"

N. Then going out, he went, as was his custom, to the Mount of Olives, and the disciples followed him. When he arrived at the place he said to them,

† "Pray that you may not undergo the test."

N. After withdrawing about a stone's throw from them and kneeling, he prayed, saying,

† "Father, if you are willing, take this cup away from me; still, not my will but yours be done."

N. And to strengthen him an angel from heaven appeared to him. He was in such agony and he prayed so fervently that his sweat became like drops of blood falling on the ground. When he rose from prayer and returned to his disciples, he found them sleeping from grief. He said to them,

† "Why are you sleeping? Get up and pray that you may not undergo the test."

N. While he was still speaking, a crowd approached and in front was one of the Twelve, a man named Judas. He went up to Jesus to kiss him. Jesus said to him,

† "Judas, are you betraying the Son of Man with a kiss?"

N. His disciples realized what was about to happen, and they asked,

C. **"Lord, shall we strike with a sword?"**

N. And one of them struck the high priest's servant and cut off his right ear. But Jesus said in reply,

† "Stop, no more of this!"

N. Then he touched the servant's ear and healed him. And Jesus said to the chief priests and temple guards and elders who had come for him,

† "Have you come out as against a robber, with swords and clubs? Day after day I was with you in the temple area, and you did not seize me; but this is your hour, the time for the power of darkness."

N. After arresting him they led him away and took him into the house of the high priest; Peter was following at a distance. They lit a fire in the middle of the courtyard and sat around it, and Peter sat down with them. When a maid saw him seated in the light, she looked intently at him and said,

C. **"This man too was with him."**

N. But he denied it saying,

V. "Woman, I do not know him."

N. A short while later someone else saw him and said,

C. **"You too are one of them";**

N. but Peter answered,

V. "My friend, I am not."

N. About an hour later, still another insisted,

C. **"Assuredly, this man too was with him, for he also is a Galilean."**

N. But Peter said,

V. "My friend, I do not know what you are talking about."

N. Just as he was saying this, the cock crowed, and the Lord turned and looked at Peter; and Peter remembered the word of the Lord, how he had said to him, "Before the cock crows today, you will deny me three times." He went out and began to weep bitterly. The men who held Jesus in custody were ridiculing and beating him. They blindfolded him and questioned him, saying,

C. **"Prophesy! Who is it that struck you?"**

N. And they reviled him in saying many other things against him.

When day came the council of elders of the people met, both chief priests and scribes, and they brought him before their Sanhedrin. They said,

C. **"If you are the Christ, tell us,"**

N. but he replied to them,

† "If I tell you, you will not believe, and if I question, you will not respond. But from this time on the Son of Man will be seated at the right hand of the power of God."

N. They all asked,

C. **"Are you then the Son of God?"**

N. He replied to them,

† "You say that I am."

N. Then they said,

C. **"What further need have we for testimony? We have heard it from his own mouth."]**

N. Then the whole assembly of them* arose and brought him before Pilate. They brought charges against him, saying,

C. **"We found this man misleading our people; he opposes the payment of taxes to Caesar and maintains that he is the Christ, a king."**

N. Pilate asked him,

V. "Are you the king of the Jews?"

N. He said to him in reply,

† "You say so."

N. Pilate then addressed the chief priests and the crowds,

V. "I find this man not guilty."

N. But they were adamant and said,

C. **"He is inciting the people with his teaching throughout all Judea, from Galilee where he began even to here."**

N. On hearing this Pilate asked if the man was a Galilean; and upon learning that he was under Herod's jurisdiction, he sent him to Herod who was in Jerusalem at that time. Herod was very glad to see Jesus; he had been wanting to see him for a long time, for he had heard about him and had been hoping to see him perform some sign. He questioned him at length, but he gave him no answer. The chief priests and scribes, meanwhile, stood by accusing him harshly. Herod and his soldiers treated him contemptuously and mocked him, and after clothing him in resplendent garb, he sent him back to Pilate. Herod and Pilate became friends that very day, even though they had been enemies formerly. Pilate then summoned the chief priests, the rulers, and the people and said to them,

V. "You brought this man to me and accused him of inciting the people to revolt. I have conducted my investigation in your presence and have not found this man guilty of the charges you have brought against him, nor did Herod, for he sent him back to us. So no capital crime has been committed by him. Therefore I shall have him flogged and then release him."

N. But all together they shouted out,

C. **"Away with this man! Release Barabbas to us."**

N. — Now Barabbas had been imprisoned for a rebellion that had taken place in the city and for murder. — Again Pilate addressed them, still wishing to release Jesus, but they continued their shouting,

C. **"Crucify him! Crucify him!"**

N. Pilate addressed them a third time,

V. "What evil has this man done? I found him guilty of no capital crime. Therefore I shall have him flogged and then release him."

N. With loud shouts, however, they persisted in calling for his crucifixion, and their voices prevailed. The verdict of Pilate was that their demand should be granted. So he released the man who had been imprisoned for rebellion and murder, for whom they asked, and he handed Jesus over to them to deal with as they wished.

As they led him away they took hold of a certain Simon, a Cyrenian, who was coming in from the country; and after laying the cross on him, they made him carry it behind Jesus. A large crowd of people followed Jesus, including many women who mourned and lamented him. Jesus turned to them and said,

The shorter form replaces this line with the words: The elders of the people, chief priests and scribes,

† "Daughters of Jerusalem, do not weep for me; weep instead for yourselves and for your children, for indeed, the days are coming when people will say, 'Blessed are the barren, the wombs that never bore and the breasts that never nursed.' At that time people will say to the mountains, 'Fall upon us!' and to the hills, 'Cover us!' for if these things are done when the wood is green what will happen when it is dry?"

N. Now two others, both criminals, were led away with him to be executed.

When they came to the place called the Skull, they crucified him and the criminals there, one on his right, the other on his left. Then Jesus said,

† "Father, forgive them, they know not what they do."

N. They divided his garments by casting lots. The people stood by and watched; the rulers, meanwhile, sneered at him and said,

C. **"He saved others, let him save himself if he is the chosen one, the Christ of God."**

N. Even the soldiers jeered at him. As they approached to offer him wine they called out,

C. **"If you are King of the Jews, save yourself."**

N. Above him there was an inscription that read, "This is the King of the Jews."

Now one of the criminals hanging there reviled Jesus, saying,

V. "Are you not the Christ? Save yourself and us."

N. The other, however, rebuking him, said in reply,

V. "Have you no fear of God, for you are subject to the same condemnation? And indeed, we have been condemned justly, for the sentence we received corresponds to our crimes, but this man has done nothing criminal."

N. Then he said,

V. "Jesus, remember me when you come into your kingdom."

N. He replied to him,

† "Amen, I say to you, today you will be with me in Paradise."

N. It was now about noon and darkness came over the whole land until three in the afternoon because of an eclipse of the sun. Then the veil of the temple was torn down the middle. Jesus cried out in a loud voice,

† "Father, into your hands I commend my spirit";

N. and when he had said this he breathed his last.

Here all kneel and pause for a short time.

N. The centurion who witnessed what had happened glorified God and said,

V. "This man was innocent beyond doubt."

N. When all the people who had gathered for this spectacle saw what had happened, they returned home beating their breasts; but all his acquaintances stood at a distance, including the women who had followed him from Galilee and saw these events.

[Now there was a virtuous and righteous man named Joseph who, though he was a member of the council, had not consented to their plan of action. He came from the Jewish town of Arimathea and was awaiting the kingdom of God. He went to Pilate and asked for the body of Jesus. After he had taken the body down, he wrapped it in a linen cloth and laid him in a rock-hewn tomb in which no one had yet been buried. It was the day of preparation, and the sabbath was about to begin. The women who had come from Galilee with him followed behind, and when they had seen the tomb and the way in which his body was laid in it, they returned and prepared spices and perfumed oils. Then they rested on the sabbath according to the commandment.]

Easter Triduum and Season of Easter

919   Holy Thursday:
Evening Mass of the Lord's Supper — ABC

At the Last Supper, on the night when he was betrayed, our Savior instituted the Eucharistic Sacrifice of his body and blood. The tabernacle should be entirely empty; a sufficient amount of bread should be consecrated at this Mass for the communion of clergy and laity today and tomorrow. The reception of the holy oils blessed at the Chrism Mass may be received by the local community during this liturgy. Mass begins with the Entrance Antiphon or an appropriate song (see #472, 477, 825, 826), followed by the Introductory Rites. During the singing of the "Gloria" the church bells are rung and then remain silent until the Easter Vigil.

Liturgy of the Word

First Reading   *Exodus 12:1–8, 11–14*

The LORD said to Moses and Aaron in the land of Egypt, "This month shall stand at the head of your calendar; you shall reckon it the first month of the year. Tell the whole community of Israel: On the tenth of this month every one of your families must procure for itself a lamb, one apiece for each household. If a family is too small for a whole lamb, it shall join the nearest household in procuring one and shall share in the lamb in proportion to the number of persons who partake of it. The lamb must be a year-old male and without blemish. You may take it from either the sheep or the goats. You shall keep it until the fourteenth day of this month, and then, with the whole assembly of Israel present, it shall be slaughtered during the evening twilight. They shall take some of its blood and apply it to the two doorposts and the lintel of every house in which they partake of the lamb. That same night they shall eat its roasted flesh with unleavened bread and bitter herbs.

"This is how you are to eat it: with your loins girt, sandals on your feet and your staff in hand, you shall eat like those who are in flight. It is the Passover of the LORD. For on this same night I will go through Egypt, striking down every firstborn of the land, both man and beast, and executing judgment on all the gods of Egypt — I, the Lord! But the blood will mark the houses where you are. Seeing the blood, I will pass over you; thus, when I strike the land of Egypt, no destructive blow will come upon you.

"This day shall be a memorial feast for you, which all your generations shall celebrate with pilgrimage to the Lord, as a perpetual institution."

RESPONSORIAL PSALM
Psalm 116:12–13, 15–16bc, 17–18

℟. Our bless-ing-cup is a com-mu-nion with the

Blood of Christ, [with the Blood of Christ.]

Music: John Schiavone, b. 1947, © 2001, OCP Publications.

▶ How shall I make a return to the LORD
for all the good he has done for me?
The cup of salvation I will take up,
and I will call upon the name of
the LORD. ℟.

▶ Precious in the eyes of the LORD
is the death of his faithful ones.
I am your servant, the son of
your handmaid;
you have loosed my bonds. ℟.

▶ To you will I offer sacrifice of
thanksgiving,
and I will call upon the name of
the LORD.
My vows to the LORD I will pay
in the presence of all his people. ℟.

SECOND READING
1 Corinthians 11:23–26

Brothers and sisters: I received from the Lord what I also handed on to you, that the Lord Jesus, on the night he was handed over, took bread, and, after he had given thanks, broke it and said, "This is my body that is for you. Do this in remembrance of me." In the same way also the cup, after supper, saying, "This cup is the new covenant in my blood. Do this, as often as you drink it, in remembrance of me." For as often as you eat this bread and drink the cup, you proclaim the death of the Lord until he comes.

GOSPEL ACCLAMATION
John 13:34

℟. Praise to you, Lord Je - sus Christ, King of end - less glo - ry!

Music: John Schiavone, b. 1947, © 2001, OCP Publications.

▶ I give you a new commandment, says the Lord:
love one another as I have loved you. ℟.

GOSPEL READING
John 13:1–15

Before the feast of Passover, Jesus knew that his hour had come to pass from this world to the Father. He loved his own in the world and he loved them to the end. The devil had already induced Judas, son of Simon the Iscariot, to hand him over. So, during supper, fully aware that the Father had put everything into his power and that he had come from God and was returning to God, he rose from supper and took off his outer garments. He took a towel and tied it around his waist. Then he poured water into a basin and began to wash the disciples' feet and dry them with the towel around his waist. He came to Simon Peter, who said to him, "Master, are you going to wash my feet?" Jesus answered and said to him, "What I am doing, you do not understand now, but you will understand later." Peter said to him, "You will never wash my feet." Jesus answered him, "Unless I wash you, you will have no inheritance with me." Simon Peter said to him, "Master, then not only my feet, but my hands and head as well." Jesus said to him, "Whoever has bathed has no need except to have his feet washed, for he is clean all over; so you are clean, but not all." For he knew who would betray him; for this reason, he said, "Not all of you are clean."

So when he had washed their feet and put his garments back on and reclined at table again, he said to them, "Do you realize what I have done for you? You call me 'teacher' and 'master,' and rightly so, for indeed I am. If I, therefore, the master and teacher, have washed your feet, you ought to wash one another's feet. I have given you a model to follow, so that as I have done for you, you should also do."

WASHING OF FEET

During the washing of feet an appropriate hymn may be sung (see #401, 402, 403).

Mass continues with the General Intercessions, followed by the Liturgy of the Eucharist. The Profession of Faith is not said at this Mass.

TRANSFER OF THE HOLY EUCHARIST

Following the prayer after communion, all kneel as the priest incenses the Blessed Sacrament on the altar. The Blessed Sacrament is then carried through the church to the place of reposition. The hosts will be distributed to the people on Good Friday. During the procession, a suitable hymn is sung (see #404, 405, 406).

After the priest incenses and places the Blessed Sacrament in the tabernacle the people are encouraged to remain for a period of quiet adoration. All depart in silence.

920   GOOD FRIDAY OF THE LORD'S PASSION — ABC

According to the Church's ancient tradition, Mass is not celebrated today. The celebration of the Lord's Passion consists of three parts: Liturgy of the Word, Veneration of the Cross, and Holy Communion.

PART I: LITURGY OF THE WORD

FIRST READING   Isaiah 52:13 — 53:12

See, my servant shall prosper,
     he shall be raised high and
          greatly exalted.
Even as many were amazed at him —
     so marred was his look beyond
          human semblance
     and his appearance beyond that of
          the sons of man —
so shall he startle many nations,
     because of him kings shall
          stand speechless;

for those who have not been told
     shall see,
     those who have not heard shall
          ponder it.

Who would believe what we have heard?
     To whom has the arm of the LORD
          been revealed?
He grew up like a sapling before him,
     like a shoot from the parched earth;
there was in him no stately bearing to
     make us look at him,

nor appearance that would attract us
  to him.
He was spurned and avoided by people,
  a man of suffering, accustomed
    to infirmity,
one of those from whom people hide
    their faces,
  spurned, and we held him in
    no esteem.

Yet it was our infirmities that he bore,
  our sufferings that he endured,
while we thought of him as stricken,
  as one smitten by God and afflicted.
But he was pierced for our offenses,
  crushed for our sins;
upon him was the chastisement that
    makes us whole,
  by his stripes we were healed.
We had all gone astray like sheep,
  each following his own way;
but the LORD laid upon him
  the guilt of us all.

Though he was harshly treated,
  he submitted
  and opened not his mouth;
like a lamb led to the slaughter
  or a sheep before the shearers,
he was silent and opened not
  his mouth.
Oppressed and condemned, he was
  taken away,

and who would have thought any
  more of his destiny?
When he was cut off from the land of
  the living,
  and smitten for the sin of his people,
a grave was assigned him among
    the wicked
  and a burial place with evildoers,
though he had done no wrong
  nor spoken any falsehood.
But the LORD was pleased
  to crush him in infirmity.

If he gives his life as an offering for sin,
  he shall see his descendants in a
    long life,
  and the will of the LORD shall be
    accomplished through him.

Because of his affliction
  he shall see the light
    in fullness of days;
through his suffering, my servant shall
    justify many,
  and their guilt he shall bear.
Therefore I will give him his portion
    among the great,
  and he shall divide the spoils with
    the mighty,
because he surrendered himself to death
  and was counted among the wicked;
and he shall take away the sins of many,
  and win pardon for their offenses.

RESPONSORIAL PSALM

Psalm 31:2, 6, 12–13, 15–16, 17, 25

R. [Fa - ther,] Fa - ther, [in - to your hands,]
in - to your hands I com - mend my spir - it.

Music: John Schiavone, b. 1947, © 2001, OCP Publications.

▶ In you, O LORD, I take refuge;
  let me never be put to shame.
  In your justice rescue me.
  Into your hands I commend my spirit;
    you will redeem me, O LORD,
    O faithful God. R.

▶ For all my foes I am an object
    of reproach,

a laughingstock to my neighbors,
    and a dread to my friends;
  they who see me abroad flee
    from me.
  I am forgotten like the unremembered
    dead;
  I am like a dish that is broken. R.

℟. **Father, into your hands I commend my spirit.**

▶ But my trust is in you, O LORD;
I say, "You are my God.
In your hands is my destiny; rescue me
from the clutches of my enemies
and my persecutors." ℟.

▶ Let your face shine upon your servant;
save me in your kindness.
Take courage and be stouthearted,
all you who hope in the LORD. ℟.

SECOND READING
Hebrews 4:14–16; 5:7–9

Brothers and sisters: Since we have a great high priest who has passed through the heavens, Jesus, the Son of God, let us hold fast to our confession. For we do not have a high priest who is unable to sympathize with our weaknesses, but one who has similarly been tested in every way, yet without sin. So let us confidently approach the throne of grace to receive mercy and to find grace for timely help.

In the days when Christ was in the flesh, he offered prayers and supplications with loud cries and tears to the one who was able to save him from death, and he was heard because of his reverence. Son though he was, he learned obedience from what he suffered; and when he was made perfect, he became the source of eternal salvation for all who obey him.

GOSPEL ACCLAMATION
Philippians 2:8–9

℟. **Praise to you, Lord Je - sus Christ, King of end - less glo - ry!**

Music: John Schiavone, b. 1947, © 2001, OCP Publications.

▶ Christ became obedient to the point of death,
even death on a cross.
Because of this, God greatly exalted him
and bestowed on him the name which is above every other name. ℟.

THE PASSION OF THE LORD
John 18:1 — 19:42

The priest and/or readers read the Passion according to St. John. Speakers in Passion Narrative are represented by these abbreviations:

N. – Narrator   V. – Voice
† – Christ   **C. – Crowd**

N. The Passion of our Lord Jesus Christ according to John

Jesus went out with his disciples across the Kidron valley to where there was a garden, into which he and his disciples entered. Judas his betrayer also knew the place, because Jesus had often met there with his disciples. So Judas got a band of soldiers and guards from the chief priests and the Pharisees and went there with lanterns, torches, and weapons. Jesus, knowing everything that was going to happen to him, went out and said to them,

† "Whom are you looking for?"

N. They answered him,

C. **"Jesus the Nazorean."**

N. He said to them,

† "I AM."

N. Judas his betrayer was also with them. When he said to them, "I AM," they turned away and fell to the ground. So he again asked them,

† "Whom are you looking for?"

N. They said,

C. **"Jesus the Nazorean."**

N. Jesus answered,

† "I told you that I AM. So if you are looking for me, let these men go."

N. This was to fulfill what he had said, "I have not lost any of those you gave me." Then Simon Peter, who had a sword, drew it, struck the high priest's slave, and cut off his right ear. The slave's name was Malchus. Jesus said to Peter,

† "Put your sword into its scabbard. Shall I not drink the cup that the Father gave me?"

N. So the band of soldiers, the tribune, and the Jewish guards seized Jesus, bound him, and brought him to Annas first. He was the father-in-law of Caiaphas, who was high priest that year. It was Caiaphas who had counseled the Jews that it was better that one man should die rather than the people.

Simon Peter and another disciple followed Jesus. Now the other disciple was known to the high priest, and he entered the courtyard of the high priest with Jesus. But Peter stood at the gate outside. So the other disciple, the acquaintance of the high priest, went out and spoke to the gatekeeper and brought Peter in. Then the maid who was the gatekeeper said to Peter,

C. **"You are not one of this man's disciples, are you?"**

N. He said,

V. "I am not."

N. Now the slaves and the guards were standing around a charcoal fire that they had made, because it was cold, and were warming themselves. Peter was also standing there keeping warm.

The high priest questioned Jesus about his disciples and about his doctrine. Jesus answered him,

† "I have spoken publicly to the world. I have always taught in a synagogue or in the temple area where all the Jews gather, and in secret I have said nothing. Why ask me? Ask those who heard me what I said to them. They know what I said."

N. When he had said this, one of the temple guards standing there struck Jesus and said,

V. "Is this the way you answer the high priest?"

N. Jesus answered him,

† "If I have spoken wrongly, testify to the wrong; but if I have spoken rightly, why do you strike me?"

N. Then Annas sent him bound to Caiaphas the high priest.

Now Simon Peter was standing there keeping warm. And they said to him,

C. **"You are not one of his disciples, are you?"**

N. He denied it and said,

V. "I am not."

N. One of the slaves of the high priest, a relative of the one whose ear Peter had cut off, said,

C. **"Didn't I see you in the garden with him?"**

N. Again Peter denied it. And immediately the cock crowed.

The message of the liturgy in proclaiming the passion narratives in full is to enable the assembly to see vividly the love of Christ for each person, despite their sins, a love that even death could not vanquish. The crimes during the Passion of Christ cannot be attributed indiscriminately to all Jews of that time, nor to Jews today. The Jewish people should not be referred to as though rejected or cursed, as if this view followed from Scripture. The Church ever keeps in mind that Jesus, his mother Mary, and the Apostles all were Jewish. As the Church has always held, Christ freely suffered his passion and death because of the sins of all, that all might be saved.

— Bishops' Committee for Ecumenical and Interreligious Affairs

Then they brought Jesus from Caiaphas to the praetorium. It was morning. And they themselves did not enter the praetorium, in order not to be defiled so that they could eat the Passover. So Pilate came out to them and said,

V. "What charge do you bring against this man?"

N. They answered and said to him,

C. **"If he were not a criminal, we would not have handed him over to you."**

N. At this, Pilate said to them,

V. "Take him yourselves, and judge him according to your law."

N. The Jews answered him,

C. **"We do not have the right to execute anyone,"**

N. in order that the word of Jesus might be fulfilled that he said indicating the kind of death he would die. So Pilate went back into the praetorium and summoned Jesus and said to him,

V. "Are you the King of the Jews?"

N. Jesus answered,

† "Do you say this on your own or have others told you about me?"

N. Pilate answered,

V. "I am not a Jew, am I? Your own nation and the chief priests handed you over to me. What have you done?"

N. Jesus answered,

† "My kingdom does not belong to this world. If my kingdom did belong to this world, my attendants would be fighting to keep me from being handed over to the Jews. But as it is, my kingdom is not here."

N. So Pilate said to him,

V. "Then you are a king?"

N. Jesus answered,

† "You say I am a king. For this I was born and for this I came into the world, to testify to the truth. Everyone who belongs to the truth listens to my voice."

N. Pilate said to him,

V. "What is truth?"

N. When he had said this, he again went out to the Jews and said to them,

V. "I find no guilt in him. But you have a custom that I release one prisoner to you at Passover. Do you want me to release to you the King of the Jews?"

N. They cried out again,

C. **"Not this one but Barabbas!"**

N. Now Barabbas was a revolutionary.

Then Pilate took Jesus and had him scourged. And the soldiers wove a crown out of thorns and placed it on his head, and clothed him in a purple cloak, and they came to him and said,

C. **"Hail, King of the Jews!"**

N. And they struck him repeatedly. Once more Pilate went out and said to them,

V. "Look, I am bringing him out to you, so that you may know that I find no guilt in him."

N. So Jesus came out, wearing the crown of thorns and the purple cloak. And Pilate said to them,

V. "Behold, the man!"

N. When the chief priests and the guards saw him they cried out,

C. **"Crucify him, crucify him!"**

N. Pilate said to them,

V. "Take him yourselves and crucify him. I find no guilt in him."

N. The Jews answered,

C. **"We have a law, and according to that law he ought to die, because he made himself the Son of God."**

N. Now when Pilate heard this statement, he became even more afraid, and went back into the praetorium and said to Jesus,

V. "Where are you from?"

N. Jesus did not answer him. So Pilate said to him,

V. "Do you not speak to me? Do you not know that I have power to release you and I have power to crucify you?"

N. Jesus answered him,

† "You would have no power over me if it had not been given to you from above. For this reason the one who handed me over to you has the greater sin."

N. Consequently, Pilate tried to release him; but the Jews cried out,

C. **"If you release him, you are not a Friend of Caesar. Everyone who makes himself a king opposes Caesar."**

N. When Pilate heard these words he brought Jesus out and seated him on the judge's bench in the place called Stone Pavement, in Hebrew, Gabbatha. It was preparation day for Passover, and it was about noon. And he said to the Jews,

V. "Behold, your king!"

N. They cried out,

C. **"Take him away, take him away! Crucify him!"**

N. Pilate said to them,

V. "Shall I crucify your king?"

N. The chief priests answered,

C. **"We have no king but Caesar."**

N. Then he handed him over to them to be crucified.

So they took Jesus, and, carrying the cross himself, he went out to what is called the Place of the Skull, in Hebrew, Golgotha. There they crucified him, and with him two others, one on either side, with Jesus in the middle. Pilate also had an inscription written and put on the cross. It read, "Jesus the Nazorean, the King of the Jews." Now many of the Jews read this inscription, because the place where Jesus was crucified was near the city; and it was written in Hebrew, Latin, and Greek. So the chief priests of the Jews said to Pilate,

C. **"Do not write 'The King of the Jews,' but that he said, 'I am the King of the Jews.'"**

N. Pilate answered,

V. "What I have written, I have written."

N. When the soldiers had crucified Jesus, they took his clothes and divided them into four shares, a share for each soldier. They also took his tunic, but the tunic was seamless, woven in one piece from the top down. So they said to one another,

C. **"Let's not tear it, but cast lots for it to see whose it will be,"**

N. in order that the passage of Scripture might be fulfilled that says:

*They divided my garments
among them,
and for my vesture they cast lots.*

This is what the soldiers did. Standing by the cross of Jesus were his mother and his mother's sister, Mary the wife of Clopas, and Mary of Magdala. When Jesus saw his mother and the disciple there whom he loved he said to his mother,

† "Woman, behold, your son."

N. Then he said to the disciple,

† "Behold, your mother."

N. And from that hour the disciple took her into his home.

After this, aware that everything was now finished, in order that the Scripture might be fulfilled, Jesus said,

† "I thirst."

N. There was a vessel filled with common wine. So they put a sponge soaked in wine on a sprig of hyssop and put it up to his mouth. When Jesus had taken the wine, he said,

† "It is finished."

N. And bowing his head, he handed over the spirit.

Here all kneel and pause for a short time.

N. Now since it was preparation day, in order that the bodies might not remain on the cross on the sabbath, for the sabbath day of that week was a solemn one, the Jews asked Pilate that their legs be broken and that they be taken down. So the soldiers came and broke the legs of the first and then of the other one who was crucified with Jesus. But when they came to Jesus and saw that he was already dead, they did not break his legs, but one soldier thrust his lance into his side, and immediately blood and water flowed out. An eyewitness has testified, and his testimony is true; he knows that he is speaking the truth, so that you also may come to believe. For this happened so that the Scripture passage might be fulfilled:

Not a bone of it will be broken.
And again another passage says:
They will look upon him whom they have pierced.

After this, Joseph of Arimathea, secretly a disciple of Jesus for fear of the Jews, asked Pilate if he could remove the body of Jesus. And Pilate permitted it. So he came and took his body. Nicodemus, the one who had first come to him at night, also came bringing a mixture of myrrh and aloes weighing about one hundred pounds. They took the body of Jesus and bound it with burial cloths along with the spices, according to the Jewish burial custom. Now in the place where he had been crucified there was a garden, and in the garden a new tomb, in which no one had yet been buried. So they laid Jesus there because of the Jewish preparation day; for the tomb was close by.

General Intercessions

The general intercessions conclude the Liturgy of the Word. The deacon , standing at the ambo, sings or says the introduction in which each intention is stated. All kneel and pray silently for some period of time, and then the priest, with hands outstretched, standing either at the chair or at the altar, sings or says the prayer. The people may either kneel or stand throughout the entire period of the general intercessions. For music, see #416.

Part II: Veneration of the Cross

The priest, clergy and faithful approach to venerate the cross in a kind of procession. They make a simple genuflection or perform some other appropriate sign of reverence according to local custom, for example, kissing the cross. During the veneration, appropriate songs may be sung (see #407, 408, 411, 414, 417).

Part III: Holy Communion

The deacon or the priest brings the vessel with the Blessed Sacrament from the place of reposition to the altar without any procession, while all stand in silence. After the Lord's Prayer is recited by all, communion is distributed to the faithful. An appropriate song may be sung during communion (see #409, 410, 412, 415).

A period of silence may be observed after communion. After a brief prayer, the priest dismisses the people and all depart in silence. The altar is stripped at a convenient time.

---

921   Easter Vigil — ABC

The entire celebration of the Easter Vigil should take place at night, that is, it should either begin after nightfall or end before the dawn of Sunday. (From the General Norms for the Liturgical Year and the Roman Calendar, no. 21) This Vigil is arranged in four parts: (I) after a brief service of light; (II) the Church meditates on all the wonderful things God has done for his people from the beginning; this is the Liturgy of the Word. As the day of resurrection approaches, new members of the Church are reborn in (III) baptism, and the whole Church is called to the table which the Lord prepared for his people through his death and resurrection; this (IV) is the Liturgy of the Eucharist.

PART I: SERVICE OF LIGHT

BLESSING OF THE FIRE AND LIGHTING OF THE EASTER CANDLE

A large fire is prepared in a suitable place. The people and the priest assemble there with the other ministers (carrying the Easter candle). The priest then greets the assembly in the usual manner and briefly instructs them about the vigil and blesses the fire. The Easter candle is then prepared and lighted from the new fire.

PROCESSION

The priest or the deacon then takes the Easter candle, lifts it high, and sings the acclamation, "Christ is our light." All respond, "Thanks be to God."

All process to the darkened church, led by the priest/deacon with the Easter candle. If incense is used, the thurifer goes before the priest/deacon. At the church door the priest/deacon lifts the candle high and sings the acclamation "Christ is our light" a second time. This is followed by the response, "Thanks be to God."

All light their candles from the Easter candle and continue in the procession. When the priest/deacon arrives before the altar, he faces the people and sings a third time, "Christ is our light," followed by the response, "Thanks be to God." Then the lights in the church are put on.

THE EASTER PROCLAMATION (EXSULTET)

If necessary, the Easter proclamation may be sung by one who is not a deacon or priest. In this case the words, "My dearest friends," up to the end of the introduction are omitted, as is the greeting "The Lord be with you." All stand and hold lighted candles. For music see "Exsultet" by Christopher Walker (edition 7151) or "Most Holy Night" by Dan Schutte (edition 10955).

After the Easter Proclamation, the candles are put aside and all are seated.

PART II: LITURGY OF THE WORD

There are seven readings from the Old Testament. After each reading a response is sung or said — or there may be a period of silent reflection. This is followed by a prayer said by the priest. The new Missale Romanum, editio typica tertia, states that all seven readings must be read "whenever it can be done, so that the character of a Vigil which takes place over some duration of time can be observed" (EV, no. 20). In cases where "grave pastoral circumstances demand it" at least three readings from the Old Testament should be chosen, always including Exodus 14 (EV, no. 21). Before the readings begin, the priest speaks to the people in these or similar words:

Dear friends in Christ, . . . the saving work he has begun in us.

FIRST READING

(Include bracketed text for Long Form)

In the beginning, when God created the heavens and the earth, [the earth was a formless wasteland, and darkness covered the abyss, while a mighty wind swept over the waters.

Then God said, "Let there be light," and there was light. God saw how good the light was. God then separated the light from the darkness. God called the light "day," and the darkness he called "night." Thus evening came, and morning followed — the first day.

Then God said, "Let there be a dome in the middle of the waters, to separate one body of water from the other." And so it happened: God made the dome, and it separated the water above the dome from the water below it. God called the dome "the sky." Evening came, and morning followed — the second day.

Then God said, "Let the water under the sky be gathered into a single basin, so that the dry land may appear." And so it happened: the water under the sky was gathered into its basin, and the dry land appeared. God called the dry land "the earth," and the basin of the water he called "the sea." God saw how good it was.

Then God said, "Let the earth bring forth vegetation: every kind of plant that bears seed and every kind of fruit tree on earth that bears fruit with its seed in it." And so it happened: the earth brought forth every kind of plant that bears seed and every kind of fruit tree on earth that bears fruit with its seed in it. God saw how good it was. Evening came, and morning followed — the third day.

Then God said: "Let there be lights in the dome of the sky, to separate day from night. Let them mark the fixed times, the days and the years, and serve as luminaries in the dome of the sky, to shed light upon the earth." And so it happened: God made the two great lights, the greater one to govern the day, and the lesser one to govern the night; and he made the stars. God set them in the dome of the sky, to shed light upon the earth, to govern the day and the night, and to separate the light from the darkness. God saw how good it was. Evening came, and morning followed — the fourth day.

Then God said, "Let the water teem with an abundance of living creatures, and on the earth let birds fly beneath the dome of the sky." And so it happened: God created the great sea monsters and all kinds of swimming creatures with which the water teems, and all kinds of winged birds. God saw how good it was, and God blessed them, saying, "Be fertile, multiply, and fill the water of the seas; and let the birds multiply on the earth." Evening came, and morning followed — the fifth day.

Then God said, "Let the earth bring forth all kinds of living creatures: cattle, creeping things, and wild animals of all kinds." And so it happened: God made all kinds of wild animals, all kinds of cattle, and all kinds of creeping things of the earth. God saw how good it was. Then] God said: "Let us make man in our image, after our likeness. Let them have dominion over the fish of the sea, the birds of the air, and the cattle, and over all the wild animals and all the creatures that crawl on the ground."

God created man in his image;
in the image of God he created him;
male and female he created them.
God blessed them, saying: "Be fertile and multiply; fill the earth and subdue it. Have dominion over the fish of the sea, the birds of the air, and all the living things that move on the earth." God also said: "See, I give you every seed-bearing plant all over the earth and every tree that has seed-bearing fruit on it to be your food; and to all the animals of the land, all the birds of the air, and all the living creatures that crawl on the ground, I give all the green plants for food." And so it happened. God looked at everything he had made, and he found it very good. [Evening came, and

morning followed — the sixth day.
Thus the heavens and the earth and all their array were completed. Since on the seventh day God was finished with the work he had been doing, he rested on the seventh day from all the work he had undertaken.]

RESPONSORIAL PSALM

Psalm 104:1–2, 5–6, 10, 12, 13–14, 24, 35

℟. Lord, send out your Spir - it, and re - new the face of the earth.

Music: John Schiavone, b. 1947, © 2001, OCP Publications.

▶ Bless the LORD, O my soul!
O LORD, my God, you are
great indeed!
You are clothed with majesty and glory,
robed in light as with a cloak. ℟.

▶ You fixed the earth upon its foundation,
not to be moved forever;
with the ocean, as with a garment, you
covered it;
above the mountains the waters
stood. ℟.

▶ You send forth springs into
the watercourses
that wind among the mountains.
Beside them the birds of heaven dwell;
from among the branches they send
forth their song. ℟.

▶ You water the mountains from
your palace;
the earth is replete with the fruit of
your works.
You raise grass for the cattle,
and vegetation for man's use,
producing bread from the earth. ℟.

▶ How manifold are your works, O LORD!
In wisdom you have wrought
them all —
the earth is full of your creatures.
Bless the LORD, O my soul! ℟.

OR

RESPONSORIAL PSALM

Psalm 33:4–5, 6–7, 12–13, 20–22

℟. The earth is full of [the good - ness,] the good - ness of the Lord.

Music: John Schiavone, b. 1947, © 2001, OCP Publications.

▶ Upright is the word of the LORD,
and all his works are trustworthy.
He loves justice and right;
of the kindness of the LORD the
earth is full. ℟.

▶ By the word of the LORD the heavens
were made;
by the breath of his mouth all
their host.
He gathers the waters of the sea as in
a flask;
in cellars he confines the deep. ℟.

▶ Blessed the nation whose God is
the LORD,
the people he has chosen for his
own inheritance.
From heaven the LORD looks down;
he sees all mankind. ℟.

▶ Our soul waits for the LORD,
who is our help and our shield.
May your kindness, O LORD, be
upon us
who have put our hope in you. ℟.

SECOND READING
Genesis 22:1–18 or 22:1–2, 9a, 10–13, 15–18

(Include bracketed text for Long Form)

God put Abraham to the test. He called to him, "Abraham!" "Here I am," he replied. Then God said: "Take your son Isaac, your only one, whom you love, and go to the land of Moriah. There you shall offer him up as a holocaust on a height that I will point out to you." [Early the next morning Abraham saddled his donkey, took with him his son Isaac and two of his servants as well, and with the wood that he had cut for the holocaust, set out for the place of which God had told him.

On the third day Abraham got sight of the place from afar. Then he said to his servants: "Both of you stay here with the donkey, while the boy and I go on over yonder. We will worship and then come back to you." Thereupon Abraham took the wood for the holocaust and laid it on his son Isaac's shoulders, while he himself carried the fire and the knife. As the two walked on together, Isaac spoke to his father Abraham: "Father!" Isaac said. "Yes, son," he replied. Isaac continued, "Here are the fire and the wood, but where is the sheep for the holocaust?" "Son," Abraham answered, "God himself will provide the sheep for the holocaust." Then the two continued going forward.]

When they came to the place of which God had told him, Abraham built an altar there and arranged the wood on it. [Next he tied up his son Isaac, and put him on top of the wood on the altar.] Then he reached out and took the knife to slaughter his son. But the LORD's messenger called to him from heaven, "Abraham, Abraham!" "Here I am," he answered. "Do not lay your hand on the boy," said the messenger. "Do not do the least thing to him. I know now how devoted you are to God, since you did not withhold from me your own beloved son." As Abraham looked about, he spied a ram caught by its horns in the thicket. So he went and took the ram and offered it up as a holocaust in place of his son. [Abraham named the site Yahweh-yireh; hence people now say, "On the mountain the LORD will see."]

Again the LORD's messenger called to Abraham from heaven and said: "I swear by myself, declares the LORD, that because you acted as you did in not withholding from me your beloved son, I will bless you abundantly and make your descendants as countless as the stars of the sky and the sands of the seashore; your descendants shall take possession of the gates of their enemies, and in your descendants all the nations of the earth shall find blessing — all this because you obeyed my command."

RESPONSORIAL PSALM
Psalm 16:5, 8, 9–10, 11

℟. You are my in - her - i - tance, O Lord.

Music: John Schiavone, b. 1947, © 2001, OCP Publications.

▶ O LORD, my allotted portion and
    my cup,
  you it is who hold fast my lot.
I set the LORD ever before me;
  with him at my right hand I shall not
    be disturbed. ℟.

▶ Therefore my heart is glad and my
    soul rejoices,
  my body, too, abides in confidence;
because you will not abandon my soul
    to the netherworld,
  nor will you suffer your faithful one
    to undergo corruption. ℟.

▶ You will show me the path to life,
    fullness of joys in your presence,
    the delights at your right hand
       forever. ℟.

THIRD READING

Exodus 14:15—15:1

The LORD said to Moses, "Why are you crying out to me? Tell the Israelites to go forward. And you, lift up your staff and, with hand outstretched over the sea, split the sea in two, that the Israelites may pass through it on dry land. But I will make the Egyptians so obstinate that they will go in after them. Then I will receive glory through Pharaoh and all his army, his chariots and charioteers. The Egyptians shall know that I am the LORD, when I receive glory through Pharaoh and his chariots and charioteers."

The angel of God, who had been leading Israel's camp, now moved and went around behind them. The column of cloud also, leaving the front, took up its place behind them, so that it came between the camp of the Egyptians and that of Israel. But the cloud now became dark, and thus the night passed without the rival camps coming any closer together all night long. Then Moses stretched out his hand over the sea, and the LORD swept the sea with a strong east wind throughout the night and so turned it into dry land. When the water was thus divided, the Israelites marched into the midst of the sea on dry land, with the water like a wall to their right and to their left.

The Egyptians followed in pursuit; all Pharaoh's horses and chariots and charioteers went after them right into the midst of the sea. In the night watch just before dawn the LORD cast through the column of the fiery cloud upon the Egyptian force a glance that threw it into a panic; and he so clogged their chariot wheels that they could hardly drive. With that the Egyptians sounded the retreat before Israel, because the LORD was fighting for them against the Egyptians.

Then the LORD told Moses, "Stretch out your hand over the sea, that the water may flow back upon the Egyptians, upon their chariots and their charioteers." So Moses stretched out his hand over the sea, and at dawn the sea flowed back to its normal depth. The Egyptians were fleeing head on toward the sea, when the LORD hurled them into its midst. As the water flowed back, it covered the chariots and the charioteers of Pharaoh's whole army which had followed the Israelites into the sea. Not a single one of them escaped. But the Israelites had marched on dry land through the midst of the sea, with the water like a wall to their right and to their left. Thus the LORD saved Israel on that day from the power of the Egyptians. When Israel saw the Egyptians lying dead on the seashore and beheld the great power that the LORD had shown against the Egyptians, they feared the LORD and believed in him and in his servant Moses.

Then Moses and the Israelites sang this song to the LORD:
    I will sing to the LORD, for he is
       gloriously triumphant;
    horse and chariot he has cast into
       the sea.

RESPONSORIAL PSALM

Exodus 15:1–2, 3–4, 5–6, 17–18

℟. Let us sing to the Lord; he has cov-ered him-self in glo - ry, [in glo - ry.]

Music: John Schiavone, b. 1947, © 2001, OCP Publications.

▶ I will sing to the LORD, for he is
    gloriously triumphant;
    horse and chariot he has cast into
      the sea.
My strength and my courage is
    the LORD,
    and he has been my savior.
He is my God, I praise him;
    the God of my father, I extol him. ℟.

▶ The LORD is a warrior,
    LORD is his name!
Pharaoh's chariots and army he hurled
    into the sea;
    the elite of his officers were
      submerged in the Red Sea. ℟.

▶ The flood waters covered them,
    they sank into the depths like a stone.
Your right hand, O LORD, magnificent
    in power,
    your right hand, O LORD, has
      shattered the enemy. ℟.

▶ You brought in the people
    you redeemed
    and planted them on the mountain
      of your inheritance —
the place where you made your seat,
    O LORD,
    the sanctuary, LORD, which your
      hands established.
The LORD shall reign forever and ever. ℟.

FOURTH READING

Isaiah 54:5–14

The One who has become your
    husband is your Maker;
    his name is the LORD of hosts;
your redeemer is the Holy One of Israel,
    called God of all the earth.
The LORD calls you back,
    like a wife forsaken and grieved
      in spirit,
    a wife married in youth and then
      cast off,
    says your God.
For a brief moment I abandoned you,
    but with great tenderness I will take
      you back.
In an outburst of wrath, for a moment
    I hid my face from you;
but with enduring love I take pity on you,
    says the LORD, your redeemer.
This is for me like the days of Noah,
    when I swore that the waters of Noah
    should never again deluge the earth;
so I have sworn not to be angry with you,

or to rebuke you.
Though the mountains leave their place
    and the hills be shaken,
my love shall never leave you
    nor my covenant of peace be shaken,
    says the LORD, who has mercy on you.
O afflicted one, storm-battered
    and unconsoled,
    I lay your pavements in carnelians,
    and your foundations in sapphires;
I will make your battlements of rubies,
    your gates of carbuncles,
    and all your walls of precious stones.
All your children shall be taught by
    the LORD,
    and great shall be the peace of
    your children.
In justice shall you be established,
    far from the fear of oppression,
    where destruction cannot come
    near you.

RESPONSORIAL PSALM

Psalm 30:2, 4, 5–6, 11–12, 13

℟. I will praise you, Lord, for you have res - cued me.

Music: John Schiavone, b. 1947, © 2001, OCP Publications.

▸ I will extol you, O LORD, for you drew
  me clear
  and did not let my enemies rejoice
    over me.
  O LORD, you brought me up from the
    netherworld;
    you preserved me from among
      those going down into the pit. ℟.

▸ Sing praise to the LORD, you his
    faithful ones,
    and give thanks to his holy name.

For his anger lasts but a moment;
  a lifetime, his good will.
At nightfall, weeping enters in,
  but with the dawn, rejoicing. ℟.

▸ Hear, O LORD, and have pity on me;
  O LORD, be my helper.
You changed my mourning
    into dancing;
    O LORD, my God, forever will I give
    you thanks. ℟.

FIFTH READING

Isaiah 55:1–11

Thus says the LORD:
All you who are thirsty,
  come to the water!
You who have no money,
  come, receive grain and eat;
come, without paying and without cost,
  drink wine and milk!
Why spend your money for what is
    not bread,
  your wages for what fails to satisfy?
Heed me, and you shall eat well,
  you shall delight in rich fare.
Come to me heedfully,
  listen, that you may have life.
I will renew with you the everlasting
    covenant,
  the benefits assured to David.
As I made him a witness to the peoples,
  a leader and commander of nations,
so shall you summon a nation you
    knew not,
  and nations that knew you not shall
    run to you,
because of the LORD, your God,
  the Holy One of Israel, who has
    glorified you.

Seek the LORD while he may be found,
  call him while he is near.
Let the scoundrel forsake his way,
  and the wicked man his thoughts;
let him turn to the LORD for mercy;
  to our God, who is generous
    in forgiving.
For my thoughts are not your thoughts,
  nor are your ways my ways, says
    the LORD.
As high as the heavens are above
    the earth,
  so high are my ways above your ways
  and my thoughts above your thoughts.

For just as from the heavens
    the rain and snow come down
and do not return there
    till they have watered the earth,
    making it fertile and fruitful,
giving seed to the one who sows
    and bread to the one who eats,
so shall my word be
    that goes forth from my mouth;
my word shall not return to me void,
    but shall do my will,
    achieving the end for which I sent it.

RESPONSORIAL PSALM

Isaiah 12:2–3, 4bcd, 5–6

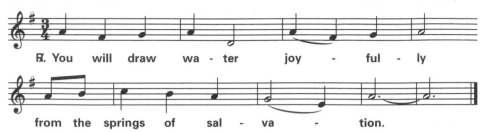

℟. You will draw wa - ter joy - ful - ly from the springs of sal - va - tion.

Music: John Schiavone, b. 1947, © 2001, OCP Publications.

▶ God indeed is my savior;
  I am confident and unafraid.
My strength and my courage is
    the LORD,
  and he has been my savior.
With joy you will draw water
  at the fountain of salvation. ℟.

▶ Give thanks to the LORD, acclaim
    his name;

among the nations make known
    his deeds,
  proclaim how exalted is his name. ℟.

▶ Sing praise to the LORD for his
    glorious achievement;
  let this be known throughout all
    the earth.
Shout with exultation, O city of Zion,
  for great in your midst
  is the Holy One of Israel! ℟.

SIXTH READING

Baruch 3:9–15, 32 — 4:4

Hear, O Israel, the commandments of life:
  listen, and know prudence!
How is it, Israel,
  that you are in the land of your foes,
  grown old in a foreign land,
defiled with the dead,
  accounted with those destined for
    the netherworld?
You have forsaken the fountain
    of wisdom!
  Had you walked in the way of God,
  you would have dwelt in
    enduring peace.
Learn where prudence is,
  where strength, where understanding;
that you may know also
  where are length of days, and life,
  where light of the eyes, and peace.
Who has found the place of wisdom,
  who has entered into her treasuries?

The One who knows all things
    knows her;
  he has probed her by his knowledge —
the One who established the earth for
    all time,
  and filled it with four-footed beasts;

he who dismisses the light, and it departs,
  calls it, and it obeys him trembling;
before whom the stars at their posts
  shine and rejoice;
when he calls them, they answer,
  "Here we are!"
  shining with joy for their Maker.
Such is our God;
  no other is to be compared to him:
he has traced out the whole way
    of understanding,
  and has given her to Jacob, his servant,
  to Israel, his beloved son.

Since then she has appeared on earth,
  and moved among people.
She is the book of the precepts of God,
  the law that endures forever;
all who cling to her will live,
  but those will die who forsake her.
Turn, O Jacob, and receive her:
  walk by her light toward splendor.
Give not your glory to another,
  your privileges to an alien race.
Blessed are we, O Israel;
  for what pleases God is known to us!

RESPONSORIAL PSALM

Psalm 19:8, 9, 10, 11

℟. **Lord, you have the words of ev - er - last - ing life.**

Music: John Schiavone, b. 1947, © 2001, OCP Publications.

▶ The law of the LORD is perfect,
   refreshing the soul;
 the decree of the LORD is trustworthy,
   giving wisdom to the simple. ℟.

▶ The precepts of the LORD are right,
   rejoicing the heart;
 the command of the LORD is clear,
   enlightening the eye. ℟.

▶ The fear of the LORD is pure,
   enduring forever;
 the ordinances of the LORD are true,
   all of them just. ℟.

▶ They are more precious than gold,
   than a heap of purest gold;
 sweeter also than syrup
   or honey from the comb. ℟.

SEVENTH READING

Ezekiel 36:16–17a, 18–28

The word of the LORD came to me, saying: Son of man, when the house of Israel lived in their land, they defiled it by their conduct and deeds. Therefore I poured out my fury upon them because of the blood that they poured out on the ground, and because they defiled it with idols. I scattered them among the nations, dispersing them over foreign lands; according to their conduct and deeds I judged them. But when they came among the nations wherever they came, they served to profane my holy name, because it was said of them: "These are the people of the LORD, yet they had to leave their land." So I have relented because of my holy name which the house of Israel profaned among the nations where they came. Therefore say to the house of Israel: Thus says the Lord GOD: Not for your sakes do I act, house of Israel, but for the sake of my holy name, which you profaned among the nations to which you came. I will prove the holiness of my great name, profaned among the nations, in whose midst you have profaned it. Thus the nations shall know that I am the LORD, says the Lord GOD, when in their sight I prove my holiness through you. For I will take you away from among the nations, gather you from all the foreign lands, and bring you back to your own land. I will sprinkle clean water upon you to cleanse you from all your impurities, and from all your idols I will cleanse you. I will give you a new heart and place a new spirit within you, taking from your bodies your stony hearts and giving you natural hearts. I will put my spirit within you and make you live by my statutes, careful to observe my decrees. You shall live in the land I gave your fathers; you shall be my people, and I will be your God.

RESPONSORIAL PSALM

(When baptism is celebrated)   *Psalms 42:3, 5; 43:3, 4*

R. Like a deer that longs for run-ning streams,
my soul longs for you, my God.

Music: John Schiavone, b. 1947, © 2001, OCP Publications.

▶ Athirst is my soul for God, the
living God.
When shall I go and behold the face
of God? R.

▶ I went with the throng
and led them in procession to the
house of God,
amid loud cries of joy and
thanksgiving,
with the multitude keeping festival. R.

▶ Send forth your light and your fidelity;
they shall lead me on
and bring me to your holy mountain,
to your dwelling-place. R.

▶ Then will I go in to the altar of God,
the God of my gladness and joy;
then will I give you thanks upon
the harp,
O God, my God! R.

OR

RESPONSORIAL PSALM

(When baptism is not celebrated)   *Isaiah 12:2–3, 4bcd, 5–6*

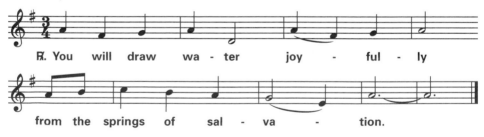

R. You will draw wa-ter joy-ful-ly
from the springs of sal-va-tion.

Music: John Schiavone, b. 1947, © 2001, OCP Publications.

▶ God indeed is my savior;
I am confident and unafraid.
My strength and my courage is
the LORD,
and he has been my savior.
With joy you will draw water
at the fountain of salvation. R.

▶ Give thanks to the LORD, acclaim
his name;
among the nations make known
his deeds,
proclaim how exalted is his name. R.

▶ Sing praise to the LORD for his
glorious achievement;
let this be known throughout all
the earth.
Shout with exultation, O city of Zion,
for great in your midst
is the Holy One of Israel! R.

OR

RESPONSORIAL PSALM
(When baptism is not celebrated)   Psalm 51:12–13, 14–15, 18–19

℟. Cre - ate   a   clean   heart   in   me,   O   God.

Music: John Schiavone, b. 1947, © 2001, OCP Publications.

▸ A clean heart create for me, O God,
  and a steadfast spirit renew
      within me.
  Cast me not out from your presence,
  and your Holy Spirit take not
      from me. ℟.

▸ Give me back the joy of your salvation,
  and a willing spirit sustain in me.

I will teach transgressors your ways,
  and sinners shall return to you. ℟.

▸ For you are not pleased with sacrifices;
  should I offer a holocaust, you
      would not accept it.
  My sacrifice, O God, is a contrite spirit;
  a heart contrite and humbled,
      O God, you will not spurn. ℟.

After the last reading from the Old Testament with its responsory and prayer, the altar candles are lighted, and the priest intones the "Gloria," which is taken up by all present (for music see #149, 176, 184, 194, 206, 218, 239, 259–265). The church bells are rung, according to local custom.

PRAYER

EPISTLE   *Romans 6:3–11*

Brothers and sisters: Are you unaware that we who were baptized into Christ Jesus were baptized into his death? We were indeed buried with him through baptism into death, so that, just as Christ was raised from the dead by the glory of the Father, we too might live in newness of life.

For if we have grown into union with him through a death like his, we shall also be united with him in the resurrection. We know that our old self was crucified with him, so that our sinful body might be done away with, that we might no longer be in slavery to sin. For a dead person has been absolved from sin. If, then, we have died with Christ, we believe that we shall also live with him. We know that Christ, raised from the dead, dies no more; death no longer has power over him. As to his death, he died to sin once and for all; as to his life, he lives for God. Consequently, you too must think of yourselves as being dead to sin and living for God in Christ Jesus.

RESPONSORIAL PSALM*   *Psalm 118:1–2, 16–17, 22–23*

℟. Al - le - lu - ia,   al - le - lu - ia,   al - le - lu - ia.

Music: John Schiavone, b. 1947, © 2001, OCP Publications.

▸ Give thanks to the LORD, for he is good,
  for his mercy endures forever.

Let the house of Israel say,
  "His mercy endures forever." ℟.

*For performance instructions, see the Missale Romanum, *editio typica tertia (EV, no. 34).*

℟. Alleluia, alleluia, alleluia.

▶ The right hand of the LORD has struck
with power;
the right hand of the LORD is exalted.
I shall not die, but live,
and declare the works of the LORD. ℟.

▶ The stone which the builders rejected
has become the cornerstone.
By the LORD has this been done;
it is wonderful in our eyes. ℟.

GOSPEL READING — A
Matthew 28:1–10

After the sabbath, as the first day of the week was dawning, Mary Magdalene and the other Mary came to see the tomb. And behold, there was a great earthquake; for an angel of the Lord descended from heaven, approached, rolled back the stone, and sat upon it. His appearance was like lightning and his clothing was white as snow. The guards were shaken with fear of him and became like dead men. Then the angel said to the women in reply, "Do not be afraid! I know that you are seeking Jesus the crucified. He is not here, for he has been raised just as he said. Come and see the place where he lay. Then go quickly and tell his disciples, 'He has been raised from the dead, and he is going before you to Galilee; there you will see him.' Behold, I have told you." Then they went away quickly from the tomb, fearful yet overjoyed, and ran to announce this to his disciples. And behold, Jesus met them on their way and greeted them. They approached, embraced his feet, and did him homage. Then Jesus said to them, "Do not be afraid. Go tell my brothers to go to Galilee, and there they will see me."

GOSPEL READING — B
Mark 16:1–7

When the sabbath was over, Mary Magdalene, Mary, the mother of James, and Salome bought spices so that they might go and anoint him. Very early when the sun had risen, on the first day of the week, they came to the tomb. They were saying to one another, "Who will roll back the stone for us from the entrance to the tomb?" When they looked up, they saw that the stone had been rolled back; it was very large. On entering the tomb they saw a young man sitting on the right side, clothed in a white robe, and they were utterly amazed. He said to them, "Do not be amazed! You seek Jesus of Nazareth, the crucified. He has been raised; he is not here. Behold the place where they laid him. But go and tell his disciples and Peter, 'He is going before you to Galilee; there you will see him, as he told you.'"

GOSPEL READING — C
Luke 24:1–12

At daybreak on the first day of the week the women who had come from Galilee with Jesus took the spices they had prepared and went to the tomb. They found the stone rolled away from the tomb; but when they entered, they did not find the body of the Lord Jesus. While they were puzzling over this, behold, two men in dazzling garments appeared to them. They were terrified and bowed their faces to the ground. They said to them, "Why do you seek the living one among the dead? He is not here, but he has been raised. Remember what he said to you while he was still in Galilee, that the Son of Man must be handed over to sinners and be crucified, and rise on the third day." And they remembered his words. Then they returned from the tomb and announced all these things to the eleven and to all the others. The women were Mary

Magdalene, Joanna, and Mary the mother of James; the others who accompanied them also told this to the apostles, but their story seemed like nonsense and they did not believe them.

But Peter got up and ran to the tomb, bent down, and saw the burial cloths alone; then he went home amazed at what had happened.

The homily follows the gospel. After the homily, the Sacraments of Baptism and Confirmation take place. If there are no candidates for baptism and confirmation, the Renewal of Baptismal Promises occurs instead.

PART III: CELEBRATION OF THE SACRAMENTS OF INITIATION

CELEBRATION OF BAPTISM

Following the homily the deacon or another minister calls the candidates for baptism, along with their godparents, forth from the assembly. The invitation to prayer and the Litany of the Saints follow (for music see #419, 525). When there are no baptisms and the font is not to be blessed, the Litany of the Saints is omitted and the blessing of water takes place at once.

BLESSING OF THE WATER

Facing the font (or vessel) containing the water, the celebrant then blesses the water which will be used for baptism. Before continuing, the celebrant pauses and touches the water with his right hand, or he may instead lower the Easter candle into the water once or three times, then hold it there for the remainder of the blessing. If the Easter candle has been held in the water during the blessing, the celebrant then raises it and the people sing a suitable acclamation (see #252, 255, 541). If there are no candidates for baptism, continue with the Renewal of Baptismal Promises.

RENUNCIATION OF SIN AND PROFESSION OF FAITH

The celebrant then asks the candidates to renounce sin. Then the celebrant, informed again of each baptismal candidate's name by the godparents, asks each of them (or the group as a whole, if it is large) to profess his or her faith.

BAPTISM

Immediately after his or her profession of faith, the celebrant baptizes each candidate either by a threefold immersion or pouring of water using the words, "N., I baptize you in the name of the Father, and of the Son, and of the Holy Spirit."

After each baptism, the assembly may sing a suitable acclamation (for music see #538, 541–548). If there are great numbers to be baptized, the baptisms may be accompanied by singing, readings from Scripture or silent prayer.

ANNOINTING AFTER BAPTISM AND CLOTHING WITH A BAPTISMAL GARMENT

If the confirmation of those baptized is separated from their baptism, the celebrant anoints them immediately. The newly baptized are then clothed with baptismal garments (this rite is optional and may be omitted). At the words "Receive this baptismal garment" the godparents place the garment on the newly baptized.

PRESENTATION OF A LIGHTED CANDLE

A godparent of each of the newly baptized goes to the celebrant, lights a candle from the Easter candle, then presents it to the newly baptized.

RENEWAL OF BAPTISMAL PROMISES

After the celebration of baptism the celebrant invites all those present, including the candidates for reception into full communion, to renew their baptismal promises. During the renewal, all stand and hold lighted candles. After all renounce sin, the celebrant then continues with the Profession of Faith.

Following this, the celebrant sprinkles the whole assembly with the blessed baptismal water, while all sing a song that is baptismal in character (for music see #252–255, 543).

If there are no candidates for reception into full communion, continue with the Celebration of Confirmation below.

CELEBRATION OF RECEPTION

The celebrant invites the candidates for reception, along with their sponsors, to come into the sanctuary and before the community to make a profession of faith. Then the candidates with their sponsors go individually to the celebrant, to be received into the full communion of the Catholic Church.

CELEBRATION OF CONFIRMATION

The newly baptized with their godparents and, if they have not received the sacrament of Confirmation, the newly received with their sponsors, now stand before the celebrant. After a brief prayer, each candidate, with godparents or sponsors, goes to the celebrant (or, if circumstances require, the celebrant may go to the candidates). Either or both godparents and sponsors place the right hand on the shoulder of the candidate; a godparent or a sponsor gives the candidate's name to the minister of the sacrament. The minister anoints each candidate using the words, "N., be sealed with the Gift of the Holy Spirit."

During the conferral of the sacrament an appropriate song may be sung (for music, see #453–465, 551). After all have received the sacrament, the newly confirmed as well as the godparents and sponsors return to their places in the assembly.

Since the Profession of Faith is not said, the General Intercessions begin immediately. The rite continues with the Liturgy of the Eucharist.

---

922   EASTER SUNDAY — ABC
THE RESURRECTION OF THE LORD

FIRST READING   *Acts of the Apostles 10:34a, 37–43*

Peter proceeded to speak and said: "You know what has happened all over Judea, beginning in Galilee after the baptism that John preached, how God anointed Jesus of Nazareth with the Holy Spirit and power. He went about doing good and healing all those oppressed by the devil, for God was with him. We are witnesses of all that he did both in the country of the Jews and in Jerusalem. They put him to death by hanging him on a tree. This man God raised on the third day and granted that he be visible, not to all the people, but to us, the witnesses chosen by God in advance, who ate and drank with him after he rose from the dead. He commissioned us to preach to the people and testify that he is the one appointed by God as judge of the living and the dead. To him all the prophets bear witness, that everyone who believes in him will receive forgiveness of sins through his name.

RESPONSORIAL PSALM   *Psalm 118:1–2, 16–17, 22–23*

℟. This is the day the Lord has made; let us re-joice and be glad.

Music: John Schiavone, b. 1947, © 2001, OCP Publications.

or: **Alleluia.**

▶ Give thanks to the LORD, for he is good,
for his mercy endures forever.
Let the house of Israel say,
"His mercy endures forever." **℟.**

▶ "The right hand of the LORD has
struck with power;
the right hand of the LORD is exalted.

I shall not die, but live,
and declare the works of the LORD." **℟.**

▶ The stone which the builders rejected
has become the cornerstone.
By the LORD has this been done;
it is wonderful in our eyes. **℟.**

SECOND READING   *Colossians 3:1–4*

Brothers and sisters: If then you were raised with Christ, seek what is above, where Christ is seated at the right hand of God. Think of what is above, not of what is on earth. For you have died, and your life is hidden with Christ in God. When Christ your life appears, then you too will appear with him in glory.

OR

SECOND READING   *1 Corinthians 5:6b–8*

Brothers and sisters: Do you not know that a little yeast leavens all the dough? Clear out the old yeast, so that you may become a fresh batch of dough, inasmuch as you are unleavened. For our paschal lamb, Christ, has been sacrificed. Therefore, let us celebrate the feast, not with the old yeast, the yeast of malice and wickedness, but with the unleavened bread of sincerity and truth.

SEQUENCE   *Victimae Paschali Laudes*

The General Instruction of the Roman Missal directs that the Sequence is to be sung before the Gospel Acclamation on Easter Sunday. For music, see #421, 422.

GOSPEL ACCLAMATION   *cf. 1 Corinthians 5:7b–8a*

℟. Al - le - lu - ia,   al - le - lu - ia,   al - le - lu - ia.

Music: John Schiavone, b. 1947, © 2001, OCP Publications.

▶ Christ, our paschal lamb, has been sacrificed;
let us then feast with joy in the Lord. **℟.**

(Options: At an afternoon or evening Mass, another Gospel may be read: Luke 24:13–35 [see 924]. The Gospel from the Easter Vigil [see 921] may also be read in place of the following Gospel at any time of the day.)

GOSPEL READING   *John 20:1–9*

On the first day of the week, Mary of Magdala came to the tomb early in the morning, while it was still dark, and saw the stone removed from the tomb. So she ran and went to Simon Peter and to the other disciple whom Jesus loved, and told them, "They have taken the Lord from the tomb, and we don't know where they put him." So Peter and the other disciple went out and came to the tomb. They both ran, but the other disciple ran faster than Peter and arrived at the tomb first; he bent down and saw the burial cloths there, but did not go in. When Simon Peter arrived after him, he went into the tomb and saw the burial cloths there, and the cloth that had covered his head, not with the burial cloths but rolled up in a separate place. Then the other disciple also went in, the one who had arrived at the tomb first, and he saw and believed. For they did not yet understand the Scripture that he had to rise from the dead.

RENEWAL OF BAPTISMAL PROMISES

The renewal of baptismal promises takes place at all Masses today. The Profession of Faith is omitted.

---

923 SECOND SUNDAY OF EASTER — ABC
DIVINE MERCY SUNDAY

FIRST READING — A   *Acts of the Apostles 2:42–47*

They devoted themselves to the teaching of the apostles and to the communal life, to the breaking of bread and to the prayers. Awe came upon everyone, and many wonders and signs were done through the apostles. All who believed were together and had all things in common; they would sell their property and possessions and divide them among all according to each one's need. Every day they devoted themselves to meeting together in the temple area and to breaking bread in their homes. They ate their meals with exultation and sincerity of heart, praising God and enjoying favor with all the people. And every day the Lord added to their number those who were being saved.

FIRST READING — B   *Acts of the Apostles 4:32–35*

The community of believers was of one heart and mind, and no one claimed that any of his possessions was his own, but they had everything in common. With great power the apostles bore witness to the resurrection of the Lord Jesus, and great favor was accorded them all. There was no needy person among them, for those who owned property or houses would sell them, bring the proceeds of the sale, and put them at the feet of the apostles, and they were distributed to each according to need.

FIRST READING — C   *Acts of the Apostles 5:12–16*

Many signs and wonders were done among the people at the hands of the apostles. They were all together in Solomon's portico. None of the others dared to join them, but the people esteemed them. Yet more than ever, believers in the Lord, great numbers of men and women, were added to them. Thus they even carried the sick out into the streets and laid them on cots and mats so that when Peter came by, at least his shadow might fall on one or another of them. A large number of people from the towns in the vicinity of Jerusalem also gathered, bringing the sick and those disturbed by unclean spirits, and they were all cured.

RESPONSORIAL PSALM

Psalm 118:2–4, 13–15, 22–24

℟. **Give thanks to the Lord for he is good, his love is ev - er - last - ing.**

Music: John Schiavone, b. 1947, © 2001, OCP Publications.

or: **Alleluia.**

▶ Let the house of Israel say,
  "His mercy endures forever."
Let the house of Aaron say,
  "His mercy endures forever."
Let those who fear the LORD say,
  "His mercy endures forever." ℟.

▶ I was hard pressed and was falling,
  but the LORD helped me.
My strength and my courage is
  the LORD,

and he has been my savior.
The joyful shout of victory
  in the tents of the just: ℟.

▶ The stone which the builders rejected
  has become the cornerstone.
By the LORD has this been done;
  it is wonderful in our eyes.
This is the day the LORD has made;
  let us be glad and rejoice in it. ℟.

SECOND READING — A

1 Peter 1:3–9

Blessed be the God and Father of our Lord Jesus Christ, who in his great mercy gave us a new birth to a living hope through the resurrection of Jesus Christ from the dead, to an inheritance that is imperishable, undefiled, and unfading, kept in heaven for you who by the power of God are safeguarded through faith, to a salvation that is ready to be revealed in the final time. In this you rejoice, although now for a little while you may have to suffer through various trials, so that the genuineness of your faith, more precious than gold that is perishable even though tested by fire, may prove to be for praise, glory, and honor at the revelation of Jesus Christ. Although you have not seen him you love him; even though you do not see him now yet believe in him, you rejoice with an indescribable and glorious joy, as you attain the goal of your faith, the salvation of your souls.

SECOND READING — B

1 John 5:1–6

Beloved: Everyone who believes that Jesus is the Christ is begotten by God, and everyone who loves the Father loves also the one begotten by him. In this way we know that we love the children of God when we love God and obey his commandments. For the love of God is this, that we keep his commandments. And his commandments are not burdensome, for whoever is begotten by God conquers the world. And the victory that conquers the world is our faith. Who indeed is the victor over the world but the one who believes that Jesus is the Son of God?

This is the one who came through water and blood, Jesus Christ, not by water alone, but by water and blood. The Spirit is the one that testifies, and the Spirit is truth.

SECOND READING — C

Revelation 1:9–11a, 12–13, 17–19

I, John, your brother, who share with you the distress, the kingdom, and the endurance we have in Jesus, found myself on the island called Patmos because I proclaimed God's word and gave testimony to Jesus. I was caught up in spirit on the Lord's day and heard behind me a voice as loud as a trumpet, which said, "Write on a scroll what you see." Then I turned to see whose voice it was that spoke to me, and when I turned, I saw seven gold lampstands and in the midst of the lampstands one like a son of man, wearing an ankle-length robe, with a gold sash around his chest.

When I caught sight of him, I fell down at his feet as though dead. He touched me with his right hand and said, "Do not be afraid. I am the first and the last, the one who lives. Once I was dead, but now I am alive forever and ever. I hold the keys to death and the netherworld. Write down, therefore, what you have seen, and what is happening, and what will happen afterwards."

GOSPEL ACCLAMATION

John 20:29

℟. Al - le - lu - ia,   al - le - lu - ia,   al - le - lu - ia.

Music: John Schiavone, b. 1947, © 2001, OCP Publications.

▶ You believe in me, Thomas, because you have seen me, says the Lord; blessed are they who have not seen me, but still believe! ℟.

GOSPEL READING

John 20:19–31

On the evening of that first day of the week, when the doors were locked, where the disciples were, for fear of the Jews, Jesus came and stood in their midst and said to them, "Peace be with you." When he had said this, he showed them his hands and his side. The disciples rejoiced when they saw the Lord. Jesus said to them again, "Peace be with you. As the Father has sent me, so I send you." And when he had said this, he breathed on them and said to them, "Receive the Holy Spirit. Whose sins you forgive are forgiven them, and whose sins you retain are retained."

Thomas, called Didymus, one of the Twelve, was not with them when Jesus came. So the other disciples said to him, "We have seen the Lord." But he said to them, "Unless I see the mark of the nails in his hands and put my finger into the nailmarks and put my hand into his side, I will not believe." Now a week later his disciples were again inside and Thomas was with them. Jesus came, although the doors were locked, and stood in their midst and said, "Peace be with you." Then he said to Thomas, "Put your finger here and see my hands, and bring your hand and put it into my side, and do not be unbelieving, but believe." Thomas answered and said to him, "My Lord and my God!" Jesus said to him, "Have you come to believe because you have seen me? Blessed are those who have not seen and have believed."

Now Jesus did many other signs in the presence of his disciples that are not written in this book. But these are written that you may come to believe that Jesus is the Christ, the Son of God, and that through this belief you may have life in his name.

THIRD SUNDAY OF EASTER — A   924

FIRST READING
Acts of the Apostles 2:14, 22–33

Then Peter stood up with the Eleven, raised his voice, and proclaimed: "You who are Jews, indeed all of you staying in Jerusalem. Let this be known to you, and listen to my words. You who are Israelites, hear these words. Jesus the Nazorean was a man commended to you by God with mighty deeds, wonders, and signs, which God worked through him in your midst, as you yourselves know. This man, delivered up by the set plan and foreknowledge of God, you killed, using lawless men to crucify him. But God raised him up, releasing him from the throes of death, because it was impossible for him to be held by it. For David says of him:

I saw the Lord ever before me,
with him at my right hand I shall
not be disturbed.
Therefore my heart has been glad and
my tongue has exulted;
my flesh, too, will dwell in hope,
because you will not abandon my

soul to the netherworld,
nor will you suffer your holy one to
see corruption.
You have made known to me the
paths of life;
you will fill me with joy in your
presence.

"My brothers, one can confidently say to you about the patriarch David that he died and was buried, and his tomb is in our midst to this day. But since he was a prophet and knew that God had sworn an oath to him that he would set one of his descendants upon his throne, he foresaw and spoke of the resurrection of the Christ, that neither was he abandoned to the netherworld nor did his flesh see corruption. God raised this Jesus; of this we are all witnesses. Exalted at the right hand of God, he received the promise of the Holy Spirit from the Father and poured him forth, as you see and hear."

RESPONSORIAL PSALM
Psalm 16:1–2, 5, 7–8, 9–10, 11

℞. Lord, you will show us the path of life.

Music: John Schiavone, b. 1947, © 2001, OCP Publications.

or: **Alleluia.**

▶ Keep me, O God, for in you
  I take refuge;
  I say to the LORD, "My LORD are you."
O LORD, my allotted portion and
  my cup,
  you it is who hold fast my lot. ℞.

▶ I bless the LORD who counsels me;
  even in the night my heart
  exhorts me.
I set the LORD ever before me;
  with him at my right hand I shall not
  be disturbed. ℞.

▶ Therefore my heart is glad and my
  soul rejoices,
  my body, too, abides in confidence;
because you will not abandon my soul
  to the netherworld,
  nor will you suffer your faithful one
  to undergo corruption. ℞.

▶ You will show me the path to life,
  abounding joy in your presence,
  the delights at your right hand
  forever. ℞.

SECOND READING

1 Peter 1:17–21

Beloved: If you invoke as Father him who judges impartially according to each one's works, conduct yourselves with reverence during the time of your sojourning, realizing that you were ransomed from your futile conduct, handed on by your ancestors, not with perishable things like silver or gold but with the precious blood of Christ as of a spotless unblemished lamb. He was known before the foundation of the world but revealed in the final time for you, who through him believe in God who raised him from the dead and gave him glory, so that your faith and hope are in God.

GOSPEL ACCLAMATION

cf. Luke 24:32

℞. Al - le - lu - ia, al - le - lu - ia, al - le - lu - ia.

Music: John Schiavone, b. 1947, © 2001, OCP Publications.

▶ Lord Jesus, open the Scriptures to us;
make our hearts burn while you speak to us. ℞.

GOSPEL READING

Luke 24:13–35

That very day, the first day of the week, two of Jesus' disciples were going to a village seven miles from Jerusalem called Emmaus, and they were conversing about all the things that had occurred. And it happened that while they were conversing and debating, Jesus himself drew near and walked with them, but their eyes were prevented from recognizing him. He asked them, "What are you discussing as you walk along?" They stopped, looking downcast. One of them, named Cleopas, said to him in reply, "Are you the only visitor to Jerusalem who does not know of the things that have taken place there in these days?" And he replied to them, "What sort of things?" They said to him, "The things that happened to Jesus the Nazarene, who was a prophet mighty in deed and word before God and all the people, how our chief priests and rulers both handed him over to a sentence of death and crucified him. But we were hoping that he would be the one to redeem Israel; and besides all this, it is now the third day since this took place. Some women from our group, however, have astounded us: they were at the tomb early in the morning and did not find his body; they came back and reported that they had indeed seen a vision of angels who announced that he was alive. Then some of those with us went to the tomb and found things just as the women had described, but him they did not see." And he said to them, "Oh, how foolish you are! How slow of heart to believe all that the prophets spoke! Was it not necessary that the Christ should suffer these things and enter into his glory?" Then beginning with Moses and all the prophets, he interpreted to them what referred to him in all the Scriptures. As they approached the village to which they were going, he gave the impression that he was going on farther. But they urged him, "Stay with us, for it is nearly evening and the day is almost over." So he went in to stay with them. And it happened that, while he was with them at table, he took bread, said the blessing, broke it, and gave it to them. With that their eyes were opened and they recognized him, but he vanished from their sight. Then they said to each other, "Were not our hearts burning within us while he spoke to us on the way and opened the Scriptures to us?" So they set out at once and returned to Jerusalem where they found gathered together the eleven and those with them who were saying, "The Lord has truly been raised and has appeared to Simon!" Then the two recounted what had taken place on the way and how he was made known to them in the breaking of bread.

THIRD SUNDAY OF EASTER — B   **925**

FIRST READING
Acts of the Apostles 3:13–15, 17–19

Peter said to the people: "The God of Abraham, the God of Isaac, and the God of Jacob, the God of our fathers, has glorified his servant Jesus, whom you handed over and denied in Pilate's presence when he had decided to release him. You denied the Holy and Righteous One and asked that a murderer be released to you. The author of life you put to death, but God raised him from the dead; of this we are witnesses. Now I know, brothers, that you acted out of ignorance, just as your leaders did; but God has thus brought to fulfillment what he had announced beforehand through the mouth of all the prophets, that his Christ would suffer. Repent, therefore, and be converted, that your sins may be wiped away."

RESPONSORIAL PSALM
Psalm 4:2, 4, 7–8, 9

℟. Lord, let your face shine on us.

Music: John Schiavone, b. 1947, © 2001, OCP Publications.

or: **Alleluia.**

▶ When I call, answer me, O my just God,
　you who relieve me when I am
　in distress;
　have pity on me, and hear my
　prayer! ℟.

▶ Know that the LORD does wonders for
　his faithful one;
　the LORD will hear me when I call
　upon him. ℟.

▶ O LORD, let the light of your
　countenance shine upon us!
　You put gladness into my heart. ℟.

▶ As soon as I lie down, I fall
　peacefully asleep,
　for you alone, O LORD,
　bring security to my dwelling. ℟.

SECOND READING
1 John 2:1–5a

My children, I am writing this to you so that you may not commit sin. But if anyone does sin, we have an Advocate with the Father, Jesus Christ the righteous one. He is expiation for our sins, and not for our sins only but for those of the whole world. The way we may be sure that we know him is to keep his commandments. Those who say, "I know him," but do not keep his commandments are liars, and the truth is not in them. But whoever keeps his word, the love of God is truly perfected in him.

GOSPEL ACCLAMATION

cf. Luke 24:32

℟. Al - le - lu - ia, al - le - lu - ia, al - le - lu - ia.

Music: John Schiavone, b. 1947, © 2001, OCP Publications.

▶ Lord Jesus, open the Scriptures to us;
  make our hearts burn while you speak to us. ℟.

GOSPEL READING

Luke 24:35–48

The two disciples recounted what had taken place on the way, and how Jesus was made known to them in the breaking of bread.

While they were still speaking about this, he stood in their midst and said to them, "Peace be with you." But they were startled and terrified and thought that they were seeing a ghost. Then he said to them, "Why are you troubled? And why do questions arise in your hearts? Look at my hands and my feet, that it is I myself. Touch me and see, because a ghost does not have flesh and bones as you can see I have." And as he said this, he showed them his hands and his feet. While they were still incredulous for joy and were amazed,

he asked them, "Have you anything here to eat?" They gave him a piece of baked fish; he took it and ate it in front of them.

He said to them, "These are my words that I spoke to you while I was still with you, that everything written about me in the law of Moses and in the prophets and psalms must be fulfilled." Then he opened their minds to understand the Scriptures. And he said to them, "Thus it is written that the Christ would suffer and rise from the dead on the third day and that repentance, for the forgiveness of sins, would be preached in his name to all the nations, beginning from Jerusalem. You are witnesses of these things."

---

926   THIRD SUNDAY OF EASTER — C

FIRST READING

Acts of the Apostles 5:27–32, 40b–41

When the captain and the court officers had brought the apostles in and made them stand before the Sanhedrin, the high priest questioned them, "We gave you strict orders, did we not, to stop teaching in that name? Yet you have filled Jerusalem with your teaching and want to bring this man's blood upon us." But Peter and the apostles said in reply, "We must obey God rather than men. The God of our ancestors raised Jesus, though you had him killed by

hanging him on a tree. God exalted him at his right hand as leader and savior to grant Israel repentance and forgiveness of sins. We are witnesses of these things, as is the Holy Spirit whom God has given to those who obey him."

The Sanhedrin ordered the apostles to stop speaking in the name of Jesus, and dismissed them. So they left the presence of the Sanhedrin, rejoicing that they had been found worthy to suffer dishonor for the sake of the name.

RESPONSORIAL PSALM *Psalm 30:2, 4, 5–6, 11–12, 13*

℟. I will praise you, Lord, for you have res - cued me.

Music: John Schiavone, b. 1947, © 2001, OCP Publications.

or: **Alleluia.**

▶ I will extol you, O LORD, for you drew
me clear
 and did not let my enemies rejoice
 over me.
O LORD, you brought me up from the
netherworld;
 you preserved me from among
 those going down into the pit. ℟.

▶ Sing praise to the LORD, you his
faithful ones,
 and give thanks to his holy name.

For his anger lasts but a moment;
 a lifetime, his good will.
At nightfall, weeping enters in,
 but with the dawn, rejoicing. ℟.

▶ Hear, O LORD, and have pity on me;
 O LORD, be my helper.
You changed my mourning
 into dancing;
 O LORD, my God, forever will I give
 you thanks. ℟.

SECOND READING *Revelation 5:11–14*

I, John, looked and heard the voices of
many angels who surrounded the
throne and the living creatures and the
elders. They were countless in number,
and they cried out in a loud voice:
 "Worthy is the Lamb that was slain
 to receive power and riches,
 wisdom and strength,
 honor and glory and blessing."
Then I heard every creature in heaven
and on earth and under the earth and

in the sea, everything in the universe,
cry out:
 "To the one who sits on the throne
 and to the Lamb
 be blessing and honor, glory
 and might,
 forever and ever."
The four living creatures answered,
"Amen," and the elders fell down and
worshiped.

GOSPEL ACCLAMATION

℟. Al - le - lu - ia,   al - le - lu - ia,   al - le - lu - ia.

Music: John Schiavone, b. 1947, © 2001, OCP Publications.

▶ Christ is risen, creator of all;
 he has shown pity on all people. ℟.

GOSPEL READING *John 21:1–19 or 21:1–14*

(Include bracketed text for Long Form)

At that time, Jesus revealed himself
again to his disciples at the Sea of
Tiberias. He revealed himself in this
way. Together were Simon Peter,

Thomas called Didymus, Nathanael
from Cana in Galilee, Zebedee's sons,
and two others of his disciples. Simon
Peter said to them, "I am going fishing."

They said to him, "We also will come with you." So they went out and got into the boat, but that night they caught nothing. When it was already dawn, Jesus was standing on the shore; but the disciples did not realize that it was Jesus. Jesus said to them, "Children, have you caught anything to eat?" They answered him, "No." So he said to them, "Cast the net over the right side of the boat and you will find something." So they cast it, and were not able to pull it in because of the number of fish. So the disciple whom Jesus loved said to Peter, "It is the Lord." When Simon Peter heard that it was the Lord, he tucked in his garment, for he was lightly clad, and jumped into the sea. The other disciples came in the boat, for they were not far from shore, only about a hundred yards, dragging the net with the fish. When they climbed out on shore, they saw a charcoal fire with fish on it and bread. Jesus said to them, "Bring some of the fish you just caught." So Simon Peter went over and dragged the net ashore full of one hundred fifty-three large fish. Even though there were so many, the net was not torn. Jesus said to them, "Come, have breakfast." And none of the disciples dared to ask him, "Who are you?" because they realized it was the Lord. Jesus came over and took the bread and gave it to them, and in like manner the fish. This was now the third time Jesus was revealed to his disciples after being raised from the dead.

[When they had finished breakfast, Jesus said to Simon Peter, "Simon, son of John, do you love me more than these?" Simon Peter answered him, "Yes, Lord, you know that I love you." Jesus said to him, "Feed my lambs." He then said to Simon Peter a second time, "Simon, son of John, do you love me?" Simon Peter answered him, "Yes, Lord, you know that I love you." Jesus said to him, "Tend my sheep." Jesus said to him the third time, "Simon, son of John, do you love me?" Peter was distressed that Jesus had said to him a third time, "Do you love me?" and he said to him, "Lord, you know everything; you know that I love you." Jesus said to him, "Feed my sheep. Amen, amen, I say to you, when you were younger, you used to dress yourself and go where you wanted; but when you grow old, you will stretch out your hands, and someone else will dress you and lead you where you do not want to go." He said this signifying by what kind of death he would glorify God. And when he had said this, he said to him, "Follow me."]

---

927   FOURTH SUNDAY OF EASTER — A

FIRST READING   *Acts of the Apostles 2:14a, 36–41*

Then Peter stood up with the Eleven, raised his voice, and proclaimed: "Let the whole house of Israel know for certain that God has made both Lord and Christ, this Jesus whom you crucified."

Now when they heard this, they were cut to the heart, and they asked Peter and the other apostles, "What are we to do, my brothers?" Peter said to them, "Repent and be baptized, every one of you, in the name of Jesus Christ for the forgiveness of your sins; and you will receive the gift of the Holy Spirit. For the promise is made to you and to your children and to all those far off, whomever the Lord our God will call." He testified with many other arguments, and was exhorting them, "Save yourselves from this corrupt generation." Those who accepted his message were baptized, and about three thousand persons were added that day.

RESPONSORIAL PSALM *Psalm 23:1–3a, 3b–4, 5, 6*

℟. The Lord is my shep-herd; there is noth-ing I shall want.

Music: John Schiavone, b. 1947, © 2001, OCP Publications.

or: **Alleluia.**

▶ The LORD is my shepherd; I shall
 not want.
 In verdant pastures he gives
  me repose;
 beside restful waters he leads me;
 he refreshes my soul. ℟.

▶ He guides me in right paths
 for his name's sake.
 Even though I walk in the dark valley
  I fear no evil; for you are at my side
 with your rod and your staff
  that give me courage. ℟.

▶ You spread the table before me
 in the sight of my foes;
 you anoint my head with oil;
  my cup overflows. ℟.

▶ Only goodness and kindness follow me
 all the days of my life;
 and I shall dwell in the house of
  the LORD
 for years to come. ℟.

SECOND READING *1 Peter 2:20b–25*

Beloved: If you are patient when you suffer for doing what is good, this is a grace before God. For to this you have been called, because Christ also suffered for you, leaving you an example that you should follow in his footsteps.

He committed no sin, and no deceit was found in his mouth.

When he was insulted, he returned no insult; when he suffered, he did not threaten; instead, he handed himself over to the one who judges justly. He himself bore our sins in his body upon the cross, so that, free from sin, we might live for righteousness. By his wounds you have been healed. For you had gone astray like sheep, but you have now returned to the shepherd and guardian of your souls.

GOSPEL ACCLAMATION *John 10:14*

℟. Al - le - lu - ia, al - le - lu - ia, al - le - lu - ia.

Music: John Schiavone, b. 1947, © 2001, OCP Publications.

▶ I am the good shepherd, says the Lord;
 I know my sheep, and mine know me. ℟.

GOSPEL READING *John 10:1–10*

Jesus said: "Amen, amen, I say to you, whoever does not enter a sheepfold through the gate but climbs over elsewhere is a thief and a robber. But whoever enters through the gate is the shepherd of the sheep. The gatekeeper opens it for him, and the sheep hear his voice, as the shepherd calls his own sheep by name and leads them out. When he has driven out all his own, he walks ahead of them, and the sheep follow him, because they recognize his voice. But they will not follow a stranger; they will run away from him, because they do not recognize the voice of strangers." Although Jesus used this figure of speech, the Pharisees did not realize what he was trying to tell them.

So Jesus said again, "Amen, amen,

I say to you, I am the gate for the sheep. All who came before me are thieves and robbers, but the sheep did not listen to them. I am the gate. Whoever enters through me will be saved, and will come in and go out and find pasture. A thief comes only to steal and slaughter and destroy; I came so that they might have life and have it more abundantly."

---

928 FOURTH SUNDAY OF EASTER — B

FIRST READING

Acts of the Apostles 4:8–12

Peter, filled with the Holy Spirit, said: "Leaders of the people and elders: If we are being examined today about a good deed done to a cripple, namely, by what means he was saved, then all of you and all the people of Israel should know that it was in the name of Jesus Christ the Nazarene whom you crucified, whom

God raised from the dead; in his name this man stands before you healed. He is *the stone rejected by you, the builders, which has become the cornerstone.* There is no salvation through anyone else, nor is there any other name under heaven given to the human race by which we are to be saved."

RESPONSORIAL PSALM

Psalm 118:1, 8–9, 21–23, 26, 28, 29

℟. The stone re-ject-ed by the build-ers has be - come the cor-ner-stone.

Music: John Schiavone, b. 1947, © 2001, OCP Publications.

or: **Alleluia.**

▶ Give thanks to the LORD, for he is good,
  for his mercy endures forever.
It is better to take refuge in the LORD
  than to trust in man.
It is better to take refuge in the LORD
  than to trust in princes. ℟.

▶ I will give thanks to you, for you have
  answered me
  and have been my savior.
The stone which the builders rejected
  has become the cornerstone.

By the LORD has this been done;
  it is wonderful in our eyes. ℟.

▶ Blessed is he who comes in the name
  of the LORD;
  we bless you from the house of
  the LORD.
I will give thanks to you, for you have
  answered me
  and have been my savior.
Give thanks to the LORD, for he is good;
  for his kindness endures forever. ℟.

SECOND READING

1 John 3:1–2

Beloved: See what love the Father has bestowed on us that we may be called the children of God. Yet so we are. The reason the world does not know us is that it did not know him. Beloved, we

are God's children now; what we shall be has not yet been revealed. We do know that when it is revealed we shall be like him, for we shall see him as he is.

GOSPEL ACCLAMATION

John 10:14

℟. Al - le - lu - ia,   al - le - lu - ia,   al - le - lu - ia.

Music: John Schiavone, b. 1947, © 2001, OCP Publications.

▸ I am the good shepherd, says the Lord;
I know my sheep, and mine know me. ℟.

GOSPEL READING

John 10:11–18

Jesus said: "I am the good shepherd. A good shepherd lays down his life for the sheep. A hired man, who is not a shepherd and whose sheep are not his own, sees a wolf coming and leaves the sheep and runs away, and the wolf catches and scatters them. This is because he works for pay and has no concern for the sheep. I am the good shepherd, and I know mine and mine know me, just as the Father knows me and I know the Father; and I will lay down my life for the sheep. I have other sheep that do not belong to this fold. These also I must lead, and they will hear my voice, and there will be one flock, one shepherd. This is why the Father loves me, because I lay down my life in order to take it up again. No one takes it from me, but I lay it down on my own. I have power to lay it down, and power to take it up again. This command I have received from my Father."

FOURTH SUNDAY OF EASTER — C   929

FIRST READING

Acts of the Apostles 13:14, 43–52

Paul and Barnabas continued on from Perga and reached Antioch in Pisidia. On the sabbath they entered the synagogue and took their seats. Many Jews and worshipers who were converts to Judaism followed Paul and Barnabas, who spoke to them and urged them to remain faithful to the grace of God.

On the following sabbath almost the whole city gathered to hear the word of the Lord. When the Jews saw the crowds, they were filled with jealousy and with violent abuse contradicted what Paul said. Both Paul and Barnabas spoke out boldly and said, "It was necessary that the word of God be spoken to you first, but since you reject it and condemn yourselves as unworthy of eternal life, we now turn to the Gentiles. For so the Lord has commanded us, *I have made you a light to the Gentiles, that you may be an instrument of salvation to the ends of the earth.*"

The Gentiles were delighted when they heard this and glorified the word of the Lord. All who were destined for eternal life came to believe, and the word of the Lord continued to spread through the whole region. The Jews, however, incited the women of prominence who were worshipers and the leading men of the city, stirred up a persecution against Paul and Barnabas, and expelled them from their territory. So they shook the dust from their feet in protest against them, and went to Iconium. The disciples were filled with joy and the Holy Spirit.

RESPONSORIAL PSALM

Psalm 100:1–2, 3, 5

℞. We are his peo-ple, the sheep of his flock, [the sheep of his flock.]

Music: John Schiavone, b. 1947, © 2001, OCP Publications.

or: Alleluia.

▶ Sing joyfully to the LORD, all you lands;
   serve the LORD with gladness;
   come before him with joyful song. ℞.

▶ Know that the LORD is God;
   he made us, his we are;
   his people, the flock he tends. ℞.

▶ The LORD is good:
   his kindness endures forever,
   and his faithfulness, to all
   generations. ℞.

SECOND READING

Revelation 7:9, 14b–17

I, John, had a vision of a great multitude, which no one could count, from every nation, race, people, and tongue. They stood before the throne and before the Lamb, wearing white robes and holding palm branches in their hands.

Then one of the elders said to me, "These are the ones who have survived the time of great distress; they have washed their robes and made them white in the blood of the Lamb.

"For this reason they stand before God's throne
   and worship him day and night in his temple.

The one who sits on the throne will shelter them.
They will not hunger or thirst anymore,
   nor will the sun or any heat strike them.
For the Lamb who is in the center of the throne
   will shepherd them
   and lead them to springs of life-giving water,
   and God will wipe away every tear from their eyes."

GOSPEL ACCLAMATION

John 10:14

℞. Al - le - lu - ia, al - le - lu - ia, al - le - lu - ia.

Music: John Schiavone, b. 1947, © 2001, OCP Publications.

▶ I am the good shepherd, says the Lord;
   I know my sheep, and mine know me. ℞.

GOSPEL READING

John 10:27–30

Jesus said: "My sheep hear my voice; I know them, and they follow me. I give them eternal life, and they shall never perish. No one can take them out of my hand. My Father, who has given them to me, is greater than all, and no one can take them out of the Father's hand. The Father and I are one."

FIFTH SUNDAY OF EASTER — A   **930**

FIRST READING   *Acts of the Apostles 6:1–7*

As the number of disciples continued to grow, the Hellenists complained against the Hebrews because their widows were being neglected in the daily distribution. So the Twelve called together the community of the disciples and said, "It is not right for us to neglect the word of God to serve at table. Brothers, select from among you seven reputable men, filled with the Spirit and wisdom, whom we shall appoint to this task, whereas we shall devote ourselves to prayer and to the ministry of the word."

The proposal was acceptable to the whole community, so they chose Stephen, a man filled with faith and the Holy Spirit, also Philip, Prochorus, Nicanor, Timon, Parmenas, and Nicholas of Antioch, a convert to Judaism. They presented these men to the apostles who prayed and laid hands on them. The word of God continued to spread, and the number of the disciples in Jerusalem increased greatly; even a large group of priests were becoming obedient to the faith.

RESPONSORIAL PSALM   *Psalm 33:1–2, 4–5, 18–19*

℟. Lord, let your mer-cy be on us,   as we place our trust in you.

Music: John Schiavone, b. 1947, © 2001, OCP Publications.

or: **Alleluia.**

▶ Exult, you just, in the LORD;
    praise from the upright is fitting.
Give thanks to the LORD on the harp;
    with the ten-stringed lyre chant
        his praises. ℟.

▶ Upright is the word of the LORD,
    and all his works are trustworthy.
He loves justice and right;
    of the kindness of the LORD the
        earth is full. ℟.

▶ See, the eyes of the LORD are
        upon those who fear him,
    upon those who hope for
        his kindness,
to deliver them from death
    and preserve them in spite
        of famine. ℟.

SECOND READING   *1 Peter 2:4–9*

Beloved: Come to him, a living stone, rejected by human beings but chosen and precious in the sight of God, and, like living stones, let yourselves be built into a spiritual house to be a holy priesthood to offer spiritual sacrifices acceptable to God through Jesus Christ. For it says in Scripture:
Behold, I am laying a stone in Zion,
a cornerstone, chosen and precious,
and whoever believes in it shall not

    be put to shame.
Therefore, its value is for you who have faith, but for those without faith:
    The stone that the builders rejected
    has become the cornerstone,
and
    A stone that will make people
        stumble,
    and a rock that will make them fall.
They stumble by disobeying the word, as is their destiny.

You are "a chosen race, a royal priesthood, a holy nation, a people of his own, so that you may announce the praises" of him who called you out of darkness into his wonderful light.

GOSPEL ACCLAMATION

John 14:6

℟. Al - le - lu - ia,   al - le - lu - ia,   al - le - lu - ia.

Music: John Schiavone, b. 1947, © 2001, OCP Publications.

▸ I am the way, the truth and the life, says the Lord;
no one comes to the Father, except through me. ℟.

GOSPEL READING

John 14:1–12

Jesus said to his disciples: "Do not let your hearts be troubled. You have faith in God; have faith also in me. In my Father's house there are many dwelling places. If there were not, would I have told you that I am going to prepare a place for you? And if I go and prepare a place for you, I will come back again and take you to myself, so that where I am you also may be. Where I am going you know the way." Thomas said to him, "Master, we do not know where you are going; how can we know the way?" Jesus said to him, "I am the way and the truth and the life. No one comes to the Father except through me. If you know me, then you will also know my Father. From now on you do know him and have seen him." Philip said to him, "Master, show us the Father, and that will be enough for us." Jesus said to him, "Have I been with you for so long a time and you still do not know me, Philip? Whoever has seen me has seen the Father. How can you say, 'Show us the Father'? Do you not believe that I am in the Father and the Father is in me? The words that I speak to you I do not speak on my own. The Father who dwells in me is doing his works. Believe me that I am in the Father and the Father is in me, or else, believe because of the works themselves. Amen, amen, I say to you, whoever believes in me will do the works that I do, and will do greater ones than these, because I am going to the Father."

---

931   FIFTH SUNDAY OF EASTER — B

FIRST READING

Acts of the Apostles 9:26–31

When Saul arrived in Jerusalem he tried to join the disciples, but they were all afraid of him, not believing that he was a disciple. Then Barnabas took charge of him and brought him to the apostles, and he reported to them how he had seen the Lord, and that he had spoken to him, and how in Damascus he had spoken out boldly in the name of Jesus. He moved about freely with them in Jerusalem, and spoke out boldly in the name of the Lord. He also spoke and debated with the Hellenists, but they tried to kill him. And when the brothers learned of this, they took him down to Caesarea and sent him on his way to Tarsus.

The church throughout all Judea, Galilee, and Samaria was at peace. It was being built up and walked in the fear of the Lord, and with the consolation of the Holy Spirit it grew in numbers.

RESPONSORIAL PSALM

Psalm 22:26–27, 28, 30, 31–32

℟. I will praise you, Lord, in the as-sem-bly of your peo-ple.

Music: John Schiavone, b. 1947, © 2001, OCP Publications.

or: **Alleluia.**

▶ I will fulfill my vows before those who
    fear the LORD.
  The lowly shall eat their fill;
they who seek the LORD shall
    praise him:
  "May your hearts live forever!" ℟.

▶ All the ends of the earth
    shall remember and turn to the LORD;
all the families of the nations
  shall bow down before him. ℟.

▶ To him alone shall bow down
    all who sleep in the earth;
before him shall bend
  all who go down into the dust. ℟.

▶ And to him my soul shall live;
    my descendants shall serve him.
Let the coming generation be told of
    the LORD
that they may proclaim to a people
  yet to be born
the justice he has shown. ℟.

SECOND READING

1 John 3:18–24

Children, let us love not in word or speech but in deed and truth.

  Now this is how we shall know that we belong to the truth and reassure our hearts before him in whatever our hearts condemn, for God is greater than our hearts and knows everything. Beloved, if our hearts do not condemn us, we have confidence in God and receive from him whatever we ask, because we keep his commandments and do what pleases him. And his commandment is this: we should believe in the name of his Son, Jesus Christ, and love one another just as he commanded us. Those who keep his commandments remain in him, and he in them, and the way we know that he remains in us is from the Spirit he gave us.

GOSPEL ACCLAMATION

John 15:4a, 5b

℟. Al - le - lu - ia, al - le - lu - ia, al - le - lu - ia.

Music: John Schiavone, b. 1947, © 2001, OCP Publications.

▶ Remain in me as I remain in you, says the Lord.
  Whoever remains in me will bear much fruit. ℟.

GOSPEL READING

John 15:1–8

Jesus said to his disciples: "I am the true vine, and my Father is the vine grower. He takes away every branch in me that does not bear fruit, and every one that does he prunes so that it bears more fruit. You are already pruned because of the word that I spoke to you. Remain in me, as I remain in you. Just as a branch cannot bear fruit on its own unless it remains on the vine, so neither can you unless you remain in me. I am the vine, you are the branches. Whoever remains in me and I in him will bear much fruit, because without me you can do nothing. Anyone who does not remain in me will be thrown out like a branch and wither; people will gather them and throw them into a fire and they will be burned. If you remain in me and my words remain in you, ask for whatever you want and it will be done for you. By this is my Father glorified, that you bear much fruit and become my disciples."

932   FIFTH SUNDAY OF EASTER — C

FIRST READING   *Acts of the Apostles 14:21–27*

After Paul and Barnabas had proclaimed the good news to that city and made a considerable number of disciples, they returned to Lystra and to Iconium and to Antioch. They strengthened the spirits of the disciples and exhorted them to persevere in the faith, saying, "It is necessary for us to undergo many hardships to enter the kingdom of God." They appointed elders for them in each church and, with prayer and fasting, commended them to the Lord in whom they had put their faith. Then they traveled through Pisidia and reached Pamphylia. After proclaiming the word at Perga they went down to Attalia. From there they sailed to Antioch, where they had been commended to the grace of God for the work they had now accomplished. And when they arrived, they called the church together and reported what God had done with them and how he had opened the door of faith to the Gentiles.

RESPONSORIAL PSALM   *Psalm 145:8–9, 10–11, 12–13*

℟. I will praise your name for ev-er, my king and my God.

Music: John Schiavone, b. 1947, © 2001, OCP Publications.

or: **Alleluia.**

▸ The LORD is gracious and merciful,
    slow to anger and of great kindness.
The LORD is good to all
    and compassionate toward all
      his works. ℟.

▸ Let all your works give you thanks,
    O LORD,
    and let your faithful ones bless you.
Let them discourse of the glory of
    your kingdom
    and speak of your might. ℟.

▸ Let them make known your might to
    the children of Adam,
    and the glorious splendor of
    your kingdom.
Your kingdom is a kingdom for all ages,
    and your dominion endures
      through all generations. ℟.

SECOND READING   *Revelation 21:1–5a*

Then I, John, saw a new heaven and a new earth. The former heaven and the former earth had passed away, and the sea was no more. I also saw the holy city, a new Jerusalem, coming down out of heaven from God, prepared as a bride adorned for her husband. I heard a loud voice from the throne saying,

"Behold, God's dwelling is with the human race. He will dwell with them and they will be his people and God himself will always be with them as their God. He will wipe every tear from their eyes, and there shall be no more death or mourning, wailing or pain, for the old order has passed away."

The One who sat on the throne said, "Behold, I make all things new."

GOSPEL ACCLAMATION   *John 13:34*

℟. Al - le - lu - ia,   al - le - lu - ia,   al - le - lu - ia.

Music: John Schiavone, b. 1947, © 2001, OCP Publications.

▶ I give you a new commandment, says the Lord:
love one another as I have loved you. ℟.

GOSPEL READING   *John 13:31–33a, 34–35*

When Judas had left them, Jesus said, "Now is the Son of Man glorified, and God is glorified in him. If God is glorified in him, God will also glorify him in himself, and God will glorify him at once. My children, I will be with you only a little while longer. I give you a new commandment: love one another. As I have loved you, so you also should love one another. This is how all will know that you are my disciples, if you have love for one another."

SIXTH SUNDAY OF EASTER — A   933

When the Ascension of the Lord is celebrated the following Sunday, the second reading and Gospel from the Seventh Sunday of Easter (see number 937) may be read on the Sixth Sunday of Easter.

FIRST READING   *Acts of the Apostles 8:5–8, 14–17*

Philip went down to the city of Samaria and proclaimed the Christ to them. With one accord, the crowds paid attention to what was said by Philip when they heard it and saw the signs he was doing. For unclean spirits, crying out in a loud voice, came out of many possessed people, and many paralyzed or crippled people were cured. There was great joy in that city.

Now when the apostles in Jerusalem heard that Samaria had accepted the word of God, they sent them Peter and John, who went down and prayed for them, that they might receive the Holy Spirit, for it had not yet fallen upon any of them; they had only been baptized in the name of the Lord Jesus. Then they laid hands on them and they received the Holy Spirit.

RESPONSORIAL PSALM   *Psalm 66:1–3, 4–5, 6–7, 16, 20*

℟. Let all the earth   cry out to God with   joy.

Music: John Schiavone, b. 1947, © 2001, OCP Publications.

or: **Alleluia.**

℟. **Let all the earth cry out to God with joy.**
or: **Alleluia.**

▶ Shout joyfully to God, all the earth,
  sing praise to the glory of his name;
  proclaim his glorious praise.
Say to God, "How tremendous are
  your deeds! ℟.

▶ Let all on earth worship and sing
  praise to you,
  sing praise to your name!"
Come and see the works of God,
  his tremendous deeds among the
  children of Adam. ℟.

▶ He has changed the sea into dry land;
  through the river they passed
  on foot;
  therefore let us rejoice in him.
He rules by his might forever. ℟.

▶ Hear now, all you who fear God, while
  I declare
  what he has done for me.
Blessed be God who refused me not
  my prayer or his kindness! ℟.

SECOND READING

1 Peter 3:15–18

Beloved: Sanctify Christ as Lord in your hearts. Always be ready to give an explanation to anyone who asks you for a reason for your hope, but do it with gentleness and reverence, keeping your conscience clear, so that, when you are maligned, those who defame your good conduct in Christ may themselves be put to shame. For it is better to suffer for doing good, if that be the will of God, than for doing evil.

For Christ also suffered for sins once, the righteous for the sake of the unrighteous, that he might lead you to God. Put to death in the flesh, he was brought to life in the Spirit.

GOSPEL ACCLAMATION

John 14:23

℟. Al - le - lu - ia, al - le - lu - ia, al - le - lu - ia.

Music: John Schiavone, b. 1947, © 2001, OCP Publications.

▶ Whoever loves me will keep my word, says the Lord,
  and my Father will love him and we will come to him. ℟.

GOSPEL READING

John 14:15–21

Jesus said to his disciples: "If you love me, you will keep my commandments. And I will ask the Father, and he will give you another Advocate to be with you always, the Spirit of truth, whom the world cannot accept, because it neither sees nor knows him. But you know him, because he remains with you, and will be in you. I will not leave you orphans; I will come to you. In a little while the world will no longer see me, but you will see me, because I live and you will live. On that day you will realize that I am in my Father and you are in me and I in you. Whoever has my commandments and observes them is the one who loves me. And whoever loves me will be loved by my Father, and I will love him and reveal myself to him."

SIXTH SUNDAY OF EASTER — B   934

When the Ascension of the Lord is celebrated the following Sunday, the second reading and Gospel from the Seventh Sunday of Easter (see number 938) may be read on the Sixth Sunday of Easter.

FIRST READING   *Acts of the Apostles 10:25–26, 34–35, 44–48*

When Peter entered, Cornelius met him and, falling at his feet, paid him homage. Peter, however, raised him up, saying, "Get up. I myself am also a human being."
    Then Peter proceeded to speak and said, "In truth, I see that God shows no partiality. Rather, in every nation whoever fears him and acts uprightly is acceptable to him."
    While Peter was still speaking these things, the Holy Spirit fell upon all who were listening to the word.

The circumcised believers who had accompanied Peter were astounded that the gift of the Holy Spirit should have been poured out on the Gentiles also, for they could hear them speaking in tongues and glorifying God. Then Peter responded, "Can anyone withhold the water for baptizing these people, who have received the Holy Spirit even as we have?" He ordered them to be baptized in the name of Jesus Christ.

RESPONSORIAL PSALM   *Psalm 98:1, 2–3, 3–4*

℞. **The Lord has re-vealed to the na-tions his sav-ing pow-er.**

Music: John Schiavone, b. 1947, © 2001, OCP Publications.

or: **Alleluia.**

▸ Sing to the LORD a new song,
    for he has done wondrous deeds;
his right hand has won victory for him,
    his holy arm. ℞.

▸ The LORD has made his salvation
    known:
    in the sight of the nations he has
    revealed his justice.

He has remembered his kindness and
    his faithfulness
    toward the house of Israel. ℞.

▸ All the ends of the earth have seen
    the salvation by our God.
Sing joyfully to the LORD, all you lands;
    break into song; sing praise. ℞.

SECOND READING   *1 John 4:7–10*

Beloved, let us love one another, because love is of God; everyone who loves is begotten by God and knows God. Whoever is without love does not know God, for God is love. In this way the love of God was revealed to us: God

sent his only Son into the world so that we might have life through him. In this is love: not that we have loved God, but that he loved us and sent his Son as expiation for our sins.

GOSPEL ACCLAMATION

John 14:23

℟. Al - le - lu - ia,   al - le - lu - ia,   al - le - lu - ia.

Music: John Schiavone, b. 1947, © 2001, OCP Publications.

▶ Whoever loves me will keep my word, says the Lord,
and my Father will love him and we will come to him. ℟.

GOSPEL READING

John 15:9–17

Jesus said to his disciples: "As the Father loves me, so I also love you. Remain in my love. If you keep my commandments, you will remain in my love, just as I have kept my Father's commandments and remain in his love.

"I have told you this so that my joy may be in you and your joy might be complete. This is my commandment: love one another as I love you. No one has greater love than this, to lay down one's life for one's friends. You are my friends if you do what I command you. I no longer call you slaves, because a slave does not know what his master is doing. I have called you friends, because I have told you everything I have heard from my Father. It was not you who chose me, but I who chose you and appointed you to go and bear fruit that will remain, so that whatever you ask the Father in my name he may give you. This I command you: love one another."

---

935   SIXTH SUNDAY OF EASTER — C

When the Ascension of the Lord is celebrated the following Sunday, the second reading and Gospel from the Seventh Sunday of Easter (see number 939) may be read on the Sixth Sunday of Easter.

FIRST READING

Acts of the Apostles 15:1–2, 22–29

Some who had come down from Judea were instructing the brothers, "Unless you are circumcised according to the Mosaic practice, you cannot be saved." Because there arose no little dissension and debate by Paul and Barnabas with them, it was decided that Paul, Barnabas, and some of the others should go up to Jerusalem to the apostles and elders about this question.

The apostles and elders, in agreement with the whole church, decided to choose representatives and to send them to Antioch with Paul and Barnabas. The ones chosen were Judas, who was called Barsabbas, and Silas, leaders among the brothers. This is the letter delivered by them:

"The apostles and the elders, your brothers, to the brothers in Antioch, Syria, and Cilicia of Gentile origin: greetings. Since we have heard that some of our number who went out without any mandate from us have upset you with their teachings and disturbed your peace of mind, we have with one accord decided to choose representatives and to send them to you along with our beloved Barnabas and Paul, who have dedicated their lives to the name of our Lord Jesus Christ. So we are sending Judas and Silas who will also convey this same message by word of mouth: 'It is the decision of the Holy Spirit and of us not to place on you any burden beyond these necessities, namely, to abstain from meat sacrificed to idols, from blood, from meats of strangled animals, and from unlawful marriage. If you keep free of these, you will be doing what is right. Farewell.' "

RESPONSORIAL PSALM
Psalm 67:2–3, 5, 6, 8

Music: John Schiavone, b. 1947, © 2001, OCP Publications.

or: **Alleluia.**

▶ May God have pity on us and bless us;
  may he let his face shine upon us.
So may your way be known upon earth;
  among all nations, your salvation. ℟.

▶ May the nations be glad and exult
  because you rule the peoples
    in equity;
  the nations on the earth you guide. ℟.

▶ May the peoples praise you, O God;
  may all the peoples praise you!
May God bless us,
  and may all the ends of the earth
    fear him! ℟.

SECOND READING
Revelation 21:10–14, 22–23

The angel took me in spirit to a great, high mountain and showed me the holy city Jerusalem coming down out of heaven from God. It gleamed with the splendor of God. Its radiance was like that of a precious stone, like jasper, clear as crystal. It had a massive, high wall, with twelve gates where twelve angels were stationed and on which names were inscribed, the names of the twelve tribes of the Israelites. There were three gates facing east, three north, three south, and three west. The wall of the city had twelve courses of stones as its foundation, on which were inscribed the twelve names of the twelve apostles of the Lamb.

I saw no temple in the city for its temple is the Lord God almighty and the Lamb. The city had no need of sun or moon to shine on it, for the glory of God gave it light, and its lamp was the Lamb.

GOSPEL ACCLAMATION
John 14:23

Music: John Schiavone, b. 1947, © 2001, OCP Publications.

▶ Whoever loves me will keep my word, says the Lord,
  and my Father will love him and we will come to him. ℟.

GOSPEL READING
John 14:23–29

Jesus said to his disciples: "Whoever loves me will keep my word, and my Father will love him, and we will come to him and make our dwelling with him. Whoever does not love me does not keep my words; yet the word you hear is not mine but that of the Father who sent me.

"I have told you this while I am with you. The Advocate, the Holy Spirit, whom the Father will send in my name, will teach you everything and remind you of all that I told you. Peace I leave with you; my peace I give to you. Not as the world gives do I give it to you. Do not let your hearts be troubled or afraid. You heard me tell you, 'I am going away and I will come back to you.' If you loved me, you would rejoice that I am going to the Father; for the Father is greater than I. And now I have told you this before it happens, so that when it happens you may believe."

---

936   ASCENSION OF THE LORD — ABC

In several ecclesiastical provinces of the United States of America, the solemnity of the Ascension of the Lord is transferred to the following Sunday. Thursday is observed as an Easter weekday in those archdioceses and dioceses.

FIRST READING
Acts of the Apostles 1:1–11

In the first book, Theophilus, I dealt with all that Jesus did and taught until the day he was taken up, after giving instructions through the Holy Spirit to the apostles whom he had chosen. He presented himself alive to them by many proofs after he had suffered, appearing to them during forty days and speaking about the kingdom of God. While meeting with them, he enjoined them not to depart from Jerusalem, but to wait for "the promise of the Father about which you have heard me speak; for John baptized with water, but in a few days you will be baptized with the Holy Spirit."

When they had gathered together they asked him, "Lord, are you at this time going to restore the kingdom to Israel?" He answered them, "It is not for you to know the times or seasons that the Father has established by his own authority. But you will receive power when the Holy Spirit comes upon you, and you will be my witnesses in Jerusalem, throughout Judea and Samaria, and to the ends of the earth." When he had said this, as they were looking on, he was lifted up, and a cloud took him from their sight. While they were looking intently at the sky as he was going, suddenly two men dressed in white garments stood beside them. They said, "Men of Galilee, why are you standing there looking at the sky? This Jesus who has been taken up from you into heaven will return in the same way as you have seen him going into heaven."

RESPONSORIAL PSALM
Psalm 47:2–3, 6–7, 8–9

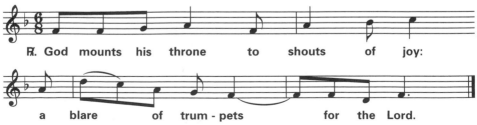

℟. God mounts his throne to shouts of joy: a blare of trum-pets for the Lord.

Music: John Schiavone, b. 1947, © 2001, OCP Publications.

or: **Alleluia.**

▶ All you peoples, clap your hands,
  shout to God with cries of gladness.
For the LORD, the Most High,
    the awesome,
  is the great king over all the earth. ℟.
▶ God mounts his throne amid shouts
      of joy;
  the LORD, amid trumpet blasts.

Sing praise to God, sing praise;
  sing praise to our king, sing praise. ℟.
▶ For king of all the earth is God;
  sing hymns of praise.
God reigns over the nations,
  God sits upon his holy throne. ℟.

SECOND READING — ABC

Ephesians 1:17–23

Brothers and sisters: May the God of our Lord Jesus Christ, the Father of glory, give you a Spirit of wisdom and revelation resulting in knowledge of him. May the eyes of your hearts be enlightened, that you may know what is the hope that belongs to his call, what are the riches of glory in his inheritance among the holy ones, and what is the surpassing greatness of his power for us who believe, in accord with the exercise of his great might, which he worked in Christ, raising him from the dead and seating him at his right hand in the heavens, far above every principality, authority, power, and dominion, and every name that is named not only in this age but also in the one to come. And he put all things beneath his feet and gave him as head over all things to the church, which is his body, the fullness of the one who fills all things in every way.

OR

SECOND READING — B

Ephesians 4:1–13 or 4:1–7, 11–13

(Include bracketed text for Long Form)

Brothers and sisters, I, a prisoner for the Lord, urge you to live in a manner worthy of the call you have received, with all humility and gentleness, with patience, bearing with one another through love, striving to preserve the unity of the spirit through the bond of peace: one body and one Spirit, as you were also called to the one hope of your call; one Lord, one faith, one baptism; one God and Father of all, who is over all and through all and in all.

But grace was given to each of us according to the measure of Christ's gift. [Therefore, it says:
  He ascended on high and took
    prisoners captive;
  he gave gifts to men.
What does "he ascended" mean except that he also descended into the lower regions of the earth? The one who descended is also the one who ascended far above all the heavens, that he might fill all things.]

And he gave some as apostles, others as prophets, others as evangelists, others as pastors and teachers, to equip the holy ones for the work of ministry, for building up the body of Christ, until we all attain to the unity of faith and knowledge of the Son of God, to mature manhood, to the extent of the full stature of Christ.

OR

Second Reading — C

Hebrews 9:24–28; 10:19–23

Christ did not enter into a sanctuary made by hands, a copy of the true one, but heaven itself, that he might now appear before God on our behalf. Not that he might offer himself repeatedly, as the high priest enters each year into the sanctuary with blood that is not his own; if that were so, he would have had to suffer repeatedly from the foundation of the world. But now once for all he has appeared at the end of the ages to take away sin by his sacrifice. Just as it is appointed that men and women die once, and after this the judgment, so also Christ, offered once to take away the sins of many, will appear a second time, not to take away sin but to bring salvation to those who eagerly await him.

Therefore, brothers and sisters, since through the blood of Jesus we have confidence of entrance into the sanctuary by the new and living way he opened for us through the veil, that is, his flesh, and since we have "a great priest over the house of God," let us approach with a sincere heart and in absolute trust, with our hearts sprinkled clean from an evil conscience and our bodies washed in pure water. Let us hold unwaveringly to our confession that gives us hope, for he who made the promise is trustworthy.

Gospel Acclamation

Matthew 28:19a, 20b

℟. Al - le - lu - ia,   al - le - lu - ia,   al - le - lu - ia.

Music: John Schiavone, b. 1947, © 2001, OCP Publications.

▶ Go and teach all nations, says the Lord;
  I am with you always, until the end of the world. ℟.

Gospel Reading — A

Matthew 28:16–20

The eleven disciples went to Galilee, to the mountain to which Jesus had ordered them. When they saw him, they worshiped, but they doubted. Then Jesus approached and said to them, "All power in heaven and on earth has been given to me. Go, therefore, and make disciples of all nations, baptizing them in the name of the Father, and of the Son, and of the Holy Spirit, teaching them to observe all that I have commanded you. And behold, I am with you always, until the end of the age."

Gospel Reading — B

Mark 16:15–20

Jesus said to his disciples: "Go into the whole world and proclaim the gospel to every creature. Whoever believes and is baptized will be saved; whoever does not believe will be condemned. These signs will accompany those who believe: in my name they will drive out demons, they will speak new languages. They will pick up serpents with their hands, and if they drink any deadly thing, it will not harm them. They will lay hands on the sick, and they will recover."

So then the Lord Jesus, after he spoke to them, was taken up into heaven and took his seat at the right hand of God. But they went forth and preached everywhere, while the Lord worked with them and confirmed the word through accompanying signs.

GOSPEL READING — C

Luke 24:46–53

Jesus said to his disciples: "Thus it is written that the Christ would suffer and rise from the dead on the third day and that repentance, for the forgiveness of sins, would be preached in his name to all the nations, beginning from Jerusalem. You are witnesses of these things. And behold I am sending the promise of my Father upon you; but stay in the city until you are clothed with power from on high."

Then he led them out as far as Bethany, raised his hands, and blessed them. As he blessed them he parted from them and was taken up to heaven. They did him homage and then returned to Jerusalem with great joy, and they were continually in the temple praising God.

SEVENTH SUNDAY OF EASTER — A   937

In those places where the observance of the solemnity of the Ascension of the Lord has been transferred to this day, the Mass and readings of the Ascension, number 936, are used.

FIRST READING

Acts of the Apostles 1:12–14

After Jesus had been taken up to heaven the apostles returned to Jerusalem from the mount called Olivet, which is near Jerusalem, a sabbath day's journey away.

When they entered the city they went to the upper room where they were staying, Peter and John and James and Andrew, Philip and Thomas, Bartholomew and Matthew, James son of Alphaeus, Simon the Zealot, and Judas son of James. All these devoted themselves with one accord to prayer, together with some women, and Mary the mother of Jesus, and his brothers.

RESPONSORIAL PSALM

Psalm 27:1, 4, 7–8

℟. I be - lieve that I shall see the good things of the Lord in the land of the liv - ing.

Music: John Schiavone, b. 1947, © 2001, OCP Publications.

or: **Alleluia.**

▸ The LORD is my light and my salvation; whom should I fear?
The LORD is my life's refuge; of whom should I be afraid? ℟.

▸ One thing I ask of the LORD; this I seek:
to dwell in the house of the LORD all the days of my life,

that I may gaze on the loveliness of the LORD
and contemplate his temple. ℟.

▸ Hear, O LORD, the sound of my call; have pity on me, and answer me.
Of you my heart speaks; you my glance seeks. ℟.

SECOND READING
1 Peter 4:13–16

Beloved: Rejoice to the extent that you share in the sufferings of Christ, so that when his glory is revealed you may also rejoice exultantly. If you are insulted for the name of Christ, blessed are you, for the Spirit of glory and of God rests upon you. But let no one among you be made to suffer as a murderer, a thief, an evildoer, or as an intriguer. But whoever is made to suffer as a Christian should not be ashamed but glorify God because of the name.

GOSPEL ACCLAMATION
cf. John 14:18

℟. Al - le - lu - ia,   al - le - lu - ia,   al - le - lu - ia.

Music: John Schiavone, b. 1947, © 2001, OCP Publications.

▶ I will not leave you orphans, says the Lord.
I will come back to you, and your hearts will rejoice. ℟.

GOSPEL READING
John 17:1–11a

Jesus raised his eyes to heaven and said, "Father, the hour has come. Give glory to your son, so that your son may glorify you, just as you gave him authority over all people, so that your son may give eternal life to all you gave him. Now this is eternal life, that they should know you, the only true God, and the one whom you sent, Jesus Christ. I glorified you on earth by accomplishing the work that you gave me to do. Now glorify me, Father, with you, with the glory that I had with you before the world began.

"I revealed your name to those whom you gave me out of the world. They belonged to you, and you gave them to me, and they have kept your word. Now they know that everything you gave me is from you, because the words you gave to me I have given to them, and they accepted them and truly understood that I came from you, and they have believed that you sent me. I pray for them. I do not pray for the world but for the ones you have given me, because they are yours, and everything of mine is yours and everything of yours is mine, and I have been glorified in them. And now I will no longer be in the world, but they are in the world, while I am coming to you."

---

938 SEVENTH SUNDAY OF EASTER — B

In those places where the observance of the solemnity of the Ascension of the Lord *has been transferred to this day, the Mass and readings of the* Ascension, *number 936, are used.*

FIRST READING
Acts of the Apostles 1:15–17, 20a, 20c–26

Peter stood up in the midst of the brothers — there was a group of about one hundred and twenty persons in the one place —. He said, "My brothers, the Scripture had to be fulfilled which the Holy Spirit spoke beforehand through the mouth of David, concerning Judas, who was the guide for those who arrested Jesus. He was numbered among us and was allotted a share in this ministry.

"For it is written in the Book of Psalms:
May another take his office.

"Therefore, it is necessary that one of the men who accompanied us the whole time the Lord Jesus came and went among us, beginning from the baptism of John until the day on which he was taken up from us, become with us a witness to his resurrection." So they proposed two, Judas called Barsabbas, who was also known as Justus, and Matthias. Then they prayed, "You, Lord, who know the hearts of all, show which one of these two you have chosen to take the place in this apostolic ministry from which Judas turned away to go to his own place." Then they gave lots to them, and the lot fell upon Matthias, and he was counted with the eleven apostles.

RESPONSORIAL PSALM

Psalm 103:1–2, 11–12, 19–20

℟. The Lord has set his throne in heav - en.

Music: John Schiavone, b. 1947, © 2001, OCP Publications.

or: **Alleluia.**

▶ Bless the LORD, O my soul;
  and all my being, bless his
    holy name.
Bless the LORD, O my soul,
  and forget not all his benefits. ℟.

▶ For as the heavens are high above
    the earth,
  so surpassing is his kindness toward
    those who fear him.

As far as the east is from the west,
  so far has he put our transgressions
    from us. ℟.

▶ The LORD has established his throne
    in heaven,
  and his kingdom rules over all.
Bless the LORD, all you his angels,
  you mighty in strength, who do
    his bidding. ℟.

SECOND READING

1 John 4:11–16

Beloved, if God so loved us, we also must love one another. No one has ever seen God. Yet, if we love one another, God remains in us, and his love is brought to perfection in us.

This is how we know that we remain in him and he in us, that he has given us of his Spirit. Moreover, we have seen and testify that the Father sent his Son as savior of the world. Whoever acknowledges that Jesus is the Son of God, God remains in him and he in God. We have come to know and to believe in the love God has for us.

God is love, and whoever remains in love remains in God and God in him.

GOSPEL ACCLAMATION

cf. John 14:18

℟. Al - le - lu - ia, al - le - lu - ia, al - le - lu - ia.

Music: John Schiavone, b. 1947, © 2001, OCP Publications.

▶ I will not leave you orphans, says the Lord.
I will come back to you, and your hearts will rejoice. ℟.

GOSPEL READING *John 17:11b–19*

Lifting up his eyes to heaven, Jesus prayed, saying: "Holy Father, keep them in your name that you have given me, so that they may be one just as we are one. When I was with them I protected them in your name that you gave me, and I guarded them, and none of them was lost except the son of destruction, in order that the Scripture might be fulfilled. But now I am coming to you. I speak this in the world so that they may share my joy completely. I gave them your word, and the world hated them, because they do not belong to the world any more than I belong to the world. I do not ask that you take them out of the world but that you keep them from the evil one. They do not belong to the world any more than I belong to the world. Consecrate them in the truth. Your word is truth. As you sent me into the world, so I sent them into the world. And I consecrate myself for them, so that they also may be consecrated in truth."

---

939 SEVENTH SUNDAY OF EASTER — C

In those places where the observance of the solemnity of the Ascension of the Lord has been transferred to this day, the Mass and readings of the Ascension, number 936, are used.

FIRST READING *Acts of the Apostles 7:55–60*

Stephen, filled with the Holy Spirit, looked up intently to heaven and saw the glory of God and Jesus standing at the right hand of God, and Stephen said, "Behold, I see the heavens opened and the Son of Man standing at the right hand of God." But they cried out in a loud voice, covered their ears, and rushed upon him together. They threw him out of the city, and began to stone him. The witnesses laid down their cloaks at the feet of a young man named Saul. As they were stoning Stephen, he called out, "Lord Jesus, receive my spirit." Then he fell to his knees and cried out in a loud voice, "Lord, do not hold this sin against them"; and when he said this, he fell asleep.

RESPONSORIAL PSALM *Psalm 97:1–2, 6–7, 9*

℟. The Lord is king, the Most High o - ver all the earth.

Music: John Schiavone, b. 1947, © 2001, OCP Publications.

or: **Alleluia.**

▶ The LORD is king; let the earth rejoice;
  let the many islands be glad.
  Justice and judgment are the
    foundation of his throne. ℟.

▶ The heavens proclaim his justice,
  and all peoples see his glory.
  All gods are prostrate before him. ℟.

▶ You, O LORD, are the Most High over
    all the earth,
  exalted far above all gods. ℟.

SECOND READING
Revelation 22:12–14, 16–17, 20

I, John, heard a voice saying to me: "Behold, I am coming soon. I bring with me the recompense I will give to each according to his deeds. I am the Alpha and the Omega, the first and the last, the beginning and the end."

Blessed are they who wash their robes so as to have the right to the tree of life and enter the city through its gates.

"I, Jesus, sent my angel to give you this testimony for the churches. I am the root and offspring of David, the bright morning star."

The Spirit and the bride say, "Come." Let the hearer say, "Come." Let the one who thirsts come forward, and the one who wants it receive the gift of life-giving water.

The one who gives this testimony says, "Yes, I am coming soon." Amen! Come, Lord Jesus!

GOSPEL ACCLAMATION
cf. John 14:18

℟. Al - le - lu - ia, al - le - lu - ia, al - le - lu - ia.

Music: John Schiavone, b. 1947, © 2001, OCP Publications.

▶ I will not leave you orphans, says the Lord.
I will come back to you, and your hearts will rejoice. ℟.

GOSPEL READING
John 17:20–26

Lifting up his eyes to heaven, Jesus prayed, saying: "Holy Father, I pray not only for them, but also for those who will believe in me through their word, so that they may all be one, as you, Father, are in me and I in you, that they also may be in us, that the world may believe that you sent me. And I have given them the glory you gave me, so that they may be one, as we are one, I in them and you in me, that they may be brought to perfection as one, that the world may know that you sent me, and that you loved them even as you loved me. Father, they are your gift to me. I wish that where I am they also may be with me, that they may see my glory that you gave me, because you loved me before the foundation of the world. Righteous Father, the world also does not know you, but I know you, and they know that you sent me. I made known to them your name and I will make it known, that the love with which you loved me may be in them and I in them."

PENTECOST: VIGIL MASS — ABC   940

These readings are used at Saturday Evening Mass celebrated either before or after Evening Prayer I of Pentecost Sunday.

FIRST READING
Genesis 11:1–9

The whole world spoke the same language, using the same words. While the people were migrating in the east, they came upon a valley in the land of Shinar and settled there. They said to one another, "Come, let us mold bricks and harden them with fire." They used bricks for stone, and bitumen for mortar. Then they said, "Come, let us build ourselves a city and a tower with its top in the sky, and so make a name for ourselves; otherwise we shall be scattered all over the earth."

The LORD came down to see the city and the tower that the people had built. Then the LORD said: "If now, while they are one people, all speaking the same language, they have started to do this, nothing will later stop them from doing whatever they presume to do. Let us

then go down there and confuse their language, so that one will not understand what another says." Thus the LORD scattered them from there all over the earth, and they stopped building the city. That is why it was called Babel, because there the LORD confused the speech of all the world. It was from that place that he scattered them all over the earth.

OR

FIRST READING

Exodus 19:3–8a, 16–20b

Moses went up the mountain to God. Then the LORD called to him and said, "Thus shall you say to the house of Jacob; tell the Israelites: You have seen for yourselves how I treated the Egyptians and how I bore you up on eagle wings and brought you here to myself. Therefore, if you hearken to my voice and keep my covenant, you shall be my special possession, dearer to me than all other people, though all the earth is mine. You shall be to me a kingdom of priests, a holy nation. That is what you must tell the Israelites." So Moses went and summoned the elders of the people. When he set before them all that the LORD had ordered him to tell them, the people all answered together, "Everything the LORD has said, we will do."

On the morning of the third day there were peals of thunder and lightning, and a heavy cloud over the mountain, and a very loud trumpet blast, so that all the people in the camp trembled. But Moses led the people out of the camp to meet God, and they stationed themselves at the foot of the mountain. Mount Sinai was all wrapped in smoke, for the LORD came down upon it in fire. The smoke rose from it as though from a furnace, and the whole mountain trembled violently. The trumpet blast grew louder and louder, while Moses was speaking, and God answering him with thunder.

When the LORD came down to the top of Mount Sinai, he summoned Moses to the top of the mountain.

OR

FIRST READING

Ezekiel 37:1–14

The hand of the LORD came upon me, and he led me out in the spirit of the LORD and set me in the center of the plain, which was now filled with bones. He made me walk among the bones in every direction so that I saw how many they were on the surface of the plain. How dry they were! He asked me: Son of man, can these bones come to life? I answered, "Lord GOD, you alone know that." Then he said to me: Prophesy over these bones, and say to them: Dry bones, hear the word of the LORD! Thus says the Lord GOD to these bones: See! I will

bring spirit into you, that you may come to life. I will put sinews upon you, make flesh grow over you, cover you with skin, and put spirit in you so that you may come to life and know that I am the LORD. I, Ezekiel, prophesied as I had been told, and even as I was prophesying I heard a noise; it was a rattling as the bones came together, bone joining bone. I saw the sinews and the flesh come upon them, and the skin cover them, but there was no spirit in them. Then the LORD said to me: Prophesy to the spirit, prophesy, son of man, and say to the spirit: Thus says the Lord GOD: From the four winds come, O spirit, and breathe into these slain that they may come to life. I prophesied as he told me, and the spirit came into them; they came alive and stood upright, a vast army. Then he said to me: Son of man, these bones are the whole house of Israel. They have been saying, "Our bones are dried up, our hope is lost, and we are cut off." Therefore, prophesy and say to them: Thus says the Lord GOD: O my people, I will open your graves and have you rise from them, and bring you back to the land of Israel. Then you shall know that I am the LORD, when I open your graves and have you rise from them, O my people! I will put my spirit in you that you may live, and I will settle you upon your land; thus you shall know that I am the LORD. I have promised, and I will do it, says the LORD.

OR

FIRST READING

Joel 3:1–5

Thus says the LORD:
I will pour out my spirit upon all flesh.
Your sons and daughters shall prophesy,
    your old men shall dream dreams,
    your young men shall see visions;
even upon the servants and
    the handmaids,
    in those days, I will pour out my spirit.
And I will work wonders in the heavens
    and on the earth,
    blood, fire, and columns of smoke;
the sun will be turned to darkness,
    and the moon to blood,
at the coming of the day of the LORD,
    the great and terrible day.
Then everyone shall be rescued
    who calls on the name of the LORD;
for on Mount Zion there shall be
    a remnant,
    as the LORD has said,
and in Jerusalem survivors
    whom the LORD shall call.

RESPONSORIAL PSALM

Psalm 104:1–2, 24 & 35, 27–28, 29, 30

℟. Lord, send out your Spir-it, and re-new the face of the earth.

Music: John Schiavone, b. 1947, © 2001, OCP Publications.

or: **Alleluia.**

▶ Bless the LORD, O my soul!
    O LORD, my God, you are
      great indeed!
You are clothed with majesty and glory,
    robed in light as with a cloak. ℟.

▶ How manifold are your works, O LORD!
    In wisdom you have wrought
      them all —
the earth is full of your creatures;
    bless the LORD, O my soul! Alleluia. ℟.

▶ Creatures all look to you
    to give them food in due time.
When you give it to them, they
    gather it;
    when you open your hand, they are
    filled with good things. ℟.

▶ If you take away their breath,
    they perish
    and return to their dust.
When you send forth your spirit, they
    are created,
    and you renew the face of
      the earth. ℟.

SECOND READING
Romans 8:22–27

Brothers and sisters: We know that all creation is groaning in labor pains even until now; and not only that, but we ourselves, who have the firstfruits of the Spirit, we also groan within ourselves as we wait for adoption, the redemption of our bodies. For in hope we were saved. Now hope that sees is not hope. For who hopes for what one sees? But if we hope for what we do not see, we wait with endurance.

In the same way, the Spirit too comes to the aid of our weakness; for we do not know how to pray as we ought, but the Spirit himself intercedes with inexpressible groanings. And the one who searches hearts knows what is the intention of the Spirit, because he intercedes for the holy ones according to God's will.

GOSPEL ACCLAMATION

℟. Al - le - lu - ia, al - le - lu - ia, al - le - lu - ia.

Music: John Schiavone, b. 1947, © 2001, OCP Publications.

▶ Come, Holy Spirit, fill the hearts of the faithful and kindle in them the fire of your love. ℟.

GOSPEL READING
John 7:37–39

On the last and greatest day of the feast, Jesus stood up and exclaimed, "Let anyone who thirsts come to me and drink. As Scripture says:
Rivers of living water will flow from within him who believes in me."

He said this in reference to the Spirit that those who came to believe in him were to receive. There was, of course, no Spirit yet, because Jesus had not yet been glorified.

---

941 PENTECOST SUNDAY — ABC

FIRST READING
Acts of the Apostles 2:1–11

When the time for Pentecost was fulfilled, they were all in one place together. And suddenly there came from the sky a noise like a strong driving wind, and it filled the entire house in which they were. Then there appeared to them tongues as of fire, which parted and came to rest on each one of them. And they were all filled with the Holy Spirit and began to speak in different tongues, as the Spirit enabled them to proclaim.

Now there were devout Jews from every nation under heaven staying in Jerusalem. At this sound, they gathered in a large crowd, but they were confused because each one heard them speaking in his own language. They were astounded, and in amazement they asked, "Are not all these people who are speaking Galileans? Then how does each of us hear them in his native language? We are Parthians, Medes, and Elamites, inhabitants of Mesopotamia, Judea and Cappadocia, Pontus and Asia, Phrygia and Pamphylia, Egypt and the districts of Libya near Cyrene, as well as travelers from Rome, both Jews and converts to Judaism, Cretans and Arabs, yet we hear them speaking in our own tongues of the mighty acts of God."

RESPONSORIAL PSALM

Psalm 104:1, 24, 29–30, 31, 34

℟. Lord, send out your Spir-it, and re-new the face of the earth.

Music: John Schiavone, b. 1947, © 2001, OCP Publications.

or: **Alleluia.**

▶ Bless the LORD, O my soul!
   O LORD, my God, you are
      great indeed!
   How manifold are your works,
      O LORD!
   the earth is full of your creatures. ℟.

▶ May the glory of the LORD
      endure forever;
   may the LORD be glad in his works!
   Pleasing to him be my theme;
   I will be glad in the LORD. ℟.

▶ If you take away their breath,
      they perish
   and return to their dust.
   When you send forth your spirit, they
      are created,
   and you renew the face of
      the earth. ℟.

SECOND READING — ABC

1 Corinthians 12:3b–7, 12–13

Brothers and sisters: No one can say, "Jesus is Lord," except by the Holy Spirit.

There are different kinds of spiritual gifts but the same Spirit; there are different forms of service but the same Lord; there are different workings but the same God who produces all of them in everyone. To each individual the manifestation of the Spirit is given for some benefit.

As a body is one though it has many parts, and all the parts of the body, though many, are one body, so also Christ. For in one Spirit we were all baptized into one body, whether Jews or Greeks, slaves or free persons, and we were all given to drink of one Spirit.

OR

SECOND READING — B

Galatians 5:16–25

Brothers and sisters, live by the Spirit and you will certainly not gratify the desire of the flesh. For the flesh has desires against the Spirit, and the Spirit against the flesh; these are opposed to each other, so that you may not do what you want. But if you are guided by the Spirit, you are not under the law. Now the works of the flesh are obvious: immorality, impurity, lust, idolatry, sorcery, hatreds, rivalry, jealousy, outbursts of fury, acts of selfishness, dissensions, factions, occasions of envy, drinking bouts, orgies, and the like. I warn you, as I warned you before, that those who do such things will not inherit the kingdom of God. In contrast, the fruit of the Spirit is love, joy, peace, patience, kindness, generosity, faithfulness, gentleness, self-control. Against such there is no law. Now those who belong to Christ Jesus have crucified their flesh with its passions and desires. If we live in the Spirit, let us also follow the Spirit.

OR

SECOND READING — C   *Romans 8:8–17*

Brothers and sisters: Those who are in the flesh cannot please God. But you are not in the flesh; on the contrary, you are in the spirit, if only the Spirit of God dwells in you. Whoever does not have the Spirit of Christ does not belong to him. But if Christ is in you, although the body is dead because of sin, the spirit is alive because of righteousness. If the Spirit of the one who raised Jesus from the dead dwells in you, the one who raised Christ from the dead will give life to your mortal bodies also, through his Spirit that dwells in you. Consequently, brothers and sisters, we are not debtors to the flesh, to live according to the flesh. For if you live according to the flesh, you will die, but if by the Spirit you put to death the deeds of the body, you will live.

For those who are led by the Spirit of God are sons of God. For you did not receive a spirit of slavery to fall back into fear, but you received a Spirit of adoption, through whom we cry, "Abba, Father!" The Spirit himself bears witness with our spirit that we are children of God, and if children, then heirs, heirs of God and joint heirs with Christ, if only we suffer with him so that we may also be glorified with him.

SEQUENCE   *Veni, Sancte Spiritus*

The General Instruction of the Roman Missal directs that the Sequence is to be sung before the Gospel Acclamation on Pentecost Sunday. For music, see #453, 454, 455, 459, 462, 464.

GOSPEL ACCLAMATION

℟. Al - le - lu - ia,   al - le - lu - ia,   al - le - lu - ia.

Music: John Schiavone, b. 1947, © 2001, OCP Publications.

▶ Come, Holy Spirit, fill the hearts of your faithful and kindle in them the fire of your love. ℟.

GOSPEL READING — ABC   *John 20:19–23*

On the evening of that first day of the week, when the doors were locked, where the disciples were, for fear of the Jews, Jesus came and stood in their midst and said to them, "Peace be with you." When he had said this, he showed them his hands and his side. The disciples rejoiced when they saw the Lord. Jesus said to them again, "Peace be with you. As the Father has sent me, so I send you." And when he had said this, he breathed on them and said to them, "Receive the Holy Spirit. Whose sins you forgive are forgiven them, and whose sins you retain are retained."

OR

GOSPEL READING — B   *John 15:26–27; 16:12–15*

Jesus said to his disciples: "When the Advocate comes whom I will send you from the Father, the Spirit of truth that proceeds from the Father, he will testify to me. And you also testify, because you have been with me from the beginning.

"I have much more to tell you, but you cannot bear it now. But when he comes, the Spirit of truth, he will guide you to all truth. He will not speak on his own, but he will speak what he hears, and will declare to you the things that are coming. He will glorify me, because he will take from what is mine and declare it to you. Everything that the Father has is mine; for this reason I told you that he will take from what is mine and declare it to you."

OR

Gospel Reading — C

John 14:15–16, 23b–26

Jesus said to his disciples: "If you love me, you will keep my commandments. And I will ask the Father, and he will give you another Advocate to be with you always.

"Whoever loves me will keep my word, and my Father will love him, and we will come to him and make our dwelling with him. Those who do not love me do not keep my words; yet the word you hear is not mine but that of the Father who sent me.

"I have told you this while I am with you. The Advocate, the Holy Spirit whom the Father will send in my name, will teach you everything and remind you of all that I told you."

SOLEMNITIES OF THE LORD DURING ORDINARY TIME

MOST HOLY TRINITY — A　　942

FIRST READING

Exodus 34:4b–6, 8–9

Early in the morning Moses went up Mount Sinai as the LORD had commanded him, taking along the two stone tablets.

Having come down in a cloud, the LORD stood with Moses there and proclaimed his name, "LORD." Thus the LORD passed before him and cried out, "The LORD, the LORD, a merciful and gracious God, slow to anger and rich in kindness and fidelity." Moses at once bowed down to the ground in worship. Then he said, "If I find favor with you, O LORD, do come along in our company. This is indeed a stiff-necked people; yet pardon our wickedness and sins, and receive us as your own."

RESPONSORIAL PSALM

Daniel 3:52, 53, 54, 55

R̰. Glo - ry and praise for ev - er!

Music: John Schiavone, b. 1947, © 2001, OCP Publications.

▶ Blessed are you, O Lord, the God of our fathers,
　　praiseworthy and exalted above all forever;
　and blessed is your holy and glorious name,
　　praiseworthy and exalted above all for all ages. R̰.

▶ Blessed are you in the temple of your holy glory,
　　praiseworthy and glorious above all forever. R̰.

℟. **Glory and praise for ever!**

▶ Blessed are you on the throne of
    your kingdom,
  praiseworthy and exalted above
    all forever. ℟.

▶ Blessed are you who look into
    the depths
  from your throne upon
    the cherubim,
  praiseworthy and exalted above
    all forever. ℟.

SECOND READING
2 Corinthians 13:11–13

Brothers and sisters, rejoice. Mend your ways, encourage one another, agree with one another, live in peace, and the God of love and peace will be with you. Greet one another with a holy kiss. All the holy ones greet you.

The grace of the Lord Jesus Christ and the love of God and the fellowship of the Holy Spirit be with all of you.

GOSPEL ACCLAMATION
cf. Revelation 1:8

℟. Al - le - lu - ia,   al - le - lu - ia,   al - le - lu - ia.

Music: John Schiavone, b. 1947, © 2001, OCP Publications.

▶ Glory to the Father, the Son, and the Holy Spirit;
  to God who is, who was, and who is to come. ℟.

GOSPEL READING
John 3:16–18

God so loved the world that he gave his only Son, so that everyone who believes in him might not perish but might have eternal life. For God did not send his Son into the world to condemn the world, but that the world might be saved through him. Whoever believes in him will not be condemned, but whoever does not believe has already been condemned, because he has not believed in the name of the only Son of God.

---

943   MOST HOLY TRINITY — B

FIRST READING
Deuteronomy 4:32–34, 39–40

Moses said to the people: "Ask now of the days of old, before your time, ever since God created man upon the earth; ask from one end of the sky to the other: Did anything so great ever happen before? Was it ever heard of? Did a people ever hear the voice of God speaking from the midst of fire, as you did, and live? Or did any god venture to go and take a nation for himself from the midst of another nation, by testings, by signs and wonders, by war, with strong hand and outstretched arm, and by great terrors, all of which the LORD, your God, did for you in Egypt before your very eyes? This is why you must now know, and fix in your heart, that the LORD is God in the heavens above and on earth below, and that there is no other. You must keep his statutes and commandments that I enjoin on you today, that you and your children after you may prosper, and that you may have long life on the land which the LORD, your God, is giving you forever."

RESPONSORIAL PSALM   *Psalm 33:4–5, 6, 9, 18–19, 20, 22*

℟. Bless'd   the   peo-ple   the   Lord has cho-sen to   be   his own.

Music: John Schiavone, b. 1947, © 2001, OCP Publications.

▶ Upright is the word of the LORD,
   and all his works are trustworthy.
He loves justice and right;
   of the kindness of the LORD the
   earth is full. ℟.

▶ By the word of the LORD the heavens
   were made;
by the breath of his mouth all
   their host.
For he spoke, and it was made;
   he commanded, and it stood forth. ℟.

▶ See, the eyes of the LORD are upon
   those who fear him,
   upon those who hope for
   his kindness,
to deliver them from death
   and preserve them in spite
   of famine. ℟.

▶ Our soul waits for the LORD,
   who is our help and our shield.
May your kindness, O LORD, be upon us
   who have put our hope in you. ℟.

SECOND READING   *Romans 8:14–17*

Brothers and sisters: Those who are led by the Spirit of God are sons of God. For you did not receive a spirit of slavery to fall back into fear, but you received a Spirit of adoption, through whom we cry, "Abba, Father!" The Spirit himself bears witness with our spirit that we are children of God, and if children, then heirs, heirs of God and joint heirs with Christ, if only we suffer with him so that we may also be glorified with him.

GOSPEL ACCLAMATION   *Revelation 1:8*

℟. Al - le - lu - ia,   al - le - lu - ia,   al - le - lu - ia.

Music: John Schiavone, b. 1947, © 2001, OCP Publications.

▶ Glory to the Father, the Son, and the Holy Spirit;
   to God who is, who was, and who is to come. ℟.

GOSPEL READING   *Matthew 28:16–20*

The eleven disciples went to Galilee, to the mountain to which Jesus had ordered them. When they all saw him, they worshiped, but they doubted. Then Jesus approached and said to them, "All power in heaven and on earth has been given to me. Go, therefore, and make disciples of all nations, baptizing them in the name of the Father, and of the Son, and of the Holy Spirit, teaching them to observe all that I have commanded you. And behold, I am with you always, until the end of the age."

944   MOST HOLY TRINITY — C

FIRST READING   *Proverbs 8:22–31*

Thus says the wisdom of God:
"The LORD possessed me, the beginning
   of his ways,
    the forerunner of his prodigies of
     long ago;
from of old I was poured forth,
  at the first, before the earth.
When there were no depths I was
    brought forth,
    when there were no fountains or
     springs of water;
before the mountains were settled
    into place,
    before the hills, I was brought forth;
while as yet the earth and fields were
    not made,
    nor the first clods of the world.

"When the Lord established the
   heavens I was there,
   when he marked out the vault over
    the face of the deep;
when he made firm the skies above,
   when he fixed fast the foundations of
    the earth;
when he set for the sea its limit,
   so that the waters should not
    transgress his command;
then was I beside him as his craftsman,
   and I was his delight day by day,
playing before him all the while,
   playing on the surface of his earth;
   and I found delight in the
    human race."

RESPONSORIAL PSALM   *Psalm 8:4–5, 6–7, 8–9*

℟. O Lord, our God, how won-der-ful your name in all the earth!

Music: John Schiavone, b. 1947, © 2001, OCP Publications.

▶ When I behold your heavens, the
    work of your fingers,
    the moon and the stars which you
     set in place —
  what is man that you should be
    mindful of him,
    or the son of man that you should
    care for him? ℟.

▶ You have made him little less than
    the angels,

and crowned him with glory
   and honor.
You have given him rule over the
    works of your hands,
    putting all things under his feet: ℟.

▶ All sheep and oxen,
   yes, and the beasts of the field,
the birds of the air, the fishes of the sea,
   and whatever swims the paths of
    the seas. ℟.

SECOND READING   *Romans 5:1–5*

Brothers and sisters: Therefore, since
we have been justified by faith, we have
peace with God through our Lord Jesus
Christ, through whom we have gained
access by faith to this grace in which
we stand, and we boast in hope of the
glory of God. Not only that, but we
even boast of our afflictions, knowing
that affliction produces endurance,
and endurance, proven character, and
proven character, hope, and hope does
not disappoint, because the love of God
has been poured out into our hearts
through the Holy Spirit that has been
given to us.

GOSPEL ACCLAMATION   *cf. Revelation 1:8*

℟. Al - le - lu - ia,   al - le - lu - ia,   al - le - lu - ia.

Music: John Schiavone, b. 1947, © 2001, OCP Publications.

▶ Glory to the Father, the Son, and the Holy Spirit;
   to God who is, who was, and who is to come. ℟.

GOSPEL READING   *John 16:12–15*

Jesus said to his disciples: "I have much more to tell you, but you cannot bear it now. But when he comes, the Spirit of truth, he will guide you to all truth. He will not speak on his own, but he will speak what he hears, and will declare to you the things that are coming. He will glorify me, because he will take from what is mine and declare it to you. Everything that the Father has is mine; for this reason I told you that he will take from what is mine and declare it to you."

MOST HOLY BODY AND BLOOD OF CHRIST — A   945

FIRST READING   *Deuteronomy 8:2–3, 14b–16a*

Moses said to the people: "Remember how for forty years now the LORD, your God, has directed all your journeying in the desert, so as to test you by affliction and find out whether or not it was your intention to keep his commandments. He therefore let you be afflicted with hunger, and then fed you with manna, a food unknown to you and your fathers, in order to show you that not by bread alone does one live, but by every word that comes forth from the mouth of the LORD.

"Do not forget the LORD, your God, who brought you out of the land of Egypt, that place of slavery; who guided you through the vast and terrible desert with its saraph serpents and scorpions, its parched and waterless ground; who brought forth water for you from the flinty rock and fed you in the desert with manna, a food unknown to your fathers."

RESPONSORIAL PSALM   *Psalm 147:12–13, 14–15, 19–20*

℟. Praise   the   Lord,   Je - ru - sa - lem.

Music: John Schiavone, b. 1947, © 2001, OCP Publications.

or: **Alleluia.**

▶ Glorify the LORD, O Jerusalem;
   praise your God, O Zion.
 For he has strengthened the bars of
   your gates;
  he has blessed your children
   within you. ℟.

▶ He has granted peace in your borders;
   with the best of wheat he fills you.
 He sends forth his command to
   the earth;
  swiftly runs his word! ℟.

℟. Praise the Lord, Jerusalem.

or: **Alleluia.**

▶ He has proclaimed his word to Jacob,
    his statutes and his ordinances
      to Israel.

He has not done thus for any
    other nation;
    his ordinances he has not
      made known to them. Alleluia. ℟.

SECOND READING
1 Corinthians 10:16–17

Brothers and sisters: The cup of blessing that we bless, is it not a participation in the blood of Christ? The bread that we break, is it not a participation in the body of Christ? Because the loaf of bread is one, we, though many, are one body, for we all partake of the one loaf.

SEQUENCE (Optional)
Lauda Sion

The General Instruction of the Roman Missal directs that the Sequence, if done, is to be sung before the Gospel Acclamation. For music, see #473.

GOSPEL ACCLAMATION
John 6:51

℟. Al - le - lu - ia,   al - le - lu - ia,   al - le - lu - ia.

Music: John Schiavone, b. 1947, © 2001, OCP Publications.

▶ I am the living bread that came down from heaven, says the Lord;
    whoever eats this bread will live forever. ℟.

GOSPEL READING
John 6:51–58

Jesus said to the Jewish crowds: "I am the living bread that came down from heaven; whoever eats this bread will live forever; and the bread that I will give is my flesh for the life of the world."

The Jews quarreled among themselves, saying, "How can this man give us his flesh to eat?" Jesus said to them, "Amen, amen, I say to you, unless you eat the flesh of the Son of Man and drink his blood, you do not have life within you. Whoever eats my flesh and drinks my blood has eternal life, and I will raise him on the last day. For my flesh is true food, and my blood is true drink. Whoever eats my flesh and drinks my blood remains in me and I in him. Just as the living Father sent me and I have life because of the Father, so also the one who feeds on me will have life because of me. This is the bread that came down from heaven. Unlike your ancestors who ate and still died, whoever eats this bread will live forever."

---

946   MOST HOLY BODY AND BLOOD OF CHRIST — B

FIRST READING
Exodus 24:3–8

When Moses came to the people and related all the words and ordinances of the LORD, they all answered with one voice, "We will do everything that the LORD has told us." Moses then wrote down all the words of the LORD and, rising early the next day, he erected at the foot of the mountain an altar and twelve pillars for the twelve tribes of Israel. Then, having sent certain young men of the Israelites to offer holocausts and sacrifice young bulls as peace offerings to the LORD, Moses took half of the blood and put it in large bowls; the other half he splashed on the altar. Taking the book of the covenant, he read it aloud to the people, who answered, "All that the LORD has said, we will heed and do." Then he took the blood and sprinkled it on the people, saying, "This is the blood of the covenant that the LORD has made with you in accordance with all these words of his."

RESPONSORIAL PSALM
Psalm 116:12–13, 15–16, 17–18

℟. I will take the cup of sal-va-tion, and call on the name of the Lord.

Music: John Schiavone, b. 1947, © 2001, OCP Publications.

or: **Alleluia.**

▸ How shall I make a return to the LORD
  for all the good he has done for me?
The cup of salvation I will take up,
  and I will call upon the name of
  the LORD. ℟.

▸ Precious in the eyes of the LORD
  is the death of his faithful ones.
I am your servant, the son of
  your handmaid;
you have loosed my bonds. ℟.

▸ To you will I offer a sacrifice
  of thanksgiving,
  and I will call upon the name of
  the LORD.
My vows to the LORD I will pay
  in the presence of all his people. ℟.

SECOND READING
Hebrews 9:11–15

Brothers and sisters: When Christ came as high priest of the good things that have come to be, passing through the greater and more perfect tabernacle not made by hands, that is, not belonging to this creation, he entered once for all into the sanctuary, not with the blood of goats and calves but with his own blood, thus obtaining eternal redemption. For if the blood of goats and bulls and the sprinkling of a heifer's ashes can sanctify those who are defiled so that their flesh is cleansed, how much more will the blood of Christ, who through the eternal Spirit offered himself unblemished to God, cleanse our consciences from dead works to worship the living God.

For this reason he is mediator of a new covenant: since a death has taken place for deliverance from transgressions under the first covenant, those who are called may receive the promised eternal inheritance.

SEQUENCE (Optional)
Lauda Sion

The General Instruction of the Roman Missal directs that the Sequence, if done, is to be sung before the Gospel Acclamation. For music, see #473.

GOSPEL ACCLAMATION   *John 6:51*

℟. Al - le - lu - ia,   al - le - lu - ia,   al - le - lu - ia.

Music: John Schiavone, b. 1947, © 2001, OCP Publications.

▶ I am the living bread that came down from heaven, says the Lord;
whoever eats this bread will live forever. ℟.

GOSPEL READING   *Mark 14:12–16, 22–26*

On the first day of the Feast of Unleavened Bread, when they sacrificed the Passover lamb, Jesus' disciples said to him, "Where do you want us to go and prepare for you to eat the Passover?" He sent two of his disciples and said to them, "Go into the city and a man will meet you, carrying a jar of water. Follow him. Wherever he enters, say to the master of the house, 'The Teacher says, "Where is my guest room where I may eat the Passover with my disciples?"' Then he will show you a large upper room furnished and ready. Make the preparations for us there." The disciples then went off, entered the city, and found it just as he had told them; and they prepared the Passover.

While they were eating, he took bread, said the blessing, broke it, gave it to them, and said, "Take it; this is my body." Then he took a cup, gave thanks, and gave it to them, and they all drank from it. He said to them, "This is my blood of the covenant, which will be shed for many. Amen, I say to you, I shall not drink again the fruit of the vine until the day when I drink it new in the kingdom of God." Then, after singing a hymn, they went out to the Mount of Olives.

---

947   MOST HOLY BODY AND BLOOD OF CHRIST — C

FIRST READING   *Genesis 14:18–20*

In those days, Melchizedek, king of Salem, brought out bread and wine, and being a priest of God Most High, he blessed Abram with these words:
"Blessed be Abram by God Most High,
the creator of heaven and earth;
and blessed be God Most High,
who delivered your foes into
your hand."
Then Abram gave him a tenth of everything.

RESPONSORIAL PSALM   *Psalm 110:1, 2, 3, 4*

℟. You are a priest for   ev - er,   in the line of Mel - chiz - e - dek.

Music: John Schiavone, b. 1947, © 2001, OCP Publications.

▶ The LORD said to my Lord: "Sit at my
right hand
till I make your enemies your
footstool." ℟.

▶ The scepter of your power the LORD
will stretch forth from Zion:
"Rule in the midst of your
enemies." ℟.

▶ "Yours is princely power in the day of
   your birth, in holy splendor;
   before the daystar, like the dew,
   I have begotten you." ℟.

▶ The LORD has sworn, and he will
   not repent:
   "You are a priest forever, according
   to the order of Melchizedek." ℟.

SECOND READING
1 Corinthians 11:23–26

Brothers and sisters: I received from the Lord what I also handed on to you, that the Lord Jesus, on the night he was handed over, took bread, and, after he had given thanks, broke it and said, "This is my body that is for you. Do this in remembrance of me." In the same way also the cup, after supper, saying, "This cup is the new covenant in my blood. Do this, as often as you drink it, in remembrance of me." For as often as you eat this bread and drink the cup, you proclaim the death of the Lord until he comes.

SEQUENCE (Optional)
Lauda Sion

The General Instruction of the Roman Missal directs that the Sequence, if done, is to be sung before the Gospel Acclamation. For music, see #473.

GOSPEL ACCLAMATION
John 6:51

℟. Al - le - lu - ia,   al - le - lu - ia,   al - le - lu - ia.

Music: John Schiavone, b. 1947, © 2001, OCP Publications.

▶ I am the living bread that came down from heaven, says the Lord;
   whoever eats this bread will live forever. ℟.

GOSPEL READING
Luke 9:11b–17

Jesus spoke to the crowds about the kingdom of God, and he healed those who needed to be cured. As the day was drawing to a close, the Twelve approached him and said, "Dismiss the crowd so that they can go to the surrounding villages and farms and find lodging and provisions; for we are in a deserted place here." He said to them, "Give them some food yourselves." They replied, "Five loaves and two fish are all we have, unless we ourselves go and buy food for all these people." Now the men there numbered about five thousand. Then he said to his disciples, "Have them sit down in groups of about fifty." They did so and made them all sit down. Then taking the five loaves and the two fish, and looking up to heaven, he said the blessing over them, broke them, and gave them to the disciples to set before the crowd. They all ate and were satisfied. And when the leftover fragments were picked up, they filled twelve wicker baskets.

948   MOST SACRED HEART OF JESUS — A

FIRST READING   *Deuteronomy 7:6–11*

Moses said to the people: "You are a people sacred to the LORD, your God; he has chosen you from all the nations on the face of the earth to be a people peculiarly his own. It was not because you are the largest of all nations that the LORD set his heart on you and chose you, for you are really the smallest of all nations. It was because the LORD loved you and because of his fidelity to the oath he had sworn to your fathers, that he brought you out with his strong hand from the place of slavery, and ransomed you from the hand of Pharaoh, king of Egypt. Understand, then, that the LORD, your God, is God indeed, the faithful God who keeps his merciful covenant down to the thousandth generation toward those who love him and keep his commandments, but who repays with destruction a person who hates him; he does not dally with such a one, but makes them personally pay for it. You shall therefore carefully observe the commandments, the statutes and the decrees that I enjoin on you today."

RESPONSORIAL PSALM   *Psalm 103:1–2, 3–4, 6–7, 8, 10*

℟. **The Lord's kind-ness is ev-er-last-ing to those who fear him.**

Music: John Schiavone, b. 1947, © 2001, OCP Publications.

▶ Bless the LORD, O my soul;
    all my being, bless his holy name.
Bless the LORD, O my soul;
    and forget not all his benefits. ℟.

▶ He pardons all your iniquities,
    heals all your ills.
He redeems your life from destruction,
    crowns you with kindness
     and compassion. ℟.

▶ Merciful and gracious is the LORD,
    slow to anger and abounding
     in kindness.
Not according to our sins does he deal
    with us,
    nor does he requite us according to
     our crimes. ℟.

SECOND READING   *1 John 4:7–16*

Beloved, let us love one another, because love is of God; everyone who loves is begotten by God and knows God. Whoever is without love does not know God, for God is love. In this way the love of God was revealed to us: God sent his only Son into the world so that we might have life through him. In this is love: not that we have loved God, but that he loved us and sent his Son as expiation for our sins. Beloved, if God so loved us, we also must love one another. No one has ever seen God. Yet, if we love one another, God remains in us, and his love is brought to perfection in us.

This is how we know that we remain in him and he in us, that he has given us of his Spirit. Moreover, we have seen and testify that the Father sent his Son as savior of the world. Whoever acknowledges that Jesus is the Son of God, God remains in him and he in God. We have come to know and to believe in the love God has for us.

God is love, and whoever remains in love remains in God and God in him.

GOSPEL ACCLAMATION

Matthew 11:29ab

℟. Al - le - lu - ia,   al - le - lu - ia,   al - le - lu - ia.

Music: John Schiavone, b. 1947, © 2001, OCP Publications.

▸ Take my yoke upon you, says the Lord;
  and learn from me, for I am meek and humble of heart. ℟.

GOSPEL READING

Matthew 11:25–30

At that time Jesus exclaimed: "I give praise to you, Father, Lord of heaven and earth, for although you have hidden these things from the wise and the learned you have revealed them to little ones. Yes, Father, such has been your gracious will. All things have been handed over to me by my Father. No one knows the Son except the Father, and no one knows the Father except the Son and anyone to whom the Son wishes to reveal him.

"Come to me, all you who labor and are burdened, and I will give you rest. Take my yoke upon you and learn from me, for I am meek and humble of heart; and you will find rest for yourselves. For my yoke is easy, and my burden light."

MOST SACRED HEART OF JESUS — B   949

FIRST READING

Hosea 11:1, 3 4, 8c–9

Thus says the LORD:
    When Israel was a child I loved him,
        out of Egypt I called my son.
    Yet it was I who taught Ephraim
        to walk,
        who took them in my arms;
    I drew them with human cords,
        with bands of love;
    I fostered them like one
        who raises an infant to his cheeks;
    Yet, though I stooped to feed
        my child,

they did not know that I was
    their healer.

My heart is overwhelmed,
    my pity is stirred.
I will not give vent to my
    blazing anger,
    I will not destroy Ephraim again;
For I am God and not a man,
    the Holy One present
    among you;
    I will not let the flames
    consume you.

RESPONSORIAL PSALM

Isaiah 12:2–3, 4, 5–6

℟. You will draw wa - ter joy - ful - ly

from the springs of sal - va - tion.

Music: John Schiavone, b. 1947, © 2001, OCP Publications.

℟. You will draw water joyfully from the springs of salvation.

▶ God indeed is my savior;
　I am confident and unafraid.
My strength and my courage is
　the LORD,
　and he has been my savior.
With joy you will draw water
　at the fountain of salvation. ℟.

▶ Give thanks to the LORD, acclaim
　his name;
　among the nations make known
　his deeds,
　proclaim how exalted is his name. ℟.

▶ Sing praise to the LORD for his
　glorious achievement;
　let this be known throughout all
　the earth.
Shout with exultation, O city of Zion,
　for great in your midst
　is the Holy One of Israel! ℟.

SECOND READING

Ephesians 3:8–12, 14–19

Brothers and sisters: To me, the very least of all the holy ones, this grace was given, to preach to the Gentiles the inscrutable riches of Christ, and to bring to light for all what is the plan of the mystery hidden from ages past in God who created all things, so that the manifold wisdom of God might now be made known through the church to the principalities and authorities in the heavens. This was according to the eternal purpose that he accomplished in Christ Jesus our Lord, in whom we have boldness of speech and confidence of access through faith in him.

For this reason I kneel before the Father, from whom every family in heaven and on earth is named, that he may grant you in accord with the riches of his glory to be strengthened with power through his Spirit in the inner self, and that Christ may dwell in your hearts through faith; that you, rooted and grounded in love, may have strength to comprehend with all the holy ones what is the breadth and length and height and depth, and to know the love of Christ which surpasses knowledge, so that you may be filled with all the fullness of God.

GOSPEL ACCLAMATION

Matthew 11:29ab

℟. Al - le - lu - ia,　　al - le - lu - ia,　　al　-　le - lu - ia.

Music: John Schiavone, b. 1947, © 2001, OCP Publications.

▶ Take my yoke upon you, says the Lord;
　and learn from me, for I am meek and humble of heart. ℟.

OR

1 John 4:10b

▶ God first loved us
　and sent his Son as expiation for our sins. ℟.

GOSPEL READING

John 19:31–37

Since it was preparation day, in order that the bodies might not remain on the cross on the sabbath, for the sabbath day of that week was a solemn one, the Jews asked Pilate that their legs be broken and they be taken down. So the soldiers came and broke the legs of the first and then of the other one who was crucified with Jesus. But when they came to Jesus and saw that he was already dead, they did not break his legs, but one soldier thrust his lance into his side, and immediately blood and water flowed out. An eyewitness has testified, and his testimony is true; he knows that he is speaking the truth, so that you also may come to believe. For this happened so that the Scripture passage might be fulfilled:

Not a bone of it will be broken.

And again another passage says:

They will look upon him whom they have pierced.

MOST SACRED HEART OF JESUS — C   950

FIRST READING

Ezekiel 34:11–16

Thus says the Lord GOD: I myself will look after and tend my sheep. As a shepherd tends his flock when he finds himself among his scattered sheep, so will I tend my sheep. I will rescue them from every place where they were scattered when it was cloudy and dark. I will lead them out from among the peoples and gather them from the foreign lands; I will bring them back to their own country and pasture them upon the mountains of Israel in the land's ravines and all its inhabited places. In good pastures will I pasture them, and on the mountain heights of Israel shall be their grazing ground. There they shall lie down on good grazing ground, and in rich pastures shall they be pastured on the mountains of Israel. I myself will pasture my sheep; I myself will give them rest, says the Lord GOD. The lost I will seek out, the strayed I will bring back, the injured I will bind up, the sick I will heal, but the sleek and the strong I will destroy, shepherding them rightly.

RESPONSORIAL PSALM

Psalm 23:1–3a, 3b–4, 5, 6

℟. The Lord is my shep-herd; there is noth-ing I shall want.

Music: John Schiavone, b. 1947, © 2001, OCP Publications.

▶ The LORD is my shepherd; I shall
    not want.
  In verdant pastures he gives
    me repose;
  beside restful waters he leads me;
    he refreshes my soul. ℟.

▶ He guides me in right paths
    for his name's sake.
  Even though I walk in the dark valley
    I fear no evil; for you are at my side

with your rod and your staff
    that give me courage. ℟.

▶ You spread the table before me
    in the sight of my foes;
  you anoint my head with oil;
    my cup overflows. ℟.

▶ Only goodness and kindness follow me
    all the days of my life;
  and I shall dwell in the house of
    the LORD
    for years to come. ℟.

SECOND READING

Romans 5:5b–11

Brothers and sisters: The love of God has been poured out into our hearts through the Holy Spirit that has been given to us. For Christ, while we were still helpless, died at the appointed time for the ungodly. Indeed, only with difficulty does one die for a just person, though perhaps for a good person one might even find courage to die. But God proves his love for us in that while we were still sinners Christ died for us.

How much more then, since we are now justified by his blood, will we be saved through him from the wrath. Indeed, if, while we were enemies, we were reconciled to God through the death of his Son, how much more, once reconciled, will we be saved by his life. Not only that, but we also boast of God through our Lord Jesus Christ, through whom we have now received reconciliation.

GOSPEL ACCLAMATION

Matthew 11:29ab

℟. Al - le - lu - ia,   al - le - lu - ia,   al - le - lu - ia.

Music: John Schiavone, b. 1947, © 2001, OCP Publications.

▶ Take my yoke upon you, says the Lord;
   and learn from me, for I am meek and humble of heart. ℟.

OR   *John 10:14*

▶ I am the good shepherd, says the Lord;
   I know my sheep, and mine know me. ℟.

GOSPEL READING

Luke 15:3–7

Jesus addressed this parable to the Pharisees and scribes: "What man among you having a hundred sheep and losing one of them would not leave the ninety-nine in the desert and go after the lost one until he finds it? And when he does find it, he sets it on his shoulders with great joy and, upon his

arrival home, he calls together his friends and neighbors and says to them, 'Rejoice with me because I have found my lost sheep.' I tell you, in just the same way there will be more joy in heaven over one sinner who repents than over ninety-nine righteous people who have no need of repentance."

ORDINARY TIME

The First Sunday in Ordinary Time is the Feast of the Baptism of the Lord (see number 899).

SECOND SUNDAY IN ORDINARY TIME — A   951

FIRST READING
Isaiah 49:3, 5–6

The LORD said to me: You are my servant,
Israel, through whom I show my glory.
Now the LORD has spoken
who formed me as his servant from
the womb,
that Jacob may be brought back to him
and Israel gathered to him;
and I am made glorious in the sight of
the LORD,

and my God is now my strength!
It is too little, the LORD says, for you to
be my servant,
to raise up the tribes of Jacob,
and restore the survivors of Israel;
I will make you a light to the nations,
that my salvation may reach to the
ends of the earth.

RESPONSORIAL PSALM
Psalm 40:2, 4, 7–8, 8–9, 10

℟. Here am I, Lord; I come to do your will.

Music: John Schiavone, b. 1947, © 2001, OCP Publications.

▶ I have waited, waited for the LORD,
and he stooped toward me and
heard my cry.
And he put a new song into my mouth,
a hymn to our God. ℟.

▶ Sacrifice or offering you wished not,
but ears open to obedience you
gave me.
Holocausts or sin-offerings you
sought not;
then said I, "Behold I come." ℟.

▶ "In the written scroll it is prescribed
for me,
to do your will, O my God, is my delight,
and your law is within my heart!" ℟.

▶ I announced your justice in the
vast assembly;
I did not restrain my lips, as you,
O LORD, know. ℟.

SECOND READING
1 Corinthians 1:1–3

Paul, called to be an apostle of Christ
Jesus by the will of God, and Sosthenes
our brother, to the church of God that
is in Corinth, to you who have been
sanctified in Christ Jesus, called to be

holy, with all those everywhere who
call upon the name of our Lord Jesus
Christ, their Lord and ours. Grace to
you and peace from God our Father
and the Lord Jesus Christ.

GOSPEL ACCLAMATION
John 1:14a, 12a

℟. Al - le - lu - ia, al - le - lu - ia, al - le - lu - ia.

Music: John Schiavone, b. 1947, © 2001, OCP Publications.

℟. **Alleluia.**

▶ The Word of God became flesh and dwelt among us.
To those who accepted him,
he gave power to become children of God. ℟.

GOSPEL READING

John 1:29–34

John the Baptist saw Jesus coming toward him and said, "Behold, the Lamb of God, who takes away the sin of the world. He is the one of whom I said, 'A man is coming after me who ranks ahead of me because he existed before me.' I did not know him, but the reason why I came baptizing with water was that he might be made known to Israel." John testified further, saying, "I saw the Spirit come down like a dove from heaven and remain upon him. I did not know him, but the one who sent me to baptize with water told me, 'On whomever you see the Spirit come down and remain, he is the one who will baptize with the Holy Spirit.' Now I have seen and testified that he is the Son of God."

---

952 SECOND SUNDAY IN ORDINARY TIME — B

FIRST READING

1 Samuel 3:3b–10, 19

Samuel was sleeping in the temple of the LORD where the ark of God was. The LORD called to Samuel, who answered, "Here I am." Samuel ran to Eli and said, "Here I am. You called me." "I did not call you," Eli said. "Go back to sleep." So he went back to sleep. Again the LORD called Samuel, who rose and went to Eli. "Here I am," he said. "You called me." But Eli answered, "I did not call you, my son. Go back to sleep."

At that time Samuel was not familiar with the LORD, because the LORD had not revealed anything to him as yet. The LORD called Samuel again, for the third time. Getting up and going to Eli, he said, "Here I am. You called me." Then Eli understood that the LORD was calling the youth. So he said to Samuel, "Go to sleep, and if you are called, reply, Speak, LORD, for your servant is listening." When Samuel went to sleep in his place, the LORD came and revealed his presence, calling out as before, "Samuel, Samuel!" Samuel answered, "Speak, for your servant is listening."

Samuel grew up, and the LORD was with him, not permitting any word of his to be without effect.

RESPONSORIAL PSALM

Psalm 40:2, 4, 7–8, 8–9, 10

℟. Here am I, Lord; I come to do your will.

Music: John Schiavone, b. 1947, © 2001, OCP Publications.

▶ I have waited, waited for the LORD,
and he stooped toward me and
heard my cry.
And he put a new song into my mouth,
a hymn to our God. ℟.

▶ Sacrifice or offering you wished not,
but ears open to obedience you
gave me.
Holocausts or sin-offerings you
sought not;
then said I, "Behold I come." ℟.

▶ "In the written scroll it is prescribed
for me,
to do your will, O my God, is
my delight,
and your law is within my heart!" ℟.

▶ I announced your justice in the
vast assembly;
I did not restrain my lips, as you,
O LORD, know. ℟.

SECOND READING
1 Corinthians 6:13c–15a, 17–20

Brothers and sisters: The body is not for immorality, but for the Lord, and the Lord is for the body; God raised the Lord and will also raise us by his power.

Do you not know that your bodies are members of Christ? But whoever is joined to the Lord becomes one Spirit with him. Avoid immorality. Every other sin a person commits is outside the body, but the immoral person sins against his own body. Do you not know that your body is a temple of the Holy Spirit within you, whom you have from God, and that you are not your own? For you have been purchased at a price. Therefore glorify God in your body.

GOSPEL ACCLAMATION
John 1:41, 17b

℟. Al - le - lu - ia, al - le - lu - ia, al - le - lu - ia.

Music: John Schiavone, b. 1947, © 2001, OCP Publications.

▶ We have found the Messiah:
Jesus Christ, who brings us truth and grace. ℟.

GOSPEL READING
John 1:35–42

John was standing with two of his disciples, and as he watched Jesus walk by, he said, "Behold, the Lamb of God." The two disciples heard what he said and followed Jesus. Jesus turned and saw them following him and said to them, "What are you looking for?" They said to him, "Rabbi" — which translated means Teacher —, "where are you staying?" He said to them, "Come, and you will see." So they went and saw where Jesus was staying, and they stayed with him that day. It was about four in the afternoon. Andrew, the brother of Simon Peter, was one of the two who heard John and followed Jesus. He first found his own brother Simon and told him, "We have found the Messiah" — which is translated Christ. Then he brought him to Jesus. Jesus looked at him and said, "You are Simon the son of John; you will be called Cephas" — which is translated Peter.

SECOND SUNDAY IN ORDINARY TIME — C   953

FIRST READING
Isaiah 62:1–5

For Zion's sake I will not be silent,
for Jerusalem's sake I will not be quiet,
until her vindication shines forth like
the dawn

and her victory like a burning torch.

Nations shall behold your vindication,
and all the kings your glory;

you shall be called by a new name
   pronounced by the mouth of the LORD.
You shall be a glorious crown in the
   hand of the LORD,
   a royal diadem held by your God.
No more shall people call you "Forsaken,"
   or your land "Desolate,"
but you shall be called "My Delight,"

and your land "Espoused."
For the LORD delights in you
   and makes your land his spouse.
As a young man marries a virgin,
   your Builder shall marry you;
and as a bridegroom rejoices in
   his bride
   so shall your God rejoice in you.

RESPONSORIAL PSALM

Psalm 96:1–2, 2–3, 7–8, 9–10

℟. Pro-claim his mar-vel-ous deeds to all the na-tions.

Music: John Schiavone, b. 1947, © 2001, OCP Publications.

▶ Sing to the LORD a new song;
   sing to the LORD, all you lands.
   Sing to the LORD; bless his name. ℟.

▶ Announce his salvation, day after day.
   Tell his glory among the nations;
     among all peoples, his wondrous
     deeds. ℟.

▶ Give to the LORD, you families
   of nations,

give to the LORD glory and praise;
give to the LORD the glory due his
   name! ℟.

▶ Worship the LORD in holy attire.
   Tremble before him, all the earth;
   say among the nations: The LORD is king.
   He governs the peoples with
     equity. ℟.

SECOND READING

1 Corinthians 12:4–11

Brothers and sisters: There are different kinds of spiritual gifts but the same Spirit; there are different forms of service but the same Lord; there are different workings but the same God who produces all of them in everyone. To each individual the manifestation of the Spirit is given for some benefit. To one is given through the Spirit the expression of wisdom; to another, the expression of knowledge according to the same Spirit; to another, faith by the same Spirit; to another, gifts of healing by the one Spirit; to another, mighty deeds; to another, prophecy; to another, discernment of spirits; to another, varieties of tongues; to another, interpretation of tongues. But one and the same Spirit produces all of these, distributing them individually to each person as he wishes.

GOSPEL ACCLAMATION

cf. 2 Thessalonians 2:14

℟. Al - le - lu - ia, al - le - lu - ia, al - le - lu - ia.

Music: John Schiavone, b. 1947, © 2001, OCP Publications.

▶ God has called us through the Gospel
   to possess the glory of our Lord Jesus Christ. ℟.

GOSPEL READING

John 2:1–11

There was a wedding at Cana in Galilee, and the mother of Jesus was there. Jesus and his disciples were also invited to the wedding. When the wine ran short, the mother of Jesus said to him, "They have no wine." And Jesus said to her, "Woman, how does your concern affect me? My hour has not yet come." His mother said to the servers, "Do whatever he tells you." Now there were six stone water jars there for Jewish ceremonial washings, each holding twenty to thirty gallons. Jesus told them, "Fill the jars with water." So they filled them to the brim. Then he told them, "Draw some out now and take it to the headwaiter." So they took it. And when the headwaiter tasted the water that had become wine, without knowing where it came from — although the servers who had drawn the water knew —, the headwaiter called the bridegroom and said to him, "Everyone serves good wine first, and then when people have drunk freely, an inferior one; but you have kept the good wine until now." Jesus did this as the beginning of his signs at Cana in Galilee and so revealed his glory, and his disciples began to believe in him.

THIRD SUNDAY IN ORDINARY TIME — A   954

FIRST READING

Isaiah 8:23 – 9:3

First the LORD degraded the land of Zebulun and the land of Naphtali; but in the end he has glorified the seaward road, the land west of the Jordan, the District of the Gentiles.

Anguish has taken wing, dispelled
   is darkness:
   for there is no gloom where but now
      there was distress.
The people who walked in darkness
   have seen a great light;
upon those who dwelt in the land
      of gloom

a light has shone.
You have brought them abundant joy
   and great rejoicing,
as they rejoice before you as at
      the harvest,
   as people make merry when
      dividing spoils.
For the yoke that burdened them,
   the pole on their shoulder,
and the rod of their taskmaster
   you have smashed, as on the day
      of Midian.

RESPONSORIAL PSALM

Psalm 27:1, 4, 13–14

℟. The Lord is my light and my sal - va - tion.

Music: John Schiavone, b. 1947, © 2001, OCP Publications.

▶ The LORD is my light and my salvation;
   whom should I fear?
   The LORD is my life's refuge;
      of whom should I be afraid? ℟.

▶ One thing I ask of the LORD;
   this I seek:

to dwell in the house of the LORD
   all the days of my life,
   that I may gaze on the loveliness of
      the LORD
   and contemplate his temple. ℟.

℟. The Lord is my light and my salvation.

▶ I believe that I shall see the bounty of the LORD
in the land of the living.

Wait for the LORD with courage;
be stouthearted, and wait for the LORD. **℟.**

SECOND READING
1 Corinthians 1:10–13, 17

I urge you, brothers and sisters, in the name of our Lord Jesus Christ, that all of you agree in what you say, and that there be no divisions among you, but that you be united in the same mind and in the same purpose. For it has been reported to me about you, my brothers and sisters, by Chloe's people, that there are rivalries among you. I mean that each of you is saying, "I belong to Paul," or "I belong to Apollos," or "I belong to Cephas," or "I belong to Christ." Is Christ divided? Was Paul crucified for you? Or were you baptized in the name of Paul? For Christ did not send me to baptize but to preach the gospel, and not with the wisdom of human eloquence, so that the cross of Christ might not be emptied of its meaning.

GOSPEL ACCLAMATION
cf. Matthew 4:23

℟. Al - le - lu - ia, al - le - lu - ia, al - le - lu - ia.

Music: John Schiavone, b. 1947, © 2001, OCP Publications.

▶ Jesus proclaimed the Gospel of the kingdom
and cured every disease among the people. **℟.**

GOSPEL READING
Matthew 4:12–23 or 4:12–17

(Include bracketed text for Long Form)

When Jesus heard that John had been arrested, he withdrew to Galilee. He left Nazareth and went to live in Capernaum by the sea, in the region of Zebulun and Naphtali, that what had been said through Isaiah the prophet might be fulfilled:
> Land of Zebulun and land of Naphtali,
> the way to the sea, beyond
> the Jordan,
> Galilee of the Gentiles,
> the people who sit in darkness have
> seen a great light,
> on those dwelling in a land
> overshadowed by death
> light has arisen.

From that time on, Jesus began to preach and say, "Repent, for the kingdom of heaven is at hand."

[As he was walking by the Sea of Galilee, he saw two brothers, Simon who is called Peter, and his brother Andrew, casting a net into the sea; they were fishermen. He said to them, "Come after me, and I will make you fishers of men." At once they left their nets and followed him. He walked along from there and saw two other brothers, James, the son of Zebedee, and his brother John. They were in a boat, with their father Zebedee, mending their nets. He called them, and immediately they left their boat and their father and followed him. He went around all of Galilee, teaching in their synagogues, proclaiming the gospel of the kingdom, and curing every disease and illness among the people.]

THIRD SUNDAY IN ORDINARY TIME — B   955

FIRST READING   *Jonah 3:1–5, 10*

The word of the LORD came to Jonah, saying: "Set out for the great city of Nineveh, and announce to it the message that I will tell you." So Jonah made ready and went to Nineveh, according to the LORD's bidding. Now Nineveh was an enormously large city; it took three days to go through it. Jonah began his journey through the city, and had gone but a single day's walk announcing, "Forty days more and Nineveh shall be destroyed," when the people of Nineveh believed God; they proclaimed a fast and all of them, great and small, put on sackcloth.

When God saw by their actions how they turned from their evil way, he repented of the evil that he had threatened to do to them; he did not carry it out.

RESPONSORIAL PSALM   *Psalm 25:4–5, 6–7, 8–9*

℟. Teach me your ways, O Lord, [your ways, O Lord.]

Music: John Schiavone, b. 1947, © 2001, OCP Publications.

▶ Your ways, O LORD, make known to me;
  teach me your paths,
  guide me in your truth and teach me,
  for you are God my savior. ℟.

▶ Remember that your compassion, O LORD,

and your love are from of old.
In your kindness remember me,
  because of your goodness, O LORD. ℟.

▶ Good and upright is the LORD;
  thus he shows sinners the way.
He guides the humble to justice
  and teaches the humble his way. ℟.

SECOND READING   *1 Corinthians 7:29–31*

I tell you, brothers and sisters, the time is running out. From now on, let those having wives act as not having them, those weeping as not weeping, those rejoicing as not rejoicing, those buying as not owning, those using the world as not using it fully. For the world in its present form is passing away.

GOSPEL ACCLAMATION   *Mark 1:15*

℟. Al - le - lu - ia, al - le - lu - ia, al - le - lu - ia.

Music: John Schiavone, b. 1947, © 2001, OCP Publications.

▶ The kingdom of God is at hand.
  Repent and believe in the Gospel. ℟.

GOSPEL READING *Mark 1:14–20*

After John had been arrested, Jesus came to Galilee proclaiming the gospel of God: "This is the time of fulfillment. The kingdom of God is at hand. Repent, and believe in the gospel."

As he passed by the Sea of Galilee, he saw Simon and his brother Andrew casting their nets into the sea; they were fishermen. Jesus said to them,

"Come after me, and I will make you fishers of men." Then they abandoned their nets and followed him. He walked along a little farther and saw James, the son of Zebedee, and his brother John. They too were in a boat mending their nets. Then he called them. So they left their father Zebedee in the boat along with the hired men and followed him.

---

956   THIRD SUNDAY IN ORDINARY TIME — C

FIRST READING *Nehemiah 8:2–4a, 5–6, 8–10*

Ezra the priest brought the law before the assembly, which consisted of men, women, and those children old enough to understand. Standing at one end of the open place that was before the Water Gate, he read out of the book from daybreak till midday, in the presence of the men, the women, and those children old enough to understand; and all the people listened attentively to the book of the law. Ezra the scribe stood on a wooden platform that had been made for the occasion. He opened the scroll so that all the people might see it — for he was standing higher up than any of the people —; and, as he opened it, all the people rose. Ezra blessed the LORD, the great God, and all the people, their hands raised high, answered,

"Amen, amen!" Then they bowed down and prostrated themselves before the LORD, their faces to the ground. Ezra read plainly from the book of the law of God, interpreting it so that all could understand what was read. Then Nehemiah, that is, His Excellency, and Ezra the priest-scribe and the Levites who were instructing the people said to all the people: "Today is holy to the LORD your God. Do not be sad, and do not weep" — for all the people were weeping as they heard the words of the law. He said further: "Go, eat rich foods and drink sweet drinks, and allot portions to those who had nothing prepared; for today is holy to our LORD. Do not be saddened this day, for rejoicing in the LORD must be your strength!"

RESPONSORIAL PSALM *Psalm 19:8, 9, 10, 15*

℟. Your words, Lord, are Spir - it and life.

Music: John Schiavone, b. 1947, © 2001, OCP Publications.

▶ The law of the LORD is perfect,
   refreshing the soul;
the decree of the LORD is trustworthy,
   giving wisdom to the simple. ℟.

▶ The precepts of the LORD are right,
   rejoicing the heart;
the command of the LORD is clear,
   enlightening the eye. ℟.

▶ The fear of the LORD is pure,
   enduring forever;
the ordinances of the LORD are true,
   all of them just. ℟.

▶ Let the words of my mouth and the
     thought of my heart
find favor before you,
O LORD, my rock and my redeemer. ℟.

SECOND READING

1 Corinthians 12:12–30 or 12:12–14, 27

(Include bracketed text for Long Form)

Brothers and sisters: As a body is one though it has many parts, and all the parts of the body, though many, are one body, so also Christ. For in one Spirit we were all baptized into one body, whether Jews or Greeks, slaves or free persons, and we were all given to drink of one Spirit.

Now the body is not a single part, but many. [If a foot should say, "Because I am not a hand I do not belong to the body," it does not for this reason belong any less to the body. Or if an ear should say, "Because I am not an eye I do not belong to the body," it does not for this reason belong any less to the body. If the whole body were an eye, where would the hearing be? If the whole body were hearing, where would the sense of smell be? But as it is, God placed the parts, each one of them, in the body as he intended. If they were all one part, where would the body be? But as it is, there are many parts, yet one body. The eye cannot say to the hand, "I do not need you," nor again the head to the feet, "I do not need you." Indeed, the parts of the body that seem to be weaker are all the more necessary, and those parts of the body that we consider less honorable we surround with greater honor, and our less presentable parts are treated with greater propriety, whereas our more presentable parts do not need this. But God has so constructed the body as to give greater honor to a part that is without it, so that there may be no division in the body, but that the parts may have the same concern for one another. If one part suffers, all the parts suffer with it; if one part is honored, all the parts share its joy.

Now] you are Christ's body, and individually parts of it. [Some people God has designated in the church to be, first, apostles; second, prophets; third, teachers; then, mighty deeds; then gifts of healing, assistance, administration, and varieties of tongues. Are all apostles? Are all prophets? Are all teachers? Do all work mighty deeds? Do all have gifts of healing? Do all speak in tongues? Do all interpret?]

GOSPEL ACCLAMATION

cf. Luke 4:18

℟. Al - le - lu - ia, al - le - lu - ia, al - le - lu - ia.

Music: John Schiavone, b. 1947, © 2001, OCP Publications.

▶ The Lord sent me to bring glad tidings to the poor, and to proclaim liberty to captives. ℟.

GOSPEL READING

Luke 1:1–4; 4:14–21

Since many have undertaken to compile a narrative of the events that have been fulfilled among us, just as those who were eyewitnesses from the beginning and ministers of the word have handed them down to us, I too have decided, after investigating everything accurately anew, to write it down in an orderly sequence for you, most excellent Theophilus, so that you may realize the certainty of the teachings you have received.

Jesus returned to Galilee in the power of the Spirit, and news of him spread throughout the whole region. He taught in their synagogues and was praised by all.

He came to Nazareth, where he had grown up, and went according to his custom into the synagogue on the sabbath day. He stood up to read and was handed a scroll of the prophet Isaiah. He unrolled the scroll and found the passage where it was written:
The Spirit of the Lord is upon me,
because he has anointed me
to bring glad tidings to the poor.
He has sent me to proclaim liberty
to captives

and recovery of sight to the blind,
to let the oppressed go free,
and to proclaim a year acceptable to
the Lord.
Rolling up the scroll, he handed it back to the attendant and sat down, and the eyes of all in the synagogue looked intently at him. He said to them, "Today this Scripture passage is fulfilled in your hearing."

---

957 FOURTH SUNDAY IN ORDINARY TIME — A

FIRST READING
Zephaniah 2:3; 3:12–13

Seek the LORD, all you humble of
    the earth,
  who have observed his law;
seek justice, seek humility;
  perhaps you may be sheltered
  on the day of the LORD's anger.

But I will leave as a remnant in
    your midst
  a people humble and lowly,

who shall take refuge in the name of
    the LORD:
  the remnant of Israel.
They shall do no wrong
  and speak no lies;
nor shall there be found in their mouths
  a deceitful tongue;
they shall pasture and couch their flocks
  with none to disturb them.

RESPONSORIAL PSALM
Psalm 146:6–7, 8–9, 9–10

℟. **Bless'd are the poor in spir-it; the king-dom of heav'n is theirs!**

Music: John Schiavone, b. 1947, © 2001, OCP Publications.

or: **Alleluia.**

▶ The LORD keeps faith forever,
    secures justice for the oppressed,
    gives food to the hungry.
  The LORD sets captives free. ℟.

▶ The LORD gives sight to the blind;
    the LORD raises up those who were
        bowed down.
  The LORD loves the just;
    the LORD protects strangers. ℟.

▶ The fatherless and the widow the
        LORD sustains,
    but the way of the wicked
    he thwarts.
  The LORD shall reign forever;
    your God, O Zion, through all
        generations. Alleluia. ℟.

SECOND READING
1 Corinthians 1:26–31

Consider your own calling, brothers and sisters. Not many of you were wise by human standards, not many were

powerful, not many were of noble birth. Rather, God chose the foolish of the world to shame the wise, and God chose the weak of the world to shame the strong, and God chose the lowly and despised of the world, those who count for nothing, to reduce to nothing those who are something, so that no human being might boast before God.

It is due to him that you are in Christ Jesus, who became for us wisdom from God, as well as righteousness, sanctification, and redemption, so that, as it is written, "Whoever boasts, should boast in the Lord."

GOSPEL ACCLAMATION

Matthew 5:12a

℟. Al - le - lu - ia, al - le - lu - ia, al - le - lu - ia.

Music: John Schiavone, b. 1947, © 2001, OCP Publications.

❯ Rejoice and be glad;
your reward will be great in heaven. **℟.**

GOSPEL READING

Matthew 5:1–12a

When Jesus saw the crowds, he went up the mountain, and after he had sat down, his disciples came to him. He began to teach them, saying:
"Blessed are the poor in spirit,
for theirs is the kingdom of heaven.
Blessed are they who mourn,
for they will be comforted.
Blessed are the meek,
for they will inherit the land.
Blessed are they who hunger and
thirst for righteousness,
for they will be satisfied.
Blessed are the merciful,
for they will be shown mercy.
Blessed are the clean of heart,
for they will see God.
Blessed are the peacemakers,
for they will be called children
of God.
Blessed are they who are persecuted
for the sake of righteousness,
for theirs is the kingdom of heaven.
Blessed are you when they insult you
and persecute you and utter every kind
of evil against you falsely because of
me. Rejoice and be glad, for your
reward will be great in heaven."

FOURTH SUNDAY IN ORDINARY TIME — B · 958

FIRST READING

Deuteronomy 18:15–20

Moses spoke to all the people, saying: "A prophet like me will the LORD, your God, raise up for you from among your own kin; to him you shall listen. This is exactly what you requested of the LORD, your God, at Horeb on the day of the assembly, when you said, 'Let us not again hear the voice of the LORD, our God, nor see this great fire any more, lest we die.' And the LORD said to me, 'This was well said. I will raise up for

them a prophet like you from among their kin, and will put my words into his mouth; he shall tell them all that I command him. Whoever will not listen to my words which he speaks in my name, I myself will make him answer for it. But if a prophet presumes to speak in my name an oracle that I have not commanded him to speak, or speaks in the name of other gods, he shall die.'"

RESPONSORIAL PSALM

Psalm 95:1–2, 6–7, 7–9

℟. If to - day you hear his voice, hard - en not your hearts.

Music: John Schiavone, b. 1947, © 2001, OCP Publications.

▶ Come, let us sing joyfully to the LORD;
  let us acclaim the rock of
    our salvation.
Let us come into his presence
  with thanksgiving;
  let us joyfully sing psalms to him. ℟.

▶ Come, let us bow down in worship;
  let us kneel before the LORD who
    made us.
For he is our God,
  and we are the people he
    shepherds, the flock he guides. ℟.

▶ Oh, that today you would hear
    his voice:
  "Harden not your hearts as
    at Meribah,
  as in the day of Massah in
    the desert,
where your fathers tempted me;
  they tested me though they had
    seen my works." ℟.

SECOND READING

1 Corinthians 7:32–35

Brothers and sisters: I should like you to be free of anxieties. An unmarried man is anxious about the things of the Lord, how he may please the Lord. But a married man is anxious about the things of the world, how he may please his wife, and he is divided. An unmarried woman or a virgin is anxious about the things of the Lord, so that she may be holy in both body and spirit. A married woman, on the other hand, is anxious about the things of the world, how she may please her husband. I am telling you this for your own benefit, not to impose a restraint upon you, but for the sake of propriety and adherence to the Lord without distraction.

GOSPEL ACCLAMATION

Matthew 4:16

℟. Al - le - lu - ia, al - le - lu - ia, al - le - lu - ia.

Music: John Schiavone, b. 1947, © 2001, OCP Publications.

▶ The people who sit in darkness have seen a great light;
  on those dwelling in a land overshadowed by death,
  light has arisen. ℟.

GOSPEL READING

Mark 1:21–28

Then they came to Capernaum, and on the sabbath Jesus entered the synagogue and taught. The people were astonished at his teaching, for he taught them as one having authority and not as the scribes. In their synagogue was a man with an unclean spirit; he cried out, "What have you to do with us, Jesus of Nazareth? Have you come to destroy us? I know who you are — the Holy One of God!" Jesus rebuked him and said, "Quiet! Come out of him!" The unclean spirit convulsed him and with a loud cry came out of him. All were amazed and asked one another, "What is this? A new teaching with authority.

He commands even the unclean spirits and they obey him." His fame spread everywhere throughout the whole region of Galilee.

FOURTH SUNDAY IN ORDINARY TIME — C 959

FIRST READING
Jeremiah 1:4–5, 17–19

The word of the LORD came to me, saying:
 Before I formed you in the womb
  I knew you,
 before you were born
  I dedicated you,
 a prophet to the nations
  I appointed you.

 But do you gird your loins;
  stand up and tell them
  all that I command you.
 Be not crushed on their account,
  as though I would leave you
  crushed before them;

 for it is I this day
  who have made you a
  fortified city,
 a pillar of iron, a wall of brass,
  against the whole land:
 against Judah's kings and princes,
  against its priests and people.
 They will fight against you but
  not prevail over you,
 for I am with you to deliver you,
  says the LORD.

RESPONSORIAL PSALM
Psalm 71:1–2, 3–4, 5–6, 15, 17

℟. I will sing of your sal - va - tion, [sing of your sal - va - tion.]

Music: John Schiavone, b. 1947, © 2001, OCP Publications.

▶ In you, O LORD, I take refuge;
 let me never be put to shame.
In your justice rescue me, and
  deliver me;
 incline your ear to me, and
  save me. ℟.

▶ Be my rock of refuge,
 a stronghold to give me safety,
 for you are my rock and my fortress.
O my God, rescue me from the hand
 of the wicked. ℟.

▶ For you are my hope, O Lord;
 my trust, O God, from my youth.
On you I depend from birth;
 from my mother's womb you are
  my strength. ℟.

▶ My mouth shall declare your justice,
 day by day your salvation.
O God, you have taught me from
 my youth,
 and till the present I proclaim your
  wondrous deeds. ℟.

SECOND READING
1 Corinthians 12:31 — 13:13 or 13:4–13

(Include bracketed text for Long Form)

Brothers and sisters: [Strive eagerly for the greatest spiritual gifts. But I shall show you a still more excellent way.
 If I speak in human and angelic tongues, but do not have love, I am a

resounding gong or a clashing cymbal. And if I have the gift of prophecy, and comprehend all mysteries and all knowledge; if I have all faith so as to move mountains, but do not have love,

I am nothing. If I give away everything I own, and if I hand my body over so that I may boast, but do not have love, I gain nothing.]

Love is patient, love is kind. It is not jealous, it is not pompous, it is not inflated, it is not rude, it does not seek its own interests, it is not quick-tempered, it does not brood over injury, it does not rejoice over wrongdoing but rejoices with the truth. It bears all things, believes all things, hopes all things, endures all things.

Love never fails. If there are prophecies, they will be brought to nothing; if tongues, they will cease; if knowledge, it will be brought to nothing. For we know partially and we prophesy partially, but when the perfect comes, the partial will pass away. When I was a child, I used to talk as a child, think as a child, reason as a child; when I became a man, I put aside childish things. At present we see indistinctly, as in a mirror, but then face to face. At present I know partially; then I shall know fully, as I am fully known. So faith, hope, love remain, these three; but the greatest of these is love.

GOSPEL ACCLAMATION

Luke 4:18

℞. Al - le - lu - ia, al - le - lu - ia, al - le - lu - ia.

Music: John Schiavone, b. 1947, © 2001, OCP Publications.

▶ The Lord sent me to bring glad tidings to the poor, to proclaim liberty to captives. ℞.

GOSPEL READING

Luke 4:21–30

Jesus began speaking in the synagogue, saying: "Today this Scripture passage is fulfilled in your hearing." And all spoke highly of him and were amazed at the gracious words that came from his mouth. They also asked, "Isn't this the son of Joseph?" He said to them, "Surely you will quote me this proverb, 'Physician, cure yourself,' and say, 'Do here in your native place the things that we heard were done in Capernaum.'" And he said, "Amen, I say to you, no prophet is accepted in his own native place. Indeed, I tell you, there were many widows in Israel in the days of Elijah when the sky was closed for three and a half years and a severe famine spread over the entire land. It was to none of these that Elijah was sent, but only to a widow in Zarephath in the land of Sidon. Again, there were many lepers in Israel during the time of Elisha the prophet; yet not one of them was cleansed, but only Naaman the Syrian." When the people in the synagogue heard this, they were all filled with fury. They rose up, drove him out of the town, and led him to the brow of the hill on which their town had been built, to hurl him down headlong. But Jesus passed through the midst of them and went away.

FIFTH SUNDAY IN ORDINARY TIME — A   **960**

FIRST READING   *Isaiah 58:7–10*

Thus says the LORD:
 Share your bread with the hungry,
  shelter the oppressed and
   the homeless;
 clothe the naked when you see them,
  and do not turn your back on
   your own.
 Then your light shall break forth like
  the dawn,
  and your wound shall quickly
   be healed;
 your vindication shall go before you,
  and the glory of the LORD shall be
   your rear guard.

Then you shall call, and the LORD
  will answer,
 you shall cry for help, and he will
  say: Here I am!
If you remove from your midst
 oppression, false accusation and
  malicious speech;
if you bestow your bread on
  the hungry
 and satisfy the afflicted;
then light shall rise for you in
  the darkness,
 and the gloom shall become for
  you like midday.

RESPONSORIAL PSALM   *Psalm 112:4–5, 6–7, 8–9*

℟. The just man is a light in dark-ness to the up-right.

Music: John Schiavone, b. 1947, © 2001, OCP Publications.

or: **Alleluia.**

▶ Light shines through the darkness for
  the upright;
 he is gracious and merciful and just.
 Well for the man who is gracious
  and lends,
 who conducts his affairs with
  justice. ℟.

▶ He shall never be moved;
 the just one shall be in everlasting
  remembrance.

An evil report he shall not fear;
 his heart is firm, trusting in
  the LORD. ℟.

▶ His heart is steadfast; he shall not fear.
 Lavishly he gives to the poor;
 his justice shall endure forever;
  his horn shall be exalted in glory. ℟.

SECOND READING   *1 Corinthians 2:1–5*

When I came to you, brothers and
sisters, proclaiming the mystery of God,
I did not come with sublimity of words
or of wisdom. For I resolved to know
nothing while I was with you except
Jesus Christ, and him crucified. I came
to you in weakness and fear and much

trembling, and my message and my
proclamation were not with persuasive
words of wisdom, but with a
demonstration of Spirit and power, so
that your faith might rest not on human
wisdom but on the power of God.

GOSPEL ACCLAMATION

John 8:12

℟. Al - le - lu - ia, al - le - lu - ia, al - le - lu - ia.

Music: John Schiavone, b. 1947, © 2001, OCP Publications.

▶ I am the light of the world, says the Lord;
whoever follows me will have the light of life. ℟.

GOSPEL READING

Matthew 5:13–16

Jesus said to his disciples: "You are the salt of the earth. But if salt loses its taste, with what can it be seasoned? It is no longer good for anything but to be thrown out and trampled underfoot. You are the light of the world. A city set on a mountain cannot be hidden. Nor do they light a lamp and then put it under a bushel basket; it is set on a lampstand, where it gives light to all in the house. Just so, your light must shine before others, that they may see your good deeds and glorify your heavenly Father."

---

961   FIFTH SUNDAY IN ORDINARY TIME — B

FIRST READING

Job 7:1–4, 6–7

Job spoke, saying:
Is not man's life on earth a drudgery?
  Are not his days those of hirelings?
He is a slave who longs for the shade,
  a hireling who waits for his wages.
So I have been assigned months
    of misery,
  and troubled nights have been
    allotted to me.

If in bed I say, "When shall I arise?"
  then the night drags on;
  I am filled with restlessness until
    the dawn.
My days are swifter than a
    weaver's shuttle;
  they come to an end without hope.
Remember that my life is like the wind;
I shall not see happiness again.

RESPONSORIAL PSALM

Psalm 147:1–2, 3–4, 5–6

℟. Praise the Lord, who heals the bro - ken - heart - ed.

Music: John Schiavone, b. 1947, © 2001, OCP Publications.

or: **Alleluia.**

▶ Praise the LORD, for he is good;
  sing praise to our God, for he
    is gracious;
  it is fitting to praise him.
The LORD rebuilds Jerusalem;
  the dispersed of Israel he gathers. ℟.

▶ He heals the brokenhearted
  and binds up their wounds.

He tells the number of the stars;
  he calls each by name. ℟.

▶ Great is our Lord and mighty
  in power;
  to his wisdom there is no limit.
The LORD sustains the lowly;
  the wicked he casts to the ground. ℟.

SECOND READING
1 Corinthians 9:16–19, 22–23

Brothers and sisters: If I preach the gospel, this is no reason for me to boast, for an obligation has been imposed on me, and woe to me if I do not preach it! If I do so willingly, I have a recompense, but if unwillingly, then I have been entrusted with a stewardship. What then is my recompense? That, when I preach, I offer the gospel free of charge so as not to make full use of my right in the gospel. Although I am free in regard to all, I have made myself a slave to all so as to win over as many as possible. To the weak I became weak, to win over the weak. I have become all things to all, to save at least some. All this I do for the sake of the gospel, so that I too may have a share in it.

GOSPEL ACCLAMATION
Matthew 8:17

℟. Al - le - lu - ia, al - le - lu - ia, al - le - lu - ia.

Music: John Schiavone, b. 1947, © 2001, OCP Publications.

▶ Christ took away our infirmities
and bore our diseases. ℟.

GOSPEL READING
Mark 1:29–39

On leaving the synagogue Jesus entered the house of Simon and Andrew with James and John. Simon's mother-in-law lay sick with a fever. They immediately told him about her. He approached, grasped her hand, and helped her up. Then the fever left her and she waited on them.

When it was evening, after sunset, they brought to him all who were ill or possessed by demons. The whole town was gathered at the door. He cured many who were sick with various diseases, and he drove out many demons, not permitting them to speak because they knew him.

Rising very early before dawn, he left and went off to a deserted place, where he prayed. Simon and those who were with him pursued him and on finding him said, "Everyone is looking for you." He told them, "Let us go on to the nearby villages that I may preach there also. For this purpose have I come." So he went into their synagogues, preaching and driving out demons throughout the whole of Galilee.

FIFTH SUNDAY IN ORDINARY TIME — C 962

FIRST READING
Isaiah 6:1–2a, 3–8

In the year King Uzziah died, I saw the Lord seated on a high and lofty throne, with the train of his garment filling the temple. Seraphim were stationed above.

They cried one to the other, "Holy, holy, holy is the LORD of hosts! All the earth is filled with his glory!" At the sound of that cry, the frame of the door shook and the house was filled with smoke.

Then I said, "Woe is me, I am doomed! For I am a man of unclean lips, living among a people of unclean lips; yet my eyes have seen the King, the LORD of hosts!" Then one of the seraphim flew to me, holding an ember that he had taken with tongs from the altar.

He touched my mouth with it, and said, "See, now that this has touched your lips, your wickedness is removed, your sin purged."

Then I heard the voice of the Lord saying, "Whom shall I send? Who will go for us?" "Here I am," I said; "send me!"

RESPONSORIAL PSALM

Psalm 138:1–2, 2–3, 4–5, 7–8

℟. In the sight of the an-gels I will sing your prais-es, Lord.

Music: John Schiavone, b. 1947, © 2001, OCP Publications.

▶ I will give thanks to you, O LORD, with all my heart,
for you have heard the words of my mouth;
in the presence of the angels I will sing your praise;
I will worship at your holy temple and give thanks to your name. ℟.

▶ Because of your kindness and your truth;
for you have made great above all things
your name and your promise.
When I called, you answered me;
you built up strength within me. ℟.

▶ All the kings of the earth shall give thanks to you, O LORD,
when they hear the words of your mouth;
and they shall sing of the ways of the LORD:
"Great is the glory of the LORD." ℟.

▶ Your right hand saves me.
The LORD will complete what he has done for me;
your kindness, O LORD, endures forever;
forsake not the work of your hands. ℟.

SECOND READING

1 Corinthians 15:1–11 or 15:3–8, 11

(Include bracketed text for Long Form)

[I am reminding you,] brothers and sisters, [of the gospel I preached to you, which you indeed received and in which you also stand. Through it you are also being saved, if you hold fast to the word I preached to you, unless you believed in vain. For] I handed on to you as of first importance what I also received: that Christ died for our sins in accordance with the Scriptures; that he was buried; that he was raised on the third day in accordance with the Scriptures; that he appeared to Cephas, then to the Twelve. After that, he appeared to more than five hundred brothers at once, most of

whom are still living, though some have fallen asleep. After that he appeared to James, then to all the apostles. Last of all, as to one born abnormally, he appeared to me. [For I am the least of the apostles, not fit to be called an apostle, because I persecuted the church of God. But by the grace of God I am what I am, and his grace to me has not been ineffective. Indeed, I have toiled harder than all of them; not I, however, but the grace of God that is with me.] Therefore, whether it be I or they, so we preach and so you believed.

GOSPEL ACCLAMATION

Matthew 4:19

℟. Al - le - lu - ia, al - le - lu - ia, al - le - lu - ia.

Music: John Schiavone, b. 1947, © 2001, OCP Publications.

▶ Come after me
and I will make you fishers of men. ℟.

GOSPEL READING

Luke 5:1–11

While the crowd was pressing in on Jesus and listening to the word of God, he was standing by the Lake of Gennesaret. He saw two boats there alongside the lake; the fishermen had disembarked and were washing their nets. Getting into one of the boats, the one belonging to Simon, he asked him to put out a short distance from the shore. Then he sat down and taught the crowds from the boat. After he had finished speaking, he said to Simon, "Put out into deep water and lower your nets for a catch." Simon said in reply, "Master, we have worked hard all night and have caught nothing, but at your command I will lower the nets." When they had done this, they caught a great number of fish and their nets were tearing. They signaled to their partners in the other boat to come to help them. They came and filled both boats so that the boats were in danger of sinking. When Simon Peter saw this, he fell at the knees of Jesus and said, "Depart from me, Lord, for I am a sinful man." For astonishment at the catch of fish they had made seized him and all those with him, and likewise James and John, the sons of Zebedee, who were partners of Simon. Jesus said to Simon, "Do not be afraid; from now on you will be catching men." When they brought their boats to the shore, they left everything and followed him.

SIXTH SUNDAY IN ORDINARY TIME — A   963

FIRST READING

Sirach 15:15–20

If you choose you can keep the
   commandments, they will save you;
   if you trust in God, you too shall live;
he has set before you fire and water;
   to whichever you choose, stretch
      forth your hand.
Before man are life and death, good
   and evil,
   whichever he chooses shall be
      given him.

Immense is the wisdom of the Lord;
   he is mighty in power, and all-seeing.
The eyes of God are on those who
      fear him;
   he understands man's every deed.
No one does he command to
      act unjustly,
   to none does he give license to sin.

RESPONSORIAL PSALM

Psalm 119:1–2, 4–5, 17–18, 33–34

℟. Bless'd are they who fol - low the law of the Lord!

Music: John Schiavone, b. 1947, © 2001, OCP Publications.

▸ Blessed are they whose way
  is blameless,
  who walk in the law of the LORD.
  Blessed are they who observe
  his decrees,
  who seek him with all their heart. ℟.

▸ You have commanded that
  your precepts
  be diligently kept.
  Oh, that I might be firm in the ways
  of keeping your statutes! ℟.

▸ Be good to your servant, that I
  may live
  and keep your words.
  Open my eyes, that I may consider
  the wonders of your law. ℟.

▸ Instruct me, O LORD, in the way of
  your statutes,
  that I may exactly observe them.
  Give me discernment, that I may
  observe your law
  and keep it with all my heart. ℟.

SECOND READING

1 Corinthians 2:6–10

Brothers and sisters: We speak a wisdom to those who are mature, not a wisdom of this age, nor of the rulers of this age who are passing away. Rather, we speak God's wisdom, mysterious, hidden, which God predetermined before the ages for our glory, and which none of the rulers of this age knew; for, if they had known it, they would not have crucified the Lord of glory. But as it is written:

*What eye has not seen, and ear has
  not heard,
  and what has not entered the
  human heart,
  what God has prepared for those
  who love him,*
  this God has revealed to us through
  the Spirit.
For the Spirit scrutinizes everything,
even the depths of God.

GOSPEL ACCLAMATION

cf. Matthew 11:25

℟. Al - le - lu - ia, al - le - lu - ia, al - le - lu - ia.

Music: John Schiavone, b. 1947, © 2001, OCP Publications.

▸ Blessed are you, Father, Lord of heaven and earth;
  you have revealed to little ones the mysteries of the kingdom. ℟.

GOSPEL READING

Matthew 5:17–37 or 5:20–22a, 27–28, 33–34a, 37

(Include bracketed text for Long Form)

Jesus said to his disciples: ["Do not think that I have come to abolish the law or the prophets. I have come not to abolish but to fulfill. Amen, I say to you, until heaven and earth pass away, not the smallest letter or the smallest part

of a letter will pass from the law, until all things have taken place. Therefore, whoever breaks one of the least of these commandments and teaches others to do so will be called least in the kingdom of heaven. But whoever obeys and teaches these commandments will be called greatest in the kingdom of heaven.] I tell you, unless your righteousness surpasses that of the scribes and Pharisees, you will not enter the kingdom of heaven.

"You have heard that it was said to your ancestors, *You shall not kill; and whoever kills will be liable to judgment.* But I say to you, whoever is angry with his brother will be liable to judgment; [and whoever says to brother, 'Raqa,' will be answerable to the Sanhedrin; and whoever says, 'You fool,' will be liable to fiery Gehenna. Therefore, if you bring your gift to the altar, and there recall that your brother has anything against you, leave your gift there at the altar, go first and be reconciled with your brother, and then come and offer your gift. Settle with your opponent quickly while on the way to court. Otherwise your opponent will hand you over to the judge, and the judge will hand you over to the guard, and you will be thrown into prison. Amen, I say to you, you will not be released until you have paid the last penny.]

"You have heard that it was said, *You shall not commit adultery.* But I say to you, everyone who looks at a woman with lust has already committed adultery with her in his heart. [If your right eye causes you to sin, tear it out and throw it away. It is better for you to lose one of your members than to have your whole body thrown into Gehenna. And if your right hand causes you to sin, cut it off and throw it away. It is better for you to lose one of your members than to have your whole body go into Gehenna.

"It was also said, *Whoever divorces his wife must give her a bill of divorce.* But I say to you, whoever divorces his wife — unless the marriage is unlawful — causes her to commit adultery, and whoever marries a divorced woman commits adultery.]

"Again you have heard that it was said to your ancestors, *Do not take a false oath, but make good to the Lord all that you vow.* But I say to you, do not swear at all; [not by heaven, for it is God's throne; nor by the earth, for it is his footstool; nor by Jerusalem, for it is the city of the great King. Do not swear by your head, for you cannot make a single hair white or black.] Let your 'Yes' mean 'Yes,' and your 'No' mean 'No.' Anything more is from the evil one."

SIXTH SUNDAY IN ORDINARY TIME — B   964

FIRST READING

Leviticus 13:1–2, 44–46

The Lord said to Moses and Aaron, "If someone has on his skin a scab or pustule or blotch which appears to be the sore of leprosy, he shall be brought to Aaron, the priest, or to one of the priests among his descendants. If the man is leprous and unclean, the priest shall declare him unclean by reason of the sore on his head.

"The one who bears the sore of leprosy shall keep his garments rent and his head bare, and shall muffle his beard; he shall cry out, 'Unclean, unclean!' As long as the sore is on him he shall declare himself unclean, since he is in fact unclean. He shall dwell apart, making his abode outside the camp."

RESPONSORIAL PSALM

Psalm 32:1–2, 5, 11

Music: John Schiavone, b. 1947, © 2001, OCP Publications.

▶ Blessed is he whose fault is taken away,
  whose sin is covered.
Blessed the man to whom the LORD
  imputes not guilt,
  in whose spirit there is no guile. ℟.

▶ Then I acknowledged my sin to you,
  my guilt I covered not.

I said, "I confess my faults to the LORD,"
  and you took away the guilt of
  my sin. ℟.

▶ Be glad in the LORD and rejoice,
  you just;
  exult, all you upright of heart. ℟.

SECOND READING

1 Corinthians 10:31—11:1

Brothers and sisters, Whether you eat or drink, or whatever you do, do everything for the glory of God. Avoid giving offense, whether to the Jews or Greeks or the church of God, just as I try to please everyone in every way, not seeking my own benefit but that of the many, that they may be saved. Be imitators of me, as I am of Christ.

GOSPEL ACCLAMATION

Luke 7:16

Music: John Schiavone, b. 1947, © 2001, OCP Publications.

▶ A great prophet has arisen in our midst,
  God has visited his people. ℟.

GOSPEL READING

Mark 1:40–45

A leper came to Jesus and kneeling down begged him and said, "If you wish, you can make me clean." Moved with pity, he stretched out his hand, touched him, and said to him, "I do will it. Be made clean." The leprosy left him immediately, and he was made clean. Then, warning him sternly, he dismissed him at once. He said to him, "See that you tell no one anything, but go, show yourself to the priest and offer for your cleansing what Moses prescribed; that will be proof for them." The man went away and began to publicize the whole matter. He spread the report abroad so that it was impossible for Jesus to enter a town openly. He remained outside in deserted places, and people kept coming to him from everywhere.

Sixth Sunday in Ordinary Time — C 965

First Reading

Jeremiah 17:5–8

Thus says the LORD:
Cursed is the one who trusts in
    human beings,
  who seeks his strength in flesh,
  whose heart turns away from the LORD.
He is like a barren bush in the desert
  that enjoys no change of season,
but stands in a lava waste,
  a salt and empty earth.
Blessed is the one who trusts in the LORD,
whose hope is the LORD.
He is like a tree planted beside
    the waters
  that stretches out its roots to
    the stream:
it fears not the heat when it comes;
  its leaves stay green;
in the year of drought it shows
    no distress,
  but still bears fruit.

Responsorial Psalm

Psalm 1:1–2, 3, 4&6

℞. **Bless'd   are   they   who   hope   in   the   Lord.**

Music: John Schiavone, b. 1947, © 2001, OCP Publications.

▸ Blessed the man who follows not
    the counsel of the wicked,
  nor walks in the way of sinners,
    nor sits in the company of
      the insolent,
  but delights in the law of the LORD
  and meditates on his law day
    and night. ℞.

▸ He is like a tree
    planted near running water,
that yields its fruit in due season,
  and whose leaves never fade.
Whatever he does, prospers. ℞.

▸ Not so the wicked, not so;
  they are like chaff which the wind
    drives away.
For the LORD watches over the way of
    the just,
  but the way of the wicked vanishes. ℞.

Second Reading

1 Corinthians 15:12, 16–20

Brothers and sisters: If Christ is preached
as raised from the dead, how can some
among you say there is no resurrection
of the dead? If the dead are not raised,
neither has Christ been raised, and if
Christ has not been raised, your faith is
vain; you are still in your sins. Then
those who have fallen asleep in Christ
have perished. If for this life only we
have hoped in Christ, we are the most
pitiable people of all.
    But now Christ has been raised from
the dead, the firstfruits of those who
have fallen asleep.

GOSPEL ACCLAMATION

Luke 6:23ab

℟. Al - le - lu - ia, al - le - lu - ia, al - le - lu - ia.

Music: John Schiavone, b. 1947, © 2001, OCP Publications.

▶ Rejoice and be glad;
  your reward will be great in heaven. ℟.

GOSPEL READING

Luke 6:17, 20–26

Jesus came down with the Twelve and stood on a stretch of level ground with a great crowd of his disciples and a large number of the people from all Judea and Jerusalem and the coastal region of Tyre and Sidon.

And raising his eyes toward his disciples he said:
"Blessed are you who are poor,
  for the kingdom of God is yours.
Blessed are you who are now hungry,
  for you will be satisfied.
Blessed are you who are now weeping,
  for you will laugh.
Blessed are you when people hate you,
  and when they exclude and
    insult you,

and denounce your name as evil
  on account of the Son of Man.
Rejoice and leap for joy on that day!
Behold, your reward will be great in heaven. For their ancestors treated the prophets in the same way.
But woe to you who are rich,
  for you have received
    your consolation.
Woe to you who are filled now,
  for you will be hungry.
Woe to you who laugh now,
  for you will grieve and weep.
Woe to you when all speak well of you,
  for their ancestors treated the false
    prophets in this way."

---

966 SEVENTH SUNDAY IN ORDINARY TIME — A

FIRST READING

Leviticus 19:1–2, 17–18

The LORD said to Moses, "Speak to the whole Israelite community and tell them: Be holy, for I, the LORD, your God, am holy.

"You shall not bear hatred for your brother or sister in your heart. Though

you may have to reprove your fellow citizen, do not incur sin because of him. Take no revenge and cherish no grudge against any of your people. You shall love your neighbor as yourself. I am the LORD."

RESPONSORIAL PSALM

Psalm 103:1–2, 3–4, 8, 10, 12–13

℟. The Lord is kind and mer - ci - ful, [kind and mer - ci - ful.]

Music: John Schiavone, b. 1947, © 2001, OCP Publications.

▶ Bless the LORD, O my soul;
  and all my being, bless his holy name.
  Bless the LORD, O my soul,
  and forget not all his benefits. ℟.

▶ He pardons all your iniquities,
  heals all your ills.
  He redeems your life from destruction,
  crowns you with kindness and
    compassion. ℟.

▶ Merciful and gracious is the LORD,
   slow to anger and abounding
      in kindness.
   Not according to our sins does he deal
      with us,
      nor does he requite us according to
      our crimes. ℟.

▶ As far as the east is from the west,
   so far has he put our transgressions
      from us.
   As a father has compassion on
      his children,
   so the LORD has compassion on
      those who fear him. ℟.

SECOND READING

1 Corinthians 3:16–23

Brothers and sisters: Do you not know that you are the temple of God, and that the Spirit of God dwells in you? If anyone destroys God's temple, God will destroy that person; for the temple of God, which you are, is holy.

Let no one deceive himself. If any one among you considers himself wise in this age, let him become a fool, so as to become wise. For the wisdom of this world is foolishness in the eyes of God, for it is written:

*God catches the wise in their
   own ruses,*
and again:
   *The Lord knows the thoughts of
      the wise,
   that they are vain.*

So let no one boast about human beings, for everything belongs to you, Paul or Apollos or Cephas, or the world or life or death, or the present or the future: all belong to you, and you to Christ, and Christ to God.

GOSPEL ACCLAMATION

1 John 2:5

℟. Al - le - lu - ia, al - le - lu - ia, al - le - lu - ia.

Music: John Schiavone, b. 1947, © 2001, OCP Publications.

▶ Whoever keeps the word of Christ,
   the love of God is truly perfected in him. ℟.

GOSPEL READING

Matthew 5:38–48

Jesus said to his disciples: "You have heard that it was said, *An eye for an eye and a tooth for a tooth.* But I say to you, offer no resistance to one who is evil. When someone strikes you on your right cheek, turn the other one as well. If anyone wants to go to law with you over your tunic, hand over your cloak as well. Should anyone press you into service for one mile, go for two miles. Give to the one who asks of you, and do not turn your back on one who wants to borrow.

"You have heard that it was said, *You*

shall love your neighbor and hate your enemy. But I say to you, love your enemies and pray for those who persecute you, that you may be children of your heavenly Father, for he makes his sun rise on the bad and the good, and causes rain to fall on the just and the unjust. For if you love those who love you, what recompense will you have? Do not the tax collectors do the same? And if you greet your brothers only, what is unusual about that? Do not the pagans do the same? So be perfect, just as your heavenly Father is perfect."

967   SEVENTH SUNDAY IN ORDINARY TIME — B

FIRST READING   *Isaiah 43:18–19, 21–22, 24b–25*

Thus says the LORD:
Remember not the events of the past,
  the things of long ago consider not;
see, I am doing something new!
   Now it springs forth, do you not
     perceive it?
In the desert I make a way,
  in the wasteland, rivers.
The people I formed for myself,

that they might announce my praise.
Yet you did not call upon me, O Jacob,
  for you grew weary of me, O Israel.
You burdened me with your sins,
  and wearied me with your crimes.
It is I, I, who wipe out,
  for my own sake, your offenses;
  your sins I remember no more.

RESPONSORIAL PSALM   *Psalm 41:2–3, 4–5, 13–14*

℟. Lord, heal my soul, for I have sinned a-gainst you.

Music: John Schiavone, b. 1947, © 2001, OCP Publications.

▸ Blessed is the one who has regard for
    the lowly and the poor;
    in the day of misfortune the LORD
    will deliver him.
  The LORD will keep and preserve him;
    and make him blessed on earth,
    and not give him over to the will of
    his enemies. ℟.

▸ The LORD will help him on his sickbed,
    he will take away all his ailment
    when he is ill.

Once I said, "O LORD, have pity on me;
  heal me, though I have sinned
  against you." ℟.

▸ But because of my integrity you
    sustain me
  and let me stand before you forever.
Blessed be the LORD, the God of Israel,
  from all eternity. Amen. Amen. ℟.

SECOND READING   *2 Corinthians 1:18–22*

Brothers and sisters: As God is faithful,
our word to you is not "yes" and "no."
For the Son of God, Jesus Christ, who
was proclaimed to you by us, Silvanus
and Timothy and me, was not "yes" and
"no," but "yes" has been in him. For
however many are the promises of God,

their Yes is in him; therefore, the Amen
from us also goes through him to God
for glory. But the one who gives us
security with you in Christ and who
anointed us is God; he has also put his
seal upon us and given the Spirit in our
hearts as a first installment.

GOSPEL ACCLAMATION   *cf. Luke 4:18*

℟. Al - le - lu - ia, al - le - lu - ia, al - le - lu - ia.

Music: John Schiavone, b. 1947, © 2001, OCP Publications.

▸ The Lord sent me to bring glad tidings to the poor,
  and to proclaim liberty to captives. ℟.

GOSPEL READING

Mark 2:1–12

When Jesus returned to Capernaum after some days, it became known that he was at home. Many gathered together so that there was no longer room for them, not even around the door, and he preached the word to them. They came bringing to him a paralytic carried by four men. Unable to get near Jesus because of the crowd, they opened up the roof above him. After they had broken through, they let down the mat on which the paralytic was lying. When Jesus saw their faith, he said to the paralytic, "Child, your sins are forgiven." Now some of the scribes were sitting there asking themselves, "Why does this man speak that way? He is blaspheming. Who but God alone can forgive sins?" Jesus immediately knew in his mind what they were thinking to themselves, so he said, "Why are you thinking such things in your hearts? Which is easier, to say to the paralytic, 'Your sins are forgiven,' or to say, 'Rise, pick up your mat and walk'? But that you may know that the Son of Man has authority to forgive sins on earth" — he said to the paralytic, "I say to you, rise, pick up your mat, and go home." He rose, picked up his mat at once, and went away in the sight of everyone. They were all astounded and glorified God, saying, "We have never seen anything like this."

SEVENTH SUNDAY IN ORDINARY TIME — C 968

FIRST READING

1 Samuel 26:2, 7–9, 12–13, 22–23

In those days, Saul went down to the desert of Ziph with three thousand picked men of Israel, to search for David in the desert of Ziph. So David and Abishai went among Saul's soldiers by night and found Saul lying asleep within the barricade, with his spear thrust into the ground at his head and Abner and his men sleeping around him.

Abishai whispered to David: "God has delivered your enemy into your grasp this day. Let me nail him to the ground with one thrust of the spear; I will not need a second thrust!" But David said to Abishai, "Do not harm him, for who can lay hands on the LORD's anointed and remain unpunished?" So David took the spear and the water jug from their place at Saul's head, and they got away without anyone's seeing or knowing or awakening. All remained asleep, because the LORD had put them into a deep slumber.

Going across to an opposite slope, David stood on a remote hilltop at a great distance from Abner, son of Ner, and the troops. He said: "Here is the king's spear. Let an attendant come over to get it. The LORD will reward each man for his justice and faithfulness. Today, though the LORD delivered you into my grasp, I would not harm the LORD's anointed."

RESPONSORIAL PSALM

Psalm 103:1–2, 3–4, 8, 10, 12–13

℟. The Lord   is   kind   and mer - ci - ful, [kind   and mer - ci - ful.]

Music: John Schiavone, b. 1947, © 2001, OCP Publications.

℟. The Lord is kind and merciful.

▶ Bless the LORD, O my soul;
  and all my being, bless his holy name.
Bless the LORD, O my soul,
  and forget not all his benefits. ℟.

▶ He pardons all your iniquities,
  heals all your ills.
He redeems your life from
    destruction,
  crowns you with kindness
    and compassion. ℟.

▶ Merciful and gracious is the LORD,
  slow to anger and abounding
    in kindness.

Not according to our sins does he deal
    with us,
  nor does he requite us according to
    our crimes. ℟.

▶ As far as the east is from the west,
  so far has he put our transgressions
    from us.
As a father has compassion on
    his children,
  so the LORD has compassion on
    those who fear him. ℟.

SECOND READING
1 Corinthians 15:45–49

Brothers and sisters: It is written, *The first man, Adam, became a living being,* the last Adam a life-giving spirit. But the spiritual was not first; rather the natural and then the spiritual. The first man was from the earth, earthly; the second man, from heaven. As was the earthly one, so also are the earthly, and as is the heavenly one, so also are the heavenly. Just as we have borne the image of the earthly one, we shall also bear the image of the heavenly one.

GOSPEL ACCLAMATION
John 13:34

℟. Al - le - lu - ia, al - le - lu - ia, al - le - lu - ia.

Music: John Schiavone, b. 1947, © 2001, OCP Publications.

▶ I give you a new commandment, says the Lord:
  love one another as I have loved you. ℟.

GOSPEL READING
Luke 6:27–38

Jesus said to his disciples: "To you who hear I say, love your enemies, do good to those who hate you, bless those who curse you, pray for those who mistreat you. To the person who strikes you on one cheek, offer the other one as well, and from the person who takes your cloak, do not withhold even your tunic. Give to everyone who asks of you, and from the one who takes what is yours do not demand it back. Do to others as you would have them do to you. For if you love those who love you, what credit is that to you? Even sinners love those who love them. And if you do good to those who do good to you, what credit is that to you? Even sinners do the same. If you lend money to those from whom you expect repayment, what credit is that to you? Even sinners lend to sinners, and get back the same amount. But rather, love your enemies and do good to them, and lend expecting nothing back; then your reward will be great and you will be children of the Most High, for he himself is kind to the ungrateful and the wicked. Be merciful, just as your Father is merciful.

"Stop judging and you will not be judged. Stop condemning and you will not be condemned. Forgive and you will be forgiven. Give, and gifts will be given to you; a good measure, packed together, shaken down, and overflowing, will be poured into your lap. For the measure with which you measure will in return be measured out to you."

EIGHTH SUNDAY IN ORDINARY TIME — A   969

FIRST READING
Isaiah 49:14–15

Zion said, "The LORD has forsaken me;
 my LORD has forgotten me."
Can a mother forget her infant,
 be without tenderness for the child of
  her womb?
Even should she forget,
 I will never forget you.

RESPONSORIAL PSALM
Psalm 62:2–3, 6–7, 8–9

℟. Rest in God a - lone, my soul.

Music: John Schiavone, b. 1947, © 2001, OCP Publications.

▶ Only in God is my soul at rest;
 from him comes my salvation.
He only is my rock and my salvation,
 my stronghold; I shall not be
  disturbed at all. ℟.

▶ Only in God be at rest, my soul,
 for from him comes my hope.

He only is my rock and my salvation,
 my stronghold; I shall not be
  disturbed. ℟.

▶ With God is my safety and my glory,
 he is the rock of my strength; my
  refuge is in God.
Trust in him at all times, O my people!
 Pour out your hearts before him. ℟.

SECOND READING
1 Corinthians 4:1–5

Brothers and sisters: Thus should one regard us: as servants of Christ and stewards of the mysteries of God. Now it is of course required of stewards that they be found trustworthy. It does not concern me in the least that I be judged by you or any human tribunal; I do not even pass judgment on myself; I am not conscious of anything against me, but I do not thereby stand acquitted; the one who judges me is the Lord. Therefore do not make any judgment before the appointed time, until the Lord comes, for he will bring to light what is hidden in darkness and will manifest the motives of our hearts, and then everyone will receive praise from God.

GOSPEL ACCLAMATION

Hebrews 4:12

℟. Al - le - lu - ia, al - le - lu - ia, al - le - lu - ia.

Music: John Schiavone, b. 1947, © 2001, OCP Publications.

▶ The word of God is living and effective;
discerning reflections and thoughts of the heart. ℟.

GOSPEL READING

Matthew 6:24–34

Jesus said to his disciples: "No one can serve two masters. He will either hate one and love the other, or be devoted to one and despise the other. You cannot serve God and mammon.

"Therefore I tell you, do not worry about your life, what you will eat or drink, or about your body, what you will wear. Is not life more than food and the body more than clothing? Look at the birds in the sky; they do not sow or reap, they gather nothing into barns, yet your heavenly Father feeds them. Are not you more important than they? Can any of you by worrying add a single moment to your life-span? Why are you anxious about clothes? Learn from the way the wild flowers grow. They do not work or spin. But I tell you that not even Solomon in all his splendor was clothed like one of them. If God so clothes the grass of the field, which grows today and is thrown into the oven tomorrow, will he not much more provide for you, O you of little faith? So do not worry and say, 'What are we to eat?' or 'What are we to drink?' or 'What are we to wear?' All these things the pagans seek. Your heavenly Father knows that you need them all. But seek first the kingdom of God and his righteousness, and all these things will be given you besides. Do not worry about tomorrow; tomorrow will take care of itself. Sufficient for a day is its own evil."

---

970   EIGHTH SUNDAY IN ORDINARY TIME — B

FIRST READING

Hosea 2:16b, 17b, 21–22

Thus says the LORD:
I will lead her into the desert
    and speak to her heart.
She shall respond there as in the days
        of her youth,
    when she came up from the land
        of Egypt.

I will espouse you to me forever:
    I will espouse you in right and
        in justice,
    in love and in mercy;
I will espouse you in fidelity,
    and you shall know the LORD.

RESPONSORIAL PSALM

Psalm 103:1–2, 3–4, 8, 10, 12–13

℟. The Lord   is   kind   and mer - ci - ful, [kind   and mer - ci - ful.]

Music: John Schiavone, b. 1947, © 2001, OCP Publications.

▸ Bless the LORD, O my soul;
  and all my being, bless his holy name.
Bless the LORD, O my soul,
  and forget not all his benefits. ℟.

▸ He pardons all your iniquities,
  heals all your ills.
He redeems your life from destruction,
  crowns you with kindness
    and compassion. ℟.

▸ Merciful and gracious is the LORD,
  slow to anger and abounding
    in kindness.

Not according to our sins does he
  deal with us,
  nor does he requite us according to
    our crimes. ℟.

▸ As far as the east is from the west,
  so far has he put our transgressions
    from us.
As a father has compassion on
  his children,
  so the LORD has compassion on
    those who fear him. ℟.

SECOND READING

2 Corinthians 3:1b–6

Brothers and sisters: Do we need, as some do, letters of recommendation to you or from you? You are our letter, written on our hearts, known and read by all, shown to be a letter of Christ ministered by us, written not in ink but by the Spirit of the living God, not on tablets of stone but on tablets that are hearts of flesh.

Such confidence we have through Christ toward God. Not that of ourselves we are qualified to take credit for anything as coming from us; rather, our qualification comes from God, who has indeed qualified us as ministers of a new covenant, not of letter but of spirit; for the letter brings death, but the Spirit gives life.

GOSPEL ACCLAMATION

James 1:18

℟. Al - le - lu - ia, al - le - lu - ia, al - le - lu - ia.

Music: John Schiavone, b. 1947, © 2001, OCP Publications.

▸ The Father willed to give us birth by the word of truth
  that we may be a kind of firstfruits of his creatures. ℟.

GOSPEL READING

Mark 2:18–22

The disciples of John and of the Pharisees were accustomed to fast. People came to him and objected, "Why do the disciples of John and the disciples of the Pharisees fast, but your disciples do not fast?" Jesus answered them, "Can the wedding guests fast while the bridegroom is with them? As long as they have the bridegroom with them they cannot fast. But the days will come when the bridegroom is taken away

from them, and then they will fast on that day. No one sews a piece of unshrunken cloth on an old cloak. If he does, its fullness pulls away, the new from the old, and the tear gets worse. Likewise, no one pours new wine into old wineskins. Otherwise, the wine will burst the skins, and both the wine and the skins are ruined. Rather, new wine is poured into fresh wineskins."

971   EIGHTH SUNDAY IN ORDINARY TIME — C

FIRST READING   *Sirach 27:4–7*

When a sieve is shaken, the husks appear;
  so do one's faults when one speaks.
As the test of what the potter molds is
    in the furnace,
  so in tribulation is the test of the just.
The fruit of a tree shows the care it
has had;
so too does one's speech disclose the
  bent of one's mind.
Praise no one before he speaks,
  for it is then that people are tested.

RESPONSORIAL PSALM   *Psalm 92:2–3, 13–14, 15–16*

℟. Lord, it is good to give thanks to you.

Music: John Schiavone, b. 1947, © 2001, OCP Publications.

▸ It is good to give thanks to the LORD,
  to sing praise to your name,
    Most High,
  to proclaim your kindness at dawn
  and your faithfulness throughout
    the night. ℟.

▸ The just one shall flourish like the
    palm tree,
  like a cedar of Lebanon shall
    he grow.

They that are planted in the house of
  the LORD
  shall flourish in the courts of
    our God. ℟.

▸ They shall bear fruit even in old age;
  vigorous and sturdy shall they be,
  declaring how just is the LORD,
    my rock, in whom there is
    no wrong. ℟.

SECOND READING   *1 Corinthians 15:54–58*

Brothers and sisters: When this
which is corruptible clothes itself with
incorruptibility and this which is mortal
clothes itself with immortality, then the
word that is written shall come about:
  Death is swallowed up in victory.
  Where, O death, is your victory?
  Where, O death, is your sting?
The sting of death is sin, and the power
of sin is the law. But thanks be to God
who gives us the victory through our
Lord Jesus Christ.
  Therefore, my beloved brothers and
sisters, be firm, steadfast, always fully
devoted to the work of the Lord,
knowing that in the Lord your labor is
not in vain.

GOSPEL ACCLAMATION   *Philippians 2:15d, 16a*

℟. Al - le - lu - ia, al - le - lu - ia, al - le - lu - ia.

Music: John Schiavone, b. 1947, © 2001, OCP Publications.

▸ Shine like lights in the world
  as you hold on to the word of life. ℟.

GOSPEL READING

Luke 6:39–45

Jesus told his disciples a parable, "Can a blind person guide a blind person? Will not both fall into a pit? No disciple is superior to the teacher; but when fully trained, every disciple will be like his teacher. Why do you notice the splinter in your brother's eye, but do not perceive the wooden beam in your own? How can you say to your brother, 'Brother, let me remove that splinter in your eye,' when you do not even notice the wooden beam in your own eye? You hypocrite! Remove the wooden beam from your eye first; then you will see clearly to remove the splinter in your brother's eye.

"A good tree does not bear rotten fruit, nor does a rotten tree bear good fruit. For every tree is known by its own fruit. For people do not pick figs from thornbushes, nor do they gather grapes from brambles. A good person out of the store of goodness in his heart produces good, but an evil person out of a store of evil produces evil; for from the fullness of the heart the mouth speaks."

NINTH SUNDAY IN ORDINARY TIME — A   972

FIRST READING

Deuteronomy 11:18, 26–28, 32

Moses told the people, "Take these words of mine into your heart and soul. Bind them at your wrist as a sign, and let them be a pendant on your forehead.

"I set before you here, this day, a blessing and a curse: a blessing for obeying the commandments of the LORD, your God, which I enjoin on you today; a curse if you do not obey the commandments of the LORD, your God, but turn aside from the way I ordain for you today, to follow other gods, whom you have not known. Be careful to observe all the statutes and decrees that I set before you today."

RESPONSORIAL PSALM

Psalm 31:2–3, 3–4, 17, 25

℞. Lord,   be my rock   of safe - ty.

Music: John Schiavone, b. 1947, © 2001, OCP Publications.

▶ In you, O LORD, I take refuge;
    let me never be put to shame.
In your justice rescue me,
    incline your ear to me,
    make haste to deliver me! ℞.

▶ Be my rock of refuge,
    a stronghold to give me safety.

You are my rock and my fortress;
    for your name's sake you will lead
    and guide me. ℞.

▶ Let your face shine upon your servant;
    save me in your kindness.
Take courage and be stouthearted,
    all you who hope in the LORD. ℞.

SECOND READING

Romans 3:21–25, 28

Brothers and sisters, Now the righteousness of God has been manifested apart from the law, though testified to by the law and the prophets, the righteousness of God through faith in Jesus Christ for all who believe. For there is no distinction; all have sinned and are deprived of the glory of God.

They are justified freely by his grace through the redemption in Christ Jesus, whom God set forth as an expiation, through faith, by his blood.

For we consider that a person is justified by faith apart from works of the law.

GOSPEL ACCLAMATION

John 15:5

℟. Al - le - lu - ia, al - le - lu - ia, al - le - lu - ia.

Music: John Schiavone, b. 1947, © 2001, OCP Publications.

▶ I am the vine, you are the branches, says the Lord; whoever remains in me and I in him will bear much fruit. ℟.

GOSPEL READING

Matthew 7:21–27

Jesus said to his disciples: "Not everyone who says to me, 'Lord, Lord,' will enter the kingdom of heaven, but only the one who does the will of my Father in heaven. Many will say to me on that day, 'Lord, Lord, did we not prophesy in your name? Did we not drive out demons in your name? Did we not do mighty deeds in your name?' Then I will declare to them solemnly, 'I never knew you. Depart from me, you evildoers.'

"Everyone who listens to these words of mine and acts on them will be like a wise man who built his house on rock. The rain fell, the floods came, and the winds blew and buffeted the house. But it did not collapse; it had been set solidly on rock. And everyone who listens to these words of mine but does not act on them will be like a fool who built his house on sand. The rain fell, the floods came, and the winds blew and buffeted the house. And it collapsed and was completely ruined."

---

973 NINTH SUNDAY IN ORDINARY TIME — B

FIRST READING

Deuteronomy 5:12–15

Thus says the LORD: "Take care to keep holy the sabbath day as the LORD, your God, commanded you. Six days you may labor and do all your work; but the seventh day is the sabbath of the LORD, your God. No work may be done then, whether by you, or your son or daughter, or your male or female slave, or your ox or ass or any of your beasts, or the alien who lives with you. Your male and female slave should rest as you do. For remember that you too were once a slave in Egypt, and the LORD, your God, brought you from there with his strong hand and outstretched arm. That is why the LORD, your God, has commanded you to observe the sabbath day."

RESPONSORIAL PSALM

Psalm 81:3–4, 5–6, 6–8, 10–11

℟. Sing with joy to God our help.

Music: John Schiavone, b. 1947, © 2001, OCP Publications.

▶ Take up a melody, and sound
the timbrel,
the pleasant harp and the lyre.
Blow the trumpet at the new moon,
at the full moon, on our solemn
feast. ℟.

▶ For it is a statute in Israel,
an ordinance of the God of Jacob,
who made it a decree for Joseph
when he came forth from the land
of Egypt. ℟.

▶ An unfamiliar speech I hear:
"I relieved his shoulder of
the burden;
his hands were freed from the basket.
In distress you called, and I rescued
you." ℟.

▶ "There shall be no strange god
among you
nor shall you worship any alien god.
I, the LORD, am your God
who led you forth from the land of
Egypt." ℟.

SECOND READING

2 Corinthians 4:6–11

Brothers and sisters: God who said, *Let light shine out of darkness,* has shone in our hearts to bring to light the knowledge of the glory of God on the face of Jesus Christ.

But we hold this treasure in earthen vessels, that the surpassing power may be of God and not from us. We are afflicted in every way, but not constrained; perplexed, but not driven to despair; persecuted, but not abandoned; struck down, but not destroyed; always carrying about in the body the dying of Jesus, so that the life of Jesus may also be manifested in our body. For we who live are constantly being given up to death for the sake of Jesus, so that the life of Jesus may be manifested in our mortal flesh.

GOSPEL ACCLAMATION

cf. John 17:17b, 17a

℟. Al - le - lu - ia, al - le - lu - ia, al - le - lu - ia.

Music: John Schiavone, b. 1947, © 2001, OCP Publications.

▶ Your word, O Lord, is truth;
consecrate us in the truth. ℟.

GOSPEL READING

Mark 2:23—3:6 or 2:23–28

(Include bracketed text for Long Form)

As Jesus was passing through a field of grain on the sabbath, his disciples began to make a path while picking the heads of grain. At this the Pharisees said to him, "Look, why are they doing what is unlawful on the sabbath?" He said to them, "Have you never read what David did when he was in need and he and his companions were hungry? How he went into the house of God when Abiathar was high priest and ate the bread of offering that only the priests could lawfully eat, and shared it with his companions?" Then he said to them, "The sabbath was made for man, not man for the sabbath. That is why the Son of Man is lord even of the sabbath."

[Again he entered the synagogue. There was a man there who had a withered hand. They watched him closely to see if he would cure him on the sabbath so that they might accuse him. He said to the man with the withered hand, "Come up here before us."

Then he said to them, "Is it lawful to do good on the sabbath rather than to do evil, to save life rather than to destroy it?" But they remained silent. Looking around at them with anger and grieved at their hardness of heart, he said to the man, "Stretch out your hand." He stretched it out and his hand was restored. The Pharisees went out and immediately took counsel with the Herodians against him to put him to death.]

---

974   NINTH SUNDAY IN ORDINARY TIME — C

FIRST READING
1 Kings 8:41–43

In those days, Solomon prayed in the temple, saying, "To the foreigner, who is not of your people Israel, but comes from a distant land to honor you — since they will learn of your great name and your mighty hand and your outstretched arm —, when he comes and prays toward this temple, listen from your heavenly dwelling. Do all that foreigner asks of you, that all the peoples of the earth may know your name, may fear you as do your people Israel, and may acknowledge that this temple which I have built is dedicated to your honor."

RESPONSORIAL PSALM
Psalm 117:1, 2

℟. Go out to all the world and tell the Good News.

Music: John Schiavone, b. 1947, © 2001, OCP Publications.

or: **Alleluia.**

▶ Praise the LORD, all you nations; glorify him, all you peoples! ℟.

▶ For steadfast is his kindness toward us, and the fidelity of the LORD endures forever. ℟.

SECOND READING
Galatians 1:1–2, 6–10

Paul, an apostle not from human beings nor through a human being but through Jesus Christ and God the Father who raised him from the dead, and all the brothers who are with me, to the churches of Galatia.

I am amazed that you are so quickly forsaking the one who called you by the grace of Christ for a different gospel — not that there is another. But there are some who are disturbing you and wish to pervert the gospel of Christ. But even if we or an angel from heaven should preach to you a gospel other than the one that we preached to you, let that one be accursed! As we have said before, and now I say again, if anyone preaches to you a gospel other than what you have received, let that one be accursed!

Am I now currying favor with humans or with God? Or am I seeking to please people? If I were still trying to please people, I would not be a slave of Christ.

GOSPEL ACCLAMATION   *John 3:16*

R. Al - le - lu - ia,   al - le - lu - ia,   al - le - lu - ia.

Music: John Schiavone, b. 1947, © 2001, OCP Publications.

▶ God so loved the world that he gave his only Son,
  so that everyone who believes in him might have eternal life. R.

GOSPEL READING   *Luke 7:1–10*

When Jesus had finished all his words to the people, he entered Capernaum. A centurion there had a slave who was ill and about to die, and he was valuable to him. When he heard about Jesus, he sent elders of the Jews to him, asking him to come and save the life of his slave. They approached Jesus and strongly urged him to come, saying, "He deserves to have you do this for him, for he loves our nation and built the synagogue for us." And Jesus went with them, but when he was only a short distance from the house, the centurion sent friends to tell him, "Lord, do not trouble yourself, for I am not worthy to have you enter under my roof. Therefore, I did not consider myself worthy to come to you; but say the word and let my servant be healed. For I too am a person subject to authority, with soldiers subject to me. And I say to one, 'Go,' and he goes; and to another, 'Come here,' and he comes; and to my slave, 'Do this,' and he does it." When Jesus heard this he was amazed at him and, turning, said to the crowd following him, "I tell you, not even in Israel have I found such faith." When the messengers returned to the house, they found the slave in good health.

TENTH SUNDAY IN ORDINARY TIME — A   975

FIRST READING   *Hosea 6:3–6*

In their affliction, people will say:
"Let us know, let us strive to know
       the LORD;
   as certain as the dawn is his coming,
   and his judgment shines forth like the
       light of day!
He will come to us like the rain,
   like spring rain that waters the earth."

What can I do with you, Ephraim?

What can I do with you, Judah?
Your piety is like a morning cloud,
   like the dew that early passes away.
For this reason I smote them through
       the prophets,
   I slew them by the words of
       my mouth;
for it is love that I desire, not sacrifice,
   and knowledge of God rather
       than holocausts.

RESPONSORIAL PSALM   *Psalm 50:1, 8, 12–13, 14–15*

R. To the up - right I will show the sav - ing pow'r of God.

Music: John Schiavone, b. 1947, © 2001, OCP Publications.

℟. **To the upright I will show the saving power of God.**

▶ God the LORD has spoken and
    summoned the earth,
  from the rising of the sun to
    its setting.
"Not for your sacrifices do I rebuke you,
  for your holocausts are before
  me always." ℟.

▶ "If I were hungry, I would not tell you,
  for mine are the world and
  its fullness.

Do I eat the flesh of strong bulls,
  or is the blood of goats my drink?" ℟.

▶ "Offer to God praise as your sacrifice
  and fulfill your vows to the
    Most High;
then call upon me in time of distress;
  I will rescue you, and you shall
  glorify me." ℟.

SECOND READING

Romans 4:18–25

Brothers and sisters: Abraham believed, hoping against hope, that he would become "the father of many nations," according to what was said, "Thus shall your descendants be." He did not weaken in faith when he considered his own body as already dead — for he was almost a hundred years old — and the dead womb of Sarah. He did not doubt God's promise in unbelief; rather, he was strengthened by faith and gave glory to God and was fully convinced that what he had promised he was also able to do. That is why *it was credited to him as righteousness.* But it was not for him alone that it was written that *it was credited to him;* it was also for us, to whom it will be credited, who believe in the one who raised Jesus our Lord from the dead, who was handed over for our transgressions and was raised for our justification.

GOSPEL ACCLAMATION

cf. Luke 4:18

℟. Al - le - lu - ia, al - le - lu - ia, al - le - lu - ia.

Music: John Schiavone, b. 1947, © 2001, OCP Publications.

▶ The Lord sent me to bring glad tidings to the poor,
  and to proclaim liberty to captives. ℟.

GOSPEL READING

Matthew 9:9–13

As Jesus passed on from there, he saw a man named Matthew sitting at the customs post. He said to him, "Follow me." And he got up and followed him. While he was at table in his house, many tax collectors and sinners came and sat with Jesus and his disciples. The Pharisees saw this and said to his disciples, "Why does your teacher eat with tax collectors and sinners?" He heard this and said, "Those who are well do not need a physician, but the sick do. Go and learn the meaning of the words, 'I desire mercy, not sacrifice.' I did not come to call the righteous but sinners."

Tenth Sunday in Ordinary Time — B   976

First Reading
Genesis 3:9–15

After the man, Adam, had eaten of the tree, the LORD God called to the man and asked him, "Where are you?" He answered, "I heard you in the garden; but I was afraid, because I was naked, so I hid myself." Then he asked, "Who told you that you were naked? You have eaten, then, from the tree of which I had forbidden you to eat!" The man replied, "The woman whom you put here with me— she gave me fruit from the tree, and so I ate it." The LORD God then asked the woman, "Why did you do such a thing?" The woman answered, "The serpent tricked me into it, so I ate it."

Then the LORD God said to the serpent:
"Because you have done this, you
    shall be banned
  from all the animals
  and from all the wild creatures;
on your belly shall you crawl,
  and dirt shall you eat
  all the days of your life.
I will put enmity between you and
    the woman,
  and between your offspring
    and hers;
he will strike at your head,
  while you strike at his heel."

Responsorial Psalm
Psalm 130:1–2, 3–4, 5–6, 7–8

℟. With the Lord there is mer - cy, and full - ness of re - demp - tion, [full - ness of re - demp - tion.]

Music: John Schiavone, b. 1947, © 2001, OCP Publications.

▶ Out of the depths I cry to you, O LORD;
  LORD, hear my voice!
Let your ears be attentive
  to my voice in supplication. ℟.

▶ If you, O LORD, mark iniquities,
  LORD, who can stand?
But with you is forgiveness,
  that you may be revered. ℟.

▶ I trust in the LORD;
  my soul trusts in his word.
More than sentinels wait for the dawn,
  let Israel wait for the LORD. ℟.

▶ For with the LORD is kindness
  and with him is plenteous
    redemption;
and he will redeem Israel
  from all their iniquities. ℟.

Second Reading
2 Corinthians 4:13 — 5:1

Brothers and sisters: Since we have the same spirit of faith, according to what is written, *I believed, therefore I spoke,* we too believe and therefore we speak, knowing that the one who raised the Lord Jesus will raise us also with Jesus and place us with you in his presence. Everything indeed is for you, so that

the grace bestowed in abundance on more and more people may cause the thanksgiving to overflow for the glory of God.

Therefore, we are not discouraged; rather, although our outer self is wasting away, our inner self is being renewed day by day. For this momentary light affliction is producing for us an eternal weight of glory beyond all comparison, as we look not to what is seen but to what is unseen; for what is seen is transitory, but what is unseen is eternal.

For we know that if our earthly dwelling, a tent, should be destroyed, we have a building from God, a dwelling not made with hands, eternal in heaven.

GOSPEL ACCLAMATION
John 12:31b–32

R̶. Al - le - lu - ia, al - le - lu - ia, al - le - lu - ia.

Music: John Schiavone, b. 1947, © 2001, OCP Publications.

▶ Now the ruler of this world will be driven out, says the Lord; and when I am lifted up from the earth, I will draw everyone to myself. R̶.

GOSPEL READING
Mark 3:20–35

Jesus came home with his disciples. Again the crowd gathered, making it impossible for them even to eat. When his relatives heard of this they set out to seize him, for they said, "He is out of his mind." The scribes who had come from Jerusalem said, "He is possessed by Beelzebul," and "By the prince of demons he drives out demons."

Summoning them, he began to speak to them in parables, "How can Satan drive out Satan? If a kingdom is divided against itself, that kingdom cannot stand. And if a house is divided against itself, that house will not be able to stand. And if Satan has risen up against himself and is divided, he cannot stand; that is the end of him. But no one can enter a strong man's house to plunder his property unless he first ties up the strong man. Then he can plunder the house. Amen, I say to you, all sins and all blasphemies that people utter will be forgiven them. But whoever blasphemes against the Holy Spirit will never have forgiveness, but is guilty of an everlasting sin." For they had said, "He has an unclean spirit."

His mother and his brothers arrived. Standing outside they sent word to him and called him. A crowd seated around him told him, "Your mother and your brothers and your sisters are outside asking for you." But he said to them in reply, "Who are my mother and my brothers?" And looking around at those seated in the circle he said, "Here are my mother and my brothers. For whoever does the will of God is my brother and sister and mother."

---

977   TENTH SUNDAY IN ORDINARY TIME — C

FIRST READING
1 Kings 17:17–24

Elijah went to Zarephath of Sidon to the house of a widow. The son of the mistress of the house fell sick, and his sickness grew more severe until he stopped breathing. So she said to Elijah, "Why have you done this to me, O man of God? Have you come to me to call attention to my guilt and to kill my son?" Elijah said to her, "Give me your son." Taking him from her lap, he carried the son to the upper room where he was staying, and put him on his bed. Elijah called out to the LORD: "O LORD, my God, will you afflict even the widow with whom I am staying by killing her son?" Then he stretched himself out upon the child three times and called out to the LORD: "O LORD, my God, let the life breath return to the body of this child." The LORD heard the prayer of Elijah; the life breath returned to the child's body and he revived.

Taking the child, Elijah brought him down into the house from the upper room and gave him to his mother. Elijah said to her, "See! Your son is alive." The woman replied to Elijah, "Now indeed I know that you are a man of God. The word of the LORD comes truly from your mouth."

RESPONSORIAL PSALM

Psalm 30:2, 4, 5–6, 11, 12, 13

℟. I will praise you, Lord, for you have res - cued me.

Music: John Schiavone, b. 1947, © 2001, OCP Publications.

▶ I will extol you, O LORD, for you drew me clear
  and did not let my enemies rejoice over me.
O LORD, you brought me up from the nether world;
  you preserved me from among those going down into the pit. ℟.
▶ Sing praise to the LORD, you his faithful ones,
  and give thanks to his holy name.

For his anger lasts but a moment;
  a lifetime, his good will.
At nightfall, weeping enters in,
  but with the dawn, rejoicing. ℟.

▶ Hear, O LORD, and have pity on me;
  O LORD, be my helper.
You changed my mourning into dancing;
  O LORD, my God, forever will I give you thanks. ℟.

SECOND READING

Galatians 1:11–19

I want you to know, brothers and sisters, that the gospel preached by me is not of human origin. For I did not receive it from a human being, nor was I taught it, but it came through a revelation of Jesus Christ.

For you heard of my former way of life in Judaism, how I persecuted the church of God beyond measure and tried to destroy it, and progressed in Judaism beyond many of my contemporaries among my race, since I was even more a zealot for my ancestral traditions. But when God, who from my mother's womb

had set me apart and called me through his grace, was pleased to reveal his Son to me, so that I might proclaim him to the Gentiles, I did not immediately consult flesh and blood, nor did I go up to Jerusalem to those who were apostles before me; rather, I went into Arabia and then returned to Damascus.

Then after three years I went up to Jerusalem to confer with Cephas and remained with him for fifteen days. But I did not see any other of the apostles, only James the brother of the Lord.

GOSPEL ACCLAMATION

Luke 7:16

℟. Al - le - lu - ia, al - le - lu - ia, al - le - lu - ia.

Music: John Schiavone, b. 1947, © 2001, OCP Publications.

▶ A great prophet has risen in our midst
God has visited his people. ℟.

GOSPEL READING

Luke 7:11–17

Jesus journeyed to a city called Nain, and his disciples and a large crowd accompanied him. As he drew near to the gate of the city, a man who had died was being carried out, the only son of his mother, and she was a widow. A large crowd from the city was with her. When the Lord saw her, he was moved with pity for her and said to her, "Do not weep." He stepped forward and touched the coffin; at this the bearers halted, and he said, "Young man, I tell you, arise!" The dead man sat up and began to speak, and Jesus gave him to his mother. Fear seized them all, and they glorified God, exclaiming, "A great prophet has arisen in our midst," and "God has visited his people." This report about him spread through the whole of Judea and in all the surrounding region.

---

978   ELEVENTH SUNDAY IN ORDINARY TIME — A

FIRST READING

Exodus 19:2–6a

In those days, the Israelites came to the desert of Sinai and pitched camp.

While Israel was encamped here in front of the mountain, Moses went up the mountain to God. Then the LORD called to him and said, "Thus shall you say to the house of Jacob; tell the Israelites: You have seen for yourselves how I treated the Egyptians and how I bore you up on eagle wings and brought you here to myself. Therefore, if you hearken to my voice and keep my covenant, you shall be my special possession, dearer to me than all other people, though all the earth is mine. You shall be to me a kingdom of priests, a holy nation."

RESPONSORIAL PSALM

Psalm 100:1–2, 3, 5

℟. We are his peo-ple: the sheep of his flock, [the sheep of his flock.]

Music: John Schiavone, b. 1947, © 2001, OCP Publications.

▶ Sing joyfully to the LORD, all you lands;
serve the LORD with gladness;
come before him with joyful song. ℟.

▶ Know that the LORD is God;
he made us, his we are;
his people, the flock he tends. ℟.

▶ The LORD is good:
his kindness endures forever,
and his faithfulness to all
generations. ℟.

SECOND READING *Romans 5:6–11*

Brothers and sisters: Christ, while we were still helpless, yet died at the appointed time for the ungodly. Indeed, only with difficulty does one die for a just person, though perhaps for a good person one might even find courage to die. But God proves his love for us in that while we were still sinners Christ died for us. How much more then, since we are now justified by his blood, will we be saved through him from the wrath. Indeed, if, while we were enemies, we were reconciled to God through the death of his Son, how much more, once reconciled, will we be saved by his life. Not only that, but we also boast of God through our Lord Jesus Christ, through whom we have now received reconciliation.

GOSPEL ACCLAMATION *Mark 1:15*

℟. Al - le - lu - ia, al - le - lu - ia, al - le - lu - ia.

Music: John Schiavone, b. 1947, © 2001, OCP Publications.

▶ The kingdom of God is at hand.
Repent and believe in the Gospel. ℟.

GOSPEL READING *Matthew 9:36 – 10:8*

At the sight of the crowds, Jesus' heart was moved with pity for them because they were troubled and abandoned, like sheep without a shepherd. Then he said to his disciples, "The harvest is abundant but the laborers are few; so ask the master of the harvest to send out laborers for his harvest."

Then he summoned his twelve disciples and gave them authority over unclean spirits to drive them out and to cure every disease and every illness. The names of the twelve apostles are these: first, Simon called Peter, and his brother Andrew; James, the son of Zebedee, and his brother John; Philip and Bartholomew, Thomas and Matthew the tax collector; James, the son of Alphaeus, and Thaddeus; Simon from Cana, and Judas Iscariot who betrayed him.

Jesus sent out these twelve after instructing them thus, "Do not go into pagan territory or enter a Samaritan town. Go rather to the lost sheep of the house of Israel. As you go, make this proclamation: 'The kingdom of heaven is at hand.' Cure the sick, raise the dead, cleanse lepers, drive out demons. Without cost you have received; without cost you are to give."

ELEVENTH SUNDAY IN ORDINARY TIME — B 979

FIRST READING *Ezekiel 17:22–24*

Thus says the Lord GOD:
  I, too, will take from the crest of
    the cedar,
    from its topmost branches tear off
    a tender shoot,
and plant it on a high and
    lofty mountain;
  on the mountain heights of Israel
    I will plant it.

It shall put forth branches and
　bear fruit,
　and become a majestic cedar.
Birds of every kind shall dwell
　beneath it,
　every winged thing in the shade
　of its boughs.
And all the trees of the field shall know

that I, the Lord,
bring low the high tree,
　lift high the lowly tree,
wither up the green tree,
　and make the withered tree bloom.
As I, the LORD, have spoken, so will
　I do.

RESPONSORIAL PSALM

Psalm 92:2–3, 13–14, 15–16

℟. **Lord, it is good to give thanks to you.**

Music: John Schiavone, b. 1947, © 2001, OCP Publications.

▸ It is good to give thanks to the LORD,
　to sing praise to your name,
　　Most High,
to proclaim your kindness at dawn
　and your faithfulness throughout
　the night. ℟.

▸ The just one shall flourish like the
　palm tree,
　like a cedar of Lebanon shall he grow.

They that are planted in the house of
　the LORD
　shall flourish in the courts of
　our God. ℟.

▸ They shall bear fruit even in old age;
　vigorous and sturdy shall they be,
declaring how just is the LORD,
　my rock, in whom there is
　no wrong. ℟.

SECOND READING

2 Corinthians 5:6–10

Brothers and sisters: We are always courageous, although we know that while we are at home in the body we are away from the Lord, for we walk by faith, not by sight. Yet we are courageous, and we would rather leave the body and go home to the Lord. Therefore, we aspire to please him, whether we are at home or away. For we must all appear before the judgment seat of Christ, so that each may receive recompense, according to what he did in the body, whether good or evil.

GOSPEL ACCLAMATION

℟. **Al - le - lu - ia, al - le - lu - ia, al - le - lu - ia.**

Music: John Schiavone, b. 1947, © 2001, OCP Publications.

▸ The seed is the word of God, Christ is the sower.
　All who come to him will live for ever. ℟.

GOSPEL READING

Mark 4:26–34

Jesus said to the crowds: "This is how it is with the kingdom of God; it is as if a man were to scatter seed on the land and would sleep and rise night and day and through it all the seed would sprout and grow, he knows not how. Of its own accord the land yields fruit, first the blade, then the ear, then the full grain in the ear. And when the grain is ripe, he wields the sickle at once, for the harvest has come."

He said, "To what shall we compare the kingdom of God, or what parable can we use for it? It is like a mustard seed that, when it is sown in the ground, is the smallest of all the seeds on the earth. But once it is sown, it springs up and becomes the largest of plants and puts forth large branches, so that the birds of the sky can dwell in its shade." With many such parables he spoke the word to them as they were able to understand it. Without parables he did not speak to them, but to his own disciples he explained everything in private.

ELEVENTH SUNDAY IN ORDINARY TIME — C   **980**

FIRST READING
2 Samuel 12:7–10, 13

Nathan said to David: "Thus says the LORD God of Israel: 'I anointed you king of Israel. I rescued you from the hand of Saul. I gave you your lord's house and your lord's wives for your own. I gave you the house of Israel and of Judah. And if this were not enough, I could count up for you still more. Why have you spurned the Lord and done evil in his sight? You have cut down Uriah the Hittite with the sword; you took his wife as your own, and him you killed with the sword of the Ammonites. Now, therefore, the sword shall never depart from your house, because you have despised me and have taken the wife of Uriah to be your wife.'"

Then David said to Nathan, "I have sinned against the LORD." Nathan answered David: "The LORD on his part has forgiven your sin: you shall not die."

RESPONSORIAL PSALM
Psalm 32:1–2, 5, 7, 11

℟. Lord, for - give the wrong I have done.

Music: John Schiavone, b. 1947, © 2001, OCP Publications.

▸ Blessed is the one whose fault is taken away,
  whose sin is covered.
Blessed the man to whom the LORD imputes no guilt,
  in whose spirit there is no guile. ℟.

▸ I acknowledged my sin to you,
  my guilt I covered not.
I said, "I confess my faults to the LORD,"
  and you took away the guilt of my sin. ℟.

▸ You are my shelter; from distress you will preserve me;
  with glad cries of freedom you will ring me round. ℟.

▸ Be glad in the LORD and rejoice, you just;
  exult, all you upright of heart. ℟.

SECOND READING

Galatians 2:16, 19–21

Brothers and sisters: We who know that a person is not justified by works of the law but through faith in Jesus Christ, even we have believed in Christ Jesus that we may be justified by faith in Christ and not by works of the law, because by works of the law no one will be justified. For through the law I died to the law, that I might live for God. I have been crucified with Christ; yet I live, no longer I, but Christ lives in me; insofar as I now live in the flesh, I live by faith in the Son of God who has loved me and given himself up for me. I do not nullify the grace of God; for if justification comes through the law, then Christ died for nothing.

GOSPEL ACCLAMATION

1 John 4:10b

℟. Al - le - lu - ia, al - le - lu - ia, al - le - lu - ia.

Music: John Schiavone, b. 1947, © 2001, OCP Publications.

▶ God loved us and sent his Son
as expiation for our sins. ℟.

GOSPEL READING

Luke 7:36 — 8:3 or 7:36–50

(Include bracketed text for Long Form)

A Pharisee invited Jesus to dine with him, and he entered the Pharisee's house and reclined at table. Now there was a sinful woman in the city who learned that he was at table in the house of the Pharisee. Bringing an alabaster flask of ointment, she stood behind him at his feet weeping and began to bathe his feet with her tears. Then she wiped them with her hair, kissed them, and anointed them with the ointment. When the Pharisee who had invited him saw this he said to himself, "If this man were a prophet, he would know who and what sort of woman this is who is touching him, that she is a sinner." Jesus said to him in reply, "Simon, I have something to say to you." "Tell me, teacher," he said. "Two people were in debt to a certain creditor; one owed five hundred days' wages and the other owed fifty. Since they were unable to repay the debt, he forgave it for both. Which of them will love him more?" Simon said in reply, "The one, I suppose, whose larger debt was forgiven." He said to him, "You have judged rightly." Then he turned to the woman and said to Simon, "Do you see this woman? When I entered your house, you did not give me water for my feet, but she has bathed them with her tears and wiped them with her hair. You did not give me a kiss, but she has not ceased kissing my feet since the time I entered. You did not anoint my head with oil, but she anointed my feet with ointment. So I tell you, her many sins have been forgiven because she has shown great love. But the one to whom little is forgiven, loves little." He said to her, "Your sins are forgiven." The others at table said to themselves, "Who is this who even forgives sins?" But he said to the woman, "Your faith has saved you; go in peace."

[Afterward he journeyed from one town and village to another, preaching and proclaiming the good news of the kingdom of God. Accompanying him were the Twelve and some women who had been cured of evil spirits and infirmities, Mary, called Magdalene, from whom seven demons had gone out, Joanna, the wife of Herod's steward Chuza, Susanna, and many others who provided for them out of their resources.]

TWELFTH SUNDAY IN ORDINARY TIME — A   981

FIRST READING
Jeremiah 20:10–13

Jeremiah said:
"I hear the whisperings of many:
    'Terror on every side!
    Denounce! let us denounce him!'
All those who were my friends
    are on the watch for any misstep
      of mine.
'Perhaps he will be trapped; then we
    can prevail,
    and take our vengeance on him.'
But the LORD is with me, like a
    mighty champion:
    my persecutors will stumble, they
      will not triumph.

In their failure they will be put to
    utter shame,
    to lasting, unforgettable confusion.
O LORD of hosts, you who test
    the just,
    who probe mind and heart,
let me witness the vengeance you
    take on them,
    for to you I have entrusted
    my cause.
Sing to the LORD,
    praise the LORD,
for he has rescued the life of the poor
    from the power of the wicked!"

RESPONSORIAL PSALM
Psalm 69:8–10, 14, 17, 33–35

℞. Lord, in your great love, an-swer me, [an-swer me.]

Music: John Schiavone, b. 1947, © 2001, OCP Publications.

▶ For your sake I bear insult,
    and shame covers my face.
I have become an outcast to
    my brothers,
    a stranger to my mother's children,
because zeal for your house
    consumes me,
    and the insults of those who
      blaspheme you fall upon me. ℞.

▶ I pray to you, O LORD,
    for the time of your favor, O God!
In your great kindness answer me
    with your constant help.

Answer me, O LORD, for bounteous is
    your kindness;
    in your great mercy turn
    toward me. ℞.

▶ "See, you lowly ones, and be glad;
    you who seek God, may your
      hearts revive!
For the LORD hears the poor,
    and his own who are in bonds he
      spurns not.
Let the heavens and the earth
    praise him,
    the seas and whatever moves
      in them!" ℞.

SECOND READING
Romans 5:12–15

Brothers and sisters: Through one man sin entered the world, and through sin, death, and thus death came to all men, inasmuch as all sinned — for up to the time of the law, sin was in the world, though sin is not accounted when there is no law. But death reigned from Adam to Moses, even over those who did not

sin after the pattern of the trespass of Adam, who is the type of the one who was to come.

But the gift is not like the transgression. For if by the transgression of the one the many died, how much more did the grace of God and the gracious gift of the one man Jesus Christ overflow for the many.

GOSPEL ACCLAMATION   *John 15:26b, 27a*

R. Al - le - lu - ia,   al - le - lu - ia,   al - le - lu - ia.

Music: John Schiavone, b. 1947, © 2001, OCP Publications.

▶ The Spirit of truth will testify to me, says the Lord;
and you also will testify. R.

GOSPEL READING   *Matthew 10:26–33*

Jesus said to the Twelve: "Fear no one. Nothing is concealed that will not be revealed, nor secret that will not be known. What I say to you in the darkness, speak in the light; what you hear whispered, proclaim on the housetops. And do not be afraid of those who kill the body but cannot kill the soul; rather, be afraid of the one who can destroy both soul and body in Gehenna. Are not two sparrows sold for a small coin? Yet not one of them falls to the ground without your Father's knowledge. Even all the hairs of your head are counted. So do not be afraid; you are worth more than many sparrows. Everyone who acknowledges me before others I will acknowledge before my heavenly Father. But whoever denies me before others, I will deny before my heavenly Father."

---

982   TWELFTH SUNDAY IN ORDINARY TIME — B

FIRST READING   *Job 38:1, 8–11*

The Lord addressed Job out of the
storm and said:
Who shut within doors the sea,
   when it burst forth from the womb;
when I made the clouds its garment
   and thick darkness its
      swaddling bands?

When I set limits for it
   and fastened the bar of its door,
and said: Thus far shall you come but
      no farther,
   and here shall your proud waves
      be stilled!

RESPONSORIAL PSALM   *Psalm 107:23–24, 25–26, 28–29, 30–31*

R. Give thanks to the Lord, his love is ev-er-last-ing, [ev-er-last-ing.]

Music: John Schiavone, b. 1947, © 2001, OCP Publications.

or: **Alleluia.**

▶ They who sailed the sea in ships,
   trading on the deep waters,
these saw the works of the LORD
   and his wonders in the abyss. R.

▶ His command raised up a storm wind
   which tossed its waves on high.
They mounted up to heaven; they
      sank to the depths;
   their hearts melted away in
      their plight. R.

▶ They cried to the LORD in their distress;
   from their straits he rescued them,
he hushed the storm to a
      gentle breeze,
   and the billows of the sea were
      stilled. ℟.

▶ They rejoiced that they were calmed,
   and he brought them to their
      desired haven.
Let them give thanks to the LORD for
   his kindness
   and his wondrous deeds to the
      children of men. ℟.

SECOND READING
2 Corinthians 5:14–17

Brothers and sisters: The love of Christ impels us, once we have come to the conviction that one died for all; therefore, all have died. He indeed died for all, so that those who live might no longer live for themselves but for him who for their sake died and was raised.

Consequently, from now on we regard no one according to the flesh; even if we once knew Christ according to the flesh, yet now we know him so no longer. So whoever is in Christ is a new creation: the old things have passed away; behold, new things have come.

GOSPEL ACCLAMATION
Luke 7:16

℟. Al - le - lu - ia, al - le - lu - ia, al - le - lu - ia.

Music: John Schiavone, b. 1947, © 2001, OCP Publications.

▶ A great prophet has risen in our midst.
   God has visited his people. ℟.

GOSPEL READING
Mark 4:35–41

On that day, as evening drew on, Jesus said to his disciples: "Let us cross to the other side." Leaving the crowd, they took Jesus with them in the boat just as he was. And other boats were with him. A violent squall came up and waves were breaking over the boat, so that it was already filling up. Jesus was in the stern, asleep on a cushion. They woke him and said to him, "Teacher, do you

not care that we are perishing?" He woke up, rebuked the wind, and said to the sea, "Quiet! Be still!" The wind ceased and there was great calm. Then he asked them, "Why are you terrified? Do you not yet have faith?" They were filled with great awe and said to one another, "Who then is this whom even wind and sea obey?"

TWELFTH SUNDAY IN ORDINARY TIME — C   983

FIRST READING
Zechariah 12:10–11; 13:1

Thus says the LORD: I will pour out on the house of David and on the inhabitants of Jerusalem a spirit of grace and petition; and they shall look on him whom they have pierced, and they shall mourn for him as one mourns for an only son, and they shall grieve over him as one grieves over a firstborn.

On that day the mourning in Jerusalem shall be as great as the mourning of Hadadrimmon in the plain of Megiddo.

On that day there shall be open to the house of David and to the inhabitants of Jerusalem, a fountain to purify from sin and uncleanness.

RESPONSORIAL PSALM

Psalm 63:2, 3–4, 5–6, 8–9

℟. My soul is thirst-ing for you, O Lord my God.

Music: John Schiavone, b. 1947, © 2001, OCP Publications.

▶ O God, you are my God whom I seek;
for you my flesh pines and my
soul thirsts
like the earth, parched, lifeless and
without water. ℟.

▶ Thus have I gazed toward you in
the sanctuary
to see your power and your glory,
for your kindness is a greater good
than life;
my lips shall glorify you. ℟.

▶ Thus will I bless you while I live;
lifting up my hands, I will call upon
your name.
As with the riches of a banquet shall
my soul be satisfied,
and with exultant lips my mouth
shall praise you. ℟.

▶ You are my help,
and in the shadow of your wings
I shout for joy.
My soul clings fast to you;
your right hand upholds me. ℟.

SECOND READING

Galatians 3:26–29

Brothers and sisters: Through faith you are all children of God in Christ Jesus. For all of you who were baptized into Christ have clothed yourselves with Christ. There is neither Jew nor Greek, there is neither slave nor free person, there is not male and female; for you are all one in Christ Jesus. And if you belong to Christ, then you are Abraham's descendant, heirs according to the promise.

GOSPEL ACCLAMATION

John 10:27

℟. Al - le - lu - ia, al - le - lu - ia, al - le - lu - ia.

Music: John Schiavone, b. 1947, © 2001, OCP Publications.

▶ My sheep hear my voice, says the Lord;
I know them, and they follow me. ℟.

GOSPEL READING

Luke 9:18–24

Once when Jesus was praying in solitude, and the disciples were with him, he asked them, "Who do the crowds say that I am?" They said in reply, "John the Baptist; others, Elijah; still others, 'One of the ancient prophets has arisen.'" Then he said to them, "But who do you say that I am?" Peter said in reply, "The Christ of God." He rebuked them and directed them not to tell this to anyone.

He said, "The Son of Man must suffer greatly and be rejected by the elders, the chief priests, and the scribes, and be killed and on the third day be raised."

Then he said to all, "If anyone wishes to come after me, he must deny himself and take up his cross daily and follow me. For whoever wishes to save his life will lose it, but whoever loses his life for my sake will save it."

13TH SUNDAY IN ORDINARY TIME — A   **984**

FIRST READING   *2 Kings 4:8–11, 14–16a*

One day Elisha came to Shunem, where there was a woman of influence, who urged him to dine with her. Afterward, whenever he passed by, he used to stop there to dine. So she said to her husband, "I know that Elisha is a holy man of God. Since he visits us often, let us arrange a little room on the roof and furnish it for him with a bed, table, chair, and lamp, so that when he comes to us he can stay there." Sometime later Elisha arrived and stayed in the room overnight.

Later Elisha asked, "Can something be done for her?" His servant Gehazi answered, "Yes! She has no son, and her husband is getting on in years." Elisha said, "Call her." When the woman had been called and stood at the door, Elisha promised, "This time next year you will be fondling a baby son."

RESPONSORIAL PSALM   *Psalm 89:2–3, 16–17, 18–19*

℟. **For ev‑er I will sing the good‑ness of the Lord.**

Music: John Schiavone, b. 1947, © 2001, OCP Publications.

▶ The promises of the LORD I will
     sing forever,
   through all generations my mouth
     shall proclaim your faithfulness.
For you have said, "My kindness is
     established forever";
   in heaven you have confirmed
     your faithfulness. ℟.

▶ Blessed the people who know the
     joyful shout;
   in the light of your countenance,
     O LORD, they walk.

At your name they rejoice all the day,
   and through your justice they
     are exalted. ℟.

▶ You are the splendor of their strength,
   and by your favor our horn
     is exalted.
For to the LORD belongs our shield,
   and to the Holy One of Israel,
     our king. ℟.

SECOND READING   *Romans 6:3–4, 8–11*

Brothers and sisters: Are you unaware that we who were baptized into Christ Jesus were baptized into his death? We were indeed buried with him through baptism into death, so that, just as Christ was raised from the dead by the glory of the Father, we too might live in newness of life.

If, then, we have died with Christ, we believe that we shall also live with him. We know that Christ, raised from the dead, dies no more; death no longer has power over him. As to his death, he died to sin once and for all; as to his life, he lives for God. Consequently, you too must think of yourselves as dead to sin and living for God in Christ Jesus.

GOSPEL ACCLAMATION

1 Peter 2:9

℟. Al - le - lu - ia, al - le - lu - ia, al - le - lu - ia.

Music: John Schiavone, b. 1947, © 2001, OCP Publications.

▶ You are a chosen race, a royal priesthood, a holy nation;
announce the praises of him who called you out of darkness into his
wonderful light. ℟.

GOSPEL READING

Matthew 10:37–42

Jesus said to his apostles: "Whoever loves father or mother more than me is not worthy of me, and whoever loves son or daughter more than me is not worthy of me; and whoever does not take up his cross and follow after me is not worthy of me. Whoever finds his life will lose it, and whoever loses his life for my sake will find it.

Whoever receives you receives me, and whoever receives me receives the one who sent me. Whoever receives a prophet because he is a prophet will receive a prophet's reward, and whoever receives a righteous man because he is a righteous man will receive a righteous man's reward. And whoever gives only a cup of cold water to one of these little ones to drink because the little one is a disciple — amen, I say to you, he will surely not lose his reward."

---

985   13TH SUNDAY IN ORDINARY TIME — B

FIRST READING

Wisdom 1:13–15; 2:23–24

God did not make death,
    nor does he rejoice in the destruction
        of the living.
For he fashioned all things that they
        might have being;
    and the creatures of the world
        are wholesome,
and there is not a destructive drug
        among them
    nor any domain of the netherworld
        on earth,

for justice is undying.
For God formed man to be imperishable;
    the image of his own nature he
        made him.
But by the envy of the devil, death
        entered the world,
    and they who belong to his company
        experience it.

RESPONSORIAL PSALM

Psalm 30:2, 4, 5–6, 11, 12, 13

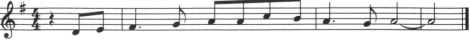

℟. I will praise you, Lord, for you have res - cued me.

Music: John Schiavone, b. 1947, © 2001, OCP Publications.

▶ I will extol you, O LORD, for you drew
    me clear
        and did not let my enemies rejoice
            over me.

O LORD, you brought me up from
    the netherworld;
        you preserved me from among
            those going down into the pit. ℟.

▶ Sing praise to the LORD, you his
    faithful ones,
and give thanks to his holy name.
For his anger lasts but a moment;
    a lifetime, his good will.
At nightfall, weeping enters in,
    but with the dawn, rejoicing. ℟.

▶ Hear, O LORD, and have pity on me;
    O LORD, be my helper.
You changed my mourning
    into dancing;
    O LORD, my God, forever will I give
    you thanks. ℟.

SECOND READING
2 Corinthians 8:7, 9, 13–15

Brothers and sisters: As you excel in every respect, in faith, discourse, knowledge, all earnestness, and in the love we have for you, may you excel in this gracious act also.

    For you know the gracious act of our Lord Jesus Christ, that though he was rich, for your sake he became poor, so that by his poverty you might become rich. Not that others should have relief while you are burdened, but that as a matter of equality your abundance at the present time should supply their needs, so that their abundance may also supply your needs, that there may be equality. As it is written:

Whoever had much did not
    have more,
and whoever had little did not
    have less.

GOSPEL ACCLAMATION
cf. 2 Timothy 1:10

℟. Al - le - lu - ia, al - le - lu - ia, al - le - lu - ia.

Music: John Schiavone, b. 1947, © 2001, OCP Publications.

▶ Our Savior Jesus Christ destroyed death
    and brought life to light through the Gospel. ℟.

GOSPEL READING
Mark 5:21–43 or 5:21–24, 35b–43

(Include bracketed text for Long Form)

When Jesus had crossed again in the boat to the other side, a large crowd gathered around him, and he stayed close to the sea. One of the synagogue officials, named Jairus, came forward. Seeing him he fell at his feet and pleaded earnestly with him, saying, "My daughter is at the point of death. Please, come lay your hands on her that she may get well and live." He went off with him, and a large crowd followed him and pressed upon him.

    [There was a woman afflicted with hemorrhages for twelve years. She had suffered greatly at the hands of many doctors and had spent all that she had. Yet she was not helped but only grew worse. She had heard about Jesus and came up behind him in the crowd and touched his cloak. She said, "If I but touch his clothes, I shall be cured." Immediately her flow of blood dried up. She felt in her body that she was healed of her affliction. Jesus, aware at once that power had gone out from him, turned around in the crowd and asked, "Who has touched my clothes?" But his disciples said to Jesus, "You see how the crowd is pressing upon you, and yet you ask, 'Who touched me?'" And he looked around to see who had done it. The woman, realizing what had happened to her, approached in fear and trembling. She fell down before

Jesus and told him the whole truth. He said to her, "Daughter, your faith has saved you. Go in peace and be cured of your affliction."]

While he was still speaking, people from the synagogue official's house arrived and said, "Your daughter has died; why trouble the teacher any longer?" Disregarding the message that was reported, Jesus said to the synagogue official, "Do not be afraid; just have faith." He did not allow anyone to accompany him inside except Peter, James, and John, the brother of James. When they arrived at the house of the synagogue official, he caught sight of a commotion, people weeping and wailing loudly. So he went in and said to them, "Why this commotion and weeping? The child is not dead but asleep." And they ridiculed him. Then he put them all out. He took along the child's father and mother and those who were with him and entered the room where the child was. He took the child by the hand and said to her, *"Talitha koum,"* which means, "Little girl, I say to you, arise!" The girl, a child of twelve, arose immediately and walked around. At that they were utterly astounded. He gave strict orders that no one should know this and said that she should be given something to eat.

986   13TH SUNDAY IN ORDINARY TIME — C

FIRST READING

1 Kings 19:16b, 19–21

The LORD said to Elijah: "You shall anoint Elisha, son of Shaphat of Abel-meholah, as prophet to succeed you."

Elijah set out and came upon Elisha, son of Shaphat, as he was plowing with twelve yoke of oxen; he was following the twelfth. Elijah went over to him and threw his cloak over him. Elisha left the oxen, ran after Elijah, and said, "Please, let me kiss my father and mother goodbye, and I will follow you." Elijah answered, "Go back! Have I done anything to you?" Elisha left him and, taking the yoke of oxen, slaughtered them; he used the plowing equipment for fuel to boil their flesh, and gave it to his people to eat. Then Elisha left and followed Elijah as his attendant.

RESPONSORIAL PSALM

Psalm 16:1–2, 5, 7–8, 9–10, 11

℟. You are my in-her-i-tance, O Lord.

Music: John Schiavone, b. 1947, © 2001, OCP Publications.

▶ Keep me, O God, for in you
    I take refuge;
    I say to the LORD, "My LORD are you.
O LORD, my allotted portion and
    my cup,
    you it is who hold fast my lot." ℟.

▶ I bless the LORD who counsels me;
    even in the night my heart
      exhorts me.
I set the LORD ever before me;
    with him at my right hand I shall not
      be disturbed. ℟.

▶ Therefore my heart is glad and my
    soul rejoices,
    my body, too, abides in confidence
because you will not abandon my soul
    to the netherworld,
    nor will you suffer your faithful one
      to undergo corruption. ℟.

▶ You will show me the path to life,
    fullness of joys in your presence,
    the delights at your right hand
      forever. ℟.

SECOND READING
Galatians 5:1, 13–18

Brothers and sisters: For freedom Christ set us free; so stand firm and do not submit again to the yoke of slavery.

For you were called for freedom, brothers and sisters. But do not use this freedom as an opportunity for the flesh; rather, serve one another through love. For the whole law is fulfilled in one statement, namely, *You shall love your neighbor as yourself.* But if you go on biting and devouring one another, beware that you are not consumed by one another.

I say, then: live by the Spirit and you will certainly not gratify the desire of the flesh. For the flesh has desires against the Spirit, and the Spirit against the flesh; these are opposed to each other, so that you may not do what you want. But if you are guided by the Spirit, you are not under the law.

GOSPEL ACCLAMATION
1 Samuel 3:9; John 6:68c

℟. Al - le - lu - ia, al - le - lu - ia, al - le - lu - ia.

Music: John Schiavone, b. 1947, © 2001, OCP Publications.

▶ Speak, Lord, your servant is listening; you have the words of everlasting life. ℟.

GOSPEL READING
Luke 9:51–62

When the days for Jesus' being taken up were fulfilled, he resolutely determined to journey to Jerusalem, and he sent messengers ahead of him. On the way they entered a Samaritan village to prepare for his reception there, but they would not welcome him because the destination of his journey was Jerusalem. When the disciples James and John saw this they asked, "Lord, do you want us to call down fire from heaven to consume them?" Jesus turned and rebuked them, and they journeyed to another village.

As they were proceeding on their journey someone said to him, "I will follow you wherever you go." Jesus answered him, "Foxes have dens and birds of the sky have nests, but the Son of Man has nowhere to rest his head." And to another he said, "Follow me." But he replied, "Lord, let me go first and bury my father." But he answered him, "Let the dead bury their dead. But you, go and proclaim the kingdom of God." And another said, "I will follow you, Lord, but first let me say farewell to my family at home." To him Jesus said, "No one who sets a hand to the plow and looks to what was left behind is fit for the kingdom of God."

14TH SUNDAY IN ORDINARY TIME — A   987

FIRST READING
Zechariah 9:9–10

Thus says the LORD:
Rejoice heartily, O daughter Zion,
 shout for joy, O daughter Jerusalem!
See, your king shall come to you;

a just savior is he,
meek, and riding on an ass,
 on a colt, the foal of an ass.
He shall banish the chariot from Ephraim,

and the horse from Jerusalem;
the warrior's bow shall be banished,
and he shall proclaim peace to
the nations.

His dominion shall be from sea to sea,
and from the River to the ends of
the earth.

RESPONSORIAL PSALM

Psalm 145:1–2, 8–9, 10–11, 13–14

℟. I will praise your name for ev-er, my king and my God.

Music: John Schiavone, b. 1947, © 2001, OCP Publications.

or: **Alleluia.**

▶ I will extol you, O my God and King,
    and I will bless your name forever
    and ever.
Every day will I bless you,
    and I will praise your name forever
    and ever. ℟.

▶ The LORD is gracious and merciful,
    slow to anger and of great kindness.
The LORD is good to all
    and compassionate toward all
    his works. ℟.

▶ Let all your works give you thanks,
    O LORD,
    and let your faithful ones bless you.
Let them discourse of the glory of
    your kingdom
    and speak of your might. ℟.

▶ The LORD is faithful in all his words
    and holy in all his works.
The LORD lifts up all who are falling
    and raises up all who are bowed
    down. ℟.

SECOND READING

Romans 8:9, 11–13

Brothers and sisters: You are not in the flesh; on the contrary, you are in the spirit, if only the Spirit of God dwells in you. Whoever does not have the Spirit of Christ does not belong to him. If the Spirit of the one who raised Jesus from the dead dwells in you, the one who raised Christ from the dead will give life to your mortal bodies also, through his Spirit that dwells in you. Consequently, brothers and sisters, we are not debtors to the flesh, to live according to the flesh. For if you live according to the flesh, you will die, but if by the Spirit you put to death the deeds of the body, you will live.

GOSPEL ACCLAMATION

cf. Matthew 11:25

℟. Al - le - lu - ia, al - le - lu - ia, al - le - lu - ia.

Music: John Schiavone, b. 1947, © 2001, OCP Publications.

▶ Blessed are you, Father, Lord of heaven and earth;
    you have revealed to little ones the mysteries of the kingdom. ℟.

GOSPEL READING

Matthew 11:25–30

At that time Jesus exclaimed: "I give praise to you, Father, Lord of heaven and earth, for although you have hidden these things from the wise and the learned you have revealed them to little ones. Yes, Father, such has been your gracious will. All things have been handed over to me by my Father. No one knows the Son except the Father, and no one knows the Father except the Son and anyone to whom the Son wishes to reveal him.

"Come to me, all you who labor and are burdened, and I will give you rest. Take my yoke upon you and learn from me, for I am meek and humble of heart; and you will find rest for yourselves. For my yoke is easy, and my burden light."

14TH SUNDAY IN ORDINARY TIME — B 988

FIRST READING

Ezekiel 2:2–5

As the LORD spoke to me, the spirit entered into me and set me on my feet, and I heard the one who was speaking say to me: Son of man, I am sending you to the Israelites, rebels who have rebelled against me; they and their ancestors have revolted against me to this very day. Hard of face and obstinate of heart are they to whom I am sending you. But you shall say to them: Thus says the LORD God! And whether they heed or resist — for they are a rebellious house — they shall know that a prophet has been among them.

RESPONSORIAL PSALM

Psalm 123:1–2, 2, 3–4

℟. **Our eyes are fixed on the Lord, plead-ing for his mer - cy.**

Music: John Schiavone, b. 1947, © 2001, OCP Publications.

▶ To you I lift up my eyes
   who are enthroned in heaven —
   as the eyes of servants
   are on the hands of their masters. ℟.

▶ As the eyes of a maid
   are on the hands of her mistress,
   so are our eyes on the LORD, our God,
   till he have pity on us. ℟.

▶ Have pity on us, O LORD, have pity
   on us,
   for we are more than sated
   with contempt;
   our souls are more than sated
   with the mockery of the arrogant,
   with the contempt of the proud. ℟.

SECOND READING

2 Corinthians 12:7–10

Brothers and sisters: That I, Paul, might not become too elated, because of the abundance of the revelations, a thorn in the flesh was given to me, an angel of Satan, to beat me, to keep me from being too elated. Three times I begged the Lord about this, that it might leave me, but he said to me, "My grace is sufficient for you, for power is made perfect in weakness." I will rather boast most gladly of my weaknesses, in order that the power of Christ may dwell with me. Therefore, I am content with weaknesses, insults, hardships, persecutions, and constraints, for the sake of Christ; for when I am weak, then I am strong.

GOSPEL ACCLAMATION

cf. Luke 4:18

℟. Al - le - lu - ia, al - le - lu - ia, al - le - lu - ia.

Music: John Schiavone, b. 1947, © 2001, OCP Publications.

▶ The Spirit of the Lord is upon me
for he sent me to bring glad tidings to the poor. ℟.

GOSPEL READING

Mark 6:1–6

Jesus departed from there and came to his native place, accompanied by his disciples. When the sabbath came he began to teach in the synagogue, and many who heard him were astonished. They said, "Where did this man get all this? What kind of wisdom has been given him? What mighty deeds are wrought by his hands! Is he not the carpenter, the son of Mary, and the brother of James and Joses and Judas and Simon? And are not his sisters here with us?" And they took offense at him. Jesus said to them, "A prophet is not without honor except in his native place and among his own kin and in his own house." So he was not able to perform any mighty deed there, apart from curing a few sick people by laying his hands on them. He was amazed at their lack of faith.

---

989   14TH SUNDAY IN ORDINARY TIME — C

FIRST READING

Isaiah 66:10–14c

Thus says the LORD:
Rejoice with Jerusalem and be glad
   because of her,
  all you who love her;
exult, exult with her,
  all you who were mourning over her!
Oh, that you may suck fully
  of the milk of her comfort,
that you may nurse with delight
  at her abundant breasts!
For thus says the LORD:
Lo, I will spread prosperity over
   Jerusalem like a river,
  and the wealth of the nations like an
   overflowing torrent.

As nurslings, you shall be carried in
   her arms,
  and fondled in her lap;
as a mother comforts her child,
  so will I comfort you;
  in Jerusalem you shall find
   your comfort.

When you see this, your heart
shall rejoice
  and your bodies flourish like
   the grass;
the LORD's power shall be known to
  his servants.

RESPONSORIAL PSALM

Psalm 66:1–3, 4–5, 6–7, 16, 20

℟. Let all the earth   cry out to God with joy.

Music: John Schiavone, b. 1947, © 2001, OCP Publications.

▸ Shout joyfully to God, all the earth,
  sing praise to the glory of his name;
  proclaim his glorious praise.
Say to God, "How tremendous are
  your deeds!" ℟.

▸ "Let all on earth worship and sing
  praise to you,
  sing praise to your name!"
Come and see the works of God,
  his tremendous deeds among the
  children of Adam. ℟.

▸ He has changed the sea into dry land;
  through the river they passed
  on foot;
  therefore let us rejoice in him.
He rules by his might forever. ℟.

▸ Hear now, all you who fear God,
  while I declare what he has done
  for me.
Blessed be God who refused me not
  my prayer or his kindness! ℟.

SECOND READING

Galatians 6:14–18

Brothers and sisters: May I never boast except in the cross of our Lord Jesus Christ, through which the world has been crucified to me, and I to the world. For neither does circumcision mean anything, nor does uncircumcision, but only a new creation. Peace and mercy be to all who follow this rule and to the Israel of God.

From now on, let no one make troubles for me; for I bear the marks of Jesus on my body.

The grace of our Lord Jesus Christ be with your spirit, brothers and sisters. Amen.

GOSPEL ACCLAMATION

Colossians 3:15a, 16a

℟. Al - le - lu - ia, al - le - lu - ia, al - le - lu - ia.

Music: John Schiavone, b. 1947, © 2001, OCP Publications.

▸ Let the peace of Christ control your hearts;
  let the word of Christ dwell in you richly. ℟.

GOSPEL READING

Luke 10:1–12, 17–20 or 10:1–9

(Include bracketed text for Long Form)

At that time the Lord appointed seventy-two others whom he sent ahead of him in pairs to every town and place he intended to visit. He said to them, "The harvest is abundant but the laborers are few; so ask the master of the harvest to send out laborers for his harvest. Go on your way; behold, I am sending you like lambs among wolves. Carry no money bag, no sack, no sandals; and greet no one along the way. Into whatever house you enter, first say, 'Peace to this household.' If a peaceful person lives there, your peace will rest on him; but if not, it will return to you. Stay in the same house and eat and drink what is offered to you, for the laborer deserves his payment. Do not move about from one house to another. Whatever town you enter and they welcome you, eat what is set before you, cure the sick in it and say to them, 'The kingdom of God is at hand for you.' [Whatever town you enter and they do not receive you, go out into the streets and say, 'The dust of your town that clings to our feet, even that we shake off against you.' Yet know this:

the kingdom of God is at hand. I tell you, it will be more tolerable for Sodom on that day than for that town."

The seventy-two returned rejoicing, and said, "Lord, even the demons are subject to us because of your name." Jesus said, "I have observed Satan fall like lightning from the sky. Behold,

I have given you the power to 'tread upon serpents' and scorpions and upon the full force of the enemy and nothing will harm you. Nevertheless, do not rejoice because the spirits are subject to you, but rejoice because your names are written in heaven."]

---

990 15TH SUNDAY IN ORDINARY TIME — A

FIRST READING
Isaiah 55:10–11

Thus says the LORD:
Just as from the heavens
     the rain and snow come down
and do not return there
     till they have watered the earth,
     making it fertile and fruitful,
giving seed to the one who sows

and bread to the one who eats,
so shall my word be
     that goes forth from my mouth;
my word shall not return to me void,
     but shall do my will,
     achieving the end for which I sent it.

RESPONSORIAL PSALM
Psalm 65:10, 11, 12–13, 14

℟. **The seed that falls on good ground will yield a fruit-ful har-vest.**

Music: John Schiavone, b. 1947, © 2001, OCP Publications.

▶ You have visited the land and
     watered it;
     greatly have you enriched it.
God's watercourses are filled;
     you have prepared the grain. ℟.

▶ Thus have you prepared the land:
     drenching its furrows,
     breaking up its clods,
softening it with showers,
     blessing its yield. ℟.

▶ You have crowned the year with
     your bounty,
     and your paths overflow with a
     rich harvest;
the untilled meadows overflow with it,
     and rejoicing clothes the hills. ℟.

▶ The fields are garmented with flocks
     and the valleys blanketed with grain.
     They shout and sing for joy. ℟.

SECOND READING
Romans 8:18–23

Brothers and sisters: I consider that the sufferings of this present time are as nothing compared with the glory to be revealed for us. For creation awaits with eager expectation the revelation of the children of God; for creation was made subject to futility, not of its own accord but because of the one who subjected it, in hope that creation itself would be

set free from slavery to corruption and share in the glorious freedom of the children of God. We know that all creation is groaning in labor pains even until now; and not only that, but we ourselves, who have the firstfruits of the Spirit, we also groan within ourselves as we wait for adoption, the redemption of our bodies.

GOSPEL ACCLAMATION

Ⓡ. Al - le - lu - ia, al - le - lu - ia, al - le - lu - ia.

Music: John Schiavone, b. 1947, © 2001, OCP Publications.

▶ The seed is the word of God, Christ is the sower.
All who come to him will have life forever. Ⓡ.

GOSPEL READING

Matthew 13:1–23 or 13:1–9

(Include bracketed text for Long Form)

On that day, Jesus went out of the house and sat down by the sea. Such large crowds gathered around him that he got into a boat and sat down, and the whole crowd stood along the shore. And he spoke to them at length in parables, saying: "A sower went out to sow. And as he sowed, some seed fell on the path, and birds came and ate it up. Some fell on rocky ground, where it had little soil. It sprang up at once because the soil was not deep, and when the sun rose it was scorched, and it withered for lack of roots. Some seed fell among thorns, and the thorns grew up and choked it. But some seed fell on rich soil, and produced fruit, a hundred or sixty or thirtyfold. Whoever has ears ought to hear."

[The disciples approached him and said, "Why do you speak to them in parables?" He said to them in reply, "Because knowledge of the mysteries of the kingdom of heaven has been granted to you, but to them it has not been granted. To anyone who has, more will be given and he will grow rich; from anyone who has not, even what he has will be taken away. This is why I speak to them in parables, because *they look but do not see and hear but do not listen or understand.* Isaiah's prophecy is fulfilled in them, which says:
*You shall indeed hear but
not understand,*

you shall indeed look but never see.
Gross is the heart of this people,
they will hardly hear with their ears,
they have closed their eyes,
lest they see with their eyes
and hear with their ears
and understand with their hearts and
be converted,
and I heal them.

"But blessed are your eyes, because they see, and your ears, because they hear. Amen, I say to you, many prophets and righteous people longed to see what you see but did not see it, and to hear what you hear but did not hear it.

"Hear then the parable of the sower. The seed sown on the path is the one who hears the word of the kingdom without understanding it, and the evil one comes and steals away what was sown in his heart. The seed sown on rocky ground is the one who hears the word and receives it at once with joy. But he has no root and lasts only for a time. When some tribulation or persecution comes because of the word, he immediately falls away. The seed sown among thorns is the one who hears the word, but then worldly anxiety and the lure of riches choke the word and it bears no fruit. But the seed sown on rich soil is the one who hears the word and understands it, who indeed bears fruit and yields a hundred or sixty or thirtyfold."]

991   15TH SUNDAY IN ORDINARY TIME — B

FIRST READING   *Amos 7:12–15*

Amaziah, priest of Bethel, said to Amos, "Off with you, visionary, flee to the land of Judah! There earn your bread by prophesying, but never again prophesy in Bethel; for it is the king's sanctuary and a royal temple." Amos answered

Amaziah, "I was no prophet, nor have I belonged to a company of prophets; I was a shepherd and a dresser of sycamores. The LORD took me from following the flock, and said to me, Go, prophesy to my people Israel."

RESPONSORIAL PSALM   *Psalm 85:9–10, 11–12, 13–14*

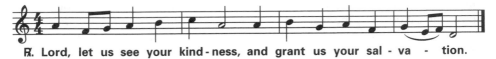

℟. Lord, let us see your kind‑ness, and grant us your sal‑va‑tion.

Music: John Schiavone, b. 1947, © 2001, OCP Publications.

▶ I will hear what God proclaims;
    the LORD — for he proclaims peace.
Near indeed is his salvation to those
    who fear him,
    glory dwelling in our land. ℟.

▶ Kindness and truth shall meet;
    justice and peace shall kiss.

Truth shall spring out of the earth,
    and justice shall look down from
    heaven. ℟.

▶ The LORD himself will give
    his benefits;
    our land shall yield its increase.
Justice shall walk before him,
    and prepare the way of his steps. ℟.

SECOND READING   *Ephesians 1:3–14 or 1:3–10*

(Include bracketed text for Long Form)

Blessed be the God and Father of our Lord Jesus Christ, who has blessed us in Christ with every spiritual blessing in the heavens, as he chose us in him, before the foundation of the world, to be holy and without blemish before him. In love he destined us for adoption to himself through Jesus Christ, in accord with the favor of his will, for the praise of the glory of his grace that he granted us in the beloved. In him we have redemption by his blood, the forgiveness of transgressions, in accord with the riches of his grace that he lavished upon us. In all wisdom and insight, he has made known to us the mystery of his will in accord with his

favor that he set forth in him as a plan for the fullness of times, to sum up all things in Christ, in heaven and on earth. [In him we were also chosen, destined in accord with the purpose of the One who accomplishes all things according to the intention of his will, so that we might exist for the praise of his glory, we who first hoped in Christ. In him you also, who have heard the word of truth, the gospel of your salvation, and have believed in him, were sealed with the promised holy Spirit, which is the first installment of our inheritance toward redemption as God's possession, to the praise of his glory.]

GOSPEL ACCLAMATION

cf. Ephesians 1:17–18

℟. Al - le - lu - ia, al - le - lu - ia, al - le - lu - ia.

Music: John Schiavone, b. 1947, © 2001, OCP Publications.

▶ May the Father of our Lord Jesus Christ
enlighten the eyes of our hearts,
that we may know what is the hope
that belongs to our call. ℟.

GOSPEL READING

Mark 6:7–13

Jesus summoned the Twelve and began to send them out two by two and gave them authority over unclean spirits. He instructed them to take nothing for the journey but a walking stick — no food, no sack, no money in their belts. They were, however, to wear sandals but not a second tunic. He said to them, "Wherever you enter a house, stay there until you leave. Whatever place does not welcome you or listen to you, leave there and shake the dust off your feet in testimony against them." So they went off and preached repentance. The Twelve drove out many demons, and they anointed with oil many who were sick and cured them.

15TH SUNDAY IN ORDINARY TIME — C   992

FIRST READING

Deuteronomy 30:10–14

Moses said to the people: "If only you would heed the voice of the LORD, your God, and keep his commandments and statutes that are written in this book of the law, when you return to the LORD, your God, with all your heart and all your soul.

"For this command that I enjoin on you today is not too mysterious and remote for you. It is not up in the sky, that you should say, 'Who will go up in the sky to get it for us and tell us of it, that we may carry it out?' Nor is it across the sea, that you should say, 'Who will cross the sea to get it for us and tell us of it, that we may carry it out?' No, it is something very near to you, already in your mouths and in your hearts; you have only to carry it out."

RESPONSORIAL PSALM

Psalm 69:14, 17, 30–31, 33–34, 36, 37

℟. Turn   to   the   Lord   in   your   need,   and   you   will   live.

Music: John Schiavone, b. 1947, © 2001, OCP Publications.

▶ I pray to you, O LORD,
for the time of your favor, O God!
In your great kindness answer me
with your constant help.

Answer me, O LORD, for bounteous is
your kindness:
in your great mercy turn
toward me. ℟.

℞. **Turn to the Lord in your need, and you will live.**

▶ I am afflicted and in pain;
  let your saving help, O God,
    protect me.
I will praise the name of God in song,
  and I will glorify him with
    thanksgiving. ℞.

▶ "See, you lowly ones, and be glad;
  you who seek God, may your
    hearts revive!

For the LORD hears the poor,
  and his own who are in bonds he
    spurns not." ℞.

▶ For God will save Zion
  and rebuild the cities of Judah.
The descendants of his servants shall
    inherit it,
  and those who love his name shall
    inhabit it. ℞.

OR

RESPONSORIAL PSALM   *Psalm 19:8, 9, 10, 11*

℞. **Your words, Lord, are Spir - it and life.**

Music: John Schiavone, b. 1947, © 2001, OCP Publications.

▶ The law of the LORD is perfect,
  refreshing the soul;
the decree of the LORD is trustworthy,
  giving wisdom to the simple. ℞.

▶ The precepts of the LORD are right,
  rejoicing the heart;
the command of the LORD is clear,
  enlightening the eye. ℞.

▶ The fear of the LORD is pure,
  enduring forever;
the ordinances of the LORD are true,
  all of them just. ℞.

▶ They are more precious than gold,
  than a heap of purest gold;
sweeter also than syrup
  or honey from the comb. ℞.

SECOND READING   *Colossians 1:15–20*

Christ Jesus is the image of the
    invisible God,
  the firstborn of all creation.
For in him were created all things in
    heaven and on earth,
  the visible and the invisible,
  whether thrones or dominions or
    principalities or powers;
  all things were created through him
    and for him.
He is before all things,
  and in him all things hold together.
He is the head of the body, the church.

He is the beginning, the firstborn from
    the dead,
  that in all things he himself might
    be preeminent.
For in him all the fullness was pleased
    to dwell,
  and through him to reconcile all
    things for him,
  making peace by the blood of his
    cross
  through him, whether those on earth
    or those in heaven.

GOSPEL ACCLAMATION

cf. John 6:63c, 68c

℟. Al - le - lu - ia, al - le - lu - ia, al - le - lu - ia.

Music: John Schiavone, b. 1947, © 2001, OCP Publications.

▸ Your words, Lord, are Spirit and life;
you have the words of everlasting life. ℟.

GOSPEL READING

Luke 10:25–37

There was a scholar of the law who stood up to test Jesus and said, "Teacher, what must I do to inherit eternal life?" Jesus said to him, "What is written in the law? How do you read it?" He said in reply, *You shall love the Lord, your God, with all your heart, with all your being, with all your strength, and with all your mind, and your neighbor as yourself.*" He replied to him, "You have answered correctly; do this and you will live."

But because he wished to justify himself, he said to Jesus, "And who is my neighbor?" Jesus replied, "A man fell victim to robbers as he went down from Jerusalem to Jericho. They stripped and beat him and went off leaving him half-dead. A priest happened to be going down that road, but when he saw him, he passed by on the opposite side.

Likewise a Levite came to the place, and when he saw him, he passed by on the opposite side. But a Samaritan traveler who came upon him was moved with compassion at the sight. He approached the victim, poured oil and wine over his wounds and bandaged them. Then he lifted him up on his own animal, took him to an inn, and cared for him. The next day he took out two silver coins and gave them to the innkeeper with the instruction, 'Take care of him. If you spend more than what I have given you, I shall repay you on my way back.' Which of these three, in your opinion, was neighbor to the robbers' victim?" He answered, "The one who treated him with mercy." Jesus said to him, "Go and do likewise."

16TH SUNDAY IN ORDINARY TIME — A　　993

FIRST READING

Wisdom 12:13, 16–19

There is no god besides you who have
　　the care of all,
　　that you need show you have not
　　unjustly condemned.
For your might is the source of justice;
　　your mastery over all things makes
　　you lenient to all.
For you show your might when the
　　perfection of your power
　　is disbelieved;
　　and in those who know you, you
　　rebuke temerity.
But though you are master of might,
　　you judge with clemency,

and with much lenience you
　　govern us;
for power, whenever you will,
　　attends you.
And you taught your people, by these
　　deeds,
　　that those who are just must be kind;
and you gave your children good
　　ground for hope
　　that you would permit repentance for
　　their sins.

RESPONSORIAL PSALM

Psalm 86:5–6, 9–10, 15–16

℟. Lord, you are good and for-giv-ing, [good and for-giv-ing.]

Music: John Schiavone, b. 1947, © 2001, OCP Publications.

▶ You, O LORD, are good and forgiving,
  abounding in kindness to all who
    call upon you.
  Hearken, O LORD, to my prayer
    and attend to the sound of
    my pleading. ℟.

▶ All the nations you have made
    shall come
  and worship you, O LORD,
  and glorify your name.

For you are great, and you do
    wondrous deeds;
  you alone are God. ℟.

▶ You, O LORD, are a God merciful
    and gracious,
  slow to anger, abounding in
    kindness and fidelity.
  Turn toward me, and have pity on me;
  give your strength to your servant. ℟.

SECOND READING

Romans 8:26–27

Brothers and sisters: The Spirit comes to the aid of our weakness; for we do not know how to pray as we ought, but the Spirit himself intercedes with inexpressible groanings. And the one who searches hearts knows what is the intention of the Spirit, because he intercedes for the holy ones according to God's will.

GOSPEL ACCLAMATION

cf. Matthew 11:25

℟. Al - le - lu - ia, al - le - lu - ia, al - le - lu - ia.

Music: John Schiavone, b. 1947, © 2001, OCP Publications.

▶ Blessed are you, Father, Lord of heaven and earth;
  you have revealed to little ones the mysteries of the kingdom. ℟.

GOSPEL READING

Matthew 13:24–43 or 13:24–30

(Include bracketed text for Long Form)

Jesus proposed another parable to the crowds, saying: "The kingdom of heaven may be likened to a man who sowed good seed in his field. While everyone was asleep his enemy came and sowed weeds all through the wheat, and then went off. When the crop grew and bore fruit, the weeds appeared as well. The slaves of the householder came to him and said, 'Master, did you not sow good seed in your field? Where have the weeds come from?' He answered, 'An enemy has done this.' His slaves said to him, 'Do you want us to go and pull them up?' He replied, 'No, if you pull up the weeds you might uproot the wheat along with them. Let them grow together until harvest; then at harvest time I will say to the harvesters, "First collect the weeds and tie them in bundles for burning; but gather the wheat into my barn."'"

[He proposed another parable to them. "The kingdom of heaven is like a mustard seed that a person took and sowed in a field. It is the smallest of all the seeds, yet when full-grown it is the largest of plants. It becomes a large bush, and the 'birds of the sky come and dwell in its branches.'"

He spoke to them another parable. "The kingdom of heaven is like yeast that a woman took and mixed with three measures of wheat flour until the whole batch was leavened."

All these things Jesus spoke to the crowds in parables. He spoke to them only in parables, to fulfill what had been said through the prophet:

I will open my mouth in parables,
I will announce what has lain
hidden from the foundation of
the world.

Then, dismissing the crowds, he went into the house. His disciples approached him and said, "Explain to us the parable of the weeds in the field." He said in reply, "He who sows good seed is the Son of Man, the field is the world, the good seed the children of the kingdom. The weeds are the children of the evil one, and the enemy who sows them is the devil. The harvest is the end of the age, and the harvesters are angels. Just as weeds are collected and burned up with fire, so will it be at the end of the age. The Son of Man will send his angels, and they will collect out of his kingdom all who cause others to sin and all evildoers. They will throw them into the fiery furnace, where there will be wailing and grinding of teeth. Then the righteous will shine like the sun in the kingdom of their Father. Whoever has ears ought to hear."]

16TH SUNDAY IN ORDINARY TIME — B   994

FIRST READING   *Jeremiah 23:1–6*

Woe to the shepherds who mislead and scatter the flock of my pasture, says the LORD. Therefore, thus says the LORD, the God of Israel, against the shepherds who shepherd my people: You have scattered my sheep and driven them away. You have not cared for them, but I will take care to punish your evil deeds. I myself will gather the remnant of my flock from all the lands to which I have driven them and bring them back to their meadow; there they shall increase and multiply. I will appoint shepherds for them who will shepherd them so that they need no longer fear and tremble; and none shall be missing, says the LORD.

Behold, the days are coming, says
    the LORD,
    when I will raise up a righteous
        shoot to David;
as king he shall reign and
        govern wisely,
    he shall do what is just and right in
        the land.
In his days Judah shall be saved,
    Israel shall dwell in security.
This is the name they give him:
    "The LORD, our justice."

RESPONSORIAL PSALM   *Psalm 23:1–3, 3–4, 5, 6*

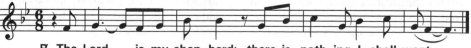

℟. The Lord   is my shep-herd; there is noth-ing I shall want.

Music: John Schiavone, b. 1947, © 2001, OCP Publications.

℟. **The Lord is my shepherd; there is nothing I shall want.**

▶ The LORD is my shepherd; I shall
    not want.
  In verdant pastures he gives
    me repose;
  beside restful waters he leads me;
  he refreshes my soul. ℟.

▶ He guides me in right paths
    for his name's sake.
  Even though I walk in the dark valley
    I fear no evil; for you are at my side
  with your rod and your staff
    that give me courage. ℟.

▶ You spread the table before me
    in the sight of my foes;
  you anoint my head with oil;
    my cup overflows. ℟.

▶ Only goodness and kindness
    follow me
  all the days of my life;
  and I shall dwell in the house of
    the LORD
    for years to come. ℟.

SECOND READING

Ephesians 2:13–18

Brothers and sisters: In Christ Jesus you who once were far off have become near by the blood of Christ.

  For he is our peace, he who made both one and broke down the dividing wall of enmity, through his flesh, abolishing the law with its commandments and legal claims, that he might create in himself one new person in place of the two, thus establishing peace, and might reconcile both with God, in one body, through the cross, putting that enmity to death by it. He came and preached peace to you who were far off and peace to those who were near, for through him we both have access in one Spirit to the Father.

GOSPEL ACCLAMATION

John 10:27

℟. **Al - le - lu - ia,**   **al - le - lu - ia,**   **al - le - lu - ia.**

Music: John Schiavone, b. 1947, © 2001, OCP Publications.

▶ My sheep hear my voice, says the Lord;
  I know them, and they follow me. ℟.

GOSPEL READING

Mark 6:30–34

The apostles gathered together with Jesus and reported all they had done and taught. He said to them, "Come away by yourselves to a deserted place and rest a while." People were coming and going in great numbers, and they had no opportunity even to eat. So they went off in the boat by themselves to a deserted place. People saw them leaving and many came to know about it. They hastened there on foot from all the towns and arrived at the place before them.

  When he disembarked and saw the vast crowd, his heart was moved with pity for them, for they were like sheep without a shepherd; and he began to teach them many things.

16TH SUNDAY IN ORDINARY TIME — C   995

FIRST READING   *Genesis 18:1–10a*

The LORD appeared to Abraham by the terebinth of Mamre, as he sat in the entrance of his tent, while the day was growing hot. Looking up, Abraham saw three men standing nearby. When he saw them, he ran from the entrance of the tent to greet them; and bowing to the ground, he said: "Sir, if I may ask you this favor, please do not go on past your servant. Let some water be brought, that you may bathe your feet, and then rest yourselves under the tree. Now that you have come this close to your servant, let me bring you a little food, that you may refresh yourselves; and afterward you may go on your way." The men replied, "Very well, do as you have said."

Abraham hastened into the tent and told Sarah, "Quick, three measures of fine flour! Knead it and make rolls." He ran to the herd, picked out a tender, choice steer, and gave it to a servant, who quickly prepared it. Then Abraham got some curds and milk, as well as the steer that had been prepared, and set these before the three men; and he waited on them under the tree while they ate.

They asked Abraham, "Where is your wife Sarah?" He replied, "There in the tent." One of them said, "I will surely return to you about this time next year, and Sarah will then have a son."

RESPONSORIAL PSALM   *Psalm 15:2–3, 3–4, 5*

℟. He who does jus-tice will live in the pres-ence of the Lord.

Music: John Schiavone, b. 1947, © 2001, OCP Publications.

▶ One who walks blamelessly and
        does justice;
    who thinks the truth in his heart
    and slanders not with his tongue. ℟.

▶ Who harms not his fellow man,
        nor takes up a reproach against
        his neighbor;
    by whom the reprobate is despised,

while he honors those who fear
        the LORD. ℟.

▶ Who lends not his money at usury
        and accepts no bribe against
        the innocent.
    One who does these things
    shall never be disturbed. ℟.

SECOND READING   *Colossians 1:24–28*

Brothers and sisters: Now I rejoice in my sufferings for your sake, and in my flesh I am filling up what is lacking in the afflictions of Christ on behalf of his body, which is the church, of which I am a minister in accordance with God's stewardship given to me to bring to completion for you the word of God, the mystery hidden from ages and from

generations past. But now it has been manifested to his holy ones, to whom God chose to make known the riches of the glory of this mystery among the Gentiles; it is Christ in you, the hope for glory. It is he whom we proclaim, admonishing everyone and teaching everyone with all wisdom, that we may present everyone perfect in Christ.

GOSPEL ACCLAMATION

cf. Luke 8:15

℟. Al - le - lu - ia, al - le - lu - ia, al - le - lu - ia.

Music: John Schiavone, b. 1947, © 2001, OCP Publications.

▶ Blessed are they who have kept the word with a generous heart and yield a harvest through perseverance. ℟.

GOSPEL READING

Luke 10:38–42

Jesus entered a village where a woman whose name was Martha welcomed him. She had a sister named Mary who sat beside the Lord at his feet listening to him speak. Martha, burdened with much serving, came to him and said, "Lord, do you not care that my sister has left me by myself to do the serving? Tell her to help me." The Lord said to her in reply, "Martha, Martha, you are anxious and worried about many things. There is need of only one thing. Mary has chosen the better part and it will not be taken from her."

---

996   17TH SUNDAY IN ORDINARY TIME — A

FIRST READING

1 Kings 3:5, 7–12

The LORD appeared to Solomon in a dream at night. God said, "Ask something of me and I will give it to you." Solomon answered: "O LORD, my God, you have made me, your servant, king to succeed my father David; but I am a mere youth, not knowing at all how to act. I serve you in the midst of the people whom you have chosen, a people so vast that it cannot be numbered or counted. Give your servant, therefore, an understanding heart to judge your people and to distinguish right from wrong. For who is able to govern this vast people of yours?"

The LORD was pleased that Solomon made this request. So God said to him: "Because you have asked for this — not for a long life for yourself, nor for riches, nor for the life of your enemies, but for understanding so that you may know what is right — I do as you requested. I give you a heart so wise and understanding that there has never been anyone like you up to now, and after you there will come no one to equal you."

RESPONSORIAL PSALM

Psalm 119:57, 72, 76–77, 127–128, 129–130

℟. Lord, I love your com - mands, [I love your com - mands.]

Music: John Schiavone, b. 1947, © 2001, OCP Publications.

▶ I have said, O LORD, that my part
  is to keep your words.
The law of your mouth is to me
  more precious
  than thousands of gold and
  silver pieces. ℟.

▶ Let your kindness comfort me
  according to your promise to
  your servants.
Let your compassion come to me that
  I may live,
  for your law is my delight. ℟.

▶ For I love your commands
more than gold, however fine.
For in all your precepts I go forward;
every false way I hate. ℟.

▶ Wonderful are your decrees;
therefore I observe them.
The revelation of your words
sheds light,
giving understanding to the simple. ℟.

SECOND READING

Romans 8:28–30

Brothers and sisters: We know that all things work for good for those who love God, who are called according to his purpose. For those he foreknew he also predestined to be conformed to the image of his Son, so that he might be the firstborn among many brothers and sisters. And those he predestined he also called; and those he called he also justified; and those he justified he also glorified.

GOSPEL ACCLAMATION

cf. Matthew 11:25

℟. Al - le - lu - ia, al - le - lu - ia, al - le - lu - ia.

Music: John Schiavone, b. 1947, © 2001, OCP Publications.

▶ Blessed are you, Father, Lord of heaven and earth;
for you have revealed to little ones the mysteries of the kingdom. ℟.

GOSPEL READING

Matthew 13:44–52 or 13:44–46

(Include bracketed text for Long Form)

Jesus said to his disciples: "The kingdom of heaven is like a treasure buried in a field, which a person finds and hides again, and out of joy goes and sells all that he has and buys that field. Again, the kingdom of heaven is like a merchant searching for fine pearls. When he finds a pearl of great price, he goes and sells all that he has and buys it. [Again, the kingdom of heaven is like a net thrown into the sea, which collects fish of every kind. When it is full they haul it ashore and sit down to put what is good into buckets. What is bad they throw away. Thus it will be at the end of the age. The angels will go out and separate the wicked from the righteous and throw them into the fiery furnace, where there will be wailing and grinding of teeth.

"Do you understand all these things?" They answered, "Yes." And he replied, "Then every scribe who has been instructed in the kingdom of heaven is like the head of a household who brings from his storeroom both the new and the old."]

997   17TH SUNDAY IN ORDINARY TIME — B

FIRST READING   *2 Kings 4:42–44*

A man came from Baal-shalishah bringing to Elisha, the man of God, twenty barley loaves made from the firstfruits, and fresh grain in the ear. Elisha said, "Give it to the people to eat." But his servant objected, "How can I set this before a hundred people?" Elisha insisted, "Give it to the people to eat. For thus says the LORD, 'They shall eat and there shall be some left over.'" And when they had eaten, there was some left over, as the LORD had said.

RESPONSORIAL PSALM   *Psalm 145:10–11, 15–16, 17–18*

℟. The hand of the Lord feeds us; he answers all our needs.

Music: John Schiavone, b. 1947, © 2001, OCP Publications.

▶ Let all your works give you thanks,
    O LORD,
    and let your faithful ones bless you.
Let them discourse of the glory of
    your kingdom
    and speak of your might. ℟.

▶ The eyes of all look hopefully to you,
    and you give them their food in
    due season;

you open your hand
    and satisfy the desire of every
    living thing. ℟.

▶ The LORD is just in all his ways
    and holy in all his works.
The LORD is near to all who call
    upon him,
    to all who call upon him in truth. ℟.

SECOND READING   *Ephesians 4:1–6*

Brothers and sisters: I, a prisoner for the Lord, urge you to live in a manner worthy of the call you have received, with all humility and gentleness, with patience, bearing with one another through love, striving to preserve the unity of the spirit through the bond of peace: one body and one Spirit, as you were also called to the one hope of your call; one Lord, one faith, one baptism; one God and Father of all, who is over all and through all and in all.

GOSPEL ACCLAMATION   *Luke 7:16*

℟. Al - le - lu - ia, al - le - lu - ia, al - le - lu - ia.

Music: John Schiavone, b. 1947, © 2001, OCP Publications.

▶ A great prophet has risen in our midst.
God has visited his people. ℟.

GOSPEL READING *John 6:1–15*

Jesus went across the Sea of Galilee. A large crowd followed him, because they saw the signs he was performing on the sick. Jesus went up on the mountain, and there he sat down with his disciples. The Jewish feast of Passover was near. When Jesus raised his eyes and saw that a large crowd was coming to him, he said to Philip, "Where can we buy enough food for them to eat?" He said this to test him, because he himself knew what he was going to do. Philip answered him, "Two hundred days' wages worth of food would not be enough for each of them to have a little." One of his disciples, Andrew, the brother of Simon Peter, said to him, "There is a boy here who has five barley loaves and two fish; but what good are these for so many?" Jesus said, "Have the people recline." Now there was a great deal of grass in that place. So the men reclined, about five thousand in number. Then Jesus took the loaves, gave thanks, and distributed them to those who were reclining, and also as much of the fish as they wanted. When they had had their fill, he said to his disciples, "Gather the fragments left over, so that nothing will be wasted." So they collected them, and filled twelve wicker baskets with fragments from the five barley loaves that had been more than they could eat. When the people saw the sign he had done, they said, "This is truly the Prophet, the one who is to come into the world." Since Jesus knew that they were going to come and carry him off to make him king, he withdrew again to the mountain alone.

17TH SUNDAY IN ORDINARY TIME — C 998

FIRST READING *Genesis 18:20–32*

In those days, the LORD said: "The outcry against Sodom and Gomorrah is so great, and their sin so grave, that I must go down and see whether or not their actions fully correspond to the cry against them that comes to me. I mean to find out."

While Abraham's visitors walked on farther toward Sodom, the LORD remained standing before Abraham. Then Abraham drew nearer and said: "Will you sweep away the innocent with the guilty? Suppose there were fifty innocent people in the city; would you wipe out the place, rather than spare it for the sake of the fifty innocent people within it? Far be it from you to do such a thing, to make the innocent die with the guilty so that the innocent and the guilty would be treated alike! Should not the judge of all the world act with justice?" The LORD replied, "If I find fifty innocent people in the city of Sodom, I will spare the whole place for their sake." Abraham spoke up again: "See how I am presuming to speak to my Lord, though I am but dust and ashes! What if there are five less than fifty innocent people? Will you destroy the whole city because of those five?" He answered, "I will not destroy it, if I find forty-five there." But Abraham persisted, saying, "What if only forty are found there?" He replied, "I will forbear doing it for the sake of the forty." Then Abraham said, "Let not my Lord grow impatient if I go on. What if only thirty are found there?" He replied, "I will forbear doing it if I can find but thirty there." Still Abraham went on, "Since I have thus dared to speak to my Lord, what if there are no more than twenty?" The LORD answered, "I will not destroy it, for the sake of the twenty." But he still persisted: "Please, let not my Lord grow angry if I speak up this last time. What if there are at least ten there?" He replied, "For the sake of those ten, I will not destroy it."

RESPONSIORIAL PSALM

Psalm 138:1–2, 2–3, 6–7, 7–8

℟. Lord, on the day I called for help, you an-swered me.

Music: John Schiavone, b. 1947, © 2001, OCP Publications.

▶ I will give thanks to you, O LORD, with
all my heart,
for you have heard the words of
my mouth;
in the presence of the angels I will
sing your praise;
I will worship at your holy temple
and give thanks to your name. ℟.

▶ Because of your kindness and
your truth;
for you have made great above
all things
your name and your promise.
When I called you answered me;
you built up strength within me. ℟.

▶ The LORD is exalted, yet the lowly
he sees,
and the proud he knows from afar.
Though I walk amid distress, you
preserve me;
against the anger of my enemies
you raise your hand. ℟.

▶ Your right hand saves me.
The LORD will complete what he has
done for me;
your kindness, O LORD,
endures forever;
forsake not the work of your hands. ℟.

SECOND READING

Colossians 2:12–14

Brothers and sisters: You were buried
with him in baptism, in which you were
also raised with him through faith in the
power of God, who raised him from the
dead. And even when you were dead in
transgressions and the uncircumcision
of your flesh, he brought you to life
along with him, having forgiven us all
our transgressions; obliterating the
bond against us, with its legal claims,
which was opposed to us, he also
removed it from our midst, nailing it
to the cross.

GOSPEL ACCLAMATION

Romans 8:15bc

℟. Al - le - lu - ia, al - le - lu - ia, al - le - lu - ia.

Music: John Schiavone, b. 1947, © 2001, OCP Publications.

▶ You have received a Spirit of adoption,
through which we cry, Abba, Father. ℟.

GOSPEL READING

Luke 11:1–13

Jesus was praying in a certain place,
and when he had finished, one of his
disciples said to him, "Lord, teach us to
pray just as John taught his disciples."
He said to them, "When you pray, say:
Father, hallowed be your name,
your kingdom come.

Give us each day our daily bread
and forgive us our sins
for we ourselves forgive everyone
in debt to us,
and do not subject us to the
final test."

And he said to them, "Suppose one of you has a friend to whom he goes at midnight and says, 'Friend, lend me three loaves of bread, for a friend of mine has arrived at my house from a journey and I have nothing to offer him,' and he says in reply from within, 'Do not bother me; the door has already been locked and my children and I are already in bed. I cannot get up to give you anything.' I tell you, if he does not get up to give the visitor the loaves because of their friendship, he will get up to give him whatever he needs because of his persistence.

"And I tell you, ask and you will receive; seek and you will find; knock and the door will be opened to you. For everyone who asks, receives; and the one who seeks, finds; and to the one who knocks, the door will be opened. What father among you would hand his son a snake when he asks for a fish? Or hand him a scorpion when he asks for an egg? If you then, who are wicked, know how to give good gifts to your children, how much more will the Father in heaven give the Holy Spirit to those who ask him?"

18TH SUNDAY IN ORDINARY TIME — A   999

FIRST READING
Isaiah 55:1–3

Thus says the LORD:
All you who are thirsty,
   come to the water!
You who have no money,
   come, receive grain and eat;
Come, without paying and without cost,
   drink wine and milk!
Why spend your money for what is
    not bread;

your wages for what fails to satisfy?
Heed me, and you shall eat well,
   you shall delight in rich fare.
Come to me heedfully,
   listen, that you may have life.
I will renew with you the
    everlasting covenant,
   the benefits assured to David.

RESPONSORIAL PSALM
Psalm 145:8–9, 15–16, 17–18

℟. The hand of the Lord feeds us; he an-swers all our needs.

Music: John Schiavone, b. 1947, © 2001, OCP Publications.

▶ The LORD is gracious and merciful,
   slow to anger and of great kindness.
The LORD is good to all
   and compassionate toward all
    his works. ℟.

▶ The eyes of all look hopefully to you,
   and you give them their food in
    due season;

you open your hand
   and satisfy the desire of every
    living thing. ℟.

▶ The LORD is just in all his ways
   and holy in all his works.
The LORD is near to all who call
   upon him,
   to all who call upon him in truth. ℟.

SECOND READING

Romans 8:35, 37–39

Brothers and sisters: What will separate us from the love of Christ? Will anguish, or distress, or persecution, or famine, or nakedness, or peril, or the sword? No, in all these things we conquer overwhelmingly through him who loved us. For I am convinced that neither death, nor life, nor angels, nor principalities, nor present things, nor future things, nor powers, nor height, nor depth, nor any other creature will be able to separate us from the love of God in Christ Jesus our Lord.

GOSPEL ACCLAMATION

Matthew 4:4b

℟. Al - le - lu - ia, al - le - lu - ia, al - le - lu - ia.

Music: John Schiavone, b. 1947, © 2001, OCP Publications.

▶ One does not live on bread alone,
but on every word that comes forth from the mouth of God. ℟.

GOSPEL READING

Matthew 14:13–21

When Jesus heard of the death of John the Baptist, he withdrew in a boat to a deserted place by himself. The crowds heard of this and followed him on foot from their towns. When he disembarked and saw the vast crowd, his heart was moved with pity for them, and he cured their sick. When it was evening, the disciples approached him and said, "This is a deserted place and it is already late; dismiss the crowds so that they can go to the villages and buy food for themselves." Jesus said to them, "There is no need for them to go away; give them some food yourselves." But they said to him, "Five loaves and two fish are all we have here." Then he said, "Bring them here to me," and he ordered the crowds to sit down on the grass. Taking the five loaves and the two fish, and looking up to heaven, he said the blessing, broke the loaves, and gave them to the disciples, who in turn gave them to the crowds. They all ate and were satisfied, and they picked up the fragments left over — twelve wicker baskets full. Those who ate were about five thousand men, not counting women and children.

1000   18TH SUNDAY IN ORDINARY TIME — B

FIRST READING

Exodus 16:2–4, 12–15

The whole Israelite community grumbled against Moses and Aaron. The Israelites said to them, "Would that we had died at the LORD's hand in the land of Egypt, as we sat by our fleshpots and ate our fill of bread! But you had to lead us into this desert to make the whole community die of famine!"

Then the LORD said to Moses, "I will now rain down bread from heaven for you. Each day the people are to go out and gather their daily portion; thus will I test them, to see whether they follow my instructions or not.

"I have heard the grumbling of the Israelites. Tell them: In the evening twilight you shall eat flesh, and in the morning you shall have your fill of bread, so that you may know that I, the LORD, am your God."

In the evening quail came up and covered the camp. In the morning a dew lay all about the camp, and when the dew evaporated, there on the surface of the desert were fine flakes like hoarfrost on the ground. On seeing it, the Israelites asked one another, "What is this?" for they did not know what it was. But Moses told them, "This is the bread that the LORD has given you to eat."

RESPONSORIAL PSALM

Psalm 78:3–4, 23–24, 25, 54

℟. The Lord gave them bread from heav - en.

Music: John Schiavone, b. 1947, © 2001, OCP Publications.

▸ What we have heard and know,
   and what our fathers have declared
      to us,
   we will declare to the generation
      to come,
   the glorious deeds of the LORD and
      his strength
   and the wonders that he wrought. ℟.

▸ He commanded the skies above
   and opened the doors of heaven;
   he rained manna upon them for food
   and gave them heavenly bread. ℟.

▸ Man ate the bread of angels,
   food he sent them in abundance.
   And he brought them to his holy land,
   to the mountains his right hand
      had won. ℟.

SECOND READING

Ephesians 4:17, 20–24

Brothers and sisters: I declare and testify in the Lord that you must no longer live as the Gentiles do, in the futility of their minds; that is not how you learned Christ, assuming that you have heard of him and were taught in him, as truth is in Jesus, that you should put away the old self of your former way of life, corrupted through deceitful desires, and be renewed in the spirit of your minds, and put on the new self, created in God's way in righteousness and holiness of truth.

GOSPEL ACCLAMATION

Matthew 4:4b

℟. Al - le - lu - ia, al - le - lu - ia, al - le - lu - ia.

Music: John Schiavone, b. 1947, © 2001, OCP Publications.

▸ One does not live on bread alone,
   but on every word that comes forth from the mouth of God. ℟.

GOSPEL READING

John 6:24–35

When the crowd saw that neither Jesus nor his disciples were there, they themselves got into boats and came to Capernaum looking for Jesus. And when they found him across the sea they said to him, "Rabbi, when did you get here?" Jesus answered them and said, "Amen, amen, I say to you, you are looking for me not because you saw signs but because you ate the loaves and were filled. Do not work for food that perishes but for the food that endures for eternal life, which the Son of Man will give you. For on him the Father, God, has set his seal." So they said to him, "What can we do to accomplish the works of God?" Jesus answered and said to them, "This is the work of God, that you believe in the one he sent." So they said to him, "What sign can you do, that we may see and believe in you? What can you do? Our ancestors ate manna in the desert, as it is written:

He gave them bread from heaven to eat."

So Jesus said to them, "Amen, amen, I say to you, it was not Moses who gave the bread from heaven; my Father gives you the true bread from heaven. For the bread of God is that which comes down from heaven and gives life to the world."

So they said to him, "Sir, give us this bread always." Jesus said to them, "I am the bread of life; whoever comes to me will never hunger, and whoever believes in me will never thirst."

1001   18TH SUNDAY IN ORDINARY TIME — C

FIRST READING
Ecclesiastes 1:2; 2:21–23

Vanity of vanities, says Qoheleth,
  vanity of vanities! All things are vanity!

Here is one who has labored with wisdom and knowledge and skill, and yet to another who has not labored over it, he must leave property. This also is vanity and a great misfortune. For what profit comes to man from all the toil and anxiety of heart with which he has labored under the sun? All his days sorrow and grief is his occupation; even at night his mind is not at rest. This also is vanity.

RESPONSORIAL PSALM
Psalm 90:3–4, 5–6, 12–13, 14, 17

℟. If to-day you hear his voice, hard-en not your hearts.

Music: John Schiavone, b. 1947, © 2001, OCP Publications.

▸ You turn man back to dust,
    saying, "Return, O children of men."
  For a thousand years in your sight
    are as yesterday, now that it is past,
    or as a watch of the night. ℟.

▸ You make an end of them in their sleep;
    the next morning they are like the
        changing grass,
  which at dawn springs up anew,
    but by evening wilts and fades. ℟.

▸ Teach us to number our days aright,
    that we may gain wisdom of heart.
  Return, O LORD! How long?
    Have pity on your servants! ℟.

▸ Fill us at daybreak with your kindness,
    that we may shout for joy and
        gladness all our days.
  And may the gracious care of the LORD
    our God be ours;
    prosper the work of our hands for us!
    Prosper the work of our hands! ℟.

SECOND READING

Colossians 3:1–5, 9–11

Brothers and sisters: If you were raised with Christ, seek what is above, where Christ is seated at the right hand of God. Think of what is above, not of what is on earth. For you have died, and your life is hidden with Christ in God. When Christ your life appears, then you too will appear with him in glory.

Put to death, then, the parts of you that are earthly: immorality, impurity, passion, evil desire, and the greed that is idolatry. Stop lying to one another, since you have taken off the old self with its practices and have put on the new self, which is being renewed, for knowledge, in the image of its creator. Here there is not Greek and Jew, circumcision and uncircumcision, barbarian, Scythian, slave, free; but Christ is all and in all.

GOSPEL ACCLAMATION

Matthew 5:3

℟. Al - le - lu - ia, al - le - lu - ia, al - le - lu - ia.

Music: John Schiavone, b. 1947, © 2001, OCP Publications.

▶ Blessed are the poor in spirit,
for theirs is the kingdom of heaven. ℟.

GOSPEL READING

Luke 12:13–21

Someone in the crowd said to Jesus, "Teacher, tell my brother to share the inheritance with me." He replied to him, "Friend, who appointed me as your judge and arbitrator?" Then he said to the crowd, "Take care to guard against all greed, for though one may be rich, one's life does not consist of possessions."

Then he told them a parable. "There was a rich man whose land produced a bountiful harvest. He asked himself, 'What shall I do, for I do not have space to store my harvest?' And he said, 'This is what I shall do: I shall tear down my barns and build larger ones. There I shall store all my grain and other goods and I shall say to myself, "Now as for you, you have so many good things stored up for many years, rest, eat, drink, be merry!"' But God said to him, 'You fool, this night your life will be demanded of you; and the things you have prepared, to whom will they belong?' Thus will it be for all who store up treasure for themselves but are not rich in what matters to God."

19TH SUNDAY IN ORDINARY TIME — A   1002

FIRST READING

1 Kings 19:9a, 11–13a

At the mountain of God, Horeb, Elijah came to a cave where he took shelter. Then the LORD said to him, "Go outside and stand on the mountain before the LORD; the LORD will be passing by." A strong and heavy wind was rending the mountains and crushing rocks before the LORD — but the LORD was not in the wind. After the wind there was an earthquake — but the LORD was not in the earthquake. After the earthquake there was fire — but the LORD was not in the fire. After the fire there was a tiny whispering sound. When he heard this, Elijah hid his face in his cloak and went and stood at the entrance of the cave.

RESPONSORIAL PSALM

Psalm 85:9, 10, 11–12, 13–14

℟. **Lord, let us see your kind-ness, and grant us your sal-va-tion.**

Music: John Schiavone, b. 1947, © 2001, OCP Publications.

▶ I will hear what God proclaims;
    the LORD — for he proclaims peace.
Near indeed is his salvation to those
    who fear him,
    glory dwelling in our land. ℟.

▶ Kindness and truth shall meet;
    justice and peace shall kiss.

Truth shall spring out of the earth,
    and justice shall look down from
    heaven. ℟.

▶ The LORD himself will give his benefits;
    our land shall yield its increase.
Justice shall walk before him,
    and prepare the way of his steps. ℟.

SECOND READING

Romans 9:1–5

Brothers and sisters: I speak the truth in Christ, I do not lie; my conscience joins with the Holy Spirit in bearing me witness that I have great sorrow and constant anguish in my heart. For I could wish that I myself were accursed and cut off from Christ for the sake of my own people, my kindred according to the flesh. They are Israelites; theirs the adoption, the glory, the covenants, the giving of the law, the worship, and the promises; theirs the patriarchs, and from them, according to the flesh, is the Christ, who is over all, God blessed forever. Amen.

GOSPEL ACCLAMATION

cf. Psalm 130:5

℟. **Al-le-lu-ia, al-le-lu-ia, al-le-lu-ia.**

Music: John Schiavone, b. 1947, © 2001, OCP Publications.

▶ I wait for the Lord;
    my soul waits for his word. ℟.

GOSPEL READING

Matthew 14:22–33

After he had fed the people, Jesus made the disciples get into a boat and precede him to the other side, while he dismissed the crowds. After doing so, he went up on the mountain by himself to pray. When it was evening he was there alone. Meanwhile the boat, already a few miles offshore, was being tossed about by the waves, for the wind was against it. During the fourth watch of the night, he came toward them walking on the sea. When the disciples saw him walking on the sea they were terrified. "It is a ghost," they said, and they cried out in fear. At once Jesus spoke to them, "Take courage, it is I; do not be afraid." Peter said to him in reply, "Lord, if it is you, command me to come to you on the water." He said, "Come." Peter got out of the boat and began to walk on the water toward Jesus. But when he saw how strong the wind was he became frightened; and, beginning to sink, he cried out, "Lord, save me!" Immediately Jesus stretched out his hand and caught Peter, and said to him,

"O you of little faith, why did you doubt?" After they got into the boat, the wind died down. Those who were in the boat did him homage, saying, "Truly, you are the Son of God."

19TH SUNDAY IN ORDINARY TIME — B   1003

FIRST READING
1 Kings 19:4–8

Elijah went a day's journey into the desert, until he came to a broom tree and sat beneath it. He prayed for death, saying: "This is enough, O LORD! Take my life, for I am no better than my fathers." He lay down and fell asleep under the broom tree, but then an angel touched him and ordered him to get up and eat. Elijah looked and there at his head was a hearth cake and a jug of water. After he ate and drank, he lay down again, but the angel of the LORD came back a second time, touched him, and ordered, "Get up and eat, else the journey will be too long for you!" He got up, ate, and drank; then strengthened by that food, he walked forty days and forty nights to the mountain of God, Horeb.

RESPONSORIAL PSALM
Psalm 34:2–3, 4–5, 6–7, 8–9

℟. [Taste and see,] taste and see the good-ness of the Lord

Music: John Schiavone, b 1947, © 2001, OCP Publications.

▶ I will bless the LORD at all times;
    his praise shall be ever in my mouth.
  Let my soul glory in the LORD;
    the lowly will hear me and be glad. ℟.

▶ Glorify the LORD with me,
    let us together extol his name.
  I sought the LORD, and he answered me
    and delivered me from all my fears. ℟.

▶ Look to him that you may be radiant
      with joy,
  and your faces may not blush
      with shame.

When the afflicted man called out, the
    LORD heard,
  and from all his distress he
    saved him. ℟.

▶ The angel of the LORD encamps
    around those who fear him and
    delivers them.
  Taste and see how good the LORD is;
    blessed the man who takes refuge
      in him. ℟.

SECOND READING
Ephesians 4:30—5:2

Brothers and sisters: Do not grieve the Holy Spirit of God, with which you were sealed for the day of redemption. All bitterness, fury, anger, shouting, and reviling must be removed from you, along with all malice. And be kind to one another, compassionate, forgiving one another as God has forgiven you in Christ.

So be imitators of God, as beloved children, and live in love, as Christ loved us and handed himself over for us as a sacrificial offering to God for a fragrant aroma.

GOSPEL ACCLAMATION

John 6:51

R. Al - le - lu - ia, al - le - lu - ia, al - le - lu - ia.

Music: John Schiavone, b. 1947, © 2001, OCP Publications.

▶ I am the living bread that came down from heaven, says the Lord;
whoever eats this bread will live forever. R.

GOSPEL READING

John 6:41–51

The Jews murmured about Jesus because he said, "I am the bread that came down from heaven," and they said, "Is this not Jesus, the son of Joseph? Do we not know his father and mother? Then how can he say, 'I have come down from heaven'?" Jesus answered and said to them, "Stop murmuring among yourselves. No one can come to me unless the Father who sent me draw him, and I will raise him on the last day. It is written in the prophets:

They shall all be taught by God.
Everyone who listens to my Father and learns from him comes to me. Not that anyone has seen the Father except the one who is from God; he has seen the Father. Amen, amen, I say to you, whoever believes has eternal life. I am the bread of life. Your ancestors ate the manna in the desert, but they died; this is the bread that comes down from heaven so that one may eat it and not die. I am the living bread that came down from heaven; whoever eats this bread will live forever; and the bread that I will give is my flesh for the life of the world."

1004   19TH SUNDAY IN ORDINARY TIME — C

FIRST READING

Wisdom 18:6–9

The night of the passover was known
    beforehand to our fathers,
  that, with sure knowledge of the
    oaths in which they put their faith,
  they might have courage.
Your people awaited the salvation of
    the just
  and the destruction of their foes.

For when you punished our adversaries,
    in this you glorified us whom you
    had summoned.
For in secret the holy children of the
    good were offering sacrifice
  and putting into effect with one
    accord the divine institution.

RESPONSORIAL PSALM

Psalm 33:1, 12, 18–19, 20–22

R. Bless'd the peo-ple the Lord has cho-sen to be his own.

Music: John Schiavone, b. 1947, © 2001, OCP Publications.

▶ Exult, you just, in the LORD;
    praise from the upright is fitting.
Blessed the nation whose God is
        the LORD,
    the people he has chosen for his
        own inheritance. ℟.

▶ See, the eyes of the LORD are upon
        those who fear him,
    upon those who hope for
        his kindness,

to deliver them from death
    and preserve them in spite of
    famine. ℟.

▶ Our soul waits for the LORD,
    who is our help and our shield.
May your kindness, O LORD, be
    upon us
    who have put our hope in you. ℟.

SECOND READING

Hebrews 11:1–2, 8–19 or 11:1–2, 8–12

(Include bracketed text for Long Form)

Brothers and sisters: Faith is the realization of what is hoped for and evidence of things not seen. Because of it the ancients were well attested.

By faith Abraham obeyed when he was called to go out to a place that he was to receive as an inheritance; he went out, not knowing where he was to go. By faith he sojourned in the promised land as in a foreign country, dwelling in tents with Isaac and Jacob, heirs of the same promise; for he was looking forward to the city with foundations, whose architect and maker is God. By faith he received power to generate, even though he was past the normal age — and Sarah herself was sterile — for he thought that the one who had made the promise was trustworthy. So it was that there came forth from one man, himself as good as dead, descendants as numerous as the stars in the sky and as countless as the

sands on the seashore.

[All these died in faith. They did not receive what had been promised but saw it and greeted it from afar and acknowledged themselves to be strangers and aliens on earth, for those who speak thus show that they are seeking a homeland. If they had been thinking of the land from which they had come, they would have had opportunity to return. But now they desire a better homeland, a heavenly one. Therefore, God is not ashamed to be called their God, for he has prepared a city for them.

By faith Abraham, when put to the test, offered up Isaac, and he who had received the promises was ready to offer his only son, of whom it was said, "Through Isaac descendants shall bear your name." He reasoned that God was able to raise even from the dead, and he received Isaac back as a symbol.]

GOSPEL ACCLAMATION

Matthew 24:42a, 44

℟. Al - le - lu - ia,   al - le - lu - ia,   al - le - lu - ia.

Music: John Schiavone, b. 1947, © 2001, OCP Publications.

▶ Stay awake and be ready!
    For you do not know on what day the Son of Man will come. ℟.

GOSPEL READING

Luke 12:32–48 or 12:35–40

(Include bracketed text for Long Form)

Jesus said to his disciples: ["Do not be afraid any longer, little flock, for your Father is pleased to give you the kingdom. Sell your belongings and give alms. Provide money bags for yourselves that do not wear out, an inexhaustible treasure in heaven that no thief can reach nor moth destroy. For where your treasure is, there also will your heart be.]

"Gird your loins and light your lamps and be like servants who await their master's return from a wedding, ready to open immediately when he comes and knocks. Blessed are those servants whom the master finds vigilant on his arrival. Amen, I say to you, he will gird himself, have them recline at table, and proceed to wait on them. And should he come in the second or third watch and find them prepared in this way, blessed are those servants. Be sure of this: if the master of the house had known the hour when the thief was coming, he would not have let his house be broken into. You also must be prepared, for at an hour you do not expect, the Son of Man will come."

[Then Peter said, "Lord, is this parable meant for us or for everyone?" And the Lord replied, "Who, then, is the faithful and prudent steward whom the master will put in charge of his servants to distribute the food allowance at the proper time? Blessed is that servant whom his master on arrival finds doing so. Truly, I say to you, the master will put the servant in charge of all his property. But if that servant says to himself, 'My master is delayed in coming,' and begins to beat the menservants and the maidservants, to eat and drink and get drunk, then that servant's master will come on an unexpected day and at an unknown hour and will punish the servant severely and assign him a place with the unfaithful. That servant who knew his master's will but did not make preparations nor act in accord with his will shall be beaten severely; and the servant who was ignorant of his master's will but acted in a way deserving of a severe beating shall be beaten only lightly. Much will be required of the person entrusted with much, and still more will be demanded of the person entrusted with more."]

1005   20TH SUNDAY IN ORDINARY TIME — A

FIRST READING

Isaiah 56:1, 6–7

Thus says the LORD:
Observe what is right, do what is just;
    for my salvation is about to come,
    my justice, about to be revealed.

The foreigners who join themselves to
        the LORD,
    ministering to him,
loving the name of the LORD,
    and becoming his servants—

all who keep the sabbath free
        from profanation
    and hold to my covenant,
them I will bring to my holy mountain
    and make joyful in my house
        of prayer;
their burnt offerings and sacrifices
    will be acceptable on my altar,
for my house shall be called
    a house of prayer for all peoples.

RESPONSORIAL PSALM

Psalm 67:2–3, 5, 6, 8

℟. O God, let all the na - tions praise you!

Music: John Schiavone, b. 1947, © 2001, OCP Publications.

▶ May God have pity on us and bless us;
may he let his face shine upon us.
So may your way be known upon earth;
among all nations, your salvation. ℟.

▶ May the nations be glad and exult
because you rule the peoples
in equity;
the nations on the earth you guide. ℟.

▶ May the peoples praise you, O God;
may all the peoples praise you!
May God bless us,
and may all the ends of the earth
fear him! ℟.

SECOND READING

Romans 11:13–15, 29–32

Brothers and sisters: I am speaking to you Gentiles. Inasmuch as I am the apostle to the Gentiles, I glory in my ministry in order to make my race jealous and thus save some of them. For if their rejection is the reconciliation of the world, what will their acceptance be but life from the dead?

For the gifts and the call of God are irrevocable. Just as you once disobeyed God but have now received mercy because of their disobedience, so they have now disobeyed in order that, by virtue of the mercy shown to you, they too may now receive mercy. For God delivered all to disobedience, that he might have mercy upon all.

GOSPEL ACCLAMATION

cf. Matthew 4:23

℟. Al - le - lu - ia, al - le - lu - ia, al - le - lu - ia.

Music: John Schiavone, b. 1947, © 2001, OCP Publications.

▶ Jesus proclaimed the Gospel of the kingdom
and cured every disease among the people. ℟.

GOSPEL READING

Matthew 15:21–28

At that time, Jesus withdrew to the region of Tyre and Sidon. And behold, a Canaanite woman of that district came and called out, "Have pity on me, Lord, Son of David! My daughter is tormented by a demon." But Jesus did not say a word in answer to her. Jesus' disciples came and asked him, "Send her away, for she keeps calling out after us." He said in reply, "I was sent only to the lost sheep of the house of Israel."

But the woman came and did Jesus homage, saying, "Lord, help me." He said in reply, "It is not right to take the food of the children and throw it to the dogs." She said, "Please, Lord, for even the dogs eat the scraps that fall from the table of their masters." Then Jesus said to her in reply, "O woman, great is your faith! Let it be done for you as you wish." And the woman's daughter was healed from that hour.

1006   20TH SUNDAY IN ORDINARY TIME — B

FIRST READING   *Proverbs 9:1–6*

Wisdom has built her house,
    she has set up her seven columns;
she has dressed her meat, mixed
      her wine,
    yes, she has spread her table.
She has sent out her maidens; she calls
    from the heights out over the city:

"Let whoever is simple turn in here;
    to the one who lacks understanding,
    she says,
Come, eat of my food,
    and drink of the wine I have mixed!
Forsake foolishness that you may live;
    advance in the way of understanding."

RESPONSORIAL PSALM   *Psalm 34:2–3, 4–5, 6–7*

℟. [Taste and see,] taste and see the good-ness of the Lord.

Music: John Schiavone, b. 1947, © 2001, OCP Publications.

▸ I will bless the LORD at all times;
    his praise shall be ever in my mouth.
Let my soul glory in the LORD;
    the lowly will hear me and be glad. ℟.

▸ Glorify the LORD with me,
    let us together extol his name.
I sought the LORD, and he answered me
    and delivered me from all my fears. ℟.

▸ Look to him that you may be radiant
    with joy,
    and your faces may not blush
    with shame.
When the poor one called out,
    the LORD heard,
    and from all his distress he
    saved him. ℟.

SECOND READING   *Ephesians 5:15–20*

Brothers and sisters: Watch carefully
how you live, not as foolish persons
but as wise, making the most of the
opportunity, because the days are
evil. Therefore, do not continue in
ignorance, but try to understand what
is the will of the Lord. And do not
get drunk on wine, in which lies

debauchery, but be filled with the Spirit,
addressing one another in psalms and
hymns and spiritual songs, singing and
playing to the Lord in your hearts,
giving thanks always and for everything
in the name of our Lord Jesus Christ to
God the Father.

GOSPEL ACCLAMATION   *John 6:56*

℟. Al - le - lu - ia,   al - le - lu - ia,   al - le - lu - ia.

Music: John Schiavone, b. 1947, © 2001, OCP Publications.

▸ Whoever eats my flesh and drinks my blood
  remains in me and I in him, says the Lord. ℟.

GOSPEL READING

John 6:51–58

Jesus said to the crowds: "I am the living bread that came down from heaven; whoever eats this bread will live forever; and the bread that I will give is my flesh for the life of the world."

The Jews quarreled among themselves, saying, "How can this man give us his flesh to eat?" Jesus said to them, "Amen, amen, I say to you, unless you eat the flesh of the Son of Man and drink his blood, you do not have life within you. Whoever eats my flesh and drinks my blood has eternal life, and I will raise him on the last day. For my flesh is true food, and my blood is true drink. Whoever eats my flesh and drinks my blood remains in me and I in him. Just as the living Father sent me and I have life because of the Father, so also the one who feeds on me will have life because of me. This is the bread that came down from heaven. Unlike your ancestors who ate and still died, whoever eats this bread will live forever."

20TH SUNDAY IN ORDINARY TIME — C   **1007**

FIRST READING

Jeremiah 38:4–6, 8–10

In those days, the princes said to the king: "Jeremiah ought to be put to death; he is demoralizing the soldiers who are left in this city, and all the people, by speaking such things to them; he is not interested in the welfare of our people, but in their ruin." King Zedekiah answered: "He is in your power"; for the king could do nothing with them. And so they took Jeremiah and threw him into the cistern of Prince Malchiah, which was in the quarters of the guard, letting him down with ropes. There was no water in the cistern, only mud, and Jeremiah sank into the mud.

Ebed-melech, a court official, went there from the palace and said to him: "My lord king, these men have been at fault in all they have done to the prophet Jeremiah, casting him into the cistern. He will die of famine on the spot, for there is no more food in the city." Then the king ordered Ebed-melech the Cushite to take three men along with him, and draw the prophet Jeremiah out of the cistern before he should die.

RESPONSORIAL PSALM

Psalm 40:2, 3, 4, 18

℟. [Lord,] Lord, come to my aid! [Come to my aid!]

Music: John Schiavone, b. 1947, © 2001, OCP Publications.

▶ I have waited, waited for the LORD,
　and he stooped toward me. ℟.

▶ The LORD heard my cry.
　He drew me out of the pit
　　of destruction,
　　out of the mud of the swamp;
　he set my feet upon a crag;
　he made firm my steps. ℟.

▶ And he put a new song into my mouth,
　a hymn to our God.
Many shall look on in awe
　and trust in the LORD. ℟.

▶ Though I am afflicted and poor,
　yet the LORD thinks of me.
You are my help and my deliverer;
　O my God, hold not back! ℟.

SECOND READING

Hebrews 12:1–4

Brothers and sisters: Since we are surrounded by so great a cloud of witnesses, let us rid ourselves of every burden and sin that clings to us and persevere in running the race that lies before us while keeping our eyes fixed on Jesus, the leader and perfecter of faith. For the sake of the joy that lay before him he endured the cross, despising its shame, and has taken his seat at the right of the throne of God. Consider how he endured such opposition from sinners, in order that you may not grow weary and lose heart. In your struggle against sin you have not yet resisted to the point of shedding blood.

GOSPEL ACCLAMATION

John 10:27

℟. Al - le - lu - ia, al - le - lu - ia, al - le - lu - ia.

Music: John Schiavone, b. 1947, © 2001, OCP Publications.

▶ My sheep hear my voice, says the Lord; I know them, and they follow me. ℟.

GOSPEL READING

Luke 12:49–53

Jesus said to his disciples: "I have come to set the earth on fire, and how I wish it were already blazing! There is a baptism with which I must be baptized, and how great is my anguish until it is accomplished! Do you think that I have come to establish peace on the earth? No, I tell you, but rather division. From now on a household of five will be divided, three against two and two against three; a father will be divided against his son and a son against his father, a mother against her daughter and a daughter against her mother, a mother-in-law against her daughter-in-law and a daughter-in-law against her mother-in-law."

1008 21ST SUNDAY IN ORDINARY TIME — A

FIRST READING

Isaiah 22:19–23

Thus says the LORD to Shebna, master of
  the palace:
"I will thrust you from your office
  and pull you down from your station.
On that day I will summon my servant
  Eliakim, son of Hilkiah;
I will clothe him with your robe,
  and gird him with your sash,
  and give over to him your authority.
He shall be a father to the inhabitants
  of Jerusalem,
  and to the house of Judah.
I will place the key of the House of
  David on Eliakim's shoulder;
  when he opens, no one shall shut
  when he shuts, no one shall open.
I will fix him like a peg in a sure spot,
  to be a place of honor for his family."

RESPONSORIAL PSALM

Psalm 138:1–2, 2–3, 6, 8

℟. Lord, your love is e-ter-nal; do not for-sake the work of your hands.

Music: John Schiavone, b. 1947, © 2001, OCP Publications.

▶ I will give thanks to you, O LORD, with
all my heart,
for you have heard the words of
my mouth;
in the presence of the angels I will
sing your praise;
I will worship at your holy temple. ℟.

▶ I will give thanks to your name,
because of your kindness and
your truth:

when I called, you answered me;
you built up strength within me. ℟.

▶ The LORD is exalted, yet the lowly
he sees,
and the proud he knows from afar.
Your kindness, O LORD, endures forever;
forsake not the work of your hands. ℟.

SECOND READING

Romans 11:33–36

Oh, the depth of the riches and wisdom
and knowledge of God! How inscrutable
are his judgments and how unsearchable
his ways!
*For who has known the mind of
the Lord*

or who has been his counselor?
Or who has given the Lord anything
that he may be repaid?
For from him and through him and for
him are all things. To him be glory
forever. Amen.

GOSPEL ACCLAMATION

Matthew 16:18

℟. Al-le-lu - ia, al-le-lu - ia, al-le-lu - ia.

Music: John Schiavone, b. 1947, © 2001, OCP Publications.

▶ You are Peter and upon this rock I will build my Church
and the gates of the netherworld shall not prevail against it. ℟.

GOSPEL READING

Matthew 16:13–20

Jesus went into the region of Caesarea
Philippi and he asked his disciples,
"Who do people say that the Son of
Man is?" They replied, "Some say John
the Baptist, others Elijah, still others
Jeremiah or one of the prophets." He
said to them, "But who do you say that
I am?" Simon Peter said in reply, "You
are the Christ, the Son of the living
God." Jesus said to him in reply,
"Blessed are you, Simon son of Jonah.
For flesh and blood has not revealed

this to you, but my heavenly Father. And
so I say to you, you are Peter, and upon
this rock I will build my church, and the
gates of the netherworld shall not
prevail against it. I will give you the keys
to the kingdom of heaven. Whatever
you bind on earth shall be bound in
heaven; and whatever you loose on
earth shall be loosed in heaven." Then
he strictly ordered his disciples to tell
no one that he was the Christ.

1009 21ST SUNDAY IN ORDINARY TIME — B

FIRST READING

Joshua 24:1–2a, 15–17, 18b

Joshua gathered together all the tribes of Israel at Shechem, summoning their elders, their leaders, their judges, and their officers. When they stood in ranks before God, Joshua addressed all the people: "If it does not please you to serve the LORD, decide today whom you will serve, the gods your fathers served beyond the River or the gods of the Amorites in whose country you are now dwelling. As for me and my household, we will serve the LORD."

But the people answered, "Far be it from us to forsake the LORD for the service of other gods. For it was the LORD, our God, who brought us and our fathers up out of the land of Egypt, out of a state of slavery. He performed those great miracles before our very eyes and protected us along our entire journey and among the peoples through whom we passed. Therefore we also will serve the LORD, for he is our God."

RESPONSORIAL PSALM

Psalm 34:2–3, 16–17, 18–19, 20–21

℟. [Taste and see,] taste and see the good-ness of the Lord.

Music: John Schiavone, b. 1947, © 2001, OCP Publications.

▸ I will bless the LORD at all times;
    his praise shall be ever in my mouth.
Let my soul glory in the LORD;
    the lowly will hear me and be glad. ℟.

▸ The LORD has eyes for the just,
    and ears for their cry.
The LORD confronts the evildoers,
    to destroy remembrance of them
    from the earth. ℟.

▸ When the just cry out, the LORD
    hears them,
and from all their distress he
    rescues them.

The LORD is close to the
    brokenhearted;
    and those who are crushed in spirit
    he saves. ℟.

▸ Many are the troubles of the just one,
    but out of them all the LORD
    delivers him;
he watches over all his bones;
    not one of them shall be broken. ℟.

SECOND READING

Ephesians 5:21–32 or 5:2a, 25–32

(Include bracketed text for Long Form, and text in parentheses for Short Form only)

Brothers and sisters: [Be subordinate to one another out of reverence for Christ. Wives should be subordinate to their husbands as to the Lord. For the husband is head of his wife just as Christ is head of the church, he himself the savior of the body. As the church is subordinate to Christ, so wives should be subordinate to their husbands in

everything.] *(Live in love, as Christ loved us.)* Husbands, love your wives, even as Christ loved the church and handed himself over for her to sanctify her, cleansing her by the bath of water with the word, that he might present to himself the church in splendor, without spot or wrinkle or any such thing, that she might be holy and without blemish.

So also husbands should love their wives as their own bodies. He who loves his wife loves himself. For no one hates his own flesh but rather nourishes and cherishes it, even as Christ does the church, because we are members of his body.

For this reason a man shall leave his father and his mother and be joined to his wife, and the two shall become one flesh. This is a great mystery, but I speak in reference to Christ and the church.

GOSPEL ACCLAMATION

John 6:63c, 68c

℟. Al - le - lu - ia, al - le - lu - ia, al - le - lu - ia.

Music: John Schiavone, b. 1947, © 2001, OCP Publications.

▶ Your words, Lord, are Spirit and life; you have the words of everlasting life. ℟.

GOSPEL READING

John 6:60–69

Many of Jesus' disciples who were listening said, "This saying is hard; who can accept it?" Since Jesus knew that his disciples were murmuring about this, he said to them, "Does this shock you? What if you were to see the Son of Man ascending to where he was before? It is the spirit that gives life, while the flesh is of no avail. The words I have spoken to you are Spirit and life. But there are some of you who do not believe." Jesus knew from the beginning the ones who would not believe and the one who would betray him. And he said, "For this reason I have told you that no one can come to me unless it is granted him by my Father."

As a result of this, many of his disciples returned to their former way of life and no longer accompanied him. Jesus then said to the Twelve, "Do you also want to leave?" Simon Peter answered him, "Master, to whom shall we go? You have the words of eternal life. We have come to believe and are convinced that you are the Holy One of God."

21ST SUNDAY IN ORDINARY TIME — C   1010

FIRST READING

Isaiah 66:18–21

Thus says the LORD: I know their works and their thoughts, and I come to gather nations of every language; they shall come and see my glory. I will set a sign among them; from them I will send fugitives to the nations: to Tarshish, Put and Lud, Mosoch, Tubal and Javan, to the distant coastlands that have never heard of my fame, or seen my glory; and they shall proclaim my glory among the nations. They shall bring all your brothers and sisters from all the nations as an offering to the LORD, on horses and in chariots, in carts, upon mules and dromedaries, to Jerusalem, my holy mountain, says the LORD, just as the Israelites bring their offering to the house of the LORD in clean vessels. Some of these I will take as priests and Levites, says the LORD.

RESPONSORIAL PSALM

Psalm 117:1, 2

℟. Go out to all the world and tell the Good News.

Music: John Schiavone, b. 1947, © 2001, OCP Publications.

or: **Alleluia.**

▶ Praise the LORD, all you nations;
   glorify him, all you peoples! ℟.

▶ For steadfast is his kindness toward us,
   and the fidelity of the LORD endures
   forever. ℟.

SECOND READING

Hebrews 12:5–7, 11–13

Brothers and sisters, You have forgotten the exhortation addressed to you as children:

"My son, do not disdain the
   discipline of the Lord
   or lose heart when reproved by him;
for whom the Lord loves,
   he disciplines;
   he scourges every son
   he acknowledges."
Endure your trials as "discipline"; God treats you as sons. For what "son" is there whom his father does not discipline? At the time, all discipline seems a cause not for joy but for pain, yet later it brings the peaceful fruit of righteousness to those who are trained by it.

So strengthen your drooping hands and your weak knees. Make straight paths for your feet, that what is lame may not be disjointed but healed.

GOSPEL ACCLAMATION

John 14:6

℟. Al - le - lu - ia, al - le - lu - ia, al - le - lu - ia.

Music: John Schiavone, b. 1947, © 2001, OCP Publications.

▶ I am the way, the truth and the life, says the Lord;
   no one comes to the Father, except through me. ℟.

GOSPEL READING

Luke 13:22–30

Jesus passed through towns and villages, teaching as he went and making his way to Jerusalem. Someone asked him, "Lord, will only a few people be saved?" He answered them, "Strive to enter through the narrow gate, for many, I tell you, will attempt to enter but will not be strong enough. After the master of the house has arisen and locked the door, then will you stand outside knocking and saying, 'Lord, open the door for us.' He will say to you in reply, 'I do not know where you are from.' And you will say, 'We ate and drank in your company and you taught in our streets.' Then he will say to you, 'I do not know where you are from. Depart from me, all you evildoers!' And there will be wailing and grinding of teeth when you see Abraham, Isaac, and Jacob and all the prophets in the kingdom of God and you yourselves cast out. And people will come from the east and the west and from the north and the south and will recline at table in the kingdom of God. For behold, some are last who will be first, and some are first who will be last."

22ND SUNDAY IN ORDINARY TIME — A

FIRST READING
Jeremiah 20:7–9

You duped me, O LORD, and I let myself
be duped;
you were too strong for me, and
you triumphed.
All the day I am an object of laughter;
everyone mocks me.

Whenever I speak, I must cry out,
violence and outrage is my message;

the word of the LORD has brought me
derision and reproach all the day.

I say to myself, I will not mention him,
I will speak in his name no more.
But then it becomes like fire burning in
my heart,
imprisoned in my bones;
I grow weary holding it in, I cannot
endure it.

RESPONSORIAL PSALM
Psalm 63:2, 3–4, 5–6, 8–9

℟. My soul is thirst - ing for you, O Lord my God.

Music: John Schiavone, b. 1947, © 2001, OCP Publications.

▶ O God, you are my God whom I seek;
for you my flesh pines and my
soul thirsts
like the earth, parched, lifeless and
without water. ℟.

▶ Thus have I gazed toward you in
the sanctuary
to see your power and your glory,
for your kindness is a greater good
than life;
my lips shall glorify you. ℟.

▶ Thus will I bless you while I live;
lifting up my hands, I will call upon
your name.
As with the riches of a banquet shall
my soul be satisfied,
and with exultant lips my mouth
shall praise you. ℟.

▶ You are my help,
and in the shadow of your wings
I shout for joy.
My soul clings fast to you;
your right hand upholds me. ℟.

SECOND READING
Romans 12:1–2

I urge you, brothers and sisters, by the
mercies of God, to offer your bodies as
a living sacrifice, holy and pleasing to
God, your spiritual worship. Do not
conform yourselves to this age but be
transformed by the renewal of your
mind, that you may discern what is the
will of God, what is good and pleasing
and perfect.

GOSPEL ACCLAMATION

cf. Ephesians 1:17–18

℟. Al - le - lu - ia, al - le - lu - ia, al - le - lu - ia.

Music: John Schiavone, b. 1947, © 2001, OCP Publications.

▸ May the Father of our Lord Jesus Christ
enlighten the eyes of our hearts,
that we may know what is the hope
that belongs to our call. ℟.

GOSPEL READING

Matthew 16:21–27

Jesus began to show his disciples that he must go to Jerusalem and suffer greatly from the elders, the chief priests, and the scribes, and be killed and on the third day be raised. Then Peter took Jesus aside and began to rebuke him, "God forbid, Lord! No such thing shall ever happen to you." He turned and said to Peter, "Get behind me, Satan! You are an obstacle to me. You are thinking not as God does, but as human beings do."

Then Jesus said to his disciples,

"Whoever wishes to come after me must deny himself, take up his cross, and follow me. For whoever wishes to save his life will lose it, but whoever loses his life for my sake will find it. What profit would there be for one to gain the whole world and forfeit his life? Or what can one give in exchange for his life? For the Son of Man will come with his angels in his Father's glory, and then he will repay all according to his conduct."

1012 22ND SUNDAY IN ORDINARY TIME — B

FIRST READING

Deuteronomy 4:1–2, 6–8

Moses said to the people: "Now, Israel, hear the statutes and decrees which I am teaching you to observe, that you may live, and may enter in and take possession of the land which the LORD, the God of your fathers, is giving you. In your observance of the commandments of the LORD, your God, which I enjoin upon you, you shall not add to what I command you nor subtract from it. Observe them carefully, for thus will

you give evidence of your wisdom and intelligence to the nations, who will hear of all these statutes and say, 'This great nation is truly a wise and intelligent people.' For what great nation is there that has gods so close to it as the LORD, our God, is to us whenever we call upon him? Or what great nation has statutes and decrees that are as just as this whole law which I am setting before you today?"

RESPONSORIAL PSALM

Psalm 15:2–3, 3–4, 4–5

℟. The one who does jus-tice will live in the pres-ence of the Lord.

Music: John Schiavone, b. 1947, © 2001, OCP Publications.

▶ Whoever walks blamelessly and
   does justice;
   who thinks the truth in his heart
   and slanders not with his tongue. ℟.

▶ Who harms not his fellow man,
   nor takes up a reproach against
   his neighbor;

by whom the reprobate is despised,
   while he honors those who fear
   the LORD. ℟.

▶ Who lends not his money at usury
   and accepts no bribe against
   the innocent.
   Whoever does these things
   shall never be disturbed. ℟.

SECOND READING
James 1:17–18, 21b–22, 27

Dearest brothers and sisters: All good
giving and every perfect gift is from
above, coming down from the Father of
lights, with whom there is no alteration
or shadow caused by change. He willed
to give us birth by the word of truth
that we may be a kind of firstfruits of
his creatures.

Humbly welcome the word that has

been planted in you and is able to save
your souls.

Be doers of the word and not hearers
only, deluding yourselves.

Religion that is pure and undefiled
before God and the Father is this: to
care for orphans and widows in their
affliction and to keep oneself unstained
by the world.

GOSPEL ACCLAMATION
James 1:18

℟. Al - le - lu - ia, al - le - lu - ia, al - le - lu - ia.

Music: John Schiavone, b. 1947, © 2001, OCP Publications.

▶ The Father willed to give us birth by the word of truth
   that we may be a kind of firstfruits of his creatures. ℟.

GOSPEL READING
Mark 7:1–8, 14–15, 21–23

When the Pharisees with some scribes
who had come from Jerusalem gathered
around Jesus, they observed that some
of his disciples ate their meals with
unclean, that is, unwashed, hands. —
For the Pharisees and, in fact, all Jews,
do not eat without carefully washing
their hands, keeping the tradition of
the elders. And on coming from the
marketplace they do not eat without
purifying themselves. And there are
many other things that they have
traditionally observed, the purification
of cups and jugs and kettles and beds.
— So the Pharisees and scribes
questioned him, "Why do your disciples
not follow the tradition of the elders

but instead eat a meal with unclean
hands?" He responded, "Well did Isaiah
prophesy about you hypocrites, as it
is written:
   This people honors me with their lips,
      but their hearts are far from me;
   in vain do they worship me,
      teaching as doctrines
         human precepts.
You disregard God's commandment but
cling to human tradition."

He summoned the crowd again and
said to them, "Hear me, all of you, and
understand. Nothing that enters one
from outside can defile that person; but
the things that come out from within
are what defile.

"From within people, from their hearts, come evil thoughts, unchastity, theft, murder, adultery, greed, malice, deceit, licentiousness, envy, blasphemy, arrogance, folly. All these evils come from within and they defile."

1013   22ND SUNDAY IN ORDINARY TIME — C

FIRST READING   *Sirach 3:17–18, 20, 28–29*

My child, conduct your affairs
  with humility,
and you will be loved more than a
  giver of gifts.
Humble yourself the more, the greater
  you are,
and you will find favor with God.
What is too sublime for you, seek not,
into things beyond your strength
  search not.
The mind of a sage appreciates
  proverbs,
and an attentive ear is the joy of
  the wise.
Water quenches a flaming fire,
  and alms atone for sins.

RESPONSORIAL PSALM   *Psalm 68:4–5, 6–7, 10–11*

℞. God, in your good-ness, you have made a home for the poor.

Music: John Schiavone, b. 1947, © 2001, OCP Publications.

▶ The just rejoice and exult before God;
  they are glad and rejoice.
Sing to God, chant praise to his name,
  whose name is the LORD. ℞.

▶ The father of orphans and the
    defender of widows
  is God in his holy dwelling.
God gives a home to the forsaken;
  he leads forth prisoners
    to prosperity. ℞.

▶ A bountiful rain you showered down,
  O God, upon your inheritance;
you restored the land when
  it languished;
your flock settled in it;
  in your goodness, O God, you
    provided it for the needy. ℞.

SECOND READING   *Hebrews 12:18–19, 22–24a*

Brothers and sisters: You have not approached that which could be touched and a blazing fire and gloomy darkness and storm and a trumpet blast and a voice speaking words such that those who heard begged that no message be further addressed to them. No, you have approached Mount Zion and the city of the living God, the heavenly Jerusalem, and countless angels in festal gathering, and the assembly of the firstborn enrolled in heaven, and God the judge of all, and the spirits of the just made perfect, and Jesus, the mediator of a new covenant, and the sprinkled blood that speaks more eloquently than that of Abel.

GOSPEL ACCLAMATION

Matthew 11:29ab

℟. Al - le - lu - ia, al - le - lu - ia, al - le - lu - ia.

Music: John Schiavone, b. 1947, © 2001, OCP Publications.

▶ Take my yoke upon you, says the Lord,
and learn from me, for I am meek and humble of heart. ℟.

GOSPEL READING

Luke 14:1, 7–14

On a sabbath Jesus went to dine at the home of one of the leading Pharisees, and the people there were observing him carefully.

He told a parable to those who had been invited, noticing how they were choosing the places of honor at the table. "When you are invited by someone to a wedding banquet, do not recline at table in the place of honor. A more distinguished guest than you may have been invited by him, and the host who invited both of you may approach you and say, 'Give your place to this man,' and then you would proceed with embarrassment to take the lowest place. Rather, when you are invited, go and take the lowest place so that when the host comes to you he may say, 'My friend, move up to a higher position.' Then you will enjoy the esteem of your companions at the table. For everyone who exalts himself will be humbled, but the one who humbles himself will be exalted." Then he said to the host who invited him, "When you hold a lunch or a dinner, do not invite your friends or your brothers or your relatives or your wealthy neighbors, in case they may invite you back and you have repayment. Rather, when you hold a banquet, invite the poor, the crippled, the lame, the blind; blessed indeed will you be because of their inability to repay you. For you will be repaid at the resurrection of the righteous."

23RD SUNDAY IN ORDINARY TIME — A · 1014

FIRST READING

Ezekiel 33:7–9

Thus says the LORD:
You, son of man, I have appointed watchman for the house of Israel; when you hear me say anything, you shall warn them for me. If I tell the wicked, "O wicked one, you shall surely die," and you do not speak out to dissuade the wicked from his way, the wicked shall die for his guilt, but I will hold you responsible for his death. But if you warn the wicked, trying to turn him from his way, and he refuses to turn from his way, he shall die for his guilt, but you shall save yourself.

RESPONSORIAL PSALM

Psalm 95:1–2, 6–7, 8–9

℟. If to - day you hear his voice, hard - en not your hearts.

Music: John Schiavone, b. 1947, © 2001, OCP Publications.

℞. If today you hear his voice, harden not your hearts.

▶ Come, let us sing joyfully to the LORD;
    let us acclaim the rock of
       our salvation.
Let us come into his presence with
    thanksgiving;
    let us joyfully sing psalms to him. ℞.

▶ Come, let us bow down in worship;
    let us kneel before the LORD who
       made us.
For he is our God,
    and we are the people he
       shepherds, the flock he guides. ℞.

▶ Oh, that today you would hear
      his voice:
    "Harden not your hearts as
      at Meribah,
    as in the day of Massah in
      the desert,
where your fathers tempted me;
    they tested me though they had
      seen my works." ℞.

SECOND READING
Romans 13:8–10

Brothers and sisters: Owe nothing to anyone, except to love one another; for the one who loves another has fulfilled the law. The commandments, "You shall not commit adultery; you shall not kill; you shall not steal; you shall not covet," and whatever other commandment there may be, are summed up in this saying, namely, "You shall love your neighbor as yourself." Love does no evil to the neighbor; hence, love is the fulfillment of the law.

GOSPEL ACCLAMATION
2 Corinthians 5:19

℞. Al - le - lu - ia, al - le - lu - ia, al - le - lu - ia.

Music: John Schiavone, b. 1947, © 2001, OCP Publications.

▶ God was reconciling the world to himself in Christ
    and entrusting to us the message of reconciliation. ℞.

GOSPEL READING
Matthew 18:15–20

Jesus said to his disciples: "If your brother sins against you, go and tell him his fault between you and him alone. If he listens to you, you have won over your brother. If he does not listen, take one or two others along with you, so that 'every fact may be established on the testimony of two or three witnesses.' If he refuses to listen to them, tell the church. If he refuses to listen even to the church, then treat him as you would a Gentile or a tax collector. Amen, I say to you, whatever you bind on earth shall be bound in heaven, and whatever you loose on earth shall be loosed in heaven. Again, amen, I say to you, if two of you agree on earth about anything for which they are to pray, it shall be granted to them by my heavenly Father. For where two or three are gathered together in my name, there am I in the midst of them."

23RD SUNDAY IN ORDINARY TIME — B   **1015**

FIRST READING

Isaiah 35:4–7a

Thus says the LORD:
  Say to those whose hearts
    are frightened:
  Be strong, fear not!
  Here is your God,
    he comes with vindication;
  with divine recompense
    he comes to save you.
  Then will the eyes of the blind
    be opened,

the ears of the deaf be cleared;
  then will the lame leap like a stag,
  then the tongue of the mute
    will sing.
Streams will burst forth in the desert,
  and rivers in the steppe.
The burning sands will become pools,
  and the thirsty ground, springs
    of water.

RESPONSORIAL PSALM

Psalm 146:7, 8–9, 9–10

℟. Praise   the   Lord,   my   soul,   [my   soul!]

Music: John Schiavone, b. 1947, © 2001, OCP Publications.

or: **Alleluia.**

▸ The God of Jacob keeps faith forever,
    secures justice for the oppressed,
    gives food to the hungry.
  The LORD sets captives free. ℟.

▸ The LORD gives sight to the blind;
    the LORD raises up those who were
      bowed down.
  The LORD loves the just;
    the LORD protects strangers. ℟.

▸ The fatherless and the widow the
    LORD sustains,
    but the way of the wicked
    he thwarts.
  The LORD shall reign forever;
    your God, O Zion, through all
      generations. Alleluia. ℟.

SECOND READING

James 2:1–5

My brothers and sisters, show no partiality as you adhere to the faith in our glorious Lord Jesus Christ. For if a man with gold rings and fine clothes comes into your assembly, and a poor person in shabby clothes also comes in, and you pay attention to the one wearing the fine clothes and say, "Sit here, please," while you say to the poor one, "Stand there," or "Sit at my feet," have you not made distinctions among yourselves and become judges with evil designs?

  Listen, my beloved brothers and sisters. Did not God choose those who are poor in the world to be rich in faith and heirs of the kingdom that he promised to those who love him?

GOSPEL ACCLAMATION
cf. Matthew 4:23

℟. Al - le - lu - ia, al - le - lu - ia, al - le - lu - ia.

Music: John Schiavone, b. 1947, © 2001, OCP Publications.

▶ Jesus proclaimed the Gospel of the kingdom
and cured every disease among the people. ℟.

GOSPEL READING
Mark 7:31–37

Again Jesus left the district of Tyre and went by way of Sidon to the Sea of Galilee, into the district of the Decapolis. And people brought to him a deaf man who had a speech impediment and begged him to lay his hand on him. He took him off by himself away from the crowd. He put his finger into the man's ears and, spitting, touched his tongue; then he looked up to heaven and groaned, and said to him, *"Ephphatha!"* — that is, "Be opened!" — And immediately the man's ears were opened, his speech impediment was removed, and he spoke plainly. He ordered them not to tell anyone. But the more he ordered them not to, the more they proclaimed it. They were exceedingly astonished and they said, "He has done all things well. He makes the deaf hear and the mute speak."

1016   23RD SUNDAY IN ORDINARY TIME — C

FIRST READING
Wisdom 9:13–18b

Who can know God's counsel,
   or who can conceive what the
      LORD intends?
For the deliberations of mortals are timid,
   and unsure are our plans.
For the corruptible body burdens
      the soul
   and the earthen shelter weighs down
      the mind that has many concerns.
And scarce do we guess the things
      on earth,
and what is within our grasp we find
      with difficulty;
but when things are in heaven, who
   can search them out?
Or who ever knew your counsel, except
   you had given wisdom
   and sent your holy spirit from
      on high?
And thus were the paths of those on
      earth made straight.

RESPONSORIAL PSALM
Psalm 90:3–4, 5–6, 12–13, 14–17

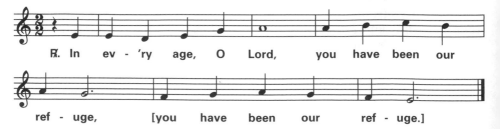

℟. In ev - 'ry age, O Lord, you have been our
ref - uge, [you have been our ref - uge.]

Music: John Schiavone, b. 1947, © 2001, OCP Publications.

▶ You turn man back to dust,
    saying, "Return, O children of men."
For a thousand years in your sight
    are as yesterday, now that it is past,
    or as a watch of the night. ℟.

▶ You make an end of them in their sleep;
    the next morning they are like the
        changing grass,
which at dawn springs up anew,
    but by evening wilts and fades. ℟.

▶ Teach us to number our days aright,
    that we may gain wisdom of heart.
Return, O LORD! How long?
    Have pity on your servants! ℟.

▶ Fill us at daybreak with your kindness,
    that we may shout for joy and
        gladness all our days.
And may the gracious care of the LORD
    our God be ours;
    prosper the work of our hands for us!
Prosper the work of our hands! ℟.

SECOND READING

Philemon 9–10, 12–17

I, Paul, an old man, and now also a prisoner for Christ Jesus, urge you on behalf of my child Onesimus, whose father I have become in my imprisonment; I am sending him, that is, my own heart, back to you. I should have liked to retain him for myself, so that he might serve me on your behalf in my imprisonment for the gospel, but I did not want to do anything without your consent, so that the good you do might not be forced but voluntary. Perhaps this is why he was away from you for a while, that you might have him back forever, no longer as a slave but more than a slave, a brother, beloved especially to me, but even more so to you, as a man and in the Lord. So if you regard me as a partner, welcome him as you would me.

GOSPEL ACCLAMATION

Psalm 119:135

℟. Al - le - lu - ia, al - le - lu - ia, al - le - lu - ia.

Music: John Schiavone, b. 1947, © 2001, OCP Publications.

▶ Let your face shine upon your servant;
    and teach me your laws. ℟.

GOSPEL READING

Luke 14:25–33

Great crowds were traveling with Jesus, and he turned and addressed them, "If anyone comes to me without hating his father and mother, wife and children, brothers and sisters, and even his own life, he cannot be my disciple. Whoever does not carry his own cross and come after me cannot be my disciple. Which of you wishing to construct a tower does not first sit down and calculate the cost to see if there is enough for its completion? Otherwise, after laying the foundation and finding himself unable to finish the work the onlookers should laugh at him and say, 'This one began to build but did not have the resources to finish.' Or what king marching into battle would not first sit down and decide whether with ten thousand troops he can successfully oppose another king advancing upon him with twenty thousand troops? But if not, while he is still far away, he will send a delegation to ask for peace terms. In the same way, anyone of you who does not renounce all his possessions cannot be my disciple."

1017   24TH SUNDAY IN ORDINARY TIME — A

FIRST READING   *Sirach 27:30—28:7*

Wrath and anger are hateful things,
   yet the sinner hugs them tight.
The vengeful will suffer the
     LORD's vengeance,
   for he remembers their sins in detail.
Forgive your neighbor's injustice;
   then when you pray, your own sins
   will be forgiven.
Could anyone nourish anger
   against another
   and expect healing from the LORD?
Could anyone refuse mercy to another
like himself,
   can he seek pardon for his own sins?
If one who is but flesh cherishes wrath,
   who will forgive his sins?
Remember your last days, set
   enmity aside;
   remember death and decay, and
   cease from sin!
Think of the commandments, hate not
   your neighbor;
   remember the Most High's covenant,
   and overlook faults.

RESPONSORIAL PSALM   *Psalm 103:1–2, 3–4, 9–10, 11–12*

℟. The Lord is kind and mer - ci - ful, slow to an - ger, and rich in com - pas - sion.

Music: John Schiavone, b. 1947, © 2001, OCP Publications.

▶ Bless the LORD, O my soul;
   and all my being, bless his holy name.
Bless the LORD, O my soul,
   and forget not all his benefits. ℟.

▶ He pardons all your iniquities,
   heals all your ills.
He redeems your life from
    destruction,
   crowns you with kindness and
   compassion. ℟.

▶ He will not always chide,
   nor does he keep his wrath forever.
Not according to our sins does he deal
   with us,
   nor does he requite us according to
   our crimes. ℟.

▶ For as the heavens are high above
   the earth,
   so surpassing is his kindness toward
   those who fear him.
As far as the east is from the west,
   so far has he put our transgressions
   from us. ℟.

SECOND READING   *Romans 14:7–9*

Brothers and sisters: None of us lives
for oneself, and no one dies for oneself.
For if we live, we live for the Lord, and if
we die, we die for the Lord; so then,
whether we live or die, we are the
Lord's. For this is why Christ died and
came to life, that he might be Lord of
both the dead and the living.

GOSPEL ACCLAMATION

John 13:34

℟. Al - le - lu - ia, al - le - lu - ia, al - le - lu - ia.

Music: John Schiavone, b. 1947, © 2001, OCP Publications.

▶ I give you a new commandment, says the Lord;
love one another as I have loved you. ℟.

GOSPEL READING

Matthew 18:21–35

Peter approached Jesus and asked him, "Lord, if my brother sins against me, how often must I forgive? As many as seven times?" Jesus answered, "I say to you, not seven times but seventy-seven times. That is why the kingdom of heaven may be likened to a king who decided to settle accounts with his servants. When he began the accounting, a debtor was brought before him who owed him a huge amount. Since he had no way of paying it back, his master ordered him to be sold, along with his wife, his children, and all his property, in payment of the debt. At that, the servant fell down, did him homage, and said, 'Be patient with me, and I will pay you back in full.' Moved with compassion the master of that servant let him go and forgave him the loan. When that servant had left, he found one of his fellow servants who owed him a much smaller amount. He seized him and started to choke him, demanding, 'Pay back what you owe.' Falling to his knees, his fellow servant begged him, 'Be patient with me, and I will pay you back.' But he refused. Instead, he had the fellow servant put in prison until he paid back the debt. Now when his fellow servants saw what had happened, they were deeply disturbed, and went to their master and reported the whole affair. His master summoned him and said to him, 'You wicked servant! I forgave you your entire debt because you begged me to. Should you not have had pity on your fellow servant, as I had pity on you?' Then in anger his master handed him over to the torturers until he should pay back the whole debt. So will my heavenly Father do to you, unless each of you forgives your brother from your heart."

24TH SUNDAY IN ORDINARY TIME — B   **1018**

FIRST READING

Isaiah 50:5–9a

The Lord GOD opens my ear that I
   may hear;
and I have not rebelled,
  have not turned back.
I gave my back to those who beat me,
  my cheeks to those who plucked
   my beard;
my face I did not shield
  from buffets and spitting.

The Lord GOD is my help,
  therefore I am not disgraced;

I have set my face like flint,
  knowing that I shall not be put
   to shame.
He is near who upholds my right;
  if anyone wishes to oppose me,
  let us appear together.
Who disputes my right?
  Let that man confront me.
See, the Lord GOD is my help;
  who will prove me wrong?

RESPONSORIAL PSALM

Psalm 116:1–2, 3–4, 5–6, 8–9

℟. I will walk be - fore the Lord, in the land of the liv - ing.

Music: John Schiavone, b. 1947, © 2001, OCP Publications.

or: **Alleluia.**

▶ I love the LORD because he has heard
my voice in supplication,
because he has inclined his ear to me
the day I called. ℟.

▶ The cords of death encompassed me;
the snares of the netherworld
seized upon me;
I fell into distress and sorrow,
and I called upon the name of the LORD,
"O LORD, save my life!" ℟.

▶ Gracious is the LORD and just;
yes, our God is merciful.
The LORD keeps the little ones;
I was brought low, and he
saved me. ℟.

▶ For he has freed my soul from death,
my eyes from tears, my feet
from stumbling.
I shall walk before the LORD
in the land of the living. ℟.

SECOND READING

James 2:14–18

What good is it, my brothers and sisters, if someone says he has faith but does not have works? Can that faith save him? If a brother or sister has nothing to wear and has no food for the day, and one of you says to them, "Go in peace, keep warm, and eat well," but you do not give them the necessities of the body, what good is it? So also faith of itself, if it does not have works, is dead.

Indeed someone might say, "You have faith and I have works." Demonstrate your faith to me without works, and I will demonstrate my faith to you from my works.

GOSPEL ACCLAMATION

Galatians 6:14

℟. Al - le - lu - ia, al - le - lu - ia, al - le - lu - ia.

Music: John Schiavone, b. 1947, © 2001, OCP Publications.

▶ May I never boast except in the cross of our Lord
through which the world has been crucified to me and I to the world. ℟.

GOSPEL READING

Mark 8:27–35

Jesus and his disciples set out for the villages of Caesarea Philippi. Along the way he asked his disciples, "Who do people say that I am?" They said in reply, "John the Baptist, others Elijah, still others one of the prophets." And he asked them, "But who do you say that I am?" Peter said to him in reply, "You are the Christ." Then he warned them not to tell anyone about him.

He began to teach them that the Son of Man must suffer greatly and be rejected by the elders, the chief priests, and the scribes, and be killed, and rise after three days. He spoke this openly. Then Peter took him aside and began to rebuke him. At this he turned around and, looking at his disciples, rebuked

Peter and said, "Get behind me, Satan. You are thinking not as God does, but as human beings do."

He summoned the crowd with his disciples and said to them, "Whoever wishes to come after me must deny himself, take up his cross, and follow me. For whoever wishes to save his life will lose it, but whoever loses his life for my sake and that of the gospel will save it."

24TH SUNDAY IN ORDINARY TIME — C 1019

FIRST READING
Exodus 32:7–11, 13–14

The LORD said to Moses, "Go down at once to your people, whom you brought out of the land of Egypt, for they have become depraved. They have soon turned aside from the way I pointed out to them, making for themselves a molten calf and worshiping it, sacrificing to it and crying out, 'This is your God, O Israel, who brought you out of the land of Egypt!' I see how stiff-necked this people is," continued the LORD to Moses. "Let me alone, then, that my wrath may blaze up against them to consume them. Then I will make of you a great nation."

But Moses implored the LORD, his God, saying, "Why, O LORD, should your wrath blaze up against your own people, whom you brought out of the land of Egypt with such great power and with so strong a hand? Remember your servants Abraham, Isaac, and Israel, and how you swore to them by your own self, saying, 'I will make your descendants as numerous as the stars in the sky; and all this land that I promised, I will give your descendants as their perpetual heritage.'" So the LORD relented in the punishment he had threatened to inflict on his people.

RESPONSORIAL PSALM
Psalm 51:3–4, 12–13, 17, 19

℟. I will rise and go to my fa - ther.

Music: John Schiavone, b. 1947, © 2001, OCP Publications.

▶ Have mercy on me, O God, in
your goodness;
in the greatness of your compassion
wipe out my offense.
Thoroughly wash me from my guilt
and of my sin cleanse me. ℟.

▶ A clean heart create for me, O God,
and a steadfast spirit renew
within me.

Cast me not out from your presence,
and your Holy Spirit take not
from me. ℟.

▶ O Lord, open my lips,
and my mouth shall proclaim
your praise.
My sacrifice, O God, is a contrite spirit;
a heart contrite and humbled,
O God, you will not spurn. ℟.

SECOND READING
1 Timothy 1:12–17

Beloved: I am grateful to him who has strengthened me, Christ Jesus our Lord, because he considered me trustworthy in appointing me to the ministry. I was once a blasphemer and a persecutor and arrogant, but I have been mercifully treated because I acted out of ignorance in my unbelief. Indeed, the grace of our Lord has been abundant, along with the faith and love that are in Christ Jesus.

This saying is trustworthy and deserves full acceptance: Christ Jesus came into the world to save sinners. Of these I am the foremost. But for that reason I was mercifully treated, so that in me, as the foremost, Christ Jesus might display all his patience as an example for those who would come to believe in him for everlasting life. To the king of ages, incorruptible, invisible, the only God, honor and glory forever and ever. Amen.

GOSPEL ACCLAMATION

2 Corinthians 5:19

℟. Al - le - lu - ia, al - le - lu - ia, al - le - lu - ia.

Music: John Schiavone, b. 1947, © 2001, OCP Publications.

▶ God was reconciling the world to himself in Christ and entrusting to us the message of reconciliation. ℟.

GOSPEL READING

Luke 15:1–32 or 15:1–10

(Include bracketed text for Long Form)

Tax collectors and sinners were all drawing near to listen to Jesus, but the Pharisees and scribes began to complain, saying, "This man welcomes sinners and eats with them." So to them he addressed this parable. "What man among you having a hundred sheep and losing one of them would not leave the ninety-nine in the desert and go after the lost one until he finds it? And when he does find it, he sets it on his shoulders with great joy and, upon his arrival home, he calls together his friends and neighbors and says to them, 'Rejoice with me because I have found my lost sheep.' I tell you, in just the same way there will be more joy in heaven over one sinner who repents than over ninety-nine righteous people who have no need of repentance.

"Or what woman having ten coins and losing one would not light a lamp and sweep the house, searching carefully until she finds it? And when she does find it, she calls together her friends and neighbors and says to them, 'Rejoice with me because I have found the coin that I lost.' In just the same way, I tell you, there will be rejoicing among the angels of God over one sinner who repents."

[Then he said, "A man had two sons, and the younger son said to his father, 'Father give me the share of your estate that should come to me.' So the father divided the property between them. After a few days, the younger son collected all his belongings and set off to a distant country where he squandered his inheritance on a life of dissipation. When he had freely spent everything, a severe famine struck that country, and he found himself in dire need. So he hired himself out to one of the local citizens who sent him to his farm to tend the swine. And he longed to eat his fill of the pods on which the swine fed, but nobody gave him any. Coming to his senses he thought, 'How many of my father's hired workers have more than enough food to eat, but here am I, dying from hunger. I shall get up and go to my father and I shall say to him, "Father, I have sinned against heaven and against you. I no longer deserve to be called your son; treat me as you would treat one of your hired workers."' So he got up and went back to his father. While he was still a long way off, his father caught sight of him, and was filled with compassion. He ran to his son, embraced him and kissed him. His son said to him, 'Father, I have sinned against heaven and against you; I no longer deserve to be called your son.' But his father ordered his servants, 'Quickly bring the finest robe and put it on him; put a ring on his finger and sandals on his feet. Take the fattened calf and slaughter it. Then let us celebrate with a feast, because this son of mine was dead, and has come to life again; he was lost, and has been found.' Then the celebration began. Now the older son had been out in the field and, on his way back, as he neared the house, he heard the sound of music and dancing. He called one of the servants and asked what this might mean. The servant said to him, 'Your brother has returned and your father has slaughtered the fattened calf because he has him back safe and sound.' He became angry, and when he refused to enter the house, his father came out and pleaded with him. He said to his father in reply, 'Look, all these years I served you and not once did I disobey your orders; yet you never gave me even a young goat to feast on with my friends. But when your son returns, who swallowed up your property with prostitutes, for him you slaughter the fattened calf.' He said to him, 'My son, you are here with me always; everything I have is yours. But now we must celebrate and rejoice, because your brother was dead and has come to life again; he was lost and has been found.'"]

25TH SUNDAY IN ORDINARY TIME — A   1020

FIRST READING   *Isaiah 55:6–9*

Seek the LORD while he may be found,
  call him while he is near.
Let the scoundrel forsake his way,
  and the wicked his thoughts;
let him turn to the LORD for mercy;
  to our God, who is generous
    in forgiving.

For my thoughts are not your thoughts,
  nor are your ways my ways, says
    the LORD.
As high as the heavens are above the
  earth,
  so high are my ways above your ways
  and my thoughts above your thoughts.

RESPONSORIAL PSALM   *Psalm 145:2–3, 8–9, 17–18*

℟. The Lord is near to all who call up - on him.

Music: John Schiavone, b. 1947, © 2001, OCP Publications.

▸ Every day will I bless you,
  and I will praise your name forever
    and ever.
Great is the LORD and highly to
    be praised;
  his greatness is unsearchable. ℟.

▸ The LORD is gracious and merciful,
  slow to anger and of great kindness.

The LORD is good to all
  and compassionate toward all
    his works. ℟.

▸ The LORD is just in all his ways
  and holy in all his works.
The LORD is near to all who call
    upon him,
  to all who call upon him in truth. ℟.

SECOND READING

Philippians 1:20c–24, 27a

Brothers and sisters: Christ will be magnified in my body, whether by life or by death. For to me life is Christ, and death is gain. If I go on living in the flesh, that means fruitful labor for me. And I do not know which I shall choose. I am caught between the two. I long to depart this life and be with Christ, for that is far better. Yet that I remain in the flesh is more necessary for your benefit.

Only, conduct yourselves in a way worthy of the gospel of Christ.

GOSPEL ACCLAMATION

cf. Acts of the Apostles 16:14b

℟. Al - le - lu - ia, al - le - lu - ia, al - le - lu - ia.

Music: John Schiavone, b. 1947, © 2001, OCP Publications.

▶ Open our hearts, O Lord,
to listen to the words of your Son. ℟.

GOSPEL READING

Matthew 20:1–16a

Jesus told his disciples this parable: "The kingdom of heaven is like a landowner who went out at dawn to hire laborers for his vineyard. After agreeing with them for the usual daily wage, he sent them into his vineyard. Going out about nine o'clock, the landowner saw others standing idle in the marketplace, and he said to them, 'You too go into my vineyard, and I will give you what is just.' So they went off. And he went out again around noon, and around three o'clock, and did likewise. Going out about five o'clock, the landowner found others standing around, and said to them, 'Why do you stand here idle all day?' They answered, 'Because no one has hired us.' He said to them, 'You too go into my vineyard.' When it was evening the owner of the vineyard said to his foreman, 'Summon the laborers and give them their pay, beginning with the last and ending with the first.' When those who had started about five o'clock came, each received the usual daily wage. So when the first came, they thought that they would receive more, but each of them also got the usual wage. And on receiving it they grumbled against the landowner, saying, 'These last ones worked only one hour, and you have made them equal to us, who bore the day's burden and the heat.' He said to one of them in reply, 'My friend, I am not cheating you. Did you not agree with me for the usual daily wage? Take what is yours and go. What if I wish to give this last one the same as you? Or am I not free to do as I wish with my own money? Are you envious because I am generous?' Thus, the last will be first, and the first will be last."

1021   25TH SUNDAY IN ORDINARY TIME — B

FIRST READING

Wisdom 2:12, 17–20

The wicked say:
   Let us beset the just one, because he
     is obnoxious to us;

he sets himself against our doings,
  reproaches us for transgressions of
    the law

and charges us with violations of
our training.
Let us see whether his words be true;
let us find out what will happen
to him.
For if the just one be the son of God,
God will defend him
and deliver him from the hand of
his foes.

With revilement and torture let us
put the just one to the test
that we may have proof of his
gentleness
and try his patience.
Let us condemn him to a
shameful death;
for according to his own words,
God will take care of him.

RESPONSORIAL PSALM

Psalm 54:3–4, 5, 6–8

℟. The Lord up - holds my life.

Music: John Schiavone, b. 1947, © 2001, OCP Publications.

▸ O God, by your name save me,
 and by your might defend my cause.
O God, hear my prayer;
 hearken to the words of my
 mouth. ℟.

▸ For the haughty have risen up
 against me,
 the ruthless seek my life;
 they set not God before their eyes. ℟.

▸ Behold, God is my helper;
 the Lord sustains my life.
Freely will I offer you sacrifice;
 I will praise your name, O LORD, for
 its goodness. ℟.

SECOND READING

James 3:16 — 4:3

Beloved: Where jealousy and selfish
ambition exist, there is disorder and
every foul practice. But the wisdom
from above is first of all pure, then
peaceable, gentle, compliant, full
of mercy and good fruits, without
inconstancy or insincerity. And the
fruit of righteousness is sown in
peace for those who cultivate peace.
 Where do the wars and where do the
conflicts among you come from? Is it
not from your passions that make war
within your members? You covet but
do not possess. You kill and envy but
you cannot obtain; you fight and wage
war. You do not possess because you do
not ask. You ask but do not receive,
because you ask wrongly, to spend it on
your passions.

GOSPEL ACCLAMATION

cf. 2 Thessalonians 2:14

℟. Al - le - lu - ia, al - le - lu - ia, al - le - lu - ia.

Music: John Schiavone, b. 1947, © 2001, OCP Publications.

▸ God has called us through the Gospel
 to possess the glory of our Lord Jesus Christ. ℟.

GOSPEL READING *Mark 9:30–37*

Jesus and his disciples left from there and began a journey through Galilee, but he did not wish anyone to know about it. He was teaching his disciples and telling them, "The Son of Man is to be handed over to men and they will kill him, and three days after his death the Son of Man will rise." But they did not understand the saying, and they were afraid to question him.

They came to Capernaum and, once inside the house, he began to ask them, "What were you arguing about on the way?" But they remained silent. They had been discussing among themselves on the way who was the greatest. Then he sat down, called the Twelve, and said to them, "If anyone wishes to be first, he shall be the last of all and the servant of all." Taking a child, he placed it in their midst, and putting his arms around it, he said to them, "Whoever receives one child such as this in my name, receives me; and whoever receives me, receives not me but the One who sent me."

1022   25TH SUNDAY IN ORDINARY TIME — C

FIRST READING *Amos 8:4–7*

Hear this, you who trample upon
   the needy
   and destroy the poor of the land!
"When will the new moon be over,"
   you ask,
   "that we may sell our grain,
   and the sabbath, that we may display
   the wheat?
We will diminish the ephah,
   add to the shekel,

and fix our scales for cheating!
We will buy the lowly for silver,
   and the poor for a pair of sandals;
   even the refuse of the wheat we
   will sell!"
The LORD has sworn by the pride
   of Jacob:
   Never will I forget a thing they
   have done!

RESPONSORIAL PSALM *Psalm 113:1–2, 4–6, 7–8*

℟. **Praise** the **Lord** who **lifts** up the **poor.**

Music: John Schiavone, b. 1947, © 2001, OCP Publications.

or: **Alleluia.**

▶ Praise, you servants of the LORD,
   praise the name of the LORD.
Blessed be the name of the LORD
   both now and forever. ℟.

▶ High above all nations is the LORD;
   above the heavens is his glory.
Who is like the LORD, our God, who is
   enthroned on high

and looks upon the heavens and the
   earth below? ℟.

▶ He raises up the lowly from the dust;
   from the dunghill he lifts up the poor
to seat them with princes,
   with the princes of his own people. ℟.

SECOND READING

1 Timothy 2:1–8

Beloved: First of all, I ask that supplications, prayers, petitions, and thanksgivings be offered for everyone, for kings and for all in authority, that we may lead a quiet and tranquil life in all devotion and dignity. This is good and pleasing to God our savior, who wills everyone to be saved and to come to knowledge of the truth.

For there is one God.

There is also one mediator between God and men,
    the man Christ Jesus,
    who gave himself as ransom for all. This was the testimony at the proper time. For this I was appointed preacher and apostle — I am speaking the truth, I am not lying —, teacher of the Gentiles in faith and truth.

It is my wish, then, that in every place the men should pray, lifting up holy hands, without anger or argument.

GOSPEL ACCLAMATION

cf. 2 Corinthians 8:9

℟. Al - le - lu - ia, al - le - lu - ia, al - le - lu - ia.

Music: John Schiavone, b. 1947, © 2001, OCP Publications.

▶ Though our Lord Jesus Christ was rich, he became poor, so that by his poverty you might become rich. ℟.

GOSPEL READING

Luke 16:1–13 or 16:10-13

(Include bracketed text for Long Form)

Jesus said to his disciples, ["A rich man had a steward who was reported to him for squandering his property. He summoned him and said, 'What is this I hear about you? Prepare a full account of your stewardship, because you can no longer be my steward.' The steward said to himself, 'What shall I do, now that my master is taking the position of steward away from me? I am not strong enough to dig and I am ashamed to beg. I know what I shall do so that, when I am removed from the stewardship, they may welcome me into their homes.' He called in his master's debtors one by one. To the first he said, 'How much do you owe my master?' He replied, 'One hundred measures of olive oil.' He said to him, 'Here is your promissory note. Sit down and quickly write one for fifty.' Then to another the steward said, 'And you, how much do you owe?' He replied, 'One hundred kors of wheat.' The steward said to him,

'Here is your promissory note; write one for eighty.' And the master commended that dishonest steward for acting prudently.

"For the children of this world are more prudent in dealing with their own generation than are the children of light. I tell you, make friends for yourselves with dishonest wealth, so that when it fails, you will be welcomed into eternal dwellings.] The person who is trustworthy in very small matters is also trustworthy in great ones; and the person who is dishonest in very small matters is also dishonest in great ones. If, therefore, you are not trustworthy with dishonest wealth, who will trust you with true wealth? If you are not trustworthy with what belongs to another, who will give you what is yours? No servant can serve two masters. He will either hate one and love the other, or be devoted to one and despise the other. You cannot serve both God and mammon."

1023   26TH SUNDAY IN ORDINARY TIME — A

FIRST READING

Ezekiel 18:25–28

Thus says the LORD: You say, "The LORD's way is not fair!" Hear now, house of Israel: Is it my way that is unfair, or rather, are not your ways unfair? When someone virtuous turns away from virtue to commit iniquity, and dies, it is because of the iniquity he committed that he must die. But if he turns from the wickedness he has committed, and does what is right and just, he shall preserve his life; since he has turned away from all the sins that he has committed, he shall surely live, he shall not die.

RESPONSORIAL PSALM

Psalm 25:4–5, 6–7, 8–9

℟. [Re - mem - ber,] re - mem - ber your mer - cies, O Lord.

Music: John Schiavone, b. 1947, © 2001, OCP Publications.

▶ Your ways, O LORD, make known to me;
   teach me your paths,
  guide me in your truth and teach me,
   for you are God my savior. ℟.

▶ Remember that your compassion,
   O LORD,
  and your love are from of old.

The sins of my youth and my frailties
  remember not;
  in your kindness remember me,
  because of your goodness, O LORD. ℟.

▶ Good and upright is the LORD;
  thus he shows sinners the way.
He guides the humble to justice,
  and teaches the humble his way. ℟.

SECOND READING

Philippians 2:1–11 or 2:1–5

(Include bracketed text for Long Form)

Brothers and sisters: If there is any encouragement in Christ, any solace in love, any participation in the Spirit, any compassion and mercy, complete my joy by being of the same mind, with the same love, united in heart, thinking one thing. Do nothing out of selfishness or out of vainglory; rather, humbly regard others as more important than yourselves, each looking out not for his own interests, but also for those of others.

Have in you the same attitude that is also in Christ Jesus,
  [Who, though he was in the form
   of God,
  did not regard equality with God
  something to be grasped.

Rather, he emptied himself,
  taking the form of a slave,
  coming in human likeness;
  and found human in appearance,
  he humbled himself,
  becoming obedient to the point
   of death,
  even death on a cross.
Because of this, God greatly exalted him
  and bestowed on him the name
  which is above every name,
  that at the name of Jesus
  every knee should bend,
  of those in heaven and on earth
   and under the earth,
  and every tongue confess that
  Jesus Christ is Lord,
  to the glory of God the Father.]

GOSPEL ACCLAMATION

John 10:27

℟. Al - le - lu - ia, al - le - lu - ia, al - le - lu - ia.

Music: John Schiavone, b. 1947, © 2001, OCP Publications.

▶ My sheep hear my voice, says the Lord;
I know them, and they follow me. ℟.

GOSPEL READING

Matthew 21:28–32

Jesus said to the chief priests and elders of the people: "What is your opinion? A man had two sons. He came to the first and said, 'Son, go out and work in the vineyard today.' He said in reply, 'I will not,' but afterwards changed his mind and went. The man came to the other son and gave the same order. He said in reply, 'Yes, sir,' but did not go. Which of the two did his father's will?" They answered, "The first." Jesus said to them, "Amen, I say to you, tax collectors and prostitutes are entering the kingdom of God before you. When John came to you in the way of righteousness, you did not believe him; but tax collectors and prostitutes did. Yet even when you saw that, you did not later change your minds and believe him."

26TH SUNDAY IN ORDINARY TIME — B   1024

FIRST READING

Numbers 11:25–29

The LORD came down in the cloud and spoke to Moses. Taking some of the spirit that was on Moses, the LORD bestowed it on the seventy elders; and as the spirit came to rest on them, they prophesied.

Now two men, one named Eldad and the other Medad, were not in the gathering but had been left in the camp. They too had been on the list, but had not gone out to the tent; yet the spirit came to rest on them also, and they prophesied in the camp. So, when a young man quickly told Moses, "Eldad and Medad are prophesying in the camp," Joshua, son of Nun, who from his youth had been Moses' aide, said, "Moses, my lord, stop them." But Moses answered him, "Are you jealous for my sake? Would that all the people of the LORD were prophets! Would that the LORD might bestow his spirit on them all!"

RESPONSORIAL PSALM

Psalm 19:8, 10, 12–13, 14

℟. The pre - cepts of the Lord give joy to the heart.

Music: John Schiavone, b. 1947, © 2001, OCP Publications.

▶ The law of the LORD is perfect,
refreshing the soul;
the decree of the LORD is trustworthy,
giving wisdom to the simple. ℟.

▶ The fear of the LORD is pure,
enduring forever;
the ordinances of the LORD are true,
all of them just. ℟.

℟. The precepts of the Lord give joy to the heart.

▶ Though your servant is careful of them,
very diligent in keeping them,
yet who can detect failings?
　Cleanse me from my unknown
　faults! ℟.

▶ From wanton sin especially, restrain
your servant;
let it not rule over me.
Then shall I be blameless and
innocent of serious sin. ℟.

SECOND READING

James 5:1–6

Come now, you rich, weep and wail over your impending miseries. Your wealth has rotted away, your clothes have become moth-eaten, your gold and silver have corroded, and that corrosion will be a testimony against you; it will devour your flesh like a fire. You have stored up treasure for the last days. Behold, the wages you withheld from the workers who harvested your fields are crying aloud; and the cries of the harvesters have reached the ears of the Lord of hosts. You have lived on earth in luxury and pleasure; you have fattened your hearts for the day of slaughter. You have condemned; you have murdered the righteous one; he offers you no resistance.

GOSPEL ACCLAMATION

cf. John 17:17b, 17a

℟. Al - le - lu - ia, al - le - lu - ia, al - le - lu - ia.

Music: John Schiavone, b. 1947, © 2001, OCP Publications.

▶ Your word, O Lord, is truth;
consecrate us in the truth. ℟.

GOSPEL READING

Mark 9:38–43, 45, 47–48

At that time, John said to Jesus, "Teacher, we saw someone driving out demons in your name, and we tried to prevent him because he does not follow us." Jesus replied, "Do not prevent him. There is no one who performs a mighty deed in my name who can at the same time speak ill of me. For whoever is not against us is for us. Anyone who gives you a cup of water to drink because you belong to Christ, amen, I say to you, will surely not lose his reward.

"Whoever causes one of these little ones who believe in me to sin, it would be better for him if a great millstone were put around his neck and he were thrown into the sea. If your hand causes you to sin, cut it off. It is better for you to enter into life maimed than with two hands to go into Gehenna, into the unquenchable fire. And if your foot causes you to sin, cut if off. It is better for you to enter into life crippled than with two feet to be thrown into Gehenna. And if your eye causes you to sin, pluck it out. Better for you to enter into the kingdom of God with one eye than with two eyes to be thrown into Gehenna, where 'their worm does not die, and the fire is not quenched.' "

26TH SUNDAY IN ORDINARY TIME — C   1025

FIRST READING   *Amos 6:1a, 4–7*

Thus says the LORD the God of hosts:
Woe to the complacent in Zion!
Lying upon beds of ivory,
    stretched comfortably on
       their couches,
they eat lambs taken from the flock,
    and calves from the stall!
Improvising to the music of the harp,
    like David, they devise their own
       accompaniment.

They drink wine from bowls
    and anoint themselves with the
       best oils;
    yet they are not made ill by the
       collapse of Joseph!
Therefore, now they shall be the first to
    go into exile,
    and their wanton revelry shall be
       done away with.

RESPONSORIAL PSALM   *Psalm 146:7, 8–9, 9–10*

℟. **Praise**   the   Lord,   my   soul,   [my   soul!]

Music: John Schiavone, b. 1947, © 2001, OCP Publications.

or: **Alleluia.**

▸ Blessed is he who keeps faith forever,
    secures justice for the oppressed,
    gives food to the hungry.
The LORD sets captives free. ℟.

▸ The LORD gives sight to the blind;
    the LORD raises up those who were
       bowed down.

The LORD loves the just;
    the LORD protects strangers. ℟.

▸ The fatherless and the widow
    he sustains,
    but the way of the wicked
    he thwarts.
The LORD shall reign forever;
    your God, O Zion, through all
       generations. Alleluia. ℟.

SECOND READING   *1 Timothy 6:11–16*

But you, man of God, pursue
righteousness, devotion, faith, love,
patience, and gentleness. Compete
well for the faith. Lay hold of eternal
life, to which you were called when you
made the noble confession in the
presence of many witnesses. I charge
you before God, who gives life to all
things, and before Christ Jesus, who
gave testimony under Pontius Pilate for
the noble confession, to keep the

commandment without stain or
reproach until the appearance of our
Lord Jesus Christ that the blessed and
only ruler will make manifest at the
proper time, the King of kings and Lord
of lords, who alone has immortality,
who dwells in unapproachable light,
and whom no human being has seen
or can see. To him be honor and eternal
power. Amen.

GOSPEL ACCLAMATION

cf. 2 Corinthians 8:9

R. Al - le - lu - ia,   al - le - lu - ia,   al - le - lu - ia.

Music: John Schiavone, b. 1947, © 2001, OCP Publications.

▶ Though our Lord Jesus Christ was rich, he became poor,
so that by his poverty you might become rich. R.

GOSPEL READING

Luke 16:19–31

Jesus said to the Pharisees: "There was a rich man who dressed in purple garments and fine linen and dined sumptuously each day. And lying at his door was a poor man named Lazarus, covered with sores, who would gladly have eaten his fill of the scraps that fell from the rich man's table. Dogs even used to come and lick his sores. When the poor man died, he was carried away by angels to the bosom of Abraham. The rich man also died and was buried, and from the netherworld, where he was in torment, he raised his eyes and saw Abraham far off and Lazarus at his side. And he cried out, 'Father Abraham, have pity on me. Send Lazarus to dip the tip of his finger in water and cool my tongue, for I am suffering torment in these flames.' Abraham replied, 'My child, remember that you received what was good during your lifetime while Lazarus likewise received what was bad; but now he is comforted here, whereas you are tormented. Moreover, between us and you a great chasm is established to prevent anyone from crossing who might wish to go from our side to yours or from your side to ours.' He said, 'Then I beg you, father, send him to my father's house, for I have five brothers, so that he may warn them, lest they too come to this place of torment.' But Abraham replied, 'They have Moses and the prophets. Let them listen to them.' He said, 'Oh no, father Abraham, but if someone from the dead goes to them, they will repent.' Then Abraham said, 'If they will not listen to Moses and the prophets, neither will they be persuaded if someone should rise from the dead.'"

1026   27TH SUNDAY IN ORDINARY TIME — A

FIRST READING

Isaiah 5:1–7

Let me now sing of my friend,
   my friend's song concerning
     his vineyard.
My friend had a vineyard
   on a fertile hillside;
he spaded it, cleared it of stones,
   and planted the choicest vines;
within it he built a watchtower,
   and hewed out a wine press.
Then he looked for the crop of grapes,
   but what it yielded was wild grapes.

Now, inhabitants of Jerusalem and
   people of Judah,
   judge between me and my vineyard:
What more was there to do for
   my vineyard
   that I had not done?
Why, when I looked for the crop
   of grapes,
   did it bring forth wild grapes?
Now, I will let you know
   what I mean to do with my vineyard:
take away its hedge, give it to grazing,

break through its wall, let it
be trampled!
Yes, I will make it a ruin:
it shall not be pruned or hoed,
but overgrown with thorns and briers;
I will command the clouds
not to send rain upon it.

The vineyard of the LORD of hosts is the
house of Israel,
and the people of Judah are his
cherished plant;
he looked for judgment, but
see, bloodshed!
for justice, but hark, the outcry!

RESPONSORIAL PSALM

Psalm 80:9, 12, 13–14, 15–16, 19–20

℟. The vine-yard of the Lord is the house of Is-ra-el.

Music: John Schiavone, b. 1947, © 2001, OCP Publications.

▶ A vine from Egypt you transplanted;
you drove away the nations and
planted it.
It put forth its foliage to the Sea,
its shoots as far as the River. ℟.

▶ Why have you broken down its walls,
so that every passer-by plucks
its fruit,
the boar from the forest lays it waste,
and the beasts of the field feed
upon it? ℟.

▶ Once again, O LORD of hosts,
look down from heaven, and see;

take care of this vine,
and protect what your right hand
has planted,
the son of man whom you yourself
made strong. ℟.

▶ Then we will no more withdraw
from you;
give us new life, and we will call
upon your name.
O LORD, God of hosts, restore us;
if your face shine upon us, then we
shall be saved. ℟.

SECOND READING

Philippians 4:6–9

Brothers and sisters: Have no anxiety at
all, but in everything, by prayer and
petition, with thanksgiving, make your
requests known to God. Then the peace
of God that surpasses all understanding
will guard your hearts and minds in
Christ Jesus.
   Finally, brothers and sisters, whatever
is true, whatever is honorable, whatever
is just, whatever is pure, whatever is
lovely, whatever is gracious, if there is
any excellence and if there is anything
worthy of praise, think about these
things. Keep on doing what you have
learned and received and heard and
seen in me. Then the God of peace will
be with you.

GOSPEL ACCLAMATION

cf. John 15:16

℟. Al-le-lu-ia, al-le-lu-ia, al-le-lu-ia.

Music: John Schiavone, b. 1947, © 2001, OCP Publications.

▶ I have chosen you from the world, says the Lord,
to go and bear fruit that will remain. ℟.

GOSPEL READING

Matthew 21:33–43

Jesus said to the chief priests and the elders of the people: "Hear another parable. There was a landowner who planted a vineyard, put a hedge around it, dug a wine press in it, and built a tower. Then he leased it to tenants and went on a journey. When vintage time drew near, he sent his servants to the tenants to obtain his produce. But the tenants seized the servants and one they beat, another they killed, and a third they stoned. Again he sent other servants, more numerous than the first ones, but they treated them in the same way. Finally, he sent his son to them, thinking, 'They will respect my son.' But when the tenants saw the son, they said to one another, 'This is the heir. Come, let us kill him and acquire his inheritance.' They seized him, threw him out of the vineyard, and killed him. What will the owner of the vineyard do to those tenants when he comes?" They answered him, "He will put those wretched men to a wretched death and lease his vineyard to other tenants who will give him the produce at the proper times." Jesus said to them, "Did you never read in the Scriptures:

The stone that the builders rejected
has become the cornerstone;
by the Lord has this been done,
and it is wonderful in our eyes?

Therefore, I say to you, the kingdom of God will be taken away from you and given to a people that will produce its fruit."

1027   27TH SUNDAY IN ORDINARY TIME — B

FIRST READING

Genesis 2:18–24

The LORD God said: "It is not good for the man to be alone. I will make a suitable partner for him." So the LORD God formed out of the ground various wild animals and various birds of the air, and he brought them to the man to see what he would call them; whatever the man called each of them would be its name. The man gave names to all the cattle, all the birds of the air, and all wild animals; but none proved to be the suitable partner for the man.

So the LORD God cast a deep sleep on the man, and while he was asleep, he took out one of his ribs and closed up its place with flesh. The LORD God then built up into a woman the rib that he had taken from the man. When he brought her to the man, the man said:

"This one, at last, is bone of my bones
    and flesh of my flesh;
this one shall be called 'woman,'
    for out of 'her man' this one has
        been taken."

That is why a man leaves his father and mother and clings to his wife, and the two of them become one flesh.

RESPONSORIAL PSALM

Psalm 128:1–2, 3, 4–5, 6

 ℟. May the Lord bless 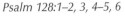 us all the days of our lives.

Music: John Schiavone, b. 1947, © 2001, OCP Publications.

▸ Blessed are you who fear the LORD,
 who walk in his ways!
For you shall eat the fruit of
  your handiwork;
 blessed shall you be, and favored. ℟.

▸ Your wife shall be like a fruitful vine
 in the recesses of your home,
your children like olive plants
 around your table. ℟.

▸ Behold, thus is the man blessed
 who fears the LORD.
The LORD bless you from Zion:
 may you see the prosperity
 of Jerusalem
all the days of your life. ℟.

▸ May you see your children's children.
 Peace be upon Israel! ℟.

SECOND READING

Hebrews 2:9–11

Brothers and sisters: He "for a little while" was made "lower than the angels," that by the grace of God he might taste death for everyone.

For it was fitting that he, for whom and through whom all things exist, in bringing many children to glory, should make the leader to their salvation perfect through suffering. He who consecrates and those who are being consecrated all have one origin. Therefore, he is not ashamed to call them "brothers."

GOSPEL ACCLAMATION

1 John 4:12

℟. Al - le - lu - ia, al - le - lu - ia, al - le - lu - ia.

Music: John Schiavone, b. 1947, © 2001, OCP Publications.

▸ If we love one another, God remains in us
 and his love is brought to perfection in us. ℟.

GOSPEL READING

Mark 10:2–16 or 10:2–12

(Include bracketed text for Long Form)

The Pharisees approached Jesus and asked, "Is it lawful for a husband to divorce his wife?" They were testing him. He said to them in reply, "What did Moses command you?" They replied, "Moses permitted a husband to write a bill of divorce and dismiss her." But Jesus told them, "Because of the hardness of your hearts he wrote you this commandment. But from the beginning of creation, *God made them male and female. For this reason a man shall leave his father and mother and be joined to his wife, and the two shall become one flesh. So they are no longer two but one flesh. Therefore what God has joined together, no human being must separate."* In the house the disciples again questioned Jesus about this. He said to them, "Whoever divorces his wife and marries another commits adultery against her; and if she divorces her husband and marries another, she commits adultery."

[And people were bringing children to him that he might touch them, but the disciples rebuked them. When Jesus saw this he became indignant and said to them, "Let the children come to me; do not prevent them, for the kingdom of God belongs to such as these. Amen, I say to you, whoever does not accept the kingdom of God like a child will not enter it." Then he embraced them and blessed them, placing his hands on them.]

1028   27TH SUNDAY IN ORDINARY TIME — C

FIRST READING

Habakkuk 1:2–3; 2:2–4

How long, O LORD? I cry for help
  but you do not listen!
I cry out to you, "Violence!"
  but you do not intervene.
Why do you let me see ruin;
  why must I look at misery?
Destruction and violence are before me;
  there is strife, and clamorous discord.
Then the LORD answered me and said:
  Write down the vision clearly upon
    the tablets,

so that one can read it readily.
For the vision still has its time,
  presses on to fulfillment, and will
    not disappoint;
if it delays, wait for it,
  it will surely come, it will not be late.
The rash one has no integrity;
  but the just one, because of his faith,
    shall live.

RESPONSORIAL PSALM

Psalm 95:1–2, 6–7, 8–9

℟. If to-day you hear his voice, hard-en not your hearts.

Music: John Schiavone, b. 1947, © 2001, OCP Publications.

▶ Come, let us sing joyfully to the LORD;
  let us acclaim the Rock of
    our salvation.
Let us come into his presence
  with thanksgiving;
  let us joyfully sing psalms to him. ℟.

▶ Come, let us bow down in worship;
  let us kneel before the LORD who
    made us.

For he is our God,
  and we are the people he
    shepherds, the flock he guides. ℟.

▶ Oh, that today you would hear his voice:
  "Harden not your hearts as
    at Meribah,
  as in the day of Massah in the desert,
  where your fathers tempted me;
    they tested me though they had
      seen my works." ℟.

SECOND READING

2 Timothy 1:6–8, 13–14

Beloved: I remind you to stir into flame
the gift of God that you have through
the imposition of my hands. For God
did not give us a spirit of cowardice
but rather of power and love and self-
control. So do not be ashamed of your
testimony to our Lord, nor of me, a
prisoner for his sake; but bear your
share of hardship for the gospel with
the strength that comes from God.

Take as your norm the sound words
that you heard from me, in the faith and
love that are in Christ Jesus. Guard this
rich trust with the help of the Holy
Spirit that dwells within us.

GOSPEL ACCLAMATION

1 Peter 1:25

℟. Al - le - lu - ia, al - le - lu - ia, al - le - lu - ia.

Music: John Schiavone, b. 1947, © 2001, OCP Publications.

▶ The word of the Lord remains for ever.
This is the word that has been proclaimed to you. ℟.

GOSPEL READING

Luke 17:5–10

The apostles said to the Lord, "Increase our faith." The Lord replied, "If you have faith the size of a mustard seed, you would say to this mulberry tree, 'Be uprooted and planted in the sea, 'and it would obey you.

"Who among you would say to your servant who has just come in from plowing or tending sheep in the field, 'Come here immediately and take your place at table'? Would he not rather say to him, 'Prepare something for me to eat. Put on your apron and wait on me while I eat and drink. You may eat and drink when I am finished'? Is he grateful to that servant because he did what was commanded? So should it be with you. When you have done all you have been commanded, say, 'We are unprofitable servants; we have done what we were obliged to do.'"

28TH SUNDAY IN ORDINARY TIME — A   1029

FIRST READING

Isaiah 25:6–10a

On this mountain the LORD of hosts
　will provide for all peoples
a feast of rich food and choice wines,
　juicy, rich food and pure,
　　choice wines.
On this mountain he will destroy
　the veil that veils all peoples,
the web that is woven over all nations;
　he will destroy death forever.
The Lord GOD will wipe away
　the tears from every face;
the reproach of his people he
　will remove

from the whole earth; for the LORD
　has spoken.
　On that day it will be said:
"Behold our God, to whom we looked
　to save us!
This is the LORD for whom we looked;
　let us rejoice and be glad that he has
　saved us!"
For the hand of the LORD will rest on
　this mountain.

RESPONSORIAL PSALM

Psalm 23:1–3a, 3b–4, 5, 6

℟. I shall live in the house of the Lord   all the days of my life.

Music: John Schiavone, b. 1947, © 2001, OCP Publications.

▶ The LORD is my shepherd; I shall
　not want.
　In verdant pastures he gives

me repose;
beside restful waters he leads me;
he refreshes my soul. ℟.

℟. **I shall live in the house of the Lord all the days of my life.**

▶ He guides me in right paths
  for his name's sake.
Even though I walk in the dark valley
  I fear no evil; for you are at my side
with your rod and your staff
  that give me courage. ℟.

▶ You spread the table before me
  in the sight of my foes;
you anoint my head with oil;
  my cup overflows. ℟.

▶ Only goodness and kindness follow me
  all the days of my life;
and I shall dwell in the house of
  the LORD
  for years to come. ℟.

SECOND READING

Philippians 4:12–14, 19–20

Brothers and sisters: I know how to live in humble circumstances; I know also how to live with abundance. In every circumstance and in all things I have learned the secret of being well fed and of going hungry, of living in abundance and of being in need. I can do all things in him who strengthens me. Still, it was kind of you to share in my distress.

My God will fully supply whatever you need, in accord with his glorious riches in Christ Jesus. To our God and Father, glory forever and ever. Amen.

GOSPEL ACCLAMATION

cf. Ephesians 1:17–18

℟. Al - le - lu - ia, al - le - lu - ia, al - le - lu - ia.

Music: John Schiavone, b. 1947, © 2001, OCP Publications.

▶ May the Father of Our Lord Jesus Christ
  enlighten the eyes of our hearts,
so that we may know what is the hope
  that belongs to our call. ℟.

GOSPEL READING

Matthew 22:1–14 or 22:1–10

(Include bracketed text for Long Form)

Jesus again in reply spoke to the chief priests and elders of the people in parables, saying, "The kingdom of heaven may be likened to a king who gave a wedding feast for his son. He dispatched his servants to summon the invited guests to the feast, but they refused to come. A second time he sent other servants, saying, 'Tell those invited: "Behold, I have prepared my banquet, my calves and fattened cattle are killed, and everything is ready; come to the feast."' Some ignored the invitation and went away, one to his farm, another to his business. The rest laid hold of his servants, mistreated them, and killed them. The king was enraged and sent his troops, destroyed those murderers, and burned their city. Then he said to his servants, 'The feast is ready, but those who were invited were not worthy to come. Go out, therefore, into the main roads and invite to the feast whomever you find.' The servants went out into the streets and gathered all they found, bad and good alike, and the hall was filled with guests. [But when the king came in to meet the guests, he saw a man there not dressed in a wedding garment. The king said to him, 'My friend, how is it that you came in here without a wedding garment?' But he was reduced to silence.

Then the king said to his attendants, 'Bind his hands and feet, and cast him into the darkness outside, where there will be wailing and grinding of teeth.' Many are invited, but few are chosen."]

28TH SUNDAY IN ORDINARY TIME — B　　1030

FIRST READING

Wisdom 7:7–11

I prayed, and prudence was given me;
　　I pleaded, and the spirit of wisdom
　　　　came to me.
I preferred her to scepter and throne,
and deemed riches nothing in
　　comparison with her,
　　nor did I liken any priceless gem
　　　　to her;
because all gold, in view of her, is a
　　little sand,
　　and before her, silver is to be
　　　　accounted mire.

Beyond health and comeliness I
　　loved her,
and I chose to have her rather than
　　the light,
　　because the splendor of her never
　　　　yields to sleep.
Yet all good things together came to me
　　in her company,
　　and countless riches at her hands.

RESPONSORIAL PSALM

Psalm 90:12–13, 14–15, 16–17

℟. **Fill us with your love, O Lord, and we will sing for joy!**

Music: John Schiavone, b. 1947, © 2001, OCP Publications.

▸ Teach us to number our days aright,
　　that we may gain wisdom of heart.
　Return, O LORD! How long?
　　Have pity on your servants! ℟.

▸ Fill us at daybreak with your kindness,
　　that we may shout for joy and
　　gladness all our days.

Make us glad, for the days when you
　　afflicted us,
　　for the years when we saw evil. ℟.

▸ Let your work be seen by your servants
　　and your glory by their children;
　and may the gracious care of the LORD
　　our God be ours;
　　prosper the work of our hands for us!
　　Prosper the work of our hands! ℟.

SECOND READING

Hebrews 4:12–13

Brothers and sisters: Indeed the word of God is living and effective, sharper than any two-edged sword, penetrating even between soul and spirit, joints and marrow, and able to discern reflections

and thoughts of the heart. No creature is concealed from him, but everything is naked and exposed to the eyes of him to whom we must render an account.

GOSPEL ACCLAMATION

Matthew 5:3

℟. Al - le - lu - ia, al - le - lu - ia, al - le - lu - ia.

Music: John Schiavone, b. 1947, © 2001, OCP Publications.

▶ Blessed are the poor in spirit,
  for theirs is the kingdom of heaven. ℟.

GOSPEL READING

Mark 10:17–30 or 10:17–27

(Include bracketed text for Long Form)

As Jesus was setting out on a journey, a man ran up, knelt down before him, and asked him, "Good teacher, what must I do to inherit eternal life?" Jesus answered him, "Why do you call me good? No one is good but God alone. You know the commandments: *You shall not kill; you shall not commit adultery; you shall not steal; you shall not bear false witness; you shall not defraud; honor your father and your mother."* He replied and said to him, "Teacher, all of these I have observed from my youth." Jesus, looking at him, loved him and said to him, "You are lacking in one thing. Go, sell what you have, and give to the poor and you will have treasure in heaven; then come, follow me." At that statement his face fell, and he went away sad, for he had many possessions.

Jesus looked around and said to his disciples, "How hard it is for those who have wealth to enter the kingdom of God!" The disciples were amazed at his words. So Jesus again said to them in reply, "Children, how hard it is to enter the kingdom of God! It is easier for a camel to pass through the eye of a needle than for one who is rich to enter the kingdom of God." They were exceedingly astonished and said among themselves, "Then who can be saved?" Jesus looked at them and said, "For human beings it is impossible, but not for God. All things are possible for God." [Peter began to say to him, "We have given up everything and followed you." Jesus said, "Amen, I say to you, there is no one who has given up house or brothers or sisters or mother or father or children or lands for my sake and for the sake of the gospel who will not receive a hundred times more now in this present age: houses and brothers and sisters and mothers and children and lands, with persecutions, and eternal life in the age to come."]

1031   28TH SUNDAY IN ORDINARY TIME — C

FIRST READING

2 Kings 5:14–17

Naaman went down and plunged into the Jordan seven times at the word of Elisha, the man of God. His flesh became again like the flesh of a little child, and he was clean of his leprosy.

Naaman returned with his whole retinue to the man of God. On his arrival he stood before Elisha and said, "Now I know that there is no God in all the earth, except in Israel. Please accept a gift from your servant."

Elisha replied, "As the LORD lives whom I serve, I will not take it"; and despite Naaman's urging, he still refused. Naaman said: "If you will not accept, please let me, your servant, have two mule-loads of earth, for I will no longer offer holocaust or sacrifice to any other god except to the LORD."

RESPONSORIAL PSALM

Psalm 98:1, 2–3, 3–4

℟. The Lord has re-vealed to the na-tions his sav-ing pow-er.

Music: John Schiavone, b. 1947, © 2001, OCP Publications.

▶ Sing to the LORD a new song,
    for he has done wondrous deeds;
his right hand has won victory for him,
    his holy arm. ℟.

▶ The LORD has made his salvation known:
    in the sight of the nations he has
    revealed his justice.

He has remembered his kindness and
    his faithfulness
    toward the house of Israel. ℟.

▶ All the ends of the earth have seen
    the salvation by our God.
Sing joyfully to the LORD, all you lands:
    break into song; sing praise. ℟.

SECOND READING

2 Timothy 2:8–13

Beloved: Remember Jesus Christ, raised from the dead, a descendant of David: such is my gospel, for which I am suffering, even to the point of chains, like a criminal. But the word of God is not chained. Therefore, I bear with everything for the sake of those who are chosen, so that they too may obtain the salvation that is in Christ Jesus, together with eternal glory. This saying is trustworthy:
    If we have died with him
      we shall also live with him;
    if we persevere
      we shall also reign with him.
    But if we deny him
      he will deny us.
    If we are unfaithful
      he remains faithful,
    for he cannot deny himself.

GOSPEL ACCLAMATION

1 Thessalonians 5:18

℟. Al - le - lu - ia, al - le - lu - ia, al - le - lu - ia.

Music: John Schiavone, b. 1947, © 2001, OCP Publications.

▶ In all circumstances, give thanks,
    for this is the will of God for you in Christ Jesus. ℟.

GOSPEL READING

Luke 17:11–19

As Jesus continued his journey to Jerusalem, he traveled through Samaria and Galilee. As he was entering a village, ten lepers met him. They stood at a distance from him and raised their voices, saying, "Jesus, Master! Have pity on us!" And when he saw them, he said, "Go show yourselves to the priests." As they were going they were cleansed. And one of them, realizing he had been healed, returned, glorifying God in a loud voice; and he fell at the feet of Jesus and thanked him. He was a Samaritan. Jesus said in reply, "Ten were cleansed, were they not? Where are the other nine? Has none but this foreigner returned to give thanks to God?" Then he said to him, "Stand up and go; your faith has saved you."

1032   29TH SUNDAY IN ORDINARY TIME — A

FIRST READING

Isaiah 45:1, 4–6

Thus says the LORD to his anointed, Cyrus,
    whose right hand I grasp,
subduing nations before him,
    and making kings run in his service,
opening doors before him
    and leaving the gates unbarred:
For the sake of Jacob, my servant,
    of Israel, my chosen one,
I have called you by your name,
    giving you a title, though you knew
    me not.

I am the LORD and there is no other,
    there is no God besides me.
It is I who arm you, though you know
    me not,
    so that toward the rising and the
    setting of the sun
    people may know that there is none
    besides me.
I am the LORD, there is no other.

RESPONSORIAL PSALM

Psalm 96:1, 3, 4–5, 7–8, 9–10

℟. Give the Lord glory and honor.

Music: John Schiavone, b. 1947, © 2001, OCP Publications.

▶ Sing to the LORD a new song;
    sing to the LORD, all you lands.
Tell his glory among the nations;
    among all peoples, his wondrous
    deeds. ℟.

▶ For great is the LORD and highly to
    be praised;
    awesome is he, beyond all gods.
For all the gods of the nations are
    things of nought,
    but the LORD made the heavens. ℟.

▶ Give to the LORD, you families
    of nations,
    give to the LORD glory and praise;
    give to the LORD the glory due
    his name!
Bring gifts, and enter his courts. ℟.

▶ Worship the LORD, in holy attire.
    Tremble before him, all the earth;
    say among the nations: The LORD
    is king,
    he governs the peoples with equity. ℟.

SECOND READING

1 Thessalonians 1:1–5b

Paul, Silvanus, and Timothy to the church of the Thessalonians in God the Father and the Lord Jesus Christ: grace to you and peace. We give thanks to God always for all of you, remembering you in our prayers, unceasingly calling to mind your work of faith and labor of love and endurance in hope of our Lord Jesus Christ, before our God and Father, knowing, brothers and sisters loved by God, how you were chosen. For our gospel did not come to you in word alone, but also in power and in the Holy Spirit and with much conviction.

GOSPEL ACCLAMATION

Philippians 2:15d, 16a

℟. Al - le - lu - ia, al - le - lu - ia, al - le - lu - ia.

Music: John Schiavone, b. 1947, © 2001, OCP Publications.

▶ Shine like lights in the world
as you hold on to the word of life. ℟.

GOSPEL READING

Matthew 22:15–21

The Pharisees went off and plotted how they might entrap Jesus in speech. They sent their disciples to him, with the Herodians, saying, "Teacher, we know that you are a truthful man and that you teach the way of God in accordance with the truth. And you are not concerned with anyone's opinion, for you do not regard a person's status. Tell us, then, what is your opinion: Is it lawful to pay the census tax to Caesar or not?" Knowing their malice, Jesus said, "Why are you testing me, you hypocrites? Show me the coin that pays the census tax." Then they handed him the Roman coin. He said to them, "Whose image is this and whose inscription?" They replied, "Caesar's." At that he said to them, "Then repay to Caesar what belongs to Caesar and to God what belongs to God."

29TH SUNDAY IN ORDINARY TIME — B **1033**

FIRST READING

Isaiah 53:10–11

The LORD was pleased
to crush him in infirmity.

If he gives his life as an offering for sin,
he shall see his descendants in a
long life,
and the will of the LORD shall be
accomplished through him.

Because of his affliction
he shall see the light in fullness
of days;
through his suffering, my servant shall
justify many,
and their guilt he shall bear.

RESPONSORIAL PSALM

Psalm 33:4–5, 18–19, 20, 22

℟. Lord, let your mer-cy be on us, as we place our trust in you.

Music: John Schiavone, b. 1947, © 2001, OCP Publications.

▶ Upright is the word of the LORD,
and all his works are trustworthy.
He loves justice and right;
of the kindness of the LORD the
earth is full. ℟.

▶ See, the eyes of the LORD are upon
those who fear him,
upon those who hope for
his kindness,
to deliver them from death
and preserve them in spite
of famine. ℟.

℟. **Lord, let your mercy be on us, as we place our trust in you.**

▶ Our soul waits for the LORD,
    who is our help and our shield.
May your kindness, O LORD, be
        upon us
    who have put our hope in you. ℟.

SECOND READING

Hebrews 4:14–16

Brothers and sisters: Since we have a great high priest who has passed through the heavens, Jesus, the Son of God, let us hold fast to our confession. For we do not have a high priest who is unable to sympathize with our weaknesses, but one who has similarly been tested in every way, yet without sin. So let us confidently approach the throne of grace to receive mercy and to find grace for timely help.

GOSPEL ACCLAMATION

Mark 10:45

℟. Al - le - lu - ia, al - le - lu - ia, al - le - lu - ia.

Music: John Schiavone, b. 1947, © 2001, OCP Publications.

▶ The Son of Man came to serve
    and to give his life as a ransom for many. ℟.

GOSPEL READING

Mark 10:35–45 or 10:42–45

(Include bracketed text for Long Form, and text in parentheses for Short Form only)

[James and John, the sons of Zebedee, came to Jesus and said to him, "Teacher, we want you to do for us whatever we ask of you." He replied, "What do you wish me to do for you?" They answered him, "Grant that in your glory we may sit one at your right and the other at your left." Jesus said to them, "You do not know what you are asking. Can you drink the cup that I drink or be baptized with the baptism with which I am baptized?" They said to him, "We can." Jesus said to them, "The cup that I drink, you will drink, and with the baptism with which I am baptized, you will be baptized; but to sit at my right or at my left is not mine to give but is for those for whom it has been prepared." When the ten heard this, they became indignant at James and John.] Jesus summoned [them] *(the Twelve)* and said to them, "You know that those who are recognized as rulers over the Gentiles lord it over them, and their great ones make their authority over them felt. But it shall not be so among you. Rather, whoever wishes to be great among you will be your servant; whoever wishes to be first among you will be the slave of all. For the Son of Man did not come to be served but to serve and to give his life as a ransom for many."

29TH SUNDAY IN ORDINARY TIME — C **1034**

FIRST READING

Exodus 17:8–13

In those days, Amalek came and waged war against Israel. Moses, therefore, said to Joshua, "Pick out certain men, and tomorrow go out and engage Amalek in battle. I will be standing on top of the hill with the staff of God in my hand." So Joshua did as Moses told him: he engaged Amalek in battle after Moses had climbed to the top of the hill with Aaron and Hur. As long as Moses kept his hands raised up, Israel had the better of the fight, but when he let his hands rest, Amalek had the better of the fight. Moses' hands, however, grew tired; so they put a rock in place for him to sit on. Meanwhile Aaron and Hur supported his hands, one on one side and one on the other, so that his hands remained steady till sunset. And Joshua mowed down Amalek and his people with the edge of the sword.

RESPONSORIAL PSALM

Psalm 121:1–2, 3–4, 5–6, 7–8

℟. Our help is from the Lord, who made heav - en and earth.

Music: John Schiavone, b. 1947, © 2001, OCP Publications.

▶ I lift up my eyes toward the mountains;
   whence shall help come to me?
My help is from the LORD,
   who made heaven and earth. ℟.

▶ May he not suffer your foot to slip;
   may he slumber not who guards you:
indeed he neither slumbers nor sleeps,
   the guardian of Israel. ℟.

▶ The LORD is your guardian; the LORD is
   your shade;
   he is beside you at your right hand.
The sun shall not harm you by day,
   nor the moon by night. ℟.

▶ The LORD will guard you from all evil;
   he will guard your life.
The LORD will guard your coming and
   your going,
   both now and forever. ℟.

SECOND READING

2 Timothy 3:14—4:2

Beloved: Remain faithful to what you have learned and believed, because you know from whom you learned it, and that from infancy you have known the sacred Scriptures, which are capable of giving you wisdom for salvation through faith in Christ Jesus. All Scripture is inspired by God and is useful for teaching, for refutation, for correction, and for training in righteousness, so that one who belongs to God may be competent, equipped for every good work.

I charge you in the presence of God and of Christ Jesus, who will judge the living and the dead, and by his appearing and his kingly power: proclaim the word; be persistent whether it is convenient or inconvenient; convince, reprimand, encourage through all patience and teaching.

GOSPEL ACCLAMATION
Hebrews 4:12

℟. Al - le - lu - ia, al - le - lu - ia, al - le - lu - ia.

Music: John Schiavone, b. 1947, © 2001, OCP Publications.

▶ The word of God is living and effective,
discerning reflections and thoughts of the heart. ℟.

GOSPEL READING
Luke 18:1–8

Jesus told his disciples a parable about the necessity for them to pray always without becoming weary. He said, "There was a judge in a certain town who neither feared God nor respected any human being. And a widow in that town used to come to him and say, 'Render a just decision for me against my adversary.' For a long time the judge was unwilling, but eventually he thought, 'While it is true that I neither fear God nor respect any human being, because this widow keeps bothering me I shall deliver a just decision for her lest she finally come and strike me.'" The Lord said, "Pay attention to what the dishonest judge says. Will not God then secure the rights of his chosen ones who call out to him day and night? Will he be slow to answer them? I tell you, he will see to it that justice is done for them speedily. But when the Son of Man comes, will he find faith on earth?"

1035   30TH SUNDAY IN ORDINARY TIME — A

FIRST READING
Exodus 22:20–26

Thus says the LORD: "You shall not molest or oppress an alien, for you were once aliens yourselves in the land of Egypt. You shall not wrong any widow or orphan. If ever you wrong them and they cry out to me, I will surely hear their cry. My wrath will flare up, and I will kill you with the sword; then your own wives will be widows, and your children orphans.

"If you lend money to one of your poor neighbors among my people, you shall not act like an extortioner toward him by demanding interest from him. If you take your neighbor's cloak as a pledge, you shall return it to him before sunset; for this cloak of his is the only covering he has for his body. What else has he to sleep in? If he cries out to me, I will hear him; for I am compassionate."

RESPONSORIAL PSALM
Psalm 18:2–3, 3–4, 47, 51

℟. [I love you,] I love you, Lord, my strength.

Music: John Schiavone, b. 1947, © 2001, OCP Publications.

▶ I love you, O LORD, my strength,
O LORD, my rock, my fortress, my deliverer. ℟.

▶ My God, my rock of refuge,
my shield, the horn of my salvation,
my stronghold!
Praised be the LORD, I exclaim,
and I am safe from my enemies. ℟.

▸ The LORD lives and blessed be
my rock!
Extolled be God my savior.

You who gave great victories to
your king
and showed kindness to
your anointed. ℟.

SECOND READING
1 Thessalonians 1:5c–10

Brothers and sisters: You know what sort of people we were among you for your sake. And you became imitators of us and of the Lord, receiving the word in great affliction, with joy from the Holy Spirit, so that you became a model for all the believers in Macedonia and in Achaia. For from you the word of the Lord has sounded forth not only in Macedonia and in Achaia, but in every place your faith in God has gone forth, so that we have no need to say anything. For they themselves openly declare about us what sort of reception we had among you, and how you turned to God from idols to serve the living and true God and to await his Son from heaven, whom he raised from the dead, Jesus, who delivers us from the coming wrath.

GOSPEL ACCLAMATION
John 14:23

℟. Al - le - lu - ia, al - le - lu - ia, al - le - lu - ia.

Music: John Schiavone, b. 1947, © 2001, OCP Publications.

▸ Whoever loves me will keep my word, says the Lord,
and my Father will love him and we will come to him. ℟.

GOSPEL READING
Matthew 22:34–40

When the Pharisees heard that Jesus had silenced the Sadducees, they gathered together, and one of them, a scholar of the law, tested him by asking, "Teacher, which commandment in the law is the greatest?" He said to him, "You shall love the Lord, your God, with all your heart, with all your soul, and with all your mind. This is the greatest and the first commandment. The second is like it: You shall love your neighbor as yourself. The whole law and the prophets depend on these two commandments."

30TH SUNDAY IN ORDINARY TIME — B   1036

FIRST READING
Jeremiah 31:7–9

Thus says the LORD:
Shout with joy for Jacob,
    exult at the head of the nations;
    proclaim your praise and say:
The LORD has delivered his people,
    the remnant of Israel.
Behold, I will bring them back
from the land of the north;
I will gather them from the ends of
    the world,
    with the blind and the lame in
    their midst,
the mothers and those with child;
    they shall return as an immense throng.

They departed in tears,
  but I will console them and
    guide them;
I will lead them to brooks of water,
on a level road, so that none
  shall stumble.
For I am a father to Israel,
Ephraim is my first-born.

RESPONSORIAL PSALM

Psalm 126:1–2, 2–3, 4–5, 6

℟. The Lord has done great things for us; we are filled with joy.

Music: John Schiavone, b. 1947, © 2001, OCP Publications.

▶ When the LORD brought back the
  captives of Zion,
we were like men dreaming.
Then our mouth was filled
  with laughter,
  and our tongue with rejoicing. ℟.

▶ Then they said among the nations,
  "The LORD has done great things
    for them."
The LORD has done great things for us;
  we are glad indeed. ℟.

▶ Restore our fortunes, O LORD,
  like the torrents in the
    southern desert.
Those that sow in tears
  shall reap rejoicing. ℟.

▶ Although they go forth weeping,
  carrying the seed to be sown,
they shall come back rejoicing,
  carrying their sheaves. ℟.

SECOND READING

Hebrews 5:1–6

Brothers and sisters: Every high priest is taken from among men and made their representative before God, to offer gifts and sacrifices for sins. He is able to deal patiently with the ignorant and erring, for he himself is beset by weakness and so, for this reason, must make sin offerings for himself as well as for the people. No one takes this honor upon himself but only when called by God, just as Aaron was. In the same way, it was not Christ who glorified himself in becoming high priest, but rather the one who said to him:
  You are my son:
    this day I have begotten you;
just as he says in another place:
  You are a priest forever
    according to the order
    of Melchizedek.

GOSPEL ACCLAMATION

cf. 2 Timothy 1:10

℟. Al - le - lu - ia, al - le - lu - ia, al - le - lu - ia.

Music: John Schiavone, b. 1947, © 2001, OCP Publications.

▶ Our Savior Jesus Christ destroyed death
  and brought life to light through the Gospel. ℟.

GOSPEL READING

Mark 10:46–52

As Jesus was leaving Jericho with his disciples and a sizable crowd, Bartimaeus, a blind man, the son of Timaeus, sat by the roadside begging. On hearing that it was Jesus of Nazareth, he began to cry out and say, "Jesus, son of David, have pity on me." And many rebuked him, telling him to be silent. But he kept calling out all the more, "Son of David, have pity on me." Jesus stopped and said, "Call him." So they called the blind man, saying to him, "Take courage; get up, Jesus is calling you." He threw aside his cloak, sprang up, and came to Jesus. Jesus said to him in reply, "What do you want me to do for you?" The blind man replied to him, "Master, I want to see." Jesus told him, "Go your way; your faith has saved you." Immediately he received his sight and followed him on the way.

30TH SUNDAY IN ORDINARY TIME — C   1037

FIRST READING

Sirach 35:12–14, 16–18

The LORD is a God of justice,
  who knows no favorites.
Though not unduly partial toward
    the weak,
  yet he hears the cry of the oppressed.
The Lord is not deaf to the wail of
    the orphan,
  nor to the widow when she pours out
    her complaint.
The one who serves God willingly
  is heard;

his petition reaches the heavens.
The prayer of the lowly pierces
    the clouds;
  it does not rest till it reaches its goal,
nor will it withdraw till the Most High
    responds,
  judges justly and affirms the right,
and the Lord will not delay.

RESPONSORIAL PSALM

Psalm 34:2–3, 17–18, 19, 23

℟. The Lord hears the cry of the poor, [the cry of the poor.]

Music: John Schiavone, b. 1947, © 2001, OCP Publications.

▶ I will bless the LORD at all times;
  his praise shall be ever in my mouth.
  Let my soul glory in the LORD;
    the lowly will hear me and be glad. ℟.

▶ The LORD confronts the evildoers,
  to destroy remembrance of them
    from the earth.
  When the just cry out, the LORD
    hears them,
  and from all their distress he
    rescues them. ℟.

▶ The LORD is close to the
  brokenhearted;
  and those who are crushed in spirit
    he saves.
  The LORD redeems the lives of
    his servants;
  no one incurs guilt who takes
    refuge in him. ℟.

SECOND READING

2 Timothy 4:6–8, 16–18

Beloved: I am already being poured out like a libation, and the time of my departure is at hand. I have competed well; I have finished the race; I have kept the faith. From now on the crown of righteousness awaits me, which the Lord, the just judge, will award to me on that day, and not only to me, but to all who have longed for his appearance.

At my first defense no one appeared on my behalf, but everyone deserted me. May it not be held against them! But the Lord stood by me and gave me strength, so that through me the proclamation might be completed and all the Gentiles might hear it. And I was rescued from the lion's mouth. The Lord will rescue me from every evil threat and will bring me safe to his heavenly kingdom. To him be glory forever and ever. Amen.

GOSPEL ACCLAMATION

2 Corinthians 5:19

℟. Al - le - lu - ia, al - le - lu - ia, al - le - lu - ia.

Music: John Schiavone, b. 1947, © 2001, OCP Publications.

▶ God was reconciling the world to himself in Christ, and entrusting to us the message of salvation. ℟.

GOSPEL READING

Luke 18:9–14

Jesus addressed this parable to those who were convinced of their own righteousness and despised everyone else. "Two people went up to the temple area to pray; one was a Pharisee and the other was a tax collector. The Pharisee took up his position and spoke this prayer to himself, 'O God, I thank you that I am not like the rest of humanity — greedy, dishonest, adulterous — or even like this tax collector. I fast twice a week, and I pay tithes on my whole income.' But the tax collector stood off at a distance and would not even raise his eyes to heaven but beat his breast and prayed, 'O God, be merciful to me a sinner.' I tell you, the latter went home justified, not the former; for whoever exalts himself will be humbled, and the one who humbles himself will be exalted."

1038   31ST SUNDAY IN ORDINARY TIME — A

FIRST READING

Malachi 1:14b—2:2b, 8–10

A great King am I, says the LORD of hosts,
  and my name will be feared among
    the nations.
And now, O priests, this commandment
  is for you:
  If you do not listen,
if you do not lay it to heart,
  to give glory to my name, says the
    LORD of hosts,
I will send a curse upon you

and of your blessing I will make
  a curse.
You have turned aside from the way,
  and have caused many to falter by
    your instruction;
you have made void the covenant of Levi,
  says the LORD of hosts.
I, therefore, have made you
    contemptible
  and base before all the people,

since you do not keep my ways,
but show partiality in your decisions.
Have we not all the one father?
Has not the one God created us?

Why then do we break faith with
one another,
violating the covenant of our fathers?

RESPONSORIAL PSALM
Psalm 131:1, 2, 3

℟. **In you, Lord, I have found my peace,** **[I have found my peace.]**

Music: John Schiavone, b. 1947, © 2001, OCP Publications.

▶ O LORD, my heart is not proud,
nor are my eyes haughty;
I busy not myself with great things,
nor with things too sublime for me. ℟.

▶ Nay rather, I have stilled and quieted
my soul like a weaned child.
Like a weaned child on its mother's lap,
so is my soul within me. ℟.

▶ O Israel, hope in the LORD,
both now and forever. ℟.

SECOND READING
1 Thessalonians 2:7b–9, 13

Brothers and sisters: We were gentle among you, as a nursing mother cares for her children. With such affection for you, we were determined to share with you not only the gospel of God, but our very selves as well, so dearly beloved had you become to us. You recall, brothers and sisters, our toil and drudgery. Working night and day in order not to burden any of you, we proclaimed to you the gospel of God.

And for this reason we too give thanks to God unceasingly, that, in receiving the word of God from hearing us, you received not a human word but, as it truly is, the word of God, which is now at work in you who believe.

GOSPEL ACCLAMATION
Matthew 23:9b, 10b

℟. **Al - le - lu - ia, al - le - lu - ia, al - le - lu - ia.**

Music: John Schiavone, b. 1947, © 2001, OCP Publications.

▶ You have but one Father in heaven
and one master, the Christ. ℟.

GOSPEL READING
Matthew 23:1–12

Jesus spoke to the crowds and to his disciples, saying, "The scribes and the Pharisees have taken their seat on the chair of Moses. Therefore, do and observe all things whatsoever they tell you, but do not follow their example. For they preach but they do not practice. They tie up heavy burdens hard to carry and lay them on people's shoulders, but they will not lift a finger to move them. All their works are performed to be seen. They widen their phylacteries and lengthen their tassels. They love places of honor at banquets, seats of honor in synagogues, greetings in marketplaces, and the salutation 'Rabbi.'

As for you, do not be called 'Rabbi.' You have but one teacher, and you are all brothers. Call no one on earth your father; you have but one Father in heaven. Do not be called 'Master'; you have but one master, the Christ. The greatest among you must be your servant. Whoever exalts himself will be humbled; but whoever humbles himself will be exalted."

1039   31ST SUNDAY IN ORDINARY TIME — B

FIRST READING

Deuteronomy 6:2–6

Moses spoke to the people, saying: "Fear the LORD, your God, and keep, throughout the days of your lives, all his statutes and commandments which I enjoin on you, and thus have long life. Hear then, Israel, and be careful to observe them, that you may grow and prosper the more, in keeping with the promise of the LORD, the God of your fathers, to give you a land flowing with milk and honey.

"Hear, O Israel! The LORD is our God, the LORD alone! Therefore, you shall love the LORD, your God, with all your heart, and with all your soul, and with all your strength. Take to heart these words which I enjoin on you today."

RESPONSORIAL PSALM

Psalm 18:2–3, 3–4, 47, 51

℟. [I love you,] I love you, Lord, my strength.

Music: John Schiavone, b. 1947, © 2001, OCP Publications.

▶ I love you, O LORD, my strength,
   O LORD, my rock, my fortress, my deliverer. ℟.

▶ My God, my rock of refuge,
   my shield, the horn of my salvation,
   my stronghold!
Praised be the LORD, I exclaim,
   and I am safe from my enemies. ℟.

▶ The LORD lives! And blessed be my rock!
   Extolled be God my savior,
you who gave great victories to your king
   and showed kindness to your anointed. ℟.

SECOND READING

Hebrews 7:23–28

Brothers and sisters: The levitical priests were many because they were prevented by death from remaining in office, but Jesus, because he remains forever, has a priesthood that does not pass away. Therefore, he is always able to save those who approach God through him, since he lives forever to make intercession for them.

It was fitting that we should have such a high priest: holy, innocent, undefiled, separated from sinners, higher than the heavens. He has no need, as did the high priests, to offer sacrifice day after day, first for his own sins and then for those of the people; he did that once for all when he offered himself. For the law appoints men subject to weakness to be high priests, but the word of the oath, which was taken after the law, appoints a son, who has been made perfect forever.

GOSPEL ACCLAMATION *John 14:23*

℟. Al - le - lu - ia, al - le - lu - ia, al - le - lu - ia.

Music: John Schiavone, b. 1947, © 2001, OCP Publications.

▶ Whoever loves me will keep my word, says the Lord;
and my Father will love him and we will come to him. ℟.

GOSPEL READING *Mark 12:28b–34*

One of the scribes came to Jesus and asked him, "Which is the first of all the commandments?" Jesus replied, "The first is this: *Hear, O Israel! The Lord our God is Lord alone! You shall love the Lord your God with all your heart, with all your soul, with all your mind, and with all your strength.* The second is this: *You shall love your neighbor as yourself.* There is no other commandment greater than these." The scribe said to him, "Well said, teacher. You are right in saying, 'He is One and there is no other than he.' And 'to love him with all your heart, with all your understanding, with all your strength, and to love your neighbor as yourself' is worth more than all burnt offerings and sacrifices." And when Jesus saw that he answered with understanding, he said to him, "You are not far from the kingdom of God." And no one dared to ask him any more questions.

31ST SUNDAY IN ORDINARY TIME — C **1040**

FIRST READING *Wisdom 11:22—12:2*

Before the LORD the whole universe is
    as a grain from a balance
  or a drop of morning dew come
    down upon the earth.
But you have mercy on all, because you
    can do all things;
  and you overlook people's sins that
    they may repent.
For you love all things that are
  and loathe nothing that you
    have made;
  for what you hated, you would not
    have fashioned.
And how could a thing remain, unless
  you willed it;

or be preserved, had it not been
    called forth by you?
But you spare all things, because they
    are yours,
  O LORD and lover of souls,
  for your imperishable spirit is in
    all things!
Therefore you rebuke offenders little
    by little,
  warn them and remind them of the
    sins they are committing,
  that they may abandon their
    wickedness and believe in you,
      O LORD!

RESPONSORIAL PSALM

Psalm 145:1–2, 8–9, 10–11, 13–14

℟. I will praise your name for ev-er, my king and my God.

Music: John Schiavone, b. 1947, © 2001, OCP Publications.

▶ I will extol you, O my God and King,
and I will bless your name forever
and ever.
Every day will I bless you,
and I will praise your name forever
and ever. ℟.

▶ The LORD is gracious and merciful,
slow to anger and of great kindness.
The LORD is good to all
and compassionate toward all
his works. ℟.

▶ Let all your works give you thanks,
O LORD,
and let your faithful ones bless you.
Let them discourse of the glory of
your kingdom
and speak of your might. ℟.

▶ The LORD is faithful in all his words
and holy in all his works.
The LORD lifts up all who are falling
and raises up all who are
bowed down. ℟.

SECOND READING

2 Thessalonians 1:11—2:2

Brothers and sisters: We always pray for you, that our God may make you worthy of his calling and powerfully bring to fulfillment every good purpose and every effort of faith, that the name of our Lord Jesus may be glorified in you, and you in him, in accord with the grace of our God and Lord Jesus Christ.

We ask you, brothers and sisters, with regard to the coming of our Lord Jesus Christ and our assembling with him, not to be shaken out of your minds suddenly, or to be alarmed either by a "spirit," or by an oral statement, or by a letter allegedly from us to the effect that the day of the Lord is at hand.

GOSPEL ACCLAMATION

John 3:16

℟. Al - le - lu - ia, al - le - lu - ia, al - le - lu - ia.

Music: John Schiavone, b. 1947, © 2001, OCP Publications.

▶ God so loved the world that he gave his only Son,
so that everyone who believes in him might have eternal life. ℟.

GOSPEL READING

Luke 19:1–10

At that time, Jesus came to Jericho and intended to pass through the town. Now a man there named Zacchaeus, who was a chief tax collector and also a wealthy man, was seeking to see who Jesus was; but he could not see him because of the crowd, for he was short in stature. So he ran ahead and climbed a sycamore tree in order to see Jesus, who was about to pass that way. When

he reached the place, Jesus looked up and said, "Zacchaeus, come down quickly, for today I must stay at your house." And he came down quickly and received him with joy. When they all saw this, they began to grumble, saying, "He has gone to stay at the house of a sinner." But Zacchaeus stood there and said to the Lord, "Behold, half of my possessions, Lord, I shall give to the poor, and if I have extorted anything from anyone I shall repay it four times over." And Jesus said to him, "Today salvation has come to this house

because this man too is a descendant of Abraham. For the Son of Man has come to seek and to save what was lost."

32ND SUNDAY IN ORDINARY TIME — A   1041

FIRST READING   *Wisdom 6:12–16*

Resplendent and unfading is wisdom,
and she is readily perceived by those
who love her,
and found by those who seek her.
She hastens to make herself known in
anticipation of their desire;
whoever watches for her at dawn
shall not be disappointed,
for he shall find her sitting by his gate.

For taking thought of wisdom is the
perfection of prudence,
and whoever for her sake keeps vigil
shall quickly be free from care;
because she makes her own rounds,
seeking those worthy of her,
and graciously appears to them in
the ways,
and meets them with all solicitude.

RESPONSORIAL PSALM   *Psalm 63:2, 3–4, 5–6, 7–8*

℟. My soul is thirst-ing for you, O Lord my God.

Music: John Schiavone, b. 1947, © 2001, OCP Publications.

▶ O God, you are my God whom I seek;
for you my flesh pines and my
soul thirsts
like the earth, parched, lifeless and
without water. ℟.

▶ Thus have I gazed toward you in
the sanctuary
to see your power and your glory,
for your kindness is a greater good
than life;
my lips shall glorify you. ℟.

▶ Thus will I bless you while I live;
lifting up my hands, I will call upon
your name.
As with the riches of a banquet shall
my soul be satisfied,
and with exultant lips my mouth
shall praise you. ℟.

▶ I will remember you upon my couch,
and through the night-watches I will
meditate on you:
you are my help,
and in the shadow of your wings
I shout for joy. ℟.

SECOND READING   *1 Thessalonians 4:13–18 or 4:13–14*

(Include bracketed text for Long Form)

We do not want you to be unaware, brothers and sisters, about those who have fallen asleep, so that you may not grieve like the rest, who have no hope. For if we believe that Jesus died and rose, so too will God, through Jesus,

bring with him those who have fallen asleep. [Indeed, we tell you this, on the word of the Lord, that we who are alive, who are left until the coming of the Lord, will surely not precede those who have fallen asleep. For the Lord himself, with a word of command, with the voice of an archangel and with the trumpet of God, will come down from heaven, and the dead in Christ will rise first. Then we who are alive, who are left, will be caught up together with them in the clouds to meet the Lord in the air. Thus we shall always be with the Lord. Therefore, console one another with these words.]

GOSPEL ACCLAMATION
Matthew 24:42a, 44

℟. Al - le - lu - ia, al - le - lu - ia, al - le - lu - ia.

Music: John Schiavone, b. 1947, © 2001, OCP Publications.

▶ Stay awake and be ready!
For you do not know on what day your Lord will come. ℟.

GOSPEL READING
Matthew 25:1–13

Jesus told his disciples this parable: "The kingdom of heaven will be like ten virgins who took their lamps and went out to meet the bridegroom. Five of them were foolish and five were wise. The foolish ones, when taking their lamps, brought no oil with them, but the wise brought flasks of oil with their lamps. Since the bridegroom was long delayed, they all became drowsy and fell asleep. At midnight, there was a cry, 'Behold, the bridegroom! Come out to meet him!' Then all those virgins got up and trimmed their lamps. The foolish ones said to the wise, 'Give us some of your oil, for our lamps are going out.' But the wise ones replied, 'No, for there may not be enough for us and you. Go instead to the merchants and buy some for yourselves.' While they went off to buy it, the bridegroom came and those who were ready went into the wedding feast with him. Then the door was locked. Afterwards the other virgins came and said, 'Lord, Lord, open the door for us!' But he said in reply, 'Amen, I say to you, I do not know you.' Therefore, stay awake, for you know neither the day nor the hour."

1042   32ND SUNDAY IN ORDINARY TIME — B

FIRST READING
1 Kings 17:10–16

In those days, Elijah the prophet went to Zarephath. As he arrived at the entrance of the city, a widow was gathering sticks there; he called out to her, "Please bring me a small cupful of water to drink." She left to get it, and he called out after her, "Please bring along a bit of bread." She answered, "As the LORD, your God, lives, I have nothing baked; there is only a handful of flour in my jar and a little oil in my jug. Just now I was collecting a couple of sticks, to go in and prepare something for myself and my son; when we have eaten it, we shall die." Elijah said to her, "Do not be afraid. Go and do as you propose. But first make me a little cake and bring it to me. Then you can prepare something for yourself and your son. For the LORD, the God of Israel, says, 'The jar of flour shall not go empty, nor the jug of oil run dry, until the day when the LORD sends rain upon the earth.'" She left and did as Elijah had said. She was able to eat for a year, and he and her son as well; the jar of flour did not go empty, nor the jug of oil run dry, as the LORD had foretold through Elijah.

RESPONSORIAL PSALM

Psalm 146:7, 8–9, 9–10

℟. **Praise** the **Lord,** my **soul,** [my **soul!**]

Music: John Schiavone, b. 1947, © 2001, OCP Publications.

or: **Alleluia.**

▸ The LORD keeps faith forever,
    secures justice for the oppressed,
    gives food to the hungry.
  The LORD sets captives free. ℟.

▸ The LORD gives sight to the blind;
    the LORD raises up those who were
    bowed down.
  The LORD loves the just;
    the LORD protects strangers. ℟.

▸ The fatherless and the widow
    he sustains,
  but the way of the wicked
    he thwarts.
  The LORD shall reign forever;
    your God, O Zion, through all
    generations. Alleluia. ℟.

SECOND READING

Hebrews 9:24–28

Christ did not enter into a sanctuary made by hands, a copy of the true one, but heaven itself, that he might now appear before God on our behalf. Not that he might offer himself repeatedly, as the high priest enters each year into the sanctuary with blood that is not his own; if that were so, he would have had to suffer repeatedly from the foundation of the world. But now once for all he has appeared at the end of the ages to take away sin by his sacrifice. Just as it is appointed that human beings die once, and after this the judgment, so also Christ, offered once to take away the sins of many, will appear a second time, not to take away sin but to bring salvation to those who eagerly await him.

GOSPEL ACCLAMATION

Matthew 5:3

℟. **Al - le - lu - ia, al - le - lu - ia, al - le - lu - ia.**

Music: John Schiavone, b. 1947, © 2001, OCP Publications.

▸ Blessed are the poor in spirit,
  for theirs is the kingdom of heaven. ℟.

GOSPEL READING

Mark 12:38–44 or 12:41–44

(Include bracketed text for Long Form, and text in parentheses for Short Form only)

[In the course of his teaching Jesus said to the crowds, "Beware of the scribes, who like to go around in long robes and accept greetings in the marketplaces, seats of honor in synagogues, and places of honor at banquets. They devour the houses of widows and, as a pretext, recite lengthy prayers. They will receive a very severe condemnation."

He] *(Jesus)* sat down opposite the treasury and observed how the crowd put money into the treasury. Many rich people put in large sums. A poor widow also came and put in two small coins worth a few cents. Calling his disciples to himself, he said to them, "Amen, I say to you, this poor widow put in more than all the other contributors to the treasury. For they have all contributed from their surplus wealth, but she, from her poverty, has contributed all she had, her whole livelihood."

1043   32ND SUNDAY IN ORDINARY TIME — C

FIRST READING

2 Maccabees 7:1–2, 9–14

It happened that seven brothers with their mother were arrested and tortured with whips and scourges by the king, to force them to eat pork in violation of God's law. One of the brothers, speaking for the others, said: "What do you expect to achieve by questioning us? We are ready to die rather than transgress the laws of our ancestors."

At the point of death he said: "You accursed fiend, you are depriving us of this present life, but the King of the world will raise us up to live again forever. It is for his laws that we are dying."

After him the third suffered their cruel sport. He put out his tongue at once when told to do so, and bravely held out his hands, as he spoke these noble words: "It was from Heaven that I received these; for the sake of his laws I disdain them; from him I hope to receive them again." Even the king and his attendants marveled at the young man's courage, because he regarded his sufferings as nothing.

After he had died, they tortured and maltreated the fourth brother in the same way. When he was near death, he said, "It is my choice to die at the hands of men with the hope God gives of being raised up by him; but for you, there will be no resurrection to life."

RESPONSORIAL PSALM

Psalm 17:1, 5–6, 8, 15

℟. Lord, when your glo - ry ap - pears, my joy will be full.

Music: John Schiavone, b. 1947, © 2001, OCP Publications.

▶ Hear, O LORD, a just suit;
    attend to my outcry;
    hearken to my prayer from lips
      without deceit. ℟.

▶ My steps have been steadfast in
     your paths,
    my feet have not faltered.

I call upon you, for you will answer
    me, O God;
incline your ear to me; hear
    my word. ℟.

▶ Keep me as the apple of your eye,
    hide me in the shadow of your wings.
But I in justice shall behold your face;
    on waking I shall be content in
    your presence. ℟.

SECOND READING

2 Thessalonians 2:16—3:5

Brothers and sisters: May our Lord Jesus Christ himself and God our Father, who has loved us and given us everlasting encouragement and good hope through his grace, encourage your hearts and strengthen them in every good deed and word.

Finally, brothers and sisters, pray for us, so that the word of the Lord may speed forward and be glorified, as it did among you, and that we may be delivered from perverse and wicked people, for not all have faith. But the Lord is faithful; he will strengthen you and guard you from the evil one. We are confident of you in the Lord that what we instruct you, you are doing and will continue to do. May the Lord direct your hearts to the love of God and to the endurance of Christ.

GOSPEL ACCLAMATION   *Revelation 1:5a, 6b*

℟. Al - le - lu - ia, al - le - lu - ia, al - le - lu - ia.

Music: John Schiavone, b. 1947, © 2001, OCP Publications.

▸ Jesus Christ is the firstborn of the dead;
  to him be glory and power, forever and ever. ℟.

GOSPEL READING   *Luke 20:27–38 or 20:27, 34–38*

(Include bracketed text for Long Form)

Some Sadducees, those who deny that there is a resurrection, came forward [and put this question to Jesus, saying, "Teacher, Moses wrote for us, *If someone's brother dies leaving a wife but no child, his brother must take the wife and raise up descendants for his brother.* Now there were seven brothers; the first married a woman but died childless. Then the second and the third married her, and likewise all the seven died childless. Finally the woman also died. Now at the resurrection whose wife will that woman be? For all seven had been married to her."] Jesus said to them, "The children of this age marry and remarry; but those who are deemed worthy to attain to the coming age and to the resurrection of the dead neither marry nor are given in marriage. They can no longer die, for they are like angels; and they are the children of God because they are the ones who will rise. That the dead will rise even Moses made known in the passage about the bush, when he called out 'Lord,' the God of Abraham, the God of Isaac, and the God of Jacob; and he is not God of the dead, but of the living, for to him all are alive."

33RD SUNDAY IN ORDINARY TIME — A   **1044**

FIRST READING   *Proverbs 31:10–13, 19–20, 30–31*

When one finds a worthy wife,
  her value is far beyond pearls.
Her husband, entrusting his heart to her,
  has an unfailing prize.
She brings him good, and not evil,
  all the days of her life.
She obtains wool and flax
  and works with loving hands.
She puts her hands to the distaff,
and her fingers ply the spindle.
She reaches out her hands to the poor,
  and extends her arms to the needy.
Charm is deceptive and beauty fleeting;
  the woman who fears the Lord is to
  be praised.
Give her a reward for her labors,
  and let her works praise her at the
  city gates.

RESPONSORIAL PSALM

Psalm 128:1–2, 3, 4–5

℟. Bless'd   are   those   who   fear   the   Lord.

Music: John Schiavone, b. 1947, © 2001, OCP Publications.

▶ Blessed are you who fear the LORD,
　who walk in his ways!
For you shall eat the fruit of
　　your handiwork;
　blessed shall you be, and favored. ℟.

▶ Your wife shall be like a fruitful vine
　in the recesses of your home;
your children like olive plants
　around your table. ℟.

▶ Behold, thus is the man blessed
　who fears the LORD.
The LORD bless you from Zion:
　may you see the prosperity
　of Jerusalem
all the days of your life. ℟.

SECOND READING

1 Thessalonians 5:1–6

Concerning times and seasons, brothers and sisters, you have no need for anything to be written to you. For you yourselves know very well that the day of the Lord will come like a thief at night. When people are saying, "Peace and security," then sudden disaster comes upon them, like labor pains upon a pregnant woman, and they will not escape.

But you, brothers and sisters, are not in darkness, for that day to overtake you like a thief. For all of you are children of the light and children of the day. We are not of the night or of darkness. Therefore, let us not sleep as the rest do, but let us stay alert and sober.

GOSPEL ACCLAMATION

John 15:4a, 5b

℟. Al - le - lu - ia,   al - le - lu - ia,   al - le - lu - ia.

Music: John Schiavone, b. 1947, © 2001, OCP Publications.

▶ Remain in me as I remain in you, says the Lord.
　Whoever remains in me bears much fruit. ℟.

GOSPEL READING

Matthew 25:14–30 or 25:14–15, 19–21

(Include bracketed text for Long Form)

Jesus told his disciples this parable: "A man going on a journey called in his servants and entrusted his possessions to them. To one he gave five talents; to another, two; to a third, one — to each according to his ability. Then he went away. [Immediately the one who received five talents went and traded with them,

and made another five. Likewise, the one who received two made another two. But the man who received one went off and dug a hole in the ground and buried his master's money.]

After a long time the master of those servants came back and settled accounts with them. The one who had received five talents came forward bringing the additional five. He said, 'Master, you gave me five talents. See, I have made five more.' His master said to him, 'Well done, my good and faithful servant. Since you were faithful in small matters, I will give you great responsibilities. Come, share your master's joy.' [Then the one who had received two talents also came forward and said, 'Master, you gave me two talents. See, I have made two more.' His master said to him, 'Well done, my good and faithful servant. Since you were faithful in small matters, I will give you great responsibilities. Come, share your master's joy.' Then the one who had received the one talent came forward and said, 'Master, I knew you were a demanding person, harvesting where you did not plant and gathering where you did not scatter; so out of fear I went off and buried your talent in the ground. Here it is back.' His master said to him in reply, 'You wicked, lazy servant! So you knew that I harvest where I did not plant and gather where I did not scatter? Should you not then have put my money in the bank so that I could have got it back with interest on my return? Now then! Take the talent from him and give it to the one with ten. For to everyone who has, more will be given and he will grow rich; but from the one who has not, even what he has will be taken away. And throw this useless servant into the darkness outside, where there will be wailing and grinding of teeth.'"]

33RD SUNDAY IN ORDINARY TIME — B   **1045**

FIRST READING

Daniel 12:1–3

In those days, I, Daniel,
    heard this word of the Lord:
"At that time there shall arise
    Michael, the great prince,
    guardian of your people;
it shall be a time unsurpassed
    in distress
    since nations began until that time.
At that time your people shall escape,
    everyone who is found written in
        the book.

Many of those who sleep in the dust of
        the earth shall awake;
    some shall live forever,
    others shall be an everlasting horror
        and disgrace.
But the wise shall shine brightly
    like the splendor of the firmament,
and those who lead the many to justice
    shall be like the stars forever."

RESPONSORIAL PSALM

Psalm 16:5, 8, 9–10, 11

℟. You are my in-her-i-tance, O Lord!

Music: John Schiavone, b. 1947, © 2001, OCP Publications.

▶ O LORD, my allotted portion and
        my cup,
    you it is who hold fast my lot.
    I set the LORD ever before me;
        with him at my right hand I shall not
            be disturbed. ℟.

▶ Therefore my heart is glad and my
        soul rejoices,
    my body, too, abides in confidence;
    because you will not abandon my soul
        to the netherworld,
        nor will you suffer your faithful one
            to undergo corruption. ℟.

℟. You are my inheritance, O Lord!

▶ You will show me the path to life,
 fullness of joys in your presence,

the delights at your right hand
 forever. ℟.

SECOND READING

Hebrews 10:11–14, 18

Brothers and sisters: Every priest stands daily at his ministry, offering frequently those same sacrifices that can never take away sins. But this one offered one sacrifice for sins, and took his seat forever at the right hand of God; now he waits until his enemies are made his footstool. For by one offering he has made perfect forever those who are being consecrated.

Where there is forgiveness of these, there is no longer offering for sin.

GOSPEL ACCLAMATION

Luke 21:36

℟. Al - le - lu - ia, al - le - lu - ia, al - le - lu - ia.

Music: John Schiavone, b. 1947, © 2001, OCP Publications.

▶ Be vigilant at all times
 and pray that you have the strength to stand before the Son of Man. ℟.

GOSPEL READING

Mark 13:24–32

Jesus said to his disciples: "In those days after that tribulation
 the sun will be darkened,
 and the moon will not give its light,
 and the stars will be falling from
 the sky,
 and the powers in the heavens will
 be shaken.
"And then they will see 'the Son of Man coming in the clouds' with great power and glory, and then he will send out the angels and gather his elect from the four winds, from the end of the earth to the end of the sky.

"Learn a lesson from the fig tree. When its branch becomes tender and sprouts leaves, you know that summer is near. In the same way, when you see these things happening, know that he is near, at the gates. Amen, I say to you, this generation will not pass away until all these things have taken place. Heaven and earth will pass away, but my words will not pass away.

"But of that day or hour, no one knows, neither the angels in heaven, nor the Son, but only the Father."

1046   33RD SUNDAY IN ORDINARY TIME — C

FIRST READING

Malachi 3:19–20a

Lo, the day is coming, blazing like
 an oven,
 when all the proud and all evildoers
 will be stubble,
and the day that is coming will set them
 on fire,

leaving them neither root nor branch,
 says the LORD of hosts.
But for you who fear my name, there
 will arise
 the sun of justice with its healing rays.

RESPONSORIAL PSALM

Psalm 98:5–6, 7–8, 9

℟. The Lord comes to rule the earth with jus - tice.

Music: John Schiavone, b. 1947, © 2001, OCP Publications.

▶ Sing praise to the LORD with the harp,
　　with the harp and melodious song.
With trumpets and the sound of
　　the horn
　　sing joyfully before the King,
　　　　the LORD. ℟.

▶ Let the sea and what fills it resound,
　　the world and those who dwell in it;
let the rivers clap their hands,
　　the mountains shout with them
　　　　for joy. ℟.

▶ Before the LORD, for he comes,
　　for he comes to rule the earth;
he will rule the world with justice
　　and the peoples with equity. ℟.

SECOND READING

2 Thessalonians 3:7–12

Brothers and sisters: You know how one must imitate us. For we did not act in a disorderly way among you, nor did we eat food received free from anyone. On the contrary, in toil and drudgery, night and day we worked, so as not to burden any of you. Not that we do not have the right. Rather, we wanted to present ourselves as a model for you, so that you might imitate us. In fact, when we were with you, we instructed you that if anyone was unwilling to work, neither should that one eat. We hear that some are conducting themselves among you in a disorderly way, by not keeping busy but minding the business of others. Such people we instruct and urge in the Lord Jesus Christ to work quietly and to eat their own food.

GOSPEL ACCLAMATION

Luke 21:28

℟. Al - le - lu - ia, al - le - lu - ia, al - le - lu - ia.

Music: John Schiavone, b. 1947, © 2001, OCP Publications.

▶ Stand erect and raise your heads
　　because your redemption is at hand. ℟.

GOSPEL READING

Luke 21:5–19

While some people were speaking about how the temple was adorned with costly stones and votive offerings, Jesus said, "All that you see here — the days will come when there will not be left a stone upon another stone that will not be thrown down."

　　Then they asked him, "Teacher, when will this happen? And what sign will there be when all these things are about to happen?" He answered, "See that you not be deceived, for many will come in my name, saying, 'I am he,' and 'The time has come.' Do not follow them! When you hear of wars and insurrections, do not be terrified;

for such things must happen first, but it will not immediately be the end." Then he said to them, "Nation will rise against nation, and kingdom against kingdom. There will be powerful earthquakes, famines, and plagues from place to place; and awesome sights and mighty signs will come from the sky.

"Before all this happens, however, they will seize and persecute you, they will hand you over to the synagogues and to prisons, and they will have you led before kings and governors because of my name. It will lead to your giving testimony. Remember, you are not to prepare your defense beforehand, for I myself shall give you a wisdom in speaking that all your adversaries will be powerless to resist or refute. You will even be handed over by parents, brothers, relatives, and friends, and they will put some of you to death. You will be hated by all because of my name, but not a hair on your head will be destroyed. By your perseverance you will secure your lives."

1047   OUR LORD JESUS CHRIST THE KING — A

FIRST READING

Ezekiel 34:11–12, 15–17

Thus says the Lord GOD: I myself will look after and tend my sheep. As a shepherd tends his flock when he finds himself among his scattered sheep, so will I tend my sheep. I will rescue them from every place where they were scattered when it was cloudy and dark. I myself will pasture my sheep; I myself will give them rest, says the Lord GOD.

The lost I will seek out, the strayed I will bring back, the injured I will bind up, the sick I will heal, but the sleek and the strong I will destroy, shepherding them rightly.

As for you, my sheep, says the Lord GOD, I will judge between one sheep and another, between rams and goats.

RESPONSORIAL PSALM

Psalm 23:1–2, 2–3, 5–6

℟. The Lord   is my shep-herd;   there is noth-ing I shall want.

Music: John Schiavone, b. 1947, © 2001, OCP Publications.

▶ The LORD is my shepherd; I shall not want.
In verdant pastures he gives me repose. ℟.

▶ Beside restful waters he leads me; he refreshes my soul.
He guides me in right paths for his name's sake. ℟.

▶ You spread the table before me in the sight of my foes;
you anoint my head with oil; my cup overflows. ℟.

▶ Only goodness and kindness follow me all the days of my life;
and I shall dwell in the house of the LORD
for years to come. ℟.

SECOND READING

1 Corinthians 15:20–26, 28

Brothers and sisters: Christ has been raised from the dead, the firstfruits of those who have fallen asleep. For since death came through man, the resurrection of the dead came also through man. For just as in Adam all die, so too in Christ shall all be brought to life, but each one in proper order: Christ the firstfruits; then, at his coming, those who belong to Christ; then comes the end, when he hands over the kingdom to his God and Father, when he has destroyed every sovereignty and every authority and power. For he must reign until he has put all his enemies under his feet. The last enemy to be destroyed is death. When everything is subjected to him, then the Son himself will also be subjected to the one who subjected everything to him, so that God may be all in all.

GOSPEL ACCLAMATION

Mark 11:9, 10

℟. Al - le - lu - ia,   al - le - lu - ia,   al - le - lu - ia.

Music: John Schiavone, b. 1947, © 2001, OCP Publications.

▶ Blessed is he who comes in the name of the Lord!
  Blessed is the kingdom of our father David that is to come! ℟.

GOSPEL READING

Matthew 25:31–46

Jesus said to his disciples: "When the Son of Man comes in his glory, and all the angels with him, he will sit upon his glorious throne, and all the nations will be assembled before him. And he will separate them one from another, as a shepherd separates the sheep from the goats. He will place the sheep on his right and the goats on his left. Then the king will say to those on his right, 'Come, you who are blessed by my Father. Inherit the kingdom prepared for you from the foundation of the world. For I was hungry and you gave me food, I was thirsty and you gave me drink, a stranger and you welcomed me, naked and you clothed me, ill and you cared for me, in prison and you visited me.' Then the righteous will answer him and say, 'Lord, when did we see you hungry and feed you, or thirsty and give you drink? When did we see you a stranger and welcome you, or naked and clothe you? When did we see you ill or in prison, and visit you?' And the king will say to them in reply, 'Amen, I say to you, whatever you did for one of the least brothers of mine, you did for me.' Then he will say to those on his left, 'Depart from me, you accursed, into the eternal fire prepared for the devil and his angels. For I was hungry and you gave me no food, I was thirsty and you gave me no drink, a stranger and you gave me no welcome, naked and you gave me no clothing, ill and in prison, and you did not care for me.' Then they will answer and say, 'Lord, when did we see you hungry or thirsty or a stranger or naked or ill or in prison, and not minister to your needs?' He will answer them, 'Amen, I say to you, what you did not do for one of these least ones, you did not do for me.' And these will go off to eternal punishment, but the righteous to eternal life."

1048 OUR LORD JESUS CHRIST THE KING — B

FIRST READING

Daniel 7:13–14

As the visions during the night
continued, I saw
  one like a Son of man coming,
    on the clouds of heaven;
  when he reached the Ancient One
  and was presented before him,
  the one like a Son of man received

dominion, glory, and kingship;
all peoples, nations, and languages
  serve him.
His dominion is an everlasting
  dominion
that shall not be taken away,
his kingship shall not be destroyed.

RESPONSORIAL PSALM

Psalm 93:1, 1–2, 5

℟. The Lord is king; he is robed in maj - es - ty.

Music: John Schiavone, b. 1947, © 2001, OCP Publications.

▶ The LORD is king, in splendor robed;
  robed is the LORD and girt about
  with strength. ℟.

▶ And he has made the world firm,
  not to be moved.
  Your throne stands firm from of old;
  from everlasting you are, O LORD. ℟.

▶ Your decrees are worthy of
  trust indeed;
  holiness befits your house,
  O LORD, for length of days. ℟.

SECOND READING

Revelation 1:5–8

Jesus Christ is the faithful witness, the
firstborn of the dead and ruler of the
kings of the earth. To him who loves
us and has freed us from our sins by
his blood, who has made us into a
kingdom, priests for his God and Father,
to him be glory and power forever and
ever. Amen.

  Behold, he is coming amid the clouds,

and every eye will see him,
  even those who pierced him.
All the peoples of the earth will
  lament him.
  Yes. Amen.

"I am the Alpha and the Omega," says
the Lord God, "the one who is and who
was and who is to come, the almighty."

GOSPEL ACCLAMATION

Mark 11:9, 10

℟. Al - le - lu - ia, al - le - lu - ia, al - le - lu - ia.

Music: John Schiavone, b. 1947, © 2001, OCP Publications.

▶ Blessed is he who comes in the name of the Lord!
  Blessed is the kingdom of our father David that is to come! ℟.

GOSPEL READING
John 18:33b–37

Pilate said to Jesus, "Are you the King of the Jews?" Jesus answered, "Do you say this on your own or have others told you about me?" Pilate answered, "I am not a Jew, am I? Your own nation and the chief priests handed you over to me. What have you done?" Jesus answered, "My kingdom does not belong to this world. If my kingdom did belong to this world, my attendants would be fighting to keep me from being handed over to the Jews. But as it is, my kingdom is not here." So Pilate said to him, "Then you are a king?" Jesus answered, "You say I am a king. For this I was born and for this I came into the world, to testify to the truth. Everyone who belongs to the truth listens to my voice."

OUR LORD JESUS CHRIST THE KING — C   **1049**

FIRST READING
2 Samuel 5:1–3

In those days, all the tribes of Israel came to David in Hebron and said: "Here we are, your bone and your flesh. In days past, when Saul was our king, it was you who led the Israelites out and brought them back. And the LORD said to you, 'You shall shepherd my people Israel and shall be commander of Israel.'" When all the elders of Israel came to David in Hebron, King David made an agreement with them there before the LORD, and they anointed him king of Israel.

RESPONSORIAL PSALM
Psalm 122:1–2, 3–4, 4–5

℟. **Let us go re - joic - ing to the house of the Lord.**

Music: John Schiavone, b. 1947, © 2001, OCP Publications.

▸ I rejoiced because they said to me, "We will go up to the house of the LORD." And now we have set foot within your gates, O Jerusalem. ℟.

▸ Jerusalem, built as a city with compact unity. To it the tribes go up, the tribes of the LORD. ℟.

▸ According to the decree for Israel, to give thanks to the name of the LORD. In it are set up judgment seats, seats for the house of David. ℟.

SECOND READING
Colossians 1:12–20

Brothers and sisters: Let us give thanks to the Father, who has made you fit to share in the inheritance of the holy ones in light. He delivered us from the power of darkness and transferred us to the kingdom of his beloved Son, in whom we have redemption, the forgiveness of sins.

He is the image of the invisible God, the firstborn of all creation. For in him were created all things in heaven and on earth,

the visible and the invisible,
whether thrones or dominions or
principalities or powers;
all things were created through him
and for him.
He is before all things,
and in him all things hold together.
He is the head of the body, the church.
He is the beginning, the firstborn
from the dead,

that in all things he himself might
be preeminent.
For in him all the fullness was pleased
to dwell,
and through him to reconcile all
things for him,
making peace by the blood of
his cross
through him, whether those on
earth or those in heaven.

GOSPEL ACCLAMATION

Mark 11:9, 10

℟. Al - le - lu - ia,   al - le - lu - ia,   al - le - lu - ia.

Music: John Schiavone, b. 1947, © 2001, OCP Publications.

▶ Blessed is he who comes in the name of the Lord!
Blessed is the kingdom of our father David that is to come! ℟.

GOSPEL READING

Luke 23:35–43

The rulers sneered at Jesus and said, "He saved others, let him save himself if he is the chosen one, the Christ of God." Even the soldiers jeered at him. As they approached to offer him wine they called out, "If you are King of the Jews, save yourself." Above him there was an inscription that read, "This is the King of the Jews."

Now one of the criminals hanging there reviled Jesus, saying, "Are you not the Christ? Save yourself and us." The other, however, rebuking him, said in reply, "Have you no fear of God, for you are subject to the same condemnation? And indeed, we have been condemned justly, for the sentence we received corresponds to our crimes, but this man has done nothing criminal." Then he said, "Jesus, remember me when you come into your kingdom." He replied to him, "Amen, I say to you, today you will be with me in Paradise."

1050   THANKSGIVING DAY

Other options for the readings are found in Volume IV of the Lectionary for Mass.

FIRST READING

Sirach 50:22–24

And now, bless the God of all,
who has done wondrous things
on earth;
Who fosters people's growth from their
mother's womb,
and fashions them according to
his will!

May he grant you joy of heart
and may peace abide among you;
May his goodness toward us endure
in Israel
to deliver us in our days.

RESPONSORIAL PSALM

Psalm 113:1–2, 3–4, 5–6, 7–8

℟. **Bless'd be the name of the Lord for ev - er.**

Music: John Schiavone, b. 1947, © 2001, OCP Publications.

Or: **Alleluia.**

▸ Praise, you servants of the LORD,
  praise the name of the LORD.
Blessed be the name of the LORD
  both now and forever. ℟.

▸ From the rising to the setting of the sun
  is the name of the LORD to
  be praised.
High above all nations is the LORD;
  above the heavens is his glory. ℟.

▸ Who is like the LORD, our God, who is
  enthroned on high
  and looks upon the heavens and the
  earth below? ℟.

▸ He raises up the lowly from the dust;
  from the dunghill he lifts up
  the poor,
To seat them with princes,
  with the princes of his own people. ℟.

SECOND READING

1 Corinthians 1:3–9

Brothers and sisters: Grace to you and peace from God our Father and the Lord Jesus Christ.

I give thanks to my God always on your account for the grace of God bestowed on you in Christ Jesus, that in him you were enriched in every way, with all discourse and all knowledge, as the testimony to Christ was confirmed among you, so that you are not lacking in any spiritual gift as you wait for the revelation of our Lord Jesus Christ. He will keep you firm to the end, irreproachable on the day of our Lord Jesus Christ. God is faithful, and by him you were called to fellowship with his Son, Jesus Christ our Lord.

GOSPEL ACCLAMATION

1 Thessalonians 5:18

℟. **Al - le - lu - ia, al - le - lu - ia, al - le - lu - ia.**

Music: John Schiavone, b. 1947, © 2001, OCP Publications.

▸ In all circumstances, give thanks,
  for this is the will of God for you in Christ Jesus. ℟.

GOSPEL READING

Luke 17:11–19

As Jesus continued his journey to Jerusalem, he traveled through Samaria and Galilee. As he was entering a village, ten persons with leprosy met him. They stood at a distance from him and raised their voices, saying, "Jesus, Master! Have pity on us!" And when he saw them, he said, "Go show yourselves to the priests." As they were going they were cleansed. And one of them, realizing he had been healed, returned, glorifying God in a loud voice; and he fell at the feet of Jesus and thanked him. He was a Samaritan. Jesus said in reply, "Ten were cleansed, were they not? Where are the other nine? Has none but this foreigner returned to give thanks to God?" Then he said to him, "Stand up and go; your faith has saved you."

SOLEMNITIES AND FEASTS
OF THE LORD AND THE SAINTS

1051   FEBRUARY 2 — PRESENTATION OF THE LORD

FIRST FORM: PROCESSION

The people gather in a chapel or other suitable place outside the church where the Mass will be celebrated. They carry unlighted candles. While the candles are being lighted, an appropriate hymn is sung (for music see #506, 661–667).

The priest greets the people as usual, and after a short introduction blesses the candles.

He sprinkles the candles in silence. The priest then takes the candle prepared for him, and the procession to the church begins. During the procession, an appropriate hymn is sung (for music see #123, 124, 507).

When the priest reaches the altar he venerates it, and may incense it. Then he goes to the chair. After the Gloria, he continues with the opening prayer and Mass proceeds as usual.

SECOND FORM: SOLEMN ENTRANCE

The people, carrying unlighted candles, assemble in the church. The priest is accompanied by his ministers and by a representative group of the faithful. They go to a suitable place (either in front of the door or in the church itself) where most of the assembly can easily take part. Then the candles are lighted and the ceremony continues as described above.

FIRST READING   *Malachi 3:1–4*

Thus says the Lord GOD:
Lo, I am sending my messenger
  to prepare the way before me;
And suddenly there will come to
    the temple
  the LORD whom you seek,
And the messenger of the covenant
  whom you desire.
  Yes, he is coming, says the LORD
  of hosts.
But who will endure the day of
  his coming?
And who can stand when he appears?

For he is like the refiner's fire,
  or like the fuller's lye.
He will sit refining and purifying silver,
  and he will purify the sons of Levi,
Refining them like gold or like silver
  that they may offer due sacrifice to
  the LORD.
Then the sacrifice of Judah
  and Jerusalem
will please the LORD,
  as in the days of old, as in years
  gone by.

RESPONSORIAL PSALM   *Psalm 24:7, 8, 9, 10*

℟. Who is this king of glo - ry? It is the Lord!

Music: John Schiavone, b. 1947, © 2001, OCP Publications.

▶ Lift up, O gates, your lintels;
    reach up, you ancient portals,
    that the king of glory may come in! ℟.

▶ Who is this king of glory?
    The LORD, strong and mighty,
    the LORD, mighty in battle. ℟.

▶ Lift up, O gates, your lintels;
    reach up, you ancient portals,
    that the king of glory may come in! ℟.

▶ Who is this king of glory?
    The LORD of hosts; he is the king
    of glory. ℟.

SECOND READING
Hebrews 2:14–18

Since the children share in blood and flesh, Jesus likewise shared in them, that through death he might destroy the one who has the power of death, that is, the Devil, and free those who through fear of death had been subject to slavery all their life. Surely he did not help angels but rather the descendants of Abraham; therefore, he had to become like his brothers and sisters in every way, that he might be a merciful and faithful high priest before God to expiate the sins of the people. Because he himself was tested through what he suffered, he is able to help those who are being tested.

GOSPEL ACCLAMATION
Luke 2:32

℟. Al - le - lu - ia, al - le - lu - ia, al - le - lu - ia.

Music: John Schiavone, b. 1947, © 2001, OCP Publications.

▶ A light of revelation to the Gentiles
    and glory for your people Israel. ℟.

GOSPEL READING
Luke 2:22–40 or 2:22–32

(Include bracketed text for Long Form)

When the days were completed for their purification according to the law of Moses, Mary and Joseph took Jesus up to Jerusalem to present him to the Lord, just as it is written in the law of the Lord, *Every male that opens the womb shall be consecrated to the Lord,* and to offer the sacrifice of *a pair of turtledoves or two young pigeons,* in accordance with the dictate in the law of the Lord.

    Now there was a man in Jerusalem whose name was Simeon. This man was righteous and devout, awaiting the consolation of Israel, and the Holy Spirit was upon him. It had been revealed to him by the Holy Spirit that he should not see death before he had seen the Christ of the Lord. He came in the Spirit into the temple; and when the parents brought in the child Jesus to perform the custom of the law in regard to him, he took him into his arms and blessed God, saying:
    "Now, Master, you may let your servant go
    in peace, according to your word,
for my eyes have seen your salvation,
    which you prepared in sight of all the peoples,
a light for revelation to the Gentiles,
    and glory for your people Israel."
    [The child's father and mother were amazed at what was said about him; and Simeon blessed them and said to Mary his mother, "Behold, this child is destined for the fall and rise of many in Israel, and to be a sign that will be contradicted — and you yourself a sword will pierce — so that the thoughts

of many hearts may be revealed." There was also a prophetess, Anna, the daughter of Phanuel, of the tribe of Asher. She was advanced in years, having lived seven years with her husband after her marriage, and then as a widow until she was eighty-four. She never left the temple, but worshiped night and day with fasting and prayer. And coming forward at that very time, she gave thanks to God and spoke about the child to all who were awaiting the redemption of Jerusalem.

When they had fulfilled all the prescriptions of the law of the Lord, they returned to Galilee, to their own town of Nazareth. The child grew and became strong, filled with wisdom; and the favor of God was upon him.]

1052   MARCH 19 — SAINT JOSEPH, HUSBAND OF THE BLESSED VIRGIN MARY

FIRST READING   *2 Samuel 7:4–5a, 12–14a, 16*

The LORD spoke to Nathan and said: "Go, tell my servant David, 'When your time comes and you rest with your ancestors, I will raise up your heir after you, sprung from your loins, and I will make his kingdom firm. It is he who shall build a house for my name. And I will make his royal throne firm forever. I will be a father to him, and he shall be a son to me. Your house and your kingdom shall endure forever before me; your throne shall stand firm forever.'"

RESPONSORIAL PSALM   *Psalm 89:2–3, 4–5, 27&29*

℟. The son of Da - vid will live for ev - er.

Music: John Schiavone, b. 1947, © 2001, OCP Publications.

▶ The promises of the LORD I will
     sing forever,
   through all generations my mouth
     shall proclaim your faithfulness,
For you have said, "My kindness is
     established forever";
   in heaven you have confirmed your
     faithfulness. ℟.

▶ "I have made a covenant with my
     chosen one;
   I have sworn to David my servant:

forever will I confirm your posterity
   and establish your throne for all
     generations." ℟.

▶ "He shall say of me, 'You are
     my father,
   my God, the Rock, my savior.'
Forever I will maintain my kindness
     toward him,
   and my covenant with him
     stands firm." ℟.

SECOND READING   *Romans 4:13, 16–18, 22*

Brothers and sisters: It was not through the law that the promise was made to Abraham and his descendants that he would inherit the world, but through the righteousness that comes from faith. For this reason, it depends on faith, so that it may be a gift, and the promise may be guaranteed to all his descendants, not to those who only adhere to the law but to those who follow the faith of Abraham, who is the father of all of us, as it is written, *I have made you father of many nations.* He is our father in the sight of God, in whom he believed, who gives life to the dead and calls into being what does not exist.

He believed, hoping against hope, that he would become *the father of many nations,* according to what was said, *Thus shall your descendants be.* That is why *it was credited to him as righteousness.*

GOSPEL ACCLAMATION

Psalm 84:5

℟. **Praise to you, Lord Je-sus Christ, King of end-less glo-ry!**

Music: John Schiavone, b. 1947, © 2001, OCP Publications.

OR (when transferred to the Easter Season)

℟. **Al-le-lu-ia, al-le-lu-ia, al-le-lu-ia.**

Music: John Schiavone, b. 1947, © 2001, OCP Publications.

▸ Blessed are those who dwell in your house, O Lord;
they never cease to praise you. ℟.

GOSPEL READING

Matthew 1:16, 18–21, 24a

Jacob was the father of Joseph, the husband of Mary. Of her was born Jesus who is called the Christ.

Now this is how the birth of Jesus Christ came about. When his mother Mary was betrothed to Joseph, but before they lived together, she was found with child through the Holy Spirit. Joseph her husband, since he was a righteous man, yet unwilling to expose her to shame, decided to divorce her quietly. Such was his

intention when, behold, the angel of the Lord appeared to him in a dream and said, "Joseph, son of David, do not be afraid to take Mary your wife into your home. For it is through the Holy Spirit that this child has been conceived in her. She will bear a son and you are to name him Jesus, because he will save his people from their sins." When Joseph awoke, he did as the angel of the Lord had commanded him and took his wife into his home.

OR

GOSPEL READING

Luke 2:41–51a

Each year Jesus' parents went to Jerusalem for the feast of Passover, and when he was twelve years old, they went up according to festival custom. After they had completed its days, as they were returning, the boy Jesus remained behind in Jerusalem, but his parents did not know it. Thinking that he was in the caravan, they journeyed for a day and

looked for him among their relatives and acquaintances, but not finding him, they returned to Jerusalem to look for him. After three days they found him in the temple, sitting in the midst of the teachers, listening to them and asking them questions, and all who heard him were astounded at his understanding and his answers. When his parents saw him, they were astonished, and his mother said to him, "Son, why have you done this to us? Your father and I have been looking for you with great anxiety." And he said to them, "Why were you looking for me? Did you not know that I must be in my Father's house?" But they did not understand what he said to them. He went down with them and came to Nazareth, and was obedient to them.

1053 MARCH 25 — ANNUNCIATION OF THE LORD

FIRST READING

Isaiah 7:10–14; 8:10

The LORD spoke to Ahaz, saying: Ask for a sign from the LORD, your God; let it be deep as the netherworld, or high as the sky! But Ahaz answered, "I will not ask! I will not tempt the LORD!" Then Isaiah said: Listen, O house of David! Is it not enough for you to weary people, must you also weary my God? Therefore the Lord himself will give you this sign: the virgin shall be with child, and bear a son, and shall name him Emmanuel, which means "God is with us!"

RESPONSORIAL PSALM

Psalm 40:7–8a, 8b–9, 10, 11

℟. Here am I, Lord; I come to do your will.

Music: John Schiavone, b. 1947, © 2001, OCP Publications.

▸ Sacrifice or oblation you wished not, but ears open to obedience you gave me.
Holocausts and sin-offerings you sought not;
then said I, "Behold I come". ℟.

▸ "In the written scroll it is prescribed for me,
To do your will, O God, is my delight, and your law is within my heart!" ℟.

▸ I announced your justice in the vast assembly;
I did not restrain my lips, as you, O LORD, know. ℟.

▸ Your justice I kept not hid within my heart;
your faithfulness and your salvation I have spoken of;
I have made no secret of your kindness and your truth
in the vast assembly. ℟.

SECOND READING

Hebrews 10:4–10

Brothers and sisters: It is impossible that the blood of bulls and goats take away sins. For this reason, when Christ came into the world, he said:
"Sacrifice and offering you did not desire,
but a body you prepared for me;
in holocausts and sin offerings you took no delight.
Then I said, 'As is written of me in the scroll,
behold, I come to do your will, O God.'"
First he says, "Sacrifices and offerings, holocausts and sin offerings, you neither desired nor delighted in." These are offered according to the law. Then he says, "Behold, I come to do your will." He takes away the first to establish the second. By this "will," we have been consecrated through the offering of the Body of Jesus Christ once for all.

GOSPEL ACCLAMATION

John 1:14ab

℟. Praise to you, Lord Je - sus Christ, King of end - less glo - ry!

Music: John Schiavone, b. 1947, © 2001, OCP Publications.

OR (when transferred to the Easter Season)

℟. Al - le - lu - ia, al - le - lu - ia, al - le - lu - ia.

Music: John Schiavone, b. 1947, © 2001, OCP Publications.

▶ The Word of God became flesh and made his dwelling among us;
and we saw his glory. ℟.

GOSPEL READING

Luke 1:26–38

The angel Gabriel was sent from God to a town of Galilee called Nazareth, to a virgin betrothed to a man named Joseph, of the house of David, and the virgin's name was Mary. And coming to her, he said, "Hail, full of grace! The Lord is with you." But she was greatly troubled at what was said and pondered what sort of greeting this might be. Then the angel said to her, "Do not be afraid, Mary, for you have found favor with God. Behold, you will conceive in your womb and bear a son, and you shall name him Jesus. He will be great and will be called Son of the Most High, and the Lord God will give him the throne of David his father, and he will rule over the house of Jacob forever, and of his kingdom there will be no end." But Mary said to the angel, "How can this be, since I have no relations with a man?" And the angel said to her in reply, "The Holy Spirit will come upon you, and the power of the Most High will overshadow you. Therefore the child to be born will be called holy, the Son of God. And behold, Elizabeth, your relative, has also conceived a son in her old age, and this is the sixth month for her who was called barren; for nothing will be impossible for God." Mary said, "Behold, I am the handmaid of the Lord. May it be done to me according to your word." Then the angel departed from her.

JUNE 23 — NATIVITY OF SAINT JOHN THE BAPTIST: 1054
VIGIL MASS

FIRST READING

Jeremiah 1:4–10

In the days of King Josiah, the word of the LORD came to me, saying:
    Before I formed you in the womb
        I knew you,
        before you were born I
            dedicated you,
        a prophet to the nations
            I appointed you.

"Ah, Lord GOD!" I said,
    "I know not how to speak; I am
        too young."
But the LORD answered me,
Say not, "I am too young."
    To whomever I send you,
        you shall go;

whatever I command you,
you shall speak.
Have no fear before them,
because I am with you to deliver
you, says the LORD.

Then the LORD extended his hand and
touched my mouth, saying,

See, I place my words in your mouth!
This day I set you
over nations and over kingdoms,
to root up and to tear down,
to destroy and to demolish,
to build and to plant.

RESPONSORIAL PSALM

Psalm 71:1–2, 3–4a, 5–6ab, 15ab & 17

℟. **Since my moth - er's womb, you have been my strength.**

Music: John Schiavone, b. 1947, © 2001, OCP Publications.

▶ In you, O LORD, I take refuge;
let me never be put to shame.
In your justice rescue me, and
deliver me;
incline your ear to me, and save me. ℟.

▶ Be my rock of refuge,
a stronghold to give me safety,
for you are my rock and my fortress.
O my God, rescue me from the hand
of the wicked. ℟.

▶ For you are my hope, O LORD;
my trust, O LORD, from my youth.
On you I depend from birth;
from my mother's womb you are
my strength. ℟.

▶ My mouth shall declare your justice,
day by day your salvation.
O God, you have taught me from
my youth,
and till the present I proclaim your
wondrous deeds. ℟.

SECOND READING

1 Peter 1:8–12

Beloved: Although you have not seen
Jesus Christ you love him; even though
you do not see him now yet believe in
him, you rejoice with an indescribable
and glorious joy, as you attain the goal
of your faith, the salvation of your souls.
Concerning this salvation, prophets
who prophesied about the grace
that was to be yours searched and
investigated it, investigating the time
and circumstances that the Spirit of

Christ within them indicated when he
testified in advance to the sufferings
destined for Christ and the glories to
follow them. It was revealed to them
that they were serving not themselves
but you with regard to the things that
have now been announced to you by
those who preached the Good News to
you through the Holy Spirit sent from
heaven, things into which angels longed
to look.

GOSPEL ACCLAMATION

cf. John 1:7; Luke 1:17

℟. **Al - le - lu - ia, al - le - lu - ia, al - le - lu - ia.**

Music: John Schiavone, b. 1947, © 2001, OCP Publications.

▶ He came to testify to the light,
to prepare a people fit for the Lord. ℟.

GOSPEL READING   *Luke 1:5–17*

In the days of Herod, King of Judea, there was a priest named Zechariah of the priestly division of Abijah; his wife was from the daughters of Aaron, and her name was Elizabeth. Both were righteous in the eyes of God, observing all the commandments and ordinances of the Lord blamelessly. But they had no child, because Elizabeth was barren and both were advanced in years. Once when he was serving as priest in his division's turn before God, according to the practice of the priestly service, he was chosen by lot to enter the sanctuary of the Lord to burn incense. Then, when the whole assembly of the people was praying outside at the hour of the incense offering, the angel of the Lord appeared to him, standing at the right of the altar of incense. Zechariah was troubled by what he saw, and fear came upon him. But the angel said to him, "Do not be afraid, Zechariah, because your prayer has been heard. Your wife Elizabeth will bear you a son, and you shall name him John. And you will have joy and gladness, and many will rejoice at his birth, for he will be great in the sight of the Lord. John will drink neither wine nor strong drink. He will be filled with the Holy Spirit even from his mother's womb, and he will turn many of the children of Israel to the Lord their God. He will go before him in the spirit and power of Elijah to turn their hearts toward their children and the disobedient to the understanding of the righteous, to prepare a people fit for the Lord."

JUNE 24 — NATIVITY OF SAINT JOHN THE BAPTIST **1055**

FIRST READING   *Isaiah 49:1–6*

Hear me, O coastlands,
  listen, O distant peoples.
The LORD called me from birth,
  from my mother's womb he gave me
    my name.
He made of me a sharp-edged sword
  and concealed me in the shadow of
    his arm.
He made me a polished arrow,
  in his quiver he hid me.
You are my servant, he said to me,
  Israel, through whom I show
    my glory.

Though I thought I had toiled in vain,
  and for nothing, uselessly, spent
    my strength,

yet my reward is with the LORD,
  my recompense is with my God.
For now the LORD has spoken
  who formed me as his servant from
    the womb,
that Jacob may be brought back to him
  and Israel gathered to him;
and I am made glorious in the sight of
    the LORD,
  and my God is now my strength!
It is too little, he says, for you to be
    my servant,
  to raise up the tribes of Jacob,
  and restore the survivors of Israel;
I will make you a light to the nations,
  that my salvation may reach to the
    ends of the earth.

RESPONSORIAL PSALM

Psalm 139:1–3b, 13–14ab, 14c–15

I praise you for I am won-der-ful-ly made.

Music: John Schiavone, b. 1947, © 2001, OCP Publications.

▶ O LORD, you have probed me and you
  know me;
  you know when I sit and when
    I stand;
  you understand my thoughts
    from afar.
My journeys and my rest you scrutinize,
  with all my ways you are familiar. ℟.

▶ Truly you have formed my
    inmost being;
  you knit me in my mother's womb.

I give you thanks that I am fearfully,
  wonderfully made;
  wonderful are your works. ℟.

▶ My soul also you knew full well;
  nor was my frame unknown to you
  when I was made in secret,
    when I was fashioned in the depths
    of the earth. ℟.

SECOND READING

Acts of the Apostles 13:22–26

In those days, Paul said: "God raised up David as king; of him God testified, *I have found David, son of Jesse, a man after my own heart; he will carry out my every wish.* From this man's descendants God, according to his promise, has brought to Israel a savior, Jesus. John heralded his coming by proclaiming a baptism of repentance to all the people of Israel; and as John was completing his course, he would say, 'What do you suppose that I am? I am not he. Behold, one is coming after me; I am not worthy to unfasten the sandals of his feet.'

"My brothers, sons of the family of Abraham, and those others among you who are God-fearing, to us this word of salvation has been sent."

GOSPEL ACCLAMATION

cf. Luke 1:76

℟. Al-le-lu-ia, al-le-lu-ia, al-le-lu - ia.

Music: John Schiavone, b. 1947, © 2001, OCP Publications.

▶ You, child, will be called prophet of the Most High,
  for you will go before the Lord to prepare his way. ℟.

GOSPEL READING

Luke 1:57–66, 80

When the time arrived for Elizabeth to have her child she gave birth to a son. Her neighbors and relatives heard that the Lord had shown his great mercy toward her, and they rejoiced with her. When they came on the eighth day to circumcise the child, they were going to call him Zechariah after his father, but his mother said in reply, "No. He will be called John." But they answered her, "There is no one among your relatives who has this name." So they made signs, asking his father what he wished him to be called. He asked for a tablet and wrote, "John is his name," and all were amazed. Immediately his mouth was opened, his tongue freed, and he spoke blessing God. Then fear came upon all their neighbors, and all these matters were discussed throughout the hill country of Judea. All who heard these things took them to heart, saying, "What, then, will this child be?" For surely the hand of the Lord was with him.

The child grew and became strong in spirit, and he was in the desert until the day of his manifestation to Israel.

JUNE 28 — SAINTS PETER AND PAUL, APOSTLES: **1056**
VIGIL MASS

For a votive Mass of Saint Peter the readings are taken from the Feast of the Chair of Saint Peter the Apostle, February 22, Lectionary for Mass n. 535.

For a votive Mass of Saint Paul the readings are taken from the Feast of the Conversion of Saint Paul the Apostle, Lectionary for Mass n. 519.

FIRST READING   *Acts of the Apostles 3:1–10*

Peter and John were going up to the temple area for the three o'clock hour of prayer. And a man crippled from birth was carried and placed at the gate of the temple called "the Beautiful Gate" every day to beg for alms from the people who entered the temple. When he saw Peter and John about to go into the temple, he asked for alms. But Peter looked intently at him, as did John, and said, "Look at us." He paid attention to them, expecting to receive something from them. Peter said, "I have neither silver nor gold, but what I do have I give you: in the name of Jesus Christ the Nazorean, rise and walk." Then Peter took him by the right hand and raised him up, and immediately his feet and ankles grew strong. He leaped up, stood, and walked around, and went into the temple with them, walking and jumping and praising God. When all the people saw the man walking and praising God, they recognized him as the one who used to sit begging at the Beautiful Gate of the temple, and they were filled with amazement and astonishment at what had happened to him.

RESPONSORIAL PSALM   *Psalm 19:2–3, 4–5*

℟. Their mes - sage goes out through all the earth.

Music: John Schiavone, b. 1947, © 2001, OCP Publications.

▶ The heavens declare the glory of God;
   and the firmament proclaims
      his handiwork.
Day pours out the word to day;
   and night to night imparts
      knowledge. ℟.

▶ Not a word nor a discourse
   whose voice is not heard;
through all the earth their
   voice resounds,
   and to the ends of the world,
      their message. ℟.

SECOND READING

Galatians 1:11–20

I want you to know, brothers and sisters, that the gospel preached by me is not of human origin. For I did not receive it from a human being, nor was I taught it, but it came through a revelation of Jesus Christ.

For you heard of my former way of life in Judaism, how I persecuted the church of God beyond measure and tried to destroy it, and progressed in Judaism beyond many of my contemporaries among my race, since I was even more a zealot for my ancestral traditions. But when God, who from my mother's womb had set me apart and called me through his grace, was pleased to reveal his Son to me, so that I might proclaim him to the Gentiles, I did not immediately consult flesh and blood, nor did I go up to Jerusalem to those who were apostles before me; rather, I went into Arabia and then returned to Damascus.

Then after three years I went up to Jerusalem to confer with Cephas and remained with him for fifteen days. But I did not see any other of the Apostles, only James the brother of the Lord. — As to what I am writing to you, behold, before God, I am not lying.

GOSPEL ACCLAMATION

John 21:17

℟. Al - le - lu - ia, al - le - lu - ia, al - le - lu - ia.

Music: John Schiavone, b. 1947, © 2001, OCP Publications.

▶ Lord, you know everything;
you know that I love you. ℟.

GOSPEL READING

John 21:15–19

Jesus had revealed himself to his disciples and, when they had finished breakfast, said to Simon Peter, "Simon, son of John, do you love me more than these?" Simon Peter answered him, "Yes, Lord, you know that I love you." Jesus said to him, "Feed my lambs." He then said to Simon Peter a second time, "Simon, son of John, do you love me?" Simon Peter answered him, "Yes, Lord, you know that I love you." He said to him, "Tend my sheep." He said to him the third time, "Simon, son of John, do you love me?" Peter was distressed that Jesus had said to him a third time, "Do you love me?" and he said to him, "Lord, you know everything; you know that I love you." Jesus said to him, "Feed my sheep. Amen, amen, I say to you, when you were younger, you used to dress yourself and go where you wanted; but when you grow old, you will stretch out your hands, and someone else will dress you and lead you where you do not want to go." He said this signifying by what kind of death he would glorify God. And when he had said this, he said to him, "Follow me."

JUNE 29 — SAINTS PETER AND PAUL, APOSTLES   **1057**

FIRST READING   *Acts of the Apostles 12:1–11*

In those days, King Herod laid hands upon some members of the church to harm them. He had James, the brother of John, killed by the sword, and when he saw that this was pleasing to the Jews he proceeded to arrest Peter also. — It was the feast of Unleavened Bread. — He had him taken into custody and put in prison under the guard of four squads of four soldiers each. He intended to bring him before the people after Passover. Peter thus was being kept in prison, but prayer by the church was fervently being made to God on his behalf.

On the very night before Herod was to bring him to trial, Peter, secured by double chains, was sleeping between two soldiers, while outside the door guards kept watch on the prison. Suddenly the angel of the Lord stood by him, and a light shone in the cell. He tapped Peter on the side and awakened him, saying, "Get up quickly." The chains fell from his wrists. The angel said to him, "Put on your belt and your sandals." He did so. Then he said to him, "Put on your cloak and follow me." So he followed him out, not realizing that what was happening through the angel was real; he thought he was seeing a vision. They passed the first guard, then the second, and came to the iron gate leading out to the city, which opened for them by itself. They emerged and made their way down an alley, and suddenly the angel left him. Then Peter recovered his senses and said, "Now I know for certain that the Lord sent his angel and rescued me from the hand of Herod and from all that the Jewish people had been expecting."

RESPONSORIAL PSALM   *Psalm 34:2–3, 4–5, 6–7, 8–9*

℟. The an-gel of the Lord will res-cue those who fear him.

Music: John Schiavone, b. 1947, © 2001, OCP Publications.

▶ I will bless the LORD at all times;
 his praise shall be ever in my mouth.
Let my soul glory in the LORD;
 the lowly will hear me and be glad. ℟.

▶ Glorify the LORD with me,
 let us together extol his name.
I sought the LORD, and he answered me
 and delivered me from all my fears. ℟.

▶ Look to him that you may be radiant
 with joy,
 and your faces may not blush
 with shame.

When the poor one called out, the
 LORD heard,
 and from all his distress he
 saved him. ℟.

▶ The angel of the LORD encamps
 around those who fear him, and
 delivers them.
Taste and see how good the LORD is;
 blessed the man who takes refuge
 in him. ℟.

SECOND READING
2 Timothy 4:6–8, 17–18

I, Paul, am already being poured out like a libation, and the time of my departure is at hand. I have competed well; I have finished the race; I have kept the faith. From now on the crown of righteousness awaits me, which the Lord, the just judge, will award to me on that day, and not only to me, but to all who have longed for his appearance.

The Lord stood by me and gave me strength, so that through me the proclamation might be completed and all the Gentiles might hear it. And I was rescued from the lion's mouth. The Lord will rescue me from every evil threat and will bring me safe to his heavenly kingdom. To him be glory forever and ever. Amen.

GOSPEL ACCLAMATION
Matthew 16:18

℟. Al - le - lu - ia, al - le - lu - ia, al - le - lu - ia.

Music: John Schiavone, b. 1947, © 2001, OCP Publications.

▶ You are Peter and upon this rock I will build my church, and the gates of the netherworld shall not prevail against it. ℟.

GOSPEL READING
Matthew 16:13–19

When Jesus went into the region of Caesarea Philippi he asked his disciples, "Who do people say that the Son of Man is?" They replied, "Some say John the Baptist, others Elijah, still others Jeremiah or one of the prophets." He said to them, "But who do you say that I am?" Simon Peter said in reply, "You are the Christ, the Son of the living God." Jesus said to him in reply, "Blessed are you, Simon son of Jonah. For flesh and

blood has not revealed this to you, but my heavenly Father. And so I say to you, you are Peter, and upon this rock I will build my Church, and the gates of the netherworld shall not prevail against it. I will give you the keys to the Kingdom of heaven. Whatever you bind on earth shall be bound in heaven, and whatever you loose on earth shall be loosed in heaven."

1058   AUGUST 6 — TRANSFIGURATION OF THE LORD

FIRST READING
Daniel 7:9–10, 13–14

As I watched:
    Thrones were set up
      and the Ancient One took his throne.
    His clothing was bright as snow,
      and the hair on his head as white
        as wool;
    His throne was flames of fire,
      with wheels of burning fire.
    A surging stream of fire
      flowed out from where he sat;
    Thousands upon thousands were

      ministering to him,
      and myriads upon myriads
        attended him.
    The court was convened, and the
    books were opened. As the visions
    during the night continued, I saw
    One like a son of man coming,
      on the clouds of heaven;
    When he reached the Ancient One
      and was presented before him,
    The one like a Son of man received

dominion, glory, and kingship;
all peoples, nations, and languages serve him.
His dominion is an everlasting dominion

that shall not be taken away,
his kingship shall not be destroyed.

RESPONSORIAL PSALM

Psalm 97:1–2, 5–6, 9

℞. The Lord is king, the Most High o - ver all the earth.

Music: John Schiavone, b. 1947, © 2001, OCP Publications.

▶ The LORD is king; let the earth rejoice;
let the many islands be glad.
Clouds and darkness are round about him,
justice and judgment are the foundation of his throne. ℞.

▶ The mountains melt like wax before the LORD,
before the LORD of all the earth.
The heavens proclaim his justice;
and all peoples see his glory. ℞.

▶ Because you, O LORD, are the Most High over all the earth,
exalted far above all gods. ℞.

SECOND READING

2 Peter 1:16–19

Beloved: We did not follow cleverly devised myths when we made known to you the power and coming of our Lord Jesus Christ, but we had been eyewitnesses of his majesty. For he received honor and glory from God the Father when that unique declaration came to him from the majestic glory, "This is my Son, my beloved, with whom I am well pleased." We ourselves heard this voice come from heaven while we were with him on the holy mountain. Moreover, we possess the prophetic message that is altogether reliable. You will do well to be attentive to it, as to a lamp shining in a dark place, until day dawns and the morning star rises in your hearts.

GOSPEL ACCLAMATION

Matthew 17:5c

℞. Al - le - lu - ia, al - le - lu - ia, al - le - lu - ia.

Music: John Schiavone, b. 1947, © 2001, OCP Publications.

▶ This is my beloved Son, with whom I am well pleased;
listen to him. ℞.

GOSPEL READING — A

Matthew 17:1–9

Jesus took Peter, James, and his brother, John, and led them up a high mountain by themselves. And he was transfigured before them; his face shone like the sun and his clothes became white as light. And behold, Moses and Elijah appeared to them, conversing with him. Then Peter said to Jesus in reply, "Lord, it is good that we are here. If you wish, I will make three tents here, one for you, one for Moses, and one for Elijah." While he was still speaking, behold, a bright cloud cast a shadow over them, then from the cloud came a voice that said, "This is my beloved Son, with whom I am well pleased; listen to him." When the disciples heard this, they fell prostrate and were very much afraid. But Jesus came and touched them,

saying, "Rise, and do not be afraid." And when the disciples raised their eyes, they saw no one else but Jesus alone.

As they were coming down from the mountain, Jesus charged them, "Do not tell the vision to anyone until the Son of Man has been raised from the dead."

GOSPEL READING — B

Mark 9:2–10

Jesus took Peter, James, and his brother John, and led them up a high mountain apart by themselves. And he was transfigured before them, and his clothes became dazzling white, such as no fuller on earth could bleach them. Then Elijah appeared to them along with Moses, and they were conversing with Jesus. Then Peter said to Jesus in reply, "Rabbi, it is good that we are here! Let us make three tents: one for you, one for Moses, and one for Elijah." He hardly knew what to say, they were

so terrified. Then a cloud came, casting a shadow over them; from the cloud came a voice, "This is my beloved Son. Listen to him." Suddenly, looking around, they no longer saw anyone but Jesus alone with them.

As they were coming down from the mountain, he charged them not to relate what they had seen to anyone, except when the Son of Man had risen from the dead. So they kept the matter to themselves, questioning what rising from the dead meant.

GOSPEL READING — C

Luke 9:28b–36

Jesus took Peter, John, and James and went up a mountain to pray. While he was praying his face changed in appearance and his clothing became dazzling white. And behold, two men were conversing with him, Moses and Elijah, who appeared in glory and spoke of his exodus that he was going to accomplish in Jerusalem. Peter and his companions had been overcome by sleep, but becoming fully awake, they saw his glory and the two men standing with him. As they were about to part from him, Peter said to Jesus, "Master, it

is good that we are here; let us make three tents, one for you, one for Moses, and one for Elijah." But he did not know what he was saying. While he was still speaking, a cloud came and cast a shadow over them, and they became frightened when they entered the cloud. Then from the cloud came a voice that said, "This is my chosen Son; listen to him." After the voice had spoken, Jesus was found alone. They fell silent and did not at that time tell anyone what they had seen.

1059   AUGUST 14 — ASSUMPTION OF THE BLESSED VIRGIN MARY: VIGIL MASS

FIRST READING

1 Chronicles 15:3–4, 15–16; 16:1–2

David assembled all Israel in Jerusalem to bring the ark of the LORD to the place that he had prepared for it. David also called together the sons of Aaron and the Levites.

The Levites bore the ark of God on their shoulders with poles, as Moses had ordained according to the word of the LORD.

David commanded the chiefs of the

Levites to appoint their kinsmen as chanters, to play on musical instruments, harps, lyres, and cymbals, to make a loud sound of rejoicing.

They brought in the ark of God and set it within the tent which David had pitched for it. Then they offered up burnt offerings and peace offerings to God. When David had finished offering up the burnt offerings and peace offerings, he blessed the people in the name of the LORD.

RESPONSORIAL PSALM

Psalm 132:6–7, 9–10, 13–14

℟. Lord, go up to the place of your rest, you and the ark of your ho - li - ness.

Music: John Schiavone, b. 1947, © 2001, OCP Publications.

▶ Behold, we heard of it in Ephrathah;
  we found it in the fields of Jaar.
Let us enter into his dwelling,
  let us worship at his footstool. ℟.

▶ May your priests be clothed with justice;
  let your faithful ones shout merrily
    for joy.

For the sake of David your servant,
  reject not the plea of your
    anointed. ℟.

▶ For the LORD has chosen Zion;
  he prefers her for his dwelling.
"Zion is my resting place forever;
  in her will I dwell, for I prefer her." ℟.

SECOND READING

1 Corinthians 15:54b–57

Brothers and sisters: When that which is mortal clothes itself with immortality, then the word that is written shall come about:

Death is swallowed up in victory.
Where, O death, is your victory?
Where, O death, is your sting?

The sting of death is sin, and the power of sin is the law. But thanks be to God who gives us the victory through our Lord Jesus Christ.

GOSPEL ACCLAMATION

Luke 11:28

℟. Al - le - lu - ia, al - le - lu - ia, al - le - lu - ia.

Music: John Schiavone, b. 1947, © 2001, OCP Publications.

▶ Blessed are they who hear the word of God
  and observe it. ℟.

GOSPEL READING

Luke 11:27–28

While Jesus was speaking, a woman from the crowd called out and said to him, "Blessed is the womb that carried you and the breasts at which you nursed." He replied, "Rather, blessed are those who hear the word of God and observe it."

1060   AUGUST 15 — ASSUMPTION OF THE BLESSED VIRGIN MARY

FIRST READING

Revelation 11:19a; 12:1–6a, 10ab

God's temple in heaven was opened, and the ark of his covenant could be seen in the temple.

A great sign appeared in the sky, a woman clothed with the sun, with the moon under her feet, and on her head a crown of twelve stars. She was with child and wailed aloud in pain as she labored to give birth. Then another sign appeared in the sky; it was a huge red dragon, with seven heads and ten horns, and on its heads were seven diadems. Its tail swept away a third of the stars in the sky and hurled them down to the earth. Then the dragon stood before the woman about to give birth, to devour her child when she gave birth. She gave birth to a son, a male child, destined to rule all the nations with an iron rod. Her child was caught up to God and his throne. The woman herself fled into the desert where she had a place prepared by God.

Then I heard a loud voice in heaven say:

"Now have salvation and power come,
  and the kingdom of our God
  and the authority of his
    Anointed One."

RESPONSORIAL PSALM

Psalm 45:10, 11, 12, 16

℟. The queen stands at your right hand, ar - rayed in gold.

Music: John Schiavone, b. 1947, © 2001, OCP Publications.

▶ The queen takes her place at your
  right hand in gold of Ophir. ℟.

▶ Hear, O daughter, and see; turn
  your ear,
  forget your people and your
    father's house. ℟.

▶ So shall the king desire your beauty;
  for he is your lord. ℟.

▶ They are borne in with gladness
  and joy;
  they enter the palace of the king. ℟.

SECOND READING

1 Corinthians 15:20–27

Brothers and sisters: Christ has been raised from the dead, the firstfruits of those who have fallen asleep. For since death came through man, the resurrection of the dead came also through man. For just as in Adam all die, so too in Christ shall all be brought to life, but each one in proper order: Christ the firstfruits; then, at his coming, those who belong to Christ; then comes the end, when he hands over the Kingdom to his God and Father, when he has destroyed every sovereignty and every authority and power. For he must reign until he has put all his enemies under his feet. The last enemy to be destroyed is death, for "he subjected everything under his feet."

GOSPEL ACCLAMATION

℟. Al - le - lu - ia,   al - le - lu - ia,   al - le - lu - ia.

Music: John Schiavone, b. 1947, © 2001, OCP Publications.

▶ Mary is taken up to heaven;
a chorus of angels exults. ℟.

GOSPEL READING   *Luke 1:39–56*

Mary set out and traveled to the hill country in haste to a town of Judah, where she entered the house of Zechariah and greeted Elizabeth. When Elizabeth heard Mary's greeting, the infant leaped in her womb, and Elizabeth, filled with the Holy Spirit, cried out in a loud voice and said, "Blessed are you among women, and blessed is the fruit of your womb. And how does this happen to me, that the mother of my Lord should come to me? For at the moment the sound of your greeting reached my ears, the infant in my womb leaped for joy. Blessed are you who believed that what was spoken to you by the Lord would be fulfilled."
    And Mary said:
"My soul proclaims the greatness of
    the Lord;
    my spirit rejoices in God my Savior
    for he has looked with favor upon
    his lowly servant.
From this day all generations will call
    me blessed:
    the Almighty has done great things
    for me,

and holy is his Name.
He has mercy on those who
    fear him
in every generation.
He has shown the strength of his arm,
    and has scattered the proud in
    their conceit.
He has cast down the mighty from
    their thrones,
    and has lifted up the lowly.
He has filled the hungry with
    good things,
    and the rich he has sent
    away empty.
He has come to the help of his
    servant Israel
    for he has remembered his promise
    of mercy,
    the promise he made to
    our fathers,
    to Abraham and his children
    for ever."
Mary remained with her about three months and then returned to her home.

SEPTEMBER 14 — EXALTATION OF THE HOLY CROSS **1061**

FIRST READING   *Numbers 21:4b–9*

With their patience worn out by the journey, the people complained against God and Moses, "Why have you brought us up from Egypt to die in this desert, where there is no food or water? We are disgusted with this wretched food!"
    In punishment the LORD sent among

the people saraph serpents, which bit the people so that many of them died. Then the people came to Moses and said, "We have sinned in complaining against the LORD and you. Pray the LORD to take the serpents from us." So Moses prayed for the people, and the LORD said to Moses, "Make a saraph and mount it on a pole, and if any who have been bitten look at it, they will live." Moses accordingly made a bronze serpent and mounted it on a pole, and whenever anyone who had been bitten by a serpent looked at the bronze serpent, he lived.

RESPONSORIAL PSALM

Psalm 78:1–2, 34–35, 36–37, 38

℟. Do not for - get the works of the Lord!

Music: John Schiavone, b. 1947, © 2001, OCP Publications.

▸ Hearken, my people, to my teaching;
  incline your ears to the words of
    my mouth.
I will open my mouth in a parable,
  I will utter mysteries from of old. ℟.

▸ While he slew them they sought him
    and inquired after God again,
  Remembering that God was their rock
    and the Most High God, their
    redeemer. ℟.

▸ But they flattered him with their mouths
    and lied to him with their tongues,
  Though their hearts were not steadfast
    toward him,
  nor were they faithful to his
    covenant. ℟.

▸ But he, being merciful, forgave their sin
    and destroyed them not;
  Often he turned back his anger
    and let none of his wrath be
    roused. ℟.

SECOND READING

Philippians 2:6–11

Brothers and sisters:
  Christ Jesus, though he was in the
      form of God,
    did not regard equality with God
      something to be grasped.
  Rather, he emptied himself,
    taking the form of a slave,
    coming in human likeness;
  and found human in appearance,
    he humbled himself,
    becoming obedient to death,
      even death on a cross.

Because of this, God greatly
    exalted him
  and bestowed on him the name
    that is above every name,
  that at the name of Jesus
    every knee should bend,
  of those in heaven and on earth
    and under the earth,
  and every tongue confess that
    Jesus Christ is Lord,
  to the glory of God the Father.

GOSPEL ACCLAMATION

℟. Al - le - lu - ia, al - le - lu - ia, al - le - lu - ia.

Music: John Schiavone, b. 1947, © 2001, OCP Publications.

▸ We adore you, O Christ, and we bless you,
  because by your Cross you have redeemed the world. ℟.

GOSPEL READING

John 3:13–17

Jesus said to Nicodemus: "No one has gone up to heaven except the one who has come down from heaven, the Son of Man. And just as Moses lifted up the serpent in the desert, so must the Son of Man be lifted up, so that everyone who believes in him may have eternal life."

For God so loved the world that he gave his only Son, so that everyone who believes in him might not perish but might have eternal life. For God did not send his Son into the world to condemn the world, but that the world might be saved through him.

NOVEMBER 1 — ALL SAINTS   1062

FIRST READING

Revelation 7:2–4, 9–14

I, John, saw another angel come up from the East, holding the seal of the living God. He cried out in a loud voice to the four angels who were given power to damage the land and the sea, "Do not damage the land or the sea or the trees until we put the seal on the foreheads of the servants of our God." I heard the number of those who had been marked with the seal, one hundred and forty-four thousand marked from every tribe of the children of Israel.

After this I had a vision of a great multitude, which no one could count, from every nation, race, people, and tongue. They stood before the throne and before the Lamb, wearing white robes and holding palm branches in their hands. They cried out in a loud voice:

"Salvation comes from our God,

who is seated on the throne,
and from the Lamb."
All the angels stood around the throne and around the elders and the four living creatures. They prostrated themselves before the throne, worshiped God, and exclaimed:
"Amen. Blessing and glory, wisdom
and thanksgiving,
honor, power, and might
be to our God forever and ever.
Amen."
Then one of the elders spoke up and said to me, "Who are these wearing white robes, and where did they come from?" I said to him, "My lord, you are the one who knows." He said to me, "These are the ones who have survived the time of great distress; they have washed their robes and made them white in the Blood of the Lamb."

RESPONSORIAL PSALM

Psalm 24:1bc–2, 3–4ab, 5–6

℟. **Lord, this is the peo - ple that longs to see your face.**

Music: John Schiavone, b. 1947, © 2001, OCP Publications.

▶ The LORD's are the earth and
    its fullness;
    the world and those who dwell in it.
For he founded it upon the seas
    and established it upon the rivers. ℟.

▶ Who can ascend the mountain of
    the LORD?
    or who may stand in his holy place?
One whose hands are sinless, whose
    heart is clean,
    who desires not what is vain. ℟.

℟. **Lord, this is the people that longs to see your face.**

▶ He shall receive a blessing from
    the LORD,
  a reward from God his savior.

Such is the race that seeks him,
    that seeks the face of the God
    of Jacob. ℟.

SECOND READING

1 John 3:1–3

Beloved: See what love the Father has bestowed on us that we may be called the children of God. Yet so we are. The reason the world does not know us is that it did not know him. Beloved, we are God's children now; what we shall be has not yet been revealed. We do know that when it is revealed we shall be like him, for we shall see him as he is. Everyone who has this hope based on him makes himself pure, as he is pure.

GOSPEL ACCLAMATION

Matthew 11:28

℟. **Al - le - lu - ia, al - le - lu - ia, al - le - lu - ia.**

Music: John Schiavone, b. 1947, © 2001, OCP Publications.

▶ Come to me, all you who labor and are burdened,
  and I will give you rest, says the Lord. ℟.

GOSPEL READING

Matthew 5:1–12a

When Jesus saw the crowds, he went up the mountain, and after he had sat down, his disciples came to him. He began to teach them, saying:
  "Blessed are the poor in spirit,
    for theirs is the Kingdom of heaven.
  Blessed are they who mourn,
    for they will be comforted.
  Blessed are the meek,
    for they will inherit the land.
  Blessed are they who hunger and
      thirst for righteousness,
    for they will be satisfied.
  Blessed are the merciful,
    for they will be shown mercy.
  Blessed are the clean of heart,
    for they will see God.
  Blessed are the peacemakers,
    for they will be called children
      of God.
  Blessed are they who are persecuted
      for the sake of righteousness,
    for theirs is the Kingdom of heaven.
  Blessed are you when they insult you
  and persecute you and utter every kind
  of evil against you falsely because of
  me. Rejoice and be glad, for your
  reward will be great in heaven."

NOVEMBER 2 — COMMEMORATION OF ALL THE FAITHFUL DEPARTED (ALL SOULS)

The following readings or those given in the Masses for the Dead, Lectionary for Mass nos. 1011-1016, may be used.

FIRST READING

Isaiah 25:6, 6–9

On this mountain the LORD of hosts
  will provide for all peoples.
On this mountain he will destroy
  the veil that veils all peoples,
The web that is woven over all nations;
  he will destroy death forever.
The Lord GOD will wipe away
  the tears from all faces;
The reproach of his people he
    will remove

from the whole earth; for the LORD
  has spoken.
On that day it will be said:
"Behold our God, to whom we looked
  to save us!
This is the LORD for whom we looked;
  let us rejoice and be glad that he has
  saved us!"

RESPONSORIAL PSALM

Psalm 23:1–3a, 3b–4, 5, 6

℟. The Lord   is my shep-herd;   there is noth-ing I shall want.

Music: John Schiavone, b. 1947, © 2001, OCP Publications.

▶ The LORD is my shepherd; I shall
    not want.
  In verdant pastures he gives
    me repose;
  Beside restful waters he leads me;
    he refreshes my soul. ℟.

▶ He guides me in right paths
    for his name's sake.
  Even though I walk in the dark valley
    I fear no evil; for you are at my side
  With your rod and your staff
    that give me courage. ℟.

▶ You spread the table before me
    in the sight of my foes;
  You anoint my head with oil;
    my cup overflows. ℟.

▶ Only goodness and kindness follow me
    all the days of my life;
  And I shall dwell in the house of
    the LORD
    for years to come. ℟.

SECOND READING

Romans 6:3–9

Brothers and sisters: Are you unaware that we who were baptized into Christ Jesus were baptized into his death? We were indeed buried with him through baptism into death, so that, just as Christ was raised from the dead by the glory of the Father, we too might live in newness of life.

For if we have grown into union with him through a death like his, we shall also be united with him in the resurrection. We know that our old self was crucified with him, so that our sinful body might be done away with, that we might no longer be in slavery to sin. For a dead person has been absolved from sin. If, then, we have died with Christ, we believe that we shall also live with him. We know that Christ, raised from the dead, dies no more; death no longer has power over him.

GOSPEL ACCLAMATION

cf. John 6:40

℟. Al - le - lu - ia, al - le - lu - ia, al - le - lu - ia.

Music: John Schiavone, b. 1947, © 2001, OCP Publications.

▸ This is the will of my Father, says the Lord.
that everyone who sees the Son and believes in him
may have eternal life. ℟.

GOSPEL READING

John 6:37–40

Jesus said to the crowds: "Everything that the Father gives me will come to me, and I will not reject anyone who comes to me, because I came down from heaven not to do my own will but the will of the one who sent me. And this is the will of the one who sent me, that I should not lose anything of what he gave me, but that I should raise it on the last day. For this is the will of my Father, that everyone who sees the Son and believes in him may have eternal life, and I shall raise him up on the last day."

1064   NOVEMBER 9 — DEDICATION OF THE LATERAN BASILICA IN ROME

FIRST READING

Ezekiel 47:1–2, 8–9, 12

The angel brought me back to the entrance of the temple, and I saw water flowing out from beneath the threshold of the temple toward the east, for the façade of the temple was toward the east; the water flowed down from the southern side of the temple, south of the altar. He led me outside by the north gate, and around to the outer gate facing the east, where I saw water trickling from the southern side. He said to me, "This water flows into the eastern district down upon the Arabah, and empties into the sea, the salt waters, which it makes fresh. Wherever the river flows, every sort of living creature that can multiply shall live, and there shall be abundant fish, for wherever this water comes the sea shall be made fresh. Along both banks of the river, fruit trees of every kind shall grow; their leaves shall not fade, nor their fruit fail. Every month they shall bear fresh fruit, for they shall be watered by the flow from the sanctuary. Their fruit shall serve for food, and their leaves for medicine."

RESPONSORIAL PSALM

Psalm 46:2–3, 5–6, 8–9

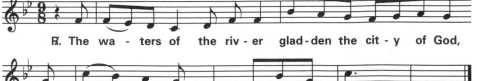

℟. The wa - ters of the riv - er glad - den the cit - y of God,

the ho - ly dwell - ing of the Most High.

Music: John Schiavone, b. 1947, © 2001, OCP Publications.

▶ God is our refuge and our strength,
　　an ever-present help in distress.
　Therefore, we fear not, though the
　　earth be shaken
　　and mountains plunge into the
　　depths of the sea. ℟.
▶ There is a stream whose runlets
　　gladden the city of God,
　　the holy dwelling of the Most High.

God is in its midst; it shall not
　　be disturbed;
　God will help it at the break
　　of dawn. ℟.

▶ The LORD of hosts is with us;
　　our stronghold is the God of Jacob.
　Come! behold the deeds of the LORD,
　　the astounding things he has
　　wrought on earth. ℟.

SECOND READING
1 Corinthians 3:9c–11, 16–17

Brothers and sisters: You are God's
building. According to the grace of God
given to me, like a wise master builder
I laid a foundation, and another is
building upon it. But each one must be
careful how he builds upon it, for no
one can lay a foundation other than the
one that is there, namely, Jesus Christ.
　Do you not know that you are the
temple of God, and that the Spirit of
God dwells in you? If anyone destroys
God's temple, God will destroy that
person; for the temple of God, which
you are, is holy.

GOSPEL ACCLAMATION
2 Chronicles 7:16

℟. Al - le - lu - ia, 　al - le - lu - ia, 　al - le - lu - ia.

Music: John Schiavone, b. 1947, © 2001, OCP Publications.

▶ I have chosen and consecrated this house, says the Lord,
　that my name may be there forever. ℟.

GOSPEL READING
John 2:13–22

Since the Passover of the Jews was
near, Jesus went up to Jerusalem. He
found in the temple area those who
sold oxen, sheep, and doves, as well as
the money-changers seated there. He
made a whip out of cords and drove
them all out of the temple area, with
the sheep and oxen, and spilled the
coins of the money-changers and
overturned their tables, and to those
who sold doves he said, "Take these out
of here, and stop making my Father's
house a marketplace." His disciples
recalled the words of Scripture,
　Zeal for your house will consume me.

At this the Jews answered and said to
him, "What sign can you show us for
doing this?" Jesus answered and said
to them, "Destroy this temple and in
three days I will raise it up." The Jews
said, "This temple has been under
construction for forty-six years, and
you will raise it up in three days?" But
he was speaking about the temple of
his Body. Therefore, when he was
raised from the dead, his disciples
remembered that he had said this, and
they came to believe the Scripture and
the word Jesus had spoken.

1065   DECEMBER 8 — IMMACULATE CONCEPTION OF THE BLESSED VIRGIN MARY

FIRST READING   *Genesis 3:9–15, 20*

After the man, Adam, had eaten of the tree, the LORD God called to the man and asked him, "Where are you?" He answered, "I heard you in the garden; but I was afraid, because I was naked, so I hid myself." Then he asked, "Who told you that you were naked? You have eaten, then, from the tree of which I had forbidden you to eat!" The man replied, "The woman whom you put here with me — she gave me fruit from the tree, and so I ate it." The LORD God then asked the woman, "Why did you do such a thing?" The woman answered, "The serpent tricked me into it, so I ate it."

Then the LORD God said to the serpent:

"Because you have done this, you
    shall be banned
    from all the animals
    and from all the wild creatures;
on your belly shall you crawl,
    and dirt shall you eat
    all the days of your life.
I will put enmity between you and
    the woman,
    and between your offspring
    and hers;
he will strike at your head,
    while you strike at his heel."
The man called his wife Eve, because she became the mother of all the living.

RESPONSORIAL PSALM   *Psalm 98:1, 2–3, 3–4*

℟. Sing to the Lord a new song,   for he has done mar-vel-ous deeds.

Music: John Schiavone, b. 1947, © 2001, OCP Publications.

▶ Sing to the LORD a new song,
    for he has done wondrous deeds;
His right hand has won victory for him,
    his holy arm. ℟.

▶ The LORD has made his salvation known:
    in the sight of the nations he has
    revealed his justice.

He has remembered his kindness and
    his faithfulness
    toward the house of Israel. ℟.

▶ All the ends of the earth have seen
    the salvation by our God.
Sing joyfully to the LORD, all you lands;
    break into song; sing praise. ℟.

SECOND READING   *Ephesians 1:3–6, 11–12*

Brothers and sisters: Blessed be the God and Father of our Lord Jesus Christ, who has blessed us in Christ with every spiritual blessing in the heavens, as he chose us in him, before the foundation of the world, to be holy and without blemish before him. In love he destined us for adoption to himself through Jesus Christ, in accord with the favor of his will, for the praise of the glory of his grace that he granted us in the beloved.

In him we were also chosen, destined in accord with the purpose of the One who accomplishes all things according to the intention of his will, so that we might exist for the praise of his glory, we who first hoped in Christ.

GOSPEL ACCLAMATION

cf. Luke 1:28

℟. Al - le - lu - ia,   al - le - lu - ia,   al - le - lu - ia.

Music: John Schiavone, b. 1947, © 2001, OCP Publications.

▶ Hail, Mary, full of grace, the Lord is with you;
blessed are you among women. ℟.

GOSPEL READING

Luke 1:26–38

The angel Gabriel was sent from God to a town of Galilee called Nazareth, to a virgin betrothed to a man named Joseph, of the house of David, and the virgin's name was Mary. And coming to her, he said, "Hail, full of grace! The Lord is with you." But she was greatly troubled at what was said and pondered what sort of greeting this might be. Then the angel said to her, "Do not be afraid, Mary, for you have found favor with God. Behold, you will conceive in your womb and bear a son, and you shall name him Jesus. He will be great and will be called Son of the Most High, and the Lord God will give him the throne of David his father, and he will rule over the house of Jacob forever, and of his Kingdom there will be no end." But Mary said to the angel, "How can this be, since I have no relations with a man?" And the angel said to her in reply, "The Holy Spirit will come upon you, and the power of the Most High will overshadow you. Therefore the child to be born will be called holy, the Son of God. And behold, Elizabeth, your relative, has also conceived a son in her old age, and this is the sixth month for her who was called barren; for nothing will be impossible for God." Mary said, "Behold, I am the handmaid of the Lord. May it be done to me according to your word." Then the angel departed from her.

DECEMBER 12 — OUR LADY OF GUADALUPE   **1066**

FIRST READING

Revelation 11:19a; 12:1–6a, 10ab (690A)

God's temple in heaven was opened, and the ark of his covenant could be seen in the temple.

A great sign appeared in the sky, a woman clothed with the sun, with the moon under her feet, and on her head a crown of twelve stars. She was with child and wailed aloud in pain as she labored to give birth. Then another sign appeared in the sky; it was a huge red dragon, with seven heads and ten horns, and on its heads were seven diadems. Its tail swept away a third of the stars in the sky and hurled them down to the earth. Then the dragon stood before the woman about to give birth, to devour her child when she gave birth. She gave birth to a son, a male child, destined to rule all the nations with an iron rod. Her child was caught up to God and his throne. The woman herself fled into the desert where she had a place prepared by God.

Then I heard a loud voice in heaven say:

"Now have salvation and
    power come,
and the Kingdom of our God
and the authority of his Anointed."

Alternate reading is Zechariah 2:14–17

RESPONSORIAL PSALM

Judith 13:18bcde, 19

℟. You are the high - est hon - or of our race.

Music: John Schiavone, b. 1947, © 2001, OCP Publications.

▶ Blessed are you, daughter, by the Most
High God,
above all the women on earth;
and blessed be the LORD God,
the creator of heaven and earth. ℟.

▶ Your deed of hope will never
be forgotten
by those who tell of the might
of God. ℟.

GOSPEL ACCLAMATION

℟. Al - le - lu - ia, al - le - lu - ia, al - le - lu - ia.

Music: John Schiavone, b. 1947, © 2001, OCP Publications.

▶ Blessed are you, holy Virgin Mary, deserving of all praise;
from you rose the sun of justice, Christ our God. ℟.

GOSPEL READING

Luke 1:39–47

Mary set out and traveled to the hill country in haste to a town of Judah, where she entered the house of Zechariah and greeted Elizabeth. When Elizabeth heard Mary's greeting, the infant leaped in her womb, and Elizabeth, filled with the Holy Spirit, cried out in a loud voice and said, "Most blessed are you among women, and blessed is the fruit of your womb. And how does this happen to me, that the mother of my Lord should come to me? For at the moment the sound of your greeting reached my ears, the infant in my womb leaped for joy. Blessed are you who believed that what was spoken to you by the Lord would be fulfilled."
And Mary said:
    "My soul proclaims the greatness of
    the Lord;
    my spirit rejoices in God
    my savior."

Alternate readings include Luke 1:26–38

As a rule, the psalm sung in response to the first reading is directly connected in the Lectionary with the individual scripture reading given for each Sunday or Feast Day. Thus, the choice of the psalm normally depends on the choice of the reading. Nevertheless, in order that the people may be able to join in the responsorial psalm more readily, some texts of responses and psalms have been chosen, according to the different seasons of the year and the class of saints, for optional use. Whenever the psalm is sung these "Seasonal Psalms" may be used in place of the text corresponding to the reading in the Lectionary (see General Instruction of the Roman Missal, no. 36). Reference is also made below to where music may be found for these responsorial psalms.

SEASON OF ADVENT
Psalm 25:4–5, 8–9, 10, 14/174
Use no. 26, 27, 28, 691

Or
Psalm 85:9–10, 11–12, 13–14
Use no. 60, 61, 62

SEASON OF CHRISTMAS
Psalm 98:1, 2–3ab, 3cd–4, 5–6
Use no. 76, 77, 78, 79, 595

Epiphany
Psalm 72:1–2, 7–8, 10–11, 12–13
Use no. 57

SEASON OF LENT
Psalm 51:3–4, 5–6, 12–13, 14, 17
Use no. 46, 47, 48

Or
Psalm 91:1–2, 10–11, 12–13, 14, 16
Use no. 67, 68, 69

Or
Psalm 130:1–2, 3–4, 4–6, 7–8
Use no. 105, 106, 107, 393

HOLY WEEK
Psalm 22:8–9, 17–18, 19–20, 23–24
Use no. 21, 22

EASTER VIGIL
Psalm 136:1–3, 4–6, 7–9, 24–26
  or 1, 3, 16, 21–23, 24–26
Use no. 108

SEASON OF EASTER
Psalm 118:1–2, 16–17, 22–23
Use no. 94, 95, 96, 97, 440

Or
Psalm 66:1–3, 4–5, 6–7, 16
Use no. 53

Ascension
Psalm 47:2–3, 6–7, 8–9
Use no. 45

Pentecost
Psalm 104:1, 24, 29–30, 31, 34
Use no. 85, 86, 87

ORDINARY TIME
Psalm 19:8, 9, 10, 11
Use no. 20, 680

Or
Psalm 27:1, 4, 13–14
Use no. 29, 30, 132, 587

Or
Psalm 34:2–3, 4–5, 6–7, 8–9
Use no. 37, 38, 39, 40

Or
Psalm 63:2, 3–4, 5–6, 8–9
Use no. 50, 51, 52

Or
Psalm 95:1–2, 6–7, 8–9
Use no. 71, 72, 73

Or
Psalm 100:2, 3, 5
Use no. 80, 81

Or
Psalm 103:1–2, 3–4, 8, 10, 12–13
Use no. 82, 83, 84

Or
Psalm 145:1–2, 8–9, 10–11, 13–14
Use no. 110, 111, 112

Last Weeks in Ordinary Time
Psalm 122:1–2, 3–4, 4–5, 6–7
Use no. 101, 102

PRAYERS

1068 NIGHT PRAYER (COMPLINE)

Night Prayer is an occasion for the Christian to remember with sorrow the day's sin and failure, and to pray for protection throughout the coming night.

VERSE AND RESPONSE
All make the sign of the cross.

HYMN
For music see no. 873, 874, 875.

A penitential rite using the formulas of the Mass may be inserted here.

PSALMODY
Psalms and their antiphons may be taken from the proper of the day.

READING

HOMILY/PREACHING *(optional)*

RESPONSORY

Presiding Minister/All: **Into your hands, Lord, I commend my spirit.**
Presiding Minister: You have redeemed us, Lord God of truth.
All: **I commend my spirit.**
Presiding Minister: Glory to the Father, and to the Son, and to the Holy Spirit.
All: **Into your hands, Lord, I commend my spirit.**

(or see no. 582)

GOSPEL CANTICLE: SONG OF SIMEON
For music see no. 123, 124, 507, 876

CONCLUDING PRAYER

The presiding minister says the concluding prayer.

BLESSING/CONCLUSION

Presiding Minister: May the all-powerful Lord grant us a restful night and a peaceful death.
All: **Amen.**

MARIAN ANTIPHON: SALVE REGINA *(For music see no. 499.)*

The Marian Antiphon "Regina Caeli," no. 436, is used during the Easter season; the antiphon "Alma Redemptoris Mater," no. 488, is used during the Advent season through the Presentation of the Lord. Other hymns approved by the Conference of Bishops may be used.

THE ANGELUS

V. The angel spoke God's message
to Mary,
R. **and she conceived of the Holy Spirit.**
Hail, Mary . . .

V. "I am the lowly servant of the Lord:
R. **let it be done to me according to
your word."**
Hail, Mary . . .

V. And the Word became flesh
R. **and lived among us.**
Hail, Mary . . .

V. Pray for us, holy Mother of God,
R. **that we may become worthy of the
promises of Christ.**

Let us pray.
Lord, fill our hearts with your grace:
once, through the message of an angel
you revealed to us the incarnation of
your Son;
now, through his suffering and death
lead us to the glory of his resurrection.
We ask this through Christ our Lord.
R. **Amen.**

MEMORARE

Remember, O most gracious Virgin Mary,
that never was it known that anyone who
fled to your protection, implored your
help, or sought your intercession, was left
unaided. Inspired by this confidence, I fly
unto you, O Virgin of virgins, my Mother.
To you I come; before you I stand sinful
and sorrowful. O Mother of the Word
Incarnate! Despise not my petitions, but
in your mercy hear and answer me. Amen.

THE ROSARY

The Joyful Mysteries
1. The Annunciation *(Luke 1:30–33)*
2. The Visitation *(Luke 1:50–53)*
3. The Nativity *(Luke 2:10–11)*
4. The Presentation *(Luke 2:29–32)*
5. The Finding of Jesus in the Temple
(Luke 2:48–52)

The Sorrowful Mysteries
1. The Agony in the Garden
(Matthew 26:38–39)
2. The Scourging at the Pillar *(John 19:1)*
3. The Crowning with Thorns
(Mark 15:16–17)
4. The Carrying of the Cross *(John 19:17)*
5. The Crucifixion *(John 19:28–30)*

The Glorious Mysteries
1. The Resurrection *(Mark 16:6–8)*
2. The Ascension *(Acts 1:10–11)*
3. The Coming of the Holy Spirit
(Acts 2:1–4)
4. The Assumption of Mary
(Song of Songs 2:3–6)
5. The Coronation of Mary
(Luke 1:51–54)

The Mysteries of Light
1. The Baptism of the Lord in the Jordan
*(2 Corinthians 5:21, Matthew 3:17
and parallels)*
2. The Wedding feast of Cana
(John 2:1–12)
3. The Proclamation of the Kingdom
of God *(Mark 1:15; Mark 2:3–13;
Luke 7:47–48 and John 20:22–23)*
4. The Transfiguration
(Luke 9:35 and parallels)
5. The Institution of the Eucharist
(John 13:1)

HAIL, HOLY QUEEN

Hail, Holy Queen, Mother of Mercy, our
life, our sweetness, and our hope! To you
do we cry, poor banished children of Eve;
to you do we send up our sighs, mourning
and weeping in this vale of tears. Turn,
then, most gracious advocate, your eyes of
mercy toward us; and after this our exile,
show unto us the blessed fruit of your
womb, Jesus. O clement, O loving, O
sweet Virgin Mary! Pray for us, O Holy
Mother of God, that we may be made worthy of the promises of Christ.

REGINA COELI

O Queen of heaven, rejoice! Alleluia.

For He whom you did merit to bear, Alleluia.

Has risen, as He said, Alleluia.

Pray for us to God, Alleluia.
℣. Rejoice and be glad, O Virgin Mary. Alleluia.
℟. For the Lord has risen indeed. Alleluia.

Let us pray. O God, Who by the resurrection of Your Son, Our Lord Jesus Christ, has given joy to the whole world, grant, we beseech You, that through the intercession of the Virgin Mary, His Mother, we may attain the same joys of eternal life. Through the same Christ Our Lord. Amen.
—*St. Ignatius of Loyola (1491–1556)*

ACT OF FAITH

O my God, I firmly believe that you are One God in Three Divine Persons, Father, Son, and the Holy Spirit; I believe that your Divine Son became man, and died for our sins, and that he will come again to judge the living and the dead. I believe these and all the truths which the Holy Catholic Church teaches, because you have revealed them, Who can neither deceive nor be deceived.

ACT OF HOPE

O my God, relying on your almighty power and infinite mercy and promises, I hope to obtain pardon of my sins, the help of your grace, and life everlasting, through the merits of Jesus Christ, my Lord and Redeemer.

ACT OF LOVE

O my God, I love you above all things, with my whole heart and soul, because you are all-good and worthy of all love. I love my neighbor as myself for the love of you. I forgive all who have injured me, and ask pardon of all whom I have injured.

ANIMA CHRISTI

Soul of Christ, sanctify me; Body of Christ, save me; Blood of Christ, inebriate me; Water from the side of Christ, wash me; Passion of Christ, strengthen me; O good Jesus, hear me; Within your wounds hide me; Separated from you, let me never be; From the evil one protect me; At the hour of my death, call me; And close to you bid me; That with your saints, I may be, praising you forever and ever. Amen.

PRAYER OF ST. FRANCIS

Lord, make me an instrument of Your peace. Where there is hatred, let me sow love; where there is injury, pardon; where there is doubt, faith; where there is despair, hope; where there is darkness, light; and where there is sadness, joy. O Divine Master, grant that I may not so much seek to be consoled as to console; to be understood as to understand; to be loved as to love; for it is in giving that we receive; it is in pardoning that we are pardoned; and it is in dying that we are born to eternal life.

PRAYER FOR ALL NEEDS

We beg you, Lord,
to help and defend us.

Deliver the oppressed.
Pity the insignificant.
Raise the fallen.
Show yourself to the needy.
Heal the sick.
Bring back those of your people who have gone astray.
Feed the hungry.
Lift up the weak.
Take off the prisoners' chains.

May every nation come to know
that you alone are God,
that Jesus is your Child,
that we are your people, the sheep that you pasture.

Amen.   —*Clement of Rome*

INDEXES

ACKNOWLEDGMENTS 1070

The publisher sincerely thanks the authors, composers and owners or holders of copyright who have so kindly granted permission to use their material. Every effort has been made to determine and acknowledge owners and administrators of each copyright. The publisher regrets any oversight that may have occurred and will gladly make proper acknowledgment in future printings after written notice has been received.

Selections copyrighted by Cooperative Ministries, Inc. are administered by OCP Publications: exclusive agent. Selections copyrighted by Gooi en Sticht, bv. Baarn, The Netherlands, are administered by OCP Publications: exclusive agent for English-language countries. Selections copyrighted by Willard Jabusch are administered by OCP Publications. All rights reserved. Selections copyrighted by North American Liturgy Resources (NALR) are owned and administered by OCP Publications. All rights reserved. Selections copyrighted by New Dawn Music are owned and administered by OCP Publications. All rights reserved.

For licensing information of all selections published or administered by OCP Publications, please write or fax your request to: Copyright Administrator, OCP Publications, PO Box 18030, Portland, OR 97218-0030; fax 503/282-3486.

NOEL ANCELL
2 Wall Street
Chadstone VIC Australia 3148

ARCHDIOCESE OF PHILADELPHIA
Music Office
222 North 17th Street
Philadelphia, PA 19103-1299
215/251-3320
Fax 215/587-3561

VIVIEN ARNOLD
RMB 19 Majors Close
Wamboin NSW Australia 2620

AUGSBURG FORTRESS, PUBLISHERS
426 S. 5th Street
PO Box 1209
Minneapolis, MN 55440
800/328-4648

THE BENEDICTINE FOUNDATION OF
THE STATE OF VERMONT, INC.
58 Priory Hill Road
Weston, VT 05161

ROSALIE BONIGHTON
27 Brinkley Avenue
Wendouree, VIC Autralia 3355

BURNS & OATES, LTD.
c/o The Continuum International
Publishing Group Ltd.
The Tower Building
11 York Road
London SE1 7NX England
44 (0) 207/922-0880
Fax 44 (0) 207/922- 0881

THOMAS H. CAIN
Walnut Hill Farmhouse, R.R. 1
Jerseyville, ON L0R 1R0 Canada

THE CHURCH PENSION FUND
445 Fifth Avenue
New York, NY 10016

COMISIÓN EPISCOPAL ESPAÑOLA
DE LITURGIA
Añastro 1
28033 Madrid, España
39 1 343 96 43

CONCACAN, INC.
2500 Don Reid Drive
Ottawa, Ontario K1H 2J2 Canada

CONCORDIA PUBLISHING HOUSE
3558 S. Jefferson
St. Louis, MO 63118
800/325-0191

CONFRATERNITY OF CHRISTIAN
DOCTRINE (CCD)
3211 Fourth Street NE
Washington, DC 20017
202/541-3098

THE COPYRIGHT COMPANY
Abingdon Press
CCCM Music
Maranatha! Music
Word of God Music
40 Music Square E
Nashville, TN 37203

BISHOP STEWART CROSS (estate of)
c/o Mrs. M. M. W. Cross
Honeybee House
Brigsteer, Kendal
Cumbria LA8 8AP England

DAMEAN MUSIC
5329 Dijon Drive, Suite 103
Baton Rouge, LA 70808-4378

EMI CHRISTIAN MUSIC
PUBLISHING
Birdwing Music/BMG Songs
Birdwing Music/Cherry Lane
Music Publishing Co., Inc.
Bud John Songs, Inc./
Crouch Music
101 Winners Circle
PO Box 5085
Brentwood, TN 37024-5085

EKKLESIA MUSIC
1434 Gaylord Street
Denver, CO 80210

FABER MUSIC, LTD.
3 Queen Square
London WC1N 3AU England

GETHSEMANI ABBEY
3642 Monks Road
New Haven, KY 40051
502/549-3117

JOYCE MACDONALD GLOVER
9202 Westmoor Drive
Richmond, VA 23229

WILLIAM BOYD GROVE
109 McDavid Lane
Charleston, WV 25311

HAROLD OBER ASSOC., INC.
425 Madison Avenue
New York, NY 10017
212/759-8600
Fax 212/759-9428

RICHARD HILLERT
1620 Clay Court
Melrose Park, IL 60160

HOPE PUBLISHING CO.
    Jubilate Hymns, Ltd.
    Stainer & Bell, Ltd.
    The Hymn Society of America
380 S. Main Place
Carol Stream, IL 60188
630/665-3200
Fax 630/665-2552

INTERNATIONAL COMMITTEE ON
ENGLISH IN THE LITURGY, INC. (ICEL)
1522 K Street, NW, Suite 1000
Washington, DC 20005
202/347-0800
Fax 202/347-1839

JOHN IRELAND TRUST
35 St. Mary's Mansions
St. Mary's Terrace
London W2 1SQ England

JAN-LEE MUSIC
PO Box 1517
Honokaa, HI 96727

ANNE K. LeCROY
1103 Cherokee Street
Johnson City, TN 37604

THE LORENZ CORPORATION
PO Box 802 (501 E. 3rd Street)
Dayton, OH 45401-0802
800/444-1144

MANNA MUSIC, INC.
35255 Brooten Road
Pacific City, OR 97135
503/965-6112

A. R. MOWBRAY & CO., LTD.
28 Margaret Street
London W1N 71B England

MRS. IRENE C. MUELLER
1441 Hillcrest, Apt. 1
Cincinnati, OH 45224

OXFORD UNIVERSITY PRESS
198 Madison Avenue
New York, NY 10016-4314
212/726-6000
Fax 212/726-6441

ROLAND F. PALMER (estate of)
c/o Canon Peter D. Wilkinson
25 Government Unit 209
Victoria, BC V8V 2K4 Canada
604/385-4444

THE PILGRIM PRESS
700 Prospect Avenue
Cleveland, OH 44115
216/736-3764
Fax 216/736-2207

PETER J. SCAGNELLI
34 Arlington Street
Framingham, MA 01702-7343

E. C. SCHIRMER MUSIC CO.
c/o ECS Publishing
138 Ipswich Street
Boston, MA 02215-3534
617/236-1935
Fax 617/236-0261

G. SCHIRMER, INC.
    J. Curwen & Sons
257 Park Avenue S., 20th floor
New York, NY 10010
212/254-2100

SCRIPTURE IN SONG
(a div. of Integrity Music, Inc.)
c/o Integrity Incorporated
1000 Cody Road
Mobile, AL 36695-3425

MRS. M. SEDDON
via Jubilate Hymns, Ltd.
Southwick House
4 Thorne Park Road
Chelston Torquay TQ2 6RX England

SELAH PUBLISHING CO.
58 Pearl Street
(PO Box 3037)
Kingston, NY 12401-0902
914/338-2816
Fax 914/338-2991

SHAWNEE PRESS, INC.
c/o Music Sales Corp.
257 Park Avenue S.
New York, NY 10010
212/254-2100
Fax 212/254-2013

DENNIS C. SMOLARSKI, SJ
Jesuit Community
Santa Clara University
Santa Clara, CA 95053

SOCIETY OF THE SACRED HEART
c/o Sr. Judith Cagney, RSCJ, Executor
Estate of Sr. Anne E. Carter
4389 W. Pine Blvd.
St. Louis, MO 63108
314/652-1500
Fax 314/534-6800

STANBROOK ABBEY
Callow End,
Worcester WR2 4TD England

WILLIAM G. STOREY
1027 E Wayne Street
South Bend, IN 46617

SUMMY BIRCHARD MUSIC
(a div. of Birch Tree Group, Ltd)
15800 NW 48th Avenue
Miami, FL 33014
305/620-1500
Fax 305/621-1094

UNITED STATES CATHOLIC
CONFERENCE (USCCB)
    National Catholic Welfare
    Conference
3211 Fourth Street NE
Washington, DC 20017
202/541-3098
Fax 202/541-3089

VERNACULAR HYMNS
PUBLISHING CO.
PO Box 2304
Bakersfield, CA 93303-2304

WALTON MUSIC CORP.
    Utryck, Sweden
76 South Road
Bloomingdale, NJ 07403

WARNER BROS.
    Belwin-Mills Publishing Corp.
10585 Santa Monica Boulevard
Los Angeles, CA 90025-4950
310/441-8600
Fax 310/470-1587

A. P. WATT, LTD.
20 John Street
London WC1N 2DR England
020 7405 6774
Fax 020 7831 2154

WESTMINSTER JOHN KNOX PRESS
100 Witherspoon Street
Louisville, KY 40202
800/227-2872
Fax 502/569-5113

THE WILLIS MUSIC CO.
PO Box 54
Florence, KY 41022-0548
800/354-9799
Fax 859/283-1784

WORD MUSIC, INC.
c/o Warner-Chappell Music
20 Music Square E
Nashville, TN 37203
Fax 615/733-1885

WORLD LIBRARY PUBLICATIONS
3825 N. Willow Road,
Schiller Park, IL 60176-2309
800/566-6150
Fax 888/957-3291

ALPHABETICAL INDEX OF HYMN TUNES 1072

METRICAL INDEX OF HYMN TUNES   1073

SCRIPTURAL INDEX   1074

TOPICAL INDEX   1075

607 Sing a New Song
605 Sing of the Lord's Goodness
610 Sing Praise to God Who
    Reigns Above
625 Sing Praise to the Lord
624 When in Our Music

NATION
644 All Good Gifts
864 America
862 America the Beautiful
865 Eternal Father, Strong to Save
866 For the Healing of the Nations
867 God of Our Fathers
618 Let All the Peoples
739 Let There Be Peace on Earth
681 Mine Eyes Have Seen
    the Glory
60 Psalm 85: Lord, Show Us
    Your Mercy
640 Sing to the Lord of Harvest
863 This Is My Song
794 We Gather Together

NATURE
See Creation

NIGHT
See Liturgical Index:
Liturgy of the Hours, Night Prayer

OBEDIENCE
533 Church of God,
    Elect and Glorious
828 Go Make of All Disciples
775 I Will Choose Christ
763 Pescador de Hombres/
    Lord, You Have Come
20 Psalm 19: Lord, You Have
    the Words
27 Psalm 25: A Ti, Señor/
    To You, O Lord
41 Psalm 40: Here I Am
73 Psalm 95: If Today You Hear
    God's Voice
72 Psalm 95: If Today You Hear
    His Voice
99 Psalm 119: Blessed Are They
98 Psalm 119: More Than Gold
104 Psalm 128: O Blessed
    Are Those
837 Servant Song
843 The Church of Christ
    in Every Age
377 Turn to Me
680 Your Words Are Spirit and Life

ORDINATION
See Liturgical Index: Rites of the
Church, Holy Orders

PARDON
See Mercy; Liturgical Index: Rites of
the Church, Penance (Reconciliation)

PASCHAL MYSTERY
See also Liturgical Index:
The Liturgical Year, Easter Triduum
432 Be Joyful, Mary,
    Heavenly Queen
411 Behold the Wood
442 Christ, the Lord, Is Risen Again
654 Jesus Died Upon the Cross
484 Jesus the Lord
522 Lift High the Cross
764 Lord of the Dance
415 My Song Is Love Unknown
443 Now the Green Blade Rises

410 O Love of God Incarnate
409 O Sacred Head, Surrounded
131 Opening Song: I Know that
    My Redeemer Lives
431 The Strife Is O'er
423 Three Days
760 Unless a Grain of Wheat
    (Farrell)
802 Unless a Grain of Wheat
    (Hurd)
521 We Should Glory in the Cross
755 What Wondrous Love Is This
823 When We Eat This Bread
682 Worthy Is the Lamb

PATIENCE
564 May Love Be Ours
314 Patience, People

PATRIOTIC
See Nation

PEACE
743 Bearers of Peace
844 Christ's Peace
744 Dona Nobis Pacem (Norbet)
742 Dona Nobis Pacem
    (Traditional)
866 For the Healing of the Nations
867 God of Our Fathers
739 Let There Be Peace on Earth
791 Let Us Go Rejoicing
734 Like a Child Rests
740 O Day of Peace that
    Dimly Shines
741 Peace
745 Peace Is Flowing Like a River
738 Prayer of St. Francis
31 Psalm 29: The Lord Will Bless
    Us with Peace
57 Psalm 72: Justice Shall
    Flourish
60 Psalm 85: Lord, Show Us
    Your Mercy
61 Psalm 85: Muéstranos, Señor/
    Show Us, O Lord
62 Psalm 85: Show Us
    Your Kindness
656 There Is a River
863 This Is My Song
842 We Shall Overcome
667 Your Light Will Come,
    Jerusalem

PENANCE
See Conversion; Liturgical Index:
Rites of the Church, Penance
(Reconciliation)

PEOPLE OF GOD
See also Church
604 All People That on Earth
    Do Dwell
546 Bathed in the Waters of Life
661 Christ Be Our Light
533 Church of God,
    Elect and Glorious
798 Gather Your People
776 Great Is the Power
    We Proclaim
383 I Will Be Your God
820 One Bread, One Body
765 Out of Darkness
813 Pan de Vida
35 Psalm 33: Blessed the People

80 Psalm 100: Nosotros Somos
    Su Pueblo/We Are
    God's People
81 Psalm 100: We Are
    God's People
852 Somos el Cuerpo de Cristo/
    We Are the Body of Christ

PETITION/PRAYER
See also Liturgical Index: Service Music
for Mass, General Intercessions
873 Abide with Me
488 Alma Redemptoris Mater
675 Blessed Jesus, at Your Word
385 Broken Cisterns Walled
    in Stone
687 Christ Be beside Me
726 Christ in the Rubble
693 Come, My Way, My Truth,
    My Life
562 Create in Me
744 Dona Nobis Pacem (Norbet)
742 Dona Nobis Pacem
    (Traditional)
865 Eternal Father, Strong to Save
242 General Intercessions
583 Give Me Jesus
686 God Be in My Head
476 Heart of Jesus
774 Holy Wisdom,
    Lamp of Learning
839 If You Believe and I Believe
727 In Every Age
757 In Perfect Charity
666 Jesus Christ, Inner Light
694 Jesus, Come to Us
701 Jesus, Lord
525 Litany of the Saints (Becker)
419 Litany of the Saints (Chant)
785 Lord God Triumphant
690 Lord of All Hopefulness
630 Many and Great
564 May Love Be Ours
550 May We See You
219 Miserere Nobis
767 Now Is the Time
551 O Breathe on Me,
    O Breath of God
670 O Christ, Our Teacher
475 O Dearest Lord,
    Your Sacred Head
284 O God, Hear Us
870 O Splendor of God's Glory
497 On This Day,
    O Beautiful Mother
695 Open My Eyes
554 Our Father, We Have
    Wandered
738 Prayer of St. Francis
28 Psalm 25: To You, O Lord
41 Psalm 40: Here I Am
48 Psalm 51: Oh Dios, Crea en
    Mí/Create in Me
50 Psalm 63: Hear Us, Lord,
    and Save Us
56 Psalm 69: Turn to God in
    Your Need
65 Psalm 90: Fill Us with Your
    Love, O Lord
105 Psalm 130: Del Señor Viene
    la Misericordia/With the
    Lord There Is Fullness
    of Redemption
107 Psalm 130: Out of the Depths

1076   INDEX OF SUGGESTED PSALMS FOR THE LITURGICAL YEAR

Suggested psalms for the church's three-year Lectionary cycle are listed below. Whenever possible, the psalm of the day has been indicated. If a suitable setting of the psalm of the day is not available, a seasonal psalm or an appropriate substitute has been recommended. Alternate settings are marked with an asterisk (*).

Gospel Acclamation (Alleluia)

Lenten Gospel Acclamation

Dismissal of the Catechumens and the Elect

See Rites of the Church, Rite of Christian Initiation of Adults, Dismissal of the Catechumens and the Elect

38 Psalm 34: Taste and See
(Willcock)
81 Psalm 100: We Are
God's People
89 Psalm 116: Alzaré la Copa
de la Salvación/I Will Take
the Cup of Salvation
92 Psalm 116: Our Blessing Cup
(Hurd)
91 Psalm 116: Our Blessing Cup
(Joncas)
111 Psalm 145: Bendeciré Tu
Nombre/I Will Praise
Your Name
110 Psalm 145: I Will Praise
Your Name (Smith)
112 Psalm 145: I Will Praise
Your Name (Willcock)
811 Seed, Scattered and Sown
793 Table of Plenty
821 Taste and See
812 This Body
816 To Be Your Bread
805 Ubi Caritas (Hurd)
754 Ubi Caritas (Rosania)
760 Unless a Grain of Wheat
(Farrell)
802 Unless a Grain of Wheat
(Hurd)
795 Ven al Banquete/
Come to the Feast
626 We Praise You
823 When We Eat This Bread
569 Where There Is Love

Eucharistic Hymn
751 Christians, Let Us Love
One Another
806 Let Us Break Bread Together
826 Lord, Who at Thy
First Eucharist
825 Shepherd of Souls

Hymn/Psalm of Praise
*See Topical Index: Charity, Church,
Good Shepherd, Joy, Kingdom/Reign
of God, Love for God, Love for
Others, Love of God for Us, Paschal
Mystery, Praise, Thanksgiving, Unity*

CONCLUDING RITE

Greeting
167 Greeting *(Celtic Mass)*
Blessing
168 Blessing *(Celtic Mass)*
Dismissal
169 Dismissal *(Celtic Mass)*
310 Easter Solemn Dismissal
Greeting, Blessing, and Dismissal
170 Easter Greeting, Blessing
and Dismissal *(Celtic Mass)*

Sending Forth
See Topical Index: Sending Forth

*The recessional song has never been
an official part of the rite; hence
musicians are free to plan music
which provides an appropriate clos-
ing to the liturgy. A song is one possible choice. However, if the people
have sung a song after communion,
it may be advisable to use only an
instrumental or choir recessional.
(Music in Catholic Worship, #73)*

SUNDAY CELEBRATIONS IN THE ABSENCE OF A PRIEST

**Entrance Song
(Gathering or Processional)**
709 A Mighty Fortress
703 Age to Age
600 All Creatures of Our God
and King
604 All People That on Earth
Do Dwell
466 All Praise and Glad
Thanksgiving
595 All the Ends of the Earth
477 Alleluia! Sing to Jesus
706 Be Not Afraid
675 Blessed Jesus, at Your Word
708 Blest Be the Lord
454 By the Waking of Our Hearts
661 Christ Be Our Light
848 Christ Is the King
830 City of God
608 Come, Christians, Join to Sing
735 Come to Me
538 Come to the River
(Mass of Glory)
790 Come, Worship the Lord
797 Draw Us in the Spirit's Tether
115 Exodus 15: To God Be
Praise and Glory
853 Father, Lord of All Creation
642 For the Beauty of the Earth
710 For You Are My God
603 From All That Dwell below
the Skies/Praise God from
Whom All Blessings Flow
777 Gather and Remember
801 Gather Us Together
798 Gather Your People
643 Give Thanks to the Lord
596 Glory and Praise to Our God
749 God Is Love
613 God, Whose Love Is Reigning
O'er Us
4 Gospel Canticle: Benedictus
673 Hail, Sov'reign Love
606 He Is the Lord
476 Heart of Jesus
593 Holy God, We Praise
Thy Name
469 Holy, Holy, Holy
396 Hosanna to the Son of David
470 How Wonderful the
Three-in-One
664 I Am the Light of the World
635 I Sing the Mighty Power
of God
647 If God Is for Us
621 Immortal, Invisible, God
Only Wise
631 In Praise of His Name
117 Isaiah 12: We Shall
Draw Water
759 Journeysong
617 Joyful, Joyful, We Adore You
659 Lead Me, Lord
618 Let All the Peoples
435 Let Heaven Rejoice
791 Let Us Go Rejoicing
800 Let Us Go to the Altar
620 Lift Up Your Hearts
645 Lord of Glory
746 Love Divine,
All Loves Excelling
871 Morning Has Broken

2 Morning Hymn: This Day
God Gives Me
503 My Soul Rejoices
623 O Bless the Lord
668 O Christ, You Speak the
Names of God
614 O God beyond All Praising
705 O God, Our Help in
Ages Past
633 Oh, Who Can Know the
Mind of God
652 Our God Provides
612 Praise, My Soul,
the King of Heaven
597 Praise to the Lord
736 Psalm 23
77 Psalm 98: All the Ends of
the Earth
76 Psalm 98: Los Confines de
la Tierra/All the Ends of
the Earth
97 Psalm 118: This Is the Day
102 Psalm 122: Con Qué Alegría/
Let Us Go Rejoicing
101 Psalm 122: Let Us
Go Rejoicing
651 Rain Down
616 Sing a Joyful Song
607 Sing a New Song
605 Sing of the Lord's Goodness
610 Sing Praise to God Who
Reigns Above
625 Sing Praise to the Lord
601 Sing to the Mountains
852 Somos el Cuerpo de Cristo/
We Are the Body of Christ
779 The Church's One
Foundation
602 The God of Abraham Praise
487 The King of Glory
748 There's a Wideness in
God's Mercy
440 This Day Was Made by
the Lord
444 This Is the Day
715 Though the Mountains
May Fall
754 Ubi Caritas
795 Ven al Banquete/
Come to the Feast
794 We Gather Together
626 We Praise You
622 We Praise You, O God
771 Where Two or Three
Have Gathered
676 Word of God,
You Spoke Creation
540 You Have Called Us

Litany in Praise of God's Mercy
553 Litany of Forgiveness
146 Penitential Rite C
(Celtic Mass)
237 Penitential Rite C
(Mass of Glory)

Responsorial Psalm
118 Daniel 3: Glory and
Praise Forever
116 Isaiah 12: Ustedes Sacarán
Agua/You Will Draw
Water Joyfully
16 Psalm 15: The One Who
Does Justice
18 Psalm 16: You Are My
Inheritance, O Lord

1078 INDEX OF FIRST LINES AND COMMON TITLES

Common titles that vary from those used in Journeysongs: 2nd Edition, *as well as the first lines of hymns, songs, and service music are given in italics.*